The Student's Guide to Law Firms

2016 - 2017

www.chambers-associate.com

Contents

1: Introduction

2: Refine Your Search

3: Becoming a Lawyer

4: Practice Areas

5: The Inside View

6: Leading Law Firms

7: Regional Guides

8: Extras

Contents

The Big Interview with famous and inspirational lawyers...

Publisher: Michael Chambers
Editor: Antony Cooke
Deputy Editor: Phil Roe
Writers: Alexis Self, Alice Saville, Amalia Neenan, Anna Winter, David Brooks, Eleanor Veryard, Michael O'Donohoe, Natalia Rossetti, Rosanna Quigley, Saskia van Emden
Contributors: Paul Rance, Sam Morris
Production: Jasper John, Paul Cummings
Business Development Director: Brad Sirott
Sales Manager: Darren Saunders
Advertising Manager: Olivia Pemberton

Published by Chambers and Partners Publishing
(a division of Orbach & Chambers Ltd)
39-41 Parker Street, London WC2B 5PQ
Tel: +44 (020) 7606 8844 **Fax**: +44 (020) 7831 5662
www.chambers-associate.com

Our thanks to the many associates, recruiters and partners who assisted us in our research.

ISBN: 978-0-85514-636-8

Chambers Associate 2016 -17

HIRING is up: that's the upbeat headline from 2016. Summer recruitment rose by 11% on last year among the firms in *Chambers Associate* – and an astonishing 73% since the gloom of 2010. The figures may look a little rosier, but our interviewees attest that competition hasn't slacked off. Even Marc Elias, Hillary Clinton's campaign lawyer, pitched in from his niche practice: *"Where good, but not great, credentials may once have been sufficient for being hired, popular areas of the law now have their pick of the most elite students on the market."* You can read our full interview with Elias on the campaign trail on p.60.

We've reviewed 14 new – and very different – firms this year: global giants like Norton Rose Fulbright and Greenberg Traurig; tech whizzes like Marshall Gerstein and Fenwick & West; and New York hard-hitters like Hughes Hubbard and Schulte Roth. These newest firms stand out for their practice area focus – Vedder Price, Mintz Levin or Goulston & Storrs to name a few more – but they also identify with a region, drawing heavily on their local markets. The result is more variety and more options for you, the student.

Our research this year has been driven by one goal: to capture the personal recommendations that help you make your mind up. Nothing is more powerful than the word-of-mouth accounts you hear on campus, but they also come replete with horror stories of BigLaw burn-out, myths of ferocious partners, or a prestigious reputation based on a single anecdote. In our interviews with junior associates, we asked them to tell us about their employers in the bluntest terms – about everything they love and everything they loathe. Each of our law firm reviews is the vivid, real-life experience of many, but presented in a balanced, considered form – word-of-mouth accounts without the bias.

The *Chambers Associate* team
June 2016

Our Editorial Team

Antony Cooke
Editor

Antony Cooke
Editor of *Chambers Associate* and *Chambers Student Guide.* Graduated from Durham University in Russian & French. Taught English at St. Petersburg State University. Previously worked at Michelin as a European project manager, and at PricewaterhouseCoopers as an associate in investment management. Fluent in Russian and French.

antonyc@chambersandpartners.com

Phil Roe
Deputy Editor

Phil Roe
Deputy editor of *Chambers Associate.* Joined Chambers & Partners in 2007 from a global executive search firm, where he advised private equity clients. Has written extensively for both *Chambers Associate* and the *Student Guide.* Graduated with an MA in English from Oxford University, and is a theater critic for London-based newspapers in his free time.

philr@chambersandpartners.com

Our Editorial Team *continued*

Sam Morris
Deputy editor. Sam graduated from the University of Leiden, The Netherlands with a first in Political Science in 2008 and from the London School of Economics with an MSc in Comparative Politics in 2009. He has worked for the Dutch Ministry of Foreign Affairs. Speaks Dutch and German.

Paul Rance
Assistant editor. Graduated from Exeter University with a first in English Literature and also spent a year abroad at the University of Toronto to read Canadian literature. He completed his MA in English at UCL in 2010.

Alexis Self
Graduated from the University of Sussex in 2012 with a BA in Modern History. Prior to joining Chambers he worked as a copywriter and freelance journalist.

Amalia Neenan
Graduated in 2014 with a degree in law from the University of Kent. Studied the Bar Professional Training Course at City University London and is also an ADR Group Accredited Civil & Commercial Mediator.

Anna Winter
Senior Researcher. Anna graduated with a BA in English Literature from Balliol College, Oxford. She took journalism qualifications following internships at *The Observer* and the *New Statesman* magazine.

David Brooks
Graduated from the University of Leicester, UK, in 2013 with a 2:1 in French & English Literature. Spent a year teaching English as a foreign language in Québec and is fluent in French. Enjoys reviewing live music in his spare time.

Eleanor Veryard
Graduated in 2011 with a bachelor's degree in History before completing a master's in Early Modern History at the University of Sheffield, UK. Previously worked as editor-in-chief of a monthly student magazine and as a teaching assistant.

Michael O'Donohoe
Graduated in 2012 with a degree in law from Trinity College Dublin, Ireland, before completing an LLM at the University of Nottingham, UK. Michael has also studied abroad in the United States and taught English in China.

Natalia Rossetti
Graduated with a First in English & Theater Studies from the University of Warwick, UK, in 2010, then completed a master's in Text & Performance at the Royal Academy of Dramatic Art. Speaks Italian and French.

Rosanna Quigley
Graduated from the University of Bristol in 2015 with a First in French and Portuguese. As part of her degree, she worked at an art magazine in Paris and studied in Rio de Janeiro. At university, she was travel editor for the student newspaper.

Tom Lewis
Graduated in 2015 with a BA In History from the University of Sheffield.

What is *Chambers Associate?*

NOW in its eighth edition and growing year on year, *Chambers Associate* gives law students an unparalleled view into the working lives of associates at the nation's leading law firms.

We're the only US legal career guide to conduct in-depth telephone interviews with thousands of junior associates on the topics that matter to juniors, like the work they do day to day, the social life (if there is one), pro bono, diversity, how hard they work you, how much money you make, personal development, and much more. We grant our interviewees anonymity so they can speak to us honestly and truthfully. We also talk to firm chairs, managing partners and hiring partners to understand who and how they recruit from law school, and the directions their firms are headed.

The qualitative approach

When finding the right career for you, there is a lot more at stake than just perceived prestige. *Chambers Associate* reviews firms on a qualitative basis. We do, however, draw on *Chambers USA*, our vast annual directory of US law firms based on client reviews. In each Inside View you will see a reference to *Chambers USA* rankings, which gives you a snapshot of a firm's practice area strengths, as rated by its clients. *Chambers USA*'s rankings cover key practice areas across all US states. For the full listing with commentary, visit www.chambersandpartners.com.

About Chambers and Partners

Since 1990, Chambers and Partners has published the world's most trusted and comprehensive guides to the legal profession. Titles include *Chambers USA, Chambers UK, Chambers Europe, Chambers Asia, Chambers Latin America, HNW Global,* and *Chambers Global.* Clients and lawyers around the globe consider Chambers to be the authority on the world's leading law firms and lawyers.

For 20 years we've also published the market-leading career guide for law students in the UK, the *Chambers Student Guide* (www.chambersstudent.co.uk).

All Chambers publications are freely accessible online at www.chambersandpartners.com.

The happiness and stress survey

Every associate we interviewed this year gave us a rating for how happy they were and how stressed they were in their firms. We've crunched the results for you below...

THE survey did pose a problem: everyone has their own version of what happiness means, and each firm attracts a different type of person with their own take on life. So how can we compare firm-to-firm? To introduce some relativity into this survey, we also asked how happy our associate sources expected to be, and then looked at the gap between reality and expectation. We found this helps anchor the results for better comparison.

What oil price?

Here we've ranked key legal markets by how happy the local lawyers are. For the second year in a row we have New England and Texas duking it out for the cheeriest place to be a lawyer. Apparently the oil price crash this year hasn't messed with Texans, who remain perennially buoyant. The table hasn't shifted dramatically apart from California's rise this year into the upper half – where we'd expect. It's in these regional rankings where we see the clearest relationship between stress and its erosion of happiness.

Regional legal market	Happiness reported out of 10
1 Texas & South	8.39
2 Boston & New England	7.95
3 California	7.81
4 DC	7.73
5 East	7.71
6 Southeast	7.65
7 New York	7.61
8 Pacific Northwest	7.50
9 Midwest	7.49

Regional legal market	Happier than expected %
1 Boston & New England	17%
2 Texas & South	16%
3 California	15%
4 East	12%
5 DC	12%
6 New York	11%
7 Southeast	9%
8 Midwest	5%
9 Pacific Northwest	1%

Regional legal market	Stress factor out of 10
1 Pacific Northwest	6.39
2 Midwest	6.12
3 Southeast	5.94
4 New York	5.79
5 California	5.60
6 DC	5.59
7 East	5.35
8 Texas & South	5.07
9 Boston & New England	4.43

Here's the data by city, singling out the top 15 happiest:

Top 15 happiest cities	Rating out of 10
1 Austin, TX	8.30
2 Atlanta, GA	8.24
3 Houston, TX	8.06
4 Philadephia, PA	8.05
5 Minneapolis, MN	8.00
6 Los Angeles, CA	7.95
7 San Francisco, CA	7.76
8 Washington, DC	7.73
9 Dallas, TX	7.68
10 Boston, MA	7.67
11 New York City, NY	7.61
12 Chicago, IL	7.52
13 Charlotte, NC	7.50
14 Seattle, WA	7.50
15 Miami, FL	7.20

"There's a mutual respect between partners and associates, and everyone is treated equally."
– Paul Hastings associate

The happiest practice areas

Pursuing shady businessmen – or women – turns out to be a real hoot, says our survey. After sorting each associate into 15 broad practice groups, white-collar crime came out as the clear winner.

Happiest associates by practice area	Rating out of 10
1 White-collar crime	8.28
2 Real estate	8.19
3 Government & regulatory	8.00
4 Healthcare	7.94
5 Tech, media & telecom	7.94
6 Labor & employment	7.93
7 Intellectual property	7.86
8 Banking & finance	7.84
9 Projects & energy	7.76
10 Tax	7.74
11 Corporate	7.72
12 Insurance	7.63
13 Bankruptcy	7.62
14 Litigation	7.61
15 Antitrust	7.54

Tech, media and telecoms lawyers are also a remarkable 22% happier than they expected to be. Both these areas and a few others at the top of the tables represent the more specialized areas populated by smaller numbers of lawyers. Lower down we find the areas that swallow up JDs in their thousands: corporate; litigation; finance. But let's not rush to conclude that the masses of litigators and corporate lawyers are less happy; rather, being on a smaller team with greater responsibility, autonomy, and likelihood of making partner are deciding factors here – and less so the subject matter, we would argue. In fact our advice before you start shortlisting firms is to pick a practice area that inspires you: a lawyer should always choose their subject matter because it's one of the few things they have control over. Do this early on, and natural enthusiasm will get you through interviews and guarantee you a more rewarding career.

Most pleasantly surprised associates, by practice area	Happier than expected %
1 Tech, media & telecom	21.9%
2 White-collar crime	17.8%
3 Labor & employment	16.8%
4 Insurance	16.3%
5 Government & regulatory	14.8%
6 Healthcare	13.6%
7 Banking & finance	12.5%
8 Tax	12.4%
9 Real estate	12.2%
10 Litigation	11.5%
11 Corporate	10.7%
12 Intellectual property	8.1%
13 Bankruptcy	5.7%
14 Projects & energy	4.5%
15 Antitrust	4.1%

Next up: the most stressed associates, grouped by practice area. Note that in many cases the most stressful practices are some of the least happy, as we'd expect. But there are a few exceptions: in particular tech, media and telecoms and healthcare, where associates appear to be both stressed and happy. This isn't uncommon in the law – stress doesn't necessarily trample on happiness. The hundreds of self-defined 'type A' characters we speak to tell us that stress motivates them to achieve. The law firms that apply pressure in the right way get some of the best results from their associates; the firms that manage its effects well are some of the most successful in the market.

Most stressed associates, by practice area	Rating out of 10
1 Healthcare	6.17
2 Tech, media & telecoms	6.14
3 Bankruptcy	6.14
4 Banking & finance	6.08
5 Corporate	5.83
6 Tax	5.76
7 Labor & employment	5.61
8 Antitrust	5.61
9 Litigation	5.57
10 Projects & energy	5.48
11 Intellectual property	5.38
12 Insurance	5.31
13 Government & reg	5.18
14 Real estate	5.03
15 White-collar crime	5.00

The best performing law firms

Top 20 happiest firms	Rating out of 10
1 Paul Hastings	9.13
2 Cozen O'Connor	9.08
3 Finnegan	9.00
4 Venable	8.76
=5 Linklaters	8.75
=5 O'Melveny & Myers	8.75
=5 Snell & Wilmer	8.75
=5 WilmerHale	8.75
=9 Choate	8.67
=9 Harris Wiltshire	8.67
11 Davis Polk	8.63
12 Waller	8.57
13 Kilpatrick Townsend	8.44
14 Baker Botts	8.43
15 Sidley Austin	8.41
16 Seward & Kissel	8.40
=17 Allen & Overy	8.38
=17 Perkins Coie	8.38
19 Fish & Richardson	8.29
20 Akin Gump	8.25

Special note should go to Paul Hastings for coming top in both tables. Our research with their associates this year revealed a down-to-earth working culture: *"you won't find any sharp elbows or crazy gunners here,"* associates reported. *"The work is tough, but it's that much easier when you're working with someone you get along with."* And a more telling quote: *"There's a mutual respect between partners and associates, and everyone is treated equally."*

Across the whole survey, associates' expected happiness before joining was a lowly 6.6/10 on average. Out of this emerges a rather gloomy picture where students are resigning themselves to a career and accepting jobs without much care for their emotional wellbeing. But as we know, the early stages of your career are much more about establishing yourself – happiness can be deferred for a while.

Top 20 most pleasantly surprised associates	Reality minus expectation out of 10
1 Paul Hastings	3.13
2 Alston & Bird	3.08
3 O'Melveny & Myers	2.75
4 Cadwalader	2.44
5 Simpson Thacher	2.31
6 Haynes and Boone	2.30
=7 Winston & Strawn	2.20
=7 Proskauer	2.20
9 Squire Patton Boggs	2.17
=10 Fried Frank	2.13
=10 Goodwin Procter	2.13
=12 Paul, Weiss	2.00
=12 Schulte Roth	2.00
=12 Willkie Farr	2.00
15 Dechert	1.94
=16 Allen & Overy	1.88
=16 Venable	1.88
=18 Irell & Manella	1.83
=18 Reed Smith	1.83
20 Norton Rose Fulbright	1.80

Top 20 least stressed associates in the US	Rating out of 10
1 Harris Wiltshire	3.83
2 Irell & Manella	4.00
3 Cadwalader	4.19
4 Marshall Gerstein	4.20
=5 Linklaters	4.33
=5 Clifford Chance	4.33
7 Sheppard Mullin	4.38
8 Nixon Peabody	4.57
9 Duane Morris	4.60
10 Fitzpatrick	4.63
=11 Hogan Lovells	4.75
=11 O'Melveny & Myers	4.75
=11 Snell & Wilmer	4.75
14 Haynes and Boone	4.80
15 Waller	4.86
16 Hunton & Williams	4.88
17 Vinson & Elkins	4.90
18 Alston & Bird	4.92
=19 Cozen O'Connor	4.94
=19 Fish & Richardson	4.94

Job satisfaction by key market metrics

If anything makes a lawyer happy it's money, surely? Well, not really. We broke our market down by a few variables that make a difference to a firm's culture and a lawyer's fulfilment, and money turned out to have little impact on happiness. This fits with research we did with law students this year which asked, 'What's the main reason you want you to be a lawyer?' And by a wide margin, 'intellectually challenging work' was the main draw into the profession (40%). The opportunity to 'make the world a better place' also trumped the 'good salary' option, which is reflected below in the pro bono test. Taking *Chambers USA* rankings as a measure of achievement, we also see that a law firm's performance correlates with happiness.

Job satisfaction by key metrics	Happier than expected %	Stress rating out of 10
The top 25 performers in *Chambers USA* by Band 1 rankings	13%	5.7
The lower 25 performers in *Chambers USA* by Band 1 rankings	8%	5.4
Top 50 biggest firms	14%	5.7
Bottom 50 smallest firms	9%	5.5
Associates starting on $160,000 or higher	12%	5.6
Associates earning under $160,000 in their first year	10%	5.5
Top 50 pro bono billers	13%	5.6
Bottom 50 pro bono billers	10%	5.5

Across all law firms, average stress ratings ranged from 7.4 to 3.8 out of 10, so variance firm-by-firm is significant. But looking at the table left, we see that the stress ratings level out no matter what portion of the market you look at. We know that pressure and workload is high across the profession, but factors like law firm size or market position appear to have little impact on how stressed lawyers are. The conclusion, then, should be that stress is less influenced by aspiration and pressure to achieve, but by how a firm manages their lawyers' stress – the cultural factors that determine how you get the best out of your lawyers. Law firms are a little preoccupied with defining their culture, so perhaps we should listen to our happiest lawyers this year at Paul Hastings, who dismissed this talk of culture: *"A lot of the time it's a load of crap."*

If we take anything from this survey, it's that you should decide what you want from your career before you start researching firms. Consider the elements you think would make life fulfilling or otherwise, then ask which law firms can match that.

'Stress is less influenced by aspiration and pressure to achieve, but by how a firm manages their lawyers' stress – the cultural factors that determine how you get the best out of your lawyers.'

Refine Your Search

How do you choose the right firm?

The menu of firms to choose between is bewildering. Researching them all would be a waste of time. Increase your prospect of getting a job by choosing the firm that suits you.

Step 1: work out what matters in your life – not what others expect of you

Consider how you respond to stress, work/life balance, how much autonomy you can handle, what subject matter gets you going, how you build and rely on personal relationships, and whether prestige motivates you. Will you become a pillar of your local business community or a jet-setting deal-maker? Do you thrive in disorder or need to control everything? Are you buttoned-up or dress down? Aggressive or collaborative?

Step 2: refine your search

Shortlist cities and regions. Then pick some practice areas you think you'd thrive in – firms will be looking for someone with focus and passion. The practice area reviews in this guide will make sense of your options. The chambers-associate.com search will round down the firms you should look at.

Step 3: read the introductions

Open the Inside View and read the first few paragraphs. Does it sound like your bag? Remember your wish list from Step 1 and have a look at our reviews of the firm culture, in particular. Bookmark all the firms that stand out.

Step 4: compare your shortlist

Use the comparison function on chambers-associate.com to compare your firms on every factor that counts: salary, pro bono, billables, diversity stats, size of firm, Chambers rankings, international offices, maternity allowance...

www.chambers-associate.com

Hours and Compensation Survey

Firm	1st year salary	2nd year salary	Billable hour requirement/ target	Average billable hours per associate 2015	Billable pro bono hours	Average pro bono hours per attorney	Total pro bono hours across US offices in 2015
Akin Gump	$160,000	$170,000	No official requirement	U	Unlimited	93	68,107
Allen & Overy	$160,000	$170,000	2,000 target	1,512	50	14	1,977
Alston & Bird	$135,000 - $160,000	U	1,900 target	U	100	67	49,465
Arnold & Porter	$160,000	U	2,000 required	U	200	124	82,998
Axinn	$150,000 - $160,000	$170,000	1,850 target	1,835	100	39	1,862
Baker & McKenzie	$130,000 - $160,000	U	2,000 required	U	U	U	U
Baker Botts	$160,000	U	2,000 required	U	Unlimited	40	28,390
Bracewell	$160,000	$170,000	2,000 target (reduced 1,800 target option)	U	100	27	10,761
Brown Rudnick	$160,000	$165,000 - $170,000	1,900 required	U	Unlimited (on approved matters)	48	6,540
Cadwalader	$160,000	$170,000	No requirement	1,627	200	45	17,104
Cahill	$160,000	$170,000	No requirement	U	Unlimited	41	13,440
Chadbourne	$160,000	$170,000	1,900 target	1,789	Unlimited (with prior approval)	87	20,266
Choate	$160,000	$170,000	1,900 required	U	Unlimited	33	5,377
Cleary Gottlieb	$160,000	$170,000	No requirement	U	Unlimited	92	63,066
Clifford Chance	$160,000	$170,000	No requirement	U	Unlimited	U (50 minimum encouraged)	U
Cooley	$160,000	$170,000	1,950 target	1,935	Unlimited	48	38,667
Cozen O'Connor	$125,000- $155,000	U	U	1,770	60	17	11,247
Cravath	$160,000	$170,000	No requirement	U	Unlimited	51	24,584
Crowell	$160,000	$170,000	1,900 target	1,711	50 (rest credited for bonus)	72	33,117
Curtis	$160,000	$170,000	No requirement	1,720	Unlimited	63	4,606
Davis Polk	$160,000	$170,000	No requirement	U	U	50	38,428
Debevoise	$160,000	$170,000	No requirement	U	U	118	58,628
Dechert	$160,000	$170,000	1,950 target	U	Unlimited (approval needed over 200)	78	49,461
DLA Piper	$145,000 - $160,000	U	2,000 target	1,807	U	79	110,000
Duane Morris	$150,000	U	1,950 required	U	100	34	22,120
Dykema	$115,000 - $145,000	Not lockstep	1,950 required	U	40 (plus additional with approval)	43	10,030

U = undisclosed

Refine your search

Refine your search

Hours and Compensation Survey *continued*

Firm	1st year salary	2nd year salary	Billable hour requirement/ target	Average billable hours per associate 2015	Billable pro bono hours	Average pro bono hours per attorney	Total pro bono hours across US offices in 2015
Epstein	U	U	1,950 required	1,728	100	20	5,000
Fenwick & West	$160,000	$170,000	1,950 required (1,800 reduced)	1,850	Unlimited	U	17,580
Finnegan	$160,000	$170,000	2,000 required	1,796	80	65	10,282
Fish & Richardson	$160,000	$170,000	1,900 required	1,972	200 (extensions authorized case-by-case)	43	14,469
Fitzpatrick	$160,000	U	2,160 target	U	Unlimited (within reason)	27	3,802
Foley & Lardner	$120,000 - $160,000	$130,000 - $175,000	1,850 required	1,867	100 (additional can be credited)	50	42,144
Fox Rothschild	$110,000 - $145,000	Not lock-step	1,850 required (1,900 required in litigation)	1,821	50 (additional with approval)	10	6,649
Freshfields	$160,000	$170,000	U	U	Unlimited	88	11,876
Fried Frank	$160,000	$170,000	2,000 target	U	300	74	30,482
Gibbons	U	$135,000 plus clerk-ship bonus	1,980 requirement	1,638	50	69	14,379
Gibson Dunn	$160,000	$170,000	U	U	1 for 1 credit	120	130,005
Goodwin Procter	$160,000	$170,000	1,950 target	U	Unlimited	68	65,120
Goulston & Storrs	$160,000	U	No requirement	1,850 – 1,900	Unlimited	62	11,823
Greenberg Traurig	$110,000 - $160,000	U	No official formal target	1,765	U	U	U
Hangley	$135,000	U	U	U	None	U	U
Harris, Wiltshire & Grannis	$168,000	$175,000	No requirement	1,648	Unlimited	40	1,779
Haynes and Boone	$160,000	$170,000	U	1,692	100 (additional with approval)	33	130,090
Hogan Lovells	$160,000	$170,000	1,800 – 2,000 re-quirement (varies by location)	U	100 (once 1,800 billable target met. Unlimited at 1,850)	79	77,199
Holland & Knight	$160,000	$170,000	1,900 required	U	100 (additional with approval)	55	60,375
Hughes Hubbard	$160,000	$170,000	1,950 target	1,800	200	131	50,922
Hunton & Wil-liams	$145,000-$160,000	U	2,000 target	1,865	50 (plus 25 com-munity service hours)	64	40,891
Irell & Manella	$160,000	$170,000	2,000 target	1,688	Unlimited	150	19,196
Jackson Walker	$160,000	U	1,950 target	U	50 (citizenship hours required, can include pro bono)	20	6,930
Jenner & Block	$160,000	$170,000	2,000 target	U	Unlimited	108	54,455

U = undisclosed

Hours and Compensation Survey *continued*

Firm	1st year salary	2nd year salary	Billable hour requirement/ target	Average billable hours per associate 2015	Billable pro bono hours	Average pro bono hours per attorney	Total pro bono hours across US offices in 2015
Jones Day	$145,000 - $160,000	U	2,000 required	U	Unlimited (but with approval)	U	104,566
K&L Gates	$115,000 -$160,000	U	No requirement	U	Unlimited	45	55,243
Kasowitz	$160,000	$170,000	U	U	Unlimited	35	9,741
Katten Muchin	$160,000	$170,000	2,000 required	U	100 (additional with approval)	42	26,635
Kaye Scholer	$160,000	$170,000	1,800 target	U	200	56	20,662
Kilpatrick Townsend	$135,000 - 160,000	$140,000 - 195,000	1,850 (level 1) 1,900 (level 2) targets	1,797	50	57	39,733
King & Spalding	$135,000 - $160,000	$140,000 - $170,000	No requirement	1,985	100	29	22,365
Kirkland & Ellis	$160,000	U	No requirement	U	Unlimited	72	103,846
Kramer Levin	$160,000	$170,000	No requirement	1,669	Unlimited	82	23,254
Latham & Watkins	$160,000	U	1,900 target	U	Unlimited	85	127,200
Linklaters	$160,000	$170,000	No requirement	U	Unlimited	79	8,685
Lowenstein	$160,000	$170,000	No requirement	U	U	84	27,279
Marshall Gerstein	$160,000	U	1,950 required	1,817	50 (additional can be credited)	32	2,281
Mayer Brown	$160,000	$170,000	2,000 required	U	Unlimited	53	42,024
McGuire-Woods	$115,000 - $155,000	U	1,950 required	1,866	50	44	27,749
Milbank	$160,000	$170,000	No requirement	U	Unlimited	96	46,091
Mintz Levin	$160,000	$170,000	No requirement	U	Unlimited	U	19,668
Morgan Lewis	$145,000 - $160,000	$150,000 - $170,000	No requirement	U	Unlimited	55	88,912
Morrison & Foerster	$160,000	$170,000	U	U	Unlimited	114	81,749
Munger Tolles	$160,000	$170,000	U	1,786	Unlimited	133	26,874
Nixon Peabody	$160,000	$165,000	1,850 required	1,717	60	62	34,000
Norton Rose Fulbright	$160,000	U	No requirement	U	100	U	U
Nutter	$145,000	Not lock-step	1,900 required	1,668	Unlimited	42	6,142
O'Melveny & Myers	$160,000	$170,000	No requirement	U	Unlimited	97	54,779
Orrick	$145,000 - $160,000	$155,000 - $170,000	1,950 target	1,879	Unlimited	92	60,248
Patterson Belknapp	$160,000	$170,000	1,850 target	U	None	135	25,261
Paul Hastings	$160,000	$170,000	2,000 target	U	Unlimited	90	68,583
Paul, Weiss	$160,000	$170,000	No requirement	U	Unlimited	63	55,151
Pepper Hamilton	$150,000 - $160,000	U	1,940 target	1,767	Unlimited	50	25,731

U = undisclosed

Hours and Compensation Survey *continued*

Firm	1st year salary	2nd year salary	Billable hour requirement/ target	Average billable hours per associate 2015	Billable pro bono hours	Average pro bono hours per attorney	Total pro bono hours across US offices in 2015
Perkins Coie	\$100,000 - \$160,000	\$105,000 - \$170,000	1,800 – 1,950 requirement	1,807 – 2,221 (dependent on location)	Unlimited	59	54,408
Pillsbury	\$160,000	\$170,000	1,950 target	U	Unlimited	56	31,132
Proskauer	\$110,000 - \$160,000	\$120,000 - \$170,000	No requirement	U	Unlimited	51	35,233
Reed Smith	\$145,000 - \$160,000	\$150,000 - \$170,000	1,900 required	1,782	120 (unlimited once billable requirement met)	55	55,516
Ropes & Gray	\$160,000	\$170,000	No requirement	U	Unlimited	96	98,174
Schulte Roth	\$160,000	\$170,000	2,000 target	U	U	33	10,457
Sedgwick	U	U	1,950 required	U	25	U	U
Seward & Kissel	\$160,000	\$170,000	2,000 target	1,665	Unlimited	31	6,671
Shearman & Sterling	\$160,000	\$170,000	No requirement	U	U	67	28,833
Sheppard Mullin	\$160,000	\$170,000	1,950 target	1,790	Unlimited	36	26,632
Sidley Austin	\$160,000	\$170,000	2,000 target	U	U	59	101,327
Simpson Thacher	\$160,000	\$170,000	No requirement	U	Unlimited	60	44,773
Skadden	\$160,000	\$170,000	1,800 requirement	U	Unlimited	89	110,516
Snell & Wilmer	\$115,000 - \$160,000	U	2,000 target	1,822	Unlimited	37	15,315
Squire Patton Boggs	\$120,000- \$160,000	U	1,950 required (1,900 for first-years)	U	100	45	31,357
Sterne Kessler	\$160,000	\$170,000	1,900 – 2,000 target	1,878	U	U	U
Stroock	\$160,000	\$170,000	1,800 target	U	200	57	15,646
Sullivan & Cromwell	\$160,000	\$170,000	No requirement	U	Unlimited	67	42,776
Thompson & Knight	\$160,000	\$170,000	2,000 target (1,900 for first-years)	2,049	Unlimited (50+ need approval)	35	4,805
Vedder Price	\$160,000	\$165,000 - \$170,000	2,000 target	U	60	U	U
Venable	\$160,000	U	1900 required	U	50	36	28,869
Vinson & Elkins	\$160,000	\$170,000	2,000 target	1,819	Unlimited	44	25,566
Waller	\$115,000	\$126,000	1,800 requirement	1,779	None	15	2,835
Weil	\$160,000	\$170,000	No requirement	U	Unlimited	60	40,000
White & Case	\$155,000 - \$160,000	\$160,000 - \$170,000	2,000 target	U	200	86	59,753
Wiley Rein	\$160,000	\$170,000	1,950 target	1,972	50	37	9,819
Willkie Farr	\$160,000	\$170,000	No requirement	U	Unlimited	62	30,458
WilmerHale	\$160,000	\$170,000	2,000 required	1,893	Unlimited	97	99,822
Winston & Strawn	\$160,000	\$170,000	2,000 required	U	100	64	50,767

U = undisclosed

Law firm horror stories we heard this year...

"You should expect to be contacted basically 24/7, and sometimes they'll call you to pull a document that it would take five minutes to pull themselves. It's very difficult especially when you've said 'I'll be at a wedding' but you're still getting emails, and you're trying to answer them but you really can't drop everything in the middle of the speeches!"

" I got assigned to work with a certain partner that everyone else at the firm had warned us about. Another partner said I would probably want to kill myself within a few months, while others just said 'good luck with that.' They weren't exaggerating and it is the sort of situation that makes you think you could just quit."

... read more online.

Class Size

Firm	Number of Summers						
	2010	2011	2012	2013	2014	2015	201
Akin Gump	34	62	61	52	54	60	54 e
Allen & Overy	27	27	24	20	23	18	24
Alston & Bird	32	63	60	50	43	46	55
Arnold & Porter						34	38
Axinn					3	4	6
Baker & McKenzie	25	26	31	28	34	37	45
Baker Botts	67	91	99	88	88	118	108
Bracewell	52	40	46	61	49	49	37
Brown Rudnick	20	22	22	20	16	14	9
Cadwalader	32	35	40	38	44	44	50
Cahill	16	37	41	51	40	36	38
Chadbourne	20	19	22	18	11	13	16
Choate		11	15	11	14	15	17
Cleary Gottlieb	89	112	145	126	99	124	102
Clifford Chance	9	25	23	24	24	27	24
Cooley	24	41	47	48	53	41	65
Cozen O'Connor						15	19
Cravath	23	53	87	97	99	105	116
Crowell	21	22	22	24	18	17	26
Curtis	10	15	13	10	9	10	10
Davis Polk	82	96	132	125	123	137	159
Debevoise	51	55	62	65	78	68	75
Dechert					49	70	74
DLA Piper	35	64	62	30	34	35	33 es
Duane Morris	10	13	16	16	15	21	17
Dykema	11	11	18	18	24	14	32
Epstein	10	11	12	11	10	10	11
Fenwick & West							34
Finnegan	20	23	24	20	16	28	29
Fish & Richardson	16	31	29	28	39	38	42
Fitzpatrick	22	15	19	11	16	7	8
Foley & Lardner					43	60	61
Fox Rothschild	12	15	14	11	15	21	28
Freshfields	19	12	14	20	22	24	27
Fried Frank	45	49	43	31	42	54	74
Gibbons	NSP						
Gibson Dunn	110	117	171	149	131	125	126
Goodwin Procter	40	42	55	50	48	65	57
Goulston & Storrs							7
Greenberg Traurig	25	28	31	33	42	46	46
Hangley	NSP						
Harris Wiltshire					2	3	3

NSP = No Summer Program

Size of starting class						
2010	2011	2012	2013	2014	2015	2016
36	40	38	50	33	33	38
18	20	21	22	16	17	21
79	49	64	52	36	34	38
					35	26
				6	4	4
23	25	24	30	14	32	32
38	48	48	48	40	52	64
33	23	19	25	34	20	23
15	21	18	20	23	14	14
27	26	31	39	37	34	40
33	41	34	34	47	38	37
18	11	17	15	12	10	9
13	18	11	13	15	10	11
110	81	93	126	99	92	90
41	30	24	20	22	29	29
38	30	46	48	46	44	45
					14	14
89	99	44	75	94	92	90
21	15	14	16	18	14	11
14	9	15	11	8	7	8
98	70	92	109	101	112	133
82	35	47	62	66	76	75
				44	54	65
62	53	49	50	30	35	31
9	9	12	13	9	10	18
6	5	6	12	8	16	10
6	7	6	9	8	8	10
						19
27	31	28	30	25	21	24
20	24	20	15	18	22	25
18	16	12	15	8	10	9
				50	36	48
13	13	13	12	11	12	19
8	15	11	7	18	17	20
53	51	39	32	26	43	52
10	10	10	10	10	6	tbd
123	89	103	125	111	109	96
						60
						6
27	21	23	27	43	37	36
					1	1 – 2
				7	4	4

Class Size *continued*

Number of Summers

Firm	2010	2011	2012	2013	2014	2015	201
Haynes and Boone	42	46	50	52	59	60	49
Hogan Lovells	65	55	76	86	69	83	110
Holland & Knight	26	39	40	27	23	41	45
Hughes Hubbard							21
Hunton & Williams	10	24	35	29	29	40	35
Irell & Manella	37	29	38	37	30	24	20
Jackson Walker	18	21	21	23	17	21	26
Jenner & Block	30	35	35	45	33	37	39
Jones Day	124	166	156	181	165	158	164
K&L Gates	34	75	77	83	122	92	81
Kasowitz	21	24	21	25	14	6	9
Katten Muchin	9	35	34	35	32	37	24
Kaye Scholer	13	18	20	24	16	19	25
Kilpatrick Townsend							32
King & Spalding	23	24	31	41	35	46	56
Kirkland & Ellis	72	140	166	132	109	139	165
Kramer Levin	19	15	18	20	16	15	15
Latham & Watkins	110	168	122	148	162	182	202
Linklaters	23	25	32	23	24	25	20
Lowenstein							24
Marshall Gerstein							3
Mayer Brown	36	35	58	71	84	63	67
McGuireWoods					16	17	22
Milbank	20	39	45	86	47	57	67
Mintz Levin						18	TBD
Morgan Lewis		63	69	57	59	61	62
Morrison & Foerster					81	88	100
Munger Tolles	19	27	25	29	30	32	22
Nixon Peabody					27	28	22
Norton Rose Fulbright							64
Nutter					6	7	7
O'Melveny & Myers					69	73	92
Orrick	28	56	45	34	40	34	50
Patterson Belknapp	9	11	9	9	7	0	NSP
Paul Hastings					63	69	132
Paul, Weiss	80	101	120	118	110	149	144
Pepper Hamilton					18	23	23
Perkins Coie	31	38	44	49	42	57	47
Pillsbury	17	25	29	31	35	37	43
Proskauer	42	47	53	42	74	75	77
Reed Smith	21	42	34	47	41	56	47

NSP = No Summer Program

Size of starting class

2010	2011	2012	2013	2014	2015	2016
33	23	26	31	31	29	30
56	86	54	58	58	57	62
36	50	34	34	24	27	38
						22
13	18	19	32	24	26	31
29	20	26	23	23	14	15
12	12	13	17	15	9	15
44	37	28	35	20	28	34
133	94	117	126	101	129	118
	104	63	51	70	85	67
19	18	22	18	16	16 (18 including clerks)	6
7	11	29	28	31	23	23
16	23	15	15	21	17	18
						16
43	26	15	22	31	24	27
130	142	140	141	111	114	140
20	14	11	16	17	12	12
203	131	150	115	133	104	156
25	20	19	26	20	23	17
						21
						5
94	59	30	47	49	60	68
				23	15	19
55	22	31	43	42	46	51
					16	17
70	51	59	62	56	86	61
				59	43	43
23	17	15	14	18	17	10
				16	23	21
						37
				6	7	4
				67	47	67
47	33	39	28	26	31	33
11	13	16	6	6	6	17
				54	61	61
86	61	66	97	92	84	120
				21	12	14
37	36	23	27	31	30	38
26	26	22	23	29	25	35
56	86	40	43	41	62	53
31	32	35	34	43	47	46

Class Size *continued*

	Number of Summers						
Firm	2010	2011	2012	2013	2014	2015	201
Ropes & Gray	82	124	125	80	100	141	144
Sedgwick	2	10	6	7	4		3
Schulte Roth							37
Seward	9	11	12	11	14	17	18
Shearman & Sterling	28	41	33	44	52	67	78
Sheppard Mullin	27	31	30	33	33	33	32
Sidley Austin	50	118	111	113	111	106	188
Simpson Thacher	72	100	107	79	105	129	140
Skadden	78	94	156	174	207	220	212
Snell & Wilmer	20	20	22	25	18	19	30
Squire Patton Boggs	8	2	32	12	16	26	28
Sterne Kessler							5
Stroock	19	25	21	27	16	14	14
Sullivan & Cromwell	77	137	122	150	126	125	144
Thompson & Knight							15
Vedder Price							14
Venable	17	29	30	29	31	37	36
Vinson	98	104	103	89	78	91	68
Waller	6	8	7	7	8	8	9
Weil	42	71	110	101	76	94	97
White & Case	47	60	56	56	57	66	102
Wiley Rein	13	15	13	19	17	10	11
Willkie Farr	18	20	43	45	54	78	64
WilmerHale	66	89	91	128	93	83	108
Winston & Strawn	43	52	61	36	59	64	67

NSP = No Summer Program

Summer hiring in 2016 is up 11.1% on 2015 among the firms in the *Chambers Associate* Survey.

Refine your search

Size of starting class						
2010	2011	2012	2013	2014	2015	2016
187	216	116	126	96	108	133
7	5	9	4	6		7
						33
10	8	11	14	11	15	14
51	70	39	31	39	48	59
28	28	26	30	31	29	32
60	154	104	115	120	101	96
83	108	112	97	96	114	104
184	92	86	135	149	186	200
23	14	18	17	22	19	13
24	1	5	12	4	16	10
						5
24	13	23	16	25	14	14
116	89	114	87	102	108	112
						8
						10
20	23	39	27	29	28	39
72	57	70	74	43	48	62
6	4	4	6	5	10	5
54	104	130	77	59	64	83
				58	55	67
13	18	13	13	16	12	8
47	27	22	42	43	55	66
88	99	85	75	105	80	49
69	36	48	41	23	43	51

Since the dismal market of 2010, summer hiring has increased by 73% among the firms in *Chambers Associate*.

Read the full analysis on www.chambers-associate.com

Work/life and Benefits Survey

Firm	Vacation	Flexible work arrangements	Paid maternity
Akin Gump	4 weeks	Reduced Workload Policy	18 weeks
Allen & Overy	4 weeks	Considered in certain circumstances	18 weeks primary caregiver, 4 weeks secondary caregiver
Alston & Bird	Discretionary	Alternative Career Path	18 weeks primary caregiver, 4 weeks non-primary caregiver
Arnold & Porter	Unlimited	Reduced hours schedule and part-time available	18 weeks
Axinn	4 weeks	Considered in certain circumstances	18 weeks
Baker & McKenzie	Discretionary	Case by case basis	18 weeks primary caregiver, 6 weeks secondary caregiver
Baker Botts	3 weeks	✓	12 weeks
Bracewell	Unlimited	Case by case basis	18 weeks primary caregiver
Brown Rudnick	4 weeks	Case by case basis	18 weeks
Cadwalader	Unlimited	Case by case basis	18 weeks
Cahill	4 weeks	Case by case basis	18 weeks (26 weeks maternity-related disability)
Chadbourne	4 weeks (5 floating days)	Case by case basis	18 weeks primary caregiver, 12 weeks non-birth primary caregiver
Choate	4 weeks	Reduced schedules available	12 weeks primary caregiver, 4 weeks non-primary caregiver
Cleary Gottlieb	4 weeks (5 weeks after four years' employment)	Case by case basis	18 weeks primary caregiver
Clifford Chance	4 weeks	Undisclosed	18 weeks
Cooley	4 weeks	Case by case basis	18 weeks primary caregiver
Cozen O'Connor	Unlimited	Reduced hours schedules	8 weeks + 6-8 weeks disability
Cravath	4 weeks	Flexible full-time	18-20 weeks primary caregiver, 12 weeks secondary caregiver
Crowell	Unlimited	Case by case basis	18 weeks
Curtis	4 weeks	Case by case basis	12 weeks
Davis Polk	4 weeks (5 weeks after five years' employment)	Part-time, flexitime and telecommuting	18 weeks
Debevoise	4 weeks	Part-time available	18 weeks (plus 2 weeks pre birth leave)
Dechert	4 weeks	Case by case basis	18 weeks
DLA Piper	Discretionary	Flexible Work Solutions including ramp-up arrangements and reduced hours schedules	18 weeks
Duane Morris	4 weeks	Part-time/flex-time policies	16 weeks
Dykema	Unlimited	Part-time available	12 weeks
Epstein	4 weeks	Alternative work schedules available	12 weeks
Fenwick & West	4 weeks	Case by case basis	18 weeks

Paid paternity	Adoption or surrogacy fees	Retirement plan	Medical and dental plans
4 weeks	✓ adoption only	✓ 401K	✓ contributory
18 weeks primary caregiver, 4 weeks secondary caregiver	NO	✓ 401K	Medical, dental, vision contributory
18 weeks primary caregiver, 4 weeks non-primary caregiver	Up to $10,000 reimbursement for adoption	✓ 401K, Roth 401K	✓ contributory
6 weeks	Up to $10,000	✓ 401K	✓ contributory
2 weeks	NO	✓ 401K	✓ contributory
18 weeks primary caregiver, 6 weeks secondary caregiver	✓ - generous	✓ contributory	✓ contributory
12 weeks	NO	✓ 401K/IRA	✓ contributory
2 weeks for secondary caregiver	NO	✓ 401K	✓ contributory
4 weeks	NO	✓ 401K	✓ contributory
4 weeks	NO	✓ 401K	✓ contributory
4 weeks	Undisclosed	✓ 401K	✓ contributory
12 weeks primary caregiver	NO	✓ 401K	✓ contributory
12 weeks primary caregiver, 4 weeks non-primary caregiver	NO	✓ 401K, Roth 401K	✓ contributory
5 weeks secondary caregiver	NO	✓ Tax Opportunity Plan for Saving	✓ contributory
8 weeks primary caregiver, 4 weeks secondary caregiver	NO	✓ 401K	✓ contributory
4 weeks secondary caregiver	NO	✓ 401K, Roth 401K	✓ contributory
8 weeks	NO	✓ 401K with profit sharing feature	✓ contributory
12 weeks primary caregiver, 4 weeks secondary caregiver	NO but 12 weeks paid leave primary caregiver, 4 weeks paid leave secondary carer	✓ 401K	✓ contributory
18 weeks primary caregiver, 4 weeks non primary caregiver	NO	✓ 401K, Roth 401K	✓ contributory
2 weeks	NO	✓ 401K	✓
10 weeks	NO	✓ 401K	✓ contributory
10 weeks primary caregiver, 4 weeks non-primary caregiver	NO	✓ 401K	✓ contributory
10 weeks primary caregiver, 4 weeks non-primary caregiver	NO	✓ 401K	✓ contributory
4 weeks	NO	✓ 401K	✓ contributory
4 weeks	NO	✓ 401K	✓ partial contributory
6 weeks	NO	✓ 401K	✓ contributory
12 weeks	NO	✓ 401K	✓
4 weeks	NO	✓ 401K	✓ contributory

Work/life and Benefits Survey *continued*

Firm	Vacation	Flexible work arrangements	Paid maternity
Finnegan	Undisclosed	Alternative work arrangement policy	18 weeks
Fish & Richardson	Discretionary	Reduced hours arrangement	16 weeks primary caregiver
Fitzpatrick	4 weeks	Case by case basis	12 weeks
Foley & Lardner	3 weeks (less than 8 years), 4 weeks (more than 8 years)	Flexible schedules	18 weeks for primary caregiver, 12 weeks for non-primary caregiver
Fox Rothschild	4 weeks	Reduced hours schedules	12 weeks
Freshfields	4 weeks	Part-time/fixed hours available	12 weeks (additional 12 weeks half salary for attorneys who have been with the firm for 15 months plus)
Fried Frank	4 weeks	Case by case basis (after two years)	18 weeks
Gibbons	3 weeks	Family-friendly schedule available	12 weeks
Gibson Dunn	Discretionary	No	18 weeks primary caregiver
Goodwin Procter	4 weeks	Case by case basis	18 weeks
Goulston & Storrs	4 weeks	✓	8 weeks
Greenberg Traurig	Undisclosed	✓	Up to12 weeks
Hangley	4 weeks	Part-time available	Covered under short-term disability policy
Harris Wiltshire	Unlimited	Case by case basis	17 weeks primary caregivers, 3 weeks non primary caregivers
Haynes and Boone	2 weeks (less than two years), 3 weeks (three to six years), 4 weeks (more than seven years)	Reduced hours schedule (after 4 years employment)	12 weeks
Hogan Lovells	Unlimited	Reduced hours and flex-time	20 weeks
Holland & Knight	4 weeks	Balanced Work/Life Policy	16 weeks
Hughes Hubbard	4 weeks	Case by case basis	18 weeks
Hunton & Williams	4 weeks	Flexible work program	18 weeks primary caregiver, 2 weeks secondary caregiver
Irell & Manella	4 weeks	Part-time available	18 weeks
Jackson Walker	Discretionary	Case by case basis	12 weeks
Jenner & Block	3 weeks	Reduced hours available	18 weeks primary caregiver
Jones Day	4 weeks	Case by case basis	18 weeks paid, 6 unpaid
K&L Gates	3-4 weeks	Balanced Hours Program	12 weeks
Kasowitz	4 weeks	Case by case basis	12 weeks
Katten Muchin	Discretionary	Reduced hours and flex-time	14 weeks
Kaye Scholer	4 weeks	Flexible Work Policy; case by case basis	18 weeks primary caregiver, 4 weeks secondary
Kilpatrick Townsend	4 weeks	Case by case basis	12 -14 weeks (6 weeks parental leave + 6-8 short-term disability)

Paid paternity	Adoption or surrogacy fees	Retirement plan	Medical and dental plans
12 weeks	NO	✓ 401K	Dental plan, health and dental insurance
8 weeks paid + 4 weeks unpaid if secondary caregiver	NO	✓ 401K, Roth 401K	✓ contributory
2 weeks	Undisclosed	✓ 401K	✓ contributory
10 weeks for primary caregiver, 4 weeks for non-primary caregiver	$5,000 + 4 weeks parental leave + 6 weeks paid leave primary caregiver	✓ 401K	✓ contributory
2 weeks	No, but paid leave is provided	✓ 401K	✓ contributory
4 weeks	NO	✓ 401K	Medical contributory, dental employer funded
10 weeks	$15,000	✓ 401K	✓ contributory
12 weeks	Undisclosed	✓ 401K	✓ contributory
10 weeks primary caregiver	NO	✓ 401K	✓ contributory
10 weeks primary caregiver, 4 weeks secondary caregiver	NO	✓ 401K	✓ contributory
8 weeks	Undisclosed	✓	✓
Up to 6 weeks	NO	✓ 401K	✓
2 weeks	NO	✓ 401K	✓ contributory
17 weeks primary caregivers, 3 weeks non-primary caregivers	NO	✓ 401K	✓
4 weeks	NO	✓	✓ contributory
12 weeks primary caregiver, 6 weeks non-primary caregiver	Up to $5,000 per child ($10,000 maximum) + up to 20 weeks paid leave for primary caregiver	✓	✓ contributory
6 weeks	NO	✓ 401K	✓ contributory
4 weeks	NO	✓ 401k	✓ contributory
18 weeks primary caregiver, 2 weeks secondary caregiver	$5,000 per adoption	✓ 401K	✓ medical contributory, dental non contributory
4 weeks	No but paid adoption and foster parent leave	✓ 401K	✓ contributory
Unofficial; arranged with department	NO	✓ 401K	✓ contributory
6 weeks secondary caregiver	NO but 1 week pre-adoption leave	✓ 401K, Roth 401K	✓ contributory
10 weeks primary caregiver, 4 weeks secondary caregiver	No but 18 weeks paid, 6 weeks unpaid for primary caregiver	✓ 401K	✓ contributory
6 weeks	NO	✓ 401K, Roth 401K	✓ contributory
0 weeks	NO	✓ 401K	✓ contributory
4 weeks	NO but 14 weeks leave if primary caregiver	✓ 401K, Roth 401K	✓ contributory
18 weeks primary caregiver, 4 weeks secondary	NO	✓ 401K	✓ contributory
6 weeks	NO	✓	✓ contributory

Work/life and Benefits Survey *continued*

Firm	Vacation	Flexible work arrangements	Paid maternity
King & Spalding	4 weeks	Case by case basis	18 weeks primary caregiver
Kirkland & Ellis	Discretionary	Flexible Work Schedule	18 weeks
Kramer Levin	4 weeks	No	18 weeks primary caregiver, 14 weeks secondary caregiver
Latham & Watkins	Discretionary	✓	18 weeks
Linklaters	22 days	Case by case basis	18 weeks primary caregiver
Lowenstein	Undisclosed	Undisclosed	Undisclosed
Marshall Gerstein	Discretionary	Part-time available after 2 years	12 weeks
Mayer Brown	Unlimited	✓	18 weeks
McGuireWoods	3 weeks	Flex time policy	18 weeks
Milbank	4 weeks	✓	18 weeks
Mintz Levin	4 weeks	Case by case basis	12 weeks
Morgan Lewis	4 weeks	Flexible work schedules	12 -16 weeks (based on individual circumstances)
Morrison & Foerster	4 weeks	Reduced hours and flex-time	18 weeks (+7 unpaid)
Munger Tolles	Discretionary	No written policy	18 weeks primary caregiver
Nixon Peabody	Discretionary	Reduced hours and flex-time	10 weeks
Norton Rose Fulbright	4 weeks (varies by market)	Reduced hours and flex-time	14 weeks primary caregiver
Nutter	4 weeks	Reduced workload schedule after parental or extended parental leave of absence	12 weeks (optional additional 4 or 12 weeks unpaid leave)
O'Melveny & Myers	3-4 weeks (depending on seniority and location)	CustOMMize program including job share, reduced workload, flex-time and PhaseBack	18 weeks
Orrick	Unlimited	Case by case basis after two years employment	22 weeks primary caregiver
Patterson Belknapp	4 weeks	✓ subject to approval	18 weeks
Paul Hastings	4 weeks days (5 weeks after seven years' employment)	No	18 weeks (8 weeks maternity + 6 weeks primary care leave + 4 weeks birthmothers child care leave)
Paul, Weiss	4 weeks	✓	18 weeks
Pepper Hamilton	4 weeks (+ 1 week carry-over if available)	✓ (after two years)	18 weeks
Perkins Coie	Unlimited	Flex-time and reduced hours	18 weeks (or 14 weeks with 140 hours ramp up/ramp down)
Pillsbury	4 weeks	Reduced hours schedules	12 weeks
Proskauer	4 weeks	Flex-time program	18 weeks
Reed Smith	3 weeks (0-3 years from law school) 4 weeks (4 years plus from law school)	Reduced hours schedule	16 weeks
Ropes & Gray	4 weeks	Flex scheduling and reduced hours schedule	18 weeks
Schulte Roth	5 weeks	Case by case basis	18 weeks (+ 6 unpaid)

Paid paternity	Adoption or surrogacy fees	Retirement plan	Medical and dental plans
18 weeks primary caregiver, 6 weeks primary caregiver	NO	✓ 401K, Roth 401K	✓ contributory
10 weeks	NO	✓ 401K	✓ contributory
10 weeks primary caregiver, 4 weeks secondary caregiver	NO	✓ 401K	✓ contributory
4 weeks non-primary caregiver	No but 18 weeks paid leave primary caregiver	✓ 401K	✓
18 weeks primary caregiver, 4 weeks secondary caregiver	NO	✓ 401K	✓ contributory
Undisclosed	Undisclosed	Undisclosed	Undisclosed
12 weeks	NO	✓ 401K	✓ contributory
6 weeks	NO	✓	✓ contributory
6 weeks	Up to $5,000	✓ 401K	✓ contributory
4 weeks	NO	✓ 401K	✓ subsidized
8 weeks	Undisclosed	✓ 401K, Roth 401K	✓ contributory
12 -16 weeks (based on individual circumstances)	No, but paid adoption leave	✓ 401K	✓ contributory
10 weeks (+2 unpaid)	NO but paid adoption leave	✓ 401K, Roth 401K	✓ contributory
6 weeks secondary caregiver	NO but paid adoption leave	✓ 401K	✓ contributory
4 weeks	✓	✓ 401K	✓ contributory
4 weeks secondary caregiver	Up to $7,500 per adoption	✓ 401K	✓ contributory
12 weeks (optional additional 4 or 12 weeks unpaid leave)	NO but 12 weeks unpaid foster care leave	✓ 401K, Roth 401K	✓
6 weeks	NO	✓ 401K	✓ contributory
4 weeks, non-primary caregiver	NO but paid adoption and surrogacy leave	✓ 401K	✓ contributory
4 weeks	NO	✓ 401K	✓ contributory
10 weeks (6 weeks primary caregiver + 4 weeks child care leave)	Undisclosed	✓ contributory, 401K	✓ contributory
4 weeks	NO	✓ 401K	✓ contributory
6 weeks	NO	✓ 401K, Roth 401K	✓ contributory
4 weeks	Up to $5,000	✓ Salary Deferral Plan	✓
6 weeks	NO	✓ 401K	✓ contributory
4 weeks	$5,000	✓ 401K	✓ contributory
10 weeks	NO	✓ 401k	✓ contributory
4 weeks	NO	✓ 401K	✓ contributory
2 weeks	NO	✓	✓ contributory

Becoming a Lawyer

What type of law firm suits you?

Researching every firm to find the right fit for you would be madness. So here's how to start a shortlist.

Wall Street firms

BY revenue, New York accounts for 17% of the nation's legal market (while the state is home to just 6% of the population). The city's most elite firms will be found in the borough of Manhattan, either near Wall Street or in Midtown. While they can range in size from under 200 to over 2,000 lawyers, all will house teams of attorneys working on high-value cases and deals for high financiers and big business, which are regularly reported on in the pages of the *Wall Street Journal*. A big pull with these firms is the prestige, but it does come at a cost: young lawyers work long hours, often as *"a cog who just has their own individual tasks."* New York is also the country's most internationally oriented market, and even though some Wall Street firms may not have legions of lawyers stationed in Chicago, Charlotte or Shanghai, their work can span the nation and the globe. Culture-wise they can be stuffy and hierarchical, even for law firms.

Global firms

Law firms have been 'international' for years. White & Case made the trip from New York to open an office in Paris in 1926, a full year before Charles Lindbergh made the same journey in the Spirit of St. Louis. However, an increasing number of firms are now more than 'international' – they are global. They figure that, in today's world, you need a foothold in every market to have a competitive advantage.

A few early movers like Baker & McKenzie have grown organically from small beginnings in other countries, but the current trend is to become global by bolting together two or more large international firms. For example, Dentons is the product of America's Sonnenschein Nath & Rosenthal, the UK's Denton Wilde Sapte, Canada's Fraser Milner Casgrain and the French-founded Salans. This amalgamation means Dentons now operates from a mind-boggling 79 locations in 52 countries across Europe, Canada, the UK, the USA, the Middle East, Asia-Pacific, Central and East Asia, and Africa.

Having flooded the Western world with offices, the global firms are now targeting emerging markets: sending delegations to charm the Chinese and Russians, beginning to open offices in Africa and South America, and keeping a close eye on India (currently off limits to foreign firms).

The work junior associates undertake is not hugely different from their peers at Wall Street firms. What is different is the strategy these firms employ to achieve their goals. This naturally has a knock-on effect on the culture. Like Wall Street firms, the work will have an international flavor.

Multi-site firms

Clients like their lawyers close at hand, so as they've grown, many firms have established networks of offices across the country. At some multi-site firms, offices work together on nationwide matters, while at others each office focuses on matters in its locality. The size of the deals will often compete with the biggest international firms, as do the salaries.

Many of these firms maintain offices abroad (though they generally have less reach than the global firms mentioned above) which have differing levels of integration with the USA (and many multi-site firms are merging with overseas counterparts to move into the 'global' category). A major benefit of a multi-site firm is that as an associate you can move cities while remaining with the same employer.

Regional firms

There can be quite a difference in the culture, working style and practice remit of firms based in different regions. Many firms take pride in the fact they are Californian, Midwestern or Bostonian. All populous states – from New Jersey and Pennsylvania to Arizona and Minnesota – have their own sophisticated legal markets, with a group of leading firms working on complex transactions and cases.

Certain regions are known for certain types of work: banking and finance in New York; government/regulatory in DC; technology and media in California; energy in Texas; private equity in Boston, etc. Many West Coast firms look toward Asia for business, while Florida firms often work in Latin America. Each region has its own set of traits and it is worth thinking about them. When researching a firm, find out about the local market in which it operates. Typically, these firms are seen as less high-stress than the New York elite, and that's reflected in the salary – which is still good, nevertheless.

Boutiques and specialists

Boutiques are firms that practice in a single area of law "Students should take advantage of job fairs. Law firms put a tremendous amount of time and money into these events... It's not just about free food! " litigation or IP, for example. Some are very small; others have hundreds of lawyers. These firms offer a great opportunity for those who know what they want to do and want to work with like-minded people, but they are not a good option if you are unsure what area of law you want to work in. Specialist firms may offer additional practice areas to support their main agenda.

Outside BigLaw: small firms

Only a fraction of the nation's 50,000 law firms employ more than 50 lawyers. The others are smaller businesses doing all kinds of legal work often with a local focus, in towns and cities from Portland, Maine to Portland, Oregon, and from Anchorage to Key West. We discuss the opportunities offered by small firms in our small firms feature elsewhere in this guide.

"Students should take advantage of job fairs. Law firms put a tremendous amount of time and money into these events, and they're a great way for you to get a sense of what different firms are about and the practice areas they cover. It's not just about free food!"

– Elizabeth Workman, Assistant Dean for Career Services, Vanderbilt Law School

Among our featured firms in this edition...

DLA Piper and **Greenberg Traurig** have the most domestic offices, with **29**

The firm with the most international offices is **Baker & McKenzie**, with **70**

Skadden has the largest summer class in 2016, with **212** summers (down from 220 in 2015 but up from 207 in 2014)

Latham has the largest number of associates – **1,001**

Skadden also has the largest starting class in 2016, with **200** juniors (up from 186 in 2015 and 149 in 2014)

Irell & Manella tops the pro bono chart this year, with attorneys here averaging **150 hours** in 2015 (closely followed by **Patterson** with 135 and **Munger** with 133)

The firm paying the highest first-year salary is once again **Harris, Wiltshire & Grannis**, at **$168,000** (up a smidgen from $167,850 in 2015)

Dykema and **Harris Wiltshire** share the top spot for proportion of female associates at **60%**, followed closely by last year's table topper, **Crowell & Moring** at 58.4%

Sedgwick has the best ratio of female partners at **30%**; **Baker & McKenzie** is the best giant firm for female partners, at **28%**

Sterne Kessler has the most ethnically diverse partnership, at 26%; Orrick and White & Case follow close behind at **21%**

Once again, **Jenner & Block** has the biggest proportion of gay lawyers among the large firms in this guide – **11.7%** of associates identify as LGBT

Allen & Overy reported a market-topping **12.5%** LGBT partnership this year

The Big Interview with... **Lindsay Cameron,** who quit BigLaw to write *BIGLAW: A Novel*

Lindsay Cameron quit BigLaw to write BIGLAW: A Novel, which came out in late 2015. One glowing review called it "The Devil Wears Prada for the legal set." She worked for several years as a corporate lawyer at large law firms in the US and Canada, including Schulte Roth & Zabel. Lindsay Cameron is a graduate of the University of British Columbia School of Law and lives in New York with her husband and two kids.

Narrated by an overworked female junior associate in New York called Mackenzie Corbett, BIGLAW is a painfully funny read that will touch a nerve with anyone who's had or is considering a career in BigLaw. Needless to say, the heroine's dreams of lawyerly bliss don't unfold quite as planned.

Why did you decide to become a lawyer?
I enjoyed academics and had a good work ethic, but wasn't a risk taker. So, I narrowed my career options down to medicine, engineering or law. I'm too squeamish for medicine, lacked the necessary skill set for engineering and that left law. So... law school here I come!

Whhat do you think your readers will get out of your novel?
I think the book gives readers a good sense of the rewarding, anxiety-provoking, maddening world of working in a large law firm and the sacrifices that go along with chasing the brass ring. For law students considering a career in BigLaw, I think it will either make them run in the opposite direction or allow them to go into that world eyes wide open.

"For law students considering a career in BigLaw, I think the book will either make them run in the opposite direction or allow them to go into that world eyes wide open."

Starting out, what did you expect from a career in the law?
I don't think I knew what to expect. In my first week of law school when I was sitting on the steps contemplating if I'd made the right decision in my process of elimination, a retired dean of the law school came up to me and sat down. He pointed to a Latin phrase written over the front entrance to the building and explained the translation. *"Let justice be done though the heavens fall."* I remember feeling proud that I was embarking on a noble profession.

Why did you choose corporate law, specifically?
I enjoyed my corporate law classes and found the type of work corporate lawyers do more appealing, but there were also some practical reasons that made it the best choice for me. I started my career in Vancouver, but knew that I wanted to transition to New York at some point and there are far more international opportunities for Canadian corporate lawyers than there are for litigators trained in the courts of Western Canada.

Mackenzie wishes at one point that *"the classes I'd taken in school had been just a little more useful"* to the realities of practicing law. Is there anything law students can be doing to better prepare themselves for life at a firm?

No professor ever drops a pile of contracts on your desk and asks you to summarize anything "relevant." I think it would be helpful for law students to shadow a lawyer to get a sense of what the day-to-day experience of practicing law actually entails. Kind of like a "bring your daughter to work day" – Bring a Law Student to Work Day. Either that or they should start recording their daily activities in six-minute intervals to get used to billing. That could help too.

"No professor ever drops a pile of contracts on your desk and asks you to summarize anything 'relevant'."

What achievement are you most proud of?
The career achievement I'm most proud of is finishing a novel with two children under the age of three. Thankfully, working in BigLaw made me accustomed to functioning with very little sleep!

What do you consider your greatest failure or regret?
My law school had a great exchange program that I wish I'd taken advantage of, but I was too Type A to deviate from the traditional path. If only I'd realized what a unique and wonderful opportunity it is to live and study in a foreign country – maybe then I'd know a second language!

What law would you change, abolish or create?
I'd create a law that would specifically limit the scope of the Second Amendment. That's right, America, I'm coming for your guns! Or, better yet, I'd like to modify the Second Amendment to make it unambiguously conform to the intent of those who drafted it. I'm pretty sure they weren't thinking about an individual right to own an assault rifle when they drafted it.

Who is your legal hero?
Without a doubt, Ruth Bader Ginsberg. The perfect lawyer, professor, judge (maybe human?). I don't think it's an exaggeration to say her commitment to human rights, and in particular gender equality, changed the American workplace and the lives of millions of women. Plus she dropped the biggest truth bomb when asked about women on the Supreme Court. *"I'm sometimes asked when will there be enough? And I say, 'When there are nine.' People are shocked. But there'd been nine men, and nobody's ever raised a question about that."* Boom!

If you could go back in time to the start of your law career, what would you do differently?
I don't think I'd do anything differently. There were a lot of highs and lows working in BigLaw, but ultimately it gave me great material for a novel.

What were your best experiences working in BigLaw?
I was fortunate in my career to work on a number of high-profile transactions and I loved the energy in the room during signing and closing. That feeling you get watching months of hard work and sacrifice finally come together and knowing that the deal you're working on is shaping an industry is what corporate lawyers live for!

And your worst?
I don't think I can pinpoint the worst, but it would probably involve being in my office at 3am, a plate of greasy Chinese food, a banker's box full of documents and a message in my inbox informing me that the timeline for our transaction has been vastly accelerated.

To what extent did your real-life experiences in BigLaw feed into the fictional world of *BIGLAW*?
The book is decidedly fiction, it's not a memoir, but there are characters and circumstances that are based on my own experience. I had the idea for the book while I was still working at a large law firm in New York, so I kept a notebook in my office to jot down my observations and thoughts. I used those notes as the basis for my novel – with some poetic license thrown in too, of course!

For any budding novelists out there, how did you set about getting *BIGLAW* published?
It wasn't a quick and easy process. When I finished the first draft of the manuscript a good friend (and former colleague) put me in touch with a literary agent she knew. I was hoping she would give me some feedback, but I was blown away to get an e-mail from her saying she loved it and wanted to represent me. My agent is a former BigLaw lawyer herself, so understood that world and totally got the book. Former BigLaw lawyers helping former BigLaw lawyers! We should start a club. After many, many revisions, my agent pitched the manuscript to publishers (more revisions) and found a good home for the novel with Ankerwycke Publishing. Then more revisions. Finally, it turned up on Barnes & Noble! Have I mentioned the revisions?

In your experience, why do BigLaw firms generally have so few female partners?
I worked in a department without a single female partner. In my experience this is completely demotivating for women. You don't have a mentor and you see women who deserve to be partner pushed into stagnant career tracks. Why stick around for that? When more firms are willing to have more women in positions of management and leadership, more women will stay in the profession and ascend the ladder.

Can we look forward to *BIGLAW: The Movie*?
I hope so! The TV and film rights have been optioned to Paramount, so I'm crossing my fingers we'll see Mackenzie on the screen.

What prompted you to take the plunge and quit BigLaw? What were your plans at the time (and did they include writing?), and what would your advice be to others thinking of doing the same?
After I came up with the idea for the book and started recording my workplace observations in my notebook every day, I was hooked. Writing in my notebook quickly became my favorite time of the day and I couldn't ignore the fact that I enjoyed it more than any legal work I was doing. It took about a year of humming and hawing, and some encouragement/insistence from family, but eventually I took the leap and decided to leave BigLaw to write a novel. My advice for others would be to take the time to really give writing a try before you quit your day job!

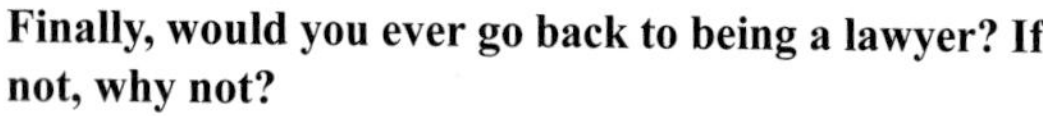

Finally, would you ever go back to being a lawyer? If not, why not?
No – been there, done that!

> ***"When more firms are willing to have more women in positions of management and leadership, more women will stay in the profession and ascend the ladder."***

Trends in the recruitment market

Entry-level hiring stats are better than they've been for years, but competition remains fierce. Here NALP's executive director and some law firm recruiters share their wisdom on how the market's looking and how best to prepare...

ONCE upon a time, in a land called '2007,' all was well with legal hiring. 60% of 2L interviews led to offers, and 92.7% of summer associates were asked to stay on. Then, in 2008, a great and terrible recession fell across the land. And, well, you know the rest. Credit crunched and boom turned to bust. By 2009, only 69% of summers got offered, and a mere 32% of 2Ls got offered places on summer associate programs. From 2010 onward, however, those numbers have been slowly clawing their way back up, and in 2015 legal recruiting *"saw more growth than we've seen in a long time,"* according to **Jim Leipold**, executive director of **NALP**. *"59% of firms made more offers than in previous years,"* he adds.

Even more impressively, in 2015 95.3% of summer associates received offers – up 1.9% from 2014 and even eclipsing 2007's high of 92.8%. Indeed, the sudden drop in recruitment back in 08/09 might even have contributed to today's recovery. *"There's a real shortage of midlevel associates with transactional experience,"* Leipold explains, *"so firms are moving their work down to junior lawyers, who they're hiring in greater numbers."*

At first blush, it looks like we've returned to the fairytale days of 2007, but it's worth sounding a note of caution. Legal recruitment remains broadly flat, according to NALP, and there is some indication that law firms are already overstaffed. 2015 was certainly a strong year for transactional work, driving demand for legal services, but it's worth noting that litigation still hasn't quite bounced back in the same way. *"This actually has nothing to do with the recession,"* notes Jim Leipold. *"It's a much longer historical trend."* The cost of litigation and discovery, as well as tighter corporate risk policies, means that the appetite for litigation has been declining for a while now, so the noncontentious side of law has been doing a lot of the heavy lifting.

City to city

This doesn't just mean that aspiring lawyers should think carefully about whether they want to be litigators or deal-doers. It also affects the legal markets of individual cities. *"Overall, litigation volume continues to decline,"* says Jim Leipold, *"so in cities like LA where law firms are more litigation-oriented, the legal market hasn't bounced back as strongly"* – especially when contrasted with transactional powerhouses like New York. Beyond this, your choice of location may also significantly affect your long-term prospects, particularly if you want to work in a certain practice area. Texas is a natural destination for aspiring energy lawyers, for example, but the collapse of oil prices has led to energy-sector bankruptcies replacing energy-sector deal work. Similarly, while *"Silicon Valley really led the rebound after the recession,"* Jim Leipold tells us, *"there's been a bit of a cooling off there as the market wonders whether there's another bubble."*

According to **Elizabeth Workman**, assistant dean for career services at **Vanderbilt Law School**, *"you'll notice that generally speaking, Midwestern firms seem to have a long-term vision for new hires, with an eye on partnership. As you head toward the East Coast there is sometimes less of a premium put on longevity, and some firms are very transparent about that."* Regardless of where the work is, one thing that employers will value is some local knowledge of the area you're applying to work in. That said, as law firm management becomes more spread out and law firms start to market themselves as 'one firm nationwide', the need to show a link with a particular area has become less important. It can't hurt, of course, but in some cases, showing an interest in an office's particular specialization is more important than demonstrating that you are a 'California person' or a 'Chicago person'.

The early firm...

"Over the last ten years we've seen OCI activity creep into the first week of August from what was September-October," NALP's Leipold tells us. For some law firms, this isn't early enough. In 2015 nearly 40 law schools reported that some of their students received pre-OCI offers, and a quarter of law firms surveyed told NALP they had made at least one offer before the OCI process even started. At the bigger end of law, firms still value OCIs for their structure and relative fairness, but they do acknowledge that they can be something of a cattle-call. *"If they can fill spots with top candidates without going through that, they will,"* explains Leipold.

Of course, there has always been pre-OCI recruiting. Students who studied in one market but wanted to return home to practice law would often write to law firms in their home cities to try and beat the OCI scramble. More and more, firms are reaching out to 1Ls in the spring in an effort to scoop up top and diverse talent before the OCI process gets underway. A common practice is to hold reception events, where applicants and recruiters mingle over drinks. Firms often collect resumes at this junkets, and candidates who make impressions may bag themselves an interview, and possibly even a pre-OCI offer.

In 2008, 37% of candidates were recruited through on-campus interviews, compared to around 23% now. Does this mean that OCIs are on the way out? Not quite. *"Currently, less than a quarter of the law firm jobs secured by new law school graduates are obtained through on-campus interviews,"* says Jim Leipold, *"but the ones that are, disproportionately are with large firms."* As ever, the bulk of legal jobs are with small and medium-sized firms, and these are often filled the old-fashioned way – networking, face time and submitting resumes.

On diversity

While diversity in recruiting continues to inch up, the law generally remains *"the least diverse of all white-collar professions,"* according to **Joseph West**, head of diversity and inclusion at **Duane Morris** (read our full interview with him in the web-only Bonus Features for our Inside View of Duane Morris). Law firms have become better at attracting diverse talent, but they're still finding it difficult to retain diverse lawyers, and minority women in particular. *"The attrition rate for minority women in large law firms hovers around 100%,"* West continues. *"I'm not talking about laterals, but home-grown attorneys who have started off with an organization. After six or seven years, almost none of them are still there. Firms are missing out on a huge amount of talent, and the next step is making sure that this talent is retained and has the opportunity to advance to leadership ranks. Inclusion is a key part of that, and that's why my role is Diversity and Inclusion Officer."*

Of course, there are many reasons why minority lawyers (or, indeed, anyone) might change jobs, but as West puts it: *"Let's not kid ourselves. A lot of people leave because their talents aren't being addressed."* A lot of firms, including West's own Duane Morris, have been recalibrating their diversity policies to focus not only on recruitment but also on retention.

Do your homework

Whether you're writing in, attending an on-campus interview or trying to schmooze your way in at a drinks reception, it's important to put your best foot forward. Good grades should really be everyone's priority in their 1L year. Your legal education was expensive, so don't throw it away by failing to do your research. *"When students bomb it's often because they treat all firms as if they're the same,"* says **Jim Leipold**. *"The more that students can do to distinguish firms in their minds the better."*

We can't stress this point enough. Every year we hear from law school hiring partners that students continue to come to interviews without even a basic knowledge of practice areas that their firm offers. Find out which practices are flourishing, and keep an eye out for less rosy developments, like senior departures or layoffs. Don't be afraid to ask tough questions at interview – that's an important part of being an attorney, and employers will value your desire for clarification. For larger firms, make sure you know which offices are hiring that year.

In their search for the partners of tomorrow, recruiters are looking for cool-headed candidates with the social skills to win and retain clients. So find a way to demonstrate this and stand out from the crowd. Get involved with extracurriculars that promote teamwork, commercial acumen and written ability. Write for your law review (and ideally edit it), work for a company or nonprofit in your 1L summer, excel in sport, show you can operate outside your comfort zone and achieve – whatever you choose to do, make sure you can talk about how it improved you.

Got an offer?

Congrats! But hold on, hotshot, you're not on the payroll yet. Take nothing for granted – even offers, if you are lucky enough to get them. Act professionally with firms you deal with at every stage of the application process, and beyond. It's understandable that you may need some more time to contemplate your decision, but remember that there are plenty more quality candidates out there who'd pawn their mothers for a job.

Bobby Weiss, director of recruiting at **Waller** recommends you *"stick to the NALP guidelines, which give you a 28-day deliberation period and are accepted by most firms across the country. Inform recruiters as soon as possible when you make a decision, and if you're waiting to hear back on another opportunity, then make sure everyone is kept in the loop. Open and honest is the way to go, and if you're holding out for something else, then let them know that you intend to accept the position unless a certain opportunity comes up."*

"When students bomb it's often because they treat all firms as if they're the same. The more that students can do to distinguish firms in their minds the better."

– Jim Leipold, executive director of NALP

Job Fairs

Below is a selection of some of the best law career fairs around the country. Dates and deadlines can change, so check in advance with ones you want to attend (and that you meet the entry criteria).

	Fair	Location	Focus
July	Bay Area Diversity Career Fair	San Francisco	Bay Area employers
	Los Angeles Off-Campus Recruitment Program	Los Angeles, CA	Regional and national law firms
	Miami Off-Campus recruitment program	Miami, FL	Regional and national law firms
	Philadelphia Walk-Around Recruitment Program	Philadelphia, PA	Regional and national law firms
	Sunbelt Minority Recruitment Program	Dallas, TX	Minority law students
	National Black Prosecutors Association Job Fair	St Louis, MO	Prosecution at local, state and federal level
	San Francisco Off-Campus Recruitment Program	San Francisco, CA	Regional and national law firms
	Southeastern IP Job Fair	Atlanta, GA	IP law in the Southeast
	Southeastern Minority Job Fair	Marietta, GA	Minority law students
	Washington DC Off-Campus Recruitment Program	Washington, DC	Regional and national law firms
TBC, usually August	Boston Lawyers Group Minority Job Fair	Boston, MA	Students of color
August	Cook County Bar Association Minority Student Fair	Chicago, IL	Minority students in the region
	Heartland Diversity Legal Job Fair	Kansas City, MO	Corporate law, non-profit, government
	Chicago Walk-Around Recruitment Fair	Chicago, IL	Regional and national law firms
	Indianapolis Bar Association Diversity Job Fair	Indianapolis, IN	Diverse law students in the Midwest
	Loyola Patent Law Interview Program	Chicago, IL	Patent law
	Minnesota Minority Recruitment Conference	Minneapolis, MN	Corporate, public interest, government
	National LGBT Bar Association (Lavender Law Career Fair)	New York, NY	Corporate, non-profit, government
	Northwest Minority Job Fair	Seattle, WA	Corporate law, public sector
	St. Louis Diversity Job Fair	St. Louis, MO	Local law firms, judicial
'early fall'	Annual Public Interest Career Reception	New York, NY	Non-profit, public sector
September	Rocky Mountain Diversity Legal Career Fair	Denver, CO	Diverse law students in the Rocky Mountain region
	Hispanic National Bar Association Annual Convention & Career Fair	Chicago, IL	Hispanic law students
Sept/Oct	National Latina/o Law Student Association Conference	Boston, MA	Latina/o students
October	Equal Justice Works Public Service Career Fair	Arlington, VA	Public interest
January	NYU International Student Interview Program	New York, NY	Foreign trained lawyers
January/ February	Nashville Bar Association Damali Booker First Year Minority Clerkship Job Fair	Nashville, TN	Minority law students
February	Midwest Public Interest Law Career Conference	Chicago, IL	Public interest
	Northwest Public Service Career Fair	Seattle, WA; Portland, OR	Government, non-profit
	NYU Public Interest Legal Career Fair	New York, NY	Government, non-profit
	UCLA LL.M. Interview Program (formerly West Coast International LLM Job Fair)	Los Angeles, CA	Foreign trained lawyers
	Nashville Bar Association Damali Booker First Year Minority Clerkship Job Fair	Nashville, TN	Minority law students
	NYU International Student Interview Program	New York, NY	Foreign trained lawyers

Who? 1Ls, 2Ls, 3Ls...	Website
2Ls and above	www.sfbar.org/
2Ls and 3Ls from participating schools	http://www.thelawconsortium.org/los-angeles.html
2Ls and 3Ls from participating schools	https://law.utexas.edu/career/interview-programs/event-type/off-campus-fairs/
2Ls and 3Ls from participating schools	http://www.thelawconsortium.org/philadelphia.html
Students from eligible schools	http://www.sunbeltjobfair.com/
Not specified	http://blackprosecutors.org/annual-conference
2Ls and 3Ls from participating schools	https://law.utexas.edu/career/interview-programs/event-type/off-campus-fairs/
Students from participating schools	http://sipjf.law.gsu.edu/
2Ls, 3Ls, recent graduates	http://www.semjf.org/
2Ls and 3Ls from participating schools	http://www.thelawconsortium.org/washington-dc.html
2Ls and 3Ls on a 4 year prgram	http://thebostonlawyersgroup.com/student/
2Ls, 3Ls	http://ccbaminorityjobfair.org/
2Ls, 3Ls and 2015 graudates	http://heartlanddiversity.org/
2Ls and 3Ls from participating schools	https://law.utexas.edu/career/interview-programs/chicago-off-campus-recruit-ment-program/
Full-time 2Ls, part-time 2Ls and 3Ls	http://www.ibadiversityjobfair.org/
2Ls, 3Ls	http://www.luc.edu/law/career/patent_students.html
2Ls, 3Ls	http://diversityinpractice.org/
Not specified	http://lgbtbar.org/annual/career-fair/
All law students	http://www.nwmjf.org/
2Ls, 3Ls	http://www.stldiversityjobfair.com/
Students from participating schools	http://law.pace.edu/public-interest-job-fairs
2Ls, 3Ls	http://www.rmdlcf.com/
2Ls, 3Ls	http://hnba.com/events/2016-annual-convention-2/
Not specified	http://nllsa.org/
2Ls, 3Ls	http://www.equaljusticeworks.org/law-school/conference-and-careerfair
Foreign-trained LLM students at sponsor schools	http://www.law.nyu.edu/isip
1Ls	http://www.nashvillebar.org/Committee/Diversity/1LJobFair.html
Open to all law students	http://www.mpilcc.org/
Law students and alumni	https://law.lclark.edu/student_groups/public_service_career_fairs/
Students from participating schools	http://pilcfair.law.nyu.edu/
Foreign trained LLM students at sponsor schools	https://law.ucla.edu/careers/employers/attend-a-job-fair-or-event/ucla-llm-interview-program/
1Ls	www.nashvillebar.org/Committee/Diversity/1LJobFair.html
Foreign-trained LLM students at sponsor schools	www.law.nyu.edu/isip/index.htm

On-Campus Interviews

Chambers Associate interviews the interviewers to help guide you through the OCIs...

The process

HIRING at most top firms follows a similar highly structured pattern: interviews on campus, followed by interviews back at the firms, then (hopefully) a summer associateship. Many components of this process are laid down by NALP's guidelines, and by law schools. Recruitment varies from school to school and from firm to firm, but here we will attempt to give you a rough overview of how the OCI process works, plus tips on how to get through it successfully.

We speak to many dozens of law firm recruiters each year during our research for this guide. Among other things, they tell us what they look for in prospective hires and what questions they're likely to ask during interviews. A number of consistent themes emerge about what they are looking for during these interviews, which we present below with some quotes from hiring partners themselves. Firms' recruiting strategies do differ, of course, and you can find out more about the particular requirements of each in the Get Hired section of our Inside View features.

Bidding

OCIs are aimed at students at the start of their 2L year for summer positions the following summer, between their 2L and 3L years. Although they occur under the banner of 'fall recruiting', OCIs are increasingly held earlier in the year, starting in August and September. Besides BigLaw firms, smaller firms, public interest organizations and government agencies (like the Federal Public Defender's Office, the IRS and Immigration and Customs Enforcement) also recruit on campus. While commercial law firms pay to attend, government and public organizations usually don't.

Students can bid on a certain number of employers (often between 20 and 50), ranking their preferences for firms and office locations. A preset system determines who they interview with: some schools allow employers to select a proportion of the students they interview; others use a lottery system which is entirely based on students' preferences. Bidding deadlines are usually in July.

Most schools request that students submit a writing sample alongside their resume when bidding for firms at OCI. This is typically a paper written on a legal subject. Good writing skills are essential for junior associates, as drafting is a big part of their staple diet. The writing sample is more important to some firms than to others. *"This firm is really, really serious about the quality of the writing sample,"* one BigLaw associate emphasized to us. *"People with excellent credentials get turned away because their writing isn't top-notch."*

Candidates are *"likely to be asked detailed questions about items on their resumes. Their capacity to speak to those topics thoughtfully, compellingly and with some imaginative insight is very important."*

Besides OCIs, some firms also interview at job fairs with a regional focus (like the Midwest Job Fair) or are focused on a specific minority (like the NBLSA Job Fair and the Lavender Law Fair), or have a specific industry focus, like the Loyola Patent Law Interview Program. Smaller firms often take applicants through a mix of direct applications and OCIs, as they don't have the resources to visit a large number of campuses. A few firms bypass the OCI process entirely. Quinn Emanuel's recruitment 'parties' are the most high-profile example, letting students mingle with the firm's associates and partners at an informal drinks event before submitting resumes.

Resumes

Firms see students' resumes before the interview. A resume should be no longer than a page long, unless you have at least five years' work experience prior to law school, which means you probably don't have space for that paper route you did in 10th grade. It also goes without saying that typos are to be avoided at all costs; even one mistake can make the difference between the 'yes' pile and the rejects, so do enlist someone to proofread your resume. Think carefully about coming up with a clear, punchy layout. Keep your resume continually up-to-date, and refine it constantly. Put your strengths somewhere where they can be clearly seen, targeting the five-second glance by a rushed recruiter. And, crucially, think carefully about how to tailor your resume to the jobs you want. It's not enough to say you're passionate about law. Give real and specific evidence which is targeted to the kind of firms you're applying to.

Often a resume will tick the right boxes, but recruiters will want to use the interview to find out if you really live up to your billing. Make sure you have plenty more to say about all the activities, experiences and hobbies you've listed. One interviewer explains that candidates are *"likely to be asked detailed questions about items on their resumes. Their capacity to speak to those topics thoughtfully, compellingly and with some imaginative insight is very important."*

The interview

Most students interview with between ten and 30 firms (assuming they can get that many interviews). OCIs usually last 20 minutes and are conducted by a mix of partners and associates. Some firms have a dedicated group of attorneys (often the hiring committee) which interviews on campus; others let a wider range of attorneys participate. Sometimes interviewers are trained by firms on how to interview and how to present the firm during OCIs. (Take a look at an OCI manual leaked to ATL – abovethelaw.com/2011/09/an-inside-look-at-sullivan-cromwells-recruiting-process/ – to get an idea of how big firms might prep their interviewers.)

Whatever's on your resume, it's how you come across during the OCI which matters most to firms. That doesn't just mean your personality – you need to be able to communicate how and why your past experiences make you right for the firm. The interview process itself is a test of character: interviewers will look at the way you speak, answer questions and make an argument to judge whether you have the qualities they are looking for. For example, many recruiters ask about candidates' undergraduate dissertations. They do this to see how well you still recall your main argument, and how well you can summarize your argument briefly for a lay audience. As one interviewer reported: *"We like to hear candidates describe and explain what they do and what they think. Through that we gain an understanding of how they organize and articulate their thoughts."* Of course, this ability to think on your feet is itself an essential quality for any attorney. Pay attention to which of its offices a firm is recruiting for on your campus. Some firms recruit for all their offices on all campuses; others allow specific offices to target specific campuses.

Callback interviews

Firms often have a maximum number of students from any school who they will 'call back' for a second interview. 'Callback interviews' usually take place in October. They involve a half-day or whole day spent on-site at one of the firm's offices. Students are usually interviewed by four to six attorneys – a mix of partners and associates. Often there will also be a lunch or coffee event with junior associates.

"Identify a couple of areas of real interest and educate yourself about those areas, both through law school courses and practice experience. In that way you can distinguish yourself from the masses."

Be aware that you are being assessed during the whole day, not just during the interviews themselves. Treat lunches and coffee dates as part of the interview process; there's no need to be formal, but you should always keep in mind that you are being judged – showing an interest in your interviewers' work and the firm in general is a good bet. *"Candidates feel more comfortable during lunches with junior associates, so these interviews will often be more illuminating than the office ones. The associates fill out assessment forms in the same way that partners do,"* a BigLaw hiring partner tells us. How you greet and talk to support staff and recruiters when you first arrive can be important too. Hiring committees usually take into consideration the views of staff and junior associates who have met with candidates.

A 'standard' callback interview will see some interviewers ask about your resume, while others might talk about hobbies, sports and academics to find out more about your skills and personality. As one recruiter pointed out, *"grades get you the interview, but once there, you need to be able to have a back and forth – we don't want someone who's very stiff."* One junior associate recalled: *"My interviewer put down my resume and said: 'Let's just have a conversation.' Then we talked about what I liked and disliked about law school, the firm and my connection to the city."* Most firms allow interviewers a lot of free rein in what they ask. *"Different interviewers will put different weights on certain aspects of a student,"* another recruiter pointed out. Some firms employ so-called behavioral interviewing techniques. This ranges from asking questions directly about skills and competencies ('give an example of when you worked in a team') to structured assessments.

For example, Philadelphia's Pepper Hamilton uses an interactive scenario in which interviewers and candidates work though a legal issue. The aim is to *"see how comfortable the candidate is in a working situation, how they work in a team and how they might counsel a client."* We reckon that this type of interviewing will become increasingly common in future.

"The worst answer I have ever had to a question was the person who told me about working on a group project at college where no-one pulled their weight, so they did all the work. They were really proud of it, but it tells me they might not work well in a team."

If a student is unsure whether to join the firm (or vice versa) they might return to the firm for a 'second look' and meet with a few more attorneys. Candidates are often asked if they want to meet attorneys from certain practice areas during the callback or 'second look'. Make use of this opportunity: asking to meet people from certain departments – even if you're not sure which you want to join – will show you're engaged with the firm's work. A short while after the callback, students will hear whether the firm wants to offer them a position as a summer associate. Students have 28 days to accept the offer.

Some top interview tips from hiring partners

- *"I like to engage students about what their passions are – say what they wrote their thesis on – to see their fluency with language and whether they have a clear world view, sophistication and maturity."*
- *"In interviews we use simple techniques to draw out aspects of someone's personality: when looking at leadership we might ask about past experiences where candidates were put into a leadership role. What was that experience like? Could they describe it in detail? How did you rise to the occasion? And so on."*
- *"We ask about their connection to the city they're interviewing in, about their outside interests and long-term plans, and what they like and don't like about law school."*
- *"One stock question I ask is: what is not on your resume that we should know about you? I like to know what's behind the resume. That's not just personality-related. I want them to go a little deeper so I can find out about their skills as a person. A wonderful response to that question is if someone relates it to a challenge they have overcome or a time when they have shown good judgment."*
- *"The worst answer I have ever had to a question was the person who told me about working on a group project at college where no-one pulled their weight, so they did all the work. They were really proud of it, but it tells me they might not work well in a team."*
- *"Show a serious interest in what the firm does, and what the people you are speaking to do."*
- *"The biggest thing you could do wrong at OCI is not be able to keep up an intelligent conversation for 20 minutes or not have any questions."*
- *"During interviews candidates should have good questions about the firm. Not just questions to which the answers are on our website, but things that show they have done their homework."*
- *"Prepare. It takes more time than some students set aside for it. Practicing to get over the jitters is good, but what's more important is thinking through what you've done in your life to understand what skills you have that can contribute to being a lawyer. When we sense that somebody's done enough thinking about themselves to know which part of their experience to talk about at an interview, we're prone to think they're analytical and will be able to perform the tasks required of them."*
- *"Identify a couple of areas of real interest and educate yourself about those areas, both through law school courses and practice experience. In that way you can distinguish yourself from the masses."*
- *"The question that I've been asking for years is: think forward a few years to when you're actually an associate. What would be a couple of things that, if you found them out after you started, would make you think you'd made the wrong choice of firm? I think a lot of students respond well to it because it puts people in the frame of mind that they're actually going to be turning up to work here every day!"*

On chambers-associate.com...

- What's your greatest weakness?
- How to deal with that annoying interview question

Examples of questions

Here are some examples of OCI and callback interview questions reported by juniors and recruiters:

- Why do you want to be a lawyer?
- Why are you applying to this firm?
- What is it you have heard or read about this firm that made you interested?
- What areas of practice are you interested in and why?
- Describe to me the central argument of your undergraduate thesis.
- What did you enjoy about law school?
- Where do you see yourself five or ten years down the road?
- What mistakes have you made in your past?
- If I called one of your referees now, how would they describe you?
- How would your law journal colleagues who worked with you describe you?
- Describe a time when you didn't succeed and what you learned from it.
- Describe a time you showed leadership. How did you rise to the occasion?
- How much time would you spend polishing a draft to get the little points right?
- Can you describe a particularly challenging circumstance in your life?
- What motivates you?
- Are you a team player?
- Can you describe a situation where you handled a difficult customer?
- Tell me about a time you worked in a team that was dysfunctional.
- Tell me about a time you helped successfully produce a certain work product.
- Tell me about a time you had to juggle several responsibilities.
- Tell me about a time you faced a setback or failure and what you did.
- What adversities have you faced in past employment?

Summers

At many BigLaw firms, getting on the summer program is tantamount to getting an associate job. Historically, many firms used the summer program as a final step in the recruitment process: a tough few months' work at the firm would weed out the weaklings, and firms would only give job offers to a certain proportion of each summer class. Some firms still use the old model, but since the recession an increasing number only hire summers who they intend to take on as first-years. Firms now pride themselves on their 100% offer rates – you'd really have to screw up during the summer not to get an offer (the economy aside...).

"If someone writes in to us and they're not from a top-50 school, but they came top of their class and were editor-in-chief of a law journal, that will certainly get our attention."

Summer programs traditionally involved a lot of wining, dining and schmoozing of participating students. This trend, too, is declining. First, a recession-induced squeeze on firms' budgets means less cash to spend on perks for summers. Second, it used to be fairly important for firms to impress (top) students to stop them seeking jobs elsewhere. With the job market as tough as it is, this is barely necessary any more.

"We like to hear candidates describe and explain what they do and what they think. Through that we gain an understanding of how they organize and articulate their thoughts."

Firms now pride themselves on offering students a summer experience which reflects the life of a junior associate.

Recruitment outside OCIs

Aside from OCIs, firms recruit from some schools by allowing students to submit their resumes via a central pool. This is known as a 'resume drop'.

Some firms also accept direct write-in applications outside OCIs. As one recruiter put it: *"If someone writes in to us and they're not from a top-50 school, but they came top of their class and were editor-in-chief of a law journal, that will certainly get our attention."* Networking is also very important if you want to get an associate job outside OCIs. Getting in touch with attorneys at the firm you are interested in either directly or via alumni events is the very least you should do. *"Our attorneys are very involved with their former alma maters,"* a hiring partner told us. Networking is also increasingly important if you are applying via OCIs. *"Students need to work hard at networking as more job opportunities are spread by word of mouth than before."*

Some firms like recruiting candidates who have completed an LL.M., especially overseas. Usually though, an LL.M. will do nothing to help your chances of getting a job as an associate.

Summer programs

The halcyon days of extravagant spending might be over, but BigLaw summer associate programs by and large remain a decent mix of solid work experience and merry social jamborees...

SUMMER associate programs are an integral part of BigLaw recruiting. Attrition rates are high across the profession, so firms run annual programs – which usually last from six to 12 weeks – in order to ensure a steady influx of first-year associates joins the ranks each year. A summer stint effectively serves as a prolonged interview, with clear benefits for applicants and recruiting attorneys alike: the former receive a preliminary taste of associate life, while the latter get an up-close and personal view of their potential colleagues in action. Provided all goes well, summers will receive an offer to return as a full-time first-year associate upon completion of their law degree.

Recent years have seen summer associate classes composed primarily of 2Ls. Many firms still hire a handful of 1Ls each year – often via scholarships or competitions – but the chances of nabbing a spot as a 3L have become slim. Although third-year hiring has risen slightly in the past couple of years, according to NALP, less than a quarter of firms reported any third-year recruiting activity in 2015, with a very minimal quantity of offers made to 3Ls. As such, many law students concentrate on their application efforts during the summer following their 1L year, when the on-campus recruiting season kicks off. For information about when and how to apply for summer spots, see our feature on the OCI process.

While class sizes took a serious hit during the economic downturn, there are definite signs of recovery: in 2015, the average class size matched pre-recession highs (the period between 2005-2009). That said, competition is still fierce so it's vital that your grades and extracurriculars are up to scratch when you apply. Check out our feature on trends in the recruitment market for more details on class sizes and employment figures.

As a summer, you'll likely get the chance to try out work across a variety of practice groups, which *"can be really helpful if you don't have a clear idea of what you want to go into,"* sources agreed. Some firms, like Willkie, Milbank and King & Spalding, even have formal rotation systems in place to ensure summer associates experience a broad mix of assignments. At the end of the program, candidates typically submit a preference for a particular practice group that is taken into consideration at the offers stage.

"I felt really integrated into my practice group when I saw that my work product was actually incorporated into the matters at hand."

The summer associate experience has historically been somewhat artificial, with many firms offering made-up tasks and discrete research assignments that bear only mild resemblance to actual responsibilities. However, the recession prompted an increased reliance on summer manpower at many a cash-strapped firm, and offering 'real' work soon became not only a priority but a necessity across the profession. That trend continues today – most of our associate interviewees now report a relatively *"authentic"* experience as summers.

"I felt really integrated into my practice group when I saw that my work product was actually incorporated into the matters at hand," one shared. *"When I returned as a first-year, I was able to pick up one of the projects that was still ongoing and see it through to the end."* Another said: *"Firms now realize the value of allowing summers to get their hands dirty with real tasks; that approach demonstrates how you will actually react under certain circumstances and prepares you for the transition into being a first-year."* Indeed, as one BigLaw hiring partner confirms, *"throwing people into the mix seems to work out best for everyone involved."*

Typical summer duties include small research tasks, drafting memos and attending negotiations or depositions to observe their seniors. The last is an important part of the learning process, according to our sources. *"We make the effort to get people on the phone to listen to the back and forth of arguing a case, and in client meetings so they can witness the kind of behavior that gets things done,"* one hiring partner tells us. *"Pro bono matters can be a real chance to stretch your wings but I never felt like I was just a flunky,"* one source said. *"It was small, short-term work, sure, but it was meaningful too."* When they're not 'learning by doing', students usually attend summer-specific training sessions and they're often able to opt into CLE classes alongside fully fledged associates. As well as general introductions to the different practices, summer training sessions cover topics as varied as advocacy, due diligence, depositions, legal writing and business development. Summers at some firms even undergo a mock trial.

In keeping with the post-recession trend of cutbacks across the legal sector, the culture of lavish wining and dining – a longstanding staple to the summer associate experience implemented with the intent of wooing top hires – has slowed down to some extent. *"Anyone summering after 2008 will find things aren't as flashy as they used to be,"* sources reported. Is this a sore spot? *"Not at all; if anything it helps prepare you for the working world,"* one associate said, looking back on their time as a summer. *"They're not trying to seduce you into thinking associate life is something that it isn't – it's not all karaoke, free bars and boat trips down the Hudson River."*

Still, socializing remains an important part of the summer experience, with frequent lunches, sports events, wine-tastings and theater trips among the standard perks. *"You can still get tickets to a Yankees game, but they won't be behind home plate,"* one source summed up. In any case, attorneys of all levels tend to look forward to the summer since *"that's when the majority of the year's social events take place,"* interviewees told us. Some of the more exciting traditions we've heard about include trips to Disneyland and a destination hike at Quinn Emanuel, a Beyonce concert at Vinson & Elkins, go-karting at Chadbourne & Parke, and falconry at Sterne Kessler. *"I'd be a summer forever if I could!"* one insider enthused. Our feature on Best BigLaw Bashes has some other great examples of events.

Savvy summers will see these kinds of events as more than just a chance to chill out – they're golden opportunities to meet and mingle. Indeed, a hiring partner at a top international firm says: *"I don't care how busy you are or how tired you are, you need to get out there and go to as many events as possible! It's as good a chance to meet and talk to people as you'll get during office hours and the more contacts you're able to make the better."*

Some firms have programs in place that let summers spend time in multiple offices or even at outside organizations with which the firm has ties. Linklaters, Debevoise and Cleary – all large international units – allow associates to spend part of their summer in an overseas office. *"Having that opportunity helped me make valuable connections with my international colleagues and offered a good insight into how the firm operates abroad,"* said one source who'd split their time between London and New York. Others – including Vinson & Elkins, Simpson Thacher and Cadwalader – offer the chance to spend several weeks working with a local public interest organization. Others still run mini client secondments for summer associates – Cleary, for example, offers a two-week stint at an investment bank. Check out our features on all of these firms for more info.

"I'd be a summer forever if I could!"

When it comes to landing an offer, a good impression is imperative – a summer stint is akin to an audition, after all. Whether you're responding to a partner's request or schmoozing at a drinks event, engage appropriately and keep to your best behavior to show you're taking the opportunity seriously. As one BigLaw hiring partner shares, *"being enthusiastic about the work is just as important as demonstrating you're capable of doing it as far as I'm concerned."* Other interviewees advised summers to *"maintain a positive attitude"* and *"show a genuine interest in what's going on at the firm and where it's heading."* That said, *"there's certainly room to relax"* during the program, our sources assured us, referring to the myriad of social events planned at most firms. *"Just don't go overboard with the booze!"* Indeed, the point of offering opportunities for associates to let their hair down is to assess candidates' overall personalities, *"including how they interact outside a work context,"* one hiring partner reveals. *"It's a good glimpse into people's attitudes and what it'll be like interacting with them on a day-to-day basis."*

Since the recession, offer rates from summer programs have been high. A tightened grip on financials has prompted a growing number of firms to limit summer hiring to those they intend to keep on for good, and the ability to claim a 100% offer rate has become something like a badge of pride on the recruiting side. *"We always aim to keep everyone, and it's rare when we don't end up with offers across the board,"* one hiring partner tells us. *"When that happens, it's because we haven't done our job perfectly and it turns out someone doesn't really fit in or didn't pan out in terms of our expectations."* The latest NALP report shows that more than 95% of summer associates in 2015 received offers, a figure up considerably from the 69.3% reported in 2009, and one that exceeds the 92.8% offer rate of 2007.

Follow @ChambersAssoc on Twitter for pics of summer socials at law firms

Clerkships

Clerking for a judge is a great way to kick-start your career as a litigator...

What is a law clerk?

A JUDICIAL clerk (or 'elbow clerk') works as a judge's assistant and typically starts after graduating law school. These clerkships normally involve working alongside a single judge. Responsibilities vary from judge to judge, but all clerks engage in research and do copious amounts of writing. Most appointments last one or two years – judges indicate the duration of the commitment at the outset. Whether you want to work in BigLaw or for a smaller outfit, the skills, connections and insights picked up while clerking are invaluable.

Why clerk?

"It's an absolutely amazing experience. If everyone could do it, there would be a lot of better lawyers," one former district court clerk told us. *"It's absolutely hands down the best way to start a legal career,"* says Melissa Lennon, a former judicial section chair at NALP. *"The training you get – really intense research and writing – is incredibly valuable."* According to former District Court of New Jersey judge Joel Pisano, *"clerking offers an opportunity to be in on the decision-making process, to understand how the courts work, to be mentored by a sitting judge and to be introduced to the members of the Bar."* Clerks learn how judges react to different briefs and styles of advocacy, and are exposed to a wide range of legal issues.

The educational value of clerkships cannot be overstated, as clerks learn directly from the arbiters of the law. A judge might ask a clerk to write a memorandum or even a first draft of a judicial opinion. *"Certainly, I was writing opinions,"* said an associate who had clerked with the District Court of Maryland. *"My writing got a lot better over the course of a year, because of the benefit of having a judge who sees you every day, guides you and shapes your writing style."* Clerks may get an insight into legal administration too. One source had clerked with a judge who sat on the Judicial Conference of the United States – a body concerned with US Courts administration – and had taken on duties related to the Conference.

The judge/clerk relationship often extends beyond the clerkship term. *"Previous clerks are always encouraged to call if they want to chat or need advice,"* according to Judge Pisano. For some this relationship is career-changing as their judge mentors them on the next step in their career. *"I didn't have a good idea of the legal scene so I asked the judge what he recommended,"* one former clerk told us. *"The firm I'm at now is the first one he recommended."* Clerks also build up a valuable network among members of the Bar, other clerks and judges. This comes in handy when practicing in the same state or district as the judge.

Different courts provide windows into different types of law. For someone who wants to be a criminal litigator, clerking in a state trial court would provide maximum exposure to criminal prosecution. Bankruptcy judges are part of the district court system and have special purview over bankruptcy filings. *"If you are interested in transactional law or corporate governance, working for the Delaware Court of Chancery is significantly advantageous,"* says Melissa Lennon. *"Delaware is the home of corporate law in the US: many groundbreaking corporate and governance issues are decided there."* Equally, those interested in green issues could look into clerking at the environmental division of the Vermont Superior Court (Vermont is one of the few states where courts have specialized environmental divisions).

Types of clerkship

Federal courts

A stint at the US Supreme Court is the most sought-after, hard-to-land position on the clerking circuit. Read our feature on SCOTUS clerkships for more information. While these clerks can practically pick a firm of their choice after this clerkship, several choose to go into academia instead (see endnote 1).

There are 13 federal courts of appeals. Federal circuit court clerks do a lot of research: assessing opposing briefs, going over the trial records, and interpreting application of the law. Many appellate court judges are known as 'feeder judges' as they have a history of having their former clerks hired by the Supreme Court.

There are 94 federal districts in the USA, and federal district courts offer clerkships with either a district judge or a magistrate judge. Federal district clerks have a more varied role than their appellate counterparts as they work in the general trial courts of the US federal system. In addition to the extensive research and writing appellate clerks undertake, district clerks coordinate with attorneys, help resolve discovery-related motions, prepare judges for settlement conferences and attend trial-related hearings.

Budding litigators should note that this is the perfect opportunity to pick up useful skills. Clerking with a magistrate judge is slightly more limited in scope as their remit is constrained by what federal district judges assign them. They do handle a wide range of work: warrants, bail hearings, arraignments, pretrial motions and civil matters related to multiparty litigation. Magistrates also write reports and recommendations to the district judge. Prospective clerks should make sure to find out what matters are referred to a magistrate judge before applying.

There are also opportunities to clerk for federal judges in subject matter-specific special courts. The Court of International Trade is one example; it has jurisdiction over international trade and customs with nine judges who often hire two clerks each (see endnote 2). Each judicial district is also home to a bankruptcy court. Clerks here are exposed to complex commercial cases, including claims made against debtors. The US Tax Court adjudicates tax disputes and arranges settlement payments to the IRS: the court comprises 19 judges, appointed for 15 years each. Other special courts include the US Court of Appeals for Veterans Claims and the US Court of Federal Claims.

State courts

Courts of last resort contribute to the development of state common law and interpret state statute, having a significant impact on state law. Clerks here have similar tasks and responsibilities to federal appellate law clerks. These clerkships are the most competitive to obtain at state level. To be considered for one, high academic standing and some journal experience are essential.

Some states have intermediary appellate courts, which operate along the lines of the federal courts of appeals – resolving appeals arising from the state's lower courts.

Many civil and criminal matters are dealt with at first instance by state trial courts. This grouping includes both general and limited jurisdiction trial courts such as city, county and probate courts. Law students looking to become criminal lawyers might be better off clerking in a state trial court than in federal court. Clerks here gain significant insight into the workings of the local Bar, state procedures and state law while assisting in trial procedures, research and drafting. This is also useful for those wishing to become public prosecutors in the region. NALP provides a detailed guide on clerkships in select state courts.

Staff attorneys

Some courts hire 'staff attorneys': clerks who work for a group of judges instead of just one. Also known as pool clerks or court attorneys, these positions can be found in both federal and state courts. The core responsibilities of staff attorneys are more limited than those of other clerks and include reviewing appeals, preparing memos and assisting in case management.

Clerkship application

Federal and state clerkships don't abide by the same deadlines. State clerkship deadlines vary from court to court and state to state. Research local deadlines to find out more.

The majority of federal appellate judges hire clerks in the fall of their 3L year. To find out more check out OSCAR (the Online System for Clerkship Application and Review) at oscar.uscourts.gov. This online system allows judges to post vacancies, and students to apply online. OSCAR used to follow a 'Hiring Plan' application schedule, but this has changed as of 2013. Now, rising second-year law students can begin researching clerkship openings on June 1, and can begin submitting applications on August 1. Judges will receive applications immediately and can offer available clerkships at any time. 2L and 3L students and alumni can access OSCAR all through the year. 73% of federal judges hold an account with OSCAR.

Different judges have different preferences for how they like students to apply. You may be able to find out how the judge you are interested in clerking with recruits by contacting their chambers. Judges usually look for a good writing sample and good personal references. Sometimes schools recommend candidates to judges. Getting a (good) clerkship can often be all about networking, recommendations and connections.

Traditional practice for interviewees has been to accept the first offer they get, as many judges expect an immediate answer. *"The crucial thing is never tell a judge, 'I don't want to work with you',"* one source advised.

At the time of writing, base salaries for federal clerks ranged from $51,811 (with no legal work experience) to $85,544 (with at least two years experience as a judicial law clerk).

Choosing a judge

Once you've chosen which judges you may want to clerk with, finding out more can be a murky process. Unfortunately there is no guide that will list the quirks of each judge, although it is extremely important to collect every last bit of information you can before applying. *"The only place where that information exists is in the halls of law schools,"* says Melissa Lennon. *"If you're lucky enough to get an interview with a judge, you need to talk to as many people as possible who have clerked or interviewed with that judge. Figure out what the judge is like and how they run their chambers."*

There are also blogs and forums where former clerks discuss their judges, their interviews and clerkships. Some clerks have been known to scoff at attempts to gather information this way but, along with networking, doing a few Google searches is a good way to find out more about a judge.

Talking to former clerks is really the best resource; we spoke with a few associates who had clerked and learned a lot. *"Some judges – like Judge Easterbrook – you just don't apply to,"* said one source. *"He and other judges on the Seventh Circuit only take people who are recommended by certain schools."* Court of Appeals Judge Danny Bloggs is known as the trivia judge – he administers a general knowledge test to prospective applicants and three of his former clerks have appeared on Who Wants to Be a Millionaire (see endnote 3). One associate had interviewed with a judge who asked them all about college basketball during the interview. *"They don't just look at your academic performance,"* said one former clerk. *"They know they will be working closely with you and want to find out if they can get along with you on a personal level."*

Should you apply?

A federal law clerk should have completed their JD and be a US citizen. Following that, there are no set academic requirements. Students who secure the most coveted clerkships are often from a highly ranked law school, were in the top quarter of their class, have worked on a law journal and have glowing academic references. Given the importance of personal recommendations, it's never too early to start forming connections with the right faculty members.

If you don't have the best grades or you're not at one of the top schools, take heart from these words from Melissa Lennon: *"It's a big country and there are opportunities for federal clerkships for candidates from different schools, not just the top 20. Judges have loyalty to their own schools."* 2015 was the ten-year anniversary of OSCAR, since its foundation there have been over 9,000 postings to the site. It would be a fair estimate that aggregate state and federal clerkships outnumber top-grade applicants, although that doesn't mean that all of those positions are open to all applicants. State judges often have strong ties to the local community, so a strong letter of recommendation from a local school could have more clout than an Ivy League recommendation. *"As with many job applications, showing you have a local link helps,"* one former clerk advised.

If you're desperate for a clerkship but don't have the right grades, journal experience or law school pedigree, try making up with practical experience: intern at a regional firm, work in-house, do pro bono work or work part-time at a small firm (these experiences can also help provide you with the writing samples which judges so love). If you haven't worked on a law journal, highlighting courses in research and writing that you've aced can help too.

Many state and federal courts offer externships to law students, often during 1L or 2L summers. It can be tough to land one of these: you will need the right combination of grades, gumption and connections. Recommendations from these externships can be key to securing a coveted clerkship later on.

Endnotes

1 - www.legalauthority.com/articles/70010/Clerkships
2 - indylaw.indiana.edu/career/judicialclerkship.htm
3 - www.newyorker.com/archive/2001/05/14/010514ta_TALK_DEPT_OF_TRIVIA
4 - http://news.uscourts.gov/federal-law-clerk-hiring-plan-discontinued
5 - www.judiciary.state.nj.us/lawclerks/

The Big Interview with... **Maureen Mahoney**, Former Deputy Solicitor General

Maureen Mahoney (born 1954; JD University of Chicago Law School, 1978) is a former deputy solicitor general and a retired partner of the appellate practice at Latham & Watkins. During her time in the solicitor general's office (between 1991 and 1993), she was nominated by President Bush to serve as a judge for the United States District Court for the Eastern District of Virginia, but her nomination was not acted upon by the Senate before Bush's time in office ended. Considered to be one of the top appellate lawyers in the USA, Mahoney was the first woman in history to be appointed to argue a case in the Supreme Court.

"Don't assume that a career in public service is more rewarding than private practice."

First of all, congratulations on winning the *Chambers USA* Outstanding Contribution to the Legal Profession award. When did you first decide to become a lawyer?
I was eight years old and made a very serious announcement of my decision during dinner with my family.

Why?
My father was a lawyer and I probably wanted to make him proud of me. It ultimately worked.

Starting out, what did you expect from a career in the law?
I hoped to have the sense of accomplishment that comes from working hard at work worth doing.

Has it lived up to your expectations?
Oh goodness, yes. I would have been more than satisfied if my career had only worked out half as well. I have absolutely loved being a lawyer. Overall, our system of justice is a beauty to behold, especially at the federal level.

How did you get into the areas of law you are known for today? By design? Chance? Both?
By default. When I started practicing law at Latham 35 years ago, I had my heart set on a career as a trial lawyer. When my children were born, I realized that I was not willing to spend weeks away from home trying complex cases. I made the switch to appellate practice to minimize my business travel.

What do you consider to have been your big break?
I had a number of very lucky breaks, but my success as a Supreme Court advocate really began when Chief Justice Rehnquist persuaded the court to appoint me to argue a case. This was the first time in history that the court had chosen a woman for this role and fortunately the press coverage of my argument was very favorable. The chief justice opened many doors for me throughout my career and it made all the difference.

What differences do you see in today's legal market compared to when you started?
Large international firms now dominate the landscape but I am one of the many lawyers (and clients) who have reaped the benefits of that change. Latham was fairly small when I joined. The intimacy was fun but my professional opportunities improved markedly as the firm grew in size and stature. As a general rule, the largest, most successful firms are handling the lion's share of the most challenging work. And intimacy can still be found within large firms at the practice group level.

What achievement are you most proud of?
It depends on the day. But today I am most proud of the fact that I only lost two of the 21 cases that I argued in the Supreme Court. There is definitely some luck associated with a win-loss record in litigation. But I would like to think that it also reflects, at least in part, the very intense effort I devoted to argument preparation in every one of my cases.

What do you consider your greatest failure or regret?
My career was practically perfect in every way. But I did want to serve as Solicitor General and was never selected.

What have you enjoyed most during your career in the legal profession?
The esteem and affection of my colleagues at Latham. But the joy of winning cases is right up there too.

And enjoyed least?
That's easy. Losing.

What law would you change, abolish or create?
I would abolish the use of elections to select state judges. We need to improve the quality of the judiciary in many states and that is one reform that could have a substantial impact.

Who is your legal hero?
If I had to name only one, then it would have to be my mentor, Chief Justice Rehnquist. But I truly admire all of the highly talented lawyers who have chosen to forgo the monetary rewards of private practice to serve on the federal bench. Judicial pay is far too low and judges have to make substantial personal sacrifices to serve our country.

What career would you have in your second life?
I would be quite content to hit the replay button.

What slogan would you like to be remembered by?
The harder I worked, the luckier I got.

What advice would you give to students trying to enter the legal profession today?
Don't assume that a career in public service is more rewarding than private practice. That seems to be the prevailing view on law school campuses now but I do not think it is accurate. Some public service jobs, like the Solicitor General's office, provide extraordinary professional opportunities. But many government offices do not offer the challenging work and excellent training available in large law firms (not to mention the compensation). I actually chose to return to Latham rather than spend my career as a deputy in the Solicitor General's office because I (accurately) perceived that I would have excellent professional opportunities with a much better work/life balance at Latham. A career that combines private practice with some public service is, in my view, the best of both worlds. So take a long view when you choose your first job. It is generally far easier to leave a great firm to work in the government than to start work in the government and then join a great firm.

And finally, to those who hope to ultimately get into appellate law?
It is important to get the experience of serving as a judicial clerk on an appellate court, so make yourself competitive for that selection process. Most of the best appellate lawyers also clerked for the Supreme Court, so aim high. I also think it is ideal to handle a mix of trial and appellate litigation in your early years in practice. Learning how to try cases will make you a stronger appellate lawyer and permit you to handle a greater range of cases. By way of example, I probably would not have been selected by the United States House of Representatives to handle litigation challenging the Commerce Department's plans to use sampling to conduct the census if I had not had some trial court experience. The case culminated in a Supreme Court argument but it started in a three judge district court.

"The harder I worked, the luckier I got."

SCOTUS clerkships

Clerking at the Supreme Court, as told by the lucky few who've been there, done that, got the judicial robe...

CLERKING at the Supreme Court of the United States is the holy grail, the most prestigious gig any law grad can get. Only 36 SCOTUS clerkships come up for grabs each year. Only the brightest and very, very best need apply. Over a thousand who consider themselves in this category (and have letters of introduction from distinguished law professors and others to back them up) do so every year. And you don't go to the Supreme Court straight from law school – usually all successful candidates have previously clerked at federal appellate level, and wowed their judges there.

"Nothing else short of being a judge will replicate this experience," one former SCOTUS clerk tells us of their year with a Justice. *"You see directly how things work, which completely changes the way you see cases."*

How do I apply?

At some point during your federal clerkship, bundle your resume, cover letter, transcript, writing sample and letters of recommendation (most Justices require at least three) and ping them to the Court. The Justices decide their own hiring schedules, so keep an eye out for announcements well in advance. *"If you've managed to get a clerkship on the circuit court, you've got some idea that you have both the grades and the recommendations to make you competitive,"* an ex-SCOTUS clerk counsels, encouragingly. A stellar reference from your judge, *"based on the couple months work you've already done for them,"* is essential. *"Many circuit judges have a great record of sending clerks to the Supreme Court."* Aside from this, the application is relatively labor-free – *"it's as brief as a resume and a cover letter."*

Your circuit court judge can help in other ways too: *"Often he can put you in touch with the SCOTUS Justice's previous clerks so you can talk with them about their experiences."* There's a lot to learn, as interviewing style varies as much as the Justices' personalities. Overall, it's important to *"be familiar with their cases and their judicial philosophy by getting your hands on as much of their writing as you can, and by reading their most high-profile cases. You also need to be familiar with all the pending cases the Court is hearing, to demonstrate you have a clear interest in that Court."*

The ex-clerks we spoke to found their interview more relaxed than anticipated. *"It tested whether you can hold an interesting conversation – very different to testing your legal reasoning skills!"* You've made it this far, so they take your legal genius as a given: *"Each Justice interviews ten to 15 people who have extremely good qualifications. They're already confident in you, so their main task is to see if they connect with you on a personal level."* Hopefully this shouldn't be too tricky as the people who recommended you *"already have a relationship with the Justice and have thought about personality and ideological fit – after all, they're sending you to live with someone for a year."* The importance of recommendations from others during the hiring process cannot be overstated: it's *"not just old guys in smoky rooms making the decisions."*

The Chief Justice is authorized to hire five clerks, the eight Associate Justices four and retired Justices one apiece.

So what do SCOTUS clerks actually do?

Something similar to what federal court clerks do. Primarily, their role is to sift through the thousands of petitions and mark the cases worthy of being granted time. *"It's the most basic task, and the constant thing that you do – during the summer it's practically your only task."* The petitions that lawyers write very cleverly argue why their cases should be granted; the clerk's job is *"to screen out those that are legitimate and write bench memos on what we think about the case."* On top of this, there's *"preparing your Justice for argument and conference. You learn very quickly how to handle yourself beyond just thinking 'wow, these people are brilliant!' You learn critical thinking and the big picture, and a sense of professionalism where it would be easy to strongly disagree with folks."* As term progresses, clerks move *"to the fun part."* Assisting with opinion-drafting is a process that can vary between Justices. *"Sometimes the Justice just wants to talk through an issue, so having a personality that won't be a distraction here is really beneficial,"* says one former clerk. Another enjoyed the close interaction when producing documents: *"We helped a lot with the drafting but ultimately every word that appeared in writing was the Justice's. The best learning experience was going back and forth on a piece of writing and seeing it changing."*

And what do I get out of it?

Being at the heart of such a profound process gives you tremendous insights, something that BigLaw recognizes by offering eye-popping SCOTUS clerkship bonuses. *"Reading and attending oral arguments is the best imaginable lesson by example you can have on being a good lawyer,"* a former clerk says. *"The practice of law has always been an apprenticeship – you learn best by example. You're privileged to see how your Justice writes out an argument, but you also see what kind of things persuade them. That alone is so beneficial in terms of your own perspective and in terms of knowing what persuades judges for when you go into private practice yourself."*

"Even if you didn't learn how to write or earn a dime during the year, it would be worth it to see a branch of government working." Equally – and altruistically – *"you're performing a public service. The issue at the heart of everything is 'what's the right answer, and how can we put it out there in the most persuasive way?'"*

"The level of aggression varies, but generally there's a two-week period where you get taken to lunch by everyone. It's a fairly ego-boosting process."

After their year at the elbow of a Supreme Court Justice, the 36 are in incredibly high demand. *"You get letters from firms as soon as you start,"* explains one. *"It's up to you and your Justice when you start to interview at firms – usually it's in June or July. The level of aggression varies, but generally there's a two-week period where you get taken to lunch by everyone. It's a fairly ego-boosting process, as they're all so nice to you!"*

Ultimately, most *"assume they'll go into BigLaw – there are loads of student loans to pay off, and the signing bonuses available go some way to making a dent in them."* But not everyone's head is turned by gold: *"It can be a real dilemma for some clerks, who'd prefer to go to a public interest group or go be a professor."*

And what of those bonuses? The latest round of SCOTUS clerks received golden hellos of $280,000 or more from their BigLaw firms (in addition to an approx $185,000 base salary) on arrival as third-year associates.

OK I'm sold. What should I do now to have a shot at a SCOTUS clerkship?

Get top grades, a place on Law Review, and glowing references from your law professors. Then you have a chance of a clerkship at federal appellate level. *"There are three ways to develop these relationships,"* explained one ex-clerk. *"The first is by taking regular classes with particular professors. The second is to get onto particular clinics – some schools have Supreme Court Litigation clinics where professors supervise students in brief writing. The professors are very experienced Supreme Court advocates – by virtue of that, they're very well known to the Justices and are impressive in their own right. These clinics are competitive to get into. The third route is to become a research assistant for a professor who has a relationship with the Supreme Court Justices."*

Depending on their particular school, our sources became aware of clerkships around their second year. *"For me it was more a by-product of the underlying material of law,"* says one. *"The professors at my school were clerkship-focused though, and they managed to convey how important they can be."*

The necessity of excellent personal recommendations means the process *"can be idiosyncratic and slightly opaque, but the overall feeling is that there is some sort of meritocracy in play. The same things students do to make themselves competitive also allow you to meet the recommendation people and have them like you."* Our sources concurred that *"you've got to have a very strong paper record before recommenders will help you."* The ex-clerks we spoke to had *"jumped through every hoop necessary,"* but not just out of a sense of duty. *"I did those things for years because I enjoyed them,"* says one. *"People you meet on Law Review come back and talk about the experience they've had and you learn a lot from it. These things may appear resume-focused, but they're also a lot of fun!"*

All of our interviewees now work at Jones Day.

"You see directly how things work, which completely changes the way you see cases."

The Big Interview with... **Marc Elias**, General Counsel for Hillary Clinton's 2016 presidential campaign

Marc Elias (JD Duke Law School 1993) is the general counsel for Hillary Clinton's 2016 presidential campaign, and is a partner at Perkins Coie, where he is chair of the political law practice. He acted as general counsel to John Kerry's presidential campaign in 2004, and in 2008 served as lead counsel for Senator Al Franken in the 2008 Minnesota Senate election recount and contest. Elias successfully argued the case which affirmed Franken had received the highest number of votes in the election. It was the largest recount and contest in American history. Elias' areas of focus include white collar & investigations, appellate, and political parties, campaigns and committees, and he is a nationally recognized expert in the Federal Election Campaign Act, Lobbying Disclosure Act, Ethics in Government Act and Foreign Agents Registration Act.

> *"Representing a presidential campaign is like sprinting a marathon."*

When did you decide to become a lawyer? Why?
I applied to law school on my brother's advice. He was already a lawyer at the time and encouraged me to take the LSAT to keep my options open. I had intended to pursue a career in academia in political science. In the end I pursued a joint degree in law and political science. I ended up in law because it opened up a new avenue for a more practical engagement with politics than the more removed perspective of academia. Taking the more practical route is something I have never regretted.

Starting out, what did you expect from a career in the law?
I really had no idea what to expect, except that it would be a lot of work.

Has it lived up to your expectations?
Well, it has been a lot of work! But it's also been a fascinating way to engage in the political process.

How did you get into the areas of law you are known for today? By design? Chance? Both?
I was interested in politics from the beginning, so political law and campaign finance law was a natural fit. I sought out this practice directly upon graduating from law school.

What do you consider to have been your big break?
I had the honor of serving as general counsel to John Kerry's presidential campaign in 2004. I had worked closely with Senate campaigns prior to this, but this was my first experience serving as the lead counsel on a presidential campaign and personally handling everything that requires. Even though we lost, it was a great experience with a tight-knit group of people, and was certainly a milestone both personally and in my legal career.

What differences do you see in today's legal market compared to when you started?
Two things: first, entry is incredibly competitive. Now that I am in the position of hiring applicants I see this every day. Where good, but not great, credentials may once have been sufficient for being hired, popular areas of the law now have their pick of the most elite students on the market. To be honest, if I were applying today, I doubt I would hire me. Second, the field of political law continues to grow and is starting to develop real subspecialties. When I started it was barely a practice area; it is now a recognized specialty.

What achievement are you most proud of?
I am very proud of having successfully managed the legal operations of Senator Al Franken's recount in his 2008 Senatorial campaign. It was a long, hard fight over eight months. We worked tirelessly to ensure that every vote cast was correctly counted. Ultimately we were successful. I have been involved in eight state-wide recounts and have been successful in all of them. This is a unique area of the law and politics to have built an expertise in and I am proud to have done so.

What do you consider your greatest failure or regret?
It is hard to pin what regret I have on only one event or one phenomenon. There are little things over the years that I can now see it would have been better to do a different way, or to have made a different decision. But I am lucky enough to have no major regrets, and I don't let the little ones hold me back. I'm always trying to do better.

What have you enjoyed most during your career in the legal profession?
Political law also offers unique opportunities to see the effects of one's practice on broader society, given the nature of the groups and individuals we represent. That has been really rewarding.

And enjoyed least?
As my career progresses, I find myself in more management and supervisory roles. Most of the time I don't mind it, but there are days when I barely feel like a real lawyer.

What law would you change, abolish or create?
I would enact universal voter registration and otherwise modernize our voting laws.

How has the practice of representing public officials, parties and organizations evolved over the years?
The field of political law has grown dramatically in size since I started, and has changed dramatically. What was once a side practice for a handful of lawyers is now a fully fledged specialty. We now deal with so many more issues than just campaign finance. We need to advise on IP, business law, leases, employment law, and litigation — to name a few areas. As campaigns grow in size so do their legal needs.

Who is your legal hero?
I have a deep and abiding respect for my mentor and fellow partner at Perkins Coie, Bob Bauer, who literally invented this area of the law.

What career would you have in your second life?
Before attending law school, I had planned to become a professor of political science. I have a Master's degree in political science that I got concurrently with my J.D., and I still teach occasionally. In another life, that's probably what I would have done.

What slogan would you like to be remembered by?
Al Franken said I was very funny. (What more could you want!)

What advice would you give to students trying to enter the legal profession today?
There is no magical advice. Go to a good law school, do well and have outside interests that make you stand out.

And secondly, to those who hope to ultimately get into political law?
Experience working on or with campaigns, party committees, or other organizations directly involved in the political process is helpful. It provides a perspective on the context of our work that you cannot get merely by reading about it. Many of our most successful associates and partners worked on campaigns before coming to work for Perkins. Aside from that, make sure to take the hard classes in law school that build skills and a useful knowledge base, even in your third year. And, of course, keep your grades up.

Finally, is there anything you'd like to highlight from the presidential campaign that you've found particularly challenging/enjoyable/interesting? Why?
Representing a presidential campaign is like sprinting a marathon. It is, by its very nature, challenging, and enjoyable, and interesting all at once. Secretly, Clinton's campaign is a great client. The team is smart and dedicated and the candidate is someone who inspires us all. It's a lot of work, but it's really rewarding.

"Where good, but not great, credentials may once have been sufficient for being hired, popular areas of the law now have their pick of the most elite students on the market."

Alternative careers: government

For graduates pursuing a legal career outside of BigLaw, the government offers myriad job opportunities on the federal, state and local levels.

AS NYU Law's former assistant dean for Public Service Deb Ellis points out: *"Working in an entry-level government job offers the opportunity to assume responsibility early in one's career for significant matters, thereby quickly developing one's skills as a lawyer, while also earning an excellent salary and benefits."* While salaries for government attorneys are admittedly lower than those working at private firms – indeed, an entry-level attorney working for the federal government can expect a minimum starting salary of between $45,932 and $79,717 (depending on experience), only about a third of what BigLaw first-year associates make – there are nevertheless many benefits to choosing a government position. These include:

Geographical flexibility – Aspiring government attorneys face fewer geographical limitations than their BigLaw counterparts, who are typically restricted to major cities: state and local governments hire attorneys across all cities in the USA, and the federal government employs around 85% of its workforce outside of Washington, DC.

Loan repayment assistance – *"A major concern of graduates in this economy is finding a position that allows them to manage their debt and still live comfortably,"* a careers adviser at Cardozo School of Law tells us. Fortunately, a number of federal agencies offer student loan repayment schemes to assist recent graduates with their debt, and many law schools have similar financial assistance programs for aspiring public interest lawyers.

Early responsibility – *"One great part of working for the government is that you get substantive work from day one,"* a recent law graduate working for the Department of Labor reflected. Indeed, attorneys in both the federal and state/local government tend to manage their own caseloads from the start of their career rather than answering to a strict hierarchical chain.

Wide variety of work – *"There is a whole slew of practice areas graduates can pursue in the government,"* a careers adviser from the University of Chicago Law School rightly points out. Indeed, federal and state/local government attorneys work in all branches of the government as well as independent agencies performing all types of legal work, including litigation, advisory and regulatory work.

Tangible results – Because government legal employees tend to deal with concrete policies rather than abstract transactions, they're often able to see first-hand the effects of their work within the community, particularly those in the local sector. *"The rewards are more intrinsic,"* explains Laura Mangini, former editor-in-chief of the University of Connecticut's Public Interest Law Journal. *"You come home feeling like you've done something good, like you've helped someone."*

Career flexibility – *"Many government attorneys stay in their jobs a long time, but those who decide to leave have developed valuable transferable skills,"* Deb Ellis tells us. With the variety of skills gained from a legal stint with the government – among them, research, communication and analytical skills – attorneys are equipped to work in a variety of jobs, from in-house or BigLaw associate positions to legal writing and teaching jobs.

Legal jobs with the government are available within two main divisions: the federal government and state/local governments. Some departments and agencies to consider in each include:

Federal
- Central Intelligence Agency
- Environmental Protection Agency
- Federal Bureau of Investigations
- Federal Trade Commission
- Internal Revenue Service

State/Local
- State Attorney General's Office
- Governor's Office
- City Law Department
- Mayor's Office
- City Council

The federal route

The federal government employs attorneys in each of its three branches – executive, legislative and judicial – as well as its independent agencies, which include the Federal Reserve System and the National Labor Relations Board. Of these divisions, the executive branch and independent agencies take on the greatest number of attorneys: In March 2015 there were more than 107,000 employees with law-related positions in executive and independent agencies.

According to the Partnership for Public Service, the federal government was looking to fill 23,596 legal positions between 2010 and 2012, nearly a quarter of which were attorney positions. Entry-level positions to consider include those that specifically require a JD – such as attorneys or law clerks for the Department of Justice (DoJ), Department of Homeland Security and Department of the Treasury (all of which have a particularly high number of jobs available each year) – as well as those for which a law degree is not required but highly recommended, such as paralegals, contact representatives, policy analysts, hearing and appeals specialists, estate tax examiners and labor relations specialists.

Contrary to popular belief, pursuing a legal career with the federal government does not restrict you to the courtroom; federal attorneys do everything from drafting legislation to handling depositions to advising on congressional inquiries. Some different areas of work include:

Litigation – Many federal litigators work for the DoJ, handling lawsuits and depositions; others are employed by agencies with independent litigating authorities, such as the Department of Labor, and typically handle drafting and other paperwork.

Advisory – Those interested in an advisory position can act as counselors or attorney advisers, providing advice and analysis for agencies like the Food and Drug Administration.

Regulatory – Regulatory agencies like the Environmental Protection Agency regularly hire lawyers to assist with the implementation of federal rules and regulations.

Public policy – Attorneys engage with public policy work in agencies like the Department of Commerce and Department of State, reinforcing the passage and interpretation of government legislation. There are several routes to landing a legal position with the federal government. While direct hiring is always an option – as all branches of government hire attorneys and other legal staff on a regular basis – there are also a number of programs designed to recruit recent graduates for which law students are eligible:

Recent Graduate Program – Under this program, which came into effect in late 2011, recent graduates are placed on a two-year career development scheme with a federal agency with the possibility of converting to a permanent position upon completion. Such jobs can include legal positions, though not typically attorney positions.

Honors Programs – The most common route for a federal agency attorney position, honors programs are tailored to specific agencies and generally entail a two-year fellowship with an agency, after which the majority of candidates are offered permanent positions. Some agencies with specific honors programs include the DoJ, CIA and Department of Homeland Security.

Presidential Management Fellows Program – Open to law, masters and doctoral graduates, this program places successful candidates in two-year management or policy positions that have the potential to result in permanent appointments. Again, positions can be legal-based but do not typically include attorney appointments.

Federal positions are highly sought after, so competition can get stiff for places. Having some type of work experience is essential when it comes to proving you're up to the task, whether it's a summer interning for a public interest organization or a full-blown fellowship with the federal government. *"Government employers view work experience like internships as extended job interviews,"* Deb Ellis tells us, pointing out that *"many graduates who land coveted government jobs have interned at a government agency."* Most law school careers development offices can offer advice on how to pursue relevant stints of work experience, some of which include externships with state US attorneys, clinical programs with the Supreme Court, summer internships with government organizations and post-graduate fellowships with federal bigwigs.

Some federal legal careers to consider in the long run include:

- Public defender
- Military attorney
- Appellate judge
- General attorney
- Trial attorney

The state/local route

Like the federal government, state governments are divided into three branches, all of which routinely recruit law graduates. The structures of local governments vary by community and work together with their respective state government to implement rules and regulations and maintain a balanced justice system. Thanks to a number of economic factors – including the impending retirement of the baby-boomer generation, the members of which occupy a significant portion of public sector jobs in the USA – the Department of Labor predicts that employment within state and local governments will rise by 4.2% between 2012 and 2022.

Entry-level jobs of interest to law graduates include honors attorneys – who typically work for city law departments or the state Attorney General's (AG) office – and in-house positions as legal counsel or general staff for various city and state agencies and departments, such as the Governor's Office, Mayor's Office and City Council.

Like their federal counterparts, state and local government attorneys practice a wide variety of law, including:

Administrative law – Many attorneys working for state agencies represent their agency in administrative proceedings and advise agency administrators and professional staff.

Environmental law – Environmental departments within AG offices employ attorneys to advise on state environmental policies and regulate initiatives.

Fraud – One of the main duties of attorneys in state AG offices is to protect citizens from various injustices, which often brings them into contact with fraud cases.

Civil rights law – Most state AG offices have a designated Civil Rights Division where attorneys handle civil rights-related litigation.

Labor law – City law department attorneys tend to practice in this area, among others, and most state AG offices have a Business and Labor Bureau that employs lawyers to handle employment matters.

The path to attaining a state or local government legal position varies depending on the sector: while both are willing to hire directly based on work experience, there are more opportunities to land a position with a local government straight after law school – particularly if you aim for a sizable office like the New York City Law Department, which hires between 40 to 50 recent law school graduates each year. There are also a few other avenues for entry-level candidates looking to get a foot in the door:

Summer internships – Many state and local agencies and offices have summer intern programs for law students, which they rely on for a certain portion of new recruits. The NYC Law Department, for example, runs a nine-week scheme for 50 interns each year, many of whom are offered permanent employment upon the completion of two summers.

Fellowships/honors programs – Because state and local agencies and offices prefer to hire those with several years of work experience, most offer paid fellowships or honors programs from which they recruit each year. The schemes range from one to three years in length and give candidates a chance to explore legal work within a particular area of the government.

Firm route

While it's a less common route than either of the aforementioned paths, there is the option of pursuing local government work through a private law firm that specializes in public sector law. Some municipalities contract out their legal work to private firms, so working as a public sector associate for a few years can provide you with enough work experience to apply directly for a legal position in local government work from there.

There's little central coordination when it comes to the hiring process within state and local governments, so it's up to students to research the recruitment process for each office and agency they're interested in and apply directly. *"Some entry-level positions are harder to find and attain than others – the key is persistence,"* advises a source from Duke's Career and Professional Development Center. A tangible interest in government-related work is a crucial factor in the hiring process, so students should look to their law school's CDO for opportunities to get involved with activities that will boost their credentials, such as judicial clerkships, legal externships, courses in public interest law and participation in government-related student groups.

Some state and local government legal careers to consider in the long run include:

- State attorney general
- State solicitor
- Honors attorney
- Policy director
- Legislator

Resources and advice

One of the best places for aspiring government employees to begin their job hunt is their law school's careers development office. CDOs at most law schools have a wing dedicated to assisting students with pursuits in public interest law and can advise on everything from summer clerkships to permanent attorney positions. The public interest departments at the following schools provide some especially useful resources:

NYU – As NYU alum Brandon Egren points out: *"NYU is known as a law school with a big public interest focus – that was definitely visible during my time there."* In addition to hosting the largest public interest law fair in the USA, which a number of government agencies attend each year, the Public Interest Law Center is the brains behind the Public Service Law Network Worldwide, an *"incredibly useful"* website that details internships and employment opportunities with government agencies, public interest organizations and private law firms with expansive public interest practices.

Cardozo – Each year, the law school's Center for Public Service Law awards selected postgraduate fellows $3,000 to participate in ten-week legal placements in public sector offices such as the Supreme Court and the District Attorney's Office. *"We have a very organized system with routine programs focused solely on helping students attain jobs in the public interest field, including government and judicial placements,"* a source in the law school's Office of Careers Services tells us.

Duke – The law school's career center publishes a career planning manual that outlines various career paths outside of BigLaw, including those with government agencies, and provides advice on interviewing, networking and preparing job applications. According to an insider, the school *"also tries to organize visits from various government departments and holds a reception so that representatives can mingle with students and alumni."*

Yale – Yale's CDO maintains a comprehensive database of job listings for students to access, including opportunities in the public interest sector, and also co-sponsors an annual Public Interest Student Career Fair, which draws over 100 representatives from public interest employers. Additionally, the law school has one of the country's most extensive programs for summer public interest work: At the time of writing, the school provided 248 fellowships in government and public interest organizations.

Harvard – The law school publishes an annual directory entitled 'Serving the Public' that details public service job opportunities for both students and graduates, including those in the government. The Bernard Koteen Office of Public Interest Advising also provides access to an online job search database and speciality guides that outline the application process for various types of public interest positions.

Our sources agreed that the avenue to a job with the government takes more focus and drive than most careers. As one points out: *"These jobs are by no means seen as a back-up plan; there are a lot of people who really want to work in the government, so you really have to be focused if you want to succeed. It's imperative to show commitment to all your work throughout law school."* Deb Ellis agrees, urging interested students to *"use your time in law school to develop the skills that will prepare you for a government career. It's helpful to take relevant courses, participate in clinics and develop excellent written and oral communication skills."*

Work experience is also key: *"The best thing you can do for yourself is actually work in government by interning because there is no substitute for having experience in the office where you want to work,"* Ellis continues. Finally: *"It's important that students are broad in their thinking when it comes to a job with the government,"* says another insider. *"The DoJ and FCC are obvious places to start because they each hire a lot of lawyers, but beyond that there are a lot of agencies hiring that students don't even think of, like the Federal Aviation Association. Think creatively and leave the DoJ aside! Some agencies are really focused on their mission and have a whole slew of practice areas available – you just have to look."*

Some good places to start:

- www.psjd.org – comprehensive guide to career opportunities in the federal and state/local government
- www.usajobs.gov – search directory for job vacancies in the federal government
- www.law.yale.edu/academics/publicinterestemployers.htm – list of employers in the federal and state/local government
- data.wherethejobsare.org/wtja/field/1498 – provides projections of future vacancies within various departments of the federal government
- www.opm.gov/hiringreform/pathways – details the upcoming reforms to the federal hiring process
- http://gogovernment.org – provides an overview of legal job opportunities in the federal government

Alternative careers: in-house counsel

Trading BigLaw's late nights and client demands for a more predictable life in a company does have its appeal, but applicants can expect to face hurdles in their pursuit – not least the lack of entry-level job opportunities.

Experience counts...

IN-HOUSE counsel are hired by a corporation's law department to handle a range of legal issues affecting the company, among them employment, policy, tax and regulatory matters. More prevalently, they play a managerial role, overseeing work that's been outsourced to attorneys at independent firms. Depending on the size of the corporation and the nature of its work, in-house attorneys may be either specialists in a certain field or general commercial practitioners; either way, there tend to be fewer litigators working in-house than transactional attorneys since most companies prefer to outsource litigious matters to lawyers at private firms, particularly at the entry level. *"When it comes to litigation, they really want people with experience,"* a prominent law school careers dean informs us. *"There are many more opportunities for entry-level corporate work in-house."*

Because corporate law departments employ significantly fewer attorneys than BigLaw firms, recent graduates have traditionally been at a disadvantage when it comes to getting hired: as another law school bigwig points out, corporate law departments *"generally prefer to hire more experienced attorneys rather than graduates straight out of law school."* Indeed, new in-house counsel positions are usually reserved for seasoned recruits with around five-plus years of legal experience, so opportunities to land an in-house position directly after law school remain scarce.

But there are some opportunities...

However, things are starting to look up for graduates as corporations look for alternative ways to minimize costs on the legal front. Fed up with the rising cost of outsourcing work to inexperienced junior associates at BigLaw firms – whose average hourly rate is approaching $300 – a growing number of companies are opting for the more cost-effective route of hiring their own lawyers fresh out of law school and training them in-house. As a result, job opportunities for in-house counsel are anticipated to grow over the next few years.

Among the pioneers of this trend are corporate giants such as Hewlett-Packard and IBM (in some years), which run formal in-house training programs with the aim of whipping recent graduates into in-house shape. *"Most in-house positions don't orient themselves to entry level, but could be an excellent opportunity when they do,"* our source continues. *"New lawyers can learn about both business and law, which is great training for a corporate lawyer, and the company gets to mould candidates in a way that allows them to understand the business better and achieve greater value for the company in the long run."*

Of the few in-house training programs available to recent graduates, Hewlett-Packard's 1st Year Attorney Graduate Program is arguably the most developed. According to a post by HP's Vice President of Operations on the In-house Access blog, the curriculum incorporates company-specific training, topical bootcamp sessions, skills-based classes on areas like drafting and negotiation, a formal mentoring system and even a sort of reverse secondment wherein some attorneys work for a brief period at a BigLaw firm.

NOT the norm...

Despite their unanimous praise for the aforementioned training schemes, our interviewees were quick to point out that such programs are hardly the norm. *"The reality is that the number of companies recruiting in-house counsel directly out of law school is extremely small, though the number could grow in the coming years,"* a careers dean reveals. *"By and large, people generally have to go to a big firm for a few years before moving in-house."*

Whether they have the potential to become so in the future is anyone's guess, as the dean points out: *"These companies are trying, but no-one's sure whether others will follow suit. It very much depends on things like the economy and whether they can maintain the capacity to bring young people on and train them."* Indeed, considering the volatile state of the economy coupled with the fact that the concept of training lawyers in-house is still relatively nascent, it's difficult to predict whether efforts to increase entry-level opportunities will pan out in the long run.

In-house in the summer

Fortunately, there appears to be a current spike in interest surrounding in-house careers that suggests the programs are safe for now. *"We're seeing more students attaining in-house summer positions,"* reveals another top law school careers adviser. *"And also more seeking fellowships with university general counsels,"* which offer the opportunity to serve for a summer or sometimes an entire year as part of a university's in-house counsel. Some law schools, like SUNY Buffalo, are even offering classes that specifically explore the role of in-house attorneys and the challenges they face. *"Direct in-house hiring from law school is still a rare thing, but it would be nice to see opportunities increase to give law students another option."*

Advantages and disadvantages

Indeed, while entry-level in-house opportunities are certainly limited, the advantages to a law career outside of a firm are undeniable. Benefits include:

- **Cross-training in several areas of law**– unlike BigLaw associates, who typically specialize very early on in their careers, in-house attorneys work as generalists, so they're able to gain experience in many areas of law, including IP, commercial litigation, real estate, M&A and antitrust, to name a few.

- **Improved work/life balance**– without the tough billing targets of corporate BigLaw, an in-house career lends itself to a more balanced lifestyle than that of a corporate associate. In-house counsel generally have a better sense of upcoming projects, which lessens the chance of unexpected all-nighters or canceled vacations and allows for a more predictable schedule overall.

- **Increased business involvement**– in many ways, the role of an in-house attorney mirrors that of a BigLaw associate: they draft documents, advise their clients and even get involved with pro bono activities; however, they have the added benefit of working in the same environment as their client, so they're able to gain an insider's point of view on how the company operates by attending business meetings and networking events. They're often also presented with unique benefits, such as stock options – all of which extends their role from that of a mere adviser to an actual stakeholder in the business.

- **Unique career opportunities**– the most common career path for those looking to advance in the in-house world is to ascend the ranks and become a general counsel, the chief lawyer of a corporation's law department. In-house attorneys also have the option of using their corporate experience as a springboard for pursuing a business-related position such as a corporate strategist or business development director.

However, every rose has its thorn, and in-house work is no exception. Among the disadvantages of pursuing a career in-house are:

- **Lower compensation**– while in-house counsel are regarded as well paid, they almost certainly receive less than their BigLaw counterparts. Case in point: Hewlett-Packard pays its first-year attorneys a $115,000 base salary, which is around $45,000 less than most first-year BigLaw associates make. Moreover, in-house attorneys rarely benefit from a lockstep compensation model or the gross salary inflation typical of private firms.

- **Little chance to specialize**– because in-house counsel are in charge of tackling all of a company's legal issues, they become well versed in a number of areas rather than experts in a single one. As such, there's little opportunity to specialize in a particular area of interest in the same manner that firm associates can.

- **Limited mobility**– an in-house experience can be sufficient preparation for moving into a non-legal career, but many find a transition back into BigLaw more difficult. The option is definitely there, but attorneys usually have to wait until they reach a rather senior position, such as a general counsel, before they become a commodity of interest to a private firm.

- **Small working environment**– corporate law departments are significantly smaller than BigLaw firms and thus lack some of the perks of a bigger workplace such as ample support staff and buffers between juniors and seniors. A small workforce also means the turnover is not as high as at a big firm, so competition for landing a position at any level is guaranteed to be fierce – even companies with graduate training programs only take on between three and six new attorneys per year.

Ultimately, an in-house career can be immensely fulfilling, but there are some serious caveats to consider before diving in, particularly at the entry level. Students who decide this career move is for them should try to get as much work experience as possible during law school in order to beef up their resumes – summer internships at big corporations like Procter & Gamble are regularly available and can do you big favors when it comes to honing workplace skills and business know-how. Relevant extracurricular activities, like writing for a business journal, won't go amiss either since they demonstrate a sustained interest in the corporate world.

However, should the elusive entry-level opportunity pass you by, all is not lost – our interviewees strongly discouraged students from discounting the option of working for a few years at a firm before moving in-house. One emphasized: *"Most corporations really want people to go out and work at a firm or a government agency before they try to move in-house. A few years down the line, you'll have gained enough experience to actually have substantive value for the company. It often works out best for everybody."*

For more information on going in-house, check out some of the following resources:

- www.goinhouse.com – legal job directory: listings for in-house counsel positions conveniently sorted by experience level.
- www.inhouseblog.com – award-winning blog run by former general counsel: features advice, information and FAQs about the in-house industry.
- www.acc.com – official site for the Association of Corporate Counsel: features articles, a job database and other legal resources for private-sector attorneys based on practice area and region.
- www.inhouseaccess.com – blog published by ACC: provides news updates and op-eds about events affecting the in-house community.
- Going In-House: A Guide for Law Students and Recent Graduates – booklet published by NALP: outlines the advantages and disadvantages of an in-house career and provides advice for getting hired.

"*The Big Interview*" on www.Chambers-Associate.com

We speak to top figures outside of BigLaw, to see how they made it...

"In my second career, I would stand firm against the mob and work toward a world in which I and others could pun with impunity."

– Bob Bauer, Obama's chief legal adviser

The Big Interview with... **Marilyn Mosby,** State's Attorney for Baltimore, and the youngest chief prosecutor of any major city in the US

Marilyn Mosby (born 1980; JD Boston College Law School) is the State's Attorney for Baltimore, and the youngest chief prosecutor of any major city in the US. An avid public servant, Mosby served as Assistant State's Attorney for Baltimore City from 2005 to 2012, before being sworn into office in January 2015. She has lobbied local and state lawmakers to bring Maryland sexual assault law into line with federal law – legislation that would allow prosecutors in sexual assault cases to use any previous sex crimes of the accused as evidence. Mosby is also an active member in her community, and has set up several initiatives of her own, including 'Aim to B'More', which provides nonviolent drug offenders an alternative to serving time in prison.

She is currently the top prosecutor in the Freddie Gray case: in 2015, she charged six police officers – who had arrested Freddie Gray prior to his death – with a variety of crimes including second-degree murder and involuntary manslaughter.

"Throughout history, every great movement toward progress began with young people unafraid to challenge the status quo in the pursuit of justice."

When did you decide to become a lawyer? Why?
At the tender age of 14 years old, my 17-year-old cousin, who grew up with me like a brother, was murdered right outside of our home in broad daylight when he was mistaken as a neighborhood drug dealer – an image that is branded into my mind to this very day.

This was a defining moment for me. I was faced with the fact that my cousin, who was actually an honors student with aspirations of becoming an architect and wanted to go onto Morehouse College, was now going to a grave. However, what was even more perplexing to me was the fact that the individual responsible for his death was also 17 years old, yet other than my family's grief, there was no sense of outrage.

I couldn't comprehend why this sort of violence was so common among communities of color, and why we collectively, as a community, had become so numb to hearing about yet another young black boy murdered at the hands of yet another young black boy.

If it weren't for the testimony of a neighbor who showed courage, cooperated with police, and testified in court, my family wouldn't have received any sort of justice. That was my introduction to the criminal justice system – dealing with the prosecutors and the court system.

This traumatic and painful event defined my purpose for me. For the first time I was intrigued as to how many African-American young men were affected and impacted by the criminal justice system. At 14 years old, I wanted to know how we could have gotten to that young man before he elected to take my cousin's life. Suffice it to say, I turned my pain into my passion to reform the criminal justice system.

As the youngest chief prosecutor of any major US city, what do you consider to have been your big break?
I consider being elected by the citizens of Baltimore City to be my big break. When I decided to run for Baltimore City State's Attorney, I embarked on a journey that was not easily rooted in an abundance of external support. I sat down with any and every politician, business owner, community and clergy leader to ask for their guidance and support in my endeavor. To my dismay, an overwhelming majority of those discussions ended with optimism for my vision, but skepticism in my ability to carry out my vision. Most of these skeptics went as far as to even discourage me from running for this position at all.

Believing in myself and having the unwavering support of my family, I realized that I had to channel my confidence, deflect the negativity, and ultimately decide

Becoming a Lawyer

that as a wife and a mother raising two little girls in the heart of West Baltimore, a woman of faith and a former prosecutor with six years of prosecutorial experience and overall 80% conviction rate, I not only possessed the vision but the passion and foresight to reform the criminal justice system. In June of 2014, I won the Democratic nomination for Baltimore City State's Attorney in a surprising upset, where I beat an incumbent who outraised me 4-to-1, by double-digit percentage points.

Much of your attention has been focused on the inequities in a criminal justice system that disproportionately affects ethnically diverse people. What do you believe to be the root of this problem, and what are the best ways to tackle it?
We have decades-old failed policies for which we are currently seeing the results. The systemic issues that plague many urban cities, such as Baltimore City, are a result of the lack of access to quality education, jobs and opportunities. For this reason, when I took office, I understood that it was not only about being tough on crime, but being smart on crime. I promised to build a future for Baltimore City where community confidence in the criminal justice system is restored, violent repeat offenders are held accountable, and communities feel safe. In order to reach these goals, my administration is taking a holistic approach to fighting crime.

"When I took office, I understood that it was not only about being tough on crime, but being smart on crime."

Within my first year in office, we made a number of changes to break down the barriers between our Office and the community through the implementation of several programs geared toward addressing these systemic issues. Our Aim to B'More program, modeled after California Attorney General Kamala Harris's Back On Track program that she launched while District Attorney of San Francisco, is tackling the issue of recidivism. The program is a pilot program that is available to first-time, nonviolent felony drug offenders, who will have their record expunged after successful completion of the program. Aim to B'More is changing lives.

Additionally, we are getting to young people before they get to the criminal justice system. Therefore, my administration has implemented two programs – the Junior State's Attorney Program and Great Expectations – which focus on introducing youth to the criminal justice profession.

What do you think law firms should be doing to better promote diversity?
At this critical point in our nation's history, it is imperative that law firms be committed to diversity and inclusion. While we can continue to talk about the disproportionate impact that the criminal justice system has on communities of color, it is incumbent on the legal community to not only talk, but to empower, collaborate, strategize, and make sure those we have around the table represent the community we serve. Then, and only then, will we ever break the systemic and structural barriers to racial and socioeconomic progress.

The Freddie Gray case has been big in the news recently. What would you say to those who think you're overreaching by taking steps to hold police officers criminally accountable?
A gag order has been issued in all matters relating to Freddie Gray. I will respect the Judge's orders.

What achievement are you most proud of?
I am most proud to be the mother of two beautiful, smart and confident little girls, and the wife of a man who is just as passionate about public service as I am, who encourages me daily, and pushes me beyond my own self-expectations.

What do you consider your greatest failure or regret?
There is no such thing as failure, only delayed triumph. I learned very early on that perceived failure is not fatal. I live by the philosophy that every setback, every roadblock, every loss is just another incredible chapter of my life's redemption story. Therefore, I have used each trial and tribulation in my life to find my passion and pursue my God-given purpose.

"There is no such thing as failure, only delayed triumph."

What have you enjoyed most during your career in the legal profession?
I have enjoyed the opportunity to pursue justice on behalf of victims and witnesses of crime. However, it is the work we are doing outside of the courtroom to address crime holistically that I have enjoyed the most. My office has several programs aimed at reaching young people in the classroom before they reach our courtrooms. The Junior State's Attorney Program and Great Expectations work to introduce young people to the criminal justice profession as opposed to the system. Last summer, one of our Junior State's Attorneys said he had lost hope of being a judge, but after participating in our program he said he would pursue his dream again.

And enjoyed least?

People always ask me if my job is hard, and I say the hardest part of my job is coming home to my babies tapping their wrists, asking "Where have you been?" As a mother it is difficult being away from my girls at times, but I have to remember that my passion to reform the criminal justice system is because of them and their future. It didn't really hit me until I was doing homework with my then-3-year-old during the campaign, and she looks up at me and she says, "Mommy, when I grow up, I want to be a state's attorney." It's moments like those that make the separation more bearable. Despite our busy schedules, my husband and I are a team, and make sure that we are there to support our daughters.

What law would you change, abolish or create?

I am currently pushing for a bill that would allow the evidence of previous sexual assault allegations to be brought in to criminal trials. One in five Maryland women will experience rape in their lifetime. However, in Maryland, the defense is legally entitled to introduce evidence regarding a victim's past sexual conduct to support their case if ulterior motives are suspected. To the contrary, the prosecution is not afforded the same right. As a result, serial sex offenders continue to win over Maryland juries, securing their freedom while endangering our public safety. We need to bring Maryland closer to compliance with the Federal Rules of Evidence, enacting laws that will allow prosecutors to introduce evidence of a defendant's relevant prior sex acts or abuse of a minor.

Who is your legal hero?

Oh wow! There are so many! I guess if I would have to pick one it would be Senatorial candidate and former Attorney General Kamala Harris.

What career would you have in your second life?

I am a public servant at heart, and my passion has always been to reform the criminal justice system. So, I don't think I would have it any other way. I am definitely living my dream.

What slogan would you like to be remembered by?

Harriet Tubman once said, "Every great dream begins with a dreamer. Always remember, you have within you the strength, the patience, and the passion to reach for the stars to change the world." It is something I say to myself daily as a reminder that there is nothing I cannot do. As long as I have the strength, the patience, and the passion to pursue my dreams, I know I will attain them.

Do you ever get compared to Rhonda Perlman from *The Wire*? Do you take it as a compliment?

I have never heard that comparison before. As a Baltimore City resident who is committed to moving this city forward, this city is so much more than what is depicted in The Wire. So, while I'm sure the fictional character of Rhonda Perlman is zealous in her pursuit of justice, I am committed to addressing the real, crippling, decades-old systemic and structural issues that have plagued the City of Baltimore for far too long.

"I am committed to the addressing the real, crippling, decades-old systemic and structural issues that have plagued the City of Baltimore for far too long."

You've set up several initiatives, including 'Aim to B'More', which provides an alternative to incarceration for nonviolent drug offenders. Why do you think it's better to take a more holistic approach to improving the criminal justice system?

We know what happens when these individuals get these felony convictions – they can no longer apply for jobs, they can no longer apply for housing, and they can't really get any sort of financial aid to further their education, so what other alternative do they have than to go back out on the street doing what they were doing before? Through this program, the participants go through a probationary period where they learn life skills, they learn job-training skills, they do community service, and at the end of their probationary period they're given a job. And it's not just something like a fast-food restaurant, five-dollar-an-hour job, but a job with benefits that allows them to provide for their families. At the completion of the probationary period, their felony record is wiped clean. It is only through programs such as this that we will really address the societal ills of poverty and crime.

What advice would you give to students trying to enter the legal profession today?

Throughout history, every great movement toward progress began with young people unafraid to challenge the status quo in the pursuit of justice by acting in that exact moment, and never letting any time, situation or circumstance define their destiny. Therefore, I encourage students to identify their passions and be resolute in their efforts to pursue them.

Alternative careers: public interest law

Pursuing a legal career in the public interest arena can be a rewarding but challenging path to take.

STUDENTS at law school often arrive in their first year with a surge of enthusiasm to use their legal knowledge for a good cause, and to help bridge the justice gap between wealthy Americans and low-income individuals. However, the reality is that by their third year, many students end up taking the path of least resistance – the path towards BigLaw.

BigLaw does make sense: for students with large debts to pay off, the offer of a job with a prestigious firm is more than tempting. These offers are usually made in September, while an offer from a nonprofit may not arrive until the following March, or later. Students are often put in an extremely difficult situation, to decide between the security of a sizable salary and a job opportunity that may never materialize.

Unfortunately, as in the private sector, the recession means it's not the greatest time to be applying to nonprofits and public interest organizations: giving is generally down in the USA, and funding has been cut, meaning that in-house opportunities are not as prevalent as they were before the economic crisis. To put it simply, many of these organizations do not have the resources to spend on training, internships and fellowships, which form the entry routes into this field of work.

We can't dress it up: pursuing this type of career is difficult and highly competitive, but not impossible. The students who ardently keep on the public interest track tend not to view it as a fall-back option. This is critical, as many public interest employers want to see that a student has a commitment and passion for their cause – a true interest in their mission. This kind of work can't be taken lightly, as it often involves handling people's lives in crisis situations – you could be negotiating child custody for an incarcerated mother, or dealing with people who have had their homes taken away from them. A single-minded focus throughout law school can therefore stand students in good stead with a potential employer.

Get involved from the get-go

While at law school, taking part in legal clinics, joining law clubs which delve into a specific area like family or environment, and pursuing pro bono projects are all essential starting points for a 1L student. Pro bono projects don't have to take up too much time, and can prove a sustained interest in this aspect of law. Using every summer wisely is also a sensible idea. Securing an internship for a nonprofit is tough, but funding opportunities are available, and many law schools will raise money to give grants to students looking to spend their summer in this way – look out for Dean Summer Service Grants, or check to see whether the school injects any money from its endowment funds to finance these summer schemes. Attending careers fairs and regularly checking websites like idealist.org can also help to get an idea of the scope of available opportunities.

"Opting for a career as a public interest attorney requires resilience and a pretty high tolerance for what feels like risk, especially when an offer from a BigLaw firm hovers on the horizon."

As a 2L, begin to lead fundraising efforts, take more of a leadership role in the campus clinics, and also consider doing an externship with a specific organization. Externships provide students with academic credit during term-time, and can be full or part-time. They're often overseen by a faculty member, and equip students with the experiential learning required to apply for positions post-law school. Some law schools also push 2Ls to apply for any available fellowships, for example those which are facilitated by Skadden and Equal Justice Works. Students first make contact with a nonprofit to develop a project, and then apply for funding through those who advertise the fellowship.

There's a reason why all of this experiential learning is so important. Due to the inability of nonprofits to provide training, it's expected that lawyers who join in-house can hit the ground running. This is not like BigLaw, where you may be tucked away doing doc review or writing up a sophisticated memo for days on end: you have to be on your game to work for a nonprofit. There are often no resources or senior figures to fall back on – you're it, and the organization will expect you to be able to potentially go to court immediately, and handle a high level of responsibility. This does feed into a problem: nonprofits won't hire anyone unless they've passed their Bar exam, which can be difficult for those who are fresh out of law school.

Luckily, some law schools do have some resources to make use of, including 'Bridge Fellowships', which are offered to those who have left law school without a job. These monetary fellowships allow postgrads to take up a position in a nonprofit, pass the Bar, and demonstrate their value to the organization in question, so that they can potentially be first in line should a job opportunity arise. The fellowships also allow nonprofits to be like BigLaw firms, in the sense that they get a chance to sample candidates before making a decision to employ them.

Paying back student debt is another issue to consider, and a prominent reason for law grads to opt for BigLaw. However, the College Cost Reduction and Access Act of 2007 has made it easier for law students to repay their loans, paving a more viable path towards a career in public interest law. Postgrads can now take out federal guaranteed debt, instead of private debt, meaning that small amounts can be paid back based on income. Law schools also have various repayment programs, and in some cases help to stump up the dollars to pay up to half of a postgrad's monthly debt. A further incentive is federal loan forgiveness, whereby the government writes off any outstanding debt after an individual has worked for a nonprofit for ten years. However, salaries are markedly lower than in private practice, and if your first nonprofit job lands you $60,000 a year, you'll be doing well.

There's no doubt that working in this field is daunting, and the ostensible dearth of opportunities can lead students to remain wary of doing so. Opting for a career as a public interest attorney requires resilience and a pretty high tolerance for what feels like risk, especially when an offer from a BigLaw firm hovers on the horizon. The good news is that if your BigLaw firm is a NALP employer (which they typically are), you can ask them to hold the offer until March, when the offer from a nonprofit may be extended. The law firm isn't obligated to do so, and it also runs the risk of demonstrating that your heart's not set on the private sector, but it is an option nonetheless.

As a general rule, it's probably better to have your heart set on one or the other, and not to try to straddle both, as nonprofits want to see a high level of dedication, just as law firms do. Furthermore, it's a tough road, and you'll be on it for the long haul. It's not all doom and gloom though: you may not be earning a six-figure salary, but many who carve out a career in this field find it to be the most meaningful and intrinsically rewarding way to utilize their expertise and spend their lives.

The Big Interview with... **Haben Girma**, the first Deafblind graduate of Harvard Law School. She's a White House Champion of Change and advocate of the civil rights of people with disabilities

Haben Girma (JD Harvard Law School 2013) is the first Deafblind graduate of Harvard Law School. She received her BA, magna cum laude, in 2010 from Lewis & Clark College. As a White House Champion of Change, she is an advocate of the civil rights of people with disabilities, and is a staff attorney at the nonprofit corporation Disability Rights Advocates. In 2015, she helped achieve a landmark legal victory in the National Federation of the Blind v Scribd case, which rules that Scribd content will now have to include accessibility features. In her free time, Haben Girma enjoys salsa, swing dance and surfing.

When did you decide to become a lawyer? Why?

As a Deafblind student in college, I witnessed advocates using the Americans with Disabilities Act (ADA) to change social attitudes. The National Federation of the Blind regularly referenced the ADA when explaining to technology developers why designing access for people with disabilities is a necessity and not some optional cherry atop the Silicon Valley sundaes. I heard how the National Association of the Deaf used the ADA to increase closed-captioning online, and how Disability Rights Advocates used the ADA to compel Target's tech team to make their website accessible to blind Americans. Impressed by the success of the advocates, I felt inspired to join them. Back then, and even now, I encountered so many barriers in the digital world. Not because of my disability, but because of attitudes among tech developers that trivialize access for people with disabilities.

"Negative stereotypes and attitudinal barriers hold the legal field back."

Starting out, what did you expect from a career in the law?

I expected to use my legal career to increase access to information for people with disabilities, and I'm successfully doing just that. A career in law allows me to work toward ending the information famine, rendering accessible the digital works that formerly had access barriers. Working on the Scribd case has thus been personally and professionally rewarding.

As the first Deafblind graduate of Harvard Law School, what skills did you learn as a student that you were able to carry forward into your legal career?

Law school teaches valuable advocacy skills, and I regularly use the skills I developed in school. My favorite class was negotiations because that's where I developed and practiced the art of negotiation.

You've worked tirelessly as an advocate for disability rights. What in your opinion should law firms be doing to promote the recruitment of people with disabilities?

Negative stereotypes and attitudinal barriers hold the legal field back. Educating law firms, spotlighting lawyers with disabilities, and including disability in diversity training will help us move in the right direction. As a first step, please sign and circulate the American Bar Association's Pledge for Change: Disability Diversity in the Legal Profession, http://www.americanbar.org/groups/disabilityrights/initiatives_awards/pledge_for_change.html.

Where should law firms be investing their money in order to best alleviate the challenges faced by their disabled employees?

Lawyers with disabilities are diverse, and most disability accommodations cost very little. Law firms should work to create inclusive environments where all employees can contribute their talents. Law firms should invest in diversity training, removing architectural barriers, and accessible digital services.

What advice would you give to someone with a disability who is hoping to go into a career in law?
Individuals with disabilities who are considering law school should reach out to law students and lawyers with disabilities to seek advice and learn strategies. Consider joining organizations for lawyers and law students with disabilities, too.

You've obviously achieved a huge amount, but what single achievement are you most proud of?
Working to increase access to Scribd's large library has been both personally and professionally rewarding. I'm excited to gain access to more digital services for the disability community.

What do you consider your greatest failure or regret?
Although I spent many hours practicing, my dancing with the Harvard Ballroom Dance Team never won me an award. I really love dancing, so I wonder sometimes where I would be now if I devoted more time to dancing.

What have you enjoyed most during your career in the legal profession?
My clients and colleagues are absolutely fantastic. I really enjoy spending time with people who believe in access and inclusion as much as I do.

And enjoyed least?
Litigation often takes a long time. I would love for positive changes to happen quickly.

What law would you change, abolish or create?
I would like to see the US develop a national program for selecting, hiring, and covering the cost of interpreters that would allow Deaf Americans greater access to their local communities.

Who is your legal hero?
Daniel Goldstein is an extraordinary attorney who has won many victories for the National Federation of the Blind. You recently helped achieve a legal victory in *National Federation of the Blind v Scribd*, meaning Scribd will now reprocess its literary content to include accessibility features.

What's the next big project on the horizon?
The vast majority of websites and apps have access barriers, so I plan to continue working to increase access to digital information.

More generally, what is your long-term career plan?
Long-term, I plan to continue working to increase access to digital information.

Finally, what slogan would you like to be remembered by?
"We all have the ability to make our world more inclusive."

"Law firms should invest in diversity training, removing architectural barriers, and accessible digital services."

Pro bono

Doing your bit for society, or advancing your legal skills – whichever way you look at it, pro bono does a world of good.

IT'S SHORT for 'pro bono publico', which, you won't need telling, means 'for the public good'. Pro bono is essentially voluntary work carried out by legal professionals – drawing on their legal nous to help out those who couldn't otherwise afford legal advice. The work offers up limitless opportunities, from advising struggling artists on the technicalities of IP law, to helping draw up new legal constitutions for war-torn African states.

Why do firms do it?

In a profession that is wedded to the billable hour, it seems even shark-like partners have a soft side. The late Esther Lardent, ex president and CEO of the Pro Bono Institute, stated when we chatted to her a few years ago: *"I think that larger law firms do pro bono for the same reason that many individual lawyers do pro bono. There's a sense that there are problems only lawyers can address – it's a special responsibility."* She continued: *"Fundamentally, this really is a question of passion and a desire to serve."* She certainly embodied that passion (look her up for more info on her fantastic work), but it turns out that giving back to the community is also a pretty smart business move:

1. A top-quality pro bono program attracts top-quality attorneys. Those who enter the profession with dreams of changing the world are more likely to join a firm that lets them run with these projects than one that denies them the chance. Increased pro bono opportunities can seal the deal for gold-standard candidates. Pro bono also serves as an incentive for more senior attorneys or partners to stick around.

2. Pro bono has come to play a central role in training for young attorneys. Juniors tend to be afforded heaps of responsibility on these matters, often taking the lead and liaising with the client directly rather than shuffling papers in the background. Not only is it an effective method of on-the-job training, but it saves both time and money on more formalized programs.

> *"A very big factor in a firm's decision to do pro bono is that it's a great training tool for younger associates, particularly for litigators."*

Litigation powerhouse Jenner & Block accumulated a whopping average of 175 pro bono hours per attorney in 2013, and remain impressive with a 108 hour average in 2015. Gabriel Fuentes and Jeffrey Koppy, the firm's previous and current pro bono chairmen, explain: *"A very big factor in a firm's decision to do pro bono is that it's a great training tool for younger associates, particularly for litigators. Given the type of work that firms like Jenner do – very high-end, with millions or billions of dollars involved in any matter – cases often settle before they go to trial. Sometimes the stakes are so high that the youngest associates don't get the participation they might want."* This is where pro bono comes into its own. *"The program allows younger attorneys to make decisions about strategy, and learn how to conduct themselves in court under our supervision. They learn all those essential elements of litigation that young attorneys need in order to develop into successful older attorneys and partners."*

3. The work is also a tremendous morale booster. Few things in BigLaw will seem as worthwhile as getting an innocent man off death row, or reuniting an asylum seeker with their family. Pro bono recognition events aren't bad for team spirit either. It's known as *"pro bono glue,"* Esther Lardent explained. *"In terms of goodwill, branding, and the retention of attorneys, large firms have the ability to use pro bono as a rallying force and a source of cross-office collaboration."*

4. A healthy pro bono caseload is a PR officer's dream. Even juniors admit that *"the website looks better when you can show that pro bono is widely available."* Then there's the fact that publicity regarding a pro bono case is cheaper and much more credible than a paid advertisement. It gets the firm's name out into the community, beyond legal circles. Studies have shown that clients are more likely to part with their money if firms are perceived to be involved with worthwhile causes. In this way, pro bono is a nifty exercise in branding.

For a prime example, look no further than Gibson Dunn. The firm's renowned litigator Ted Olson teamed up with David Boies, his opposing counsel in Bush v Gore, to challenge Prop 8, a California state constitutional amendment banning same-sex marriage. His work on the lawsuit earned him a place among Time 100's greatest thinkers, and an ABA Medal (the highest award of the American Bar Association). The case caused such a furore it was even turned into a play, 8, which saw Olson played by John Lithgow and Martin Sheen, and Boies by Morgan Freeman and George Clooney. Not bad publicity for a bit of pro bono work.

So, from a business perspective, pro bono makes sense. Why, then, do some firms do so much more than others? According to our figures, in 2015 attorneys at Patterson Belknap Webb & Tyler stacked up an impressive average of 135 pro bono hours each, Munger, Tolles & Olson followed closely with133, Arnold & Porter wowed with 124, Debevoise & Plimpton reached 117.5, and Jenner & Block did their thing with 108. Compare this to Allen & Overy (14 hour average in 2015), Waller (15), Cozen O'Connor (17.4), and Jackson Walker (20) and you'll be asking yourself some questions.

There's a clear correlation between gross revenue and firm size and the amount of pro bono racked up.

Like so many things in business, this often comes down to the bottom line: there's a clear correlation between gross revenue and firm size and the amount of pro bono racked up. Take Haynes and Boone: their revenue in 2013 was $311.2 million, their pro bono hours totalled 11,169 and the average per attorney was 22.2; by 2015 these figures had risen to $362 million, 13, 090 and 33.3 respectively. Even more staggeringly, look at Sheppard, Mullin, Richter & Hampton: $466.5 million, 14,607 and 23.3 in 2013; $510.71 million, 21,693 and 32.6 in 2014; and $559.5 million, 26,632 and 36.2 in 2015. Our 2015/16 stats show that the 50 biggest firms by associate class-size averaged 68.9 hours of pro bono per attorney, whereas the smaller half averaged 54 hours. Honing in further, the 20 biggest recruiters record an average of 73.5 hours. The 20 smallest recruiters record 47.1 hours.

This is largely down to a lack of resources. Your Sullivan & Cromwells (67 hours) and Ropes & Grays (95.6 hours) can afford to hire a full-time pro bono coordinator or put together a robust pro bono committee. Many of these law firms have also fostered longstanding relationships with public service organizations. At smaller firms, full-time partners are likely to be juggling pro bono coordination tasks with their already hefty workload, which has a knock-on effect on the program's ultimate impact.

The ratio of associates to partners also plays a part, as does geography. If your biggest office is in Phoenix, Arizona – like Snell & Wilmer (37 hours average in 2015) – fewer pro bono opportunities are likely to present themselves compared to a firm based in New York or DC like Shearman & Sterling (67 hours in 2015).

Why do attorneys do it?

After a hard week of training, networking and racking up an obscene amount of billable hours, why spend your time rifling through immigration documents when you could be eating chocolate mousse in front of Netflix? As one associate put it, *"there are two kinds of time: time you're billing hours that count, and time you could be spending on the couch."*

Well, for starters, doing pro bono work just feels good. One junior associate told us: *"It's really nice to step outside of what you're doing for the big clients and help people who wouldn't otherwise be able to afford it."* Plus, on a more cynical note: *"It's often a more interesting topic of conversation at a party than what financing transaction you just closed."*

Secondly, as we've already mentioned, pro bono projects provide some of the best on-the-job training you're likely to receive as an attorney. Another massive bonus is that juniors can actually seek out the type of skills and experience they want to gain, and make a beeline for those cases.

The integral issue of billable hours complicates things. Every firm has a different policy when it comes to pro bono work. Some count time spent on pro bono in exactly the same way as paid client hours (Cleary, Jones Day). Most only count a certain number of pro bono hours as billable (Haynes and Boone, Gibbons). A select few only begin to count pro bono once juniors have reached their billable hour target (Venable, Epstein Becker & Green), while others don't count time spent on pro bono at all (Hangley Aronchick Segal Pudlin & Schiller, although they do say that a minimum of 50 hours is *"expected"*). Of course, within these broad categories fall myriad variations, but generally *"it's considered part of firm citizenship,"* one source explained. All in all, the billable hour/pro bono equilibrium is well worth taking into consideration when choosing the firm to kick-start your career.

State requirements

In 1969, the ABA adopted the Code of Professional Responsibility, which stated: *"Every lawyer, regardless of professional prominence or professional workload, should find time to participate in serving the disadvantaged."* This still stands today, as does the aspirational goal that every lawyer in the USA should spend at least 50 hours a year working on pro bono matters. In most states, however, these rules aren't enforced (apart from Florida, Hawaii, Illinois, Maryland, Mississippi, Nevada and New Mexico). They recognize that attorneys may not be dead on 50 hours each year, but suggest that over the entire course of their career it should pretty much balance out. Some states have also departed from the 50-hour rule, choosing their own aspirational pro bono goal. Virginia, for instance, requires attorneys to dedicate 2% of their professional time to pro bono. In Oregon, the target is 80 hours.

One of the biggest talking points in the pro bono world recently has been New York's adoption of a new hours requirement. On May 1, 2012, New York's Chief Judge Jonathan Lippman announced that all applicants for admission to the New York Bar from January 2015 would be required to have completed 50 hours of pro bono. Go online to read more about the impact of this.

What sort of pro bono work is on offer?

The opportunities for pro bono work may well be endless; some firms have an enormous list of options, and strongly encourage associates to bring in their own projects from outside. Others are more limited in their range, working closely with a couple of organizations or insisting that juniors only take on pro bono work that complements their practice area. A lack of pro bono options is a regular grumble among our transactional-focused associates.

That said, in the past few years we've spoken to associates involved in a whole range of fascinating projects, like assisting with Hurricane Sandy relief efforts, volunteering for a presidential election protection helpline to combat corruption, defending families who are having their homes foreclosed, and helping survivors of sex trafficking have their convictions for prostitution overturned (to name but a few).

But it is true that certain types of pro bono matters are likely to crop up more than most. In 2012, firms in the Am Law 200 spent the most time on death penalty cases, with over 64,000 hours clocked up in total. Matters surrounding civil rights (56,481), prisoners' rights (33,699), criminal defense (26,072) and veterans (21,639) make up the rest of the top five.

Current issues in pro bono

After the recession, the 'justice gap' – the divide between the legal needs of low-income people and the ability of civil legal mechanisms to meet these needs – visibly grew. Already bending under pressure, the system came under additional strain. The Legal Services Corporation (LSC), the largest single funder of civil legal services in the USA, has for several years been reporting on the depressingly low percentages of low-income people with civil legal problems who are actually able to obtain the necessary legal assistance. The March 2013 sequestration didn't help matters.

It's perhaps no surprise then that Jonathan Lippman took arguably drastic measures a few years back and implemented a scheme whereby all applicants to the New York bar must have carried out a minimum of 50 hours of legal pro bono work. The new rule has been active since January 2015, and while it may be a bit early to check on results, it was estimated that it would add 500,000 hours of voluntary legal assistance in the area.

While Lippman's move shows that the problem is an urgent one, it's also important to acknowledge that pro bono has become a central aspect being a lawyer for the younger generations, with many of our respondents citing it as a priority when selecting a firm. Economic turbulence might signify a dip in pro bono (since individuals aren't the only ones suffering: BigLaw firms can also struggle to put in the free work when general business is bad), but the changing landscape of social justice can also bring new opportunities for fascinating pro bono work.

Recently, firms have been busy working out the changes in laws surrounding the legal recognition of same-sex unions globally. Jones Day launched a website, www.samesexrelationshipguide.com, designed to survey and track these changes. *"The site summarizes the status of legal recognition of same-sex relationships in all U.N. recognized countries worldwide,"* the firm told us, adding that lawyers and staff together have spent almost 6,000 hours on the project with an estimated value of over $2.5 million in fees. Similarly White & Case *"partnered with Bank of NY Mellon to create a free, online database of tax rules and regulations for same-sex couples filing their taxes in the US."*

The issues of rape, consent, and the way cases of sexual violence are treated by the police and the public at large have also been prevalent in the news in the past few years. As part of their pro bono roster Goodwin Procter represent the Joyful Heart Foundation, a non profit dedicated to supporting victims of sexual assault. Goodwin's attorneys also support its "End the Rape Kit Backlog" initiative, which seeks to shed light on the number of rape kits that go untested every year *"by sending public records requests to police departments and state agencies in over a dozen U.S. jurisdictions."* At K&L Gates, associates can work with the firm's Cyber Civil Rights Legal Project on revenge porn cases. *"A lot of young associates work on these matters; I think we have a better understanding of the things you can do on a smart phone."* Check out our website for more on this.

On chambers-associate.com...

10 pro bono organizations you need to know about.

Practice Areas

Antitrust: Cartel – an overview by White & Case

Legal trends

- Criminal and civil cases can be brought for a violation of Section 1 of the Sherman Act (15 U.S.C. §1), the principal statute governing cartel activity under US law. Cartel activity includes agreements between competitors on price, output, market or customer allocation and bid-rigging. The US Department of Justice, Antitrust Division (the DOJ) is charged with criminal enforcement. Private parties can bring civil actions for monetary damages and injunctive relief for alleged Sherman Act violations.
- The DOJ has intensified its investigations into alleged cartel activity in recent years with a focus on international cartels. This is an important development for global businesses because companies found liable for cartel activity are exposed to large criminal penalties, and company executives may face prosecution.
- Recent DOJ cartel investigations into the automotive parts, financial services, optical disk drive and air cargo industries, among others, have resulted in billions of dollars in fines and substantial jail time for numerous executives. For fiscal year 2015, DOJ criminal prosecution of companies and individuals engaged in cartel behavior resulted in US$3.6 billion in criminal penalties. Also in 2015, 66 individual defendants were charged for cartel-related activity, with an average sentence of 25 months for those who received prison terms.
- There also has been an increase in recent years in foreign regulatory agencies investigating cartel activity, which has led to a rise in cooperation between competition enforcement agencies around the world, including the United States, the European Union, Japan, Korea, Canada and many others. Although this cooperation allows the international agencies to coordinate the gathering of evidence and general theories of the case, as the trend continues, questions of overlapping jurisdiction and the ability to order overlapping sanctions have become issues of increasing importance.
- Given the global nature of many recently uncovered cartels, a key issue in US cartel enforcement is the extraterritorial reach of the Sherman Act. The Foreign Trade Antitrust Improvements Act (FTAIA) (15 U.S.C. §6a) limits the extraterritorial reach of the Sherman Act. FTAIA applies to both criminal and civil enforcement. Under FTAIA, the Sherman Act applies to antitrust conduct occurring outside the United States only if that conduct is import commerce or has a direct, substantial and reasonably foreseeable effect on domestic commerce, and such effect proximately caused a plaintiff's foreign injury. The Seventh Circuit recently issued an opinion that indicates that the application of FTAIA will be different in criminal and civil cases. *Motorola Mobility, LLC v. AU Optronics*, 775 F.3d 816 (7th Cir. 2015), *cert. denied*, 135 S.Ct. 2837 (2015).
- Once the DOJ begins an investigation into a particular industry, civil actions typically follow in the form of class actions and direct actions. Civil actions are often broader in scope than criminal investigations, and the absence of criminal liability does not ensure protection from civil liability. Damages in private actions typically are measured by the *"overcharge"* resulting from the cartel, with actual damages being automatically trebled if liability is proven. Civil damages can be substantial in cartel cases.
- Purchasers at different levels of the distribution chain may have standing to bring causes of action for the same alleged cartel behavior. Problems with multiple recoveries arise when purchasers at different levels of the distribution chain bring actions and both purchasers claim they suffered injury from the same overcharge. Direct purchasers will argue that they absorbed any overcharge that resulted from the cartel, while indirect purchasers will argue that the direct purchasers passed on any overcharges. Given the potential for duplicative recoveries, treble damages, and joint and several liability, the mere filing of a class action creates settlement leverage regardless of the merits of a claim.
- Recently the pharmaceutical industry has seen an onslaught of antitrust cases that include Section 1 claims that defendants conspired to restrain trade. In the recent "product hopping" case, Mylan Pharmaceuticals Inc. v. Warner Chilcott PLC et al., 2015 WL 1736957 (April 16, 2015), plaintiffs claimed that the brand manufacturer and its licensee conspired to extend the brand's monopoly by deploying a scheme to develop subsequent versions of the same drug, and discontinuing older versions, thereby extending its patent. The court granted summary judgment for the defendants and found that product hopping almost never constitutes exclusionary conduct. In so-called "reverse payment" or "pay for delay" cases, plaintiffs challenge patent infringement settlements

between a brand name drug manufacturer and a generic competitor that include terms that plaintiffs allege will provide for payments from the brand manufacturer to delay generic competition. Many of these cases include claims that the settlement agreements were an unlawful conspiracy to restrain trade.

What an up-and-coming lawyer in this area can expect

- Representing and counseling clients in connection with a variety of complex and often headline-grabbing investigations and litigations
- Advocating for clients at meetings with the DOJ and foreign regulatory agencies during investigations
- Advising clients on the development of comprehensive compliance programs and policies
- Preparing and representing witnesses in providing testimony in grand jury investigations, civil depositions, and civil and criminal trials
- Drafting motions to dismiss, motions for summary judgment and various substantive nondispositive motions
- Working with economic experts in determining the viability of overcharge claims and examining a cartel's effect on prices

White & Case LLP's antitrust practice

White & Case has experience in all aspects of global cartel investigations and litigation, including parallel civil Sherman Act class actions, EU proceedings, extradition and extraterritorial discovery. With more than 180 antitrust lawyers in 23 offices on four continents, White & Case's Antitrust practice offers our clients an integrated worldwide team with deep competition law capabilities, providing a coordinated approach to the increasingly global competitive issues facing our clients. White & Case is recognized by Global Competition Review, the leading international authority on competition law and practice, as one of the world's elite competition practices. White & Case also was named "Competition Group of the Year" by Law360 in 2011, 2012, 2013, 2014 and 2015, making it the only firm to win the award five years in a row.

About the authors

J. Mark Gidley chairs the White & Case Global Antitrust practice. His practice focuses on mergers, acquisitions and cartel cases, frequently with a transnational focus. In December 2014, Mark was named one of the inaugural Litigation Trailblazers by The National Law Journal. (University of Kansas (BS) and Columbia University (JD))

Martin M. Toto is a partner in the firm's Global Antitrust practice, concentrating in US antitrust law and complex commercial litigation. He has served as trial counsel and successfully defended clients in several recent price-fixing and monopolization trials. Martin also has advised companies on virtually all aspects of antitrust law. (Lehigh University (BS) and New York University (JD))

Jack Pace is a partner in White & Case's Global Antitrust practice and Executive Partner of the firm's New York office. He represents clients in complex litigation matters, particularly class actions, involving claims under the antitrust, RICO, consumer protection and other laws. (Fordham University (BA and JD))

John Chung is a partner in the firm's Global Antitrust and Commercial Litigation practices. His practice focuses on antitrust, complex commercial disputes, international arbitration and white-collar investigations, often involving cross-border and international law issues. (Northwestern University (BS), Temple University (JD) and New York University (LLM))

Heather Abrams is an associate in the Global Antitrust practice. She represents clients in civil and criminal antitrust cases, including several complex multidistrict litigations. (Boston College (BA) and Fordham University (JD))

WHITE & CASE

Antitrust

In a nutshell

Antitrust attorneys advise clients on whether their business practices comply with regulations domestically and abroad so that markets function effectively on the basis of fair and open competition. In doing so, they undertake a broad range of different legal activities, including litigation, government investigations, merger advice and counseling.

Within litigation, generally there are cases alleging improper single company conduct and those alleging anti-competitive agreements or collusion among two or more entities. The former refers to claims against a single entity for monopolistic conduct, such as predatory pricing or abuse of monopoly power. The latter refers to an agreement or conspiracy among two or more entities that could include conduct such as boycotting, bid-rigging, price-fixing and dividing markets or customers. Many of these cases are brought by a class of affected customers or consumers. Both types are private and civil.

Government investigation, or enforcement, can be brought as a civil or criminal proceeding. Civil enforcement involves investigating companies for certain conduct, asking them to change their behavior, and sometimes fining them. Criminal investigations revolve primarily around cartels and price-fixing, and carry steep criminal penalties.

Merger advice (often called merger control) is another big piece of antitrust work, whereby attorneys shepherd their client through major regulations associated with M&A transactions, which generally result in a greater market share, the likely elimination of competitors and a greater risk of monopolistic conduct. Counseling involves providing clients with advice about their current and future business practices, such as co-marketing or distribution.

What lawyers do

Civil litigation on the defense side

- Receive complaint and file for motion to dismiss. This can often go through several rounds, as the claimant amends the complaint.
- If working on a class action, attorneys conduct 'class' discovery, during which they work with experts to attempt defeating class action certification. They will depose the experts and file and defend their reports.
- If class certification is granted, or if the case was never a class action to begin with, lawyers conduct 'merits' discovery. This requires producing all the relevant documents and conducting depositions about liability and damages.
- Apply for summary judgment. If summary judgment is denied, attorneys prepare for trial, which involves determining what evidence and depositions to use and whether they will be admitted, drawing up the exhibit list, and deciding what sort of discovery or motions to push for.
- Go to trial. Handle post-trial steps.
- Attorneys for plaintiff conduct due diligence before filing a complaint, oppose motions to dismiss, defend class action certification and oppose summary judgment.

Civil government investigation

- Receive Civil Investigative Demand (CID) from the Federal Trade Commission or Department of Justice, requesting documents. State attorneys general can also initiate investigations.
- Negotiate with the government to narrow the categories of violations, limit the bounds of discovery and win more time.
- Produce the requested documents, ensuring those provided comply with the government's demand. **Jay Srinivasan** of **Gibson Dunn** describes this portion as capable of being a *"massive implementation effort"* in larger cases.
- Negotiate and maybe give interviews to the government while waiting for its decision. Depending on the three possible outcomes, attorneys close the investigation, negotiate, or defend the client in court or before an administrative law judge.

Criminal government investigation

- Receive grand jury subpoena or FBI warrant.
- Conduct investigation into possible wrongdoing.
- Produce materials requested by the subpoena or warrant.
- If evidence suggests possible wrongdoing, counsel client on strategies to defend against a possible charge or advise on possible plea arrangements.
- Client decides whether to fight or plea. If the latter, negotiate plea agreement (including scope of charge and fine amount).
- Enter into a plea agreement.
- If negotiations fail and the client does not enter into plea, or chooses to fight the charge, attorneys will go to trial.

Mergers

- If the merger meets one or more of the government's enumerated thresholds, attorneys file a Hart-Scott-Rodino form (HSR), indicating the intent to merge.
- Conduct due diligence and spot issues.
- Determine the likelihood that the merger will be challenged, reviewed or investigated.
- Depending on the government's response to the HSR, lawyers wait, go ahead with the merger, agree to a consent decree, or defend the client in an injunctive trial or administrative hearing.

Realities of the job

- Attorneys must know how markets work, how they are defined and how different forces will affect them. You don't need to have studied economics as an undergraduate but it will certainly help if you have.
- The Sherman Antitrust Act of 1890 and the Clayton Antitrust Act of 1914 are the body of law most antitrust attorneys work with and which forms the foundation for most state antitrust laws.
- Legal precedent plays the largest role in antitrust matters. Lawyers must know their case law, especially US Supreme Court decisions, and the issues that have and have not been resolved.
- Even the smallest antitrust case can take two to three years to make its way through litigation. If it's only a two-party case of smaller companies, it could still take two years or more.
- Because the cases tend to be large and high-profile, young associates often have to share responsibility among a larger team. If the case is big enough, however, associates may get an opportunity to second-chair depositions.
- Discovery is a crucial part of the litigation process and is document and time-intensive. Associates will play a key role in document review and become integral members of the team, because nobody is more valuable to litigation than those who know the documents well.
- The stakes in criminal cases are higher than in civil ones, since there is more potential for individual exposure. Public companies will tend to plead if there is a substantial basis for criminal charges, since trial will carry significant risk and uncertainty.
- The DOJ, the only agency that handles criminal matters, has historically lost more than half its cases. Juries are very particular in applying an exacting burden of proof on the government. Recent Supreme Court decisions have also been favorable to antitrust defendants.
- Whereas the antitrust section of the DOJ is a small part of a large department, the FTC is an independent regulatory agency and handles some matters the DOJ doesn't, such as unfair competition and advertising. Attorneys will have different experiences with people at both the DOJ and FTC, based on the different rules and procedures of each, as well as on personalities.
- Generally speaking, antitrust work on mergers will increase when the economy is good, while a downturn will bring more litigation work.
- Antitrust will also be affected by intellectual cycles and en vogue economic theories. **Daniel Swanson** of **Gibson Dunn** says: *"We're currently in an upswing of thought calling for greater activism, internationalization, and coordination in jurisdictions."*
- **Steven Newborn** at **Weil, Gotshal & Manges** says: *"One of the advantages of working on mergers is that they have a beginning, a middle and an end and they normally last only a few months. I find it very attractive to be able to have a decision within a relatively short period of time."*

Current issues

- A significant number of antitrust litigation has emerged in recent years, in part due to the US' general economic climate. Cravath Chairman Evan Chesler explains: *"After a significant downturn in the economy there is often an after effect and echo effect on antitrust litigation which follows. This is either because people believe that during a downturn companies did things they shouldn't have done or during the recovery from a downturn there is a belief that companies engaged in that sort of conduct. It's not that unusual for there to be an uptick in antitrust litigation after a recession."*
- Twenty-five merger investigations in the USA during 2015 were subject to merger remedies while one deal was banned outright and five more were abandoned after coming under regulatory scrutiny.
- The antitrust landscape varies from administration to administration. The recent rise in federal prosecutions has also been driven by the adoption of a much tougher enforcement stance under Obama than the preceding Bush administration. The first year of Obama's presidency saw the total in fines for criminal antitrust cases top $1 billion for the first time ever while in 2015 alone that figure rocketed to $3.6 billion. It remains to be seen how much of an effect the coming administrative change will have on this area.
- Private antitrust claims – these are brought alongside Department of Justice investigations or prosecutions – continue to hit companies hard, with some of the largest ever civil antitrust settlements being awarded in 2015. Until the DOJ's tough enforcement stance is relaxed, this trend won't be waning any time soon.
- The US has traditionally been the most popular venue for antitrust litigation, especially when it comes to class actions suits. In recent years, however, the number of claims being brought in Europe and Asia is steadily increasing as enforcement regimes within these jurisdictions rapidly develop. US lawyers need

to become increasingly familiar with antitrust regulations in these locations and their affect on issues arising in the USA.

- In March 2016 it was announced that Japan and the EU would expand the extent to which their antitrust regulators share information. This extension should allow more comprehensive enforcement in both jurisdictions while also decreasing the chances of conflicting rulings.
- Concerns were raised in early 2016 by the US Treasury that the European Commission (the EU's regulatory body) is unfairly targeting US companies in tax regulations, pointing out that three out of four EU investigations into tax deals with EU countries revolve around US corporations. The EU has denied the allegations but with both sides intent on hammering home their point, it doesn't look like this difference of opinion will be resolved any time soon.
- At the time of going to press, debates were currently ongoing in the US House of Representatives over a bill that would see the merger review procedures of the Federal Trade Commission and Department of Justice more closely aligned.

Rankings in *Chambers USA*

Top ranked

Alston & Bird	Morgan Lewis
Cleary	Norton Rose Fulbright
Davis Polk	O'Melveny & Myers
Dechert	Ropes & Gray
Gibson Dunn	Sidley Austin
Jones Day	Simpson Thacher
Kirkland & Ellis	Skadden
Latham	White & Case
Mayer Brown	Wilmer Hale

Highly recommended

Allen & Overy	Morgan Lewis
Arnold & Porter	MoFo
Axinn	Munger
Baker & McKenzie	Orrick
Baker Botts	Paul Hastings
Cadwalader	Paul, Weiss
Choate	Pepper Hamilton
Cooley	Reed Smith
Cravath	Shearman
Crowell	Sheppard
Freshfields	Sullivan
Haynes and Boone	Thompson & Knight
Hogan Lovells	Vinson
Hunton	Weil
King & Spalding	Willkie
McGuireWoods	Winston

For more detail on ranking tiers and locations, visit www.chambersandpartners.com

Appellate

"If you like to play with language, prose and sentence structure, if you consider writing to be an art, then appellate law is a great opportunity to immerse yourself in that." – Evan Tager, Mayer Brown

In a nutshell

In simple terms, appellate law is a stage of dispute resolution. More specifically, it involves handling cases on appeal, but the best appellate practices think of it more broadly and consider sophisticated legal analysis, strategy and issue identification – even at the trial level – to be part of their core function.

Appellate lawyers, though all experts in appellate advocacy per se, often come to specialize in different areas. This includes the likes of antitrust, state and federal taxation, corporate law, punitive damages, telecommunications, labor and employment, environment and intellectual property.

They will also often have a court-specific focus, developing expertise in state appellate courts, federal courts of appeal, state supreme courts, or the US Supreme Court.

What lawyers do

- Evaluate the issues in the case.
- Review motions filed by lawyers in trial court, because they tend to identify the important issues.
- Read the trial transcript.
- Work with trial lawyers to understand the facts of the case.
- Conduct legal research to assess the strength of the issues raised at trial.
- Write an 'issues memo' after the research and analysis, and consult with the client and trial lawyers to identify the most promising issues.
- Write the brief. This process takes time.
- Share the brief with the client and trial counsel; incorporate their comments and reactions.
- Continue to refine the brief until it must be filed.
- Present the oral argument.
- Manage post-hearing steps.

Realities of the job

- Oral argument *"is an incredibly adrenalin-fueled experience,"* says **Evan Tager** of **Mayer Brown**. *"It adds spice to your ordinary research and writing routine."*
- It is, however, a relatively small part of the case. The strength of the appeal rests on the shoulders of the brief, though most clients still hire appellate lawyers based on their oral argument capabilities.
- Prior to an oral argument, appellate lawyers should go through one or more moot court sessions in preparation for the real thing. *"Appellate judges appreciate the extra preparation,"* explains **Stephen Shapiro** of **Mayer Brown**.
- *"The reality is that appellate work is far more people-centric than most assume,"* **Carter Phillips** of **Sidley Austin** says. *"You're going in as part of a much broader team, and if you're successful it's because you have the right skills to work effectively with others."*
- Appellate law is a highly intellectual area that involves cutting-edge legal issues. Phillips adds: *"Those who practice appellate law tend to have remarkably strong credentials coming out of law school."*
- Associates must enjoy spending countless hours doing research and crafting written statements. This work decreases with seniority.
- *"If you like to play with language, prose and sentence structure, if you consider writing to be an art, then appellate law is a great opportunity to immerse yourself in that,"* says Tager.
- There is no law stating that you have to do a clerkship in order to become an appellate lawyer, but *"it's much easier and a natural progression for those who have,"* Phillips tells us. Working in government in an appellate division can also be beneficial.
- Courts around the country are constantly issuing decisions that appellate lawyers need to keep up with, though practitioners can generally limit their focus to decisions made in the courts or areas of law that apply

to their practice.

- *"It's useful to develop a wider array of litigation skills in the first year or two,"* according to Phillips. **Seth Waxman** of **WilmerHale** confirms: *"I could never have been the kind of appellate lawyer that I am without putting together cases from scratch, learning how to establish facts in a trial record and developing a facility for never doing the same kind of substantive case twice."*
- Another key difference between appellate law and litigation is the considerable shift toward answering questions as opposed to asking them. This is done by *"meeting the obvious questions head on in a brief, or being prepared to quickly and thoughtfully provide answers to questions that judges ask during oral advocacy,"* says Waxman.
- Judges are human. They have predispositions and find it difficult not to view a case through the lens of their biases, often frustrating even the best-laid plans – although this is less of an issue in the Supreme Court compared to the lower court levels.

Rankings in *Chambers USA*

Top ranked

Gibson Dunn	WilmerHale
Sidley Austin	

Highly recommended

Akin Gump	Mayer Brown
Arnold & Porter	MoFo
Hogan Lovells	Munger
Jenner	O'Melveny
Jones Day	Orrick
King & Spalding	Reed Smith
Kirkland	Vinson
Latham	

For more detail on ranking tiers and locations, visit www.chambersandpartners.com

Current issues

- Appellate lawyers are being brought onto cases at increasingly earlier stages such as immediately after jury verdicts or even when winning a case starts to look unlikely. Some clients are even requesting that an appellate lawyer be staffed from the get-go, with the purpose of keeping an eye on potential appeal strategies. Specialised appellate lawyers have also become increasingly common in recent years.
- The death of Justice Antonin Scalia has weakened its far right, conservative strength among Supreme Court Justices. The appointment of a new justice will shift the balance among the Justices so the nomination process was always going to be hotly contested; at time of going to press, Merrick Garland is the nominee Republicans and Democrats are preparing to do battle over. Areas most likely to be affected by the changing makeup of the Supreme Court Judges are class actions and arbitrations, which have previously seen decisions revolve toward a pro-business.
- Numerous new 'pro se' or 'pro bono' appellate programs have been developed throughout the country over recent years, to tackle the influx of self-represented civil litigants in appellate courts and to improve efficiency in this regard. Public Counsel operates two clinics to assist pro se litigants: the Appellate Self-Help Clinic and the Federal Pro Se Clinic.
- In Texas, a trend has been observed: the state's leaders are increasingly turning to appellate litigators to fill top government legal positions. Former Texas Assistant Solicitor General Jimmy Blacklock was appointed general counsel to the incoming governor, while another alum of the Texas Solicitor General's office, Brantley Starr, was appointed the new Deputy Attorney General for Legal Counsel. These big-shot appellate litigators were appointed because of their ability to handle the thorniest of legal issues: an ability which had been honed thanks to the complex issues generated within the Appellate Bar. Whether this trend will surface in other states remains to be seen, but it indicates something about the potential career progression of a successful appellate lawyer, and the value of handling intricate appellate cases.
- Sample briefs and arguments are available at www.appellate.net

Banking & Finance

"*This area allows you to push yourself and increase the percentage of time spent doing things that are new, interesting, challenging and occasionally frightening.*" – James Florack, Davis Polk

In a nutshell

Banking and finance lawyers deal with the lending and borrowing of money, and the management of financial liabilities. Their task is to help structure their clients' transactions, to protect their clients' best legal and commercial interests, and to negotiate and document the contractual relationship between lenders and borrowers. It's a hugely technical, ever-evolving and jargon-heavy area of law. For anything banks do with capital raising or financial instruments, see Capital Markets.

Straightforward bank lending: a bank or other financial institution lends money to a borrower on documented repayment terms. Bank loans may be bilateral (made by one bank to the borrower) or syndicated (arranged by one or more financial institutions and made by a group of lenders). **Acquisition finance:** a loan made to a corporate borrower or private equity sponsor for the purpose of acquiring another company. This includes **leveraged finance**, where the borrower finances the cost of an acquisition by borrowing most of the purchase price without committing a lot of its own capital (as typically done in leveraged buyouts).

Real estate finance: a loan made to enable a borrower to acquire a property or finance the development of land, commonly secured by way of a mortgage on the acquired land/buildings. **Project finance:** the financing of long-term infrastructure (eg roads or power plants) and public services projects (eg hospitals) where the amounts borrowed to complete the project are paid back with the cash flow generated by the project. **Asset finance:** this enables the purchase and operation of large assets such as ships, aircraft and machinery. The lender normally takes security over the assets in question. **Islamic finance:** Muslim borrowers, lenders and investors must abide by Shari'a law, which prohibits the collection and payment of interest on a loan. Islamic finance specialists ensure that finance deals are structured in a Shari'a-compliant manner.

Financial services regulation: lawyers advise financial and other businesses on everything that they might need to know about the legal limits of their financial and investment activities. They focus especially on new and complex federal and state regulations. Major clients are usually banks, hedge funds, private equity firms, broker-dealers and insurance firms. Post-recession there has been a multifold increase in the volume of legislation governing the financial sector.

What banking and finance lawyers do

Bank lending

- Meet with clients to establish their specific requirements and the commercial context of a deal.
- Carry out due diligence – an investigation exercise to verify the accuracy of information passed from the borrower to the lender or from the underwriter of securities to potential investors. This can involve on-site meetings with the company's management, discussions with the company's auditors and outside counsel, and review of material agreements and other documents.
- Negotiate with the opposite party to agree the terms of the deal and record them accurately in the facility documentation. Lenders' lawyers usually produce initial documents (often based on a standard form or an agreed precedent) and borrowers' lawyers try to negotiate more favorable terms for their clients. Lawyers on both sides must know when to compromise and when to hold out.
- Assist with the structuring of complicated or groundbreaking financing models, and ensure innovative solutions comply with all relevant laws.
- Gather all parties to complete the transaction, ensuring all agreed terms are reflected in the loan documents, all documents have been properly signed and delivered and all conditions to closing have been met.
- In a secured loan (most bank loans to below investment-grade borrowers require collateral), ensure that the agreed-upon collateral has been properly granted

and that all filings, registrations and other procedures necessary to 'perfect' the security have been or will be made.

Financial services regulation

- Receive calls from banks and other financial institutions that seek guidance as to how business initiatives can be implemented most effectively in US markets, in full compliance with the letter and policy of US law.
- Sit down with the client – speaking to individuals at a very senior level – to find out what the client's business plan and intentions are.
- Analyze the implications of implementing that plan based on what current or future regulation looks like, or can be expected to look like, and what the legal, compliance, reputational, strategic, cross-border and related risks of that plan might be.
- Give advice on what changes may need to be made to the business initiative to achieve regulatory compliance and minimize risk.
- Regulatory lawyers are not just involved with compliance counseling: they also advise on enforcement and internal and external investigations; the restructuring and disposition of bank assets; the organization of bank units and subsidiaries; acquisitions, investments, strategic alliances and joint ventures; capital raising initiative and the creation and distribution of bank securities and deposit and other financial instruments; the structuring of 'living wills' and recovery and resolution plans; and the implementation and evaluation of bank marketing, cross-selling and similar initiatives.

Rankings in *Chambers USA*

Top ranked

Bracewell	McGuireWoods
Cahill	MoFo
Cleary	Mintz Levin
Cravath	Proskauer
Davis Polk	Reed Smith
Foley & Lardner	Ropes & Gray
Gibson Dunn	Sidley
Goodwin Procter	Simpson
Greenberg	Skadden
Jones Day	Squire Patton Boggs
K&L Gates	Sullivan
King & Spalding	White & Case
Latham	WilmerHale

Highly recommended

Allen & Overy	Milbank
Alston & Bird	Morgan Lewis
Arnold & Porter	Nixon Peabody
Baker & McKenzie	Norton Rose Fulbright
Baker Botts	Nutter
Cadwalader	Orrick
Choate	Paul Hastings
Debevoise	Paul, Weiss
Dechert	Shearman
Duane Morris	Sheppard
Fried Frank	Thompson & Knight
Goulston	Vedder
Haynes and Boone	Venable
Hogan Lovells	Vinson
Hunton	Waller
Katten	Weil
Kilpatrick	Willkie
Kirkland	Winston
Mayer Brown	

For more detail on ranking tiers and locations, visit www.chambersandpartners.com

Realities of the job

- Some firms act for investment or commercial banks on highly complex and often cross-border financings, whereas the work of others generally involves more mainstream domestic finance deals.
- A good working knowledge of the bankruptcy laws is critical for lawyers practicing in the area of leveraged finance. Banking lawyers advise for the worst-case scenario, which is often a bankruptcy filing by the borrower. Understanding how the rules change once that filing is made is critically important, even for lawyers who never expect to set foot in a bankruptcy courtroom.
- Lawyers need to appreciate the internal policies and sensitivities of their clients in order to deliver pertinent advice and warn of the legal (and reputational) risks involved in the transactions. Deals may involve the movement of money across borders and through different currencies and financial products. International deals have an additional layer of difficulty: political changes in transitional economies can render a previously sound investment risky.
- Banking clients are ultra-demanding and the hours can be long. On the plus side, clients will be smart and dynamic. It is possible to build up long-term relationships with investment bank clients, even as a junior associate.
- Working on deals can be exciting. The team and the other side are all working to a common goal, often under significant time constraints and other pressures. Deal closings bring adrenalin highs and a sense of satisfaction.
- You need to become absorbed in the finance world. Start reading *The Wall Street Journal*, the various deal-related trade publications or other good business-oriented websites.
- Regulatory lawyers need to remain constantly aware of the latest political developments (potentially) af-

fecting regulations. *"We are not management consultants, but our role involves a huge amount of market-based business analysis. Lawyers who want to work in this area need to become very knowledge-focused. Staying on top of the latest news in all the areas involved is a great ongoing challenge of the job,"* says **Robert Tortoriello** (who is senior counsel at **Cleary Gottlieb** and has been actively involved in the firm's financial institutions practice).

- Regulatory lawyers operate on shifting sands. *"Abnormal is the new normal,"* says **Tortoriello**. *"It is a constantly evolving practice. At present lawyers are advising on the 'likely' implications of the emerging regulatory framework that continues to develop and change in the context of historic and emerging financial issues."*

Banking & Finance: an overview by White & Case

Business Climate and Recent Trends

- Since its development in the 1980s, the syndicated loan market has become the primary source of loan financing for corporate borrowers.
- In 2015, global syndicated loan volume reached US$4.7 trillion (10,561 deals), a 3 percent deal volume decrease compared to 2014 (10,889 deals), but still the second-highest annual total on record since 2007 (US$4.8 trillion). US loans accounted for 49 percent of the global loan volume, totaling US$2.2 trillion.
- The syndicated loan market can be divided into two sections: the market for investment-grade borrowers and the market for non-investment-grade borrowers (the leveraged loan market). Investment-grade transactions involve large, highly creditworthy borrowers and although the amounts involved can be very large, the deals are generally more straightforward and unsecured, with the funds provided mainly by commercial banks. Leveraged loan transactions involve borrowers with lower credit ratings. They are riskier and more complex and typically involve taking a security interest in the assets of the borrower as well as more extensive and more heavily negotiated documentation provisions.
- The market is highly dynamic, with deal terms and structures rapidly evolving in response to economic conditions, fluctuations in interest rates, the ebb and flow of the M&A market and changes in business sentiment. A variety of forces shaped US market activity in 2015. Regulations (particularly the Leveraged Lending Guidance, CLO capital requirements under Basel III and new EU "bail-in" rules), macro-economic conditions, increased competition between financial institutions and non-traditional lending sources, and higher purchase price multiples in M&A transactions all served to influence the US loan market. Although US syndicated lending experienced an estimated 2 percent volume decline in 2015, it was helped by stability in the investment-grade lending market.
- The large supply of capital has resulted in strong competition among lenders and has allowed companies and financial sponsors to push for lower interest rates and more borrower-friendly terms (such as those seen in so-called "covenant-lite" transactions). In addition, in recent years, large financial sponsors who are active consumers of debt products with significant market power have had a strong influence on loan terms.
- Debt financing is incurred by companies for a variety of purposes, such as financing acquisitions, refinancing maturing or more expensive debt, financing dividends paid to equity owners and for general corporate purposes. The predominance of one purpose over another tends to vary over time in line with market conditions and borrower needs.
- Global economic trends also have significant impact – macroeconomic uncertainty and regulatory constraints in the European and Asian markets in recent years have resulted in a dramatic increase in the number of European and Asian borrowers accessing the US loan market in transactions that utilize New York-law governed documents.
- With regulators increasingly focused on banks' underwriting standards and the impact the performance of high-risk loans could have on the banks' "stress test" results, regulatory scrutiny and the challenges that banks face as a result are likely to remain the key focal points for market players in 2016. In particular, it is anticipated that a shift towards "non-regulated" alternative capital providers as a source of finance for riskier credits will continue as a consequence of the regulatory clampdown.

What an Up-and-Coming Attorney in This Area Can Expect

- Representing a mix of banks, financial institutions, private equity firms, hedge funds, top-tier financial sponsors and corporate borrowers in connection with a variety of complex and often headline-grabbing financing transactions
- Structuring, negotiating and documenting complex financing arrangements for clients in a vast array of industries and across multiple jurisdictions
- Counseling clients on changes in current market trends and regulatory changes and remaining at the forefront of developing innovative financing solutions, structures and techniques
- Leading deal teams across a global network of offices to address local law issues in complex cross-border transactions and liaising with counsel in focused areas of legal experience to provide one-stop solutions for clients
- Working directly with clients and senior lawyers to provide top-quality service and technical advice in a high-performance and collaborative environment
- Access to extensive training and professional development resources

White & Case LLP's Bank Finance Practice

White & Case has a market-leading Global Banking Practice that focuses on advising banks, sponsors and corporations in connection with a broad range of financing transactions, including leveraged buyouts, asset-based lending transactions, real estate, structured, trade and investment-grade financings, workouts, restructurings, and debtor-in-possession and exit financings. Our group comprises more than 320 lawyers with established teams in all the major financial markets globally, including New York, London, Frankfurt, Paris, Hong Kong, Tokyo and Singapore, and in many regional financial centers. The international strength of our Global Banking Practice is reflected not only in White & Case's recognition for its banking work in *Chambers Global* 2015, but also in more than a dozen *Chambers* individual market and regional rankings, including rankings for USA Nationwide, Europe-wide, Latin America, United Kingdom, Germany, France and Asia.

About the Authors

Eric Leicht, a partner in White & Case LLP's New York office, is head of the firm's Americas Bank Finance Practice. Eric represents major commercial and investment banks, as lead agents and arrangers and borrowers, in a variety of lending transactions, with an emphasis on acquisition and leveraged financings.

Eliza McDougall is a partner in the Bank Finance Practice of White & Case LLP. Based in the firm's New York office, Eliza represents lenders and corporate borrowers in connection with a wide range of domestic and international secured and unsecured lending transactions, including leveraged and investment-grade acquisition financings, general syndicated financings, asset-based financings and project financings.

WHITE & CASE

Bankruptcy & Restructuring

In a nutshell

The essential task of bankruptcy and restructuring lawyers is to avoid a client's bankruptcy. The term 'bankruptcy' itself is a technical term that refers to when financially distressed companies, unable to restructure on their own, file for Chapter 11 to undergo a court-supervised restructuring.

In order to avoid this scenario, a company must successfully *"restructure its debt to keep the company together and retain its value,"* head of **Davis Polk**'s insolvency and restructuring practice **Don Bernstein** explains. But the path to financial viability – through court or not – can be convoluted.

Bankruptcy and restructuring attorneys must be adept at **transactional** work and **litigation** across a range of areas like M&A, securities, banking, labor and employment, environment, tax and IP. *"Bankruptcy is the last bastion of the generalist,"* the late Harvey Miller, partner and founder of **Weil Gotshal's** restructuring group, told us.

Troubled companies will first attempt out-of-court restructuring, or corporate reorganization, in which they try to reach an agreement with their creditors. This has become an increasingly important stage. *"Traditional Chapter 11 cases can be expensive, inefficient and harmful to the business,"* according to **Jay Goffman**, global head of **Skadden**'s corporate restructuring group. *"This means it's important to advise companies on how to avoid Chapter 11 or shorten their time in Chapter 11 and similar insolvency proceedings, rather than convincing them to do it."*

Chapter 11 provides for a **court-supervised restructuring** and, crucially, protection from creditors, who are barred from seeking to retrieve their money until the company is restructured. A notable feature of Chapter 11 work is the growing prevalence of 'distressed M&A', which describes the selling of parts – or the whole – of the ailing company. Such sales are done under the provisions of Section 363 of the Bankruptcy Code and often referred to as '363 deals'.

The number of parties involved in a restructuring can be vast. They come from all walks of a company's life and often have competing interests. Acting for the **debtor** is a challenge on its own, because then *"everyone's problem is your problem. You have to deal with every creditor and ensure the pie is allocated fairly,"* Bernstein explains.

Representing **creditors** is often simply about trying to recover as much as you can from a debtor, but there are many different types of creditors to choose from. 'Secured' creditors include commercial and investment banks, insurance companies and hedge funds, while 'unsecured' creditors include bondholders and vendors, or 'trade creditors' (eg, auto parts suppliers). In Chapter 11, there are official committees of unsecured creditors and debtor in possession (DIP) lenders, while out-of-court proceedings will have bondholder committees.

Other parties involved may include strategic buyers and private equity firms and hedge funds interested in acquiring distressed assets. They engage in the purchase, sale and trading of debt claims. This has become one of the biggest administrative components of Chapter 11 cases. A special committee set up by the board to oversee the restructuring may also be involved and, in instances of 'gross mismanagement' by the company, a trustee is appointed to handle matters.

What bankruptcy/restructuring lawyers do

Out-of-court restructuring for debtor

- Analyze the situation in order to determine the feasibility of staying out of bankruptcy. What's the problem? What caused it? How big is it? Will it result in a default that is uncontrollable? Who's in the creditor body? Are they secured or unsecured? What's the litigation status? What's the liquidity status? Are there sufficient funds to stay in business while being restructured?
- Look for 'red flags', such as jurisdiction. *"You need to know if the entity has international operations, how it operates, how it's interconnected,"* explains Miller.
- Work with financial advisers to create a model of how the crisis will be dealt with.
- Try to persuade creditors to *"just stand still"* and not pursue immediate payback. *"You need to focus on the nature of the debt in order to determine who you approach to get a standstill or moratorium,"* Miller says.
- Negotiate with creditors and try convincing them that the problem is best solved out of bankruptcy.
- If negotiations are successful, work out payment plans for each creditor.
- If not successful, file for Chapter 11.

Court-supervised restructuring for debtor

- Initiate a Chapter 11 case to pursue restructuring within the protective provisions of the Bankruptcy Code.
- Create a detailed communication plan to include regulators, shareholders, employees, vendors and clients. *"Entry into Chapter 11 should be made as smooth and unruffled as possible,"* says **Davis Polk**'s insolvency and restructuring group co-head **Marshall Huebner**.
- Secure financing. *"Without liquidity to pay the bills, all is for naught,"* Huebner explains.
- Once liquidity is secured, work with the management team and financial advisers to decide what's core and non-core to the business.
- Build creditor consensus around the chosen exit strategy. This can be a lengthy process and require delicate negotiations.
- If creditors think they are being economically harmed, there could be extensive litigation.
- Document and effectuate the eventual agreement.

Realities of the job

- *"You need to be psychologically ready to handle the stress and strain inherent in being involved in a practice in which, by definition, there are huge amounts of failure,"* says **James Sprayregen** of **Kirkland & Ellis**.
- He adds, however, that *"there is the positive and gratifying side, which is helping businesses and saving peoples' jobs."*
- The extent to which transactional work and litigation cross paths during a restructuring cannot be overstated. *"There is a transactional aspect even when in court. You litigate by day and negotiate by night,"* Bernstein describes.
- The nature of cases can vary enormously. Sprayregen adds: *"Our work involves dozens of industries and that really does give you the opportunity to learn a lot."*
- Debtors face innumerable difficulties. They have no political muscle, whereas creditors do – and flex it. Though bankruptcy laws are constantly amended, they continue to favor creditors. *"Nobody likes being a debtor, even those who successfully go through the labyrinth of reorganization,"* states Miller.
- In order to lead such a diverse group of parties to a consensus, debtor attorneys must possess strategic, tactical and managerial skills.
- Steering clients clear of Chapter 11 through out-of-court restructuring often requires a creative and innovative approach.
- The current Chapter 11 was passed in 1978, but it comes from Chapter X, which was passed in the 1930s. *"The Bankruptcy Code has its roots in the Great Depression,"* Bernstein says.
- Chapter 15 is the provision for cross-border bankruptcies that dictates proceedings in the USA when the main proceeding is in another country. Designed to ensure that all creditors and debtors are treated fairly irrespective of jurisdiction, it may also involve Chapter 11 proceedings if the debtor's assets are sufficiently complex.
- Restructuring is a lengthy process that requires a considerable amount of work before an outcome can be reached. *"There are so many different stakeholders and other components, and you spend a lot of time on*

Rankings in *Chambers USA*

Top ranked

Akin Gump	Lowenstein
Alston & Bird	McGuireWoods
Arnold & Porter	Milbank
Brown Rudnick	Mintz Levin
Davis Polk	Norton Rose Fulbright
Greenberg	Paul, Weiss
Haynes and Boone	Perkins Coie
Hunton	Reed Smith
Jones Day	Skadden
K&L Gates	Vinson
King & Spalding	Weil
Kirkland	

Highly recommended

Baker Botts	Kilpatrick Townsend
Bracewell	Kramer Levin
Chadbourne	Latham
Choate	Mayer Brown
Cleary	Morgan Lewis
Debevoise	MoFo
Dechert	O'Melveny
Duane Morris	Orrick
Dykema	Paul Hastings
Foley	Pepper Hamilton
Fox Rothschild	Proskauer
Gibbons	Ropes & Gray
Gibson Dunn	Schulte
Goodwin Procter	Sheppard
Goulston	Sidley
Hangley	Simpson
Hogan Lovells	Squire Patton Boggs
Holland & Knight	Stroock
Hughes Hubbard	Thompson & Knight
Irell	Vedder
Jackson Walker	Venable
Jenner	White & Case
Kasowitz	Willkie
Katten	WilmerHale
Kaye Scholer	Winston

For more detail on ranking tiers and locations, visit www.chambersandpartners.com

Practice Areas

the process itself – which I didn't expect as a young associate," Sprayregen tells us.

- Bankruptcy and restructuring is considered a countercyclical practice. When the market is healthy, bankruptcy attorneys may find themselves working on more diverse corporate matters.
- While the debtors' lawyers negotiate with the creditors to try to persuade them to *"just stand still,"* creditors' lawyers do a similar analysis to *"determine where they have the most leverage and figure out what the consequences would be if they forced bankruptcy upon their debtors,"* Miller says, adding that *"you have to be much more innovative working for a debtor because they generally have less in the way of leverage."*
- Lenders' needs have to be attended to carefully, Huebner explains, because *"very frequently if lenders have a vested interest in a company, they're the ones who will get wiped out; more typical than not they become Chapter 11 financiers."* As such financiers, lenders tend to impose very difficult and sometimes onerous terms on the debtor to stimulate sales and liquidations.
- Sprayregen notes that, *"ultimately, the most successful cases will be the ones that are the least problematic. Those cases are less interesting from the media's perspective, but that's when you really see success."*

Current issues

- Although the recession saw a rise in bankruptcy filings in the USA, these numbers have been plummeting since. The American Bankruptcy Institute calculates that all filings in the US dropped by 10% in 2015 compared to 2014 (commercial filings fell by 14% and consumers' by 10%). The total number of commercial and personal bankruptcies added up to 819,285 (the lowest number since 2006), and 96% of these were filed by consumers.
- With the crash in oil prices however, things might be set to change again. Around 67 US oil and natural gas companies filed for bankruptcy in 2015, in a 379% rise from 2014. At the start of 2016, as oil prices dipped further, several more companies resorted to bankruptcy. While good for the consumer, cheap energy prices can have catastrophic circumstances for producers and their employees.
- Traditional Chapter 11 bankruptcy is already an expensive and lengthy process, which companies try to avoid, but recently it's been rumored to have become even more costly. *The Wall Street Journal* reviewed numerous bankruptcy filings to report on rising legal fees at top US firms, discovering that partner rates are reaching $1,500 per hour. Bankruptcy is known to be expensive because the stakes are so high and the work lawyers do is of vital importance to clients in dire straits.
- In the news recently: a judge ruled that an insurance salesman who decided to moonlight as an Uber driver to avoid bankruptcy doesn't have to pay back $10,000 in auto loan debt, accrued after his plan went wrong. He got a new, bigger car on Uber's suggestion, borrowing from GM, but the Chevrolet SUV was repossessed after he filed for bankruptcy less than a month after the purchase, failing even to make the first payment. GM re-sold the car and sued him for the difference since you can't cancel such a large debt for a *"luxury good"* so soon, but he was exonerated on account of the judge ruling that a car bought to make an extra income to support oneself is not a *"luxury good."*
- Also in the news, rapper and father-of-two 50 Cent filed for bankruptcy recently, but while the process was ongoing he also Instagrammed himself lying with (allegedly fake) wads of cash, sparking questions from his angry creditors. Get rich or die tryin' indeed.

Advice from the bankruptcy/restructuring gurus

Harvey Miller, former partner, **Weil, Gotshal & Manges**
"The common assumptions one makes about bankruptcy – be they informed or uninformed – in law school are generally erroneous. I never thought I would end up in this area of law. It sounds mundane but it's really not."

"It's rare to get well-informed applicants, because bankruptcy law is a one-semester class at most law schools, so I wouldn't expect our new attorneys to be up-to-date on the most current legal issues. It's definitely a 'learn on the job' type of practice. In essence, you get an MBA on the job."

James Sprayregen, partner, **Kirkland & Ellis**
"When you start working on a matter, try to imagine what the vision of success will look like and then develop the strategy and tactics that will allow you to accomplish that vision – and make sure that vision is shared by everyone on your team. But even if you succeed, you have to be flexible as the matter won't always end up like what's drawn on the blackboard. You have to embrace the chaos!"

"The restructuring process can be difficult and ugly so don't become a prisoner of emotion if you want to be valuable to the client."

Corporate Finance and Capital Markets: an overview by Cahill Gordon & Reindel

Legal trends and business climate

Whether a company is a startup, needs acquisition financing, is looking to raise capital in an IPO or private equity transaction, is the subject of a leveraged buyout by a private equity fund, or simply wants to refinance existing debt at lower interest rates, the financing needs of companies of all sizes and across all sectors will involve the input of legal specialists in corporate finance.

Many of the most complex, interesting, and creative financing situations involve companies with lower credit ratings, or significant other debt already on their balance sheets, known as 'leveraged' finance scenarios. A major focus of corporate finance is helping clients – whether they are borrowers or financial institutions acting as arrangers, lenders or underwriters – design and negotiate creative leveraged financing structures and terms.

Flexibility is important. Companies looking for financing solutions have a broad array of products to choose from, any of which may be more or less desirable at a given moment due to market forces, current political events, strength of the company's own projected business profile, the company's corporate structure, and other pre-existing indebtedness. While historically there were two separate and distinct sources of funding in these scenarios – traditional bank lenders providing secured senior debt on the one hand, versus a broader market of investment funds, CLOs, hedge funds and others playing for high returns in the capital markets, often through unsecured or subordinated bonds – these two markets, while still distinct in terms of legal process and deal execution, now see many crossover investors.

Ever-changing lending regulations have opened up new opportunities for non-traditional sources of funds to enter the lending market, particularly following the recession. Innovative non-traditional products such as covenant-lite loans and second lien loans and bonds have become common as ideas and concepts from one product are adopted into another. With this confluence of funding sources and investor requirements, it is important to be agile enough to discuss all alternatives with clients and understand the considerations required in choosing a financing path (or creating a new one!).

"With multinational corporations and private equity investment becoming more global in nature, pressure grows to expand traditional lending structures to include new locations in creative cross-border financings."

Corporate finance is a collaborative practice, even with the parties 'across the table'. The interests of funding sources and those of issuers or borrowers will not be aligned completely, but all of the parties to each transaction are interested in generating a solution that brings each of the parties what they need. Financing sources and borrowers look to their legal advisers to help them structure increasingly creative options that work for all parties on a long-term basis in the face of challenging and potentially volatile financial environments.

Keeping abreast of market trends and financing considerations is a must in this dynamic environment. Because both the capital markets and the leveraged lending worlds are subject to significant fluctuation based on a number of factors – including everything from recent case law involving financings, collateral security, and bankruptcies, to the global political and regulatory environment – the 'best' answer for a client in a given scenario can change at any time. Recent developments may require new investor risk protections on any given transaction, or may dictate that companies in a specific sector or geopolitical area will be viewed as more or less stable. Our depth of market knowledge allows us to help clients structure creative solutions to complex situations while understanding the parameters of what investors will require, whether during a peak or a trough moment in the financial markets.

In addition, the practice of corporate finance requires a global view. As markets of the world previously viewed as unstable or less legally mature begin to evolve and set up legal structures that allow them to be seen as viable jurisdictions for investment, the complexity of transaction structures and the volume of financing alternatives increases. With multinational corporations and private equity investment becoming more global in nature, pressure grows to expand traditional lending structures to include new locations in creative cross-border financings. Corporate finance lawyers are often called upon to find balance between allowing an issuer or borrower to capitalize on its assets on a more global basis, while maintaining the integrity of the investors' risk.

The life of a junior corporate finance associate

- Corporate finance associates act as the 'hub' of the transaction wheel. In order to be sure a financing is executed efficiently and properly, he or she will coordinate with experts in other areas relevant to the transaction, including bankruptcy attorneys where there are questions of enforcement or protection in a 'worst-case' scenario, tax attorneys involved in structuring the issuance or loan on a cost-efficient basis, real estate and environmental attorneys where real property will be taken as collateral, and litigators involved to evaluate various risks existing at an issuer or potentially created by a financing.
- Corporate finance associates work directly with clients; junior members of the client team are similarly involved, which affords the opportunity to develop long-term client relationships in the process.
- Corporate finance associates at all levels are crucial to the drafting of disclosure documents for securities offerings, and junior associates often are the real 'experts' on the issuer, having conducted much of the due diligence evaluating the company's operations and business, through review of corporate documents and material contracts, discussions with management, and on-site visits.
- Corporate finance associates will be involved in drafting contracts from a very early stage in their careers, and will participate in the negotiation and documentation of final deal terms on an increasing basis as they become more familiar with market terms and client desires.
- Junior corporate finance associates serve as 'masters of ceremonies' as a financing transaction reaches conclusion. Particularly on a transaction involving secured debt, many documents will have to be executed, certifications delivered, and filings made – and the junior associates will be tasked with verifying all is done properly in order to ensure the business deal is reflected accurately and security has been granted properly.

Suggested coursework for a future corporate finance attorney

Junior corporate finance attorneys may find it helpful to complete a basic accounting or finance course, preferably at the business school affiliated with their law school. Learning the language and fundamental elements of these disciplines provides one with a foundation upon which to set the day-to-day experiences as a corporate finance lawyer.

"Courses in securities regulation, secured transactions, contract negotiation and drafting all prove helpful after law school graduation.'"

For capital markets transactions, aspects of the US securities laws, including SEC rules and guidelines and general disclosure issues, are central to the work we do. On transactions involving leveraged lending, knowledge of the regulatory landscape, creditors' rights and Uniform Commercial Code matters all play a primary role. Courses in securities regulation, secured transactions, contract negotiation and drafting all prove helpful after law school graduation.

Because corporate finance associates bring together expertise from specialists in other relevant areas, a basic familiarity with related areas such as M&A, corporate tax, bankruptcy or real property law is beneficial in helping round out an associate's skill set and foster an appreciation of the 'bigger picture' surrounding a finance transaction.

About the author, Jennifer B Ezring

Jennifer B Ezring is a partner in Cahill's corporate practice. She advises commercial and investment banks in leveraged finance transactions, including acquisition financings, leveraged buyouts, going-private transactions, recapitalizations, project financings, bridge lending and loan commitments, out-of-court debt restructurings, exit facilities and other secured lending transactions. Jennifer received her BA from Princeton University and her JD from NYU.

About Cahill Gordon & Reindel LLP

Cahill has a prominent global corporate finance practice operating from New York and London. In 2015, it was ranked #1 by Bloomberg for representing investment banks in the over $250 billion (2015) US corporate high yield debt markets and #1 by Thomson Reuters for representing lenders and arrangers in the over $900 billion (2015) US corporate leveraged (i.e. non-investment grade) syndicated loan markets.

Capital Markets

In a nutshell

Capital markets lawyers feel all the highs and lows of market forces, and when the recession hit the practice did suffer; however, the vast sums exchanged and the technicality of the transactions mean that it will always remain an important area for BigLaw firms. Essentially, the world's capital markets are trading floors (either real or virtual) on which cash-hungry businesses obtain funding by selling a share of their business (equity) or receiving a loan (debt) from lenders. These 'markets' are used by companies with unique financing needs which traditional bank loans cannot satisfy. They offer more freedom to companies than obtaining cash via bank loans, which tie both parties into the term of the loan. Capital markets allow for companies to obtain massive sums with more flexibility; they also offer up limitless investment opportunities. Large financial institutions offer customized services to companies seeking funding on the capital markets. These services include advice on debt and equity offerings, on securitization and on the creation of derivatives. Debt (bonds), equity (stocks) and derivatives are all types of security, and capital markets law is sometimes referred to as 'securities law'.

Attorneys advise companies ('issuers') and investment banks ('underwriters') on these complex capital markets transactions. Issuer and underwriter will both engage a separate law firm. The issuer's attorneys will sometimes help their client analyze which type of security to issue. This decision depends on the nature of the company, the desired duration of the loan, who the buyers are likely to be, and market demand. If an issuer is new to the market, they may begin by seeking their lawyers' advice on the processes involved, before approaching an underwriter.

Equity capital markets

Within equity, there are initial public offerings (IPOs) and follow-on offerings of common and preferred stock. An IPO is a transformational event for a company. *"The IPO is the 'ne plus ultra' of capital markets work,"* says Josh Bonnie, capital markets partner at Simpson Thacher. *"The decision of whether or not to become a public company is incredibly commercial and requires a great deal of strategy. It's unlikely the client will have IPO experience, so they will be reliant on their attorneys."* The New York Stock Exchange and NASDAQ are the major exchanges in the USA and most American public companies will be listed on one of them. Companies can list on multiple exchanges around the world.

Debt capital markets

This generic category covers many types of debt instrument, but generally speaking it deals with a borrower raising capital by selling tradable bonds to investors, who expect the full amount lent to be paid back to them with interest. Bonds (also called 'notes') come in all shapes and sizes, from investment grade to high-yield ('junk') bonds. The terms of the bond – including the interest rate (or 'coupon') and maturity date – are decided on by the underwriter and issuer.

Why would a company issue bonds rather than take out a bank loan? As mentioned above, the terms of a bank loan can be restrictive to both parties: bank debt can prevent companies from making equity or debt issuances or from acquiring other companies until the loan is paid off. The terms of a bilateral loan tie both parties in, so a bank can't transfer risk or sell this debt with the same flexibility that the bonds market allows. Bonds are tradable; risk and its rewards can be sold on and spread across numerous lenders (bondholders), meaning that a company can raise much larger sums that can only be matched by arranging a syndicated loan (a group of banks chipping in on the principal), but without the same bank loan obligations that syndications entail. Plus bondholders can be anyone, not just a bank.

Structured finance and securitization

Structured finance can get gloriously complicated, but its aims are simple: to increase liquidity and structure risk, which in turn offers up extra funding for borrowers. Securitization is the core of the process, which takes a lowly untradable piece of debt, such as a mortgage, vehicle loan or a credit card receivable, bundles it together with debt of the same class, and sells the bundle of debt on to investors, such as pension funds, hungry for the cash flows that come with the debt.

To securitize debt a bank will first set up a special-purpose entity (SPE) to isolate the debt risk from the bank's main operations, and separate the legal rights to the debt, enabling it to be transferred to new holders. Within the SPE are the bundled loans which enable the SPE to issue bonds, where the interest on the bundled debt forms the cash flows or bond yields. Mortgage securities like residential mortgage-backed securities (RMBS) and commercial mortgage-backed securities (CMBS) are among the most common in the market, but *"the range of capital-raising that companies pursue is almost end-*

less, and is limited only by human creativity," says Josh Bonnie of Simpson Thacher. Collateralized debt obligations (CDOs) are a unique structure in that they group a variety of types of debt and credit risk, where different classes are called 'tranches', and the higher the tranche's risk, the greater the yield.

Securitization shouldered much of the blame for the credit crunch and the ensuing global economic havoc. Complicated structures led to a murky tangle of debt obligations, grouping different debt classes and exploiting credit enhancement. All was rosy until the housing bubble burst, mortgages defaulted and the ugly truth emerged. Don't let this put you off; there still is and will be demand for structured finance lawyers, but the order of the day is caution.

Derivatives

At its most basic, a derivative is a financial instrument used by banks and businesses to hedge risks to which they are exposed due to factors outside of their control. They can also be used for speculative purposes by betting on the fluctuation of just about anything, from currency exchange rates to the number of sunny days in a particular region. The value of a derivative at any given time is derived from the value of an underlying asset, security or index. Futures, forwards, options and swaps are the most common types of derivatives. **Forwards** are agreements between two parties that one will buy a certain product from the other for a fixed price at a fixed date in the future. Hedging against future price risks and speculation over the price movement of the underlying assets are the big attractions. **Futures** are standardized forwards, which can be traded on the futures market. **Options** are optional futures, where a buyer has the right but not the obligation to purchase or sell a product at a certain date in the future for a certain price. **Swaps** are agreements between two parties to exchange assets at a fixed rate, for example to protect against fluctuations in currency exchange rates.

What lawyers do

IPO or other equity offering

- Work with the client and its accounting firm to prepare and file a registration statement with the Securities and Exchange Commission (SEC).
- Do due diligence on the issuer company and draft a prospectus (as part of the registration statement) that provides a welter of information about the company and its finances, as well as past financial statements.
- Help the accountants draft a comfort letter, assuring the financial soundness of the issuer.
- File with the SEC and wait 30 days before getting initial comments from them.
- Undergo multiple rounds of commentary back and forth with the SEC. This can take one or two months.
- Negotiate approval of a listing on the stock exchange. This involves the submission of documentation, certifications and letters that prove the client satisfies the listing requirements.
- Finalize the underwriting agreement and other documentation.

Debt offering

- Plan out the deal with issuer and underwriter. A timeline is drawn up and tasks are allocated between the different parties.
- Draft a prospectus for SEC registration or a Rule 144A offering memorandum.
- Conduct due diligence on the issuer to examine its creditworthiness, make the disclosure accurate and highlight any associated risks.
- Deliver to the underwriters at closing a legal opinion and a disclosure letter on the offering based on due diligence.
- Draft the indenture: a document describing the bond's interest rate, maturity date, convertibility and so on.
- Draft the purchase (or 'underwriting') agreement.

Securitization

- Work with the underwriter and issuer to draw up the structure of a security, and help the parties negotiate the terms of that structure. *"We will literally sit down with all the parties and draw boxes, charts and arrows on a whiteboard in order to come up with new ideas,"* explains **John Arnholz**, structured finance transactions partner at **Morgan, Lewis & Bockius**.
- Draft the disclosure document and the prospectus or private placement memorandum. *"It is a descriptive piece – almost like a magazine article,"* says John Arnholz. *"It covers all the risks and other characteristics of owning a security."*
- Draft the purchase agreement documenting the transaction. *"This involves a lot of negotiation back and forth between issuer, underwriter, trustees, service providers and insurers,"* says John Arnholz.

Derivatives

- Be approached by a financial institution client (eg, a hedge fund) with an idea to create a new derivatives product.
- Communicate back and forth with the client discussing legal issues and risks related to various possible structures for the product.
- Home in on a specific structure for the product.
- Prepare a memo explaining the problems, issues and legal risks associated with the derivative's agreed-upon structure, as well as suggesting ways to resolve or mitigate those problems and issues.

Practice Areas

- If all has gone well, and if the new structure has sufficient prospects for legal and commercial success, lawyers will draft new documentation describing the makeup of the derivative.

Realities of the job

- Notwithstanding the differences mentioned in the descriptions above, there are big similarities between the work of lawyers on debt, equity and other securities transactions.
- The nature of lawyers' involvement in a capital markets transaction depends on its novelty. *"If someone is doing a securitization or designing a derivatives product they must address those issues which are novel,"* says **Josh Cohn**, head of US derivatives and structured products at **Mayer Brown**. *"If you are working on a product based on a preexisting structure, you may be asked to look at certain details like new swaps arrangements."*
- Junior lawyers usually practice in all areas of capital markets law, sometimes combining this with other corporate work too. Some top firms have specialist departments for each capital markets subgroup. Partners often specialize in debt, equity, securitization or derivatives work, but they may continue to dabble in other areas too. *"I would advise junior associates to get involved with as many different types of transactions as possible,"* says **Robert Gross**, capital markets partner at **Clifford Chance**. *"You'll end up getting more to do that way, and it will be more burdensome, but you will get a ton of experience."*
- Clients in the world of finance are incredibly demanding and attorneys usually work very long hours. On the plus side, clients are also smart, sophisticated and dynamic. Large law firms usually have strong and close relationships with investment bank clients, meaning that juniors can get frequent client contact. *"I love working with companies' management teams and with bankers,"* says **Arthur Robinson**, head of the capital markets practice at **Simpson Thacher**. *"On each deal I do I 'meet' a new company and learn about the business from the inside from the CEO and CFO. It may sound odd, but companies do have their own personality, so it's akin to meeting a new person each time."*
- The content and organization of prospectuses tends to be fairly standard, but lawyers consider working on them a rewarding exercise because a good deal of creative writing is required to communicate a company's narrative.
- The purchase agreement is a lengthy contract in which the underwriter agrees to buy the securities and resell them to investors.
- As soon as a company undergoes an IPO, it will be subject to all the rules and requirements of a public company, so the necessary organizational structure must be in place before the IPO.
- Follow-on offerings of common equity are much simpler than an IPO because most of the basic disclosure has already been drafted and will only need to be updated.
- Underwriter's counsel draft most documents related to a bond issue. An issuer's lawyers will comment on them and negotiate changes.
- Due diligence is conducted by both underwriter's and issuer's counsel, but is most important to the underwriter. A due diligence investigation may help in establishing a 'due diligence defense' in any future investor lawsuits claiming a violation of securities laws.
- A debt offering can be registered with the SEC or unregistered under Rule 144A of the 1933 Securities Act. In the latter case bonds can only be bought by certain large registered institutional buyers.
- Issuer's and underwriter's counsel work together with a team of bankers, accountants, insurers and an issuer's management to get securities issued. *"There is a very collaborative atmosphere,"* says **Bill Whelan**, corporate partner at **Cravath, Swaine & Moore**. *"The*

Rankings in *Chambers USA*

Top ranked

Cadwalader	Morgan Lewis
Cahill	Sidley
Cleary	Simpson
Cravath	Skadden
Davis Polk	Sullivan
Latham	Vinson
Mayer Brown	

Highly recommended

Akin Gump	Kirkland
Allen & Overy	Kramer Levin
Baker Botts	Milbank
Bracewell	MoFo
Cooley	O'Melveny
Debevoise	Orrick
Dechert	Paul Hastings
Fenwick	Paul, Weiss
Freshfields	Pillsbury
Fried Frank	Proskauer
Gibson Dunn	Ropes & Gray
Goodwin Procter	Schulte
Haynes and Boone	Shearman
Hunton	Stroock
Jones Day	Thompson & Knight
Katten	Weil
Kaye Scholer	White & Case

For more detail on ranking tiers and locations, visit www.chambersandpartners.com

team has the common goal of getting the deal done. There are moments when we have disagreements, but rarely does it get acrimonious." If teams get on particularly well, deals may end with a closing dinner or drinks event.
- The bond market is huge and influential. It is generally considered to have a large influence on the health of the US and global economy.
- Market conditions are very important to the success of capital market deals – more important even than the willingness of the parties to get the deal done. *"The one negative in this area of practice is that the markets are always unpredictable,"* says Bill Whelan of Cravath, Swaine & Moore. "You ca*n invest a lot of time in getting a deal organized, but market conditions can mean it falls through."*
- Practitioners recommend that those interested in the field should take law school classes in securities regulation, corporate finance and the Uniform Commercial Code (UCC). Knowledge of bankruptcy, property and tax law is useful too, as is gaining an understanding of the basic principles of accounting. Reading the financial press – starting with The Wall Street Journal – is a must.

Current issues

- 2014 saw a 14 year high in US IPOs, topping 2013 by 23% as per Renaissance Capital's findings, with 273 IPOs. 2015 was set to be another stable year, with an approximated total of around 200 IPOs. Instead, 2015 ushered in an unwelcome six-year low in IPO activity. According to Renaissance Capital, only a 169 IPOs amassing a measly $30 billion were recorded. While it is fair to say that the IPOs of Shake Shack (5 million shares totaling $105 million), Go Daddy (23 million shares totaling $460 million) and Fitbit (36.6 million shares totaling $732 million), over half of all IPOs ultimately traded below issue.
- Reasons for the slump have been a mixture of Federal Reserve panic, uncertainty about the Chinese economy, European monetary issues, the oil market drop and increased M&A and private market deals. These trends look set to continue well into 2016.
- Looking at the FED interest rate hike in December 2015 in particular, the increase between the rate of 0.25% and 0.5% caused so many ripples, that the scheduled re-raise in March 2016 was postponed indefinitely because of the uncertainty surrounding global markets. If it's raised again, you can expect volatility in the aftermath.
- 2016 has been billed 'The Year of the Mega-Merger.' In the wake of Pfizer Allergan and Dow Chemicals, it's likely that other companies will follow suit. Plus, there's an increased level of consolidation among exchanges to chase market share, with new challengers emerging such as Hong Kong and Toronto. This means more lucrative M&A activity for lawyers.
- Look out for all things tech. With greater focus on Blockchain and cloud services like the Google Cloud and Amazon Web services, the financial industry is starting to streamline and store data like this to save costs. Cutting expenditure here means that banks will likely grow their practices. Ripple effects into FinTech growth should also be mentioned as IDC Research projections pinpoint this specific market to reach $48.6 billion by 2019.
- According to the Goldman Sachs outlook report for 2016, emerging markets are predicted to pick up after six years of slow growth. A particular focus should be on Mexico as well as central and eastern Europe. Poland and Hungary are the favorites and are likely to be important as prominent targets for capital flows.
- The crash has created a 'lost generation' of lawyers (and bankers) who were unable to develop their deal experience and become sophisticated practitioners during their middle-level associate years.
- Expert economists are predicting an upward trend in inflation rates in the USA, Europe and Japan in the coming months. This could mean that inflation-linked securities might become an essential part of investment portfolios.
- New regulations – especially the Dodd-Frank Act – are having a major effect on the rules governing securities. For example, Title VII of the Act requires certain types of previously unregistered derivatives to be registered with exchanges. Other key provisions also encompass rules that require the public availability of security-based swap transactions and pricing data, to enhance price discovery.
- Prompted by studies required by Dodd-Frank, six federal agencies proposed new rules which required sponsors of asset-backed securities to hold back at least 5% of the credit risk of the assets underlying any securities they issue. After various revisions, the Office of the Comptroller of the Currency, Treasury, the Board of Governors of the Federal Reserve System, Federal Deposit Insurance Corporation, US Securities and Exchange Commission, Federal Housing Finance Agency and Department of Housing and Urban Development agreed to adopt and implement these requirements on October 20, 2014. But for the full effect of the Act to be known, we have to wait until different regulatory agencies have finished writing the rules that can implement the rest of the sections.
- The JOBS Act – signed into law in April 2012 – is having a major impact. It entails easing all kinds of securities regulations to stimulate investment in small business, including lifting the ban on general sales of securities issued under Rule 144A of the Securities Act. The final rules and forms of the Act are effective as of May 16, 2016.

- But, it's an election year and only time will tell how the results affect the markets and the ways in which the USA regulates them.
- *"Securities law is changing dramatically,"* John Arnholz of Morgan, Lewis & Bockius comments. *"In the old days, rules about securities weren't written down. They were based on lore. Many regulations in the industry are new. That means old hands like me have a smaller advantage over new people entering the field than we used to. Industrious young associates can learn about new regulations and outsmart the partners!"*
- Despite new rules and regulations, securitization and derivatives lawyers are still able to be very creative in determining what securities look like and how they are structured. John Arnholz further adds that *"for young associates eager to get client contact, no practice area provides more of an opportunity to work directly with clients."*

Doing M&A in the middle market: Jenner & Block's perspective

A strong transactional practice group can assist clients in a wide variety of complex transactions. For example, Jenner & Block LLP assists clients in areas including mergers and acquisitions, corporate finance, securities, and private equity and investment management. A broad understanding of companies and the markets is key to helping clients decide how to structure transactions to attain the most desired outcome.

Business Climate

In 2015, improved economic conditions resulted in record-setting M&A activity, both in terms of deal volume and proceeds. Among the largest transactions was Pfizer's planned merger with Allergan for $160 billion. This transaction became a hot topic in April 2016, when the deal fell apart after the US Department of the Treasury announced a new regulation that some argue was designed specifically to block the Pfizer–Allergan merger. Also in 2015, Anheuser-Busch InBev proposed to acquire rival SABMiller for $107 billion.

Middle-market transactions remained the dominant arena for private equity investors.

Given the flurry of activity in 2015, it was not surprising to see activity slow in the first quarter of 2016. First-quarter deal volume declined by 16 percent from 2015, year to date. Sectors that have remained strong and growing include industrials, which saw a 3 percent increase in deal volume, and utilities, which saw a 213 percent increase in deal proceeds.

Private equity sponsors were able to quickly raise funds and saw strong distributions from exits in 2015. The year saw a continuing trend of distributions exceeding contributions, inspiring more limited partners to invest and reinvest in funds. Middle-market transactions remained the dominant arena for private equity investors.

Life of an Associate

This climate provides excellent opportunities to junior corporate associates. Specifically, associates can get exposure to a variety of businesses, industries, cultures and clients. Companies continue to look to do deals, and with more regulatory regimes, corporate lawyers are needed as much as they have ever been.

Savvy junior associates take the initiative to figure out where their assignments fit in to the bigger picture.

Deals are like puzzles, and associates must be prepared to understand how pieces fit together. Savvy junior associates take the initiative to figure out where their assignments fit in to the bigger picture and how they can develop their skill sets so as to take on additional responsibilities in future transactions.

While all transactions are different, junior corporate associates at Jenner & Block may find themselves doing any number of the following on a day-to-day basis:

- conducting due diligence and preparing due diligence reports;
- assisting senior associates and partners in drafting and revising transaction documents;
- preparing corporate resolutions and attending to general corporate housekeeping matters;
- drafting and reviewing ancillary documents related to a transaction (for instance, a junior associate may be asked to prepare an escrow agreement for use in an M&A transaction or to check a company's securities filing against the relevant securities rules);
- coordinating the drafting of transaction documents and review of due diligence materials by the firm's subject matter experts; and
- conducting research on a specific issue raised by a client or a general topic applicable to numerous clients or matters.

While all of the above may require practice-specific skills, they also require certain fundamental skills that apply to lawyers at all levels. Specifically, associates need to be organized and communicate well. A willingness to work hard and pitch in as a team player is also important.

Law school does not always prepare you for life as a junior corporate associate.

As a junior associate, you should not wait for the work to come to you. Go out and find assignments, especially assignments that interest you. Consider not only the type of transaction (e.g., M&A versus securities), but also the industry involved and the size of the transaction. Larger transactions provide associates with the opportunity to observe and learn from the resolution of complex legal issues, while smaller transactions allow junior associates to draft, negotiate and handle other components of a transaction. You should continue to seek opportunities for training, learn from senior lawyers about the work you are doing, and ask for tips and feedback. Such interactions help your professional development.

Law school does not always prepare you for life as a junior corporate associate. For instance, law school doesn't teach you how to call a specialty partner – perhaps someone in tax, IP or labor – to request that he or she take on a task related to the transaction. While you should take appropriate courses, including contracts, business organizations and secured transactions, be aware that many of those courses are theoretical in nature. The best courses will be taught by practitioners, often adjunct professors, who are in the field and can give practical insight about the day-to-day nuances of the role. Look for opportunities to take classes in contract drafting, mergers and acquisitions and anything that has to do with accounting. These are skills that will serve you well.

Life as a junior corporate associate varies with the peaks and valleys of deal flow. You may go a few weeks with very little work, then get slammed when a transaction gets underway. Being flexible, prepared and up to speed on all of your matters are key to successfully navigating your time as a junior associate. If you work hard, demonstrate a genuine interest in the area and produce high-quality work, the opportunities to work on more complex matters will present themselves.

You need to appreciate your client's business and be interested in what the client wants to accomplish.

More and more, clients expect their counsel to be true advisers who advise not just on the relevant legal issues, but also the full scope of the business. Clients do not want to always hear *"that is a business issue"* or *"we should ask the business people what they think."* They want your perspective on those points, too. To effectively counsel your client in these areas, you need to appreciate your client's business and be interested in what the client wants to accomplish. The concepts can sometimes be difficult, and the work will vary from industry to industry, but if you develop an understanding of the underlying aspects of the business, you will be more likely to succeed.

This is a time of technological and innovative change, and the new economy offers challenges and opportunities for innovation in the practice of corporate law. At Jenner & Block, we hope that by leveraging improvements in technology and thinking creatively, we can continue to provide excellent service to our clients and remain competitive in the changing legal market.

Michael Bolos focuses his practice primarily on mergers and acquisitions, domestic and cross-border complex business transactions and other general corporate matters for public and privately held companies.

Hannah K. Costigan Cowles focuses her practice primarily on middle market mergers and acquisitions and private equity transactions and works with private equity and mezzanine funds on matters that arise throughout the lives of those funds.

Brendan A. Donahue's practice includes corporate law, mergers and acquisitions and private equity. He represents public and private companies in a variety of domestic and cross-border transactions.

JENNER & BLOCK

Corporate/M&A

In a nutshell

Corporate is sometimes defined as a catchall practice area that includes everything that isn't litigation or tax. The higher you go in the BigLaw tree, however, the more corporate becomes synonymous with mergers and acquisitions (M&A) and corporate governance. Some big firms include capital markets and private equity under this umbrella, but these areas are so complex and distinct that *Chambers Associate* prefers to treat them separately.

This practice area can involve advising clients from cradle to grave: from starting up and going public, to raising capital, selling, acquiring and combining businesses, to looking at the overall framework for operations and advising the board of directors on special transactions. Typical M&A work involves advising on selling, combining and acquiring businesses. BigLaw firms often focus on public M&A, advising either the buyer or seller in a transaction involving a public company. This area of corporate law routinely provides the biggest deals, is often cross-border and can involve cash and/or stock considerations. Private M&A takes place between private companies and can also be multifaceted, particularly where partnerships are involved. M&A lawyers can act as transactional coordinators too, because for every takeover or disposal, there will be employment, antitrust or tax implications to consider.

Corporate governance involves advising companies on crucial board affairs (including director duties) and their relationships with shareholders, which are paramount during transactions or shareholder disputes.

What lawyers do

Public M&A for buyer

- Identify the client's business objectives.
- Identify the legal issues – these vary depending on factors like whether the deal is friendly or unfriendly.
- Build a 'road map' for the client from start to finish, and include a timeframe.
- Advise on deal and negotiating tactics.
- Conduct due diligence on other side.
- Determine – with the help of tax attorneys – the tax implications and if they require special structuring.
- Work with antitrust attorneys to assess regulatory obstacles, gain regulatory approval and analyze any other required regulatory approvals.
- If cross-border, work with local counsel. Review all the client's contracts: business, employment, outsourcing, debt instruments, preferred stock, etc.
- Obtain third-party consents from lenders or parties to other contracts.
- Negotiate agreement, sign, announce publicly, close the deal.
- Attorneys for the target decide whether to negotiate, refuse the buyer's overtures, sell, or do a deal with another company.

Realities of the job

- *"The most important thing for a corporate lawyer is to develop an understanding of what's most important to your client – what they are really trying to accomplish and what issues really matter to them and why,"* explains **Victor Lewkow** of **Cleary Gottlieb Steen & Hamilton.**
- An M&A transaction can have *"a whole laundry list of tactics to choose from and issues to consider, depending upon what side you're on,"* says **Alison Ressler** of **Sullivan & Cromwell**, meaning that no two deals are exactly the same. Similarly, each deal will have a unique life cycle and so some will naturally take longer to complete than others.
- A key part of M&A work is explaining issues in a way that makes sense to the client. *"Lawyers often use enormous amounts of jargon, with great expertise and complexity, which is not necessarily helpful for the businesspeople involved,"* Lewkow tells us. He adds: *"Often there is no perfect answer, so some of the time you'll be helping the client figure out what the least 'bad' alternative is."*
- Due diligence will largely fall to associates and, though it can be tedious, it's crucial for attorneys to understand what's in the documents. *"Law students tend to think of us as just reading and marking up documents, but a key characteristic of a top corporate lawyer is the ability to negotiate and construct arguments on your feet,"* states Ressler.
- Delaware, where many corporations are incorporated, has among the most pronounced and expansive laws on the duties of the board and rules concerning special committees, which have tremendous implications for M&A transactions and corporate governance work. Lewkow confirms: *"Many of the corporate law court decisions in Delaware influence how we address problems and generally go about structuring transactions."*
- Public companies, particularly those in the Fortune 500, are slick operations with considerable legal budg-

ets and expertise, and usually need less hand-holding than smaller, less sophisticated clients.

- The high-pressure nature of the work is a result of *"not only having the chance to be involved in issues that are very important to your client, but also making a genuine difference to those issues,"* says **Adam Emmerich** of **Wachtell, Lipton, Rosen & Katz**.
- *"Many deals have a lot of moving pieces, whereby solving one problem could actually create another problem,"* according to Lewkow. *"What works well for IP purposes, for example, might not work well for tax purposes."*
- Clients often expect transactions to be completed in a matter of days, which can mean working 18-hour days and weekends. This expectation can create an atmosphere of cooperation and expediency among parties. *"You break down the walls between who's doing what, and just dive in and do it,"* **Josh Bonnie** of **Simpson Thacher & Bartlett** says.
- It also means that flexibility is key. *"Sometimes you may have a plan to go on holiday, then find out that you need to be on the spot and fully engaged,"* says Emmerich. However, this comes with the territory of it being *"a dynamic, interesting and exciting practice."*
- *"I don't think there is one style which makes you an excellent or effective M&A lawyer,"* explains **Louis Goldberg** of **Davis Polk & Wardwell**. He adds that at one end of the spectrum you have those who are *"thoughtful, determined and tactical,"* while at the other end there are the 'deal junkies': *"They have the charisma and love the ins and outs of the deal climate."*
- The broader category of corporate finance includes representing borrowers in lending transactions with banks, though most firms organize themselves so that the lawyers who advise the lenders and borrowers are part of the banking and finance team.

Rankings in *Chambers USA*

Top ranked

Alston & Bird	Latham
Baker Botts	Lowenstein
Cooley	McGuireWoods
Cravath	Morgan Lewis
Davis Polk	MoFo
Dechert	Perkins Coie
Fenwick & West	Reed Smith
Foley & Lardner	Ropes & Gray
Gibson Dunn	Sidley
Goodwin Procter	Simpson
Greenberg Traurig	Skadden
Hogan Lovells	Snell & Wilmer
Holland & Knight	Squire Patton Boggs
Hunton & Williams	Sullivan
Jones Day	Venable
K&L Gates	Vinson
King & Spalding	Waller
Kirkland	WilmerHale

Highly recommended

Akin Gump	Kramer Levin
Allen & Overy	Mayer Brown
Arnold & Porter	Milbank
Baker & McKenzie	Mintz Levin
Bracewell	Munger
Cadwalader	Nixon Peabody
Choate	Norton Rose Fulbright
Cleary	O'Melveny
Cozen O'Connor	Orrick
Crowell & Moring	Paul Hastings
Debevoise	Paul, Weiss
Duane Morris	Pepper Hamilton
Dykema	Pillsbury
Fox Rothschild	Proskauer
Freshfields	Schulte
Fried Frank	Seward & Kissel
Gibbons	Shearman
Haynes and Boone	Sheppard Mullin
Hughes Hubbard	Thompson & Knight
Jackson Walker	Vedder Price
Jenner	Weil
Katten	White & Case
Kaye Scholer	Willkie
Kilpatrick Townsend	Winston & Strawn

For more detail on ranking tiers and locations, visit www.chambersandpartners.com

Global giant Skadden Arps on life as an M&A lawyer

The M&A practice entails advising clients on mergers, acquisitions, divestitures, spin-offs, proxy contests, joint ventures and consideration of strategic alternatives. Additionally, M&A attorneys advise clients on corporate governance, securities law and general corporate matters.

The practice affords the opportunity to represent a diverse array of U.S. and international, public and private clients, including multinational corporations, emerging companies, private equity funds and hedge funds, individual investors, sovereign governments and other stakeholders. Clients are often undergoing fundamental changes in their strategy and business, and M&A attorneys help them navigate this period of profound change.

Business Climate

Key Drivers of the M&A Market: In 2015, the economic environment continued to be conducive to M&A activity, particularly in the U.S. Corporate balance sheets were in good shape, equity markets were relatively stable and access to debt financing was generally available on attractive terms, although there was some dislocation in the high-yield market in the fourth quarter.

Corporations face a continued imperative to grow at a rate that exceeds economic growth – and M&A is an important tool to achieve that goal. At the same time, there are risks and uncertainties in the global economy and equity markets that could impact activity levels. For example, finding financing on acceptable terms has become more difficult for lower-rated issuers.

'Corporations face a continued imperative to grow at a rate that exceeds economic growth – and M&A is an important tool to achieve that goal.'

On the regulatory front, robust antitrust enforcement and scrutiny will continue, but boards and advisers have shown resilience to sign deals, allocate risk and ultimately get deals done.

Many of the biggest deals in 2015 were stock-for-stock transactions, so financing considerations weren't at the forefront. Investment-grade and the better ranked high-yield issuers continued to have favorable access to the credit markets. Private equity firms, which accounted for approximately 6 percent of global M&A activity in 2015, and other acquirers that rely on leverage weren't key drivers of M&A activity in 2015 and aren't likely to be in 2016.

Geographies and Industries: 2015 M&A activity was generally robust across the globe. The U.S. was particularly strong, but European and Asian activity also increased. Activity in Latin America was relatively slow.

In terms of industries, technology and health care were very strong. Within tech, the semiconductor space was a real standout, with long-anticipated consolidation finally happening in 2015 and expected to continue in 2016. With technology, products and markets evolve quickly. Entire industries emerge and disappear within a span of just a few years, so even very large, established companies have to constantly reinvent themselves, and that continues to be a driving force for M&A. In health care, mega pharma deals, as well as interest in biotech companies, were big drivers. Pharmaceutical companies face the challenge of patents expiring on big drugs in coming years, so biotech companies, particularly at current price levels and with only spotty capital market windows, present attractive buying opportunities.

On the private equity front, PE firms haven't been as prominent in the current M&A landscape, but they've still been involved, perhaps in different roles. For example, Silver Lake played a significant role in the Dell-EMC deal. To a certain extent, we're going back to a world where synergies and strategic imperatives are driving deals and valuations. That's an environment which probably favors strategic over financial buyers. In 2016, it will also be important to see how the debt markets evolve and whether cheap financing remains available.

Looking Ahead: There is a stratum of transactions that will remain difficult to get done, and private equity activity may continue to be constrained in 2016. Leveraged transactions are likely to be constrained if current conditions persist given where the high-yield markets seem to be, at least for now. Absent adverse developments, however, strategic transactions should continue because the needs for growth, consolidation and a global footprint aren't going away.

Preparing for life as an M&A associate

Do you like being in the center of the action? Do you like being challenged and thinking on your feet? Do you enjoy making sense out of organized chaos? If so, you would most likely enjoy being an M&A associate.

In the context of a deal, the M&A team serves as the quarterback – calling the play in consultation with the client and successfully executing with the help of legal specialist teams. Your job as an M&A is as complex as the clients you serve and, accordingly, M&A transactions are multifaceted. Each deal requires you to work closely with lawyers in other groups, such as corporate finance, banking, executive compensation and benefits, IP, labor, real estate, tax, antitrust and litigation, to name a few. Often, there will be a regulatory component that adds even more complexity. From the career development standpoint, a major perk of being an M&A associate is exposure to each of these areas of law.

In the height of a transaction, the M&A team's role exists somewhere between emergency room triage and a good game of whack-a-mole. Although this can be stressful, it's also completely exhilarating. Law school teaches you to issue-spot; being a lawyer requires you to find solutions. Some issues in the context of a deal are straightforward while others require out-of-the-box thinking and skillful creativity. The job is challenging to be sure, but ask any M&A lawyer why they enjoy their job and you're likely to get a uniform response: It's fun.

How should you prepare for life as an M&A associate? Look at your education as a chance to amalgamate the skill sets that will enable your success. Many of these skills won't be listed in the course catalog, but don't worry, you've unknowingly been preparing all along. Multitasking, setting and meeting deadlines, time management, attention to detail and the ability to think critically are all skills that are cultivated in law school and will prove immensely valuable as an M&A associate.

Many law schools offer specific classes in M&A and contract drafting. These classes introduce you to the different sections of M&A agreements, expose you to relevant legal vernacular and provide you with an understanding of many key transaction drivers. Classes in securities law, corporations, business taxation, finance and accounting are all useful as well. However, these are suggestions, not prerequisites. There is no one class without which you will not succeed and there is no substitute for the real world experience you will gain at a firm. Given the diversity of deals and clients, there are always areas of law you will need to learn on the job. Perhaps the best preparation you can have is getting comfortable saying, *"I don't know, but I'll find out."*

As an M&A associate, you will jump into different industries and have clients across varied geographies. You will learn to make sense of the unknown and leverage past experience to assist on your next deal. Remember, no transaction takes place in a vacuum – clients and their businesses exist within the wider, global business, financial and regulatory markets. To that end, start reading The Wall Street Journal, Financial Times and other business news publications. Neither your colleagues nor your clients will quiz you on the front page, but familiarity with the business world will pay dividends. As you will see when you draft M&A documents, your firm is regularly referred to as your client's "advisor"; that role is based on legal expertise but often extends beyond.

Authors

Thomas Kennedy

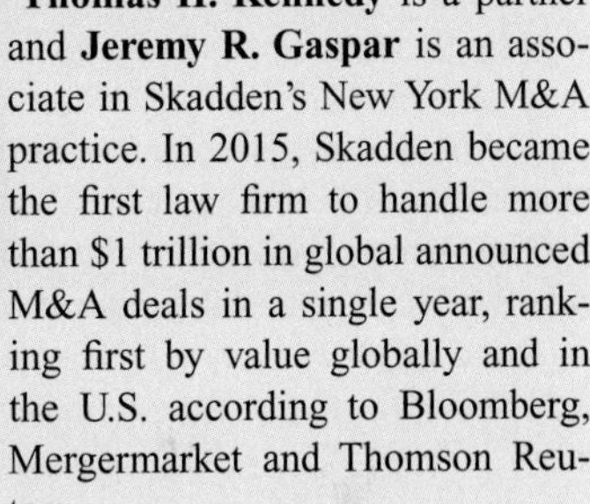

Thomas H. Kennedy is a partner and **Jeremy R. Gaspar** is an associate in Skadden's New York M&A practice. In 2015, Skadden became the first law firm to handle more than $1 trillion in global announced M&A deals in a single year, ranking first by value globally and in the U.S. according to Bloomberg, Mergermarket and Thomson Reuters.

Jeremy Gaspar

'In the height of a transaction, the M&A team's role exists somewhere between emergency room triage and a good game of whack-a-mole.'

Skadden
Skadden, Arps, Slate, Meagher & Flom LLP
& Affiliates

Energy & Projects
"Never in my long practice has it been in such rapid flux as it is currently. So it's never boring, never static." – Thomas Eastment, Baker Botts

In a nutshell
Energy and projects are two distinct but overlapping areas of law. When combined, they focus on the development, construction and financing of major natural resource (oil/gas, mining), power and infrastructure projects. The construction of pipelines, refineries, mines, power plants and petrochemical plants is a massive business, with high stakes and massive dollar values. Emerging economies are frequently the most hungry for infrastructural improvements, meaning a lawyer's work increasingly takes on an international flavor.

In addition, the projects component of an energy practice consists of both transactional and regulatory work (with regulatory work more prevalent in US domestic projects). There is a clear demarcation between transactional and regulatory work, and lawyers usually specialize in one of the two.

Non-energy projects are all about infrastructure. Typical examples might be road, airports, rail, shipping, telecoms and, most glamorously, sewage and water systems. The work would also include the construction of major multi-investor public buildings such as jails and stadiums.

What lawyers do

Energy – transactional & regulatory
- Transactional work can cover anything across M&A, joint ventures, capital markets, private equity, venture capital and project development and finance work.
- Energy lawyers deal with three types of clients: **upstream, midstream** and **downstream**. **Upstream** businesses deal with getting energy out of the ground – oil, gas, coal, sometimes geothermal. This includes mining and minerals companies. **Midstream** clients are in the refining, treating and transportation of resources industry and its offshoots. **Downstream** clients are energy distributors: gas stations, electricity providers, gas companies.
- Lawyers advise clients on negotiating and drafting agreements related to things like energy projects, the sale of power companies, investment in and development of upstream resources and the financing of various energy investments.
- Many firms' energy work focuses either on infrastructure and construction projects or on representations in front of the Federal Energy Regulatory Commission (FERC). FERC is a US government regulatory agency. It regulates electricity sales, electric rates, hydropower projects, natural gas pricing and oil pipeline rates. Its decisions can be reviewed by federal courts.
- *"Practicing in energy regulation and litigation is exciting because you're dealing with ever-changing government policies. It's always in flux. But never in my long practice has it been in such rapid flux as it is currently. So it's never boring, never static,"* says **Thomas Eastment**, partner and head of the energy regulatory section, **Baker Botts**.

Projects
- Projects lawyers have three or four types of clients: sponsors/developers who put together the project; financiers (banks, international development agencies, foreign export credit agencies); the provider or contractor (who supplies raw materials or undertakes construction); and sometimes the 'offtaker' who purchases the products produced by the project. The most significant roles for lawyers are representing either the sponsors/developers or the financiers.
- **Keith Martin,** partner and co-head of the project finance group at **Chadbourne & Parke**, says: *"Project finance transactions are complicated exercises in risk allocation that take a lot of time and generate lots of paper. The complexity is increased by the involvement of different countries and the number of people in different roles – sponsors, senior and subordinated lenders, tax and true equity investors, landowners, offtakers. These are interesting puzzles to put together – they take an ability to listen carefully, spot common ground and solve problems."*

Realities of the job

- Texas is *"the land of opportunity"* for energy lawyers focused on US-based projects. Its law schools – most notably the University of Texas – are some of the only ones in the country to provide energy classes. In Texas the energy industry is regulated by the Railroad Commission of Texas. Alaska is the country's second oil state.
- The overwhelming majority of international work for projects lawyers is handled in New York – which remains the 'money center' for transactions in Latin America. The Energy Policy Act of 2005 created a host of new regulations by which companies in the industry are required to abide. These include loan guarantees for technologies that avoid greenhouse gases, subsidies for alternative energy producers and incentives to drill for oil in the Gulf of Mexico.
- Work is often international or related to projects overseas, as there is hyperactive development of infrastructure and the energy sector in many economies. *"Just look at where development is roaring to find out where we work: China, India, Brazil, Mexico, Indonesia, Peru, the Gulf states. There are giant infrastructure developments there – things are moving much faster than in the developed world."*
- The international nature of work means lawyers often have to deal with *"shaky jurisdictions. Structuring a deal to take into account political risk is very much a part of being an international projects lawyer. And that's not just in less developed countries – there could be similar issues surrounding a mining deal in California."*
- **Thomas Eastment** tells us: *"With so much evolution in the market and government, flexibility is required to solve problems. You can't just look at the last deal or memo for answers to new questions that a client poses. Energy law isn't for someone who wants to feel like, 'I've got all this mastered, now I can use my cookie cutter'."*
- Eastment continues: *"A nice broad understanding of the key areas of law is crucial. This would include classic energy law but also environmental, finance and general commercial law. The issues we grapple with span all these, so you need to be nimble. The answer is not simply taking an energy course."*
- **Jonathan Green**, partner and cochair of the project finance group at **Milbank**, says: *"Projects lawyers get the opportunity to do many different transactions without a whole lot of repetition. For young lawyers I think that presents benefits and challenges. The work tends to be extremely varied for many years, even for partners, and that keeps the learning curve very steep for a good part of your career. The challenge is that you don't have the opportunity to repeat transactions and hone your expertise early on, as you might in other areas. It takes longer to become an expert."*

Rankings in *Chambers USA*

Top ranked

Bracewell	Skadden
Latham	Vinson
Morgan Lewis	Winston & Strawn
Nixon Peabody	
Orrick	

Highly recommended

Akin Gump	K&L Gates
Alston & Bird	King & Spalding
Baker Botts	Kirkland & Ellis
Cadwalader	McGuireWoods
Chadbourne	Munger
Cleary	Norton Rose Fulbright
Crowell & Moring	Pillsbury
Gibson Dunn	Sidley
Greenberg Traurig	Simpson
Haynes and Boone	Sullivan
Hogan Lovells	Thompson & Knight
Hunton & Williams	Venable
Jackson Walker	White & Case
Jones Day	

For more detail on ranking tiers and locations, visit www.chambersandpartners.com

Current issues

- The oil price drop is one of the most talked-about news stories of the past twelve months. Although at the time of writing, prices had begun to increase, they plummeted to below $30 per barrel around December 2015. This has had drastic ripple effects across the sector.
- In the wake of the slump, oil and gas-dependent states across the USA like Texas, Oklahoma, Wyoming, Louisiana, North Dakota, Alaska, New Mexico and West Virginia, have taken an economic downturn after mass layoffs and oil rig shut-downs. For example, projections in North Dakota indicate that between 2015 and 2017, there will be a 32.6% drop in extraction jobs in the state.
- On the (slightly) brighter side, attorneys with bankruptcy specialisms will likely find more work in this sector than ever before. Around 48 oil and gas companies in North America had filed for bankruptcy since the beginning of 2015, compared to only eight filed in 2014. According to energy consultancy Graves & Co. energy companies have announced that at least a further 319,000 jobs will be cut since late 2014.
- The knock-on effect is that there will be a surge in M&A. After a disappointing 2015, with Wood Mackenzie placing last year's deal quota at only 14 M&As over $1 billion, There is a surplus in private funding that still remains after deals were canceled. This means that small to medium-sized independent com-

panies are likely to merge more in 2016, to ride the slump. For everyone else, assets-targeted acquisitions appear to be key.

- **Scott Barshay**, Paul, Weiss' global head of mergers and acquisitions tells us that *"there is normally a lag before we see an increase in M&A in that space. It's a function of psychology. Directors need to get used to the fact that their stock prices aren't going to be back to the same level as their 52 week high. It takes time for people to accept that oil won't be back at $75 or $80 per barrel. Once this happens, then there will be a come-back for M&A. But in the meantime, I think now deals will be mostly dominated by stock transactions. If prices don't rise again, then I think we're likely to see a phenomenon in 2016 where there will be more cash deals taking place."*
- The Federal Reserve Bank of Dallas observes that a sustained 50% lower crude oil price is likely to raise US growth by 0.5 of a percentage point for around a year. For the next year or so, it's likely that growth in the USA will be on the up if things stay the way they are.
- Shale oil exploitation has been a big thing since the 2000s, with a nearly 80% increase from the 2006 levels being reported by the US Energy Information Administration. But in the aftermath of the oil price plummet, smaller companies who got rich quick from the earlier shale boom are now going out of business.
- The emerging trend of US shale gas exportation has already begun to have an impact on other oil-producing countries. Many foreign companies tied into deals requiring them to purchase set amounts of oil at prices far above spot-price have gone to arbitration in order to renegotiate the terms of their contracts. The first export took place on March 15, 2016, when a tanker transported 3 billion cubic feet of natural gas to Brazil. The USA is now set to become the third largest exporter of liquefied natural gas (LNG), which is poised to raise sustainable job creation.
- Internationally, Brazil, East Africa, Australia and the North Sea are attracting increasing attention. Chinese and Indian companies especially are investing heavily in infrastructure and exploration in these new areas, as well as existing markets. South Africa looks ripe to become a key player in shale gas exploration come 2017.
- **Thomas Eastment** says: *"An incredible sea-change has arisen in the USA from shale oil and gas development. It has transformed the debates about so many issues. There are serious environmental questions posed over the fracking techniques used to develop oil and gas. There's also a concern that by exporting these commodities domestic prices will go up."*
- **Jonathan Green** says: *"Cross-border work continues to be very strong, particularly related to developing nations and in energy and natural resources. This allows you to work in different legal systems and cultures. We're seeing very large international projects often supported by governmental lenders and multilateral institutions."*

"An incredible sea-change has arisen in the USA from shale oil and gas development."

Environment
"The practice of environmental law... involves politically controversial subjects that one reads about in the papers every day." – Bill Brownell, Hunton & Williams

In a nutshell

Environment attorneys advise companies on federal, state and local laws and regulations relating to public health, welfare and the environment. The type of conduct that is regulated includes industrial activity, the development of natural resources, the use of land and everyday activities like driving a car. BigLaw attorneys primarily defend companies that are subject to these laws and regulations.

The laws attorneys' work will depend on the environmental medium: for example, air, water, waste and natural/cultural/historical resources (this touches on historical preservation, land use and endangered species) all have their own statutes and programs. The Clean Air Act – *"one of the most complex pieces of legislation on the books,"* according to **Hunton & Williams** partner **Bill Brownell** – is one example.

The types of proceedings handled by environmental lawyers are also varied. Administrative agency work involves dealing with agencies. In federal government, that includes the Environmental Protection Agency (EPA), the Department of the Interior (DOI), the Department of Agriculture (DOA), the Department of Energy (DOE) and the Nuclear Regulatory Commission (NRC). Legislative work involves working with Congress and advising companies on federal legislation and lobbying.

What lawyers do

- *"I tell students that the practice of environmental law touches on everything a lawyer can do. An environmental lawyer will practice before Congress, administrative agencies, federal and state courts, and international tribunals and organizations. The practice of environmental law also involves politically controversial subjects that one reads about in the papers every day,"* says Hunton's Brownell.
- He adds: *"When a statute or law is changed it initiates a process that can last for years, from lobbying legislators, to working with agencies that develop rules, to challenging or defending those rules in court, to seeking permits and licenses under those rules, to defending clients in enforcement proceedings."*

Realities of the job

- The laws and regulations have become increasingly complicated over the years. Thus, much of what environmental lawyers do on a daily basis is to *"make sure that clients understand all the rules to which they are subject and work with them to ensure they are complying with those rules,"* says **Hunton & Williams** partner **Andrea Field.**
- *"Often, the first time a client realizes that there's a problem is when the EPA starts an enforcement action, charging the client with breaking federal law."* Because the laws are often unclear, *"it is the attorney's job to determine if legitimate arguments can be made that, in fact, the client has not violated the law. And if there are violations, then it is the lawyer's job to negotiate a reasonable – and, if possible, nonpunitive – way for the client to come into compliance."*
- This field of law is *"constantly changing,"* according to Field. *"International tribunals, Congress and state legislatures enact complicated laws. That prompts regulators to adopt complicated rules and issue guidance to implement the laws."* And then there are the advocacy groups, which can *"file lawsuits and do other things to try to push regulators into taking (or not taking) additional actions."* Staying abreast of all such changes *"necessarily keeps practitioners on their toes."*
- The legislation is sometimes politically motivated, so environmental lawyers can end up wading into controversies among different branches of government. *"And just as you start getting a handle on a program, there is a national or state election, and that ushers in new legislators and new regulators, which restarts the cycle of change,"* says Field. But the changing players and changing requirements make things interesting.*"As an environmental lawyer, I not only deal with nuts-and-bolts factual and legal issues, I also get to argue important issues of administrative and constitutional law."*

Rankings in *Chambers USA*

Top ranked

Arnold & Porter	King & Spalding
Baker Botts	Latham & Watkins
Cravath	Lowenstein
Davis Polk	McGuireWoods
Gibbons	Nixon Peabody
Gibson Dunn	Perkins Coie
Greenberg Traurig	Sidley Austin
Hunton	Simpson
Jenner	Snell & Wilmer
K&L Gates	Squire Patton Boggs
Kilpatrick	Waller

Highly recommended

Allen & Overy	Mayer Brown
Alston & Bird	Mintz Levin
Baker & McKenzie	MoFo
Bracewell	Morgan Lewis
Brown Rudnick	Norton Rose Fulbright
Cahill	Nutter
Crowell	O'Melveny & Myers
Debevoise	Paul Hastings
Fox Rothschild	Pillsbury
Goodwin Procter	Shearman & Sterling
Goulston & Storrs	Sheppard Mullin
Haynes and Boone	Sullivan & Cromwell
Hogan Lovells	Thompson & Knight
Holland & Knight	Venable
Jackson Walker	White & Case
Katten Muchin	Vinson & Elkins
Kirkland & Ellis	

For more detail on ranking tiers and locations, visit www.chambersandpartners.com

- *"Practicing environmental law requires an aptitude for sophisticated legal analysis, an aptitude for simplifying complex issues, and an ability for written and oral advocacy,"* Bill Brownell says. Andrea Field adds: *"And just like full-time litigators, you have to roll up your sleeves and become fully familiar with the facts in your cases. Tempting as it may be to delegate doc review to others, you have to stay involved because you have to know the facts."* A lot of reading case law and doc review can be involved. And there can be a lot of documents.
- **Robert Wyman**, partner and environment don at **Latham & Watkins**, says: *"Almost everything one does touches on an important area of public policy. Most environmental law practitioners find the job personally rewarding because they have strong views about how environmental risk should be addressed. The practice of law can become routine, but if you're passionate then it never gets old."*
- Wyman adds: *"Day to day we might be involved in rulemaking, consulting with clients or defending an enforcement action, but in each of those contexts we are essentially engaging in the larger debate about how to use the world's resources in a responsible way."*
- **Betty Moy Huber**, co-head of the environmental group at **Davis Polk**, says: *"An environmental lawyer must have solid communication skills. Even at the most junior level you'll be analyzing very complex environmental issues or laws and having to explain these in plain English to a senior lawyer or a client in a very clear and crisp manner."*
- She adds: *"You become part of the client's team. They depend on you and often there's a real feeling of camaraderie. This is very rewarding, but the responsibility also creates pressure."*

Current issues

- The political debate surrounding climate change has led to increasingly complex legislative proposals and regulation. *"Environmental lawyers will be busy in the next few years preparing clients for possible legislative and regulatory changes,"* says Betty Moy Huber of Davis Polk.
- In 2013, President Barack Obama outlined a new national action plan centered on climate change. This included steps to reduce carbon pollution and ensure communities are fully prepared for the effects of climate change – like increased storms, droughts and wildfires.
- The same year, the Natural Resources Defense Council – an environmental group that has had a strong influence on Obama's climate change agenda – recently suggested changes that could lead to even steeper reductions in carbon pollution than those outlined by the President.
- The government has begun to put forth measures to combat global warming, but without the need for legislation from Congress. As an example, it recently announced plans to start cutting emissions of methane as a means of addressing climate change.
- Climate change (and the environment generally) may be a top priority for the government, but it doesn't seem to be as high on the list of concerns for the US public. According to a poll by research company Gallup, only 24% of those who participated worried about climate change 'a great deal'. Similarly, a mere 31% worried a great deal about the quality of the environment. Both were near the bottom of the list, with race relations the only issue to have been ranked lower.
- In August 2015, President Obama established the Clean Power Plan – the first-ever carbon pollution standards for existing power plants. However, in February 2016 the Supreme Court voted to block the plan and debates about its implementation are ongoing.

- After two weeks of talks in Paris in late 2015, world leaders came to an agreement governing greenhouse gases, emissions mitigation, adaptation and finance from 2020. Conference head Laurent Fabius, France's foreign minister, said this 'ambitious and balanced' plan was a 'historic turning point' in the goal of reducing global warming. At the time of writing, the Paris Agreement has yet to be adopted.
- In 2014, the California Legislature passed the Sustainable Groundwater Management Act, a statute designed to create comprehensive sustainable management of groundwater. While the legislation conferred oversight authority to government bodies, primary implementation rests with local groundwater sustainability agencies (GSAs). At the beginning of 2016 the GSAs began implementing legislation to improve California's groundwater supplies. There has been support for GSAs in Berkeley and Stanford law journals as well as in state legislatures further afield and one hopes they will succeed in their endeavors.
- Contaminated water supplies due to aging pipes in Flint, Michigan led to the exposure of between 6,000 and 12,000 children to drinking water with high levels of lead. The children may experience a range of serious health problems as a result of the exposure. In response to the crisis, on January 5th 2016, the city was declared to be in a state of emergency by the Governor of Michigan, Rick Snyder, before President Obama declared it as a federal state of emergency. The Flint water crisis has become a big issue among the nominees for the 2016 Presidential election candidacies.
- *"Economics can have a large effect on how you handle specific environmental matters. A client may start off wanting to litigate every conceivable issue in an enforcement case, but the cost of doing that – and the animosity that can create in dealing with regulators with whom the client might need to do business – usually prompts clients to try to find a reasonable middle ground to resolve cases,"* Andrea Field says. A down economy is therefore likely to lead to more cases settling out of court in this area.

"Even at the most junior level you'll be analyzing very complex environmental issues or laws and having to explain these in plain English to a senior lawyer or a client in a very clear and crisp manner."

The Big Interview with **Philip K. Howard**, bestselling author, law reformer and Covington partner

Philip K. Howard (born 1948; JD UVA School of Law, 1974), is a senior counsel at Covington & Burling, bestselling author and an advocate of American government and legal reform. After law school, Howard joined Sullivan & Cromwell, and later went on to found Howard, Derby & Levin in 1983. The latter firm merged with Covington & Burling in 1999.

Howard is also a renowned commentator and author, focusing on the impact of modern law and bureaucracy on human behavior. He is chair of Common Good, a legal reform coalition which he founded in 2002. The think-tank proposes a radical simplification of law and government, in an effort to restore common sense to American bureaucracy.

> ***"I saw the ways in which detailed regulations prevented officials from acting sensibly."***

When did you decide to become a lawyer? Why?
I was interested in public policy and law seemed the best training. I took a year off after college, working as a photographer in New York and generally observing various trendy professions. Law still seemed the best bet.

Starting out, what did you expect from a career in the law?
I wanted a platform from which I could get involved in a wide range of interesting projects.

Has it lived up to your expectations?
Yes.

How did you get into the areas of law you are known for today? By design? Chance? Both?
My practice evolved by chance. My policy writings grew out of a decade of civic activism, observing government officials paralyzed by bureaucracy.

What do you consider to have been your big break?
My biggest break was my summer job in college – working at the Oak Ridge National Lab as the gopher in a small group of brilliant scientists led by Nobel laureate Eugene Wigner. I saw how smart people do things.

What differences do you see in today's legal market compared to when you started?
The legal market is much more commoditized. There are fewer generalists, and there is less demand for outside lawyers to steer the ship.

What achievement are you most proud of?
Oh gosh, I'm proud of the law firm we started and built (now part of Covington). I'm proud of my books. I'm also proud of my four nice successful children.

What do you consider your greatest failure or regret?
I have few regrets. There are one or two clients that should have done better.

What have you enjoyed most during your career in the legal profession?
I have wonderful, bright, funny colleagues and have thoroughly enjoyed working with them.

And enjoyed least?
Dealing with lawyers on the other side who are mendacious or more interested in their own ego or self-interest than their client's. Over time, I'd like to think, it catches up with them.

What law would you change, abolish or create?
I write books about the need to modernize regulatory laws. They need to be radically simplified so that people on the ground can 1) understand what's expected, and 2) have flexibility to deal reasonably with particular situations.

Who is your legal hero?
I admire the humanistic approach of Holmes and Cardozo. I think Justice Anthony Kennedy is wise and practical.

What career would you have in your second life?
I think I am well suited to be a lawyer, and glad that I can take advantage of that training to try to accomplish public goals.

What slogan would you like to be remembered by?
Common sense.

What advice would you give to students trying to enter the legal profession today?
Figure things out for yourself. Don't accept underlying assumptions.

What key personal experiences have shaped your ideas?
Two influences: I was an intern for three summers for Nobel physicist Eugene Wigner at the Oak Ridge National Lab, where he and his colleagues emphasized the personal nature of all accomplishments. As a young lawyer, I was active as a civic leader, chairing zoning hearings and getting involved in local land use disputes. I saw the ways in which detailed regulations prevented officials from acting sensibly.

"Figure things out for yourself. Don't accept underlying assumptions."

Government

In a nutshell

Government contracts lawyers *"don't necessarily focus on one area and have to be jacks of all trades,"* according to **Tom McGovern** of **Hogan Lovells**. They help contractors navigate the regulations and special rules involved with providing goods and services to federal government, as well as advising on subcontracts, scheduling and organizational conflicts. Bid protests form the bulk of contentious work, along with disputes involving costs recovery or performance problems, and defending contractors accused of fraud or other misconduct.

"Law firms who lobby are not selling access, they are selling skills," says **Nick Allard**, former chair of **Patton Boggs'** lobbying, political and election law practice, and current President and Joseph Crea Dean of Brooklyn Law School. *"They are litigators being advocates in a broader array of arenas."* More specifically, government relations lawyers directly lobby the federal and state government on behalf of a variety of businesses – healthcare, education and defense – on specific legislation or ongoing issues. They promote or oppose new initiatives to Congress or the administration, attempt to persuade government to amend legislation, and try to convince courts to reinterpret laws.

Political law specialists advise on the organization and financing of election campaigns, and help corporations and other groups with election-related activities. On the litigation side they engage in challenges to decisions made by electoral authorities, such as the Federal Election Commission.

What lawyers do

Government contracts

- Virtually every government agency procures external services, but the Department of Defense is far and away the largest consumer. Other major areas are aerospace, construction, healthcare, Homeland Security, education and IT.
- When external services or goods are required, the government will issue a procurement solicitation (or 'Request for Proposal'). The process of procurement and contracting is run by a government official called the Contracting Officer.
- Lawyers help guide potential contractors through the solicitation procedures: pointing out the key risk issues, how the evaluation factors will influence the selection decision and how this contract differs from previous ones. However, they do not advise clients on how to obtain a contract or how to market themselves.
- **Rand Allen** of **Wiley Rein** says: *"We advise a lot of companies on how to get into the government contracts arena without creating undue compliance risk, for instance by qualifying for a status which will minimize the intrusiveness of government in their business."*
- Government contracts tend to use 'boilerplates' or standardized terms and conditions. There is not as much room to negotiate the requirements which form part of the contract as there is in a commercial setting. Lawyers negotiate subcontracts and teaming agreements between contractors.
- After the formation of the contract, lawyers act for both plaintiffs (the disappointed bidders) and defendants (the awardees) during bid protests. A typical bid protest challenges the award of a contract at an administrative forum, the Government Accountability Office (GAO) or the US Court of Federal Claims (CFC). These cases are resolved over a period of about three months, which means associates don't get bogged down for long periods in document review. The GAO is required by statute to issue a ruling within 100 days. Plaintiffs have ten days to put together protest documents, and government agencies have 30 days to respond. CFC proceedings take about the same time, sometimes slightly longer. Associates prepare drafts of protest filings and identify applicable legal precedent. This involves close scrutiny of the original Request for Proposal, the government agency's award decision and the proposals and negotiation responses submitted by both the awardee and the protester.
- There are also disputes over the performance of existing contracts. Lawyers represent contractors in alternative dispute resolution or litigation in front of the Armed Services Board of Contract Appeals, the Civilian Board of Contract Appeals or the Court of Federal Claims.
- Lawyers also defend contractors against allegations of fraud, waste and misconduct under various federal criminal and civil statutes, including the False Claims Act.
- Lawyers also act in litigation between prime contractors and subcontractors in federal and state courts.

Government relations

- Government relations lawyers are approached by clients from all industries who believe a certain piece of legislation will benefit or harm their business, in order to get it promoted or changed.

- The service that government relations lawyers provide involves *"analyzing laws, writing memoranda to clients advising on legal provisions – telling them what their responsibilities are under new legislation – and preparing advocacy pieces for hearings,"* Allard tells us.
- Besides advocacy there's legal research into current statutes, drafting of proposed rules and legislation, and drafting of clients' comments on legislation.
- Government relations lawyers are a link between their clients and politicians and administrators. But Allard wants us to clear up a misunderstanding: *"Lobbying involves so much more than this image people have of the glad-handing door-opener. That is not interesting or high-end work. What we do is analyze, advise and advocate. We seek to understand our clients' business, their mission and what they want to accomplish."*

Rankings in *Chambers USA*

Top ranked

Akin Gump	Perkins Coie
Arnold & Porter	Skadden
Crowell	Wiley Rein
Jenner	

Highly recommended

Alston & Bird	King & Spalding
Cozen O'Connor	Mayer Brown
Fried Frank	Pillsbury
Gibson Dunn	Sheppard
Hogan Lovells	Squire Patton Boggs
Holland & Knight	Venable
Jones Day	Vinson & Elkins
K&L Gates	WilmerHale

For more detail on ranking tiers and locations, visit www.chambersandpartners.com

Realities of the job

- *"Government contracts is a very litigation-oriented area,"* explains **John Chierichella** of **Sheppard Mullin**. *"You don't just have the opportunity to litigate, though; you get to do so in relation to things that are incredibly interesting, whether it be a bid protest, debarment proceeding, False Claims Act case or subcontract dispute."*
- Bid protests are typically intense affairs, with a lot of information that must be absorbed in a short space of time. *"If your eyes glaze over when reading a detailed technical or cost proposal, this is not the area for you,"* says McGovern.
- Associates working on a smaller bid protest may have the opportunity to actually lead the case, while in a larger bid protest it's more likely that they'll work on a particular aspect of it.
- Cost issues can be daunting to look at because of the vast regulations and complex wording involved. According to Chierichella, however, *"if you can understand that logic chain and overcome those concerns, there's a lot of benefit you can give clients in working through cost issues to maximize the amount to be paid and the amount they will retain."*
- While most traditional law practices deal with questions of what the law is, political law mainly involves the question of what the law should be.
- Lobbyists' main clients include corporations, trade associations, universities, healthcare institutions, states and municipalities.
- There is also pro bono lobbying work for charities and other nonprofit organizations.
- *"One of the most important things to understand is that every company in the USA is affected by the government's policies,"* **Tom Boyd** of **DLA Piper** tells us. *"Whether it's in the form of legislation, regulation or the exercise of executive power, it's going to impact the marketplace and every one of our clients."*
- Allard describes the public policy process as *"never-ending,"* adding that *"anything that is done can be undone."*
- It is usually easier to shoot down a planned bill than to get one passed.
- *"Whenever you're representing a corporation, part of the picture will involve a high-profile public official,"* says **Ken Gross** of **Skadden**. *"So it's vital to understand how decisions will play out if they get picked up by the media."*
- The famous 'revolving door' relationship between the administration and lobbying shops provides lawyers at all levels with the opportunity to work in-house for the government.
- *"I think having some exposure to government service is very helpful in this practice,"* explains Gross. *"You're essentially seeing the picture from the inside, which certainly helps when dealing with the regulation side of things."*
- Government lawyers are also active at the state level. Smaller state-based firms – grouped together into the State Capital Global Law Firm Group – advise on business regulation, ethics codes, campaign finance and state government procurement.
- *"Clients come from all over the globe,"* Boyd says. *"So we're not only interested in the political issues concerning Washington, DC, but also the likes as they relate to client interests in London, Paris, Berlin and Brussels."*
- *"There is a relatively small Bar and you deal with the same people regularly on the other side,"* states Allen.*"That generates more comity and less hostile behavior than some lawyers are used to."*

Current issues

- Contractors and government are always at odds as they attempt to achieve the best prices from their respective positions. **Tom McGovern**, the government contracts practice area leader at **Hogan Lovells**, explained that *"contractors are consulting us for advice as to how to protect themselves from government budget cuts and austerity measures."*
- A significant issue for government contract lawyers has been advising their clients on potential budget cuts in light of the 'fiscal cliff', including assessing what their rights would be should the government decide to cease financing certain services or projects. While a deal was reached to avoid such substantial spending cuts – albeit narrowly – a lot of work still needs to be done and it remains a primary concern for contractors.
- The budget cuts and reductions in overall government spending have made the competition for any government work available all the more competitive. *"With tighter budgets come fewer contract awards, so contractors are more likely to seek redress through the bid protest process if they lose contracts they previously held,"* according to McGovern.
- An area which has seen significant activity, unsurprisingly considering the ongoing impact of Edward Snowden's revelations about the activities of the security services, has been data security. This affects all contractors who have access to government information, whether they store it on their own systems or are tasked with securing the government's own storage facilities.
- *"Contractors are concerned about mounting cybersecurity threats, both in relation to their own networks and those they maintain for government customers. The government is greatly concerned about the security of its own data entrusted to contractors and expects contractors to adhere to strict information assurance guidelines and to cooperate and share data about cyber attacks in order to counter such threats. At the same time, there have been news reports of government intelligence agencies attempting to access data in commercial networks, including those operated by their own contractors, which is somewhat ironic,"* explained McGovern.
- Government contractors have also been integral in the implementation of Obamacare, and not all has gone smoothly. They have been *"at the forefront of setting up government websites, health insurance exchanges and providing navigators to inform consumers of their various options,"* explains McGovern. *"This development is typical of this area of practice where the focus shifts depending on the government's priorities of the day."*
- Technology is having a major impact on the relationship between government, the public and corporations. The amount of information provided online is driving up the quality of counseling and advice demanded from lawyers.

Advice from the government law gurus

Nick Allard, former partner and chair of the lobbying, political and election law practice, **Patton Boggs**: *"Take legislation and regulatory courses, get involved in a political campaign, consider government service on the Hill or in an agency. And I think you need to be more of an extrovert and a people person, because you have to make connections with people in government."*

"I would encourage law students to consider a career in this area because it's interesting, worthwhile and you can make a difference. I love it all."

John Chierichella, partner, **Sheppard, Mullin, Richter & Hampton**:
"The only way to become a good government contracts lawyer is to do a lot of government contracts work – and the only way to do that is by going to a firm with a well-established practice group, which has a cadre of highly regarded lawyers and a vast number of widely recognized clients. That's where you're going to see a real breadth of issues and proceedings, and it's also where you're going to have the opportunity as a young lawyer to take a significant role in cases at an earlier point in time."

Tom McGovern, partner, **Hogan Lovells:**
"In representing Rutgers University in a dispute with the US Navy over a sonar invention, I had to learn all about piezoelectric polymers. On other cases, I've learned about helicopter flight controls and the efficacy of cancer medications. The federal government buys virtually everything, so if you have intellectual curiosity, this area presents a great opportunity to learn."

Healthcare

In a nutshell

"Our practice is more defined by who our clients are and the industry – as well as the substantive laws – than it is by the process of what we do," Jeffrey Schneider of Hogan Lovells tells us. Typically though, health law practitioners provide regulatory advice on the implementation of (new) legislation, and advise healthcare companies in transactions, commercial litigation and government investigations.

Healthcare is a massive part of the US economy. In October 2012 this was a sizable 18%, and by 2021 it is predicted to account for just under one-fifth of the country's economy. Many major firms have healthcare practices and there are many niche or boutique health firms, with many of them tied to specific states. Why is there a need for so many health lawyers? *"The main difference with other sectors of the economy is the unique and intensive regulatory environment,"* explains Doug Hastings, chair of Epstein Becker & Green and a member of its healthcare and life sciences practice.

It is also a practice that is *"constantly in flux because of the ever-changing laws,"* says Schneider. The passing of the Patient Protection and Affordable Care Act in March 2010 (aka Obamacare), for example, remains a landmark moment. One thing is for certain: the nationwide demand for healthcare advice and representation has never been greater.

Rankings in *Chambers USA*

Top ranked

Akin Gump	K&L Gates
Alston & Bird	King & Spalding
Duane Morris	Norton Rose Fulbright
Epstein	Proskauer
Hogan Lovells	Ropes & Gray
Jones Day	Waller

Highly recommended

Arnold & Porter	Latham
Cadwalader	McGuireWoods
Choate	Mintz Levin
Cozen O'Connor	Morgan Lewis
Crowell	Nixon Peabody
Foley & Lardner	Paul Hastings
Fox Rothschild	Pepper Hamilton
Gibbons	Reed Smith
Greenberg Traurig	Ropes & Gray
Haynes and Boone	Sheppard Mullin
Holland & Knight	Sidley Austin
Jackson Walker	Skadden
Katten Muchin	Thompson & Knight
King & Spalding	Venable

For more detail on ranking tiers and locations, visit www.chambersandpartners.com

What lawyers do

Healthcare: transactional

- Healthcare lawyers are sometimes brought in as troubleshooters at the same stage of a deal that tax and antitrust attorneys are brought in (see Corporate section). This is often the case for smaller BigLaw health practices and local healthcare boutiques.
- At other times healthcare lawyers will run a deal from soup to nuts. This happens when there are numerous health industry clients or statutes involved, so lawyers who understand the regulatory context of a deal need to be involved from the outset. This happens more often in larger BigLaw healthcare practices and boutiques, but is increasingly common given the complexity of new healthcare reforms.
- Healthcare transactional work involves putting a deal together and doing the due diligence as normal. According to Schneider, however, *"these are usually very complicated deals because of the regulatory constraints that exist, so you have to structure them in ways that you might not in other industries."*

Healthcare: litigation

- Litigation work – especially in relation to government investigations – is *"the high end of regulatory healthcare work for people who have been at it for a long time and are really good,"* Hastings says.
- Government-funded Medicare and Medicaid payments are a major source of litigation and government investigations. *"There is a whole set of rules on how you can get paid as a healthcare provider for Medicare and Medicaid services,"* explains Hastings. *"Anyone that provides healthcare – hospitals, physicians, hospices, home care providers – will have some Medicare patients. Not only are there questions surrounding the eligibility and amount of payment, but providers might face anything from a routine government audit to an investigation into healthcare fraud."*
- Healthcare and life sciences practices see a lot of qui

Practice Areas

tam litigation – cases in which someone who assists with a government prosecution can receive all or part of the penalty imposed.

Healthcare: advice

- Outside the times when healthcare lawyers are called in for litigation and transactions, they are constantly providing regulatory advice. Schneider says: *"It's about making sure clients comply with the vast array of regulations out there that limit a company's conduct, as well as helping clients think through problems and do things in the correct manner."*
- The advice covers more than just the regulatory side. *"There are nonregulatory issues to deal with as well, such as contractual issues with physicians and medical staff relationships,"* Dennis Barry of King & Spalding states.
- Among the key pieces of legislation governing Medicare fraud and abuse are the Anti-Kickback Statute and the Stark Law. The latter governs physicians' referral of patients to medical facilities in which that physician has a financial interest.
- Federal antitrust laws and Food & Drug Administration regulations also form an important component of health lawyers' work.

Healthcare: an overview by Waller

Since the enactment of Medicare in 1965 and through the ongoing implementation of the Affordable Care Act, service to the healthcare industry has been the cornerstone of Waller's legal practice. From a single physician-owned hospital in Nashville, Waller helped HCA Inc. grow into the world's largest investor-owned operator of healthcare facilities. We continue to represent investor-owned and not-for-profit hospitals and health systems throughout the United States, and over the past 50 years our healthcare practice has evolved with the industry itself. Today we also represent clients focused on outpatient healthcare services, post-acute care, behavioral health, life sciences and healthcare information technology. Our experience extends across virtually every segment of the healthcare industry.

For more than a decade Waller has been recognized among the nation's 10 largest healthcare law firms by Modern Healthcare, and we are top-ranked in the South for membership in the Health Law Section of the American Bar Association (ABA). We are recognized annually among the nation's largest healthcare law firms by American Health Lawyers Association (AHLA) for our continued commitment to the advancement of professional development in healthcare law. Additionally, our healthcare practice has earned a top ranking from Chambers USA. Waller attorneys are frequently quoted on healthcare topics in Modern Healthcare, The Wall Street Journal, The New York Times and myriad other industry publications. Our healthcare attorneys serve in key leadership positions in the AHLA and the ABA Health Law Section, and they are also highly sought-after speakers at healthcare industry and professional conferences held throughout the country. In addition, many leading healthcare companies and organizations are now led by former Waller attorneys who fill C-Suite, General Counsel, Compliance, Operational and other key roles across the healthcare industry.

Waller's multidisciplinary healthcare department comprises more than 100 attorneys across our four offices in Austin, Birmingham, Memphis and Nashville. Waller has earned a national reputation for our experience in high-profile healthcare transactions, having provided counsel in healthcare mergers, acquisitions, joint ventures and divestitures with a combined value of more than $14 billion since 2010. As Chambers USA noted: "Waller stands out for the quality of services in the corporate arena. Aimed at the middle market, the team operates on a national level." Our capabilities in corporate transaction are complemented by attorneys with specialized experience across the full spectrum of healthcare legal services, including:

- Regulatory compliance and operations
- Government investigations, False Claims Act matters and qui tam litigation
- Commercial finance and securities
- Real estate
- Environmental law
- Labor and employment
- Immigration
- IP
- Software licensing and IT outsourcing
- Data security and patient privacy

Healthcare Compliance and Government Enforcement Defense

For healthcare providers and investors, the counsel provided by Waller's Healthcare Compliance and Government Enforcement Defense team is now more critical than ever. Scrutiny from government enforcement agencies continues to escalate, and financial recoveries

Practice Areas

in the form of penalties and settlements from healthcare organizations remain at historic levels. In the wake of recent high profile cases, businesses and individuals in the healthcare industry increasingly find themselves the subject of government investigations and enforcement. Waller's expanding Healthcare Compliance and Government Enforcement Defense Team focuses on healthcare compliance, government enforcement, internal and external investigations, and white collar defense and includes attorneys with experience gained in-house, at other top-ranked law firms, and in various U.S. Attorneys' Offices.

This complex regulatory overlay creates the need for highly specialized attorneys who are experienced with the technical aspects of federal and state laws, rules and regulations. Equally critical is the need for attorneys who understand healthcare regulatory law as it applies to a wide range of facilities and service providers. The expansion of Waller's Healthcare Compliance and Government Enforcement Defense Team comes in response to the increased government enforcement actions brought against healthcare providers since the creation of the Health Care Fraud Prevention and Enforcement Action Team (HEAT) - a joint effort between the U.S. Department of Justice (DOJ) and Department of Health and Human Services (HHS). HHS and the Centers for Medicare & Medicaid Services (CMS) are increasingly focused on developing approaches to monitor, limit and remediate such payments, all of which makes compliance more complex for providers.

Healthcare Compliance

Healthcare organizations turn to Waller every day for assistance with navigating the federal and state regulations that impact both their day-to-day operations and their long-term objectives. Our goal is to provide peace of mind as we guide them through a virtual regulatory minefield. Their confidence is based on our more than 50 years of experience with healthcare regulatory law and the fact that many of the solutions to complex problems we have developed are now models used throughout the healthcare industry.

Healthcare organizations require assistance with navigating the federal and state regulations that impact both their day-to-day operations and their long-term objectives. To be successful, healthcare associates need to be both highly technical and detail oriented to align client objectives with the constantly changing regulatory environment. Healthcare compliance attorneys work closely with clients to understand their objectives and then develop creative approaches to achieve those goals. Typical areas in which healthcare compliance associates will be involved include:

- Medicare enrollment and reimbursement, Stark, state and federal anti-kickback compliance, along with the Emergency Medical Treatment and Active Labor Act, Joint Commission standards and numerous other regulations
- Structuring mergers, acquisitions and joint ventures to ensure compliance with federal and state regulations
- Innovative models for hospitals and physicians to work together, e.g., through clinical co-management agreements and foundation models, within Physician-Hospital Organizations and Accountable Care Organizations, and through joint venture arrangements
- State survey and certification issues, including Certificate of Need applications
- HIPAA patient privacy/security regulations, the electronic storage and transfer of medical records and electronic payment systems, security programs under the HITECH Act and security breaches
- Regulatory investigations, audits and appeals involving Medicare reimbursement, including Zone Program Integrity Contracts (ZPIC), Recovery Audit Contractors (RACs) and Medicare Administrative Contractors (MACs)

Government Enforcement and Defense

Healthcare businesses today face an environment in which regulatory issues can quickly turn into government investigations or enforcement actions. Waller's attorneys help clients navigate this dynamic environment to prevent otherwise simple regulatory issues from morphing into something far more damaging and costly. We understand what to expect and how to respond to a government investigation because many of our attorneys actually investigated allegations of fraud and abuse for the government. When faced with a government investigation or enforcement action, our attorneys help clients respond appropriately with strategies aimed at minimizing – or completely avoiding – penalties, negative publicity and disruptions to core business operations.

In fiscal year 2015, the United States Department of Justice obtained $1.9 billion in healthcare fraud settlements and judgments from False Claims Act cases for a total of $16.5 billion recovered in healthcare cases since January 2009. These settlements underscore both the federal government's continuing commitment to pursuing healthcare fraud and abuse cases and the increasingly important roles played by compliance attorneys and government enforcement defense attorneys. False Claims Act cases known as qui tam actions can also be filed by private citizen whistleblowers on behalf of the government. In actions in which the government prevails, the whistleblower is eligible to receive up to

30 percent of the amount recovered in the form of fines, penalties, and/or settlements. Until 1992, the majority of new healthcare-related matters opened each year were classified as non-qui tam matters by the DOJ. Since 1992, however, the percentage of qui tam actions has skyrocketed. In 2013, 500 new healthcare matters were classified as qui tam actions compared to a mere 15 non-qui tam matters. In the healthcare context, a significant percentage of False Claims Act enforcement actions center on alleged violations of the Stark Law or the Anti-kickback Statute.

Even for a healthcare organization with an effective compliance program and plan overseen by strong internal counsel and a compliance officer, there are still instances when it is necessary to involve outside counsel. Such instances include:

- Any contact, subpoena, or inquiry from a governmental entity such as the DOJ or the OIG
- Credible allegations of criminal conduct
- Senior management or board members directly involved in a complaint or investigation
- A nuanced analysis when the hospital or health system needs an outside written opinion
- An overtaxed or understaffed compliance department, which is unable to conduct a thorough internal investigation
- A matter when maintaining legal privilege is particularly important and where third parties may need to be hired for investigation or review purposes
- A potential settlement with a governmental agency or relator is being negotiated
- External validation of the compliance department's effectiveness is needed

Conclusion

The complex and constantly changing nature of federal and state healthcare regulations and the government's aggressive enforcement of False Claims Act cases have combined to create a high demand for healthcare compliance and enforcement defense attorneys. To be successful, these attorneys will need critical thinking skills and a commitment to mastering a highly specialized area of the law. For attorneys with the ability to navigate the technical regulatory interplay governing the healthcare industry, however, significant career opportunities are available in both private practice and in-house legal roles.

Intellectual Property

In a nutshell

There are four different types of intellectual property: patents, trademarks, copyright and trade secrets. Patents are issued by the US Patent & Trademark Office to the creators of new inventions or processes. They're practically a monopoly on the manufacture and sale of the patented invention, but they only last for 15 years. Trademarks can potentially last forever, but only protect the words, symbols or phrases used to distinguish the brand or identity of a good or service.

Somewhere in between is copyright, which protects works of authorship such as books, movies, music and plays. Copyright is a complicated system of restrictions on copying, performing and otherwise profiting from protected works, and lasts for the life of the author plus seventy years. Finally, trade secret law protects the holders of proprietary information from having their information stolen or disclosed to the public in certain circumstances. Think Coke's secret formula.

Companies big and small rely on IP to give them an edge over their competitors, and In 2010 IP-intensive industries directly or indirectly accounted for 40 million US jobs, or 27.7% of the workforce. Clients can include a tech startup looking to patent the latest gizmo to a film distributor trying to stop its content from being pirated. As well as being financially rewarding, IP law also offers some fascinating ethical questions, including;

- Do pharmaceutical patents give life-sciences companies an incentive to invest in creating life-saving drugs, or do they just keep their prices high?
- Should people named 'McDonald' be able to name their restaurants after themselves?
- And is your *Happy Potter* fanfiction copyright infringement, fair use, or just weird?

What IP lawyers do

- Engage in written correspondence to see if the alleged infringement can be resolved through a license and royalty agreement or other amicable resolution.
- If not resolved, attorneys representing the rights-holder file an infringement claim. Defense attorneys then respond with a counterclaim stating that either their client has not infringed or that the IP is invalid and unenforceable.
- Engage in discovery. Examine public records held in the USPTO that document the correspondence between the patent holder and the USPTO. Prepare interrogatories, requests for admission, and document requests seeking more information about the other side's positions. On average, discovery will take three years.
- Engage in the summary judgment motion phase. Engage in a Markman hearing, during which the judge interprets the language of the claims, ruling on any disagreements between parties on their interpretation. Markman hearings can take place any time before the case goes to the jury, but usually occur before trial.
- Go to trial, normally in front of a jury. This normally takes between four and ten days.
- Perform IP due diligence – review a third party's IP portfolio prior to your client entering into a transaction with them. Assess the strengths and weaknesses of the portfolio so that the client can understand the risks of doing business with the rights-holder.
- Draft commercial agreements between owners of IP rights and those who want to use the protected invention, design or artistic work. The most common agreements will either transfer ownership or grant a license.

Realities of the job

- In order to become a member of the patent Bar, you must pass an exam administered by the USPTO, which requires you to have completed a minimum number of technical or scientific courses in college or university. You don't actually need to be a member of the patent Bar to appear in federal district court on a patent case. Membership of the patent Bar is only necessary for attorneys who want to do patent prosecution work.
- Most patent attorneys have a scientific or technology background, either academic or work-related. That being said, it is possible for lawyers with non-scientific backgrounds to do patent litigation work. Non-scientists have to show some initiative, and a bit of hustle, in order to break in, but it's certainly doable. *"Go to a general practice firm that has a patent litigation practice, and volunteer,"* advises **Professor Tim Holbrook** of **Emory University**. *"Your first patent assignment won't be very patent law heavy, but if you do a good job, and make a good impression, you'll be invited back."*
- Good communication skills are a must, particularly in transactional IP and IP litigation. Lawyers need to be able to simplify and explain complex technical matters to lay judges, juries and clients.
- Patent owners can file claims in any district court they want; some districts are considered more patent-

Rankings in *Chambers USA*

Top ranked

Alston & Bird	Kilpatrick
Arnold & Porter	Kirkland
Baker Botts	McGuireWoods
Cooley	MoFo
Debevoise	Norton Rose Fulbright
Finnegan	Perkins Coie
Fish & Richardson	Pillsbury
Foley & Lardner	Sidley Austin
Goodwin Procter	Sterne Kessler
Hunton	WilmerHale
Irell	Winston
Jones Day	

Highly recommended

Akin Gump	Marshall Gerstein
Baker & McKenzie	Mayer Brown
Bracewell	Milbank
Choate	Morgan Lewis
Cravath	O'Melveny
Crowell	Orrick
Dechert	Patterson Belknap
Duane Morris	Paul Hastings
Fenwick & West	Paul, Weiss
Fitzpatrick	Pepper Hamilton
Gibbons	Proskauer
Gibson Dunn	Reed Smith
Greenberg Traurig	Ropes & Gray
Haynes and Boone	Skadden
Hogan Lovells	Thompson & Knight
Jenner & Block	Venable
K&L Gates	Vinson
Katten Muchin	Weil
Kaye Scholer	White & Case
King & Spalding	Wiley Rein
Latham	
Lowenstein	

For more detail on ranking tiers and locations, visit www.chambersandpartners.com

friendly and are therefore more popular than others. The most notable of these is the Eastern District of Texas, based in Marshall, TX (population 24,000). Critics say its unorthodox rules and conservative jury pool favor patent-owners, while its supporters cite the court's efficiency.

- Every patent infringement appeal is filed with the US Court of Appeals for the Federal Circuit. If parties don't like the result there, the only option is to file a petition for certiorari with the Supreme Court, which has taken more patent cases in the last decade.
- Patent cases bring great risk to Fortune 500 companies, which can incur enormous damages dating back up to six years from the filing of the complaint. This explains the rise of non-practicing entities or patent trolls, which buy up portfolios of patents and make their money threatening to sue other businesses for patent infringement. Faced with such stiff penalties, and without the resources to fight the case in court, smaller companies and inventors pay the patent trolls hefty license fees.
- Different types of IP work means differing workloads, explains Professor Tim Holbrook. *"Patent prosecutors tend to work more independently, as it's often just you and the PTO,"* he explains. *"Patent litigation often goes on for years, and requires long term thinking,"* he adds, *"while trademark litigation is all about speed. Cases are decided off a preliminary injunction, so if something's happening, it's happening now."*
- An IP portfolio can be the most valuable of a business's assets, particularly in the pharmaceutical sector. This means that IP lawyers need to form part of the deal team from an early stage.

Current Issues

- Copyright protects the rights of creatives, but for copyright lawyers there's no escaping the reach of technology. This is because copyright infringers are often very technologically sophisticated and often based abroad, according to **George P Wukoson** of **Davis Wight Tremaine**. In addition to *"keeping up to date with new technologies"* copyright litigators need to think around corners and *"craft equally robust enforcement measures."*
- The patent world continues to assess the effects of the America Invents Act, and in particular its inter-partes review proceedings. This allows anyone to challenge the validity of patents, and was designed to thwart non-practicing entities, or patent trolls. Inter-partes review has given the tech sector some relief, but has itself been abused by so-called reverse patent trolls; hedge funds which challenge strategic patents, causing the patent holder's share price to drop. They then make a profit shorting the rights-holder's stock.
- The America Invents Act fundamentally altered the position in US patent law from a 'first to invent' system to a 'first to file'. This brings the United States in line with most other countries and means that the first party to file an application will hold the patent over the technology.
- Although they've calmed down a little from their 2012 heyday, the Apple-Samsung patent wars will continue to keep lawyers (and the 9th Circuit's Judge Lucy Koh) busy for some time to come. Her honor can look forward for a fourth retrial (on the subject of damages, natch) in March or April 2016.
- Another issue that continues to vex the patent world is patentable subject matter or, in English, what can you patent? Back in the eighties, the Supreme Court held

that *"anything under the sun that is made by man,"* could be patented. Since 2012, however, the circumstances under which business methods and software can be considered elligible for patents have been fiercely rightened yet largely unspecified following the Supreme Court's ruling in Alice Corpo v CLS Bank.

- Between 1946 and 2015 a law called the Lantham Act prevented the federal registration of disparaging trademarks. Over the years, this has allowed the government to cancel or refuse to register a number of potentially inflammatory trademarks, including the Washington Redskins. Note that this does not prevent the trademark holder from using or enforcing their trademarks. It merely denies them a range of additional benefits, including the right to sue in federal court.
- Even so, in December 2015 the Federal Circuit ruled that this provision violated the First Amendment. This contradicted an earlier 2015 decision of the Fourth circuit. With the circuits split, pundits are taking bets on whether this rule will last the year. And that's not all folks. The Federal Circuit has also speculated that the provisions of the Lantham Act allowing the refusal of scandalous or immoral trademarks may also be unconstitutional.
- Trade secrets are traditionally the province of state law, but this may all change if the Defend Trade Secrets Act of 2016, currently in the Senate Judiciary Committee, is adopted into law. If enacted, the bill would create a federal cause of action where someone steals a trade secret related to a product or service intended for use in interstate or foreign commerce. There is some debate on whether this is even necessary; all states already protect trade secrets under federal law, and the vast majority have based their laws on the Uniform Trade Secrets Act, which means that trade secrets laws are already fairly harmonized across the USA.

International Arbitration

"At the most basic level, international arbitration attorneys are international litigators in a transnational justice system." – Donald Donovan, Debevoise.

In a nutshell

International arbitration addresses any case or potential dispute between parties – usually located in two different countries – and is the most common form of alternative dispute resolution (ADR). *"At the most basic level, international arbitration attorneys are international litigators in a transnational justice system,"* says **Donald Donovan** of **Debevoise & Plimpton.** *"It's a system that's validated by both national and international law, but not run directly by any given state."*

Arbitrations often arise from clauses included by companies in their commercial contracts with one another. This means that, if a dispute arises between them, they are obliged to arbitrate their dispute rather than pursue traditional litigation. Arbitration provides a binding solution to the dispute by way of an arbitral 'award'. The award can be enforced internationally through the provisions of the 1958 New York Convention on the Recognition and Enforcement of Arbitral Awards, which more than 140 states have ratified. *"Private parties often prefer international arbitration because it provides a neutral and relatively confidential forum, specialist arbitrators and greater ease of enforcement of the award in multiple jurisdictions. The New York Convention is unique in that there is no equivalent international treaty in force around the globe to ensure the international currency and enforcement of domestic court judgments,"* explains **David Lindsey**, partner and cofounder of international arbitration boutique **Chaffetz Lindsey** in New York.

The types of cases heard in international arbitration are typically cross-border commercial disputes that occur in situations like joint ventures or corporate transactions (including M&A). *"The types of disputes run the gamut, but they are all really linked to investment and transactions outside the home jurisdiction of the claimant,"* **Nigel Blackaby** of **Freshfields Bruckhaus Deringer** says. Disputes commonly originate in the oil and gas, telecom, privatized public utilities and construction industries.

One specific type of international arbitration is 'investment arbitration', where a claim is brought by a foreign investor directly against the host state of its investment. This arises from the likes of multinational ventures, such as energy projects, and can be instigated in two ways: investors and host states either consent in contracts to use international arbitration to resolve disputes, or investors make claims under bilateral (or multilateral) investment treaties (BITs). BigLaw firms – as well as specialist boutique firms in some instances – represent both claimants and defendants in such cases, though they must be careful about conflicts.

The disputes are often considered under a foreign applicable law and resolved under the arbitration rules of the International Chamber of Commerce (**ICC**), the International Centre for Dispute Resolution of the American Arbitration Association (**ICDR**), the London Court of International Arbitration (**LCIA**), The World Bank's International Centre for Settlement of Investment Disputes (**ICSID**), or the United Nations Commission on International Trade Law (**UNCITRAL**). The nature of the dispute largely determines the relevance of each set of rules. Investor-state disputes, for example, are usually arbitrated under UNCITRAL or ICSID, while the LCIA and ICC rules are suitable for virtually all types of arbitration – though the latter is more appropriate for commercial disputes.

What lawyers do

- Receive instructions from the client, who thinks, for example, that their contract has been breached or that their rights under an applicable investment treaty have been infringed.
- Review the contract or treaty, solicit and review relevant documentation and speak to potential witnesses.
- Provide the client with a memo on the merits of the case. This may involve working with local counsel in the relevant jurisdiction.
- If a client wants to proceed, draft the necessary ini-

Practice Areas

tiation papers – usually a 'Request for Arbitration' in accordance with the applicable arbitration rules, such as ICDR, ICC or ICSID – and submit to the relevant arbitral institution.

- The case is then registered and the request is communicated to the respondent, usually by the arbitral institution. The respondent answers, possibly with an objection to the jurisdiction and with a response to the case's merits. They name an arbitrator.
- In order to establish the tribunal, each party proposes an impartial and independent 'party-nominated' arbitrator. The party-nominated arbitrators then usually seek to agree on a 'president' or 'chair' of the tribunal, failing which, the president/chair will be nominated by the institution. Once constituted, the tribunal will invite parties to the first procedural hearing at the (usually neutral) seat of hearing (often jurisdictions with favorable arbitration laws and culture such as New York, London, Paris, Geneva and Singapore), where the calendar and procedural order for the next steps will be established.
- In commercial arbitration, there is a period for exchanging documentary evidence, during which each side will produce the documents upon which it intends to rely. This does not typically include 'US-style' discovery, but a far more limited disclosure process.
- The next steps usually include a very detailed presentation of the facts and evidence by the claimant (including written witness/expert statements and all relevant documentation). This is called a 'Memorial'– it may also be included in a pre-hearing brief shortly before the hearing on the merits.
- Defense attorneys submit a 'Defense Memorial' or response brief with a similar presentation.
- There will often be a further round of 'Reply' and 'Rejoinder' memorials or briefs.
- Final hearing takes place, where witnesses are questioned and cross-examined before the tribunal, and oral argument is made. The written witness statements filed with the Memorials often take the place of direct testimony at the hearing.
- Submit final, post-hearing briefs. In complex cases, these can be lengthy.
- Tribunal determines award, which must be 'reasoned' (ie, the tribunal's reasoning for the award must be set out), in writing, and signed by the members of the tribunal. With a three-person tribunal, a majority determines the award.

Realities of the job

- *"The international context is fascinating because, regardless of whether it's a commercial or investor-state arbitration, you're always experiencing different cultures, countries, languages and personalities. It really is such a wonderful dynamic and mix,"* says **Carolyn Lamm** of **White & Case**.
- *"You can assist yourself greatly by having a real command of more than one language,"* Donovan explains. *"English is of course important, but having a command of other languages as well really helps."* Spanish, Chinese and Russian are three languages in demand. Portuguese is also increasingly valuable for international arbitrators, in conjunction with the growth of the Brazilian market in particular.
- *"International arbitration isn't entirely different from courtroom advocacy,"* according to Lamm. Compared to US litigation, however, international arbitration typically relies more on written, instead of oral, advocacy and on contemporaneous documents, rather than on witness testimony from parties. In final hearings, for example, written witness statements often take the place of oral direct testimony.
- Much like litigation, international arbitration requires great discipline and a thorough understanding of large quantities of documents, some of which can be technical and need to be structured into databases.
- The job involves a lot of travel to identify relevant documents and interview witnesses. Depending on the circumstances, associates may also travel.
- It's important for international arbitration lawyers to build up their knowledge of economic and financial issues, as these form an important component of the work.
- *"Currently there is no overarching set of rules to account for all the various national backgrounds that lawyers in an international proceeding come from, so if you have lawyers from different legal systems they may not be conducting themselves in the same way,"* Lamm tells us. Despite this, the differences between European, US and Asian practices, and between civil law and common law, are not as great as they once

Rankings in *Chambers USA*

Top ranked

Debevoise
White & Case

Highly recommended

Arnold & Porter	King & Spalding
Baker & McKenzie	Norton Rose Fulbright
Baker Botts	Shearman & Sterling
Chadbourne	Sidley Austin
Cleary	Simpson
Curtis	Skadden
Freshfields	Sullivan
Hogan Lovells	Weil
Hughes Hubbard	WilmerHale
Jenner	

For more detail on ranking tiers and locations, visit www.chambersandpartners.com

Practice Areas

were. Some say a more universal practice is developing; the International Bar Association's now widely used evidence rules are an example of this.

- In commercial arbitration, demands for documents from the other side are allowed, but not as much as in the discovery phases of US litigation. Depositions are rarely allowed, unless US parties are involved and the arbitration clause itself calls for them. (See the aforementioned IBA evidence rules for a good summary.)
- International arbitration has provided an effective platform for female practitioners to excel, which is demonstrated by organizations such as ArbitralWomen.
- David Lindsey says: *"Participants in the international arbitration Bar share a mutual respect and camaraderie that I have not witnessed in other areas of legal practice."*
- International arbitration is generally a difficult profession to enter, and so it's typical for juniors to develop their skills as trial lawyers first. *"The bottom line is you must learn advocacy – how to present on your feet with care, thoroughness and confidence. You also need to know whether you love to do that, because some people just don't excel in that kind of situation,"* Lamm informs us.

Current issues

- New York, London, Paris and Geneva have traditionally been favored as the arbitrators, venue of choice, but Hong Kong and Singapore are quickly becoming popular alternatives. Don't expect newcomers to displace old favorites, commentators reckon the growth of Asian venues is thanks to a wider increase in international arbitration and a desire to emulate successful models found in the Europe and the USA.
- Arbitral decisions have been being increasingly challenged over the last ten years; while most of these failed to overturn initial rulings, the last five years have seen a few succeed.
- **Jenner & Block's Anton Valukas** tells us: *"Arbitration has become as complex as civil litigation. It's not unusual for arbitrations to involve extensive discovery, motion practice and protracted resolutions. As a result, arbitration may not continue to be the alternative choice for resolving matters."*
- Reacting to complaints that arbitration has become increasingly costly and slow, at the start of 2016 the International Chamber of Commerce (ICC) announced new time scale expectations for the submission of awards to try and combat the problem.
- Class arbitrations have been around in the USA for some time but thanks to some companies prohibiting customers from pursuing class arbitrations these actions are on the decline. Outside the USA it's a different story; although still infrequent, class arbitrations are increasingly springing up and commentators expect this to continue in the coming years.
- Alternative funding, such as third-party funding, will continue to finance arbitrations. Third-party financing sees external investors stump up the cash for companies to pursue arbitrations, on condition the investors pocket a proportion of any settlement awarded. Despite some hostility to arrangements in certain areas, some jurisdictions are warming up to the method; Hong Kong is set to review its restrictions on third-party funding.
- The number of investor-state disputes has increased considerably in recent years, with energy, oil, gas and mining companies leading the charge. As governments begin imposing limitations and conditions on investors' abilities to take on foreign governments, this incline in cases could soon start leveling off.
- The world's largest arbitral settlement was awarded in 2014 to the shareholders of Yukos Oil after it emerged that Russia had attempted to transfer Yukos' assets to a state-owned company after falsely accusing and prosecuting Yukos over alleged tax evasion. Russia's currently disputing the award and refusing to pay out, so the next year will test just how well arbitral awards can be enforced. Keep an eye on the dispute between ConocoPhillips and Venezuela over the illegal expropriation of oil investments to watch how another sovereign state attempts to push back against arbitral decision: Venezuela is currently trying to get the ruling overturned.

"Arbitration has become as complex as civil litigation. It's not unusual for arbitrations to involve extensive discovery, motion practice and protracted resolutions. As a result, arbitration may not continue to be the alternative choice for resolving matters."

International Arbitration: an overview by Freshfields Bruckhaus Deringer

What is international arbitration and what do arbitration lawyers do?
International arbitration concerns the resolution of disputes involving parties from different countries that have agreed to resolve their differences before international arbitral tribunals instead of domestic courts. International arbitration can be divided between two main categories: (i) investment arbitration, which concerns the resolution of disputes between states and foreign investors arising under instruments providing for the protection of the latter's investments (eg investment treaties or investment legislation); and (ii) commercial arbitration, which concerns the resolution of disputes between individuals or companies arising out of contracts.

Aside from representing parties in all stages of arbitration, lawyers practicing in this area may also work on litigation relating to arbitrations – including with respect to the enforcement of arbitral awards – and in alternative methods of dispute resolution. Moreover, arbitration lawyers typically provide advisory services to clients, especially with respect to the merits of potential claims and the drafting of sophisticated arbitration and dispute resolution clauses.

The life of a junior associate in international arbitration
Junior associates practicing international arbitration get heavily involved in cases from the outset of their careers. The tasks that a junior associate will be asked to do include:

- assisting with the drafting of memoranda of advice;
- legal research and writing internal memoranda;
- preparing for and attending interviews/meetings with fact and expert witnesses;
- reviewing documents and developing the factual narrative of a case;
- drafting sections of briefs and witness statements;
- coordinating the logistics surrounding the filing of submissions before the tribunal; and
- assisting with the preparation of oral advocacy (eg opening and closing statements, examination of witnesses) and attending hearings.

Given the international nature of these disputes, associates are expected to be willing to travel frequently in order to meet the demands of the cases.

How international is international arbitration?
As the name suggests, this practice is truly international in nature. Aside from involving parties from two (or, in multiparty arbitrations, more) jurisdictions, these disputes typically:

- involve the application of laws from different jurisdictions (including, in investment arbitration, the application of public international law);
- are before arbitrators from different countries and legal backgrounds;
- require the participation of fact and expert witnesses who are often located around the world;
- involve multiple languages; and
- are interrelated with, and require knowledge of, geopolitical developments.

A single case may therefore require work to be performed in many countries and across several continents. To give an illustration, a recent case in which Freshfields was involved concerned a power plant in Eastern Africa. The dispute was between Eastern African and Asian companies. The case required the application of Canadian law and the law of an Eastern African country. Fact and expert witnesses were scattered across Canada, Cuba, the United States of America, the United Kingdom, Ghana, Ethiopia, Korea, China and Madagascar. The tribunal was comprised of arbitrators from the United States of America, the United Kingdom and New Zealand.

The growth of international arbitration
The vast majority of arbitrations – especially commercial disputes – are confidential and are therefore not in the public domain. The most reliable statistics regarding the growth of international arbitration are those published by the institutions that administer the cases. The growing caseload of the world's largest arbitration institutions is a testament to the growth of the practice of international arbitration.

Commercial arbitration has for many years been the dispute resolution method of choice for contracting parties from different jurisdictions. Among the benefits is the neutrality of the forum and the international enforceability of arbitral awards. Cases have steadily increased over the last decade. For example, the International Chamber of Commerce – one of the largest arbitration institutions in the world – increased its number of newly registered cases from just over 500 cases in 2005 to over 800 cases in 2015.

As for investment arbitration, while many cases are confidential, there is significantly more publicly-available information as compared to commercial disputes. The International Centre for Settlement of Investment Disputes (**ICSID**) is the leading institution for the administration of investment disputes. In 2015, it registered more cases than in any previous year and more cases than had been registered throughout the 1990s.

The proliferation of investment arbitration is the product of several overlapping developments. Globalization has removed trade barriers leading to increased foreign direct investment and, with that, an increase in the number of disputes arising out of such investments. Also, the proliferation of international treaties providing for investment protections and investor-state dispute settlement (such as the recently signed Trans-Pacific Partnership) means that more investors find that they have rights and remedies in the face of Government measures adversely affecting their investments. Finally, many states that were historically considered as capital-importing states are now also capital-exporting states, which has increased the pool of foreign investors seeking to make use of those rights and remedies. All of this points to the continued growth of investment arbitration.

About Freshfields' arbitration practice

Freshfields is widely recognized as one of the world's leading practices in this area. The team is consistently ranked in the top tier of every major legal directory, across all regions. We have the world's premier investment arbitration practice, and are involved in advisory and contentious matters arising under bilateral and multilateral treaties all over the world.

The group is currently managing a caseload of some 200 matters that span the globe and are being conducted in eight different languages. Aside from the volume of its cases, the firm routinely works on the largest, groundbreaking and most complex arbitrations in the market. Our lawyers have acted as counsel in a large array of industrial sectors in some of the most significant investment treaty arbitrations, many of which have contributed to shaping the legal landscape of investment treaty law. The team has achieved great successes for its clients, including, most recently, securing one of the largest awards ever rendered in an ICSID arbitration.

FRESHFIELDS BRUCKHAUS DERINGER

Practice Areas

International Trade

In a nutshell

The work of international trade lawyers is split between two main areas: the application of domestic law to international trade, and treaty-based international law governing trade flows. On the domestic side, work covers export controls, embargoes and economic sanctions, import relief actions such as antidumping, countervailing duties and safeguards, and customs classifications, valuation and rules of origin matters. In relation to international treaties, attorneys advise on World Trade Organization (WTO) rules, preferential trade regimes such as the North American Free Trade Agreement (NAFTA) and bilateral investment treaties (BITs).

Lawyers advise on the implementation of these domestic and international rules, and counsel clients in disputes related to their violation. Clients include US organizations doing business in foreign jurisdictions and foreign businesses operating in the USA; they include major corporations, trade associations and national and regional governments.

What lawyers do

Domestic

- Lawyers represent clients before the International Trade Commission (ITC) and the Department of Commerce (DOC), the two main bodies that review petitions related to import laws. They are the first port of call for disputes and protests related to issues such as dumping, countervailing duties and safeguards.
- The first port of call for protests over customs classifications, valuation and rules of origin matters is US Customs and Border Protection (CBP).
- Lawyers assist US companies to secure a license from the DOC for the export of 'dual use' goods (with both military and commercial applications), or from the Department of State for the shipment of military goods.
- They also assist clients before the Treasury Department's Office of Foreign Assets Control (OFAC), which administers and enforces economic and trade sanctions against targeted foreign countries, terrorism-sponsoring organizations and international narcotics traffickers.
- Parties can protest determinations made by the ITC, DOC and CBP at the Court of International Trade. This court also hears protests against trade-related worker assistance decisions made by the Departments of Labor and Agriculture.
- Antidumping duties are imposed on imports to combat 'dumping'– selling a product in an export market at a price less than its home market value, which injures a domestic industry.
- Countervailing duties are similar to antidumping duties, but are imposed by a country to counter the effects of subsidies in foreign markets.
- Safeguards are 'emergency' measures in response to an unforeseen increase in imports which damages or threatens to damage a specific domestic industry. Unlike 'unfair' activities like subsidies and dumping, increased shipments by themselves are not deemed to be unfair, so safeguards must be applied in a nondiscriminatory fashion.
- Section 337 of the Tariff Act of 1930 provides an alternative to US court actions to challenge imports that infringe patents or other intellectual property rights. These cases are dealt with by administrative law judges in the ITC.
- Lawyers also assist companies involved in an acquisition of a US target under review by the Committee on Foreign Investment in the United States (CFIUS). Established in 1975, CFIUS (pronounced 'sifius') is tasked with reviewing the national security implications of investment in US assets.

International

- On the treaty side, trade lawyers practice *"global regulatory law,"* according to **Andy Shoyer**, partner and chair of **Sidley Austin**'s international trade and dispute resolution practice.
- Disputes are the largest source of work. The WTO is the main international arbitrator of trade disputes. Its Dispute Settlement Body makes rulings on agreements made between member states under WTO negotiations. Only sovereign states can bring disputes to the WTO so lawyers for private stakeholders will be involved in lobbying governments to bring cases or in assisting to defend them.
- Neither the US government nor the EU hires outside counsel to represent them in front of the WTO, so US attorneys often find themselves representing other nations, such as Brazil. Disputes relating to BITs are heard in arbitral tribunals administered by the International Centre for Settlement of Investment Disputes (ICSID), an arm of The World Bank, or similar arbitration centers.
- Treaty-focused attorneys will also engage in lobbying to influence the development of new international rules. *"We listen to what companies tell us about the*

Practice Areas

regulatory barriers they face and translate that into potential treaty language. Then we will help businesses affect the negotiations within the USA and internationally," Andy Shoyer explains.

Realities of the job

- **F Joseph Warin**, partner and chair of the Washington, DC litigation department at **Gibson Dunn**, advises: *"Adventurousness and a willingness to take risks are necessary in this practice. If you're dealing with, for instance, stock options in Norway, you need a sense of intellectual curiosity to understand and process all this and then give advice that's nuanced to the environment. Cultural sensitivity is a must. Being a good listener is imperative. I urge young associates to be keen listeners and not to leapfrog that step because it's absolutely essential in order to give good solid advice."*
- International trade work is often closely tied to headline-making current events, and associates grapple with key policy as well as legal issues. As **Beth Peters**, co-director of **Hogan Lovells**' International Trade and Investment group, explains: *"This practice appeals to students who both have an interest in international relations as well as a separate passion for litigation or regulatory work; it can attract many kinds of lawyers."*
- One associate who works in an international trade department told us: *"I had focused on international studies throughout college and demonstrated an interest in international trade."* Peters comments that *"working for a US government agency or international organization in the international trade area can provide very useful perspective. It will give a student some insight as to whether they would be interested in this area."*
- *"Unlike domestic litigation we don't have substantial document production and discovery work in WTO or other treaty disputes,"* Shoyer informs us. *"That saves junior associates from some of the drudge work. But that doesn't mean that lawyers don't have to get on top of the facts! Arbitrations can involve hundreds of pages of documents and younger associates will get involved in that."*
- *"International trade practices with a significant policy focus tend to be partner-heavy because clients demand high-profile advice,"* Shoyer explains. *"It's hard to generate the knowledge base required just by reading the case law: you need to have the experience. You build up your knowledge base slower."*
- Trade lawyers need to be politically aware and keep track of negotiations at the WTO and other multilateral, regional and bilateral regimes. **Joe Dorn**, former partner at **King & Spalding** says: *"Many WTO cases are very intellectually challenging. You're often covering new ground, so that's very stimulating."*
- Andy Shoyer tells us: *"The greatest challenge and joy in this area is that you are really practicing the law of globalization. You're at the forefront of those business and policy forces that drive the world. Anyone in this practice needs to appreciate that the nexus of law and policy is very important."*
- Shoyer adds: *"While the ability to work comfortably in several languages is so helpful, a fluency with culture is vital. You need to be comfortable putting yourself in the shoes of someone from another culture. Creativity and openness is a must, perhaps more so than in any other area of the law because it's still emerging."*
- F Joseph Warin says: *"I'm constantly globe-trotting. I'll go to London, then Abu Dhabi, then two weeks later I'll be in New Delhi. It's fascinating but it also keeps me away from my family, so this big plus is also the biggest negative."*

Current issues

- The nature of international trade means that it is important for lawyers to be aware of ongoing diplomatic and political developments across the globe.
- International trade laws increasingly intersect other regulatory frameworks and cut across multiple borders, which makes compliance challenging. Beth Peters informs us that *"typically regulations within the US, EU, UK and other regions may be triggered simultaneously when trade issues arise, whether that's in international trade litigation or in international trade compliance matters. Some examples are export controls, sanctions, anti-money laundering, cybersecurity and securities reporting regulations."*
- Lawyers in this practice have to be acutely aware of the sanctions imposed on foreign nations. *"In the last year governments have continued the use of 'smart sanctions' – those that are targeted to particular industries and transactions,"* Peters reports. *"They have been implemented in particular with respect to Russia and Ukraine, as well as in Latin America, where they relate to narcotics traffickers and other designated nationals."*
- In addition, US sanctions on North Korea have been strengthened and expanded recently. In February 2016, President Obama signed into law the North Korea Sanctions and Policy Enhancement Act in response to Pyongyang's recent ballistic missile activities.
- From an export perspective, **Matthew Nicely**, a partner in **Hughes Hubbard & Reed**'s International Trade and Customs practice group, explains that *"the opening up of Myanmar and its re-entry into the world economy will be important. Many companies are interested in changing the way they go about doing business in the country now that USA and other countries' trade and investment restrictions are being lifted."*
- In February 2016, the Trans-Pacific Partnership (TPP)

Practice Areas

trade deal was signed by the United States and 11 other Asia-Pacific countries: Australia, Brunei Darussalam, Canada, Chile, Japan, Malaysia, Mexico, New Zealand, Peru, Singapore and Vietnam. TPP writes the rules for global trade among members, seeking to promote trade and strengthen relationships between the nations.

- The upcoming election has seen *"some interesting dialogue"* with respect to TPP and a range of other multilateral and regional agreements, according to Beth Peters.
- President Obama's trip to Cuba in March 2016 marks the most recent development in US-Cuba diplomatic relations; commercial air travel was also restored in February 2016. Peters notes that *"dialogue with respect to Cuba will continue to come up in this election."*
- The potential for Britain's exit from the EU – the so-called Brexit – would completely change the legal basis of Britain's trade links with the world. *"This is an area that requires complex study,"* Peters tells us, as *"the USA and Britain have a very close trade and national security relationship."*
- Matthew Nicely stressed that *"there's always a lot of focus on the origin of goods imported into the United States. This is true with all products, but particularly those that have been subjected to antidumping or countervailing duty cases, which inevitably lead to allegations of transhipment."* In the recent past the most frequent target of antidumping and countervailing duty cases was China, but recent cases include *"multiple other countries, including Korea, Japan and Turkey, and others, particularly as the US steel industry has resumed its heavy use of this kind of import relief."*
- Increasingly, both US and foreign clients are becoming more aware that nations outside the USA also have complicated and important trade laws. Peters highlights that *"we've certainly experienced clients addressing trade issues in Singapore, Brazil and India,"* in particular.

Rankings in *Chambers USA*

Top ranked

Fish & Richardson	Skadden
Hogan Lovells	White & Case
Sidley Austin	

Highly recommended

Akin Gump	Kirkland & Ellis
Alston & Bird	Latham & Watkins
Arnold & Porter	Mayer Brown LLP
Baker & McKenzie	MoFo
Crowell & Moring	O'Melveny
Curtis	Pillsbury
Davis Polk	Stroock
Finnegan	Vinson
Gibson Dunn	Wiley Rein
Hughes Hubbard	WilmerHale
King & Spalding	Winston & Strawn

For more detail on ranking tiers and locations, visit www.chambersandpartners.com

Practice Areas

Labor & Employment

In a nutshell

Labor and employment law governs the workplace and the relationships between employers and employees; managers and unions; and employers and the government. BigLaw firms tend to represent employers.

Employment work involves both litigation and counseling. The former tackles claims of discrimination, including age, disability, national origin, race, religion, whistle-blower/retaliation, sex and sexual harassment. Such claims are brought by individuals or administrative agencies like the US Equal Employment Opportunity Commission (EEOC). Other common disputes concern unpaid overtime ('wage and hour' claims) under the Fair Labor Standards Act (FLSA), and claims relating to the Family and Medical Leave Act (FMLA), both of which may be filed with the US Department of Labor (DOL).

Lawyers who offer employment counseling advise on compliance with various employment laws. This involves advising on clients' wholesale employment policies and practices, as well as on 'difficult situations', be they sexual harassment complaints or reductions in force. They will often advise on the employment aspects of business transactions like M&A or restructurings. Attorneys will either provide both litigation and counseling advice, or specialize in one discipline.

BigLaw labor lawyers commonly advise management on union matters governed by the National Labor Relations Act (NLRA), which is administered by the National Labor Relations Board (NLRB). They have expertise in collective bargaining, union and strike avoidance, and strike breaking. They will also advise on Occupational Safety and Health Act (OSHA) matters, which the DOL (via the Occupational Safety and Health Administration) enforces. Labor attorneys may also engage in litigation of NLRA and OSHA disputes.

Employee Benefits, Executive Compensation & ERISA

Many firms have a distinct practice focused on executive compensation, employee benefits and ERISA work. For the uninitiated, ERISA is the Employee Retirement Income Security Act of 1974 – the federal statutory framework that governs the administration of employee benefit plans and the rights of the beneficiaries. **Kyoko Takahashi Lin**, a partner at **Davis Polk**, tells us: *"The work we do is really about people: how do you motivate them? How do you get them to be incentivized and work hard and do the right thing and treat employees well? That is what we are trying to advise companies on."* There is much, much more to this specialization, however.

What lawyers do

Employment litigation

- Receive notice of a charge or complaint filed with the EEOC or DOL, respectively.
- Advise clients on how to respond to the EEOC, DOL or other government investigations.
- Negotiate with the agencies, work with them in investigations, and try to come to settlement in appropriate cases.
- If a class action, oppose class certification.
- If no settlement can be reached, begin discovery – paper and electronic. Settlement can occur at any stage of a case.
- Provided the case is not settled, standard litigation will commence.

Employment counseling

- Review and draft employment contracts and policy documents.
- Advise client on the steps to take when problems arise.
- Keep client abreast of new changes to laws and regulations, often by way of newsletters or seminars.
- Advise on the employment implications of business transactions. Focus on minimizing risk for the client, by instilling a proactive and preventive approach.

Labor relations

- Act as a liaison between management and unions.
- Lead negotiations between the different sides.
- Litigate cases before the NLRB and in federal courts.

Realities of the job

- Only a small percentage of cases filed in the courts are putative class actions. Most are wage and hour or discrimination cases.
- Cases are heard in state and federal courts, as well as before administrative and regulatory boards.
- Many labor and employment laws will sound familiar: Americans with Disabilities Act, Civil Rights Act of 1964, Equal Pay Act, Age Discrimination in Employment Act and National Labor Relations Act.
- Most charges are found to have 'no reasonable cause'

and many others will be settled before litigation.

- The EEOC and NLRB are separate administrative agencies and are not part of the DOL. The best labor lawyers will have good people skills, because they will be interacting with both management and unions. The most successful ones will be able to convince both management and unions that they have common goals.
- According to **Thomas Linthorst**, a partner in **Morgan Lewis & Bockius**' labor & employment practice: *"Those that really can get close to their clients, understand what the client needs, and can think creatively about meeting the client's needs will find that to be a successful approach."*
- When the economy is down, clients are concerned about surviving, which often involves downsizing. Advising on reductions in force is never pleasant.
- **Alison Marshall** of **Jones Day** says: *"I do think that we move more quickly in comparison to some of the big commercial litigation cases. Also, our cases are not always as big, so associates often get more responsibility. That is a plus, but juniors need to be prepared to take on that responsibility."*
- Sometimes the intensity of the workload is high, especially when lawyers are gearing up for a big trial. Being responsive is critical.
- Often lawyers will be dealing with a non-lawyer – a HR professional for example – so they need to be able to translate complex legal principles into clear concepts for them. It's critical to be able to write well, with a view toward addressing practical problems, and not overwhelming the client. This is also true when it comes to explaining elements of a case or situation to the judiciary.
- **Bettina Plevan**, partner at **Proskauer Rose**, says: *"Sometimes clients have pressing emergencies, and you have to be responsive immediately."*
- **Joseph Costello**, partner at **Morgan Lewis**, warns: *"This is an area of law that requires flexibility and adaptability. Every day there's a new challenge, and the issues are not always predictable: an employee may have a disability that needs to be accommodated; there might be a union-organizing drive; or maybe an employee has complained about a posting on a social media website, which another employee has published. Any of these situations could trigger a call to us."*
- **Stephen Poor**, chairman of **Seyfarth Shaw** informs us that in this field, *"there is still that focus on the real world, which can be messier and stickier than the relatively sterile laboratory of the justice system. In other words, success in this field requires a practical bent and a propensity to solve problems rather than win arguments."*

Rankings in *Chambers USA*

Top ranked

Alston & Bird	Morgan Lewis
Baker & McKenzie	Nixon Peabody
Cleary	Paul Hastings
Davis Polk	Perkins Coie
Gibson Dunn	Proskauer
Goodwin Procter	Ropes & Gray
Greenberg	Simpson
Hunton	Skadden
Jones Day	Sullivan
Latham	Venable
Lowenstein	Waller
McGuireWoods	

Highly recommended

Akin Gump	MoFo
Bracewell	Munger
Cozen O'Connor	Norton Rose Fulbright
Dechert	Nutter
Duane Morris	O'Melveny
Dykema	Orrick
Epstein	Pepper Hamilton
Foley & Lardner	Reed Smith
Fox Rothschild	Sheppard
Gibbons	Sidley Austin
Haynes and Boone	Snell & Wilmer
Holland & Knight	Squire Patton Boggs
Jackson Walker	Thompson & Knight
K&L Gates	Vedder Price
Kilpatrick	Vinson
King & Spalding	Weil
Mayer Brown	Winston
Mintz Levin	

For more detail on ranking tiers and locations, visit www.chambersandpartners.com

Current issues

- A very significant development is the death of Justice Scalia in February 2016. He was part of a Supreme Court majority that issued a number of significant decisions in labor and employment, *"including in the areas of class actions, arbitration agreements, and on the merits of wage and hour issues,"* Thomas Linthorst informed us. *"I'm looking with great interest at who his replacement will be for their impact on those areas."*
- *"Whistle-blowing is an area that is clearly on the rise, by virtue of additional legislation under Dodd-Frank, and some high-profile announcements from the SEC,"* Linthorst reported. Recently, the SEC announced that a $30 million bounty was given to someone who provided original information to them, which led to a successful enforcement action.
- The extent of the protection afforded by the Sarbanes-

Practice Areas

Oxley (SOX) whistle-blower anti-retaliation provision was expanded by a 2014 decision of the Supreme Court. The Annual Report on the Dodd-Frank Whistleblower Program, released by Office of the Whistleblower (OWB), reports an increase of 8% of tips from whistle-blowers in 2015 compared to 2014.

- An increase in SOX retaliation claims has resulted from *"a series of decisions by the Department of Labor extending SOX protections for conduct not previously considered protected,"* according to Linthorst. In February 2016, the Whistleblower Augmented Reward and Nonretaliation Act of 2016 (or WARN Act) was introduced, and aims to strengthen the protections and incentives available to financial crimes whistle-blowers.
- One area that has also been very active is the SEC's stance on policies and agreements that it contends may chill reporting to regulators, such as overbroad confidentiality agreements and non-disparagement provisions. *"The SEC has brought several enforcement actions against companies where it claimed the policies or agreements were overbroad,"* Linthorst informed us. *"This means companies are generally reviewing their policies and agreements to make sure they don't preclude or chill employees from reporting potential violations of law to regulators."*
- Another *"hot area"* is that of wage and hour claims. According to Linthorst: *"There has been lots of class and collective action litigation as everyone seems to be suing for overtime."* Some of the claims are being brought by those covered by the 'white-collar exemptions' to the overtime requirements, while others have been brought by employees claiming that they have not been properly compensated for 'off-the-clock' work. *"One of the reasons for this spike,"* explains Linthorst, *"is that under the federal overtime law, the Fair Labor Standards Act, a claim can be filed on behalf of all those who are 'similarly situated' to the plaintiff and, upon a determination by the court that the case is appropriate for notice, notice can be sent to all others 'similarly situated'. When that happens, there can suddenly be hundreds of claims."*
- More generally, Linthorst pointed to *"the rise of labor and employment laws, regulations and ordinances at the state and local level."* He continued that *"a lot of state and local governments are passing laws; some of them are around wage theft, some relating to paid sick leave, and some are just new posting requirements for existing laws, but it creates a real challenge for those employers that operate nationally."*

"In other words, success in this field requires a practical bent and a propensity to solve problems rather than win arguments."

Litigation: an overview by Allen & Overy

Characteristics of US litigation

US litigation encompasses a broad range of methods for resolving disputes or potential disputes, including internal investigations, government and regulatory investigations, informal negotiations, mediation, arbitration, and state and federal court litigation. Litigators are also brought in to assess litigation risk in transactions and when litigation is threatened, and to advise on aspects of US law that may be relevant to disputes pending abroad.

The substantive areas of civil litigation as practiced at Allen & Overy are vast, encompassing disputes arising out of transactions of all kinds (real estate, financial, consumer, public works, commercial contracts), administrative laws and regulations (including actions by agencies such as the Department of Justice, Securities & Exchange Commission (SEC) and the Commodity Futures Trading Commission (CFTC)), enforcement of intellectual property rights, and bankruptcy proceedings. Litigation in the areas of criminal (other than white-collar crime), immigration and family law tends to be handled by smaller firms.

Due to the globalization of the world economy, use of US law in foreign transactions, coordination among regulators and US courts' openness to foreign parties, US litigation frequently involves an international element. Some examples:

- New York state law permits high-value contracts drafted under New York law to be litigated in New York by agreement of the parties, even if the dispute has nothing to do with New York. Parties to a New York-law governed contract may bring a contract action in a New York court and also assert other causes of action, such as fraud claims, under the law of a foreign jurisdiction.
- US litigation increasingly involves foreign companies and events that occurred abroad, and litigants frequently face similar claims in multiple jurisdictions, including the US, at once. As a result, defending or prosecuting US litigation often requires coordination with counsel outside the US to develop a deep understanding of relevant foreign law and, where parallel proceedings are involved, to develop a global strategic approach.
- A significant trend in financial regulatory investigations and prosecutions is the coordination of enforcement action among multiple US agencies (such as the Department of Justice, SEC, CFTC, and state attorneys general and financial services regulators), and between US regulators and those abroad, particularly in the UK and Hong Kong. Such investigations require banks to coordinate their responses across multiple languages and legal regimes to develop a global strategic approach, and often result in 'follow-on' litigation by private plaintiffs such as customers or shareholders.
- Foreign companies involved in US litigation have to navigate the data privacy and bank secrecy laws of their home countries (and for some, the EU as well) in responding to US discovery requests or subpoenas. Banks in particular may face a conflict between the order of a US court and the requirements of their domestic regulator if directed to freeze bank accounts or provide customer information.

Substantive areas of litigation grow or contract according to the economic forces at work in the sectors to which they relate. For example, commercial contract disputes and bankruptcy litigation may see an increase during periods of economic downturn, and shareholder litigation challenging corporate transactions may see an increase during an up economy. Similarly, in the wake of the Great Recession, companies, particularly financial institutions, have seen a significant increase in regulatory investigations and enforcement actions.

Life as a litigation associate at Allen & Overy

- Research applicable law and develop case strategy, such as the arguments to raise in a motion to dismiss or motion for summary judgment and the evidence to develop to succeed at trial
- Draft pleadings, motions, discovery requests and responses, and deposition and interview outlines
- Liaise with clients to identify, preserve and collect relevant documents
- Review documents for production and those that have been produced by opposing parties, and managing other litigation support vendors, such as data hosting companies and court reporters
- Develop a deep understanding of the facts of the case
- Research legal issues that arise throughout the course of the case, and draft internal and client memos

- Prepare presentations to investigating regulatory agencies on factual findings and legal arguments
- Provide US litigation advice for the firm's other offices and for other departments within the New York office
- Subpoena witnesses and documents
- Coordinate, attend and conduct witness interviews
- Take and defend depositions (first and second chair)
- Assist experts in the preparation of their reports and testimony
- Prepare for and attend settlement negotiations and mediations
- Prepare witnesses and exhibits for trial
- Assist in drafting opening and closing statements
- Draft jury instructions, motions to exclude evidence and other pre-trial filings, appellate briefs, and settlement agreements
- Second-chair the examination and defense of witnesses
- Identify assets and draft pleadings to enforce judgments
- Assist clients with remediation measures in response to regulatory investigations

Outside the litigation process, our associates also draft articles and materials on developments in the law for publication and presentation, assist with preparation of continuing legal education presentations, attend internal and external trainings (such as the National Institute for Trial Advocacy deposition workshop), participate in Bar associations, and contribute to pitches to new clients. Our department also handles an array of pro bono matters, including immigration and domestic violence matters and contract disputes for not-for-profit corporations.

Litigation is constantly evolving through developments in legislation, case law and society. People who like to be constantly learning are well suited to litigation.

The best litigators are those who can shape the facts of the client's case into a compelling story that persuades the court, jury or other decision maker. This requires excellent research, writing and oral communication skills.

A&O's US litigation practice

Allen & Overy's US litigation practice serves clients in complex disputes including financial institutions litigation, antitrust, internal investigations and special investigations for boards, securities litigation, real estate litigation, regulatory and white-collar defense, corruption investigations and regulatory compliance, complex commercial litigation, and international disputes. Our attorneys, who include three partners who are former federal prosecutors, have experience litigating and trying cases in a wide variety of forums, work closely with our highly ranked UK, European, Middle East and Asia litigation and dispute resolution practices to provide unmatched international coverage.

About the authors

Laura Hall is a litigation partner in Allen & Overy's New York office. Laura focuses on cross-border financial and bankruptcy litigation. One example of her recent work includes a six-week trial held simultaneously in the US and Canada concerning Canada's largest-ever bankruptcy. Laura graduated from Georgetown University and Harvard Law School.

Justin Ormand is a litigation associate in Allen & Overy's New York office. Justin focuses on complex commercial litigation and internal investigations. Justin graduated from the University of Cincinnati College-Conservatory of Music and Brooklyn Law School.

Michael Westfal is a litigation associate in Allen & Overy's New York office. Michael focuses on complex commercial litigation and regulatory investigations. Michael graduated from Emory University and Emory University School of Law.

ALLEN & OVERY

Litigation

In a nutshell

Litigation attorneys help their clients resolve disputes. If disputes are not settled by negotiation, they will be concluded either by court litigation or by an alternative form of dispute resolution, such as arbitration or mediation, both of which are potentially more expeditious, less costly and out of public view.

Disputes may concern anything from unpaid bills or unfulfilled contract terms to problems between landlords and tenants, infringement of IP rights, construction-related claims, the liabilities of insurers, shipping cases, defective products, entertainment industry wrangles... the list is endless.

Some litigators will concentrate on specific types of claims, making use of particular industry knowledge; others will remain generalists, applying their legal experiences – especially trial experience – to all manner of cases and clients. Some will focus on appellate matters, and there is a separate explanation of this type under Appellate Law.

What litigators do

- Pre-litigation counseling and advisory work. Part of the job involves mitigating the risk of future wrangles by counseling clients on the ramifications of business decisions and ensuring compliance with laws and regulators. *"We focus on risk analysis,"* **Anton Valukas** of **Jenner & Block** stresses. *"All good litigators understand that an appropriate evaluation of a matter in the first instance can significantly reduce exposure to litigation."*
- Advise clients on whether they have a valid claim, or whether to settle or fight a claim made against them. *"One of the biggest mistakes lawyers can make is to oversell the chances of winning,"* **Robert Giuffra** of **Sullivan & Cromwell** tells us. *"The client needs the best possible assessment of the chances of victory and what it will entail to get them there."*
- Draft pleadings; for example, if acting for a defendant a litigator will prepare a motion to dismiss or an answer.
- Assuming that the case goes beyond the pleading stage, litigators will ordinarily proceed to the discovery phase, where each side serves discovery requests on the other in order to gain access to evidence that is relevant to the case.
- There is a vast amount of document review, during which litigators attempt to find the 'smoking gun' that will win the case – for example, an email that indicates strong evidence of a conspiracy. *"There is a perception that a stunning moment in a trial will turn it all around,"* Valukas tells us. *"The reality is if you have two really talented lawyers who work exceedingly hard, the facts will determine the case. For every hour in the courtroom there have been dozens of hours spent outside it, getting ready for that moment. All that preparatory work for trial is so important."*
- Draft evidentiary objections. This involves constructing arguments on the admissibility of evidence that may be prejudicial, or beneficial, to either side. Represent clients at pretrial hearings.
- Prepare and conduct depositions.
- Senior litigators, normally at partner level, are responsible for the way the case is presented and conduct the trial itself, deciding which arguments will resonate with jurors and undertaking witness cross-examination and closing arguments. *"You always want to litigate a case through the rubric of your main themes. One mistake lawyers make is to overcomplicate a case,"* says Giuffra. *"It's very important to figure out and focus on the four or so issues that matter most."*

Realities of the job

- *"The great thing about litigation is the variety; everything is new almost all of the time,"* says **Carey Dunne** of **Davis Polk**. *"The legal issues can be similar of course, but the industries are frequently different and so are the facts, which means the strategy and analysis is always challenging and evolving."*
- Everything is driven by procedural rules and the timetable of the courts. Good litigators understand how best to maneuver within the system, while also developing case-winning strategies.
- As litigators need to abide by tight deadlines, the nature of the work is often cyclical. *"There may be periods when you just have a tremendous volume of work that needs to be accomplished in a short amount of time, but there's also a level of rush and excitement about that,"* says **David Zinn** of **Williams & Connolly**.
- *"You have to be someone who is willing to deal with uncertainty; litigation is inherently uncertain,"* Giuffra tells us. *"Planning goes out the window; I've had to learn how not to plan,"* confirmed one Fried Frank associate. *"It's an adjustment and some people aren't ready for that. You need to be adaptable."*
- *"Searching through documents is often like looking*

for a needle in a haystack; it can be a taxing and tiring process," explains **F Joseph Warin** of **Gibson Dunn**. However, for junior attorneys this is not as prominent a task as it once was. While initial document review is often outsourced to contract attorneys, litigators at all levels of seniority need to have excellent knowledge of the key documents in a case.

- Juniors do also perform written work, like first drafts of pleadings, and the preparation of questions to be asked, and sometimes conduct depositions.
- Litigators need to express themselves succinctly and precisely in all their communications.
- *"Taking apart a set of arguments is like a labyrinth of pros and cons,"* Warin says. *"You need to figure out which are likely to be the most persuasive for a judge or jury, as well as discarding arguments that you eventually find out are flawed."*
- Deciding upon which arguments will be the most effective is made easier by jury simulations. *"You don't go to trial in a big case without having some testing of which key points resonate with potential jurors,"* according to **Jonathan Lerner** of **Skadden**.
- Front-line participation in full-blown trial advocacy generally isn't something that litigators experience until later in their careers. *"Sometimes young lawyers don't get the opportunity to be in the courtroom,"* says **Randy Mastro** of **Gibson Dunn**. *"I always encourage them to take on additional pro bono assignments where they can get that experience."*
- Litigators may be known for having the gift of the gab but it's just as important to put your ears to good use. **Brad D Brian** of **Munger, Tolles and Olsen** tells us: *"If you're in a courtroom you need to listen to what the judge and opposing counsel are saying. So many lawyers at the beginning and end of their careers are tied to their scripts for their outline or witness examinations and are not listening to what the judge, opposing counsel or witnesses are saying."*
- The overwhelming majority of cases will settle before reaching trial.

Current issues

- As clients tighten their budgets for full-blown trials, law firms are having to compete far more for the fewer matters that are going around. Cash-conscious companies are turning instead to mediation or arbitration to settle disputes or directing their lawyers to keep costs down. While the amount of litigation may have fallen, cases that do make it to trial are increasingly complex or high value.
- Recent high-profile data breaches have catapulted cyber security and privacy into the spotlight. It's now one of the fastest-growing practices out there. Data breaches; a growing push for consumer protection; and regulatory shifts concerning privacy and data sharing have highlighted the need for businesses to have a strong understanding of the law in this area. For example, the Federal Communication Commission's (FCC) 2015 ruling on the Telephone Consumer Protection Act increased the scope of liability businesses face, while in Europe the European Court of Justice ruled that national regulators have the power to stop companies transferring EU citizens' data to the US.
- Class action suits are forming another booming area. Privacy class actions are increasingly hitting the courts as consumers take on companies whose data breaches exposed personal data. More consumers are also bringing suits over inaccurate food and beverage labeling. Other areas attracting class action fever include fraud and securities.
- The Securities Exchange Commission (SEC) has ratcheted up its enforcement actions in recent years. With the upcoming departure of the current administration and potential legislation changes looming, this looks unlikely to slow down. While mortgage-related matters stemming from the financial crisis are starting to tail off, litigators are getting stuck into more SEC actions that focus on financial institutions and trading activity such as price fixing.
- Contentious IP matters in the healthcare and pharmaceutical space are tipped for an uptick. *"There's a growing need for litigation services in the biosimilar area,"* **Evan Chesler** of **Cravath** highlights. 'What on earth are biosimilars?' we hear you cry: they're basically generic copies of branded bio-pharmaceutical drugs. *"The legal issues with biosimilars are similar to those which surround the development of generic drugs in the traditional chemical pharma space,"* Chesler continues. *"I think that will be a very big litigation focus in the coming years."*
- Litigators are also seeing a significant amount of antitrust litigation largely due to the tough enforcement stance of the Obama administration. Keep an eye out for any changes once the administration switches.
- Several upcoming trials in the healthcare sphere are set to have a resounding impact on this area in the coming year. Challenges to abortion rights in Texas, the House of Representatives taking on Affordable Care Act subsidies and several cases concerning overbilling brought under the False Claims Act are all on the docket.
- Environmental nongovernmental organizations (ENGOs) are increasingly fighting new energy developments with regulatory and legal challenges. Using social media to mobilize support, ENGOs are drumming up considerable funding to enable them to pursue these challenges.
- In late 2015, the Department of Justice revealed it new white-collar crime policy which places an increased focus on the naming of individuals involved in corporate wrongdoing. Previously companies could cooper-

ate with investigators and hand over information about improper practices without having to identify those involved but, in part thanks to criticism that Wall Street execs have remained largely unscathed in the fallout from the financial crisis, the DOJ has toughened its stance. Credit will be given to companies who hand over such details but commentators are concerned that in the interest of protecting employees, organizations may refuse to cooperate with the DOJ.

"The reality is if you have two really talented lawyers who work exceedingly hard, the facts will determine the case. For every hour in the courtroom there have been dozens of hours spent outside it, getting ready for that moment. All that preparatory work for trial is so important."

Rankings in *Chambers USA*

Top ranked

Alston & Bird
Cadwalader
Cahill
Cleary
Cravath
Davis Polk
Debevoise
Dechert
Foley & Lardner
Gibbons
Gibson Dunn
Goodwin Procter
Hogan Lovells
Hunton & Williams
Jenner & Block
Jones Day
King & Spalding
Kirkland
Latham
Lowenstein
McGuireWoods
Morgan Lewis
Munger
Nixon Peabody
Paul, Weiss
Pepper Hamilton
Perkins Coie
Proskauer
Reed Smith
Ropes & Gray
Shearman
Sidley
Simpson
Skadden
Snell & Wilmer
Sullivan & Cromwell
Waller
Willkie
WilmerHale
Winston & Strawn

Highly Recommended

Akin Gump
Allen & Overy
Arnold & Porter
Axinn
Baker & McKenzie
Baker Botts
Bracewell
Choate
Cooley
Cozen O'Connor
Crowell
Duane Morris
Dykema
Fenwick & West
Fox Rothschild
Freshfields
Fried Frank
Goulston & Storrs
Greenberg Traurig
Hangley
Haynes and Boone
Holland & Knight
Irell & Manella
Jackson Walker
K&L Gates
Kasowitz
Katten
Kaye Scholer
Kilpatrick
Kramer Levin
Mayer Brown
Milbank
Mintz Levin
MoFo
Norton Rose Fulbright
Nutter
O'Melveny
Orrick
Patterson Belknap
Paul Hastings
Sheppard
Squire Patton Boggs
Stroock
Thompson & Knight
Vedder Price
Venable
Vinson
Weil
White & Case

For more detail on ranking tiers and locations, visit www.chambersandpartners.com

White-Collar Defense: an overview by Cahill Gordon & Reindel

Legal trends and business climate

In Cahill's white collar practice, we advise public companies, boards, committees, and executives of publicly held companies in corporate governance matters, corporate and governmental investigations and crisis management.

Cahill lawyers are called upon to assist clients with particularly sensitive matters involving corporate governance and ethical malfeasance, including accounting fraud and earnings management, market manipulation, disclosure violations, insider trading and fraud in connection with mortgages, conflicts of interest, director and management responsibilities and business practices. The firm is widely regarded for its ability to develop remedial and compliance plans that appropriately address potential liabilities and provide appropriate responses to governmental and regulatory inquiries.

Cahill has managed some of the most significant investigations arising from existing and emerging regulation in the white collar arena, including for some of the largest public companies and banks with transnational operations as well as the largest credit rating agency and important government organizations. Our lawyers have extensive experience conducting multinational investigations involving alleged violations of the Foreign Corrupt Practices Act (FCPA), the Office of Foreign Assets Control (OFAC) regulations, commercial anti-bribery laws and the Bank Secrecy Act.

Cahill lawyers represent parties in proceedings before Congress, the Securities and Exchange Commission, Department of Justice, United States Attorneys' Offices, Department of the Treasury, Federal Trade Commission, Office of the Inspector General, and State Attorneys General as well as the New York Stock Exchange, FINRA and other prosecutorial and regulatory agencies.

What type of clients does this practice area serve?

Cahill devotes a substantial focus to representation of public companies and their boards of directors and committees in transnational business operations. We frequently represent audit committees responsible for the global regulatory oversight of their organization. We also maintain a very active practice representing board members and senior executives in compliance and enforcement matters.

Our clients include or have recently included some of the world's largest banks (HSBC, Credit Suisse and others), some of the world's largest public companies and their boards (Wal-Mart Stores, Qualcomm, Diageo, Teva Pharmaceuticals), and the largest largest credit rating agency (Standard & Poor's), as well as the Federal Reserve Bank of New York and Freddie Mac, to name a few. These clients turn to us to handle high profile matters that are complex and international in scope. The matters we have handled for HSBC and Credit Suisse are, for example, among the most significant regulatory matters in the long histories of those banks. Teams of Cahill litigators have also assisted a Cahill partner appointed as a Monitor to oversee various operations at Toyota and Biomet.

Is there much of an international element?

Yes. For example, Cahill is overseeing a global internal investigation for the Audit Committee of Wal-Mart Stores, and the company's response to DOJ and SEC investigations, as well as global compliance evaluations and program modifications arising out of its operations at subsidiaries around the world. We represented the Audit Committee of London-based Diageo plc in connection with possible FCPA violations arising from the company's business dealings in South Korea, Thailand and India. We represented the Audit Committee of Pride International in one of the largest FCPA investigations ever, spanning Venezuela, India, Mexico, Kazakhstan, Nigeria, Saudi Arabia, the Republic of the Congo and Libya.

What are some of the drivers of growth for this practice area?

We deal in complex and expansive regulatory schemes affecting many different industries, coupled with enforcement by government agencies worldwide that has recently become significantly more aggressive.

What might a junior associate in this practice area expect to do day-to-day?

A junior associate might expect foreign travel and a wide range of responsibilities that make up the typical internal investigation assignment, including:

- Compiling evidence
- Researching
- Drafting reports
- Supporting more senior associates in preparing and conducting interviews of witnesses

What experience, qualifications and personal qualities are needed to succeed in this practice area?

Critical thinking skills and healthy skepticism, especially relating to witness testimony, will serve a junior lawyer well in this practice area. Those who have an ability to digest large volumes of evidence and documentary materials and have the perspective to pull it all together into a cohesive whole as it relates to the situation will excel. Successful lawyers practicing white collar investigations and defense have the ability to compare, contrast and find the truth in conflicting evidence.

CAHILL

What are the pros and cons of being a lawyer in this practice area?

Lawyers practicing in this area are exposed to a wide range of industries, disciplines and specialties, providing an intellectual dimension that keeps things interesting. One must have an ability to understand with sufficient depth various types of business operations to be an effective investigator and/or advocate. Frequent travel and the ability to meet and work with a variety of people from all over the world is very rewarding.

Practicing in white collar investigations and defense can allow lawyers to get from behind their desks and interact with clients and witnesses. Young lawyers in this area can achieve broad perspectives, learning about a wide variety of issues and controversies while they progress as attorneys. In one moment, a white collar defense attorney could be learning the secrets of the retail industry, and in the next, deep in conversation about preparing an oil rig for its next expedition. It's an intellectually stimulating area in which to practice.

About the author, David N. Kelley

David N. Kelley is a senior advisor to public companies, boards of directors, audit committees, and officers and directors in significant matters involving business crime and investigations by federal and state government prosecutors and regulators. Representations include federal securities and commercial litigation as well as Grand Jury investigations, prosecutions and Congressional inquiries. Prior to joining Cahill in September 2005, David served as the US Attorney for the Southern District of New York, overseeing the 255 lawyer Office and supervising some of the nation's most significant investigations and prosecutions involving white collar crime, securities fraud, international terrorism and national security issues as well as the Foreign Corrupt Practices Act and matters involving the Office of Foreign Assets Control. David received his AB from The College of William and Mary, and his JD from New York Law School.

Private Equity & Investment Management

In a nutshell

Private equity and investment companies operate funds that pool the investments of anybody prepared to part with their money for a sustained period of time. The private equity firm takes this cash – often alongside a large portion of bank debt (making it a 'leveraged buyout', or 'LBO') – to buy companies or other assets with the goal of selling them on at a massive profit. Investment management lawyers, therefore, have two primary functions: they form the funds (which are typically structured as limited partnerships) and help the private equity firm negotiate the terms on which investors contribute their money, and they act for the private equity fund when it buys and sells its investments.

Venture capital is a subset of private equity that sees investors put money into startup companies or small businesses in the hope they will be sold to a private equity firm or taken public. Although this typically entails high risk for the investor, it has the potential for above-average returns. The higher risk compared to private equity proper is offset by investing smaller amounts over a shorter timespan, typically.

Investment management is the professional management of various securities (shares, bonds, etc) and assets in order to meet the specified investment goals of investors. Investment management lawyers may work in any of the specialist areas described below, but ultimately advise on the structuring, formation, taxation and regulation of all types of investment funds.

A **hedge fund** is a private, actively managed investment fund. It aims to provide returns to investors by investing in a diverse range of markets, investment instruments and strategies. Hedge funds' investment strategies aim to make a positive return on investment regardless of whether markets are rising or falling. Expertise on the derivative markets helps hedge funds achieve this.

A **mutual fund** is a collective investment vehicle that pools money from many investors to purchase securities. The term is most commonly applied to collective investments that are regulated and sold to the general public.

A **real estate investment fund/trust** is a publicly traded investment vehicle that uses investors' money to invest in properties and mortgages.

Both hedge funds and mutual funds generally operate as **open funds**. This means that investors may periodically make additions to, or withdrawals from, their stakes in the fund. An investor will generally purchase shares in the fund directly from the fund itself rather than from the existing shareholders. It contrasts with a closed fund, which typically issues all the shares it will issue at the outset, with such shares usually being tradable between investors thereafter.

What private equity/investment management lawyers do

- Advise clients on how to structure new funds.
- Help private equity firms negotiate the terms on which investors contribute their money.
- Act for the private fund when it buys and sells its investments.
- Assist clients throughout the fund-raising process. This includes the preparation of offering materials, the preparation of partnership agreements, advising on and documenting management and compensation arrangements, and closing fund formation transactions.
- Draft the numerous organizational documents necessary to form an investment fund, including a private placement memorandum, a limited partnership agreement (if the fund is a limited partnership) or an operating agreement (if the fund is a limited liability company), and investor subscription agreements.
- Conduct diligence and negotiate contracts.
- Inform and advise clients on the constantly changing regulatory and compliance issues arising under US and international securities, tax and ERISA laws.
- Provide day-to-day advice with respect to issues such as performance and advertising, and brokerage and portfolio trading practices.

Realities of the job

- Funds lawyers often work for clients in very small teams, meaning there is the chance for even the most junior associates to gain great experience. *"When you start out, you will work on private placement memos, draft key documents and review the transfer agreements,"* says **Bruce Ettelson** of **Kirkland & Ellis**. *"In funds, you may negotiate with hundreds of parties at the same time so typically you get the chance to work in negotiations as a young associate."*
- Structuring funds requires an intimate familiarity with

Practice Areas

relevant securities and investment company rules. Understanding and being able to apply knowledge of key legislature, such as the Securities and Exchange Commission (SEC) guidelines as well as federal and state laws, is a vital skill.

- Setting up funds also requires a significant amount of tax, ERISA and industry knowledge. Funds lawyers often work in close collaboration with their tax and finance colleagues to realize the best value for clients.
- Private placement memoranda must contain risk factors and material disclosures about the investment manager and the strategy to be employed by the fund.
- Form ADV is the uniform form used by investment advisers to register with both the SEC and state securities authorities. It consists of two parts: part one requires information about the investment adviser's business, ownership, clients, employees, business practices, affiliations, and any disciplinary events of the adviser or its employees; part two requires investment advisers to prepare narrative brochures written in plain English that contain information such as the types of advisory services offered, the adviser's fee schedule, disciplinary information, conflicts of interest, and the educational and business background of management and key advisory personnel of the adviser.
- Being responsive to client needs and understanding the time-sensitive nature of fund organization is essential. *"A lot of work involves helping clients to understand what the market is and how they can best use such information. As private funds attorneys, we often play a strategic counseling role,"* says Bruce Ettelson.
- *"I would recommend taking a securities regulations course,"* says **Lisa Schneider** of **Fried Frank**. *"Having a basic understanding of securities law is an important foundation for the practice of asset management and other areas of corporate law."*
- *"A key personality trait often overlooked that you need in this practice area is emotional intelligence – people skills. One of the things I love about this practice is that in fund-raisings I don't really do one-on-one negotiations, and in terms of large private securities offerings you will be dealing with numerous different law firms. Finding a common denominator and getting everyone to agree to pretty much the same terms means that being able to read, understand and gently move people helps tremendously,"* explains **Jordan Murray** of **Debevoise & Plimpton**.
- *"Attention to detail and the ability to take a step back and understand the big picture"* are key attributes for success, according to Lisa Schneider.

Current issues

- The private equity market had another solid year in 2015. Despite the slightly sluggish economic outlook, investment multiples reached new peaks.
- However, the number of deals and their value were only incrementally higher than previous years.
- Global fundraising dropped by 15.4% from the 2014 total of $339 billion, to $287 billion in 2015 according to Prequin.
- Of that $287 billion, $151 billion was made up of buyout strategies. $47.5 billion was from venture capital. $49.264 billion was contributed by asset owners, such as US public defined benefit plans.
- The three largest funds that closed in 2015 raised $40.1 billion. They were Blackstone Capital Partners VII, Warburg Pincus Private Equity XII and Lexington Capital Partners VIII.
- Private equity-backed IPOs fell to roughly half of 2014's record breaking year value. But this still means that 2015 was the second most active year on record. Only 155 deals were recorded compared to 2014's 211. Which accounted for a 74% decline in the number and value of private equity-backed deals in the Americas.
- IPOs accounted for only 14% of total private equity exit value, compared to almost 25% in 2014.
- IPO follow-on activity however had an increase of about 2% in value and 24% in volume, raising $107.1 billion.
- Following 2010's Dodd-Frank Act, the SEC is concerned with regulating private equity and hedge funds. The level of disclosure concerning fund fees and expenses, as well as their allocation into different meth-

Rankings in *Chambers USA*

Top ranked

Cooley LLP	Proskauer
Debevoise	Ropes & Gray
Dechert	Schulte
Fenwick & West	Sidley
Goodwin Procter	Simpson
Kirkland	WilmerHale

Highly recommended

Akin Gump	Orrick
Choate	Paul Hastings
Cleary	Paul, Weiss
Davis Polk	Perkins Coie
Fried Frank	Seward & Kissel
Gibson Dunn	Skadden
Goodwin Procter	Stroock
K&L Gates	Sullivan & Cromwell
Latham	Vedder Price
Linklaters	Weil, Gotshal
Lowenstein	White & Case
MoFo	Willkie
Morgan Lewis	WilmerHale
Nixon Peabody	

For more detail on ranking tiers and locations, visit www.chambersandpartners.com

ods of investment, has come under increased scrutiny recently. *"Private equity has become less private,"* says Jordan Murray.

- Private equity managers are now required to register under Dodd-Frank with the SEC. The SEC's enforcement work in this area, along with the Presence Examination Initiative carried out by the Office of Compliance Inspections and Examinations (OCIE) increased in 2014 and 2015.
- President Barack Obama signed into law the Jumpstart Our Business Startups (JOBS) Act in April 2012 with bipartisan support from Congress. This allows hedge funds to advertise responsibly to investors through normal channels. Hedge funds had been banned from soliciting or advertising their private offerings to the general public in exchange for being exempt from having to register their interests or shares with the SEC under Rule 506 of Regulation D. More investors will therefore be allowed to enter a single fund.
- The Private Fund Investment Advisers Registration Act eliminated the so-called private adviser exemption for advisers with fewer than 15 clients, upon which most private fund managers relied to avoid registration under the Investment Advisers Act of 1940. That provision provided an exemption from registration for any adviser that did not hold itself out as an adviser and had fewer than 15 clients during the preceding twelve-month period. Now, hedge funds and private equity funds of over $150 million are required to register with the SEC.
- A new Bill was proposed in March 2016 to close the 'carried interest loophole,' which has allowed partners at private equity firms and hedge funds to pay drastically reduced federal tax rates on their income. Until now, a large portion of their income has been treated as capital gain, entitling them to pay at the capital gains rate of 20% (19.6% less than the rate taxed on normal income.) Despite urges from President Obama to close the loophole sooner, this new Bill has strong support now.

Advice from the investment management gurus:

Bruce Ettelson, head of the private funds group, **Kirkland & Ellis**:
"A real benefit of funds work is that you meet very senior people at the clients early on in your career and become a general corporate counsel to those clients. You're able to represent clients from cradle to grave. You're not only doing the transfers, but also helping them with reports, regulatory compliance, structuring transactions within a fund's permitted transaction parameters and other issues. A wealth of challenges will come up over ten years of working with a client. It's a very dynamic and challenging practice. The work doesn't end with structuring and closing a fund."

Lisa Schneider, corporate partner, focused primarily on the structuring and representation of hedge funds and other alternative investment products, at **Fried Frank**:

"One of the great things about this area of law is that the role of a junior associate is not that different from that of a senior associate or partner. In many fields, junior associates are often relegated to lower-level tasks, such as diligence, and are not exposed to high-level deal negotiations. Juniors in this practice really get exposure to the whole picture. Transactions are leanly staffed, so that junior associates are able to be involved in all aspects of a transaction, including drafting and negotiations."

"The private fund space is dynamic and is continuously evolving. As the client businesses and products adapt to changes in the market, our practice must change and evolve as well. This is what keeps the private funds practice both challenging and rewarding. It's great to be at the cutting edge of the industry."

Jordan Murray, deputy chair of the firm's corporate department and member of the private equity funds and investment management groups, **Debevoise & Plimpton**:

"I really view myself as a commercial business lawyer who does everything for these private investment firms other than their acquisitions and dispositions. We handle their private securities offerings – which could be viewed as the sexy part of the job – and deal with a whole range of projects, including opening non-US offices, high-level personnel changes, firm restructurings and liquidity events, securities filings, investor reports and communications, incentive arrangements and regulatory and compliance issues, which have become ever more burdensome. My job often involves marshaling the right teams within Debevoise for our clients. It's like being the quarterback who directs everything."

"For me the real reward is that our clients are so easy to work with. So many of the folks I work with are so entrepreneurial and smart and grasp onto issues and concepts so quickly that it really is quite fun. They are also the type of people who recognize the good work and loyalty we bring to the table – they let you know they appreciate that. For most of my clients I feel like I'm an extension of their organizations. When I speak of my clients it's about 'we'. We enjoy our clients' successes and, thankfully with less frequency, suffer and fight through their challenges as well."

Product Liability

Product liability

Product liability involves personal injury or property damage litigation arising from alleged design and manufacturing defects, or information/warning deficiencies, in products. Litigation can consist of individual cases arising from one-off injuries, though in recent years much of it has been conducted through mass torts. Mass torts comprise class actions and/or multiple related individual cases brought by plaintiffs. Most cases within a mass tort do not usually go to trial as they tend to be resolved early through mediation or settlement.

Product liability lawyers also advise on how to avoid litigation, since clients are increasingly interested in prevention and mitigation of the costs and risks of significant product liability litigation. Attorneys are also often required to advise on related, nontraditional product claims, such as government investigations, which frequently arise alongside private claims. This quasi-criminal aspect involves defending the client against suits filed by state attorneys general and investigations conducted by the Department of Justice, often simultaneously.

The major industries that see the lion's share of product liability suits are tobacco, pharmaceutical, consumer products, chemicals and medical devices. BigLaw firms normally defend the manufacturers of the products.

What lawyers do

- Meet with company witnesses to put together the company's defense.
- Fact investigation and discovery – find out what actually happened.
- Product investigation – get to know the product.
- Choose and prepare experts; arrange for experiments if necessary.
- File motions under the Frye or Daubert doctrines to dismiss inadequate plaintiffs' experts.
- Write briefs on evidentiary, class action and dispositive motion issues, as well as legal analysis.
- Take and defend fact and expert depositions.
- Argue cases before juries.
- Manage post-trial steps.

Realities of the job

- Mass torts will typically include some form of consolidation or aggregation of the claims, ranging from a class action – in which plaintiffs have significant issues in common – to a federal multidistrict proceeding coordinating all the cases for pretrial purposes.
- Cases are heard all across the country, though plaintiffs may like certain jurisdictions better than others for tactical reasons. These include East Texas, Atlantic County in New Jersey, and Philadelphia. The 'bank district' in Los Angeles is popular for its history of awarding multimillion and billion-dollar verdicts. It has been described by advocates of tort law reform as *"judicial hell on earth."*
- Not all cases are tried the same way. There are a variety of different trial models that judges are experimenting with, including the bifurcated, reverse-bifurcated and bellwether models. Depending on the model, different strategies will be needed, and will sometimes require a mock jury exercise to see what will work best. Attorneys can suggest alternate trial plans, though the judge has the final say. Once the trial has begun, it is difficult to change how it is tried, though with mass tort, which involves many cases, it is possible to try iterative cases differently. Judges experimented extensively with the thousands of cases in the fen-phen litigation in the Philadelphia courts.
- The main drivers of complex product liability litigation are the business and strategic decisions made by the plaintiffs' Bar, which do not necessarily involve pure scientific analysis of a product.
- Plaintiff lawyers jump from product to product and industry to industry, and try to apply the same model to different cases. The tobacco industry has often seen plaintiffs' innovations before any other, whereafter plaintiffs will experiment with those approaches in different industries.
- Many clients work extensively with the FDA, so current FDA employees cannot be used by the defense as expert witnesses, due to the conflict of interest. Instead, attorneys will work with retired FDA employees to learn about the regulatory and approval processes.
- Much of the work done preparing for trial will turn out to be for cases that never make it to trial, since most mass torts are resolved before then. But attorneys do not know which of the 20,000-30,000 claims filed will actually be tried. There is, however, a winnowing process whereby judges eventually select a smaller pool of cases to be tried.
- There is a large amount of routine paper and electronic discovery required, though many firms use staff and contract attorneys to do this job.
- You don't have to have a background in science to be a

Rankings in *Chambers USA*

Top ranked

McGuireWoods	Sidley Austin

Highly recommended

Arnold & Porter	Mayer Brown
Baker Botts	Morgan Lewis
Dechert	MoFo
Gibbons	Norton Rose Fulbright
Goodwin Procter	O'Melveny
Greenberg	Orrick
Holland & Knight	Pepper Hamilton
Hughes Hubbard	Perkins Coie
Jones Day	Reed Smith
Kaye Scholer	Skadden
King & Spalding	Venable
Kirkland	

For more detail on ranking tiers and locations, visit www.chambersandpartners.com

product liability lawyer, though to be a successful one you will have to learn about areas outside the law like engineering, medicine and science. You will also have to be able to communicate complicated scientific ideas to a judge or jury in a clear and simple fashion.

- You may work with some of the leading scientists and doctors in the country and the world.
- The job often involves extensive travel for trials and meeting with experts.
- Most product liability work is domestic.

Current issues

- Consumer fraud class actions continue to be on the rise in venues across the United States, particularly in California. These actions tend to be filed when plaintiffs' counsel allege that *"defendants mislead consumers as to the benefits of their products,"* explains **Michael Davis**, head of **Sidley Austin**'s product liability and mass torts practice. These actions often arise when a product *"claims to be 'natural' or have a specific health benefit, or when there are technical issues with labeling."*
- Some frequently named defendants, in addition to the traditional consumer, food and pharmaceutical companies, are *"energy drink manufacturers who allegedly fail to adequately label their products, helmet manufacturers, and NFL franchises for concussion injuries players allegedly suffered over time,"* according to Michael Davis.
- Another interesting development has been the advent of 'innovator liability'. According to **Paul Boehm**, partner at **Williams & Connolly**, this has been driven *"by plaintiffs lawyers' desire to circumvent the Supreme Court's decision in Mensing. Since plaintiffs, under Mensing, cannot sue a generic drug manufacturer for failure to warn, plaintiffs' attorneys have advanced the theory that the 'original innovator' of the product, rather than the manufacturer of the product plaintiff actually used, can be liable under state-based 'failure to warn' claims. This theory would represent a fundamental change in some basic principles of tort law. Three state courts have allowed 'failure to warn' cases founded on the theory of 'innovator liability', but most courts continue to reject it."*
- Plaintiffs' attorneys continue to bring cases on purely speculative bases. These actions are often based on supposed economic loss or the mere risk of a loss in future. *"Such cases are often brought when the actual product works as it should, but it is claimed that negative press coverage about possible damage has reduced the product's value,"* according to Davis.

Real Estate

In a nutshell

Real estate has multiple branches. Certainly, the practice no longer simply involves the sale of property by A to B; it now encompasses acquisitions and disposals, financing, leasing, development, joint ventures and funds.

Financing is a significant component of most transactions, and can involve sophisticated structuring, capital markets transactions, mortgage and mezzanine loans, debt restructurings, private placements, sale and leaseback financings, governmental incentives and tax aspects.

Another branch of real estate is land use, which requires attorneys to advise on state and local laws, such as zoning regulations, which affect the behavior and development of the real estate market. There are also aspects of real estate work that sometimes require advice on tax, litigation, restructuring and bankruptcy, and environmental law.

What lawyers do

- Draft a letter of intent, which sets forth the basic parameters of a transaction.
- Conduct due diligence. Make sure what the client is purchasing or underwriting holds no unwelcome surprises.
- Obtain municipal and/or state approval, where needed. Negotiate the contract, which allocates responsibilities among the parties.
- Negotiate financing documentation.
- Close the contract, joint venture and/or financing.

Realities of the job

- According to **Joseph Shenker** of **Sullivan & Cromwell**, there are three aspects to every deal: *"Of course you have the legal element, but on top of that there are the business and psychological elements to take into account."*
- These are also integral to the practice as a whole. *"The practice of real estate law involves the confluence of legal and business strategy,"* he adds. *"It's ideal for someone who is interested in both business and law, as well as in meeting entrepreneurial people and understanding their mindset."*
- Typical clients include developers, owners, institutional investors, lenders, tenants, underwriters, pension funds, insurance companies, private equity and hedge funds.
- Working in real estate requires sensitivity to each client's needs and expectations. While private clients are motivated by profit margins, the public ones are driven

Rankings in *Chambers USA*

Top ranked

Alston & Bird	Jones Day
Arnold & Porter	Katten
Baker Botts	King & Spalding
Cleary	Kirkland
Cooley	Latham
Foley & Lardner	McGuireWoods
Fried Frank	Paul Hastings
Gibson Dunn	Perkins Coie
Goodwin Procter	Sidley
Goulston & Storrs	Simpson
Greenberg	Skadden
Haynes and Boone	Snell & Wilmer
Hogan Lovells	Sullivan
Holland & Knight	Thompson & Knight
Hunton & Williams	Venable
Jackson Walker	Waller

Highly recommended

Allen & Overy	Morgan Lewis
Bracewell	MoFo
Brown Rudnick	Munger
Cadwalader	Nixon Peabody
Cozen O'Connor	Norton Rose Fulbright
Debevoise	Nutter
Dechert	Orrick
Duane Morris	Patterson Belknap
Dykema	Paul, Weiss
Fox Rothschild	Pepper Hamilton
Fried Frank	Pillsbury
Gibbons	Proskauer
Hangley	Reed Smith
Hunton & Williams	Ropes & Gray
Jenner	Schulte
K&L Gates	Shearman
Kaye Scholer	Stroock
Kilpatrick	Vinson
Kirkland	Weil
Kramer Levin	White & Case
Lowenstein	Willkie
Mayer Brown	WilmerHale
Mintz Levin	

For more detail on ranking tiers and locations, visit www.chambersandpartners.com

by policy and politics. Lenders tend to be cautious in their approach, while developers are bold and visionary. Harmonizing parties' competing goals can be tricky.

- Real estate is cyclical by nature. When the economy is bad, the real estate sector is often adversely affected. This means that *"if you have skills to put a deal together, you should also have the skills to take it apart – if and when it gets into trouble,"* says **Laura Ciabarra**, partner at **Dechert**. *"Prior to the financial crisis you didn't need to know both sides, but now there's a wonderful opportunity for young attorneys to acquire both sets of skills and they should definitely take advantage of that."*
- A transaction is truly a team-oriented affair; there will always be more than one attorney working on the deal. Therefore, having the ability to collaborate well with others is a must, in addition to coping with the stressful nature of deadlines.
- *"In the week or so leading up to the completion of a deal, you'll probably find yourself in the office every day working until midnight,"* explains Ciabarra. *"I don't think I've ever worked on a transaction without there being that final week or two of craziness."* However, she describes real estate lawyers as *"deal junkies"* who thrive on the hectic nature of the closing stages, with everyone pulling together to reach a successful conclusion.
- Real estate lawyers tend to have a variety of projects in hand at any one time, which requires exceptional organizational skills.
- The work is often highly tax-driven. When it comes to the more complex transactions, understanding the tax goals and limitations that exist is particularly useful.
- Unlike corporate lawyers, who may have no more than a CD-ROM to mark the end of a deal, real estate lawyers have a physical result that can be seen, touched, visited, lived in and worked in.

Visit www.chambers-associate.com for real estate gurus Fried Frank's insight on Real Estate: Dirt

Real Estate: an overview by Allen & Overy

While traditional real estate practices focus either on real estate investment or finance, at Allen & Overy, our real estate team regularly represents clients on complex domestic and cross-border real estate investment and finance matters across all asset classes (i.e. both single asset and portfolio deals for a multitude of asset classes, including multifamily, retail, office, industrial and hospitality). Our practice represents world-leading financial institutions, corporations, REITs, hedge funds and private equity funds and encompasses acquisitions, sales, development, equity investment, finance, and the exercise of remedies for commercial real estate throughout the United States. Our real estate associates therefore develop a 360-degree perspective of all aspects of the real estate industry and are recognized for their commercial awareness and ability to more naturally find common ground acceptable to all parties during difficult negotiations.

A typical real estate transaction involves several stages and aspects of the law, including corporate law, contract law, real estate law, tax law, finance law and sometimes litigation. Our team regularly collaborates with other practice groups and offices outside the US to provide an integrated offering for our clients and brings all of these resources to bear in planning and executing on our matters.

Real estate is often acquired and held with a mix of debt and equity capital. The equity capital is obtained by bringing investment partners into the transaction (by way of a joint venture agreement) and the debt capital is obtained from a variety of institutional and private financing sources (by way of a suite of loan documents). The same institutional investors may serve as an equity investor in one transaction and may act as a lender on another transaction.

The financing arrangements that our team handles often go beyond simple mortgage borrowing and lending. Representing both borrowers and lenders, our team handles mezzanine financing (i.e. a form of financing where the shares in a company owning real property is the collateral, rather than the real property itself), preferred equity arrangements and loan-on-loan financing (i.e. loans made to lenders secured by loans in such lender's portfolio). This diversity of experience has made our team a market leader and firm of choice for distressed loan/asset workouts, restructurings and foreclosures.

Recent trends

Real estate expertise continues to be in high demand. The real estate industry is notably cyclical. These cycles often correspond to changing interest rates and greater global economic trends. However, certain markets and asset classes may also be affected by particular industries that indirectly impact real estate investment. For example, with the fall of oil prices, real estate investments in energy sector dependent regions have started to depress. While many practices see a slowdown in legal work during these down markets, our group often gets busier. With a unique expertise in mezzanine lending and a proven track record on high-profile mezzanine loan foreclosures, our group is seeing an increase in workouts on distressed assets and foreclosures. While this may not bode well for some clients, others are opportunistic investors with the ability to use these down markets to their advantage. For the attorneys in our group, the down market further broadens their knowledge base, improves their drafting and enhances their ability to develop innovative methods to protect clients from worst-case scenarios.

What can new attorneys can expect to see?

Given the wide variety of clients, deal structures and asset classes to which attorneys in our group are exposed, no two days or deals are alike. Associates can expect to be involved in every phase of a transaction, including:

- Drafting and negotiating purchase and sale agreements, and real property transfer documents, such as deeds and assignments, leases and management agreements.
- Drafting and negotiating corporate formation and governance documents, such as limited liability company operating agreements, limited partnership agreements and by-laws for various types of entities, including property owners, joint ventures and other tax-driven structures and entities.
- Drafting and negotiating loan agreements, security agreements, including mortgages and pledge agree-

ments, financing statements and other loan documents.
- Participating in meetings and conference calls with clients which address both the commercial and legal issues arising in the transaction.
- Performing due diligence in a variety of areas, including title and survey, environmental, leasing agreements and service contracts.
- Coordinating with attorneys in other practice groups where specialized expertise is needed.
- Coordinating with local counsel in domestic and international jurisdictions where a property is located to analyze relevant issues under local law.
- Reviewing and negotiating third party contracts for clients who are investing in a real estate project, including leasing agreements and service contracts.
- Managing the closing of transactions, including compilation and tracking of documents and deliverables and coordinating document execution and recording.
- Participating in marketing activities, such as attending lunches, dinners and events with current and prospective clients.

Real estate deals move quickly, often spanning just a few months, but sometimes closing within a week. This pace can be quite different from other transactional practice areas where transactions may take anywhere from several months to a few years. This expedited timeline provides associates with the opportunity to work on substantive aspects of transactions at early stages in their careers and to see a large number of deals in a short period of time. As a result, it is very easy for associates to gain extensive experience within their first six months and to get exposure to a variety of our group's clients.

The learning curve for our real estate associates is steep. Due to the complexity of the transactions, as well as the high stakes and often short timeframes of these transactions, the associates who perform best in real estate tend to be those who are well organized, flexible and highly inquisitive. While much of the work is technical and requires strong organizational skills, all of the work is highly substantive and requires critical thinking and analysis from day one. Junior attorneys are thrown right into deals as soon as they start working and begin tackling issues and facing clients immediately. To that end, the more senior attorneys in our group work hard to ensure that even the most junior attorney understands the fundamentals of every transaction and to build his/her confidence and knowledge base as quickly as possible.

About the authors

Yaakov Sheinfeld is a partner in the real estate group at Allen & Overy in New York. His practice focuses on representing major investment banks, institutional lenders and private equity firms in loan workouts and modifications, loan origination, repurchase/warehouse financing, and the acquisition and sale of all debt tranches including whole loans, mezzanine loans, preferred equity investments, junior notes and participations (including CMBS bonds and fair value options), as well as serving as counsel to both purchasers/borrowers and sellers of commercial property.

Jeremy Schonfeld is an associate in the real estate group at Allen & Overy in New York. His practice focuses on representing major investment banks, institutional lenders and private equity firms in loan workouts and modifications, loan origination, repurchase/warehouse financing, and the acquisition and sale of all debt tranches including whole loans, mezzanine loans, preferred equity investments, junior notes and participations (including CMBS bonds and fair value options), as well as serving as counsel to both purchasers/borrowers and sellers of commercial property.

ALLEN & OVERY

Practice Areas

The Big Interview with **Matt Ritter**, Big Law stand-up-comedian

Matt Ritter (JD Penn Law) is one of the founders of comedy group Comedians-at-Law, who tour the country performing for firms and law schools. Before his career on the big stage, Ritter worked for four years as a corporate attorney at Mayer Brown and Kirkland & Ellis, focusing on M&A, PE and finance. He is currently a director of recruitment firm Lateral Link in LA and New York. He's had great success as a standup comedian, and has also turned his hand to writing and producing. He produced the shows Duck Dynasty *and* Fat N' Furious *for the Discovery Channel, and has created his own TV show called* Chained to My Ex.

"Don't try to be the funny guy at your office party, it will only end up with you in an HR seminar the next day. Call a professional!"

What made you decide to leave the law and embrace the laughs?
Truthfully, I had a great life as a midlevel associate in New York at a top firm, but I didn't feel fulfilled and I knew exactly why. I always had this feeling that I was meant to be performing for a living, I was always the guy "performing" for his friends throughout my life. So when I moved to New York and started work, I also started performing at night at the open mic and clubs for a few years until finally I just felt that feeling inside you that says, *"I just can't keep going to work anymore. I'm meant to be doing this other thing. Stop being a coward."* Also, I felt I was good enough to pursue comedy. I didn't leave my job after my first open mic bomb.

Was it a fairly smooth transition or is comedy a hard nut to crack?
No, it was smooth sailing. I quit my job and then the next day I landed a Comedy Central special. All kidding aside, it was painful. I moved to LA immediately after I left the law, and I thought I had saved enough money to have a cushion, but like every other struggling artist, there's no escaping the struggle. The comedy world is not only fiercely competitive and filled with brilliant minds, there's no road map. I think that's the toughest part. It's very hard to gauge success and failure, like you would in a normal job. I know lots of "successful" comedians that still work as waiters or drive Ubers.

For me, the creation of the Comedians-at-Law group was a way to carve out my own stage time, not wait around for someone to hand me anything. You have to be proactive about creating opportunities and that's what I did. Of course, it didn't happen overnight. It's been seven years since I left law for comedy and I still feel I have a long way to go.

Are there any skills you learnt in BigLaw that are useful for the big stage?
I think there's something to be said for crafting words as a lawyer that help you craft jokes. Every word in both cases has to be in its proper place for the desired effect. Also, angry partners are like hecklers. They think it's their job to give you shit when you just want to be like, *"Shut up, I know what I'm doing, that's why you hired me!"*

Has the Comedians-at-Law group lived up to your expectations?
Absolutely, I've managed to tour and headline the entire country, entertain thousands of lawyers, give law students a nice stress relief from their finals. On a personal level, I ended up getting a comedy manager, selling my first TV show, working on a bunch of other hit TV shows partially because of CAL.

You currently balance TV producing, acting, writing and comedy with your position as the director of a recruitment firm – where do you find the time?
I sleep very little. I try to focus on the recruiting during the early part of the day, that's my first order of business when I wake up. And that's pretty much ongoing throughout the day chatting with candidates. In between, I work on my personal projects, writing a new TV pilot, etc. Nighttime is for standup! Then I binge Narcos at 3am like every other multitasker in this world. It's 2016, doesn't everyone have five jobs?

How's life as a recruiter? Would you recommend it?
Hmm, I don't really know who's reading this. You shouldn't quit your job as a lawyer to be a recruiter if you are remotely content at your job. Most lawyers are naturally risk-averse and like having a steady paycheck. In some ways this commission-based recruiting gig is worse than the entertainment industry. You're counting checks that never come for whatever reason, it's got big highs and lows.

If you like chatting with lawyers and you feel that helping others fulfill their goals is something you want to pursue, then sure, have at it. I personally think it suits me because A) I've already worked in BigLaw so the candidates know I can empathize, B) I'm well connected to many big firms that people want jobs at, and C) I've done almost everything you can do with a law degree, so they know I'll give them my honest assessment of where I think they should be headed. If you are thinking about recruiting, the company I work for, Lateral Link, is by far the best in the biz, so give us a call!

You tour law schools with the comedy group – have you had any particularly fun (or difficult) audiences?
Oh, I have had so many fun audiences. Ohio Northern Law took us out to drinks at their local bar. The crowds at Standup Live in Phoenix are always phenomenal. The audiences in San Francisco are always so sharp, I think that might be a stereotype, but it's a good one.

Difficult ones, hmm. Well, when the law school or firm doesn't give you mic, a sound system or any sort of lighting, yeah, it's not fun. But you just have to plow through it. Probably the worst was when I did a joke (that killed) in front of three hundred people about how Sandra Day O'Connor had the worst one-night stand ever, because she slept with Bill Rehnquist in law school and then had to see him every day for decades. Apparently the guy who organized the event brought his 11-year-old daughter and then told me I should go back on stage and apologize, which I refused to do. Our show is pretty clean, but don't bring your pre-teen!

What was the most hilarious thing you saw or heard about as a BigLaw associate?
I saw a friend get divorced, experiment with their sexuality, get pretty wild, have the firm actually change the name on their door and on the website, then get back together with their spouse, and have the firm change it all back. I don't think the spouse knew about any of the interim stuff! Basically, an attorney decided to have a midlife crisis and I got to witness it. I think the funniest is when attorneys pretend they aren't hooking up with their co-workers. I call them *"secret couples."* It's really only a secret in their mind, because everyone can tell. Also, nobody cares.

Are there any experiences you had as a lawyer that you now use as comedy material?
Quite a few of my screw-ups at work. We had a huge summer program where we would take summers out to fancy restaurants, theater, ballgames... I was the guy that always decided to take it up a notch and take them out to a bar for tequila shots. Every time I handed our summer coordinator a bill for reimbursement, she gave me a warning that I had gone too far. Finally, I dropped a $3,000 bar tab on her at the end of the summer. She politely slid it right back at me and told me to *"eat it."* That one hurt. I wouldn't exactly call it hilarious, but now looking back on it, I can laugh about it.

Also, I do a bit about the abhorrent conditions of work as a document review attorney. (I also created a web series about this called *"The Bottom Rung."*) I briefly toiled in a few of these gigs after I moved to LA and the money ran out. The bit goes something like this: It's 20 people in a 6x8 room, no water, no air, no breaks. Doc review is so bad that sometimes I would drive by a tollbooth operator and go, *"How the hell did he get his own office?"*

What achievement are you most proud of?
I don't really like to take stock of my accomplishments because I feel like I'm just getting started. But I did go from being a BigLaw attorney to writing jokes on Duck Dynasty, which was the highest-rated reality show ever. Not sure there are too many white-collar to blue-collar stories like that. :) And I got that job because the owner of the company originally wanted me to be his lawyer. I refused and said I only want to do creative work. He liked me enough to give me a shot. Also, I've performed comedy for injured troops at Walter Reed hospital, that was pretty great.

What do you consider your greatest failure or regret?
I don't really have any regrets. Live your life, take chances. I definitely am happy I went to law school and worked as a lawyer, because I wouldn't be where I am today without the crazy road I've taken. I still haven't sold a comedy script about the legal world. I sold a web series,

but I really want to create a comedy about the BigLaw world. Still working on it!

Also, maybe not registering our trademark! Recently, someone decided to start a site called *"Comedian-at-Law"* and we politely asked him to change the name because it was a pretty obvious case of infringement in our opinion, so now the *"Comedians-at-Law"* may have to sue the *"Comedian-at-Law."* That's high comedy. But also really sad because the guy is a constitutional law professor who apparently has no ethics. So make sure when you're trying to book us to type "www.comediansatlaw.com*"*.

What's your best lawyer joke?
I don't really tell *"lawyer jokes"* but here's one of my all-time favorites that I've heard. What do lawyers use for birth control?... Their personalities.

Do you think lawyers can take a joke, or do they sometimes take themselves a bit too seriously?
I can say definitely from performing in front of thousands of lawyers, they can (for the most part) take a joke. Though, I'm sure all the ones with sticks up their ass probably haven't been coming out to our shows.

Have Comedians-at-Law done any gigs at law firms, for example during happy hours or at holiday parties? What would your pitch be to firms to hire you for the night?
Of course we have. That's pretty much our bread and butter! Our pitch: Don't try to be the funny guy at your office party, it will only end up with you in an HR seminar the next day. Call a professional!

Do you have any words of advice for law students trying to get into BigLaw right now?
Yes, take it seriously. As a recruiter, I see what firms look at. Many of them are sticklers for grades. Don't let a Law Review drinking session affect your ability to land a big-firm job, especially now that the economy has turned around and the market is hot. That *"C"* is like a scarlet *"A"* you will wear for a long time.

What about advice for those lawyers who can only dream about taking the plunge and doing something else?
If you're *"dreaming"* about doing something else, start doing it. Today. Don't wait till you quit your job. That tells me you're not really serious about this dream of yours.

Do you see Comedians-at-Law growing in future? If there are any funny lawyers out there, can they get involved?
Sure, send us a clip and a bio. We get a lot of *"Hey, I'm a lawyer, I think I'm funny"* emails. Those don't work for us! Everyone in our group is a professional comic with years of experience. Go get some comedy experience under your belt, don't be the guy that thinks you're ready to jump into something because it sounds awesome. We worked our asses off to get here. But yeah, I'd like to have some international members too!

Finally, what slogan would you like to be remembered by?
It took him three decades, but he finally paid off those Sallie Mae loans.

You can reach Matt for recruiting at Mritter@lateral-link.com or rittercomedy@gmail.com for bookings!

"Angry partners are like hecklers. They think it's their job to give you shit when you just want to be like, "Shut up, I know what I'm doing, that's why you hired me!"

Sports, Media, Entertainment & Advertising

In a nutshell

Media and entertainment, advertising and sports are distinct yet overlapping areas of the law. Some aspects of their practice are common to them all – contracts law, for example – but ensuring a '100% beef burger' abides by the rules stated by the Federal Trade Commission (FTC) is clearly a matter for an advertising specialist.

Whichever strand you practice, one thing is for certain: the work is incredibly varied. None of these specialisms has its own distinct branch of law. Rather, they involve piecing together elements of a broad range of legal disciplines and applying them to one particular industry sector.

Media and entertainment

Media and entertainment lawyers provide legal advice and representation to those working in the entertainment industries, including the fields of theater, television, music, publishing, gambling, film and digital media. The practice has a major fault-line down the middle, with most lawyers falling on either the transactional or the contentious side. Many entertainment lawyers hone one particular specialism – the music industry, for example – while others remain generalists.

Advertising

Advertising lawyers advise on every aspect of brand promotion, from drawing up contracts and deploying 'viral' campaigns to settling false advertising disputes. Again, the role of 'advertising lawyer' is somewhat of a misnomer as its attorneys tend to fall into subspecialisms – generally using their expertise to advise on regulatory, transactional or false advertising matters.

Sports

Split between transactional and litigation work, sports lawyers help out individuals and companies involved in the sports industry. That involves anything from drawing up player signing contracts, purchasing and selling stadiums and negotiating branding agreements to litigating licensing issues.

What lawyers do

Media and entertainment

- Draft and negotiate record, publishing, producer, management, distribution, touring, merchandising, corporate sponsorship, licensing and internet agreements.
- Consult with artists, record companies and publishers regarding their financing, entertainment and internet strategies, plus the protection of their IP rights.
- Advise media and entertainment companies on their M&A and merger activities.
- Provide pre-publication content advice to broadcasters and publishers.
- Litigate matters including contractual, copyright and trademark, employment, and payment disputes.
- First Amendment law is a substantial specialism in itself – advising on issues of free speech, censorship and defamation, among other contentious issues.

Advertising

- Advise advertisers on playing by the rules according to advertising watchdogs including the FTC, and legislation such as the Children's Online Privacy Protection Act.
- Counsel manufacturers on all facets of food and drug labeling, marketing and advertising requirements.
- Advise on sweepstakes and other commercial promotions.
- Litigate false advertising claims, from single party to consumer class actions – particularly those falling under the Lanham Act, the federal false advertising statute.
- Provide copyright advice on advertising issues.
- Negotiate advertising-based content licensing agreements, for a whole range of different media.

Sports

- Advise broadcasters and other sports bodies on audiovisual media piracy issues.
- Sports-related litigation – anything from athlete contractual disputes to stadium construction and copyright issues.
- Advise professional sports leagues, club owners, investors and other financial institutions on sports-related licensing agreements, project finance, securitizations, and security offerings.
- Involved in M&A transactions involving sports-related bodies, and in the purchase and sale of sports teams.
- Advise sports administrators, commercial bodies and municipal authorities on hosting major sporting events.

Realities of the Job

- *"It's a great deal of fun, in part because of the personalities involved,"* says **Bruce Wilson**, a senior corporate partner from **Covington & Burling** with expertise in sports law. But mingling with the stars also brings its own set of challenges. *"You need to be willing to stand up to people unaccustomed to hearing the word 'no',"* he explains. This demands attorneys to *"be exceptionally creative, and learn how to say 'perhaps there's an alternative option'."*
- Media clients are generally accustomed to a more informal working style than you find in the world of BigLaw. To succeed in this industry, you'll need to demonstrate that you're clued in on what makes the entertainment industry tick. A healthy understanding of the media is just as important as your knowledge of the law.
- CEOs and senior management of corporate businesses are particularly interested in advertising litigation. Why? *"Because advertising significantly impacts market share,"* says **Larry Weinstein**, co-head of **Proskauer's** false advertising and trademark group. *"Market share is really how corporate America stays alive and thrives, particularly in the areas of consumer products and pharmaceuticals."* Attorneys in these areas tend to work not just with in-house counsel but with people at every level of their clients' business.
- It's also worth noting that these cases – advertising in particular – often involve complex issues of technology, consumer research or product testing methodology. You don't need to be a science whiz-kid, but it's essential to be open to learning about new techy concepts and products.
- Attorneys in each of these fields should expect a heavy workload, strict deadlines and an extremely fast-paced lifestyle. On the advertising side, cases tend to go to trial more than the average commercial litigation in the US. *"On average, each partner in our advertising practice at Proskauer tries one or two cases a year,"* says Weinstein. *"That's a lot for a big corporate law firm, and it's very exciting."*
- Whether you're a transactional or litigation lawyer, there are a number of different disciplines you'll need to master in order to succeed in the competitive world of media and entertainment. **Scott Edelman**, cochair of **Gibson Dunn's** media, entertainment and technology practice group, stresses: *"I'd encourage people who want to end up as media and entertainment litigators to acquire a broad set of skills in litigation. It doesn't matter if it's environmental, real estate or employment litigation, but acquire a broad set of skills before narrowing."*
- Many newbies waltz into the world of media law expecting glitz and glamor. There's an element of that: *"If you're an associate telling your friends about a deal you've worked on they'll understand who the company is and what they do. It makes it more glam and exciting,"* says **Faiza Saeed**, head of **Cravath's** M&A group. However, *"in terms of nuts and bolts, it's basic M&A skills."*
- Choose your law firms carefully. As a generalization, in media and entertainment law, big corporate firms tend to deal with industry clients, and smaller boutiques with the 'talent'. They're very different career paths, and there's not as much crossover between them as you might expect.
- Finally, media and entertainment, advertising and sport are extremely competitive areas to break into. There are far more associates looking to work here than there are job opportunities. Weinstein stresses: *"If you want to have a chance to work on advertising cases, you'll be far better off working at a firm with 30 or 40 cases a year in this area, than one with a few."*

Rankings in *Chambers USA*

Top ranked

Akin Gump	Munger
Cahill	Patterson
Cravath	Paul, Weiss
Debevoise	Proskauer
Gibson	Skadden
Jenner & Block	Weil
Kramer Levin	Wiley Rein
Latham & Watkins	Winston & Strawn

Highly recommended

Arnold & Porter	Kirkland
Cooley	Morgan Lewis
Davis Polk	O'Melveny
Foley & Lardner	Reed Smith
Greenberg	Sheppard Mullin
Hogan Lovells	Sidley Austin
Holland & Knight	Stroock
Hughes Hubbard	Venable
Irell & Manella	Waller
Katten	WilmerHale

For more detail on ranking tiers and locations, visit www.chambersandpartners.com

Media & Entertainment Law: an overview by Sidley Austin

With two offices in Southern California, and lawyers across the globe who provide services to numerous clients on media and entertainment-related projects, Sidley has a dynamic and growing media and entertainment practice and is involved in virtually all phases of content creation, protection, production, financing and distribution.

Sidley represents various media businesses including commercial banks, financiers and investors, film and television studios, production companies, and producers of entertainment and new media content. Sidley assists our clients in a range of entertainment-related transactional work, including with M&A and finance deals, general corporate governance and corporate organizational work. As a transactional media attorney, day-to-day life is dictated by the transactions, which tend to build in intensity until a scheduled closing date. Transactional lawyers serve as deal team leaders, and oversee the negotiations, diligence and drafting efforts of a team of specialist lawyers.

"Working in Sidley's media and entertainment transactional group, I regularly engage with media power players in Hollywood and around the world. My practice in Sidley's Century City office is focused on entertainment M&A, although I also work on entertainment-focused finance deals. My experience working at Sidley has been challenging and filled with long hours and late nights, but extremely professionally rewarding. As a film and television fan, it has been quite rewarding to the see the fruits of our clients' labor on billboards, television, streaming online, and on the big screen."

– Aerin Snow, fourth year associate in the Century City office, Corporate and Finance group

Sidley's litigation lawyers handle a variety of entertainment matters, including breach of contract, copyright infringement, trademark infringement, and appeals, and provide general legal guidance to entertainment and media clients. The clients that Sidley serves include television and film studios, television networks, production companies, music companies, recording labels, fashion companies, and online and print publishing companies. A litigation attorney will handle all facets of the litigation process, from drafting the initial complaint or answer, through motion practice and discovery, all the way until the case is resolved. Litigation associates in particular can expect a hands-on experience, as these types of cases are typically staffed with a single partner and a single associate. This lean staffing enables litigation associates to take leadership roles in drafting pleadings, interfacing with the client and opposing counsel, attending hearings, and conducting discovery.

"Already in my short time at Sidley, I have had the opportunity to work on several intellectual property matters for media and entertainment clients. I think what makes these matters fun and exciting is the challenging areas of law, the sometimes unbelievable facts, and the popular, well-known clients."

– Lauren M. De Lilly, second-year associate in the Los Angeles office, Complex Commercial Litigation

Becoming a Media and Entertainment Lawyer

Sidley assigns its associates to a single practice group such as litigation, bankruptcy or real estate when they begin practicing. However, associates have a few years to experiment with different practice areas within a group to determine their best fit. In Sidley's Los Angeles and Century City offices transactional associates are assigned to the corporate and finance group and have the opportunity to work in areas such as structured finance, restructuring, M&A, technology transactions and investment funds. Associates interested specifically in transactional media deals have the opportunity to try their hands at media-related deals to gauge whether they enjoy the work. Sidley places a strong emphasis on formal and informal mentoring, and associate and partner mentors frequently assist with navigating the tricky decision of selecting a practice area.

"Sidley's transactional media partners are some of the best in the business, and they take an unparalleled interest in mentoring their associates. I feel lucky to be working with them, and grateful for the interest they have taken in my professional development, and the professional development of every other member of our team of media deal lawyers."

– Aerin Snow

Sidley's litigation attorneys are placed into the general litigation group where they have the opportunity to be staffed on all types of litigation matters, including those for media and entertainment clients. In the Los Angeles office, a distinct group of partners form the backbone of the entertainment and media practice. Associates interested in working on entertainment-related cases will likely find themselves working for this core group. Litigation associates have several options as to how to become involved in media and entertainment matters. For example, an associate can express interest to the litigation group staffing partners, who then work to pair the associate with an entertainment-related matter. Alternatively, a partner in the entertainment practice may reach out directly to an associate to assist on projects for a media client. Associates working on entertainment matters frequently also work on cases in other litigation areas including product liability, class actions, copyright, trademark, appeals, complex commercial litigation, and investigations.

"One of my more memorable cases was defending multiple television networks and a former television executive against claims of copyright infringement related to a popular reality television show. This case was leanly staffed, allowing me to work one-on-one with one of the co-heads of the Los Angeles litigation group and to take on key responsibilities in the case including an ownership role over drafting our motion to dismiss, reply brief, discovery responses and requests, as well as communicating with opposing counsel. This case gave me hands-on experience during my first year as an associate and proved a stepping stone in terms of building my media and entertainment litigation practice, as now I find myself recommended by partners to assist on media and entertainment-related intellectual property cases."

– Lauren De Lilly

Current Issues for Media and Entertainment Lawyers

Transactional

- Technological change continues to disrupt the media industry resulting in massive disaggregation. Deal making across the industry is requiring practitioners to be aware of the latest innovations while anticipating future changes and their impact on deal making.
- Significant consolidation of the media industry is occurring in response to continuing disaggregation. Horizontal and vertical consolidation strategies are being pursued, as well as sponsor-driven roll-up strategies and branded content strategies. Demand for M&A practitioners with media deal-making expertise will remain strong for the foreseeable future.
- Deals require capital. There are significant financial resources looking for alternative investment strategies, and media investments remain an attractive option for everyone from wealthy individuals to banks, hedge funds, private equity, family offices, sovereign funds and others. Practitioners adept in representing those deploying or obtaining capital will remain in high demand.

Litigation

- Technology has disrupted the traditional business models of content delivery. There is considerable friction between content owners and those developing new means to deliver content outside of traditional channels, resulting in a fair amount of litigation.
- We should see continued publicity rights litigation in light of the Supreme Court's refusal to hear the *Electronic Arts v Davis* case, where former NFL players objected to the use of their images in the Madden NFL games. The lines between regarding "fair use" and what uses are protected under the First Amendment are quite murky now, and that breeds litigation.
- Litigation respecting the scope of copyright fair use should play out in interesting and unexpected ways.

Practice Areas

Tax & Wealth Management

In a nutshell

Tax

"Tax touches virtually every aspect of the economy," says **Les Samuels**, senior tax counsel at **Cleary Gottlieb**. Accordingly, tax law encompasses a variety of activities, from transactional support and structuring to tax planning and tax controversy.

Working alongside corporate lawyers, tax attorneys ensure that transactions are as tax-efficient as possible, be they centered on public or private M&A, capital markets, investment funds (private equity, REITs and mutual funds), joint ventures or partnerships. Tax planning advice requires familiarity with all relevant domestic and international laws, and it is essential to have an understanding of clients' overall objectives and the structuring of their businesses.

Tax controversy is more of an independent category, covering a range of contentious tax issues. These include tax-based litigation, IRS examinations and tax shelter investigations. Disputes are usually resolved at the administrative level. Transfer pricing is also grouped with tax controversy.

Practice Areas

Wealth management / private client

Private client lawyers advise wealthy families, individuals, trustees and fiduciaries on all aspects of estate planning, tax planning, wills and trusts, plus various types of estate litigation. This can be domestic in scope, for families living within the US, or it can have an international element if the family has a branch in the US, is seeking asylum in the country, or has invested wealth overseas, for example.

A great deal of private client work is tax-based, particularly involving income and estate tax. Specialists in this area also need their corporate tax knowledge to be up to scratch, as it's not unusual for the families they work for to have multimillion-dollar businesses to their names.

What lawyers do

Tax

- Advise clients on the tax elements of transactions.
- Analyze cases and regulations to develop a real understanding of the tax implications of transaction structures. Findings are summarized as memoranda or given through direct counseling.
- Negotiate terms dealing with the tax aspects of transactions.
- Draft agreements, especially for M&A and joint ventures, which are particularly tax-intensive. An important element is the drafting of tax disclosures.
- Liaise with other non-tax lawyers and clients to ensure the smooth running of transactions.
- If working in tax controversy, negotiate with the IRS, respond to IRS questions, and draft memoranda and briefs.

Wealth management

- Work with families in regard to their offshore trusts and the implications of bringing them onshore.
- Advise families on their international estates, including multijurisdictional legal advice.
- Liaise with private client lawyers around the world.
- Represent trustees in litigation as to their conduct of an estate.
- Draft wills, trusts and estate documents.
- Regularly meet with clients.
- Aid families and wealthy individuals on their personal tax liabilities and solutions.
- Legal research.
- Strategic thought.
- Communicate and discuss strategy within a team.

Realities of the job

Tax

- Tax lawyers need to keep up with all new developments in both the law and the economy as a whole. This is especially important for a young lawyer, who needs to build expertise. The law is always changing.
- By keeping up to date, tax lawyers can become real experts and even innovators within the legal landscape. With experience, they may be able to offer a solution to a tax issue that has previously been unsolvable. For example, the tax lawyer will produce a new financial instrument that becomes accepted by the market. This will sometimes prompt the government to review its regulations.
- It's vital to have an affinity for reading case law and regulations, as this is how juniors will spend some of their time. They must be able to rationalize their findings and summarize them accurately.

- Tax lawyers must have full confidence in their advice. The research must be methodical and complete.
- In order to ensure that commercial transactions are as tax-efficient as possible, tax practices work closely with corporate departments and understand the non-tax issues that drive transactions. A successful tax department can be a useful marketing tool for firms looking to attract new clients.
- Tax lawyers need to express themselves clearly and concisely. Solid technical knowledge is essential, as is the ability to explain technical information to non-experts.
- Excellent interpersonal skills are a must. Tax controversy can sometimes involve liaising with the IRS, and it is important that lawyers be upfront and straight-talking. They may also work with international clients, so cultural awareness is important.
- Lawyers have the chance to work on a variety of matters, including charity and pro bono. They are expected to comment on proposed regulations and may also give tutorials to colleagues and clients.
- Tax lawyers sometimes break up their career by spending time working for the government, notably the IRS.

Wealth management

- **Basil Zirinis**, a leading wealth management partner at **Sullivan & Cromwell**, says: *"Our practice is a mix of drafting, meeting, advising and research."*
- Wealth management tends to offer young lawyers more direct client contact than they'd generally get in a larger corporate or litigation department. *"If you're a strong associate and you show drive, there is always the opportunity to be very involved with families face to face,"* says Zirinis.
- Research plays a large role. *"We're fortunate enough to have a practice where the questions are unusual and complex and there are often no clear answers,"* Zirinis notes. *"We add value where the answer is unsettled. So the associates are doing research, but it's creative research. This makes it more challenging and more interesting."*
- One challenge for private client lawyers is juggling several different matters at once. They don't just focus on one thing at a time. *"This element is a challenge, but at the same time it's a high point. There's so much variety and you never see the same thing over and over again. It's thrilling and exciting and fresh,"* Zirinis confirms.
- It helps to have an interest in tax and an appreciation of numbers – there's a large amount of this sort of work involved in private client and wealth management – but by no means is it a math-based area of the law. Tax work tends to be integrated with corporate elements, with the more complex parts being handled by the firm's corporate tax teams. **McDermott Will & Emery** partner **Amy Heller** says: *"You need to have a strong analytical mind, but the work is more conceptual than adding and subtracting figures."*

Rankings in *Chambers USA*

Top ranked

Alston & Bird	King & Spalding
Baker & McKenzie	Kirkland
Baker Botts	Latham
Cleary	Mayer Brown
Cravath	McGuireWoods
Davis Polk	Pepper Hamilton
Gibson Dunn	Ropes & Gray
Goodwin Procter	Skadden
Greenberg	Sullivan
Holland & Knight	Vinson

Highly recommended

Akin Gump	Munger
Arnold & Porter	Norton Rose Fulbright
Bracewell	O'Melveny
Cadwalader	Paul Hastings
Choate	Paul, Weiss
Debevoise	Pillsbury
Dechert	Proskauer
Fenwick & West	Reed Smith
Fried Frank	Schulte
Haynes and Boone	Shearman
Irell & Manella	Sidley
Jenner	Simpson
Jones Day	Thompson & Knight
Katten	Venable
Kilpatrick	Weil
Kramer Levin	White & Case
Milbank	Willkie
Morgan Lewis	WilmerHale
MoFo	Winston

For more detail on ranking tiers and locations, visit www.chambersandpartners.com

Current issues

Tax

- Congress remains divided over the topic of comprehensive tax reform. Much of this is centered on the issue of revenue – namely whether it should be raised or be revenue-neutral. Readers may be interested to discover that fantasy sports betting has come under some scrutiny: its current status as a game of skill means that its tax exemptions on expenses are more generous than in gambling-related pursuits.
- Globally, there has been more cooperation regarding

Practice Areas

tax havens and information exchange to address the role of businesses in eroding countries' tax bases. So far, 79 countries have signed Foreign Account Tax Compliance Act agreements with the IRS, which has helped create greater lines of communication between the IRS and foreign financial firms. As of October 2015 financial account information has been automatically exchanged with foreign tax authorities online. The IRS's offshore voluntary disclosure program allows overseas account holders to rectify any tax shortcomings, thus warding off the threat of penalty action.

- Heads up, readers, this one could affect you. Effective as of the 2016 fiscal year, students who wish to qualify for tax breaks on educational expenses must now file a copy of the 1098-T Tuition Statement form before applying.
- The US is the only major economy not to have a value-added tax (VAT) system. However, there is a belief among some experts that a federal VAT system could be introduced in future.
- In response to the rising threat of cybercrime, the IRS held a security summit in March 2015. It subsequently announced that tax returns will now be validated using 20 new pieces of data. Such revisions tend to prompt a rise in advisory work for tax attorneys. The IRS also launched an awareness campaign in November 2015, to inform taxpayers of the importance of cybersecurity.
- Following the Supreme Court's approval of same-sex marriage in June 2015, gay and lesbian married couples may now file joint tax returns at state and federal levels.

Wealth management

- *"The global nature of wealth certainly has an impact on the practice,"* says Amy Heller. *"It's increasingly common for wealthy families to have family members and assets in multiple jurisdictions, so it's important to have at least an awareness of other countries' laws and a sensitivity to other cultures."*
- The changing nature of the law means that lawyers must be flexible in their drafting of wills, trusts and other documents. They must be packed full of additional clauses, which means they can be adapted to fit current regulations at any given time.
- Wealth transfer tax laws and thresholds are constantly being amended. This includes gift tax, estate tax and generation-skipping transfer tax, among others. The fluctuations impact the clients' financial planning, so you have to keep abreast of the shifts.

Technology & Telecoms

In a nutshell

Technology lawyers are experts on the rapidly changing laws and regulations surrounding complex communication technologies. Their classification as an attorney can vary – some fall under the IP umbrella, while others work within corporate or trial departments – but tech lawyers are united in their specialized industry expertise. Many narrow their focus to the telecommunications field, which deals with media such as telephones, cable, radio and the internet; others focus on information technology – which involves software, e-commerce and data privacy issues – or outsourcing, which oversees the provision of third-party services.

Whatever their specialty, a tech lawyer's primary role is to help clients abide by the complicated policies that pertain to certain technologies. In the US, such policies are by and large enforced by the Federal Communications Commission (FCC). Typical matters range from working on behalf of the government to promote fair market competition, to overseeing disputes between telecom corporations, to advising merging companies on contract negotiations.

Rapid advances in technology mean each generation of tech lawyers faces a shifting workload – attorneys today regularly contend with smartphone and internet-related matters, while their 20th century counterparts mainly dealt with telephone line technology, and attorneys in the 19th century grappled with the telegraph and other disruptive innovations.

What lawyers do

- Advise companies on commercial transactions, including mergers, acquisitions, investments and the purchase of services, particularly those with antitrust issues.
- Negotiate contract terms for companies acquiring new technologies or enhancing existing ones.
- Handle diligence and draft transaction documents.
- Assist with dispute resolution, often between telecom companies. Many disputes are cross-border and often fall under the IP bracket – for example, patent infringement cases.
- Represent clients at trial, usually in the State Court.
- Counsel communications companies, such as cable or internet providers, on their regulatory obligations.
- Help companies learn how to protect their IT and web-based assets and defend themselves against cybersquatting and other data protection issues.
- Represent clients seeking the provision of IT services through a third party.
- Assist the government to promote competition between telecom and other technology companies, and ensure services don't interfere with national security.

Realities of the job

- Technology transactions often require attorneys to work as part of a multidisciplinary team that incorporates lawyers from multiple fields, including IP, tax and corporate. *"My role is like that of a quarterback,"* **Baker Botts'** technology sector chair **John Martin** tells us. *"I coordinate lawyers from other practice areas and disciplines to develop and implement an integrated solution and to address the client's many issues. It's a multifaceted approach."*
- The field is constantly changing thanks to developments in technology, which means *"every deal is different and every transaction has its own challenges,"* Martin says. *"There's no cookie-cutter matter out there; each deal is unique, which makes this a challenging and intellectually stimulating field. Nothing is rote or routine, and the learning curve never plateaus."* This shifting workload also means *"practitioners should be comfortable with ambiguity,"* advises **Chérie Kiser**, a partner in **Cahill Gordon & Reindel's** communications practice. *"The law surrounding communications issues is constantly changing because the technology is dynamic. Developments are happening in real time in this sector, and lawyers are called upon by their clients to help shape and influence those laws. One should be comfortable with that lack of stability."*
- Because technology lawyers are specialists, they typically *"handle the majority of matters themselves rather than delegating projects or issues completely,"* Kiser says. This means even top-level partners are obliged to contend with grunt work like diligence at times. *"Fortunately, matters are interesting!"* she adds. Technology and telecom matters have *"a language of their own that's highly technical and full of acronyms,"* Kiser warns. As such, attaining a good grasp of the relevant jargon – accessible through industry trade journals and magazines – is a crucial aspect of the job. Though not strictly required, a technical background is often preferred in the field. It's not unusual for a tech lawyer to have an undergraduate degree in engineering, business or computer science, and many have held

Rankings in *Chambers USA*

Top ranked

Baker & McKenzie	MoFo
Harris, Wiltshire & Grannis	Pillsbury
Latham	Wiley Rein
Mayer Brown	Willkie

Highly recommended

Akin Gump	McGuireWoods
Arnold & Porter	Milbank
Baker Botts	Mintz Levin
Bracewell	Morgan Lewis
Cahill	Norton Rose Fulbright
Choate	Proskauer Rose
Cooley	Sidley Austin
Gibson Dunn	Simpson
Goodwin Procter	Skadden
Greenberg	Squire Patton Boggs
Haynes and Boone	Venable
Hogan Lovells	Vinson
Jenner	Weil
K&L Gates	White & Case
Kirkland	WilmerHale

For more detail on ranking tiers and locations, visit www.chambersandpartners.com

previous careers in those industries before making the change to law.

- A job as a tech lawyer isn't limited to a BigLaw firm, though an increasing number of matters are now handled by teams at private firms, thanks to the manpower and other resources such establishments have at their disposal. Options outside of BigLaw include serving as legal counsel for the FCC and going in-house with a telecom firm.

Current Issues

- The rapid rise of cloud computing has made it a *"very hot topic"* in the sector, Baker Botts' John Martin tells us. *"It's at an active and evolving stage, which lends itself to many interesting issues in terms of stability of service and allocation of risk. Think about your mobile device and all the data it contains – that's now being stored in the cloud rather than the device itself, which means you as a consumer will require on-demand services and updated info from the technology provider."*
- The sector used to center around the US regulatory landscape exclusively; however, thanks to an increasingly global market, most technology and telecom companies have expanded their business internationally, *"which in turn requires us to broaden our capability as legal advisers by collaborating with foreign counsel to apply our US-based knowledge transnationally."*
- A good example of the need for cross-border savvy took place in October 2015 when a ruling by the European Court of Justice that a data-sharing agreement (known as 'Safe harbor') between the US and EU was invalid left US tech firms (and their lawyers) scrambling. US tech giants like Facebook, Google and Amazon relied on this agreement to ferry users' personal data back and forth across the Atlantic. In February 2016, the EU and US reached agreement on a new safe harbor provision that should remedy the Europeans' concerns, but with the deal yet to be approved by EU member states, US tech firms are likely to remain jumpy for some time yet.
- And it's not just our friends across the pond that are worried about privacy. Controversy is growing over government surveillance, sparked by Edward Snowden's revelations that the National Security Agency (NSA) is keeping records of citizens' phone calls. Apple recently got into a courtroom brawl with the FBI, which demanded that it help them access an iPhone formerly belonging to San Bernardino shooter Syed Rizwan Farook.
- Tech companies and privacy advocates worried that granting the FBI's request would give the government a permanent backdoor into everyone's phones. Had Apple co-operated with the government, this might also have lead to pressure from more repressive governments for Apple to help them spy on their citizens. The FBI dropped the case after figuring out how to access the phone on their own. The courtroom struggle's not over, though: now Apple wants the FBI to tell them how they hacked the phone, so they can beef up their security.
- Yet companies are increasingly anxious about their own vulnerability to cyber intrusions. The Sony hack of 2014 did more than provide *The Interview* with free publicity. Sony wound up paying out over $5.5 million to a group of former employees whose data had been left exposed by the attack. A number of firms, including Crowell & Moring and Patterson Belknap have been beefing up their cybersecurity offerings.
- From delivering pizza to filming to helping to find lost mountaineers, the potential civilian and commercial uses of unmanned aerial vehicles (more commonly, and awesomely, known as drones) have proliferated. Clients are increasingly keen to discover how best to utilize these flying machines, and that means navigating a host of legal and regulatory issues. With all these unmanned aircraft whizzing about the sky, safety is a prime concern, but considering that drones were developed for intelligence purposes, so is privacy. Law firms have been setting up practice groups to help their clients navigate this spaghetti-esque tangle of regulations.

- 3D printers have also created quite a stir, particularly in the IP and product liability worlds. All that is needed to 3D-print something is an electronic schematic and a 3D printer, and the technology is already capable of producing prosthetics, aircraft parts and even rudimentary firearms. 3D printers are becoming more affordable and accessible, which raises the specter of their being used to produce unauthorized copies of patented inventions.
- Job prospects for tech lawyers are especially robust, Kiser tells us. *"I think we can safely predict that the demand to share information in a variety of formats will continue to grow!"* Indeed, as Martin points out, *"the landscape in the technology sector is constantly evolving, so there's a high demand for smart, hard-working lawyers to get involved. Technology is an attractive sector for new lawyers because there's always something over the horizon. This will be the case for the foreseeable future."*

"Developments are happening in real time in this sector, and lawyers are called upon by their clients to help shape and influence those laws. One should be comfortable with that lack of stability."

The Inside View

The Inside View

As you will read in The Inside View, law firms can vary massively – all have their own quirks – but most share common features as businesses. Here's what JD grads should expect...

What firms have in common

- At most BigLaw firms juniors join a **single department** on their first day. Some firms allow rotations either within a broad practice area (like corporate) or across the whole firm.
- Usually entry-level associates begin life at a firm with low-level **'junior' tasks** – the grunt work like due diligence, document review, document production, collecting closing signatures and so on. You have to start somewhere, but things do get better: drafting, advising clients, negotiating with opposing counsel. How steep the learning curve is depends on the firm, but there are usually certain responsibilities that fall to individuals at each level. For instance, a BigLaw junior is unlikely to be taking depositions, but they may second-chair one. The higher the dollar value of a matter, the lower a junior's level of responsibility tends to be.
- If a firm is known for a certain area of practice, don't assume this is all it does (for example, there's a lot more to Weil Gotshal & Manges than just bankruptcy). Boutiques aside, at most BigLaw firms corporate and litigation are the two biggest departments. Either a **specialist department** – like IP or labor & employment – will exist alongside these, or specialisms will be discernible in a firm's corporate or litigation work (for example, a focus on product liability or energy).
- Junior associates usually **have their own office**, although at the largest firms – especially in New York – juniors will share with another lawyer for their first one or two years.
- The most common cliché about BigLaw is true: lawyers do work some **long hours**. Client and partner demands can mean long days and all-nighters when the going gets tough. Where firms differ is in how often such 'firedrills' occur, how regularly you're expected to work weekends and late at night, and how frequently you end up canceling events in your private life for work.
- Many firms have a formal **billable target**. Others don't. But that doesn't mean lawyers work any less. All firms expect attorneys to work an amount which reflects how active their department is. If you're significantly below the average, that's bad news. Billing is the be all and end all of lawyer life.
- Law firms are increasingly relaxed about where lawyers do their work. Most juniors try to be in the office during **business hours**, but few partners expect juniors to be at their desks every day from 9am to 9pm. At the same time, many firms allow and expect flexibility from their juniors. This means that working from home in the evenings and on weekends is common. Associates are expected to check emails on their smartphones and be communicative outside office hours.
- Devoting a proportion of your time to **pro bono** is encouraged at most firms. Some allow a certain number to be counted as billable; at others this number is essentially unlimited. In practice, juniors are usually free to pursue pro bono projects provided they do not interfere with paid work. Only rarely do juniors devote more than 5–10% of their time to pro bono.

Akin Gump Strauss Hauer & Feld LLP

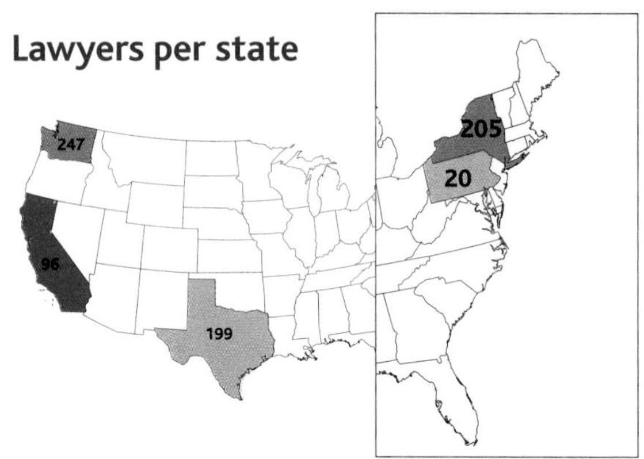

Largest US office: Washington, DC
US offices: 12
International offices: 9
First-year salary: $160,000
Billable hours: no requirement
Summers 2016: 54 2Ls (1Ls & 3Ls TBD)
Revenue 2015: $930 million (+7.1%)
Partners made 2016: 12 globally (8 in US)
Famous for: transatlantic restructuring powerhouse; helping Native Americans; gobbling up Bingham McCutchen's London, Frankfurt and Hong Kong offices

Combining Southern charm with a global outlook, this top Texan is a great place to wrangle up a career.

LIKE the 20th century Texan economy, which jumped abruptly from agricultural to oil-pumping powerhouse, Akin Gump looks unstoppable. Founded just after WW2, it now has 12 branches across the US and nine more around the world. In 2014, the firm acquired all of the lawyers in Bingham McCutchen's London, Frankfurt and Hong Kong offices – almost 60 in total. With its expertise in bankruptcy work, the London office complemented Akin's *Chambers USA* top-ranked US restructuring practice.

Bankruptcy is far from the only practice area to pick up accolades on this side of the Atlantic. *Chambers USA* also gives the firm nods for litigation, corporate, lobbying, healthcare, Native American law, international trade, labor & employment, telecoms, and energy law, among others.

ASSOCIATES SAY...

The Work

Litigation gets most new associates, with over twice as many juniors as the next-biggest practice group, corporate. Next in line are labor and Texas specialty oil & gas – the latter being a pervasive sector focus across all the firm's practices groups – and the remaining newbies sprinkled lightly across the other practices. These can range from intellectual property and financial restructuring to highly specialized areas like investment funds and cross-border transactions. The larger departments have a formal assignment system, with a firmwide partner responsible for making sure that work is fairly distributed. In the smaller niche practices there's less of a need for such a formal system.

> *"Sending the client the documents and answering their questions."*

Corporate is a good place to go if you're looking for client contact. *"It's very common for the junior to be the one sending the client the documents and answering their questions,"* one explained. Responsibility increases as juniors progress, with those slightly more experienced *"drafting ancillary documents and managing the due diligence process."* Responsibility doesn't just vary with seniority, but also with the size of the deal: *"If it's staffed with a lot of people, I'm more likely to do fewer high-level tasks."*

Over in litigation *"we go to trial more than other firms, or so the partners claim."* This means attorneys stay busy researching and writing briefs, drafting motions, second-chairing depositions and, yes, *"some doc review."* Not as much as we've heard about at other firms, though. *"I don't know if we outsource doc review, or if I've just been lucky,"* wondered one. Another source here described the

On chambers-associate.com...

- Akin Gump's Native American law and policy group

The Inside View

See firm profile on p.605

Rankings in *Chambers USA*

Appellate Law	Investment Funds
Bankruptcy/Restructuring	Labor & Employment
Capital Markets	Litigation
Corporate/M&A	Media & Entertainment
Energy & Natural Resources	Native American Law
Government	Projects
Healthcare	Tax
Intellectual Property	Technology
International Trade	Telecommunications

For detail on ranking tiers and ranking locations, visit www.chambersandpartners.com

Recent work highlights

- Negotiated the inclusion of the Passamaquoddy Tribe's sustainable forestry industry in the State of California's Cap-and-Trade program
- Represented Emerging Capital Partners in its investment in African telecommunications firm IHS Holdings
- Represented the trustee of Saint Vincent's Catholic Medical Centers, helping recovery $610 million worth of assets while maintaining patient care
- Helped nonprofit education group KIPP LA issue a $28 million bond to finance the acquisition and construction of new charter schools serving underprivileged children in LA

workload as *"too varied to describe,"* but intimated that there's a lot of contract and insurance litigation, as well as a good helping of class action defense and the odd bit of antitrust. *Chambers USA* ranks Akin's white-collar defense practice too.

"A robust curriculum"

Litigation often works hand-in-glove with the financial restructuring group, particularly at the junior end. *"Juniors quite often do the litigation side of the work, because it tends to be time-intensive,"* which means *"if you're interested, and I am, you can help them do research, draft pleadings and take depositions."* Similarly, the transactional side *"works closely with the finance and corporate groups,"* for example when disposing of distressed assets. What Texas firm would be complete without an oil & gas department? Akin Gump deals with both the regulatory and transactional sides of energy law. *"We get involved in both 'note and comment' litigation and arguments in front of administrative law judges,"* said one energy junior. This necessitates *"a lot of research,"* followed swiftly by *"drafting pleadings."*

Training & Development

Akin Gump's first year orientation program won't cover you from the cradle to the grave, but in the firm's words it will get you from 'backpack to briefcase.' Orientation teaches juniors how to do everything from work with secretaries to mandatory litigation or transactional training. The former was described as *"a more in-depth version of the stuff you'll cover in civil litigation."* This is followed by *"constant CLE programs"* and *"a robust curriculum of technology training."* If this isn't enough, it's *"not hard to find somebody to ask for help,"* particularly in the smaller offices. Those core competencies pop up again in discussions about the review process. As with interviewees, they are the standard the firm measures attorneys against. Management seeks input from each attorney as well as the bigshot in charge of *"every project you've worked 40 hours on,"* which is followed by meeting. *"Everyone takes it seriously,"* said an attorney who'd been through the process a few times, *"and everyone gives substantive feedback, which makes it work."*

Offices

Everything is famously bigger in Texas, but DC is actually the firm's largest homestead. Its DuPont Circle location was described as *"perfect"* – centrally sited, an easy commute from outside the city, but removed from *"the craziness and politicos"* of K Street. Unfortunately, the building itself is a little tired: *"It's not one of those trendy new offices,"* said one associate. The associates we spoke to were more impressed with New York, which they characterized as *"what you would expect from a well-appointed BigLaw office."* We hear the entrance hall is particularly impressive: *"I think the lobby might have sealed the deal for me,"* quipped one New Yorker.

"The craziness and politicos"

Akin hasn't forgotten its roots. Half of its US offices are scattered across the plains and prairies of Texas: specifically, situated in the state's major economic areas. We heard that the Dallas branch has been experimenting with *"more collaborative office designs,"* with part of the building given over to open-plan workspaces, treadmills and *"glass doors to let in more light."* So far this is only a trial, and for the time being Texans, like their colleagues in other offices, *"all get our own offices, even juniors."*

Pro Bono

Law students with an interest in public service can apply to take part in Akin Gump's pro bono scholars' program. Think of it as an extended summer associate program, with a student's 1L summer spent at a pro bono organization of their choice, followed by an orientation at the firm's DC office. This is followed up by a more traditional summer offering in the student's 2L summer. *"We're incredibly proud of it,"* says hiring partner David Botter. *"It's a two-year commitment by the firm to the student, and by the student to the firm,"* he elaborates, *"and an*

See firm profile on p.605

opportunity for them to do work that's valued by the law firm before coming to work at the firm itself." Attorneys appreciated being able to *"do pro bono without worrying about our bonus,"* thanks to Akin's matching hours policy, although according to one source there was an understanding that *"it shouldn't interfere with our billable work."*

"A two-year commitment by the firm to the student."

The firm recently hired a second pro bono head. Between the two of them they *"help attorneys do the sort of work that they want to do."* From the juniors we spoke to, this could include everything from suing the French government on behalf of those who suffered under the Vichy regime to assisting animal welfare societies enforce judgments against people convicted of mistreating animals.

Pro bono hours

- For all attorneys across all US offices: 68,107
- Average per US attorney: 93

Culture

"Texas is wide open and entrepreneurial," explained an attorney, *"and Akin Gump is the same."* We heard of a partner with an interest in African infrastructure *"befriending experts in African businesses,"* and of junior associates *"speaking to specialized newspapers, publishing articles and developing a public presence,"* at an early stage of their careers. Beyond that, the good ol' folksy Texan charm is in evidence with *"approachable"* partners, and associates who are *"very friendly and willing to help each other out."* Some sources even claimed to *"enjoy coming to work..."*

"Willing to help each other out."

Hours & Compensation

With such a heady mix of enthusiasm and entrepreneurship in the air, we weren't surprised to come across a few early-bird attorneys who start their day at eight or even 7am. That said, if you aren't a morning person, most attorneys get in between the more sensible hours of nine and 9.30am. The working day tends to finish around 7pm, unless deadlines are approaching. *"I have something due in a few weeks, so I'll stay later and get it done,"* one told us, while another was more blunt: *"When a deal is on, it's nuts!"* There's no formal billable hours target, which takes some of the pressure off, but associates can find themselves staffed on international deals, which can take its toll. *"I once did a deal that spanned ten time zones,"* recalled one shell-shocked attorney. *"The day never really ended."*

"I once did a deal that spanned ten time zones"

Most of the lawyers we spoke to went into BigLaw with their eyes wide open, so were fairly sanguine about having to work hard. *"I knew it was a big firm with big-firm expectations when I joined,"* explained one, *"but the partners do a great job of managing your time so you don't get stressed."* Another agreed, telling us that *"when it's slow the partners insist that we take the time to relax and enjoy it."* And *"a little pressure is healthy, but I'm not at the point of tearing my hair out."*

Diversity

"The firm is very welcoming toward diverse lawyers," thought one interviewee, *"but there's a long way to go when it comes to diversity."* While *"the overall majority of partners are still white men,"* we heard that Akin has *"a good number of female partners,"* including the current chairperson, Kim Koopersmith. Associates told us about a number of initiatives to attract diverse lawyers, and the firm places an *"emphasis on diversity when it recruits for the summer associate and pro bono scholars' programs."* Some thought that these were starting to pay off in terms of recruitment: *"My summer associates were ethnically diverse and there was an even split between men and women."* Nevertheless, *"retaining diverse lawyers is a trickier subject."* One diverse attorney opined that *"retention is a very individual decision. Having diverse partners that attorneys can look up to plays a big role in their decision to stay."*

"Retaining diverse lawyers is a trickier subject."

Strategy & Future

"We're not looking to be all things to all people," head honcho Kim Koopersmith tells us, *"but we're focusing on making sure that every practice area we have is strong and able to meet client needs."* She cites financial restructuring, funds, tax, energy, policy, litigation, corporate and international trade as the areas that *"brought us notoriety and client recognition,"* and therefore *"the ones we want to concentrate on doing well."* Internationally, the firm is still digesting the Bingham acquisition. While there are no plans to stake a claim on any new frontier, according to Kim Koopersmith this shouldn't stop the firm reaching new markets from its existing bases. In particular, *"we're working on a Cuba initiative,"* she explains, *"and our corporate and energy practices have extensive experience in the African and Latin American markets."*

"Working on a Cuba initiative"

See firm profile on p.605

Get Hired

Good grades are a must, obviously, but as *"only accomplished and capable"* people make it to the interview stage, would-be associates must show they offer a little extra. The firm has a list of core competencies against which it tests interviewees. According to hiring partner David Botter, these include *"ownership, professional excellence, service, teamwork and client focus."* Associates who'd been involved in recruitment sought similar traits in their interviewees: *"I'm looking for someone I think I'll enjoy working with,"* said one, *"as well as someone who'll be able to handle the stressful periods without freaking out."* Another associate thought interviewees used an informal 'Des Moines airport' test, *"as in, would you mind having an overnight layover in Des Moines with this person?"*

"Would you mind having an overnight layover in Des Moines with this person?"

The interview process had been less a grilling and more a pleasant discussion for our sources. *"They looked at my resume, asked some general questions and chatted about my travels,"* recalled one. *"It was a really easy conversation."* Another told us that *"my interviewer seemed really thoughtful and interested in finding out what I could bring to the firm."*

"At the other places I interviewed I felt like I was under a microscope. At Akin it felt like a conversation..."

See firm profile on p.605

Allen & Overy LLP

Lawyers per state

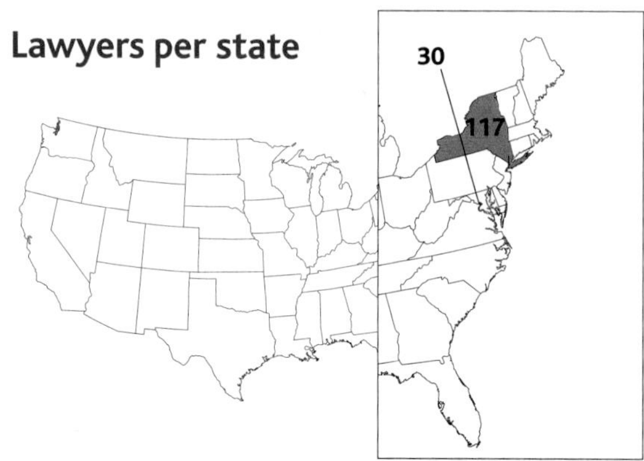

Largest US office: New York
US offices: 2
International offices: 42
First year salary: $160,000
Billable hours: 2,000 target
Summers 2016: 24 (all 2Ls)
Revenue 2015: $2.06 billion (-0.03%)
Partners made in 2016: tbd
Famous for: high-end international corporate and finance work; social culture; British elite firm

Allen & Overy offers global work and the camaraderie of a much smaller firm.

WHAT kind of law firm do you want to work at? One that does BigLaw quality work for BigLaw quality clients? How about a global behemoth that has the tight-knit atmosphere of a smaller firm? Perhaps you want to be in regular contact with colleagues and clients overseas, with the chance to spend some time in another office? If your answer is 'all of the above', then consider Allen & Overy. It's a member of London's 'magic circle' of elite law firms, and its US attorneys are plugged into a worldwide network of offices that give them access to big, meaty cross-border transactions. At the same time, A&O's two smallish US offices – nearly 120 in NYC and 30 in DC – give it a more intimate feel here.

In the US, A&O is particularly known for its project finance work, but it also picks up *Chambers USA* rankings for areas including general commercial litigation, M&A, real estate, regulatory and capital markets. The associates we spoke to felt that while A&O was still growing in the US, it had the edge on most American firms when it came to international work. *"Home-grown firms are starting to look globally,"* explained one source, *"but A&O is so far ahead of most competitors internationally that it'll be a struggle for another firm to match us."*

On chambers-associate.com...

- Allen and Overy's connection to the British Monarchy

ASSOCIATES SAY...

The Work

Allocation varies between New York and the smaller Washington, DC office. In the latter *"you're assigned to a general group, such as banking, and the expectation is that you'll get most of your work from within that group,"* explained a junior in the capital. In New York, incoming associates submit a list of their preferences to the firm, which rotates them through *"at least two, but sometimes up to three, different departments."* Management *"guarantees that at least one rotation will be your first choice,"* we're told. The associates we spoke to appreciated being able to try before buying *"I came in thinking I wanted to work in one area of law,"* explained one, *"only to find that what I thought was my first choice wasn't my first choice at all."*

> *"The deals can span two, three or even four jurisdictions."*

"A lot of people come here wanting to do project finance work," said one associate. *"It's the sexy group."* Juniors reported taking charge of closings, where *"there's a lot of drafting, a lot of conditions precedent to monitor, and a lot of documents in play. Your job is to keep track of them all."* There's also the opportunity to *"look at the legal opinions that have to be delivered."* After completion, associates can find themselves *"reopening the finance documents to see if they permit borrowers to do something."* When this happens, it's the younger

See firm profile on p.606

Rankings in *Chambers USA*

Antitrust	Latin American Investment
Capital Markets	Litigation
Corporate/M&A	Projects
Environment	Real Estate
Financial Services Regulation	

For detail on ranking tiers and ranking locations, visit www.chambersandpartners.com

Recent work highlights

- Advised Guyana Goldfields on the Aurora Gold Project, the first ever project financing in Guyana's history
- Acted on Coca-Cola Iberian Partners' transatlantic merger with two other bottling companies to form the world's largest independent Coke bottler
- Counseled the Import-Export Bank of Korea on the world's first ship-covered bond deal

associates who are in charge of *"combing through the paperwork, targeting the relevant provisions and doing the initial draft of any amendments or waivers."*

The work frequently crosses borders, but our sources were at pains to stress that the US offices were far from just outposts. *"We have our own clients, independent of London,"* said a New Yorker. *"In capital markets deals can span two, three or even four jurisdictions, so you'll be in constant contact with your colleagues abroad,"* said an associate in that department. *"In litigation, where you're in a jurisdiction practicing before a court, there's less interaction."* In addition to liaising with colleagues in other offices, there are ample opportunities to spend a bit of time abroad. *"Secondments tend to come about two years after qualification,"* said a source, *"but recently a first-year got to spend six months in London."*

Hours & Compensation

Associates are expected to bill 2,000 hours a year. There were mixed feelings on the target: *"I had no problem hitting it,"* said one associate, *"but some of the people in my class did."* With different patterns of allocation in different departments, and much of the work cyclical, some juniors struggled to do enough billable work. *"We do a lot of non-billable work, which takes up more time than people think."* It certainly isn't fatal if you fall a little short though: *"2,000 is the target, but I've known people who've billed below that and still received a full bonus."* Salary is market rate, and there were generally no complaints, especially regarding hours worked. *"I get paid the same as other lawyers in New York, but I probably work better hours."*

"I don't think I could have asked for a better work-life balance."

So the hours are good, then? *"Yes-ish,"* replied a New Yorker. *"This isn't A&O's fault, it's a BigLaw-wide problem, but they expect you to always be available, and this does affect quality of life."* In fact, people we chatted to spoke highly of the firm's commitment to work/life balance. *"I don't think I could have asked for a better work/life balance,"* said one, while another described the firm as *"as good as it gets among BigLaw firms in New York."* Of course, you shouldn't expect to work nine to five: average days tend to begin around 9am and, depending on the department, usually end anywhere between 7pm and 10pm.

Diversity

A&O's standout diversity initiative is called '20:20', a firmwide drive to increase the female membership of the firm's global partnership by 20% by 2020. Associates described this as a *"sincere and concerted effort to increase the female percentage of the partnership."* Overall, our sources thought that there was a *"good split between males and females"* at associate level, and a few mentioned that *"there's a lot of diversity in terms of national origin."* That said, our sources weren't able to identify any other diversity initiatives, and there was agreement that the firm could do more to reach out to ethnic minority candidates.

Pro Bono

"I think the firm genuinely values pro bono work," felt one associate, *"and you can pretty much do anything you want to."* Others were a little more hesitant: *"They support the idea of pro bono, but partners won't stop assigning billable work just because you're doing pro bono,"* explained a project financier. This is borne out by the fairly low figure of 14 hours' pro bono associates did on average in 2015. There's certainly a lot of choice in the kind of matters associates can get involved in – one of our sources used the word 'menu' to describe the range of options on offer, which include everything from representing Russian LGBT people in asylum cases to providing tax advice. The firm is also open to associates 'bringing in' new pro bono work; we heard of one associate who brought some wrongful conviction appellate work with them from law school. Associates can count 50 pro bono hours toward their billable hours target of 2,000.

Pro Bono hours

- For all attorneys across all US offices: 1,977
- Average per US attorney: 14

See firm profile on p.606

Culture

Our sources described A&O as the sort of place *"that attracts people who want to work hard but who respect others."* Overall, people are *"kinder and nicer than your typical New York firm,"* an associate told us, adding wryly *"it was a bit of a culture shock for me."* In the New York office *"nobody closes their door unless they're on a call,"* and *"we don't have any screamers."* One source in Washington described that office as having an *"entrepreneurial culture,"* something they put down to the fact it's small but growing. With regular contact between branches in different countries, people felt there was definitely an A&O-wide culture. *"People are quite worldly, with international backgrounds."* Departments tend to socialize together, and naturally some are more active than others, but there are bi-weekly happy hours, monthly get-togethers for food and annual summer and holiday parties.

Offices

New York is the larger of A&O's US offices. It's situated in plum Manhattan real estate in Midtown and is *"connected to the Rockefeller Center concourse, so it's theoretically possible to go shopping without ever seeing the outside world."* DC is smaller and newer, and our sources there described it as *"much nicer than New York."* We'll let them settle this between themselves, but both offices benefit from central locations and that close-knit, small firm feel we mentioned earlier. *"We're scattered over three floors of a building,"* said someone in the city that never sleeps, *"but I'm still very close with the people I summered with."*

"People who want to work hard but who respect others."

Whichever office you go to, one of A&O's big attractions is the opportunity to spend time in one of the overseas offices. Twice a year the firm sends an email around all its offices, and each office lists available secondment opportunities. There's also the chance to do some-on-the-job training in an overseas office. Some groups take their newbies to London for two weeks of training at the home office. Departments also hold offsites where the entire worldwide practice group descends on a chosen city for a few days of training.

Training & Development

All incoming attorneys attend two weeks of orientation followed by department-specific training. Orientation takes the form of a series of ninc-to-fivc days, and includes internal presentations about each of the departments and their work, general information about the firm, and administrative stuff. *"I find the more intermittent CLE training more useful,"* admitted a junior, *"but at the end of the day, you do need to know how the computers work."* There's also a formal appraisal system in which *"you can nominate anyone you've worked with to evaluate you,"* but associates found the informal, off the cuff feedback delivered by partners and associates they had worked with to be the most helpful. *"It's entirely dependent on the person,"* a source in projects found, *"but in my group there are some very talented associates who are always willing to lend a hand."*

Strategy & Future

If associates were drawn to how many borders Allen & Overy crosses, then so too are clients, US managing partner David Krischer tells us. The US is a tough nut for Brits to crack but A&O thinks its global reach gives it the edge. *"It's not the world's biggest secret that New York is an incredibly competitive market,"* admits David Krischer, *"but clients who deal in multiple jurisdictions are beginning to realize the benefits of a one-firm approach."* Of course, simply planting flags everywhere isn't enough. There are no plans in the immediate future to open other US offices, but there is a big push to grow both New York and Washington. *"We need to have high-quality people at all levels, and we're very keen on promoting our associates to partner,"* says Krischer, contrasting A&O with other firms where *"partnership opportunities are more limited."*

"We're very keen on promoting our associates to partner."
David Krischer, US managing partner

Get Hired

Because of all the different markets the firm operates in, recruiters look for the ability to think a little differently: *"Of course we want bright, skilled people who are willing to work hard and put in the time, but that's what everybody wants,"* US MP David Krischer explains. To stand out, candidates need to show that they're *"intellectually rigorous enough to grapple with a number of legal systems bumping up against each other."* He also advises law students to keep an open mind about their futures: *"It's almost trite to say that the profession is changing, but it is."* New starters should *"stay flexible about the kind of law they want to practice, while spending their first few years getting in the best possible training."*

"They don't want someone who's going to treat the firm like their own plane ticket."

See firm profile on p.606

Junior interviewees flagged *"language skills"* as something the firm looks favorably on, although they noted that the lack of them isn't a deal breaker. Similarly, while *"moot court and law review experience would definitely be welcomed,"* they aren't essential. *"They were interested in me as a person, rather than just as a set of exam results,"* recalled one interviewee. *"Questions focused on what I could bring to the business, rather than a set of grades."* An interest in the firm's international work was a recurring theme raised by the associates we interviewed, but they warned against overdoing it. *"Interviewers like to hear that you're interested in the international aspects of working here,"* explained one, *"but they don't want someone who's going to treat the firm like their own plane ticket."*

"A&O is so far ahead of most competitors internationally that it'll be a struggle for another firm to match us."

The Inside View

See firm profile on p.606

Alston & Bird LLP

Lawyers per state

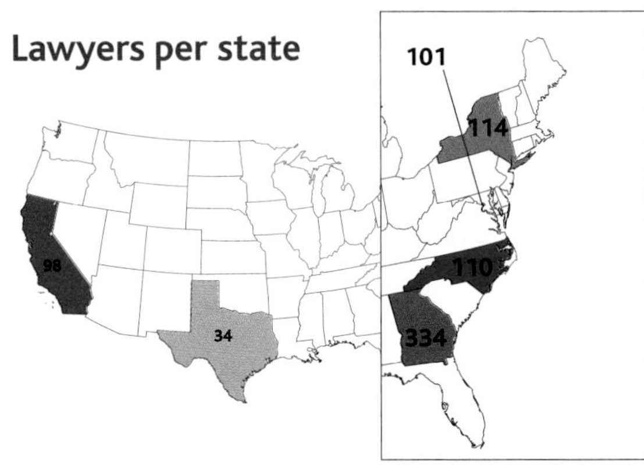

Largest US office: Atlanta
US offices: 8
International offices: 2
First-year salary: $135,000 - $160,000
Billable hours: 1,900 target
Summers 2016: 55 (44 2Ls, 11 1Ls)
Revenue 2015: $688 million (+6.6%)
Partners made in 2016: 16 (all US)
Famous for: warm and friendly Southern culture

Birds of a feather flock together, and associates hired here have all demonstrated "*a hunger, appetite, enthusiasm and creativity.*"

ALSTON & Bird added another chick to its nest at the end of 2015 with the hatching of its Beijing office. Managing partner Richard Hays chirps: *"We had a growing practice from clients based in China over the last several years, with more of our lawyers spending an increasing amount of time there. Opening an office in Beijing was a natural step."* The new addition, Hays assures us, is already hungry and gobbling up far more than its initial diet of IP matters: *"Our inbound corporate/M&A work has been greater than we had anticipated."* Beijing is Alston's second international office (the first is in Brussels) and joins a brood of eight US offices.

Alston's Atlanta HQ is at the top of the pecking order for corporate/M&A work in the region, according to *Chambers USA,* while its large IP group is also highly regarded. You'll also find the firm roosting among the top branches of the antitrust, bankruptcy/restructuring, healthcare, labor & employment, litigation, real estate and tax trees. Alston might be a golden eagle in Atlanta for these practice areas, but it was high-flying reputation of another kind that first attracted interviewees here: *"Alston gives young attorneys national level work without burning them out. A lot of firms promise a work/life balance, but I've found it to be true here."*

On chambers-associate.com...

- We speak with managing partner Richard Hays
- Professional personal partner Liz Price gives us the lowdown on hiring
- Human trafficking pro bono

ASSOCIATES SAY...

The Work

Many of the firm's 30-odd entry-level associates swoop into the litigation or IP department (including IP litigation, securities, and trial). The rest are spread across transactional practices including finance, financial services & products, corporate transactions, and real estate. Finally, a few usually go into the tax department.

"You're just the new kid on the block."

Work allocation is *"pretty group-dependent. The smaller groups have no formal process; you're just the new kid on the block and people check your availability with the practice group leader before getting in touch with you. My group requires associates to fill out a workload report to indicate if you're jammed up and off limits."* Larger groups like IP litigation or litigation & trial operate a formal pairing system where associates are attached to two partners and an associate. One litigator explained: *"I got most of my work from them in first year but it wasn't a bar to getting projects from other people I wanted to work with."* By the time associates hit their third year, *"the system acts as more of a back up"* than first point of call, but *"there is a concerted effort from the partnership*

See firm profile on p.607

Rankings in *Chambers USA*

Antitrust	Healthcare
Banking & Finance	Immigration
Bankruptcy/Restructuring	Intellectual Property
Construction	International Trade
Corporate/M&A	Labor & Employment
Employee Benefits & Executive Compensation	Litigation
	Privacy & Data Security
Energy & Natural Resources	Real Estate
Environment	REITs
ERISA Litigation	Tax
Government	

For detail on ranking tiers and ranking locations, visit www.chambersandpartners.com

Recent work highlights

- Advised flooring manufacturers Mohawk Industries in its $1.2 billion acquisition of Belgian vinyl tile manufacturers IVC Group
- Represented Mazda Motor in litigation arising from allegedly defective airbags sold to numerous automakers by Takata Corp, which prompted the recall of over 374,000 Mazda vehicles
- Assisted global pharmaceutical company Mylan in securing $13.7 million in damages against GlaxoSmithKline concerning a breach of contract over the production and sale of an antidepressant drug

to ensure associates update them every couple of weeks on capacity so no-one is over burdened or under served."

Alston's IP litigators primarily handle patent litigation (pursuing patent infringement claims) on the defense side, although there's also scope to sample things like trademark litigation. Newbies in litigation & trial spend their first few years as generalists, flitting their way through areas like antitrust, white collar, healthcare and class actions. Litigators in both groups pointed out that a current busy spell at the firm meant they'd seen higher levels of responsibility than expected: *"There are definitely times when I'm helping out on a higher level by assisting with deposition prep and writing motions for the court, but there has been a good mix of tasks. I can sit back and not worry about things while doing doc review and at other times make a lot of effort with a memo."*

Training & Development

Litigation juniors felt *"the firm makes an effort to fill the gap created by the lack of trial experiences for young associates, in a world where cases don't go to trial as often as they used to."* Alston & Bird Litigation University schools associates in practical areas such as *"conducting depositions or handling discovery disputes. We submit mock assignments and receive feedback; it's been helpful in broadening our horizons when the client work isn't bringing us to those stages. We'll be a bit more prepared when we see it."*

"Fill the gap created by the lack of trial experiences."

IP litigators can also jump on IP training with their transactional counterparts every couple of months to discuss areas like *"patents, trademarks and trade secrets, so those who don't encounter those areas learn what each section does."* Deal-doers in corporate and transactional groups receive regular rundowns on skills such as conducting due diligence and negotiating agreements. They also participate in mock acquisition agreements, with associates acting as either buyers or sellers.

Way before they get into all the nitty gritty training, all new starters attend a week long orientation on the usual nuts and bolts, topped off with discussions on *"how to manage being a young associate."*

Pro Bono

Up to 100 hours of pro bono count toward the firm's bonus eligible target. One junior told us *"there are associates who've never done it and some who bill over 300 hours a year. We can tackle whatever we feel comfortable with."* Others felt there was more of a concerted *"push from senior associates and partners to make sure we're involved with it. We might not otherwise get the opportunity to be able to stand up in court as a first or second-year."*

"We might not otherwise get the opportunity."

Most matters are sourced through the firm's internal pro bono portal where juniors can pick up *"opportunities helping artists write contracts or sell and protect their work. We also help victims of domestic violence and write wills and offer estate planning for folks,"* one associate outlined. *"A big pro bono opportunity in Atlanta is human trafficking cases."* Visit our website to read more about Alston's work concerning human trafficking.

Pro bono hours

- For all attorneys across all US offices: 49,465
- Average per US attorney: 67

Hours & Compensation

Alston & Bird has no formal billable hours requirement but associates are bonus eligible at 1,900 hours (including 100 hours of pro bono). Bonus amounts increase for every 100 hours above the target and the firm also offers

See firm profile on p.607

discretionary bonuses tied to non-billable work such as business development or high levels of pro bono. Juniors believed the bonus target was a *"reasonable figure but it's dependent on which group you're in and your seniority so not everyone makes it."* For those who don't, *"it's a little disheartening that the number is so rigid and doesn't take work flow into consideration."*

"Past 7pm there are only a few lights on around the office."

One typical target-hitter reassured us: *"I don't feel like I have to work 12 hours a day to make the 1,900."* Most interviewees put the daily attorney exodus home time at around 6.30pm. *"If I'm here past 7pm there are only a few lights on around the office. There is really is an acceptance and encouragement to work remotely. People don't care where you are so long as the work is done."* That said, several sources generally didn't have to plug in from home more than a couple of days a week, if at all: *"I've not had to do it for a few weeks."* Even those who do consistently put in a couple of extra evening and weekend hours told us they had *"tons of time for a social life, gym, vacations and all that other stuff while still hitting bonus hours."*

Culture

Alston & Bird's decade and a half on *Fortune*'s list of the '100 Best Companies to Work For' sets expectations high, so do attorneys think Alston actually lives up to the hype? *"Generally everyone has this perception that they wouldn't want to work anywhere else,"* one junior reckoned. *"That's not to say it's a cake walk here. Expectations are very high for everyone but they come with a lot of respect too."*

A leisurely stroll through the firm's hallways doesn't usually afford attorneys the sight of *"people with their doors closed or their heads down looking like they haven't slept in two months."* Several sources noted the firm's knack of diffusing any slip toward BigLaw's notorious highly strung environment: *"I'm stressed but it's not like despair,"* clarified one upbeat associate. *"It's more that I'm involved in work that places a lot of expectations on me. I don't dread working with anyone in particular, which makes pretty stressful projects easier to do."* Another shared similar emotions: *"I'm normally an anxious person – law school made me anxious! – but everyone is so upfront there are no real surprises here. People are warm and understanding, so my stress is low."*

"The Southern culture is warmer and friendlier."

Alston's Atlanta origins topped our poll of the main drivers behind its culture. *"We're more congenial and laid back than the traditional stuffy firm; the Southern culture is warmer and friendlier,"* one Atlanta-based rookie revealed. *"The partners take an interest in associates' personal lives. I see that day-to-day in the hallways and it carries into the work environment when partners want to make sure I'm not overburdened and I'm getting the kind of work I want to do."*

"Generally everyone has this perception that they wouldn't want to work anywhere else."

The HQ's atmosphere appears infectious to varying degrees. In Washington, DC, the smaller office *"feels more formal than Atlanta,"* but head up country to the Big Apple and you find that *"being a Southern firm, Alston's culture is a little different to New York institutions which grind associates out."*

Offices

Sources believed there is a good amount of *"collaboration across offices"* when it comes to staffing cases. *"It creates an environment where we feel like one firm, not different firms spread across the country."* Even juniors who were yet to see substantial cross-office action noted, like this New Yorker: *"We often call other bases just to ask what their particular thoughts on a matter are. I think we're very integrated."*

"We feel like one firm."

Atlanta handles *"a bit of everything."* New York tackles cases with more of a financial bent and *"our California offices have a really strong environment group."* DC houses a robust healthcare practice while Charlotte's IP group is regarded by *Chambers USA* as one of three top-ranked IP groups in the region.

Diversity

"Alston makes a sincere commitment to diversity," associates said. *"During orientation we had presentations in unconscious bias in the workplace and visited The* [Martin Luther] *King Center in Atlanta."* Happily, diversity initiatives stretch somewhat further than a quick Powerpoint and jaunt to the local memorial site. Alston's active Women's Initiative, for example, throws events like happy hours, client dinners and associate dinner parties at partners' homes.

"A coffee and a chit chat every quarter."

See firm profile on p.607

While the Women's Initiative operates its own mentoring system, other minorities (LGBT, ethnically diverse etc) are also assigned a mentor. *"We have coffee and a chit chat every quarter."* But are these initiatives having any effect on Alston's attorney make up? *"The partner level is not as diverse as the associates. I don't know how to feel about that,"* one source admitted. *"Variety takes time to bubble up to senior levels, especially as the odds of making partner are hard anyway. We'll see how it goes."*

Get Hired

Setting aside the obligatory good grades, Alston is *"not looking for people who just want to punch a clock, but those seeking to be part of our firm in a meaningful and complete way. We want new associates to come in with an appetite for sophisticated and meaningful work, and personal and professional growth and development, "* professional personnel partner Liz Price stresses.

"Act like a regular person."

But bear in mind that *"at some point you have to step back and be yourself,"* one associate involved in hiring told us. *"If I see someone just putting on an act, that's strikes one, two and three. I don't know who you are if you're trying to be a super associate for 30 minutes rather than yourself."* Visit our website to read more from Liz Price about Alston's hiring practices.

Strategy & Future

Late 2015 saw the addition of a Beijing office to Alston's roster. *"It's the next frontier,"* one associate exclaimed. Sources pegged the move as *"very much work driven; we're not expanding internationally just for the sake of it."*

While no more new offices are on the horizon, the firm's concentrating on its existing bases: *"We've had a good bit of expansion in our Dallas office; at the beginning of the year we brought in about eight lawyers into our financial team and just added an additional five lawyers within the last couple of weeks to our financial services and banking groups,"* managing partner Richard Hays tells us. Read his full take on the firm's future and strategy on our website.

"A lot of firms promise a work/life balance, but I've found it to be true here."

See firm profile on p.607

Arnold & Porter LLP

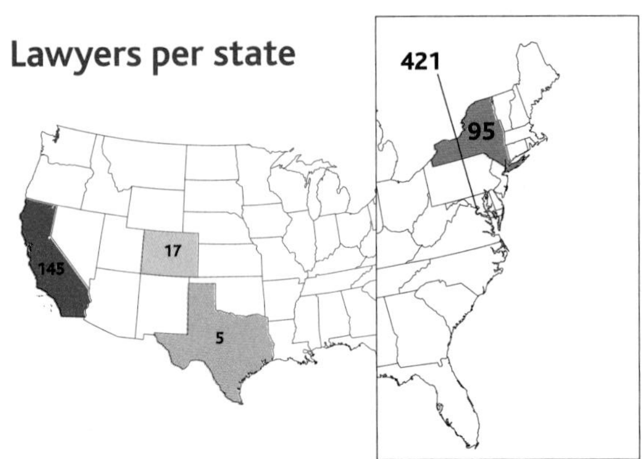

Largest US office: Washington, DC
US offices: 7
International offices: 2
First-year salary: $160,000
Billable hours: 2,000 target
Summers 2016: 38 (all 2Ls)
Revenue 2015: $649.8 million (–6.5%)
Partners made in 2016: 7 (all US)
Famous for: one of DC's finest; all things pro bono

This DC leader mixes "*top-notch talent with a friendly vibe*" and actively encourages pro bono.

"JUST because DC is our largest office it doesn't mean that everything happens here," highlights Richard Alexander, chairman since January 2016. *"45% of our lawyers work outside DC and we have 140 attorneys in California alone."* A&P is famed for its work around public policy and business, plus a commitment to pro bono that sees it urge each of its lawyers to volunteer 15% of their time to worthy causes. This ethos has been around since the firm's birth in 1946 as Arnold & Fortas. Paul Porter joined the following year. It dropped the 'Fortas' in 1965 (which referred to cofounder Abe Fortas, later a Supreme Court Justice).

"When I was interviewing," an insider told us, *"I talked to loads of juniors at different firms and asked them which I should apply to if I wasn't going to apply to theirs. They all said A&P."* But why? A glance at *Chambers USA* reveals top rankings in litigation, government contracts, bankruptcy & restructuring, environment, real estate, and IP, plus a swath of commendations in other areas. But it's not the work alone that attracts recruits here. *"The people won me over, and several of them are true friends,"* another associate was keen to stress. *"Also, the serious commitment to pro bono, which goes back as long as the firm has been around."* Richard Alexander confirms: *"We want to be the number-one pro bono firm in the world."* For the full interview with Alexander, read our Bonus Features on A&P online.

On chambers-associate.com...

- Interview with chairman Richard Alexander
- Interview with cochairs of the hiring committee, Darren Skinner and Ellen Fleishhacker

ASSOCIATES SAY...

The Work

Traditionally, around half of the incoming first-year class starts in litigation. Associates explained: *"Within that there are sub-categories that include product liability, white-collar crime and IP litigation. The second biggest regulatory group is antitrust and then environmental, followed by government contracts."* Others continued that *"more of our IP work comes out of California. New York has a strong corporate and real estate practice, but otherwise I don't think there's a segregation of practice specialisms by location."* Normally litigators enter as generalists, *"but there is opportunity to steer your own ship if you want specific work."* Rookies revealed that *"from day one there is very little doc review. I've created the first draft of motions to dismiss, motions of reply to oppositions, I've spoken to opposing counsel in discovery dispute calls and even taken the lead in some. I've conducted work on implementing settlement agreements, drafted appeals and at one point had to write four short briefs each week."*

> *"I don't feel like I'm just spinning in a gerbil wheel."*

See firm profile on p.608

Rankings in *Chambers USA*

Antitrust
Appellate Law
Bankruptcy/Restructuring
Corporate Crime & Investigations
Corporate/M&A
Environment
Financial Services Regulation
Government
Healthcare
Intellectual Property
International Arbitration
International Trade
IT & Outsourcing
Leisure & Hospitality
Life Sciences
Litigation
Media & Entertainment
Privacy & Data Security
Products Liability
Real Estate
Securities
Tax
Telecommunications
Transportation

For detail on ranking tiers and ranking locations, visit www.chambersandpartners.com

Recent work highlights

- New York partners achieved a $655.5 million judgment after a seven-week jury trial on behalf of Americans killed or injured during six terrorist attacks in Israel between 2002 and 2004
- Devoted a substantial amount of time and resources to pro bono matters relating to the treatment of mentally ill prisoners at a supermax prison in Colorado
- Successfully helped sexual assault victims navigate the military justice system
- Advised GE in its $13 billion acquisition of Alstom
- Represented AT&T before the FCC in seeking approval of its proposed acquisition of DIRECTV, and coordinated competition approvals for the deal in several Latin American countries

Antitrust is a hybrid between litigation and corporate work. *"As a first-year, I've worked on deposition prep with expert witnesses calculating damages and impact."* Second-years recounted that larger deals are *"phenomenal experiences where I had to assess risk evaluations, engage early with regulators and conduct depositions. I don't feel like I'm just spinning in a gerbil wheel."* IP interviewees *"get awesome assignments right out of the gate. I've drafted Federal Circuit appellate briefs."* Some *"traveled abroad to take declarations from 45 people."* Tax newbies similarly praised responsibility levels, saying: *"You start out marking up purchase agreements, then you move onto negotiating tax provisions with opposing counsel. You're certainly not going to grow without advocating for yourself. State your interest and then the trust will either build or it won't."*

Life science & healthcare regulatory sources advised that *"usually everyone has a background in this area and it dictates how the work is assigned."* Third-years get a hefty amount of client contact, but first-years also do a *"substantive amount of statute interpretation, explaining the life cycle of new products on the market and going through regulatory compliance risk and liability with clients."* Novices in larger groups described the assignment process as a blend between formal and informal means. *"We have an assignment partner for each group, but as people get more senior they tend to organically work with certain partners."*

Pro Bono

Back in the 1950s, Arnold & Porter represented the first victims of McCarthyism. It later won the landmark *Gideon v Wainwright* case, which gave anyone accused of serious crimes the right to be represented by counsel, regardless of their financial means. *"We are proud of* Gideon *and now our work on the 'supermax' prison in Colorado. It's front and center, they even mention it at orientation."* Others added: *"The cases don't really differ from commercial cases in responsibility, it's more about getting different work experiences."* As well as the *"15% of our time to pro bono,"* practice group leaders *"encourage us to obtain at least 200 hours which can count toward billables, as can business development work."*

"It looks just like a commercial case, but my responsibility is more substantive."

Pro bono cases have included *"applying for tax exemption status on behalf of three organizations. It's good practice because we would do the same for commercial clients."* Others had worked *"on a straight litigation case, where we're representing the plaintiff. I'm in charge of drafting the complaint, interrogatories and requests for production."* A DC insider mused: *"I've had a little bit of trouble finding the right pro bono work for me. There's just so much to choose from!"*

Pro Bono hours

- For all attorneys across all US offices: 82,998
- Average per US attorney: 124

Training & Development

"I'm never given an assignment and just sent away." Several we spoke to praised the *"extensive set of programs for all new lawyers. The A&P Academy covers everything you need as a new associate, like how to manage and report your time."* There are practice group specific schemes too. Antitrust sources remembered that *"it's bifurcated with demonstrations on e-discovery, how to read financial statements and write briefs and motions. There's even pro bono training."*

"I'm never given an assignment and just sent away."

See firm profile on p.608

Subsequent training isn't mandatory but is strongly encouraged. Transactional interviewees detailed that *"we have a license with PLI* [Practising Law Institute] *that provides online CLE training in any area. We can go to conferences which our group will sponsor as we usually have partners speaking there. Our clients are normally there so we get great training and the chance to network."* Interviewees mentioned a training forum/retreat that occurs once for first-years and then again when they're midlevels. After the first year, *"everyone goes to DC for two days. Litigators get specialist training on depositions and corporate attorneys focus on the transactional side, but we all get the same program."*

Associates receive *"a formal evaluation once a year where you ask partners to evaluate you on matters where you've billed more than five hours."* Feedback is then relayed by a senior partner. Insiders appreciated the firm's effort as *"it takes them a very long time to put it together."*

Diversity

Like most firms, *"we're fairly good with gender diversity. However, it skews toward males a little at the top."* DC insiders explained that *"the firm has developed a new mentoring program for women* (Mentoring Circles) *and we meet in groups twice a month. It's phenomenally valuable, as we all have different experiences to share."*

"It's about focusing on experiences outside of your own."

There are various affinity groups at A&P promoting racial and other diversity, and several juniors were impressed by the mandatory diversity training for all new employees. *"It's four hours long and we do role-playing exercises where we put ourselves in another employee's shoes. It's about focusing on experiences outside of your own."* Cochairs of the hiring committee Darren Skinner and Ellen Fleishhacker point out the firm also awards yearly Diversity Scholarships worth $10,000 each. Applicants must be first-years from any ABA accredited school and *"must explain how they've contributed to diversity in their community, either at law school or writ large."* The affinity groups are: Minorities at Arnold & Porter (MAP), Women Lawyers at Arnold & Porter (WLAP), LGBT Lawyers, and Arnold & Porter Veterans & Affiliates (APVA).

Offices & Culture

"The new space is phenomenal." In October 2015, the DC HQ relocated to the Penn Quarter neighborhood. *"The old building had an outdated law firm setup. Now everyone has their own exterior windowed offices."* With seven domestic bases plus hubs in London and Brussels, lawyers often work with colleagues elsewhere. *"DC works a lot with San Francisco and New York,"* for example.

However, some New Yorkers felt that *"there is a mothership mentality in DC and they sometimes forget to consider the implications for those off-site. Team meetings in Washington mean that Californians can't always attend."* San Franciscans felt that *"it's interesting, our office is the product of a merger with Howard Rice so we do things more independently."*

"It's a good balance for BigLaw. People are just nice and caring."

However, all associates stressed that A&P is *"inviting to first-years. It's a good balance for BigLaw. People are just nice and caring."* This environment is further encouraged by *"regular happy hours and snacks in each office's Garden Room."* DC inhabitants revealed they'd even *"seen conference rooms set up for people to work together on a big puzzle. It's very odd, but great."* Historically, summers have been treated to *"an office Olympics with miniature golf and basketball in the stairwells."*

Hours & Compensation

Attorneys must bill 2,000 hours to be bonus-eligible. To reach this goal, most insiders work ten-hour days and insisted that *"it's necessary to log back on to the system from home sometimes."* New Yorkers similarly revealed that *"there have been times when people have been here till 2am. It really fluctuates."* San Franciscans are slightly more *"laid back, with everyone leaving around 6pm."* Even so, *"partners aren't afraid to email you at 5am."*

"As people get more senior they tend to organically work with certain partners."

"There have been times when people have been here till 2am. It really fluctuates."

Once bonus-eligible, many felt that the system was *"unclear as the firm is keeping its cards pretty close to its chest. It's a moving target. My understanding is that if you reach 2,000 hours you get a bonus in line with the market rate. But last year DC's rate was less than New York, so the bonuses reflected that."* However, others countered that *"we are changing our bonus structure to soon take more of a merit component into account."*

See firm profile on p.608

Get Hired

"There's a thin line between stalking and preparing."

One of the hiring attorneys, Darren Skinner, tells us that *"we find that the candidates who will be terrific associates are the ones who demonstrate that they have done research on the firm and intelligently discuss how they fit in here."* Associates felt that *"once you've passed the grade threshold, it's whether you're personable and have interesting experiences that lend well to the practice of law."* They advised that *"you should prepare by looking at a firm's website, but keep in mind that it's from a marketing perspective. Do the diligence, read the cases we're working on so you can talk about them in an interview. But remember, there's a thin line between stalking and preparing."* For more on hiring, go online.

Strategy & Future

Darren Skinner explains that *"we were essentially founded as a pro bono law firm, so this has become an essential part of our history."* Pro bono is also an essential part of A&P's future, as Richard Alexander confirms that *"we will continue to stick to our knitting and do the things we are known for."* Additionally, Alexander continues that *"all firms need to become more business-oriented as our clients hold us accountable."* With this in mind, A&P's HQ move has attempted to shrink the firm's *"footprint by 25%"* by reducing real estate expenditure. *"We now have a 20-year lease that will give us the facilities to deal with market changes."*

"There is a lot going on though, it's buzzing."

Workwise, associates informed us *"there is a lot going on. It's buzzing. Most practice groups are really busy."* Among many, *"I think governmental contracts and life science & healthcare regulatory as well as appellate litigation are building."*

"We were essentially founded as a pro bono law firm, so this has become an essential part of our history."

See firm profile on p.608

Axinn, Veltrop & Harkrider LLP

Lawyers per state

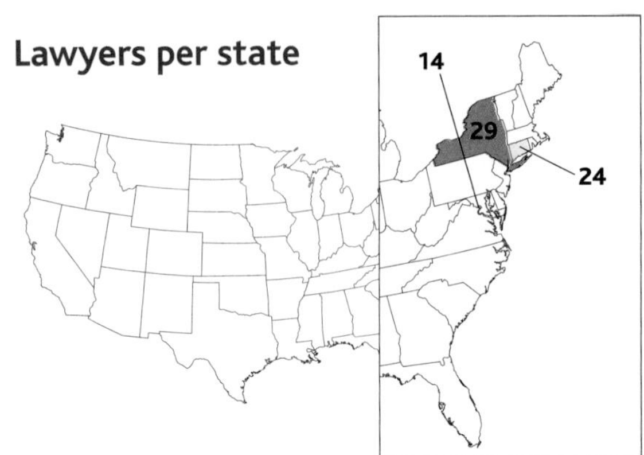

Largest US office: New York
US offices: 3
International offices: 0
First-year salary: $150,000 (Hartford) – $160,000
Billable hours: 1,850 target (2,000 for full bonus)
Summers 2016: 6 (all 2Ls)
Revenue 2015: undisclosed
Partners made in 2016: 0
Famous for: antitrust and IP work; being a young, growing firm

Despite its youth and boutique size, Axinn handles some of the world's biggest deals, and is a veritable teenage dream for antitrust.

"IT'S been an extraordinary year for us," managing partner Jim Veltrop enthuses, with justification. Having turned 18 in 2015, Axinn's coming of age little resembles that of your average late teen. This feisty firm spent the past year advising on billion-dollar mergers and representing the heavyweights of the pharmaceutical and technology industries; notches in Axinn's legal bedpost feature the names of huge corporations including Google, Black & Decker, and most recently Dell (see Work Highlights).

Axinn's expertise is further demonstrated by its rankings in *Chambers USA*, where it is among the front runners both for general commercial litigation in Connecticut, and antitrust in New York and DC. And while 2015 might be Axinn's *"best year ever,"* according to Jim Veltrop, *"2016 looks just as good, if not better."* With a growing antitrust practice and several major cases pending, including one he describes as *"possibly the largest antitrust class action in US history,"* it's no wonder this young firm's hard-working partners and associates alike are excited about its future.

On chambers-associate.com...

- How to succeed at the boutique end of BigLaw
- Interview with managing partner Jim Veltrop

ASSOCIATES SAY...

The Work

All of Axinn's lawyers are litigators, and newbies are evenly divided between antitrust and IP, with just one in the general litigation group. The latter does a lot of corporate-level insurance and commercial contract litigation, as well as some high-level labor & employment cases. Work is allocated formally via an assigning partner: *"Every week we turn in our projected hours and he will use that information to task people on matters."* While the firm is *"working on a system to align associates better with what they want to do,"* assignment is mainly based on associates' availability.

In IP, the firm's *"bread and butter for many years,"* the team works a lot with medical devices and generic pharmaceutical companies (generic drugs being those whose patents have expired). Technology has also been a growing industry for the firm in recent years. Associates mentioned cases related to developments in the biotech field, like spinal implants. A large portion of work in this group is devoted to patent litigation, although there is also *"counseling work and Freedom to Operate projects: the client comes to us to see if they can put the project on the market without infringing existing patents."* For first-years, this mainly translates into discrete research projects as newbies familiarize themselves with particular topics. Although doc review in the traditional sense is mostly contracted out, *"you still have to manage that,"* and attorneys review documents to prepare for deposi-

See firm profile on p609

Rankings in *Chambers USA*

Antitrust	Litigation

For detail on ranking tiers and ranking locations, visit www.chambersandpartners.com

tions. Second and third-year associates described tasks such as writing first drafts of briefs and motions, prepping expert witnesses for depositions, and defending depositions: *"I have a far more central role. I'm not the captain, but I'm squad leader."*

"The most rewarding part of antitrust is getting to dive deep into those markets."

Over in antitrust, Axinn does *"everything from deal work to counseling to litigation, and we're also trying to grow our criminal practice."* How does this break down day-to-day? *"The main ball of work is getting to know the markets and the products, finding out who your client is and what they sell. It's all about pricing and competition – the most rewarding part of antitrust is getting to dive deep into those markets."* The compliance side involves *"looking into current compliance programs, and finding out what would be effective, and what regulators would consider a good compliance program."* Merger control is *"like an investigation, working hand in glove with regulators. Then at the end of the tunnel there may be litigation, so it's a hybrid."* Antitrust associates described clients ranging in size and industry, from the portfolio companies of private equity firms, to large lab equipment and computer technology corporations.

Training & Development

Aside from a few days *"getting to know the IT systems,"* Axinn doesn't have much by way of initial orientation, and *"you basically learn everything on the job."* That said, there is the odd training session on topics such as taking depositions, how to bring in clients, and *"recently someone came in to teach us about oral presentation skills."* As far as practice area-specific training goes, attorneys will *"get together once or twice a month to discuss new issues and developments in the legal field. If something particularly interesting happens in a case, we'll go through that too."* While associates agreed that the training schedule *"isn't very systematic,"* efforts are being made to increase the amount of formal instruction.

"I've never thought twice about asking questions."

Although juniors are assigned mentors, associates also find guidance more informally: *"I look for coaching and advice from those people that I have developed a close relationship with. I've never thought twice about asking questions."* But while most felt well supported, some said high rates of turnover among midlevel associates means that *"as a junior, there's not a whole lot of accessibility to somebody who is above me. It's hard to ask a partner a stupid question!"*

Recent work highlights

- Serving as lead antitrust counsel to Dell on its $67 billion acquisition of EMC
- Successfully represented Alvogen before the FTC in connection with Alvogen's approval to buy the divestiture products in the proposed Mylan/Perrigo transaction
- Representing Interactive Data Corporation (IDC) in its $5.2 billion acquisition by Intercontinental Exchange

Offices & Culture

The New York HQ is mainly focused on the merger control side of antitrust work. The building is *"spectacular,"* with *"a very black and white, hipster-style décor. It's very modernistic."* Another added: *"It's kind of monochrome with splashes of color, not the wood paneling of your typical New York firm."* Although New Yorkers don't have a gym, being Midtown means there's a lot of choice for restaurants, and *"frankly it's good to get out of the building sometimes."* The DC office, which works on a broader mix of antitrust matters, does have its own gym, and is *"in a great location; all of the metro lines are close to us, and there's a lot of options for places to eat around the office. It's a very vibrant area."*

Over in Hartford, the office is awash with *"light colors and dark, stained woods; it's very light and inviting."* The building offers various amenities such as banks and a food court, and associates have access to a YMCA gym on the first floor. One Hartford associate told us that *"it's almost like they're a different firm in New York."* By comparison, New York and DC *"work together a lot."*

"It's almost like they're a different firm in New York."

Associates revealed that attitudes to work differ between offices, and that DC and Connecticut are more *"laid back"* than their counterparts in New York. So is the Big Apple is more BigLaw? *"That would be the tactful way to say it,"* one DC associate responded carefully. *"When you're working on a deal for somebody in New York, the hours are much more unpredictable. Well, they're predictable in that they're inconvenient!"* Another remarked that working with New York means *"I will regularly have to sign back on at around 10pm in order to receive edits for the next three hours, whereas if I'm working with somebody in DC, I might get those first thing in the morning."* New York associates themselves agreed: *"We*

See firm profile on p.609

work longer hours here and it's a little more intense." That said, the sophisticated matters that the firm takes on mean that regardless of where you are, *"people work really hard. Although Axinn is a smaller firm, it's not for somebody who wants a small-firm lifestyle."*

Working habits aside, the firm's small proportions give it a universally *"amiable atmosphere."* A junior in the Hartford office mentioned that *"I know every single person in the office, and that's also starting to be true in the New York and DC offices, because I travel there for business."* Another added: *"We'll get lunch together, and stop by offices to chat."* This doesn't necessarily translate into a lot of external socializing, however, and while there was talk of the odd happy hour, a quarterly office get-together, and lunches with other associates, *"a lot of us just want to get home to our families and lives."*

"We're not holding hands singing Kumbaya, but I will ask partners questions."

In general, associates felt that partners were approachable, to an extent: *"I mean, we're not holding hands singing Kumbaya, but I will ask them questions."* Another associate was equally imaginative, explaining that *"I view the partners as half-coach, half-captain of the team. For the most part you're doing the work and they're coaching you through, and at the end of the game they enter and score the winning goal."*

Hours & Compensation

Interviewees agreed that *"the reality at Axinn is a lot of hours, so there are a fair number of late nights and weekends."* A few felt, therefore, that *"the firm could benefit from respecting associates' time more. It's not the amount of work, it's getting the weird late-night and weekend e-mails."* Juniors were generally quite accepting of the demanding hours, unless *"we're working into the middle of the night because a case wasn't well managed."*

Associates need to bill 1,850 hours to eligible for a portion of their bonus, and 2,000 for the full amount. While most reported achieving their target, some IP associates had struggled as *"things have been a little slow"* in the department this year. Antitrust associates, meanwhile, highlighted that *"if you're on an investigation or a litigation your hours could range from seven to ten a day, whereas if you're on a big deal, they could be more like ten to 14. And the big deals can last for six to ten months, so if you don't get put on one, your hours could come in as significantly lower."* As far as vacation goes, Axinn's formal policy is four weeks, and while *"the firm is fairly accommodating"* if you plan in advance, the consensus was that *"it would be very strange if somebody were able to take the full four weeks."*

Pro Bono

100 pro bono hours can count toward billables at Axinn, and the firm sends out regular e-mails with opportunities. But while some juniors were enthusiastic about pro bono, and had exceeded even the 100 billable hours, others felt *"pretty overwhelmed by billable matters, so taking on pro bono seems very daunting."*

Opportunities that were mentioned varied from veterans' rights affairs to taking on refugee cases through the International Rescue Committee. Attorneys in New York had worked for Volunteer Lawyers for the Arts, which provides legal representation for low-income artists and nonprofit arts organizations.

"Taking on pro bono seems very daunting."

Pro bono hours

- For all attorneys: 1,862
- Average per attorney: 39

"Although Axinn is a smaller firm, it's not for somebody who wants a small-firm lifestyle."

Diversity

"This is a very white place," one associate informed us, another noting: *"We have a few minorities and certainly a good number of women associates, but in terms of partner ranks both are very much underrepresented."* The firm's figures tell us that 12.5% of partners are women, while 100% are white. What is being done to improve this? *"I'm not aware of any initiatives,"* one associate admitted. There is in fact a diversity committee, as well as an initiative for female attorneys. The latter get together in New York once a month for a conference: *"Sometimes we get speakers in who help us think through developing various skills like oral communication."*

Get Hired

Given Axinn's young status and ambitions to grow, antitrust hiring partner Daniel Bitton looks for *"people with an entrepreneurial spirit."* And if you think you're the cream of the crop, think again: *"We need our attorneys to excel beyond the best in order to get the business. They need to be smart and have creative ideas, and be committed to working hard and outworking others."*

See firm profile on p.609

"You have to have a demonstrable interest in antitrust."

Antitrust associates were very clear that *"you have to have a demonstrable interest in antitrust. We take that very seriously into consideration."* A background in economics for this practice area is also *"pretty much a must-have. It probably could be picked up but it would be pretty difficult."* Read more from the hiring partners online.

Strategy & Future

"We're growing rapidly; it's a really exciting startup environment to be in."

"I'm super-excited about Axinn," HP Daniel Bitton tells us. *"I started in 2004 when there were 18 of us, and now there are more than 60 here. We're growing rapidly: it's a really exciting startup environment to be in."* And associates echoed this, with one antitrust newbie adding that *"we expect to grow from our summer associate program and from laterals this year, because we've been very busy."* MP Jim Veltrop points to some challenges within the IP market of late, adding that *"there's a storm going on within IP, but we're weathering it quite well. The practice remains very vibrant, with lots of very high-level cases."* Read the full interview in our Bonus Features.

"We need our attorneys to excel beyond the best in order to get the business. They need to be smart and have creative ideas, and be committed to working hard and outworking others."

Daniel Bitton, antitrust hiring partner

The Inside View

See firm profile on p.609

Baker & McKenzie

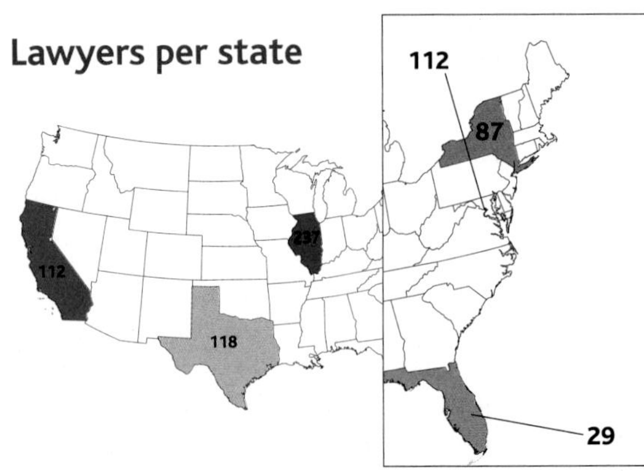

Largest US office: Chicago
US offices: 7
International offices: 70
First-year salary: $130,000 (+$5k signing bonus) - $160,000
Billable hours: 2,000 required
Summers 2016: 45 (42 2 Ls, 3 1Ls)
Revenue 2015: $2.43 billion (-4.3%)
Partners made 2016: 26
Famous for: its bigness; Chicago heritage

Global legal brands don't get much bigger than Baker & McKenzie.

CHICAGO-born globetrotter Baker & McKenzie converted to a Swiss Verein structure in 2004, which essentially means that offices operate semi-autonomously, with their own profit centers. Associates suggested that perhaps as a result there is a concerted effort to unify the business, which benefits them because *"not only do we get the chance to regularly work with colleagues around the world, but the firm has also invested extensively in programs that allow us to move between offices."* The firm's sheer size and rapid expansion led inevitably to the 'McLaw Firm' tag years ago, but it's one that Baker Mac has largely shaken off. *"We're not aiming for all of our offices to be uniform,"* confirms North America managing partner Rick Hammett. *"We hold separate events for new associates, mid-levels, seniors and partners. It means that our lawyers can discuss the challenges and opportunities they face with colleagues who are up against the same situations."*

Though Baker & McKenzie continues to broaden its reach – now boasting over 4,200 attorneys in a mind-boggling 78 offices across the globe – the past few years have focused far more on integrating existing operations. One of the nation's leading tax outfits, Baker's eight US offices work in conjunction with their colleagues overseas to assist multinational corporations based at home and abroad. *Chambers USA* highly ranks a range of domestic and international practices including tax, climate change, litigation, immigration, international trade and arbitration, outsourcing, and cross-border M&A. *"Though we're known as a Chicago firm, every office has its own market to cover and expertise to add,"* associates told us. *"We're always working across offices to help clients whose interests take them here, there and everywhere, so Baker feels much more like a global entity than a Chicago firm with regional satellites."*

On chambers-associate.com...

- Baker's movers and shakers

ASSOCIATES SAY...

Training & Development

Though practice groups hold orientation meet-ups to get rookies up to speed, the vast majority of their substantive legal training comes on the job. Monthly cross-office webinars and annual reviews help to fill in any gaps along the way. As of 2015, each new associate is assigned a formal mentor as well as a small budget which *"allows you to meet once or twice a month over lunch."* But it's the informal mentoring that had our insiders really licking their lips. *"Partners and associates take a real interest in training you,"* gushed one. *"Some like to check in regularly, whereas others prefer to brief you and then talk over assignments when you're done. People have different styles, but whatever the method, when something big comes in Baker does a good job of limiting those face-drop moments."*

"Partners and associates take a real interest in training you."

See firm profile on p.611

Rankings in *Chambers USA*

Antitrust	Intellectual Property
Climate Change	IT & Outsourcing
Corporate/M&A	Labor & Employment
Employee Benefits & Executive Compensation	Litigation
	Outsourcing
Environment	Privacy & Data Security
FCPA	Tax
Franchising	Technology
Immigration	

For detail on ranking tiers and ranking locations, visit www.chambersandpartners.com

Recent work highlights

- Helped poultry production heavyweight Pilgrim's Pride overturn a $30 million fine for unpaid taxes
- Guided FedEx through its $1.4 billion acquisition of GENCO
- Defended The University of Chicago's priceless collection of Persian artifacts, on academic loan from the Islamic Republic of Iran. The artifacts were sought as compensation by US victims of a terrorist bombing in Jerusalem, who held Iran culpable for the attack
- Handling portfolio management and trademark work for the C.S. Lewis Company

The Work

As the firm's biggest department, it's no surprise that a sizable portion of juniors join the tax team. Here they take on a mix of both planning and controversy matters. Planning helps large corporations – usually those with parent companies in the USA and a number of international subsidiaries – to restructure their financial framework in such a way that minimizes clients' tax obligations. Such necessities often arise out of mergers, which for large clients *"can entail subsidiaries in up to 60 different jurisdictions."* Controversy focuses more on clients' relationship with the IRS, and the firm regularly defends corporations' stated positions in disputed tax returns and filings. Insiders in both groups typically begin with *"very discrete research issues,"* but *"as you progress you learn to see more of global picture, and think more about how corporations should approach their tax obligations. Once you've started developing that more contextual oversight, you'll notice your client involvement opportunities begin to grow."*

"It's not uncommon to spend your morning on a conference call with clients in three different continents."

Elsewhere, rookies are split between the corporate & securities, IP, litigation, international commercial, compensation & employment, or banking & finance/major projects practices. Corporate greenhorns are encouraged to work as generalists, though opportunities arise *"predominantly on cross-border M&A transactions and internal reorganizations."* The latter of the two involves dealing with the logistics of moving money, shares and employees to assist the tax planning team's cost-cutting wizardry. *"Reorganization work is probably the front runner for Baker's corporate department,"* but it's an area the drew a few grumbles for being *"a fairly dull money spinner."* That said, it does provide ample opportunity for international involvement: rookies had kept busy with *"a lot of document drafting to set up foreign companies,"* and *"it's not uncommon to spend your morning on a conference call with clients in three different continents."*

Most of our corporate callers had started off as part of an assignment pool, whereas those in tax and disputes had been taken in by a partner whose practice met their interests. Juniors are still free to scout out work from elsewhere. *"It's the type of place where everyone does their best to accommodate your preferences,"* the majority agreed. *"The goal is for everyone to be happy, so if you can communicate which clients or transactions you're interested in then people will try and make it happen."*

Hours

Associates who clock up 2,000 hours are eligible for a bonus. Most overshoot that mark, though *"extenuating circumstances are always taken into account. If the work's not there then you certainly won't be ushered out the back door."* There's a bit of an East/West divide when it comes to facetime expectations. In New York, *"you're expected to be here at least ten hours per day,"* and those in DC sighed: *"If it's a bad week then you're not leaving. Working from home isn't really an option."* California sources felt *"no expectation to be sat in your seat at 8pm,"* and Chicago is similarly *"a little more chilled than New York,"* with most shooting home before 7pm and putting in an hour or two remotely in the evening. Those interested in joining Baker & McKenzie should be aware that *"whichever office you end up in you'll inevitably pull some strange hours at some point. We're a global firm, so negotiating time zones to fit in calls is just a fact of life."*

"Negotiating timezones to fit in calls is just a fact of life."

Over the course of our research, Baker's 'unlimited vacation' policy (which sounds great on the face of it) was a recurring gripe. One insider moaned: *"You can take it when you're free, or so they say, but there's always work to be done! I wish there was a more formal policy."*

See firm profile on p.611

The Inside View

Pro Bono

Associates felt that pro bono is very much viewed as additional to paying matters, so volunteers should be aware that *"you have to manage it around your existing commitments. No room will be made in your schedule at the expense of billed time."* Nevertheless, most of our sources had war stories to share.

"You have to manage it around your existing commitments."

Palo Alto interviewees liked the fact that *"much of what we do relates to local municipal law. Representing non-profit organizations in land use disputes can be extremely rewarding, as you feel like a force for good in your community."* In Chicago, several sources had worked on U visa cases for victims of domestic violence, whereas those in DC had capitalized on the firm's strong ties with the Public International Law & Policy Group. This peace negotiation nonprofit proved particularly popular, as *"it sometimes stages mock arbitrations in the office for associates to have a crack at."*

Pro bono hours

- For all attorneys across all US offices: undisclosed
- Average per US attorney: undisclosed

Offices & Culture

Baker's Chicago hub, which featured in the movie *Transformers 4*, looms over the Millennium Park and offers associates *"waterside views of Lake Michigan"* from their desks. As if that wasn't enough, there's also a reflecting pond on its 50th floor lobby, supposedly to wow clients with its Zen-like charm. *"Sometimes it's hard to see the water as it's so smooth,"* revealed one source. *"Several people have even stepped into it, thinking it was a marble floor!"* The Windy City heart is big on tax and corporate & securities, but offers a full breadth of other services too. *"San Francisco and New York are similarly wide-ranging,"* one insider explained, *"but in smaller offices like Miami or Dallas the choice is a bit more limited."*

"For us to prosper it's important to put faces to names."

Fortunately associates get plenty of opportunities to compare notes, because as one noted: *"Baker goes out of its way to bring together its attorneys. We do a lot of cross-office work, and the firm recognizes that for us to prosper it's important to put faces to names."* Beyond annual practice area gatherings, associates have access to a number of social meet-ups based on their position in the hierarchy. *"We hold separate events for new associates, mid-levels, seniors, and partners,"* North America MP Rick Hammett explains. *"It means that our lawyers can discuss the challenges they face with colleagues who are up against the same difficulties."* As one Chicago insider corroborated: *"Knowing that you can pick up your phone and seek advice from colleagues nationwide has been a big perk."*

"Baker feels much more like a global entity than a Chicago firm."

Further afield, summer associates have the option to spend a few weeks abroad in one of the firm's sister offices, and fully-fledged associates can even jet off for between three months and two years thanks to Baker's 'Associate Training Program.' *"There are always one or two ATPs visiting at any one time,"* according to one New Yorker. *"We've had Polish, Mexican and Australian colleagues pass through the office, which is a great way to build up your global contact list."* To learn more about travel opportunities at B&M, head to chambers-associate.com.

Get Hired

As a behemoth of the BigLaw global league, Baker & McKenzie prizes candidates who are willing to embrace international opportunities. Grades are a given, and those wishing to impress at interview *"must be able to convince us that they're team players,"* says hiring partner Scott Brandman. *"You're just as likely to collaborate with a team the next floor up as you are with another US office, or even an office on another continent. We invest time and resources into promoting a global culture that makes Baker an enjoyable place to work, and we want people who will fit into that."* Those boasting foreign language skills, previous international work experience, or notable team-based achievements should take note.

"Applicants must be able to convince us that they're team players."

Diversity

With so many offices across the globe *"Baker is inherently diverse,"* and rookies relished the fact that *"there are always colleagues of different nationalities passing through."* When it comes to recruitment, insiders had noticed *"a big effort to address the gender gap,"* with those in the Windy City particularly reassured by the presence of *"a lot of young female partners,"* and a 50:50 female/male split at associate level. Ethnic minority hiring is *"not where is should be,"* and respondents highlighted a *"fairly inactive"* affinity group network as an area in need of improvement. That being said, New Yorkers were

See firm profile on p.611

encouraged by the establishment of diversity round table events for 1Ls, which *"are full of useful panels and discussions to help to address the industry's shortcomings."*

"There are always colleagues of different nationalities passing through."

Strategy & Compensation

Baker Mac's expansive international network incorporates a Swiss Verein structure, which keeps offices financially independent. In last year's Inside View, associates had noted a shift toward economic unity, with offices increasingly sharing work instead of hoarding it. This year there were further developments, the most notable being the implementation of a universal North American bonus structure. *"Before every office had a different compensation policy,"* recounted one DC caller, *"so if you made your hours then you were more-or-less guaranteed a certain bonus amount. Now first years can earn more depending on the number of hours they've billed and their profitability, among other considerations."* One New Yorker grumbled that *"the firm could have communicated the particularities of the change a little better."*

The truth is that the move forms part of Baker's overarching strategy to grow its North American offering. *"First and foremost we're a global law firm,"* Rick Hammett explains, *"and we'll continue to look at investing in emerging markets to better serve our clients. To better serve our global platform our focus at the moment is to dramatically increase our North American presence. We see real opportunity in pushing expansion in New York and the Bay Area."* A New Yorker added: *"Our Chicago office is definitely more established than New York, and we'd like to compete with other New York firms for elite work and clients to put those standings on a level setting."*

"Expansion in New York and the Bay Area."

"When something big comes in Baker does a good job of limiting those face-drop moments."

The Inside View

See firm profile on p.611

Baker Botts LLP

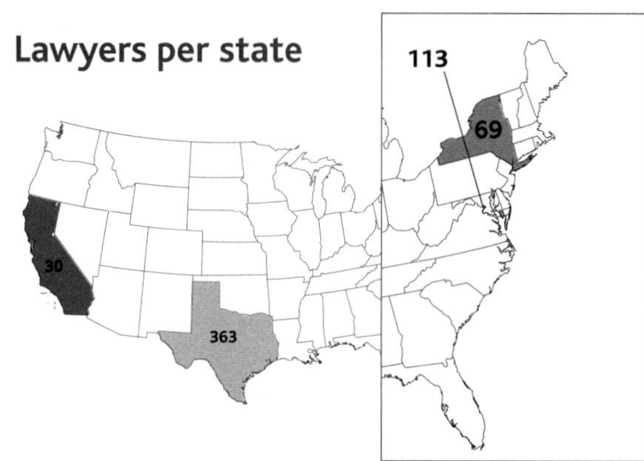

Largest US office: Houston
US offices: 7
International offices: 7
First-year salary: $160,000
Billable hours: 2,000 requirement
Summers 2016: 108 (80 2Ls, 28 1Ls)
Revenue 2015: $704.5 million (+7.9%)
Partners made 2016: 12 globally (10 in US)
Famous for: being the oldest firm in Texas; a stellar energy portfolio

Once the original Texan energy firm, Baker Botts is now an international, diversified practice with a "*terrific reputation.*"

TEXAS was an independent republic when Baker Botts opened for business in 1840. Born into an age of upheaval, the firm has weathered just about every trial history can throw at it, and now its knack for survival has come to the fore once more, as it rides out the bumps in oil prices. *"We're the oldest firm in Texas and proud of it!"* insiders proclaimed. And their high spirits are deserved: over the past year, the firm opened its latest addition to the network in San Francisco, and watched revenue jump to $704.5 million.

Juniors were drawn by the *"familiar atmosphere coupled with the sophistication of big-firm work."* In Texas the giant clients like Shell, BP and Halliburton take center stage, but *Chambers USA* doesn't overlook the breadth of the work in the state, awarding top-tier rankings in IP, real estate, tax and corporate – alongside the expected first prize for its energy practices. Nationwide, the firm picks up a diverse bunch of rankings too: as usual, energy looms large, but climate change, international arbitration, M&A and environment are just a few of the areas attracting high praise.

On chambers-associate.com...

- Interview with hiring partner Van Beckwith

ASSOCIATES SAY...

The Work

Candidates should know which location specializes in what practice area. Most beginners join one of the three Texan offices and they gave us the run-down of who practices what and where: *"Houston is huge and has basically everything. DC's focus is energy regulation and antitrust. Manhattan is mainly corporate and energy projects. Palo Alto is known for IP as is Austin, with the latter also doing State regulatory work. And Dallas is pretty big in real estate."* Associates in New York can also expect some high profile IP and corporate work. A large number of rookies join litigation, corporate and IP, with projects, environmental and tax following not far behind.

Assignment was generally described as a *"free for all."* Initially, starters are given their first work by mentors so that *"you know you have projects when you come in. After that partners can reach out and so can you, but there isn't an assignment system."* Others divulged that *"there's an email once a month which tells us what's coming down the pipeline. We also have luncheons within our practice groups and half the time is spent talking about work opportunities."*

Once staffed on cases, litigators commonly spend time *"drafting motions and various odd jobs throughout discovery like deposition prep. I've also argued minor discovery motions."* Those who specialized in antitrust

See firm profile on p.610

Rankings in *Chambers USA*

Antitrust	International Arbitration
Banking & Finance	Latin American Investment
Bankruptcy/Restructuring	Litigation
Capital Markets	Products Liability
Climate Change	Projects
Corporate/M&A	Real Estate
Energy & Natural Resources	Tax
Environment	Technology
Intellectual Property	

For detail on ranking tiers and ranking locations, visit www.chambersandpartners.com

Recent work highlights

- Won a jury trial in a breach of contract case for LyondellBasell against GIM Channelview. The jury awarded LyondellBasell $8.8 million
- Represented Halliburton in an agreement that Halliburton will acquire all the outstanding shares of Baker Hughes in a stock and cash transaction worth $38 billion
- Represented Repsol, the Spanish energy giant, in its acquisition of Talisman Energy, a Canadian oil and natural gas producer, for $8.3 billion
- Represented Shell Midstream Partners in its landmark IPO

litigation devoted *"80% of the time to government investigations, criminal investigations and internal company audits."* One DC source felt that *"they staff matters leanly, so if you are the only junior you have to do everything."* New joiners in corporate reported similar staffing models. Respondents pondered that *"it's a mix of larger M&A work in due diligence and drafting smaller ancillary documents."* Those in Palo Alto considered that *"a third of the time is venture capital finance startup work. I have the chance to take a substantial role drafting first round finance documents."*

"It doesn't hurt to say 'I can do this' because people let you try."

Interviewees in global projects were *"amazed how much responsibility we have. I've taken first shots at drafts fixing client problems after sitting in on their meetings. It doesn't hurt to say 'I can do this' because people let you try."* As an associate progresses in projects, *"second-years often help draft purchase and sale agreements. There's a lot of chart and matrix work for precedent agreements that have 30 different provisions."* Those we spoke to in global projects enjoyed travel opportunities. Some had gone to *"Mexico and others got to go to Chile in their first year."*

IP juniors detailed that *"there's a strong patent prosecution docket so I'll research patent trails and source-code scans. If another entity holds a patent, I have to make sure that there isn't an open source license that could cause problems during a transfer."* The Austin branch *"is fairly prominent in IP so several new IP partners were brought in."* Sources also revealed that *"in prosecution you're normally writing a patent application or working with the patent office to issue it. The work hasn't substantively changed as we've progressed; you just get more autonomy."*

Training & Development

New starters are given *"a series of classes on our different systems,"* then associates divide up and get training on their respective practice groups. In the second and third years litigators have Houston-based deposition and trail advocacy training. Global projects newbies received *"guidance on basic contract writing on energy issues and the market. We also have lunchtime events called 'EnergyU' where we can talk about industry issues."* Others went to a *"two-day deposition and negotiation workshop at Columbia University."* However, the majority of instruction is *"ad hoc and happens organically."* As associates progress through the years there's evidence of partnership-track training, too.

"The assessments took me a day and a half to complete."

Reviews are *"taken seriously. The assessments took me a day and a half to complete!"* shared one insider. *"Self-evaluations are based on a model of skills that we should be developing,"* we were told. *"We're then sent a list of all matters that we've billed more than 20 hours on and from this we choose the supervisors we want to review us."* Some intimated that *"the senior associates are better at giving feedback, but no news is good news right?"*

Offices & Culture

Baker Botts has developed seven domestic offices and seven overseas. *"For the firm's 175th anniversary there has been an initiative to remind us of our Texan rooted history, so we've had articles about our founders."* But our associate sources needed no reminders about the firm's identity: *"We're definitely a Texan firm."* Even New Yorkers commented that *"it's relatively laid back for New York. It must be our Texas roots."* Juniors were anxious to point out that *"we're not rigid like other old firms. It's very easy-going: everyone calls each other by first names. It's a team-orientated environment."* We noted a collaborative, non-hierarchical vibe from our interviewees.

"We have giant canisters of candy and we rotate flavors."

See firm profile on p.610

The biggest office is Houston, which was remodeled recently. It's located at One Shell Plaza, conveniently positioned for Shell – one if its big clients. Greenhorns observed that *"all the surrounding buildings are energy-related. Most of our clients are either within walking distance or an elevator ride away."*

Those in DC are *"close-ish to the White House. We're in a central location so people come here for the fourth of July fireworks."* Dallas locals spoke of firm festivities *"on Friday afternoons: there's ping-pong with beer and wine. There's also a lunch culture here."* While all locations told of regular *"happy hours,"* Houston trumps the rest because *"every Friday is 'M&M' day. We have giant canisters of candy and we rotate flavors. We also have soda fountains on most of the floors. It's horrible and wonderful at the same time."*

Hours & Compensation

While this may sound like *"candy-land,"* it is still BigLaw with its demanding hours. Most juniors work around ten hours per day on average, with some logging back onto the system from home. As with most firms of this caliber, *"it can fluctuate dramatically. In a single week I had a two-hour day and then a 17 hour day."* However, insiders liked that *"if it's a long night, partners also get down in the dirt."*

"If it's a long night, partners also get down in the dirt."

Attorneys have a 2,000 hour billable target. While pro bono work can feed into this number uncapped, insiders were tentative to suggest that it was easily achievable. *"It's been a little rough with the oil price problem. But the partners have gone out of their way to tell us not to worry,"* because the firm is so well diversified. Once the target is reached, an associate becomes *"bonus eligible."* However, many suggested that *"the bonus system is a little nebulous."* When asked to explain, insiders stated that *"we operate on a level, not a lockstep system. There are four levels of associates and each level is two to three years."*

Pro Bono

All interviewees spoke highly of the pro bono work at Baker Botts: *"We take it very seriously."* All first-years are assigned a case usually in teams with a partner mentor. However, *"you're ultimately responsible for managing it. It's a formative experience as a new lawyer."*

"I'm now more comfortable talking to judges and thinking on my feet."

Austin IP sources recounted their time *"at immigration court with a government attorney in opposition. It's given me more experience in drafting briefs and motions. I'm now more comfortable talking to judges and thinking on my feet."* Others discussed their roles *"staffing the Dallas legal clinic and a housing clinic once a month."* The Houston cohort felt that *"we have really good co-operative agreements with organizations."* The firm collaborates with many institutions including Lone Star Legal Aid, Human Rights First and the Houston Volunteer Lawyers Association.

Pro bono hours

- For all attorneys across all US offices: 24,777
- Average per US attorney: 39.7

Diversity

"Law firms think that they can say the word 'diversity' and it will fix the problem," retorted one respondent. New York litigators weren't so enthusiastic about ethnicity. Those in Dallas explained that *"there are a lot of women associates who then get more senior and leave. It's a tough puzzle the industry hasn't figured out yet."* However, all associates agreed that *"being 100% truthful, the firm knows it needs to work on this."* And it is.

"It's a tough puzzle the industry hasn't figured out yet."

There's a firmwide diversity committee, and juniors were most aware of its efforts in the context of the Global Women's Forum. We heard about the Forum's *"Enterprising Women's Series which has quarterly meetings and events. There was an event on 'grit and mindset'."* Austin insiders spoke of *"sub-group mentoring circles of five to eight women. The firm pays for lunch in an informal setting where you can ask partners and senior associates questions and also be a resource for younger associates."* Juniors have also been treated to presentations from *"the female CEOs or general counsel of our major clients."* Hiring partner Van Beckwith stresses that diversity in recruitment is paramount. For example, *"in partnership with Duke law school, we run a resume review and help workshop for the entire first-year class."* Most newbies felt that despite the industry-wide deficiency, *"the firm is trying to create an environment where people from diverse backgrounds can succeed."*

Get Hired

"Be grateful to work with the smartest people in the room."

"Each year, we visit close to 40 campuses and job fairs," explains Beckwith. He asks candidates to *"show us your*

See firm profile on p.610

past success in law school, but then go further: we want examples of open and obvious leadership successes either in a student organization or job. The more a student can tell me about this in a granular way, the better the interview." Associates added that "*I feel fortunate to be working here. A client once told me that I should be grateful to work with the smartest people in the room.*" Intellect aside, juniors elaborated that "*people have to fit in culturally. When everyone needs to be on deck, there's no separation between sixth-years and third-years. We just have to get the work done, so people can't take themselves too seriously.*" Beckwith emphasizes that "*we are looking for people who have the drive and determination to be successful on our platform.*" For the full interview with Van Beckwith, go online.

Strategy & Future

The energy market slump recently caused a dip in this work across the country. However, insiders were keen to stress that "*we've bucked the trend.*" Associates mused that "*initially when prices dropped, no one knew what to do. People stopped buying and selling, but it stabilized and I don't think it affected us like other firms.*" Others proffered that "*there were some slow years, but in oil and gas it's always volatile.*"

"There is more than enough work to go round."

Van Beckwith reassures us that "*antitrust is booming and IP litigation is very strong. Corporate/M&A is well known to continue to grow especially in the wake of the energy market difficulties.*" Associates could see this in play at the time of our interviews. DC sources disclosed that "*we will see a lot of M&A activity. Antitrust has been the busiest it's ever been and there is more than enough work to go round.*"

"We have people who enjoy working together and respect the intellect we all bring to the table."
Van Beckwith, hiring partner

See firm profile on p.610

Bracewell LLP

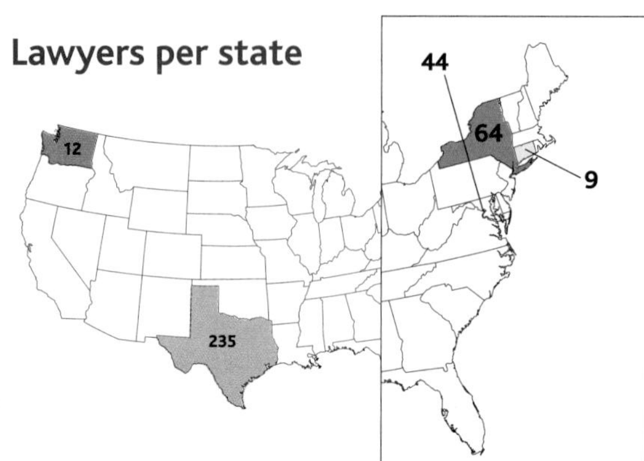

Largest US office: Houston
US offices: 8
International offices: 2
First-year salary: $160,000
Billable hours: 2,000 target (or 1,800 reduced compensation track)
Summers 2016: 37 (27 2Ls, 10 1Ls)
Revenue 2015: $296.5 million (–12.1%)
Partners made in 2016: 5
Famous for: energy work, Southern culture

This Texan powerhouse has more than just energy tricks up its check shirt sleeves...

WHAT do Steve Martin, Stephen Stills, and Bracewell all have in common? Aside from sharing Texan roots of course, they all celebrated their 70th birthday in 2015. And with age, the firm has certainly got more impressive (we can't speak for the other two). Founded with just four attorneys in 1945, Bracewell has swelled to an international outfit of nearly 400 lawyers across the US, and further afield in Dubai and London.

But while it's historically been known for its energy work, the firm is strong in other areas too, with top *Chambers USA* rankings for banking & finance and technology outsourcing, for example. *"Even for people who aren't interested in energy, I think Bracewell is definitely a place you'd want to be,"* one third-year associate told us. *"There's a lot going on outside the energy world."* Texas is still at the heart of Bracewell, though, and many of our interviewees agreed that the firm is trying to keep it that way: *"We are international but we try really hard to keep a small-town feel, even while we're fighting with the big dogs."* In January 2016, former NYC mayor and Bracewell name partner Rudy Giuliani left the firm for greener pastures – Greenberg Traurig – and Bracewell & Giuliani became simply Bracewell.

On chambers-associate.com...

- Getting into Bracewell: what is the firm really looking for? Director of attorney employment Jean Lenzner tells us
- Interview with managing partner Mark Evans

ASSOCIATES SAY...

The Work

Nearly half of this year's group of interviewees were based in the corporate field, while a quarter were in litigation and a quarter were in finance. The remaining handful were spread across the white-collar, labor, tax, and IP litigation groups. Juniors at Bracewell are allocated work though a pooling system, meaning they aren't necessarily assigned their 'own' supervising partner to help them with work flow. This means that *"you have to get out there,"* and *"take on more work with certain partners and organically move to the group that you're interested in."* While most of our sources felt this was a great way to develop their contacts and get involved in a range of cases, others felt that the system made it *"harder to build strong partner-associate relationships."*

"You have to get out there."

On the corporate side, juniors work in a range of areas, including transactions, project finance and bankruptcy & restructuring. *"We do pipeline and power plant projects, then there's a transactional component where we help out with buying and selling energy assets."* Day to day, corporate newbies described *"doing research, writing memos and briefs, reviewing documents for enforcement*

See firm profile on p.612

Rankings in *Chambers USA*

Banking & Finance	Intellectual Property
Bankruptcy/Restructuring	Labor & Employment
Capital Markets	Litigation
Climate Change	Projects
Corporate/M&A	Real Estate
Energy & Natural Resources	Tax
Environment	Technology
Financial Services Regulation	

For detail on ranking tiers and ranking locations, visit www.chambersandpartners.com

Recent work highlights

- Represented Sysco Corporation in a $2 billion public offering of senior notes
- Currently advising Kinder Morgan in connection with its development of the Palmetto Pipeline project, for the shipment of petroleum products from Louisiana, Mississippi and South Carolina, to Georgia and Florida
- Represented Wells Fargo as administrative agent in a $1.5 billion unsecured revolving credit facility to Rowan Companies, a global provider of offshore contract oil and gas drilling services
- Advised Citibank on $5 billion of debt financings related to the merger between energy infrastructure company Williams Partners and Access Midstream Partners

cases and prepping witnesses for depositions." Those in litigation told us: *"I write a lot of motions and briefs. I also do legal research and some doc review, although that's not the bulk."* Other tasks included preparing depositions and attending mediations and hearings.

Most of our interviewees agreed that they were offered a high level of responsibility at Bracewell: *"My first week of work I was assigned to draft several motions right off the bat."* This was particularly common for the smaller cases, which associates can *"handle from start to finish, taking depositions and doing all of the interaction with the client."* The prevalence of energy clients was also, unsurprisingly, very apparent. One corporate associate told us that *"I probably do about 70-80% of work for energy partners right now,"* another adding: *"We've been working on projects where they turn natural gas to liquid products, so it's not all traditional oil and gas."* Even in the white-collar group, *"we're doing defense and investigations of energy clients, from very large international companies to smaller local companies."*

Energy isn't the only thing on Bracewell's agenda, however, particularly in the younger New York office, where lateraled-in partners have brought in their own clients from different sectors. *"Only a few out of my busiest cases have been in the energy sector,"* noted one junior New Yorker. Sources mentioned non-energy clients including Wells Fargo and Bank of America, as well as automobile companies and online retailers.

Training & Development

All new starters are introduced to Bracewell with a short training program in Houston: *"One day was more administrative, another day we focused on big topics like client confidentiality, and the third day was more of a meet and greet."* Although juniors are usually assigned partner mentors, many felt that *"the people you become most reliant on are the people who weren't assigned to you."* Indeed, the support offered by the partners themselves was something that our interviewees were keen to highlight. *"We're not just blindly drafting,"* one finance junior told us. *"After a partner has made corrections on my draft, they'll go over it with me – sometimes for up to two hours. It's invaluably helpful."*

"We're not just blindly drafting."

Finance and corporate associates talked about a boot camp which takes place every Friday for the first few months, that *"brought in partners in different specialisms, from finance-specific matters to securities matters. Now if something comes up for us to work on from another group, we have a bit of background."* The training process in litigation is more informal, the learning method being to *"just throw you in the fire, and let you experience a variety of legal work."*

Offices

The firm's head office in Houston – covering eight floors of the angular, asymmetrical Pennzoil Place – is certainly a well-known landmark, although some felt the interior of the building could use a facelift. One associate described some of the floors as *"retro,"* although Bracewell's managing partner, Mark Evans, assures us that over the coming year *"we're going to make a lot of changes, such as stripping out the attorney floors and putting in a lot of glass to bring in much more natural light."* The New York office is located in central Manhattan, and around a quarter of juniors start their careers here. One associate proudly stated: *"When people say the center of world is New York, we're right in the middle of the center. There's a great feel to it."* Meanwhile in DC, the firm moved to a brand new building in April 2016, which is *"all glass inside and out; a really high-quality office."*

"We don't limit ourselves to our local office."

The high level of connectivity across the offices was frequently mentioned by our interviewees, part of this

See firm profile on p.612

being an 8.30am (CT) Monday morning video conference, when *"all the offices get together and deliver reports based on new deals, transactions, cases or wins."* For those in time zones west of Texas it's an even earlier start. In the work, too, Bracewell associates noted that *"we don't limit ourselves to our local office; if there's somebody in another office who we can ask for help, we will."* One Houston junior described working on a case with *"partners in New York and Seattle, and I worked at the Dallas office for few days last week."*

Culture

While laid back is one way to describe the Bracewell environment, a junior in Houston added that *"it's a good mix between conservative and relaxed; it's not over-the-top Southern."* Nonetheless, some associates reported seeing the occasional cowboy boot, and there is a 'go Texan day' once a year, with all the offices getting involved to crown the best-dressed Texan.

"It's hard to hide here."

Associates in the New York office described the atmosphere as *"more traditionally BigLaw,"* although it seemed the Texan friendliness still reached the Big Apple. Describing the partners, one source noted that *"if you screw something up they'll let you know, but no-one is going to yell at you."* And this attitude filters down to the associate level: *"We're passionate and good at what we do, but we're not so tightly wound that if one thing goes wrong we'll go unhinged; we're here to work together to solve issues."* But laid back certainly does not mean passive, and an entrepreneurial spirit goes a long way at Bracewell. As one New York associate told us, *"the short line is that it's hard to hide here. People will talk to you and ask things like 'What are you working on? What do you want to do?'"*

Our interviewees mostly agreed that *"socializing is important; people like to interact as friends,"* whether that's playing tennis, going to happy hours, or taking part in a fantasy football league, as one New York junior reported. *"A group this year pooled together to get season tickets for New York City FC."* Litigators in Houston told us that relationships between associates and partners were also sociable, helped by the fact that *"there's a close one-to-one ratio of associates to partners, and most of the partners are quite young."* A DC associate added: *"Our managing partner likes to play pranks on the other partners."*

Hours & Compensation

To be eligible for a bonus, associates at Bracewell are expected to bill 2,000 hours, although this target was described as *"flexible."* One second-year told us that *"they understand that because of the regulatory work we do, there will be people that fall under 2,000. I was below 2,000 in my first year and they still gave me a bonus."* Others reported receiving a token bonus if they fell just short of the target. While the vast majority of associates aim for the 2,000 hours, there is also a 1,800 track available.

"If you want to hit those hours, the work is there for it."

That said, most of the associates had no difficulty in reaching this number, and *"if you want to hit the hours, the work is there for it."* On average, our sources reported working nine-hour days, although at busy times this would increase to around 11 or 12 hours, as well as work most weekends.

Pro Bono

Attitudes to pro bono were generally enthusiastic among the juniors we interviewed, with many hitting the 100 billable pro bono hours, and some going above and beyond this: *"Last year I billed about 150 hours."* The cases in the DC office are largely linked to immigration and work for a veterans' legal aid clinic, while in Houston, it was common for associates to be on multiple cases: *"I'm on one very large death row case, and I have another two smaller divorce cases."* New York lawyers described a variety, many working for NYLAG [New York Legal Assistance Group] to defend the city against law suits, as well as cases involving immigration and domestic violence. One associate added that *"we've partnered with a local community center where we provide a housing clinic, taking on cases involving tenant and landlord disputes."*

Pro bono hours

- For all attorneys across all US offices: 10,761
- Average per US attorney: 27

Diversity

The associates we spoke to felt that *"there's somewhat of an issue with diversity at Bracewell, but the reality is in the legal profession there's an issue generally."* That said, the firm is aware of where it needs to improve, and *"there's definitely been a move over the past couple of years toward recruiting more diverse people."* Another added that *"HR has a great list of all the affinity groups within law schools, and we circulate that when interviewing, so if we see an acronym from a certain group we know what it means."*

See firm profile on p.612

Get Hired

"It's not a good place to go to bide out a few years in BigLaw doing doc review."

"The firm likes someone who can take ownership of a case," one associate told us, adding that Bracewell is *"not a good place to go to bide out a few years in BigLaw doing doc review."* That doesn't mean you have to be a workaholic, though: *"I think they're really looking for people with a balance, who are hard-working but know when to relax,"* another junior deliberated. Jean Lenzner, Bracewell's director of attorney employment, adds to this: *"We're not the kind of firm where someone can sit in their office and have no contact with other people."* Read more on our website.

Strategy & Future

In general, the juniors we spoke to were aware of the firm's strategy. Aside from the firmwide Monday morning meeting, associates talked about how *"our MP comes once a year and sits down with associates and goes over the firm's finance from the last year, its profits, practice groups, the ten largest clients – various key factors that let associates know about the behind-the-scenes health of Bracewell."*

"They wanted to support her, so they let the deal happen."

Our interviewees felt that the firm was also very active in helping them develop their legal careers: *"I interviewed with a finance associate who had brought in a relatively small case, not a case that a large firm would normally take on, but they really wanted to support her, so they let the deal happen."* As Mark Evans, Bracewell's managing partner emphasizes: *"We encourage client contact early on; that's always been a Bracewell trademark, because we do not put a lot of people on things. A lot of the associates get to go to front lines pretty quickly."* This strategy means that many of the associates *"see a long-term future"* for themselves at the firm.

"We are international but we try really hard to keep a small-town feel, even while we're fighting with the big dogs."

See firm profile on p.612

Brown Rudnick LLP

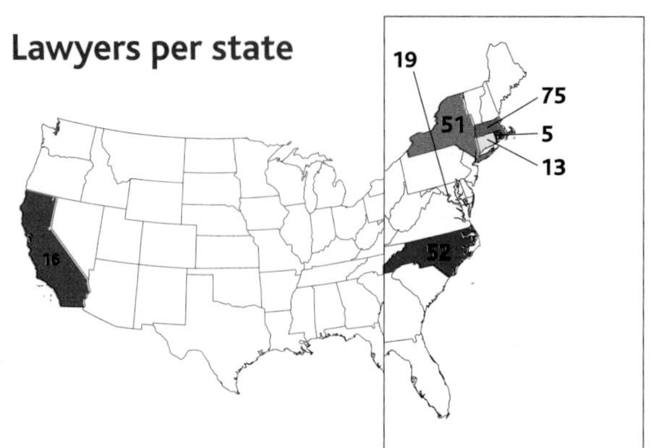

Largest US office: Boston
US offices: 6
International offices: 3
First-year salary: $160,000
Billable hours: 1,900 target
Summers 2016: 9 (all 2Ls)
Revenue 2015: $192.4 million (+0.4%)
Partners made in 2016: 9 globally (5 in US)
Famous for: bankruptcy expertise

Bankruptcy is the beating heart of this Bostonian.

LIKE a Boston terrier, Brown Rudnick is small, strong-willed and sociable. Despite the firm's relatively petite proportions, its bankruptcy expertise enables it to take on the legal big dogs in the restructuring sphere. Imagine an 'American Gentleman' (as the canine is so nicknamed) with a snazzy scarlet collar to set off its monochrome markings: image-conscious Brown Rudnick's offices are decorated according to the firm's black, white and red color scheme, with the Beantown base featuring a 'zebra wall.' And although this sort of hound might have dainty white paws, sources insisted that the firm is *"not white shoe at all."* One explained that *"this place revolves around restructuring – most work touches on bankruptcy in some way. Usually, the firm acts for unsecured creditors and in order to get what we want for these clients we have to be tenacious, creative, roll up our sleeves and claw our way through problems."*

ASSOCIATES SAY...

The Work

Most new associates join the Boston or New York office, with smaller numbers heading to Hartford, DC or Orange County. At the time of our calls, around two-thirds of juniors were in litigation & restructuring. The corporate & capital markets department covers subgroups like tax, finance and IP.

On chambers-associate.com...

- Interview with co-hiring partner Jeff Jonas
- More about Cambridge tech

When it comes to getting hold of work, there's a formal system in place. Both departments (litigation & restructuring and corporate & capital markets) have an associate development manager who assigns work to juniors based on their availability. *"It's sort of protection – they can funnel work to you if you're not busy or stop you from getting slammed."* However, *"there is the flexibility to find your own assignments and partners will come directly to you."*

What do restructuring juniors get up to? *"First-years do a lot of research assignments,"* declared a second-year. *"Obviously I still do some research, but I also write most of the pleadings and have a lot of client contact. Cases are run pretty leanly here so on smaller cases I'm often the most senior associate."* It's also common to get stuck into a lot of marketing work, which entails *"putting together pitch materials and overviews of how companies are doing."* Another restructuring associate highlighted that *"historically the firm has represented creditors' committees and ad hoc bond holder groups who are usually unsecured. That's why we have a reputation for being very litigious: our clients need us to be hard-nosed fighters. Lately we've been getting more secured lender groups as clients, which gives us a little bit more control in bankruptcy proceedings and makes the deals more cooperative. But we still do a large share of unsecured creditor work."*

Commercial litigators noted that they take on *"a broad range of work, although it's inevitable that you'll be doing bankruptcy work at some point because the department is so strong here. In my commercial litigation prac-*

See firm profile on p.613

Rankings in *Chambers USA*

Bankruptcy/Restructuring
Real Estate
Environment

For detail on ranking tiers and ranking locations, visit www.chambersandpartners.com

Recent work highlights

- Represented the committee of unsecured creditors of New England Compounding Pharmacy, including personal injury tort victims who had received tainted steroid injections
- Acted for Target Stores on its $300 million development of a three-story 'City Target' shop in Boston
- Represented Christopher Wilson, the former head of legal at J.P. Morgan in Hong Kong, in SEC, DOJ, Federal Reserve and Hong Kong Monetary Authority investigations relating to the hiring of the sons and daughters of Chinese officials

tice I've handled contract disputes in New York federal and state court as well as taking on some white-collar matters." According to sources, *"there's a fair amount of doc review when you first start. Bankruptcy cases moves so quickly and they often need a lot of people to be on a doc review."* Drafting briefs and discovery requests were also cited as common tasks.

"There is the flexibility to find your own assignments."

Over in corporate, juniors had *"done a mix of general corporate counsel work and M&A. The majority of clients are public companies, although I've done a fair amount of private transactions for equity companies."* The daily grind often consists of *"quite a lot of diligence and collecting signature pages, although I've also gotten some drafting experience."* Interviewees concurred that *"lean staffing helps you to get experience. Sometimes on deals the other side has twice as many attorneys working on it. You're often put in a situation where you're not entirely comfortable – you're aware of your responsibility and the time limit."*

Training & Development

Incoming juniors head to Boston for a week of orientation, where *"we get to know the firm's policies and the different departments."* After this, *"we have formal trainings for both departments and as a first-year you're obligated to go to all of them. The bankruptcy training is helpful because at some point your work will touch on bankruptcy cases or come from a bankruptcy client."* In addition to this, *"there are other in-depth programs like a two-day deposition training, and last year we had a financial adviser come in to discuss how to read financial statements."* Sources agreed that there's an extensive range for newcomers. *"They kinda beat you over the head with training in your first year!"* chortled one.

"The bankruptcy training is helpful."

Interviewees had mixed opinions about informal feedback. *"I get it on a constant basis,"* exclaimed a New Yorker. *"Sometimes it's unsolicited! It's a function of our size here. It's easy to go back to a partner and ask about what you could've done better and partners will call me to say 'great job!'"* Others agreed that, inevitably, time constraints and individual personalities affect the amount of informal feedback on offer. *"I haven't gotten much at all. I don't feel like I have a particularly clear impression of how the firm thinks I'm doing. I get the occasional e-mail saying 'well done,' but I haven't had much of an opportunity to sit down with anyone. I'd like to have more of that."* First-years have a formal review after six months, after which it's an annual occurrence.

Culture

"The firm tries to have people work across offices and likes it that way – a one-firm approach. However, different offices have very different cultures and it's difficult to work closely with people you don't see on a daily basis who work according to different practices and expectations," noted a Bostonian carefully. A junior in the Big Apple shed more light on the matter. *"In New York specifically you have to be a certain type of person to work here. There has been a turnover in litigation because the personalities of the partners here are aggressive and pretty blunt. I personally think it's good for development but it might not be the best fit for some people. The partners like it when you take the reins on cases and stay one step ahead of them by reaching out to clients for things and suggesting to them what needs to be done. When you do something wrong or something they don't love then you're probably gonna get yelled at. It never bothers me but causes stress for some. These are old-school New York trial lawyers. In Boston the partners are more relaxed and bubbly."*

"Different offices have very different cultures."

Other New Yorkers noted that *"it's close-knit here – there's no real division between the practice groups and that makes it easy to get experience and work with different people. There's also a real collegiality between associates, rather than a sense of competition. Everyone helps each other."* In Boston, an interviewee characterized the office as *"a fairly laid back environment. People are busy and work hard but they take breaks and chat in the hallways."* Over in DC, *"there's a strong sense of*

See firm profile on p.613

camaraderie." According to attorneys, the official Brown Rudnick social calendar isn't full to bursting – but there are occasional happy hours and holiday parties. However, associates emphasized that *"among ourselves we often go out for drinks."*

Hours & Compensation

Juniors had mixed feelings about the 1,900 billable hour target for the year. *"It's a reasonable number, but if your workload is inconsistent then it can be difficult and stressful. I have had concerns about not meeting it,"* admitted one. Most sources described *"having slow months then super-heavy months"* but a typical stretch in the office tends to be from 9.30am until 7.30pm. *"There's no face time thing or expectation to be here late into the night just to be available. This past week I just finished a deal and was able to leave at 4pm to go home and sleep."*

"Working into the wee hours is rare."

Of course, if the matter at hand is critical then *"you're expected to get the work done, including working weekends and late nights, but working into the wee hours is rare. It's no different than any other big law firm."* Those who hit the billable target automatically get a bonus, according to class year, with a discretionary amount on top.

Pro Bono

"The firm encourages pro bono – we have a coordinator who farms out assignments and an associate who oversees availability." All hours of pro bono work (with approval) can count toward the billable target. Restructuring juniors help out with *"a bankruptcy assistance program which helps indigent individuals to file Chapter 7 personal bankruptcies."* Other sources mentioned helping with immigration cases and unemployment insurance matters.

Pro bono hours

- For all attorneys across all offices: 6,540
- Average per attorney: 48

Diversity

"There are very few racial minority attorneys here, but the firm is trying to address it – there's a diversity committee which reaches out to the entire firm," commented a New Yorker, while a Bostonian concurred that *"it's a really white office, although the firm tries hard to recruit diverse candidates."* The women's initiative *"organizes events every once in a while. We recently had a dinner for the holidays and they've done lunch meetings where we discussed ways to improve networking skills. They also put together a group to try to come up with a system to encourage retention including alternative work schedules and setting up systems to work from home."* In addition, the firm puts on compulsory unconscious bias training, and recently appointed a diversity partner.

"The firm tries hard."

Get Hired

When it comes to selecting summers, co-hiring partner Jeff Jonas tells us that *"the starting point, like at most firms, is academic excellence. Probably just as important is a person with initiative, a person with drive or entrepreneurial spirit."* But how can someone fresh out of law school demonstrate this? *"It's not always self-evident but on a personal level when you get to meet somebody and hear about their background and what they've done then it's apparent. They don't have to have founded a company or something, but if they show drive and ambition then that leads to the conclusion that they have an entrepreneurial spirit."*

"We have to be tenacious, creative, roll up our sleeves and claw our way through problems."

Strategy & Future

Brown Rudnick holds a *"unique position in the legal industry,"* according to chairman and CEO Joe Ryan. *"We were once described as a global boutique... we're not a thousand-lawyer firm, we're much smaller, but we're very international in our outreach and work. Almost 40% of our lawyers are located in Europe and we compete against firms five to ten times our size."* There's always scope for growth. *"If you look at our growth in recent years, we've focused on Paris and London. Last year we added a great restructuring team to complement international arbitration in Paris."* Looking to the future, Ryan cites IP litigation, life sciences and white-collar as areas of development for the firm.

"We were once described as a global boutique."
Joe Ryan, chairman and CEO

See firm profile on p.613

Cadwalader, Wickersham & Taft LLP

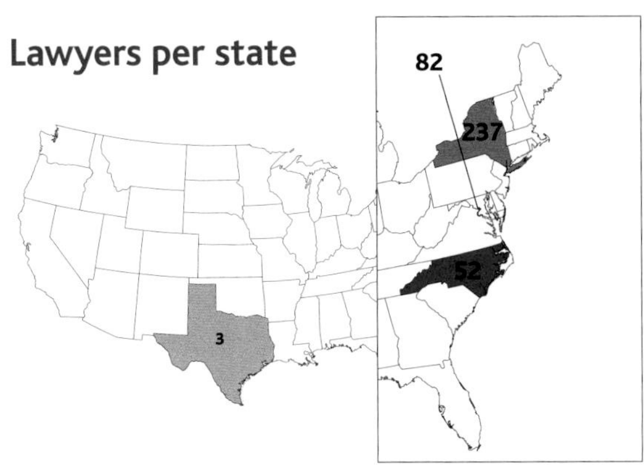

Largest US office: New York
US offices: 4
International offices: 4
First-year salary: $160,000
Billable hours: no requirement
Summers 2016: 50 (44 2Ls, 3 1Ls, 3 SEOs)
Revenue 2015: $463.5 million (-3.8%)
Partners made in 2016: 5 globally (all US)
Famous for: not being a shark tank any more; being a top destination for capital markets

You may have heard about Cadwalader's capital markets capabilities and tough culture (once upon a time), but what's it really like working at this Wall Street icon?

YOU don't become one of the juiciest worms in the Big Apple without a large appetite and plenty of wriggle. Yes, we're talking about Cadwalader. A fixture of the New York scene for nearly 225 years, the past couple of decades saw the firm establish itself as a national leader in capital markets and other transactional practices, in the process building itself a reputation for housing aggressively energetic deal-makers. But forget anything you may have heard on the grapevine about Cadwalader's intimidating culture: these days, it consciously tries to cultivate a much pleasanter associate experience.

Is it succeeding? Well, many junior interviewees told us that as well as being attracted to Cadwalader's powerful practice areas, they were sold on the human aspect too encountered during positive summer experiences. *"I knew I wanted to be in New York doing capital markets, and when I visited this firm everyone was really down to earth and easy to talk to. I summered here and had the best time. We all got really close and even ended up going on holiday together to Six Flags."* Another added that *"here summers sit with attorneys, so you feel you're integrated and interacting truthfully with the whole firm."*

On chambers-associate.com...

- Interview with managing partner Pat Quinn
- Cadwalader's pro bono work: Malala Yousafzai
- More tips on getting hired

Capital markets, corporate/M&A and litigation were big draws in New York, while DC sources were magnetized by Cadwalader's strong antitrust and white collar groups, among others here.

ASSOCIATES SAY...

The Work

Work assignment is not a regimented affair at Cadwalader. Each team has its own style: some have availability reports and assignment databases while others operate a *"traffic light"* system which allows associates to indicate if they're swamped, pretty free, or actively looking for work. Everyone found that *"eventually you become partner-oriented; they approach you for their next project."* New York is the firm's largest office, best known for its capital markets, corporate and M&A expertise. At the time of our calls, 42 of 57 juniors were based in Manhattan. While most occupied the aforementioned bigger groups, there were also associates in IP, financial services and tax. DC claimed 11 associates, spread out equally between the office's main areas of practice: antitrust, energy and white collar defense & investigations. The cohort's remaining four members were based in Charlotte, mostly working in the capital markets team. Cadwalader also has an office in Houston, which is far smaller in size and doesn't currently house any junior associates.

See firm profile on p.614

Rankings in *Chambers USA*

Antitrust	Financial Services Regulation
Capital Markets	Healthcare
Corporate/M&A	Litigation
Employee Benefits & Executive Compensation	Real Estate
Energy & Natural Resources	Tax

For detail on ranking tiers and ranking locations, visit www.chambersandpartners.com

It came as no surprise that New York associates in the capital markets group were *"really busy,"* but we also heard that *"you can always approach the staffing partner to find someone else to take something on if you're swamped."* This was a pro of working in an *"associate heavy group,"* but did it mean juniors were stuck with menial tasks and little responsibility? *"Not at all. If it's a bigger deal, there might be a junior, a second-year, a mid-level and a partner, but on smaller deals it could just be you and the partner."* This meant taking on meatier tasks, as well as *"much more client contact than expected, although it's sometimes with a junior member of the client's team."*

A DC associate in antitrust put it simply when we asked what sort of tasks were handed out to juniors: *"I've always done everything. Our group staffs lightly, so I've never worked alongside another junior associate. I get to do the initial processing, client interviews, influx documents, discovery requests, prep for DoJ investigations, motions... it's pretty much the full gamut of the civil and criminal sides of antitrust work. And there's no downtime, so you immediately have to learn to manage your time."*

"I feel like a detective."

Commercial, corporate and securities associates in New York reported feeling *"really happy"* with their trajectory so far. *"During our first year there was a lot of research, but not very much doc review. After that I ended up writing a section of a brief, and running the entire document production."* Here clients are *"pretty big"* so client contact varied, but *"on a smaller case you get to go to client meetings."* In straight corporate *"every day is different. Today I came in and drafted a voting agreement. It's an ancillary document to a merger agreement for a deal we're working on. Sometimes we do in-depth research, and I feel like a detective."* In the second year, *"responsibility doubles."* The team is known for advising on IPOs, securities and M&A matters, as well as for advising big-name companies on governance issues.

Elsewhere, *"the white-collar group covers a wide area: there's DEA investigations, independent internal investigations, auditing, and investigating fraud, as well as other criminal antitrust matters."* Matters range in size, and again smaller cases mean more responsibility: *"It was just me and a partner on a congressional investigation, and the amount of client interaction exceeded my expectations."*

Recent work highlights

- Client Deutsche Bank with Cadwalader's support won 'CLO of the Year' at a capital markets industry conference in New York
- DC lawyers supported Brussels-based team representing Irish airplane company Aer Lingus throughout its ten year battle to reject bids from rival Ryanair, until the latter finally agreed to sell its Aer Lingus shares to IAG
- Represented Credit Suisse when the company was sole financial advisor to specialist pharmaceutical company AcelRx during the $65 million partial sale of one of its drugs to PDL BioPharma
- Successfully represented Nestlé USA in an ongoing litigation concerning chocolate price-fixing

Hours & Compensation

"BigLaw means big hours," one put it plainly, *"but no one is creating work for you: when it's busy you can end up staying late for long periods, but when it's a bit quieter you get more free time. The firm respects your need to have a life outside work."* Some chose to get in earlier than most of their colleagues (meaning around 8am) to ensure they stuck to working during the week and kept weekends (mostly) free. Others preferred to stick around a bit later in the evenings.

"BigLaw means big hours."

Cadwalader's hours requirement was scrapped in January 2014. *"Some people were pretty suspicious about it at first,"* a source reported, *"but I haven't heard a single complaint about it in two years. Or praise."* Another agreed and added: *"It hasn't changed much, people still use the old target as a guideline and they tend to stick to it or – more often – exceed it. The only difference is that you could fall short and potentially still get a bonus, which takes some stress away."* Some commented that *"removing the requirement means those who are thus inclined can do more marketing and pro bono."* Since the 2014 move the firm has also introduced new guidelines for added clarity: if associates bill 1,600 plus 200 non-billables they will get 50% of the standard bonus, if they bill 1,800 plus 200 they will get the full bonus, and a total of 2,000 will bag them 120% of the base amount.

See firm profile on p.614

Pro Bono

All agreed that the firm is very active in providing pro bono opportunities, but most of our sources hadn't yet found the time to get involved. We did hear that *"the firm is signed up to Obama's Clemency Project, and a bunch of our attorneys are looking at that. It aims to look at petitions for clemency from people who have been in prison for a long time for non-violent crimes."* Some corporate associates bemoaned that *"pro bono opportunities are mostly for litigators,"* but a few had still found ways to get involved. Read our Bonus Features for more on one pro bono case: Malala Yousafzai.

Pro bono hours

- For all attorneys across all US offices: 17,104
- Average per US attorney: 45

Diversity

Interviewees were mostly able to reel off the firm's various diversity initiatives, and acknowledged a vigorous effort is being made to improve on numbers and to demonstrate commitment. One even commented that they *"were used to having only white friends at school, but looking around my colleagues there's more than just passing words given to the idea of diversity."* Still, another admitted that *"like with all law firms, overall we're not as diverse as we should be."* One referred specifically to gender diversity in the higher ranks and lamented: *"I can count our female partners in DC on one hand"* (there are five women out of 22 partners in total).

"We're not as diverse as we should be."

The firm does offer *"mentorships and sponsorships targeted at helping women and other groups figure out the next steps needed to become partner,"* as well as opening up positions exclusively for 1L candidates. Managing partner Pat Quinn explains that affinity groups have now become part of the firm's business strategy: *"Each affinity group has developed a business plan and a set of tasks to help the firm, so they're no longer just support groups. The aim is to make sure diverse individuals have all the tools and skills to become future leaders."*

Training & Development

"There's no shortage of training," associates agreed. It starts with *"First Year Fundamentals,"* Cadwalader's training week for new starters. *"Everyone went up to New York, the training felt substantive, and we all got to know each other."* Subsequently, *"there's a training on some topic or other at least every fortnight,"* a source explained, adding: *"I'm actually going to be teaching one soon! The firm tries to give associates a chance to get involved."* On a less formal level, one interviewee pointed out that *"it's a free and collaborative environment, where everyone is happy to sit down and explain something to you – not just vertically, but among peers."*

"The best way to handle it is by not forcing the relationship."

Support is also available from mentors. Each associate is allocated a junior and senior mentor and a quarterly budget to go out for a coffee or a meal. *"You make of it what you want,"* one explained. *"I don't do much with my partner mentor even though we get on great, but I get lunch with my associate mentor every week without exception. The best way to handle it is by not forcing the relationship."*

"We have identified a set of core values, which we're on the cusp of publishing internally. What makes Cadwalader Cadwalader? They're firmwide and not limited to lawyers, so everyone's singing from the same song sheet."

Pat Quinn, managing partner

Culture

Most of our sources made a point of voicing that *"the culture varies depending on the office,"* and even, *"depending on the team."* Unlike many firms that take great pains to operate homogeneously *"as one,"* Cadwalader's atmosphere is defined by supportive relationships and healthy group dynamics, associates said, rather than by a firmwide effort to subscribe to a particular one-firm ethos. At the same time, as mentioned earlier, there's been an extensive and radical re-branding of the firm's culture following years of Cadwalader's less than peachy *"shark tank"* reputation. Pat Quinn informs us that *"we have identified a set of core values, which we're on the cusp of publishing internally. What makes Cadwalader Cadwalader? They're firmwide and not limited to lawyers, so everyone's singing from the same song sheet. They are values that already exist at the firm, we've just defined them."*

"My friends at other firms are jealous."

As part of the cultural refurb, the hours requirement was scrapped and vacation became unlimited: *"These things have made a big difference. Now when I talk about where I work my friends at other firms are jealous,"* one shared. In spite of starting with the caveat that they were merely

See firm profile on p.614

describing the atmosphere of their own office or group, our sources pointed to largely similar factors: *"It's a relaxed atmosphere where everyone respects each other, there's a focus on quality rather than hours spent at the office, and they've done a really good job at improving morale."*

Offices

Sources in the Big Apple expressed their appreciation of the office in their own ways, from the practical *"it's well painted,"* to the more poetic: *"The views are outstanding. Sometimes turning a corner becomes a breathtaking moment, when you're suddenly staring at the sunset over the Hudson, or at a beautiful sunny day over the harbor."* Once associates get their breath back, they can head to the *"subsidized cafeteria, or to one of the many restaurants in the area."*

"A breathtaking moment."

In DC, the office is based in Chinatown, *"meaning there are countless places you can take summers for lunch without ever having to repeat!"* The building was described as *"a small building, very pretty inside, clean and new."* All associates get their own office, and if that gets lonely *"you can always meet up with colleagues and head to the food truck haven outside the National Portrait Gallery."* In Charlotte, which houses under 50 lawyers, juniors also get their own office.

Get Hired

Who gets into Cadwalader? *"There's no personality test as part of the recruitment process,"* one joked, *"but they do put an emphasis on intellectual curiosity. They like people who are intelligent but also laid back."* A willingness to *"chime in"* and *"learn from mistakes"* was mentioned by sources, who added that *"approachable and hard working"* was an apt description for Cadwalader attorneys. A few also mentioned the *"collaborative"* feel of the firm, substantiating this by observing that *"Pat* [Quinn] *makes a point of knowing the attorneys. That there's a genuinely nice person at the helm sets a tone for the rest of the firm."* One did have a word of warning though: *"An inability to handle stress would be a bad quality. You would break down the machine."* Yoga, anyone?

"A genuinely nice person."

Strategy & Future

On the question of Cadwalader's strategy going forward, managing partner Pat Quinn predicts: *"We think about expansion as a means to an end, rather than a goal in itself. At the moment, our practices fit together in strategic ways, and we're focused on being world-class at what we do rather than being all things for all people. If we have an opportunity to expand because clients need more depth in a certain area, we'll grow in that area. If we sense that there are significant client demands in a certain geography, we might move there. But we're not trying to be a mega-firm."*

"I summered here and had the best time. We all got really close and even ended up going on holiday together to Six Flags."

See firm profile on p.614

Cahill Gordon & Reindel LLP

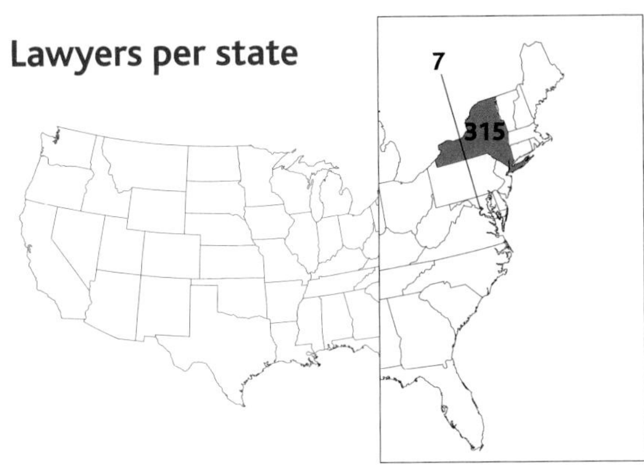

Largest US office: New York
US offices: 2
International offices: 1
First-year salary: $160,000
Billable hours: no requirement
Summers 2016: 38 (all 2Ls)
Revenue 2015: $364.5 million (–4.3%)
Partners made in 2016: 3
Famous for: Floyd Abrams; its corporate prowess; working associates hard and paying accordingly

Cahill thrives on finance and famously forgoes the frills, though associates are more than happy to collect two bonuses a year.

CAHILL means business: an enticing reputation for corporate work and a formidable litigation practice lure intrepid associates into this century-old Wall Street fortress. *Chambers USA* recognizes Cahill's mastery, awarding it top gongs for banking & finance, capital markets, insurance disputes, and media & entertainment litigation. Insiders told us one or more of these practice strengths attracted them here, litigators saying the First Amendment practice, headed by superstar Floyd Abrams, is a particular magnet. A word of warning, though: *"Some people are drawn to Cahill and think they'll be First Amendment lawyers. It sets Cahill apart but it's never something you're doing full-time."* Roughly half of junior associates work in the corporate group, and half in litigation (of which Abrams' team is a part).

With just two US offices (NY and DC), Cahill felt *"smaller"* to sources *"compared to other firms of similar caliber. When you're narrowing down your job search it acts as a promise of face-to-face interaction and meaty tasks."* Such hands-on responsibility comes at a price, and Cahill expects its associates to work harder than most. But in return they get a bigger pay packet: for the past few years they've received a welcome midyear windfall in addition to the end-of-year bonus (jump to the Hours section for more info).

On chambers-associate.com...

- Interview with managing partner Jonathan Schaffzin
- Landmark Cahill cases
- Cahill's spotlight on white collar defense and capital markets

ASSOCIATES SAY...

The Work

Cahill's free-market system for getting work appealed to many interviewees when they applied, and didn't disappoint now they're here. Associates approach partners, and vice versa. *"The way they sell it is pretty much the way it plays out, but initially work might not be as free-flowing as you expected. You might agree to take something on, and then something else comes along. As you learn to navigate the system, though, you can achieve real control over how much and when you work. Rigid assignment systems at other firms sound horrible!"*

"Rigid assignment systems at other firms sound horrible!"

Juniors in the corporate group had worked on *"credit agreements and debt capital markets, a lot of leverage finance and some equity work."* Sources concurred: *"When you start you're doing diligence, then it evolves to drafting ancillary documents, and eventually you're the first one to hold the pen to credit agreements and major transactional documents. As a third-year you get to do almost everything, including communicating directly with clients."* Corporate associates felt that *"deals being*

See firm profile on p.615

The Inside View

Rankings in *Chambers USA*

Banking & Finance	Litigation
Capital Markets	Media & Entertainment
Environment	Telecommunications
Insurance	

For detail on ranking tiers and ranking locations, visit www.chambersandpartners.com

leanly staffed helps juniors get substantive experience: midlevel and senior associates nurture you and guide you, and soon enough you're able to take some of the drafting off their plate and do it yourself."

Litigators informed us that *"a lot of the group's work is financial services litigation, representing banks and other financial services companies. Investigations are definitely on the up."* Associates found *"there's a big difference between large and small cases in terms of tasks. As a junior on a large case like an FCPA* [Foreign Corrupt Practices Act] *or SEC investigation, there can be a lot of doc review. Some people choose to take on one big case for a year or two, with smaller cases on top to get more experience."* As they gain experience, tasks vary to include *"preparing witnesses for depositions, and being involved in strategy."* Overall, insiders felt fulfilled, describing the work as *"not run of the mill"* and enthusing that *"it's the stuff that appears in newspapers, which is pretty cool."*

Some litigators can choose to *"take a year out to do a judicial clerkship. The firm supports you and writes you a recommendation when needed. When you get back you're given a lot of responsibility."*

Pro bono

"Some people spend a whole month billing pro bono and no-one minds."

Responsibility can also be sought via Cahill's *"very active"* stream of pro bono. *"Opportunities are mostly for litigators, which doesn't mean a corporate associate can't take them on,"* we heard, and indeed most interviewees were able to reel off past or current experiences of pro bono. *"We have a partnership with Sanctuary for Families, who gave me the opportunity to go to family court and take a testimony from a client."* Another spoke of links with the Legal Aid Society, *"involved in criminal appeals."* There's no minimum hours requirement nor a cap on pro bono, and one reckoned *"it accounts for about 10% of my billables. Some people spend a whole month billing pro bono and no-one minds."* Opportunities also come in the form of *"non-legal stuff"* (which doesn't count as pro bono hours, though) like *"tutoring kids through Sanctuary for Families, and going into schools to get students interested in law. It's made easy for us to do this kind of thing."*

Recent work highlights

- Represented the financing sources in nearly $50 billion of new debt for the buyout of EMC Corporation by Dell in a transaction valued at about $67 billion
- Successfully represented occupational therapist Debra Fisher in a lawsuit she brought against the NYC Department of Education, who suspended her for helping a disabled boy set up a Kickstarter campaign to fund his novel
- Cahill litigators successfully acted for biopharmaceutical company Amarin in a high-profile, precedent-setting First Amendment lawsuit
- Represented J.P. Morgan, Merrill Lynch and Citigroup in connection with a $6.6 billion corporate high-yield bond offering by telephone company Frontier

Pro bono hours

- For all attorneys across all US offices: 13,440
- Average per US attorney: 41

Culture

Overwhelmingly, sources described Cahill's culture as *"comfortable and relaxed. Not in that California jeans-and-flip-flops way, only in the sense that the firm values and fosters independence so it doesn't need to impose many rules."* This relative lack of strictures extends to exonerating associates from *"being in the office late at night when you could be working from home,"* and from a *"strict dress code."*

Most felt the free-market system had something to do with this as *"it affords you freedom and allows you to work for people you like. When there's camaraderie and people get on, the atmosphere benefits hugely."* Generally, interviewees felt that senior lawyers were *"accepting of juniors' insights and always prepared to explain something."* One shared: *"Unlike the last firm I worked at, here when a first-year is ready to do a 'second-year' task, nothing's stopping them."*

"The firm values and fosters independence so it doesn't need to impose many rules."

Some sources socialize with peers outside the office *"every week, multiple times. They're my friends."* Associates can also gather at *"monthly happy hours, cupcake breaks, a fishing trip the firm organizes every year, and our extravagant Christmas shindig at the Ritz, inclusive of a videoed skit where associates make fun of partners."* Cahill summers can enjoy *"watching a Mets game from*

See firm profile on p.615

the firm's party deck, going to Broadway for dinner and a show, and several cocktail events."

Offices

The *"slightly old and scrappy"* offices were seen affectionately by associates as *"another symbol of a culture that values personality. There's no beautiful marble floor or incredible art collection. We get our work done, we do it well, and that speaks for itself."* That's all very well, but how scuzzy are we actually talking? *"They're probably on the lower end of fanciness,"* said one, still skirting around the subject, *"but they're comfortable."* Another was similarly diplomatic: *"They're understated."* Ultimately though, there were no real complaints; in fact, we heard about different coffee machines (*"they tried them all"*), a whole new floor *"with a glass conference room,"* and *"generous tech stipends for your office. You get your own office a year and a half in, at the latest."* The weirdest office accessory among associates? *"A dartboard."*

"There's no beautiful marble floor or incredible art collection."

The Cahill mothership is located *"in the financial district, which is better than Midtown because it's far less busy,"* sources agreed. *"I heard traffic in Midtown is horrendous,"* one mused. Associates enjoyed *"being next to the water and sitting outside on the seaport for lunch,"* as well as appreciating that *"there's a bunch of subways nearby."*

Hours & Compensation

While a comparative study of the best machine-made cappuccinos and a picturesque seafront lunch may be wonderful ways to take a break, make no mistake: Cahill associates' working days are serious business. *"No one would say this job is easy in that respect,"* one admitted, *"but the hardest part isn't the hours themselves, just how unpredictable they can be."* A quiet day could see an associate arriving for 9.30 or 10am, and strolling out at 5.30pm, *"to probably log in later that evening for a bit."* But a busy one can take home-time right up to midnight. Working *"many weekends"* was considered a given. *"Working from home is definitely an option, and it needs to be because you're always on call. At any given time you might get an email that requires a couple of hours of work."* So while interviewees did complain that *"it's hard to take control of your schedule, and you can't just say to your friends, 'See you on Wednesday at 8',"* they also conceded that *"this is where the free-market system comes in to help you if you've learned to say no. You can choose when to give yourself a break."*

"No one would say this job is easy."

There's no billable hours requirement, but sources reckoned *"you're expected to do 1,800, most people aim for 2,000, and you usually end up with 2,200."* We've previously reported on Cahill's rep for giving its lawyers super-sized bonuses. One of the exec committee bosses, Jonathan Schaffzin, is quick to assert that this isn't just free money: *"We expect our associates to work harder than their peers at other firms, and we're committed to taking account of that. We paid a midyear bonus in 2015 which I don't think other firms did. We do review it annually, but I've no reason to believe we won't continue this practice."*

Training & Development

To prepare juniors for the hard work ahead, their time at Cahill begins with a week-long training program aptly referred to as *"boot camp. It's helpful, but it's hard to contextualize so early on. The informal training we receive on the job is more useful."*

"A promise of face-to-face interaction and meaty tasks."

Where other firms might refer to *"mentors,"* Cahill has adopted the term *"liaison partners."* Each associate is paired up with one upon arrival, though after that the scheme is a bit hit and miss: *"Your liaison partner is theoretically the person you'd reach out to if you're stressed or have any questions,"* we heard, *"but most of us don't know that partner very well at all. It's more likely you'll have picked up an informal mentor from the people you frequently work with."* Liaison partners also deliver annual reviews to their assigned associates, and insiders shared their hopes that *"the firm is working on making formal reviews more frequent."* We checked with hiring partner Brian Markley, who clarifies that *"we've incorporated reviews from a greater number of reviewers and expect to provide more feedback on assignments at regular intervals throughout the year."*

Diversity

While respondents were divided on whether their law schools *"did a good job at diversity"* or not, they all agreed that *"Cahill could do better. It's clearly on the partnership's radar. There are committees designed to help and quarterly newsletters, but looking around it's not very diverse."* Sources seemed to think that *"we do better in terms of gender than race."* Jonathan Schaffzin echoes this candidly: *"We're still striving to improve and increase diversity at the firm. It's a challenge but it's one that's a high priority."* As of spring 2016, 20% of partners are female, and 93% of partners are white.

See firm profile on p.615

Get Hired

On the subject of law schools represented by the associate cohort, our interviewees were more approving. *"We all come from a pretty wide variety of schools, and it's particularly evident in the younger classes."* Individual qualities perceived as valuable included *"being highly self-motivated and comfortable taking control of your own career, since there's not much hand-holding here."* Some also reflected that *"people tend to be outgoing and sociable but no-one is going to fault you if you're not. There's a lot of individuality, which makes for a varied and interesting environment."* Insiders were also keen to dish out tips they picked up along the way. One opined: *"Don't be intimidated by the free-market system; it doesn't create a cut-throat environment, it just demands maturity and initiative. Think about whether you're prepared to work very hard, and if you are then make sure you look after yourself physically."*

"Don't be intimidated by the free-market system."

Strategy & Future

Corporate juniors and midlevels felt confident that if they aspired to partnership it would be *"achievable. It's up to you if you want to pursue it, though it's not like you become partner and suddenly work nine to five."* Litigators, meanwhile, vented their concern regarding *"the recent lateral hires born out of the firm's expansion in the field of investigations. The corporate department seems to be grown more organically, with most partners being people who summered with the firm, while litigation seems to be growing laterally recently. If I was an eighth-year, it would make me mad."* We quizzed exec committee member Jonathan Schaffzin, who was adamant this is not the case: *"We are a firm with a strong emphasis on promotion from within and that philosophy hasn't changed. We've had some great development opportunities in the regulatory area that have required bringing in the necessary expertise with a few lateral hires. But overall we've done very little, and we promote litigation associates to partner on a basis commensurate with our corporate associates."*

Speaking of Cahill's future strategy in general, Schaffzin states: *"We will continue to focus on growing our litigation and regulatory investigations practices. Our clients include a number of sophisticated financial institutions that face continued complexity in terms of government regulation."* He adds that *"on the corporate side we will continue to provide the highest-quality service to clients"* and that *"an important facet of our strategy is associate development and retention. We have become more transparent in recent years and our internal review process has become more robust."*

"An important facet of our strategy is associate development and retention. We have become more transparent."

Jonathan Schaffzin, managing partner

See firm profile on p.615

Chadbourne & Parke LLP

Lawyers per state

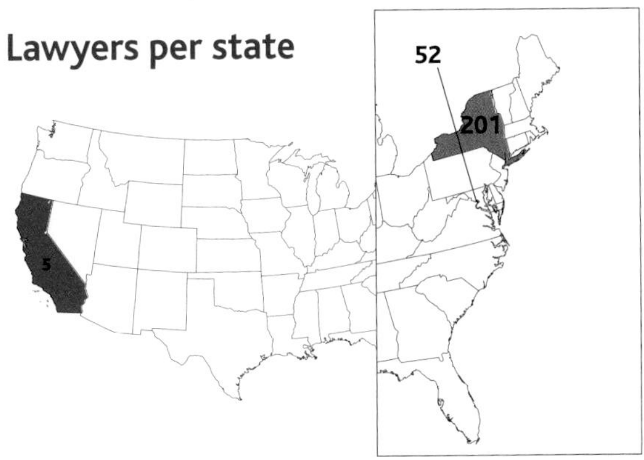

Largest US office: New York
US Offices: 3
International offices: 8
First-year salary: $160,000
Billable hours: 1,900 target
Summers 2016: 16 (all 2Ls)
Revenue 2014: $254.5 million
Partners made 2016: 4 US; 6 globally
Famous for: heavyweight projects practice; presence in emerging markets; servicing the Wright brothers, Edison and James Joyce

A small summer intake makes for big opportunities at this projects whizz.

"IT'S not a paper airplane!" chuckles Chadbourne's managing partner Andy Giaccia of the New York firm's new logo – a product of its 2014 re-brand. The pointy, fast-looking Concorde-like symbol is *"designed to reflect the modernity and innovativeness of our practices,"* he adds. In response to a tricky economy, this project finance heavyweight certainly has a sleeker look these days. It closed offices a long-haul flight away from the NYC HQ in Almaty (2012), Kyiv (2014), and Beijing (2015). Despite this trimming, January 2015 saw the firm establish a base in Johannesburg, putting it in a strong position to capitalize on the growing amount of energy and infrastructure transactions in Africa. Desire to grow in the energy sector and emerging markets has also prompted *"dramatic additions to our international practice, through the hiring of Ben Donovan and Andrei Baev in London."*

The jewel in Chadbourne's crown continues to be its project finance team, for whom energy sector clients are a massive source of trade and income. Over the first half of 2015, the firm advised on a chart-topping $36 billion worth of project finance transactions. $30 billion of this was in the oil and gas sector, so it's no surprise that Chadbourne notches up top rankings in *Chambers USA* for LNG and renewables projects. Also in 2015, the firm was reportedly in merger talks with Pillsbury, although these came to nothing.

On chambers-associate.com...

- Chadbourne's new Johannesburg office

ASSOCIATES SAY...

The Work

Litigation and corporate are common destinations for new associates. Others go to project finance, while tax also welcomes one or two. Held in the head office, the firm's summer program won unanimous plaudits from associates for its ability to ease the transition into full-time practice. With the flexibility to navigate through project finance, litigation, tax and corporate, New York-bound newbies are afforded *"a good feel for what life would be like in different teams,"* which proved *"particularly helpful when it came to expressing practice group preferences at the exit interview."* Much more limited in its uptake, rookies heading to DC are usually channeled toward project finance, though litigation is occasionally an option. Irrespective of final destination, all summers get the chance to work on live matters. This can result in *"more than a few late nights,"* but on the whole interviewees felt that *"working to the real-life demands of clients so early on really helps you to find your feet as soon as possible."*

"A lot more chances than expected to work directly with partners and play central roles on huge deals."

Opportunity isn't merely a lure for the summers however: lean staffing means that those who had joined the project finance team had received *"a lot more chances than expected to work directly with partners and play central roles on huge deals."* The department advises on projects relating to the financing and development

See firm profile on p.616

Rankings in *Chambers USA*

Bankruptcy/Restructuring	International Arbitration
Energy & Natural Resources	Latin American Investment Projects
Insurance	

For detail on ranking tiers and ranking locations, visit www.chambersandpartners.com

of power, renewable energy, PPP and LNG projects, so cases *"can be incredibly complex."* Matters *"regularly hit the headlines,"* so whether you're keeping a checklist on a transaction or drafting an agreement, *"each step requires a great deal of individual thought."*

Elsewhere, litigation rookies boasted of *"very little doc review,"* instead keeping busy researching and writing memos, and drafting sections of briefs and motions. *"Far from just a support department for project finance,"* lit is split into subgroups such as IP, securities regulation, project finance and white-collar crime, the latter of which is headed up in DC. Corporate comprises groups including private funds, securities, public companies and corporate finance, and transactional interviewees were similarly glad to announce that *"we win a lot of our own clients."* That said, *"there is a lot of cross-selling between groups, so whatever team you're in, you can expect to work with people outside of your team and your office."* Internationally speaking, the firm's Latin American offices were cited as regular points of collaboration.

"move at a pace you're comfortable with"

Irrespective of which department they head to, juniors' first instructions always come from an assigning partner or practice group manager. It's a popular set-up as *"there's no pressure on you to ask partners for work when you've hardly met them."* Reliance upon this centralized allocation system is expected to lessen as relationships with more senior colleagues blossom, but having the reassurance of a backup source *"allows you to move at a pace you're comfortable with."* Associates' ties to their assigning partner aren't completely cut, as *"they're always available to help you to manage your workload should you need it."*

Training & Development

First-years begin with a few days of orientation in the New York office, which *"covers billing, professional conduct, and anything else you'll need to know to hit the ground running."* Juniors then return to their respective offices to undertake departmental training. Those in project finance, litigation, and corporate/tax/bankruptcy are treated to training 'bootcamps': the aim here being to flesh out newbies' market knowledge and provide a few pointers on the kinds of tasks they're likely to encounter

Recent work highlights

- Helped a joint venture of Flatiron and Dragados to bid and secure the contract to design, build and operate the new Harbor Bridge in Corpus Christi, Texas. At 1,655 feet, it'll be the longest cable-stayed bridge in the USA
- Represented a syndicate of 25 commercial banks and other financial institutions in the $4.6 billion financing of liquefaction and purification facilities at the Sabine Pass LNG Terminal in Cameron Parish, Louisiana
- Acted for TerraForm Power in its $350 million purchase of five wind farms in Idaho and Oklahoma from Atlantic Power Corporation
- Reached settlements and claim dismissals while defending Argentinian oil and gas producer YPF. The multibillion-dollar claims were raised by the State of New Jersey and Occidental Chemical Corporation, and related to the pollution of the Passaic River

down the line. Follow-up training comes on the job, with formal reviews every six months and senior colleagues *"always forthcoming with encouragement, comments and suggestions."* You *"soon learn how people like things done."* Litigation training comes more routinely, with a few hours a week penciled in for the first couple of months. These sessions touch upon *"every aspect of a case: whether it's sending an email to a partner to ask for work, captioning a brief, conducting the initial client interview, or understanding the court process. It's all covered."*

"It's all covered."

The biannual reviews are held with a member of the management committee, and are based on comments given by attorneys who juniors have spent over ten hours working with. *"Informal feedback is great for improving your work, but the appraisals are done with an eye on the future,"* enthused one interviewee. *"It's done in a 'we think you can handle this, so why not try this' kind of way."*

Pro Bono

Fronted by the *"incredibly dedicated"* coordinator Maureen Schad (a former associate), pro bono at Chadbourne affords juniors *"even greater involvement in cases, and the opportunity to try out new areas while receiving hands-on training."* We heard of first-year litigators who'd given depositions in the federal court, and other juniors who'd given filings in the supreme court on behalf of death row prisoners. Meanwhile, corporate rookies were *"astonished by the number of transactional opportunities available,"* so whether it's helping a small

See firm profile on p.616

business whose budget wouldn't otherwise stretch to BigLaw representation, instructing an individual on how to form an entity, or undertaking routine transactions for charities, there's plenty of exposure to be gained.

"I was astonished by the number of transactional opportunities."

Pro bono hours

- For all attorneys across all US offices: 20,266
- Average per US attorney: 87

Hours & Compensation

Chadbourne sets a quality non-billable target of 200 hours. These could be spent doing pro bono, writing articles or working on the hiring committee, and 100 plus pro bono hours can be used against the firm's billable requirement of 1,900 hours. Hit 2,100 combined – a target that associates described as *"challenging in your first year"*– and you'll make your bonus.

"Very few people who come here don't realize what they signed up for."

As far as work/life balance is concerned, new starters *"do get lots of substantive work earlier on, but that does translate into putting in more hours to do things properly."* Not that this was a problem: perhaps as a result of the summer program's success, *"very few people who come here don't realize what they signed up for."* Nine in the morning to 6.30pm-ish seemed a pretty ordinary day at the DC office, though this was usually followed by an hour or so working remotely in the evening. Despite being the city that never sleeps, New York was ruled *"a later starter,"* with ten till 8.30pm fairly routine. Interviewees from all practices had spent the odd night working until the very early hours, but project finance was deemed most subject to fluctuations, with a fortnight of 12 hour days followed by a fortnight of seven hour days not uncommon.

Offices and Culture

With plenty of substantive work to be getting on with, and *"less of a 'bro' culture than at other places,"* associates in the New York office found themselves *"more likely to forge relationships in the daytime than in a bar after work."* Thankfully, Chadbourne's move to a *"dazzling"* new Sixth Avenue HQ in September 2014 has made long nights in the Big Apple all the more comfortable. First and second-years double up on offices, and with *"homely common areas to encourage interaction"* and *"an incredible cafe where you can watch the news, or take in the fantastic views of Central Park and the rest of Manhattan,"* there are *"plenty of spots where you can have a breather and shoot the breeze."*

"You're more likely to forge relationships in the daytime than in a bar after work."

As far as dress code goes, interviewees found DC a little more laid back than its NY cousin. *"On my first day I came in all gussied up,"* explains one DC junior, *"and people gave me a hard time for it. We're more slacks than suits here, though that's not the case for New York."* But when it comes to the office's social scene, DC boasts a similar vibe, with one source mentioning that *"a lot of people here have kids so there's no bar-after-work culture."* Furthermore, *"with the level of responsibility we get, we couldn't go and drink every night and do our jobs well. We usually go get coffee together instead, and if you're in for a late night, someone'll always come and see if you fancy a top-up."*

LA completes Chadbourne's stateside showing. Beyond the USA, the firm has offices in Dubai, Istanbul, Johannesburg, London, Mexico City, Moscow, São Paulo and Warsaw.

Diversity

Chadbourne's internal diversity program was thought to be pivotal in cultivating such a symbiotic office environment. Associates had attended lunchtime discussions, movie screenings, and seminars led by guest speakers, with the latter proving particularly popular: *"One encouraged us to describe ourselves according to the stereotypes that we may fall into, and then give a true and accurate account of our personalities in light of that. It really helped us to realize how much we create that's not there."*

"Any future lack of women partners will not be due to lack of opportunity."

When it comes to minority representation Chadbourne's upper echelons, *"like most law firms, are quite Caucasian male-heavy."* However, sources felt that *"there have been some huge efforts to push this in the right direction,"* and according to director of associate recruiting Lisa Featherson, *"the firm is proud of our dedication to recruit a diverse set of attorneys: over 50% of our 2016 summer associates come from diverse backgrounds."* Standing at 15%, associates felt that *"there aren't as many women partners as there should be,"* though one female source was keen to add that *"this is bound to shift in the years ahead. There's a good female showing among associates, and any future lack of women partners will not be due to lack of opportunity."*

See firm profile on p.616

Get Hired

Lisa Featherson highlights Columbia, Fordham, Georgetown and NYU as *"some of the core schools that hold an important place in our recruiting initiative, due to their strong alumni base at the firm and history of cultivating excellent attorneys. But we're not just looking for great grades from a small group of schools,"* she adds. *"We're looking to recruit attorneys from many schools who have the skillsets we value: leadership and entrepreneurial abilities; dynamic work experience before law school; foreign language skills, and a devoted interest in our core practice areas."*

"We look for confident, calm and collected team members."

Personality is a big consideration too. With advanced responsibilities early on and a small summer program, Chadbourne wants candidates who *"can encourage and support others while working to be successful themselves. This job can be stressful, particularly when you're working against tight timelines: we look for confident, calm and collected team members who will work together towards a common goal."*

Strategy

At the time of our calls there had been much talk of a proposed merger between Chadbourne and San Fran's Pillsbury. *"Overall I've loved my time here,"* reviewed one interviewee, *"but I'd dock a point for the firm's efforts to keep us in the loop on such big strategic decisions. It's never fun to discover merger talks via Google."* That said, interviewees had noticed *"an uptick in management's efforts to improve our formal correspondence."* With an increased number of committee meetings – now held once every two months – rookies do have access to a forum from which they can voice their views on the way that the firm is being managed. *"It's positive to see that they're seeking out our opinions,"* one associate glowed. *"Whether they listen is another story!"*

"It's never fun to discover merger talks via Google."

New starters at Chadbourne *"do get lots of substantive work earlier on, but that does translate into putting in more hours to do things properly."*

See firm profile on p.616

Choate Hall & Stewart LLP

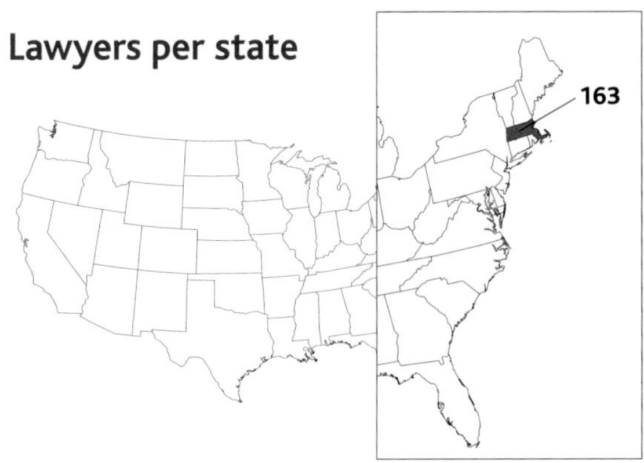

Largest US office: Boston
US offices: 1
International offices: 0
First-year salary: $160,000
Billable hours: 1,900 required (2,000 for bonus)
Summers 2016: 17 (15 2Ls, 2 1Ls)
Revenue 2015: $202.7 million (+4.3%)
Partners made 2016: 2
Famous for: its one-office model

A senior statesman of the Boston market, Choate condenses a lot of exciting development opportunities into its one office.

"WE'RE a one-office firm. We all operate under the same roof, and that mentality runs through everything we do," declared junior associates at this plucky Boston firm. Comprising some 163 attorneys in its Massachusetts homestead, Choate has made its name by turning the traditional BigLaw model on its head. And it's a model that's paying off.

Hot off the heels of a record-breaking 2014, when the firm posted revenue of $194.37 million, Choate registered its best ever financials in 2015, smashing through the $200 million mark for the first time to post a 4.3% rise in revenue. Focus is the name of the game here: Choate's prolific success stems from its formidable prowess in a cherry-picked bunch of practices, which draw in clients from way beyond the confines of the Bay State. In *Chambers USA*, antitrust, banking & finance, bankruptcy, general commercial litigation and technology all secure high rankings.

Our associate sources couldn't speak highly enough of Choate's strategic approach: *"We're involved in top-quality complex work for an impressive host of clients nationwide, but don't have the hassle of having to co-ordinate with a partner three thousand miles away!"* relished one. In fact, *"everyone knows everyone, so it's much easier for partners to keep an eye on your progress."* In terms of associates' development, Choate's cozy setup lends itself to a learning environment where *"there's no sense that you're part of a rigid hierarchy,"* so *"it's not the case that junior associates do all of the doc review, and the midlevels get the writing opps. It's all about proving yourself here."*

On chambers-associate.com...

- Choate gets a makeover

ASSOCIATES SAY...

The Work

Juniors are split roughly 50:50 between the litigation and business streams, though patent & IP and wealth management also snap up one or two. Practice area preferences are highlighted during summer exit interviews, but *"the hiring team calls in during the 3L summer. There's sometimes the odd 180, and Choate is really receptive to changes in opinion."*

Irrespective of where they end up, rookies' workloads are managed by an assigning partner, to whom they send weekly capacity reports. *"There's also space to convey your interests,"* explained one insider. *"They want us to enjoy our work, so if you have a burning desire to try something, you're encouraged to reach out."* Practicing as generalists for at least their first three years, associates eventually build up work streams from partners they've previously worked with. This work still goes through the assigning partner, which sources found *"a good protective measure."*

See firm profile on p.617

Rankings in *Chambers USA*

Antitrust	Intellectual Property
Banking & Finance	Litigation
Bankruptcy/Restructuring	Private Equity
Corporate/M&A	Tax
Healthcare	Technology

For detail on ranking tiers and ranking locations, visit www.chambersandpartners.com

Recent work highlights

- Counseled app development tool FeedHenry during its $65 million takeover by Red Hat, the world's leading open-source software company
- Successfully thwarted a suit raised by consumers against Samsung, whose Galaxy S smartphone was alleged to be malfunctioning
- Helping Wells Fargo to oversee $200 million worth of liquidation proceedings stemming from the bankruptcy of its debtor client, supermarket giant A&P
- Providing strategic, corporate and regulatory advice to Foundation Medicine, whose sequencing testing technology is used to flag and highlight appropriate treatment methods for genetic mutations in tumors and blood cancers

Litigators work their way through a varied mix of tasks, stemming from Choate's appellate, bankruptcy, general commercial, government enforcement, insurance & reinsurance, IP and labor & employment subgroups. *"One week you'll be drafting motions in a patent litigation case and the next you'll be preparing corporate executive witnesses for interview in a government investigation,"* recalled one interviewee. *"It's great exposure and really keeps it exciting."* Juniors begin with legal research and doc review tasks, but *"the teams are pretty small so once you're comfortable on the basics the intensity soon ramps up."*

"Once you're comfortable on the basics the intensity soon ramps up."

It's a similarly mixed bag over in business, where finance & restructuring, business tech and private equity are king. Whether undertaking their *"fair share of diligence on a private equity deal,"* or *"assisting with the logistics of a Series A business tech financing,"* newbies' responsibilities here are *"undeniably low-level"* until they feel ready to take on more. Our second and third-year sources weren't complaining, however, having drafted ancillary documents for credit facilities, held one-to-one client calls and meetings, and even advised clients following consultation with partners. Such opportunities for client contact *"really put your substantive legal training and business development skills to the test."*

Training & Development

Such rapid progression means that *"there are definitely times when you're terrified,"* but it's a small trade-off for feeling like *"you're growing as a lawyer with every day that passes."* Thankfully senior colleagues are *"very open to questions. I've even asked people working on different transactions for help,"* bragged one rookie. *"There were no excuses or 'maybe laters,' they just took the time to sit down with me and talk it through."*

Starters cover the logistical nuts 'n' bolts with a few days' orientation training. Over the next six months, lunchtime sessions led by individual practice groups cover more substantive legal areas. Further food for thought comes during 'lunch 'n' learn' sessions, which though not compulsory, are *"definitely popular."* Open to all disciplines, the itinerary is curated based on associates' requests. *"If a few people want to learn about patent licenses, then the development team will tie up with certain partners to arrange informal Q&A seminars. You can just fire away!"*

"There are definitely times when you're terrified."

Every six months juniors' progress is reviewed by all partners and seniors for whom they have spent ten or more hours working. Submitted online, this feedback is summarized and presented by a reviewing partner. *"We're also able to request copies of partners' original reviews, so you can see exactly where you went wrong or excelled on individual matters."*

A new pilot scheme is scrapping the surveys and instead interviewing partners individually. *"It'll help the review go into even greater depth,"* explained one respondent. A 'firm compact' aims to objectively set forth all of the skills that Choate expects associates to have mastered each year. Associates are also made aware what they should expect from partners.

Office & Culture

Housing some 163 attorneys, Choate's Boston digs have been treated to a facelift in the past year. *"It was always a nice building: right on the edge of the financial district with great views of Boston Harbor,"* enthused one resident. But now it's been renovated, *"it's looking pretty sexy!"* Styled with a *"modern, startup feel,"* the HQ features *"lots of glass, and lots of collaborative spaces,"* making it *"much easier to get together and chat over a draft, or just shoot the breeze for five minutes."*

Rookies also saw real value in Choate's single-office setup. *"If you ever have any questions, you can just go*

See firm profile on p.617

and knock on someone's door. If we had to schedule calls with someone in California to get a simple point clarified, then our ability to get work done would suffer." On a more social level, *"there are very few partners or seniors who you won't have had a coffee or chat with. That's rare in a firm of Choate's stature."* Such familiarity *"helps you to further your understanding of the kinds of work covered here."* After sussing out colleagues' areas of expertise, *"you know who to go to when there's something you need help with, or would like to try out,"* so all in all, it was thumbs-up for the one-roof approach.

"There are very few partners or seniors who you won't have had a coffee or chat with."

Further integration opportunities arise through more formally organized means. For instance, the first Thursday night of each month is pizza night. Held in Choate's staff cafeteria – groan-inducingly named 'The Firm Bite' – it's *"well attended by partners and associates"* alike. And to top it all off, there's the annual lawyers' field day. Held in *"a high-end country club,"* the day treats Choate's attorneys to a bit of downtime over rounds of golf, yoga classes or a few sets on the tennis courts. Best of all is the firm dinner, where first-years traditionally premiere a video skit that makes fun of partners. *"We tried to stay between bounds of decency,"* one chuckled, *"and in fairness they all took it pretty well!"*

Hours & Compensation

Choate's integration efforts seem to be paying off, and it's just as well. *"We all work long hours,"* sighed an insider, *"so it really helps that we all take an interest in each other's lives."* The amount of hours spent in the office *"depends on personal preference."* Many will work nine until six and then head home for dinner, finishing off the day with an hour or two remotely. Others prefer to get everything done in the office. The odd late night does crop up, but *"you never feel like you're grinding out useless hours. If you're in past midnight, it's because it's important and we need all hands on deck."*

"You never feel like you're grinding out useless hours."

To qualify for a bonus, grafters must hit 2,000 billable hours. Pro bono work counts hour for hour, and rookies can also count up to 100 hours of on-the-job training (OTJ) toward billables. OTJ credit was a big hit, not only because it facilitates bonus achievement, but also because *"it really puts the direction of your training into your hands."* One enthusiast elaborated: *"If you want to observe the negotiation of a credit agreement on a deal, then there's a strong possibility that the client won't want to pick up the bill. That's understandable. The firm gives us the option to bill that as OTJ, which means that you're still learning, and clients still get good value for money."*

Pro Bono

As a key player in the Boston legal community for over a century, *"giving back is really important"* at Choate. *"There's no hard cap"* when it comes to pro bono, so though *"you wouldn't get away with working exclusively on pro bono"* matters, juniors felt that *"if a case is taking a lot of your time, it's not a problem."*

"If a case is taking a lot of your time, it's not a problem."

A dedicated pro bono team, comprising a partner and two senior associates, is responsible for broadcasting up-for-grabs matters. *"They're extremely knowledgeable, and are open to questions if you're taking on something new."* As well as having close ties with the Center for Women in Enterprise, the firm also works with the Lawyers Clearinghouse, a Bostonian organization tackling homelessness and housing troubles by matching pro bono lawyers with individuals in need of legal aid. With asylum cases also common fare, Choate's juniors did concede that *"opportunities tend to fall in favor of litigators."* That said, we did hear of more transactionally minded associates who'd chipped in to organize founding documents or dissolutions for nonprofit organizations.

Pro bono hours

- For all attorneys across all US offices: 5,377
- Average per US attorney: 33

Diversity

Though its attorneys are *"predominantly white, and at partnership level white and male,"* Choate's associates felt that *"the firm is doing its best to recruit fairly, in a market that is still pretty homogenous."* A diversity 1L summer fellowship is helping to boost Choate's numbers for ethnic minority representation, and sources were also resolute that efforts were being made to retain female attorneys. A big part of this is Choate's *"fabulous"* maternity leave program, which sees *"most beneficiaries take about six months, four of which are paid."* The firm also considers part-time scheduling for parents with young children, so all in all juniors felt that *"the firm will always do its best to find a workable outcome."* The firm takes an egalitarian view towards paternity, especially when the father is the primary caregiver.

See firm profile on p.617

Get Hired

Choate's one-office Bostonian heritage is an important consideration for applicants. The firm takes on some 15 summers each year, following OCIs at a smattering of East Coast law schools. Key targets include Boston College, NYU, Georgetown, Cornell, BU, Columbia, Harvard, Suffolk, UVA and Yale, though write-ins are also accepted. Juniors aren't expected to walk around in 'I ♥ Beantown' T-shirts, but a vested interest in the local area is important. *"Don't be afraid to take on pro bono work during your summer program,"* advised one insider. *"It's a great way to show you're interested in exploring Boston's legal scene."*

"I know a lot of us would be willing to grab a coffee and talk about our experiences if asked."

"One of our key strengths is having all of our talent and expertise under one roof," Recruiting director Elaine Cohen Bortman adds, *"so we're looking for strong collaborators. Candidates should be ambitious, smart and interested in working hard, but beyond that we need to see an interest in the firm's work, and the work of our clients."* Behavioral interviewing techniques are used to ascertain such traits. *"If we ask for evidence of team-based accomplishments and the interviewee uses 'I' a lot instead of 'we,' we'd be inclined to probe further on their collaborative skills,"* she continues.

For more insider info, *"don't be afraid to reach out,"* nudged one junior associate. *"It's often said at law school but rarely taken advantage of. I know a lot of us would be willing to grab a coffee and talk about our experiences if asked."*

Strategy & Future

Keen to strengthen Choate's position as a venerable Bostonian institution, chairman John Nadas expresses particular excitement at the city's current economic health. *"General Electric's recent announcement of plans to relocate its corporate headquarters to Boston illustrates the strength and vibrancy of the Greater Boston economy,"* he delights. *"GE is one of the largest companies in the world. After considering many, many attractive options, GE chose Boston on the announced basis that Boston has the most dynamic and creative ecosystem in the country."*

"Our model won't be changing any time soon."

But Choate's reputation stems far beyond its home city. *"Being distinct in the market is important,"* proclaims John Nadas. *"We are unusual in that, from a single central location, we focus on a select group of practices in which we are able to provide our clients with market-leading expertise, experience, service and success."* As such, *"clients seek our guidance from all over, seeking our help not because of our geographical location, but because of the unusual expertise, experience, service and success we provide."* The one-roof strategy is key to ensuring such success, and *"we don't anticipate that we will be changing that strategy any time soon,"* Nadas asserts. *"In terms of efficiency, collaboration and cohesion it works unusually well. Our clients understand and appreciate it, and we continue to thrive under this model."*

"We're involved in top-quality complex work for an impressive host of clients nationwide, but don't have the hassle of having to coordinate with a partner three thousand miles away!"

See firm profile on p.617

Cleary Gottlieb Steen & Hamilton LLP

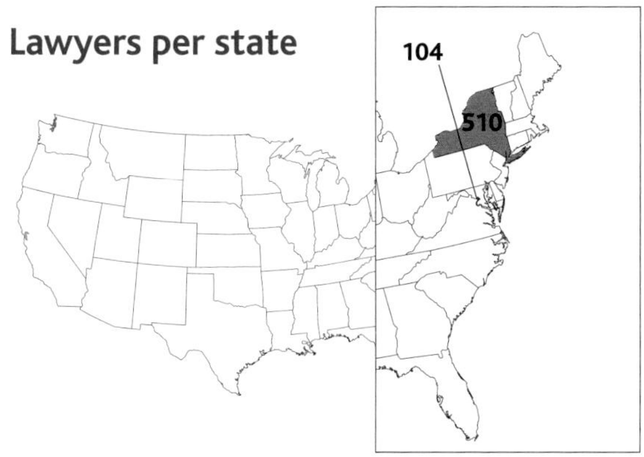

Largest US office: New York
US offices: 2
International offices: 14
First-year salary: $160,000
Billable hours: no requirement
Summers 2016: 102 (97 2Ls, 1 3L, 4 others)
Revenue 2015: $1.213 billion (-3%)
Partners made in 2016: 7 globally (6 in US)
Famous for: informal work practice and historic prestige

Prestigious Cleary is 70 years old in 2016 but still redefining what it means to be a junior associate.

CLEARY is clear on one thing: *"It doesn't like its lawyers to be pigeon-holed."* Summer associates are encouraged to *"try everything"* – including offices overseas, if they want to and have the requisite language skills – and when they join as first-years they can continue to fly between practice areas. According to junior associates here, Cleary considers itself a *"coalition of talents"* rather than a *"rigid top-down operation,"* and the fact that outside interests are so valued in the recruitment process reflects the premium the firm places on high-flyers with a diverse skill set.

But it's not just the relative freedom to choose your work that leaves associates cooing appreciatively. Cleary's lawyers work on some of the biggest assignments around. Its M&A work, for example, has seen it ranked eighth globally by Thomson Reuters for 2015 with a total of 86 deals worth $575.8 billion. This includes the recent acquisition of medical manufacturer Actavis by Allergan – the largest acquisition financing ever, at the time – which included over $70 billion worth of cash and stock. It's no surprise then that *Chambers USA* ranks Cleary in the elite for corporate/M&A work; other top-ranked practices include capital markets, antitrust, financial services regulation, Latin American investment and white-collar crime.

On chambers-associate.com...

- Interview with head hiring partner Lisa Schweitzer
- Cleary's work for sovereign states

ASSOCIATES SAY...

The Work

Cleary encourages summer and junior associates to sample a variety of work flavors so they can find out what taste they like. During the summer, New York recruits (the vast majority) receive *"a form with 20 areas"* and are asked to *"list their preferences,"* which then forms the basis for their early assignments. In DC – owing to that office's smaller size – there are three main choices: *"Corporate, litigation and antitrust,"* though structured finance and bank regulatory are also options. Fluidity is the name of the game and many we spoke to echoed the view that *"the odds of you doing the same work in your third year as when you joined are far less than in other firms."* One source confirmed: *"I'm starting my third year and have been in three different groups."* Those that take a lot of junior associates in New York include capital markets, M&A, litigation/arbitration, private equity/fund formation, and real estate.

"You should work on the deals you like."

From their first day, Cleary's associates are spurred to *"get up and go."* For transactional folks this means *"you should work on the deals you like,"* and that *"if you aren't proactive it can be easy to get side-tracked into work you*

See firm profile on p.618

Rankings in *Chambers USA*

Antitrust
Banking & Finance
Bankruptcy/Restructuring
Capital Markets
Corporate Crime & Investigations
Corporate/M&A
Employee Benefits & Executive Compensation
Energy & Natural Resources
Financial Services Regulation
International Arbitration
Investment Funds
Latin American Investment
Litigation
Private Equity
Projects
Real Estate
Securities
Tax

For detail on ranking tiers and ranking locations, visit www.chambersandpartners.com

Recent work highlights

- Secured the dismissal of $5.5 billion worth of civil RICO and related state law claims against HSBC and BNP Paribas
- Acted as counsel for drug-makers Actavis in its acquisition of Allergan, at the time the largest healthcare equity offering ever
- Acted as lead counsel to medical manufacturer Medtronic in its $49.9 billion acquisition of Covidien

don't want to do." A capital markets junior explained: *"I have approached partners many times. I just drop by a partner's office (it's an open-door firm) and say 'hey, I am available'. I think you need some guidance at the beginning."* For those who enter the corporate realm, *"when you first show up they give you a corporate client, and you are encouraged to build up a relationship and do most of your work with them."*

Litigators likewise found they had *"iterative discussions"* to get and help determine their assigned work: *"I got put on my first case from a conversation I had when I started. I geared up for a trial and it was a huge team. Later I went and spoke with one of the litigation assigners and said I was interested in being on a smaller team."* An M&A New Yorker disclosed that *"after your first year they'll ask if you want to move on. I think most people prefer not to continue to stay on. I actually chose to stay on because the work is so different and variable. It is just what you make it."* Most sources praised the role of assignment coordinators who *"will contact you, see your hours and ask 'do you have the time for this'? If you communicate with them, they listen and give me a call if there's something I might be interested in."*

This isn't a place for shrinking violets, and Cleary recruits those it believes will thrive in a more proactive environment. As one lawyer put it: *"We are all type-A and don't like saying 'no'."* That said, the coordinators are responsible for distributing assignments and checking that associates are doing a spread of work they're interested in. Faith in the recruitment process is also evident in the amount of responsibility associates are given early on: *"Traditionally, most new associates do document review but at Cleary we have staff attorneys who do that kind of stuff."*

Training & Development

All new associates are eased in to this environment with a *"two-week mini MBA program"* in New York that deals with numerous things like *"using Excel and understanding how financial structuring works."* This was widely hailed as *"extremely useful,"* though some admitted that *"it's a little basic if you've been to law school."* Sources praised the social opportunities the training affords: *"It kind of turned into talking to friends at the back of the class, which was great!"* DC newbies are *"put up in a nice hotel"* where there is, unsurprisingly, *"plenty of socializing."*

After this initial flurry of classroom activity, there are fairly regular CLEs, which are *"helpful though pretty poorly attended."* These are complemented by two quirkily-named annual programs, 'Corporate College' and 'Litigation Academy'. The first takes place *"twice a week and occurs over a period of about six months."* It's mandatory for corporate associates to attend and *"consists of lectures and Powerpoint presentations on corporate work,"* usually given by a partner or mid-level associate. Litigation Academy runs over a shorter space of time but is more intensive. *"Everyone participates, from juniors to partners,"* and activities include *"courtroom scenarios and fictional depositions."*

"Feedback is not anonymous, so people soften their punches."

The appraisal system veers off a bit from the more straightforward curriculum. In New York, for their first two years, associates' annual reviews are given by Mary Watson, a senior attorney and director of professional development. During junior appraisals her job is to *"solicit feedback from everyone you've worked with and deliver it to you in an evaluative format."* Most of those we spoke to were quick to praise this process, some even describing her as a *"motherly figure."* However, a few voiced concerns about the effectiveness of an appraisal delivered by someone who you've never worked closely with. While she *"encourages you to go to the person who gave your initial feedback, many people are shy"* and might be reluctant to follow-up on this. Moreover, *"feedback is not anonymous, so people soften their punches."* Things are a little different in DC: there's *"a six month review, which is truncated. And then a full review after about a year and a half"* with a partner of your choosing.

See firm profile on p.618

Hours & Compensation

Interviewees resoundingly approved the firm's policy of having no formal billing target. *"It takes away unnecessary competition"* because *"you never worry about what other people are doing."* Cleary's bonus system is *"completely lockstep."* As one associate put it, *"if there was a bonus for higher hours, I'd definitely have been in the higher tier,"* adding: *"But I don't think I'd have had as much fun doing it."*

"I've never had anyone pressure me not to take a vacation."

After working on a big deal or case – where *"days are 18-hours long"* – associates can at least look forward to taking some of their 20 days' vacation allowance, which increases with seniority. Many echoed one junior who reported: *"I've never had anyone pressure me not to take a vacation, and mine have always fallen at inopportune times for the rest of my team."* Even so, if your iPhone does start beeping on the beach, *"you get those days back."*

Culture

"We are more highly leveraged than firms we consider our peers," associates pointed out. *"That means there are fewer partners, so responsibility flows down."* High levels of responsibility can mean *"associates in the final years of being an associate are treated like partners."* Partners themselves often appear conscious of this, interviewees said, and are therefore *"extremely approachable"* and *"always want to spend time with associates – if we are traveling, we will all get dinner."* All of this contributes to a *"collegial and collaborative"* environment.

"the first-year class puts together skit movies usually poking fun at the firm"

Notable social events include Cleary's famous 'Wranglers.' *"We obviously have a lot during the summer when our summers are here. One of the more unique events is Wranglers, an event where the first-year class puts together skit movies usually poking fun at the firm. Last year we had an '80s cover band and the theme was '80s movies. We had a live vote to decide the winner."* Alas, outside of the summer, get-togethers are rather more mundane: *"CLEs with lunches"* and such like. *"Whenever you have a new group of lawyers coming to the firm, there are dinners. If you have the time, you go."* One fun-loving DC attorney lamented: *"There's wine and cheese once a month but it's not the most social office."* Lucky New Yorkers get these tasty spreads weekly.

Pro Bono

"If you are interested in it you can do as much as you want," juniors told us. It is *"almost completely self-driven"* in terms of how much you do, and a pro bono director in New York manages the assignments. Cleary doesn't impose a cap on the amount you can do. Lawyers here have links to organizations including Bronx Defenders, Sanctuary for Families, IRAP [International Refugee Assistance Project] and many others. For those able to find the time, *"there is an award and recognition if you bill 100 pro bono hours."*

Pro bono hours

- For all attorneys across all offices: 63,065
- Average per US attorney: 92

Diversity

A New York lawyer was fairly representative when she told us that *"in terms of young associates – over 50% in my class are female."* Among other initiatives, Cleary has *"hired multiple consultants to work on the promotion and retention of women."* Existing programs include Women Lawyers, a firmwide committee that holds *"lunches once a month for Cleary's female lawyers"* and whose raison d'être is to *"work on the promotion and retention of women."*

"Over 50% in my class are female."

In terms of helping ethnic minority representation, there are affinity groups – including ones for African-American and Latin American attorneys – that hold regular lunches and provide discussion forums for members. Generally speaking, as is often the case in BigLaw, *"at the associate level the firm is pretty diverse but unfortunately that tails off quite considerably moving up to partner."*

"There are fewer partners, so responsibility flows down."

Offices

Another area where there's room for improvement is attorneys' office space, some said. Due to high numbers, in One Liberty Plaza in New York *"most people have an office mate for their first eight to 18 months."* During this time, their view of the outside world improves: *"You start with no windows then, after six months to a year, you get one. Then, by the end of two years, you usually have two!"* Associates spoke positively about the size and layout of the offices. However, one pointed out that *"once you get the two-window, this is pretty much the*

See firm profile on p.618

office you'll have forever!" In DC *"you have your own office from the first day."*

Get Hired

Associates stressed that having diverse interests is smiled upon by recruiters at Cleary. One associate spoke of how *"everybody in my Cleary OCI asked me the same question: what subject my BA thesis was on. Nobody at any other firm asked me that."* The point of all this is to find interesting people *"who they'd want to be with in a conference room at 3am."* Hiring partner Lisa Schweitzer stresses that the firm's criteria for recruitment are the same as that for making partner: *"Based on attorneys who are excellent, are collegial and who have the potential to be leaders in their field."*

Strategy & Future

When pressed on what the future holds for the firm, HP Lisa Schweitzer replies that after opening offices in China, South Korea, São Paulo and Abu Dhabi in recent years, the firm is *"very comfortable with its coverage."* She stresses that the lockstep approach permeates all aspects of Cleary's strategy and *"because we have that model as a crucial component, we don't just expand for expansion's sake."*

"We don't just expand for expansion's sake."
- Lisa Schweitzer, hiring partner

See firm profile on p.618

Clifford Chance US LLP

Lawyers per state

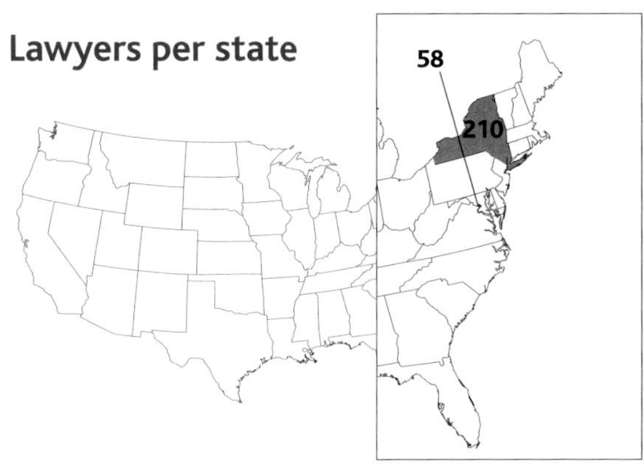

Largest US office: New York
US offices: 2
International offices: 33
First-year salary: $160,000
Billable hours: no requirement
Summers 2016: 24 (23 2Ls, 1 other)
Revenue 2015: $2.139 billion (April 2015)
Partners made in 2016: 24 (3 in US)
Famous for: being a member of the UK 'magic circle'; the king of *Chambers Global*

Peer beyond Clifford Chance's petite Stateside bases and you'll find a prodigious international organization.

IN the UK, where Clifford Chance originated as long ago as 1802 when the Napoleonic Wars hadn't even started, the firm is synonymous with prestige. It's one of the renowned 'magic circle' of elite outfits that all the best wannabe lawyers long to join. But banish any thoughts of quaint afternoon teas, tweed jackets and stiff upper lips. This is a modern global beast, not an English antique. Since its beginnings in Georgian London, the firm has expanded to massive proportions – nowadays it has 35 offices spread over 26 countries. In fact, CC has more top-tier *Chambers Global* rankings than any other firm, period.

With such a walloping presence on the global legal scene, it's unsurprising that associates in DC and New York emphasized the firm's *"international appeal and the chance to work with lawyers around the world"* as major draws. That said, the modest sizes of the US bases mean that *"you get a small-practice, hands-on feel, along with all the benefits of being at a firm with an enormous network."* Summer associates usually spend two weeks in a foreign office – we heard from interviewees who'd jetted off to London, Frankfurt, Amsterdam, Beijing and Hong Kong.

On chambers-associate.com...

- Interview with hiring partner Nick Williams

ASSOCIATES SAY...

The Work

At the time of our calls, there were 30 second and third-years in the New York office and ten in DC. In the Big Apple, around a third were litigators while most attorneys were to be found in the transactional department. The transactional team is divided into corporate, banking & finance or capital markets (though there are further subdivisions within each of these, like the insurance team, which is part of corporate). Tax, pensions & employment also had a sprinkling of associates. Just over half the DC juniors were in litigation.

In previous years, transactional juniors did three six-month rotations through corporate, banking and capital markets. However, *"deals don't work in neat six month segments, and the ramp-up and ramp-down period for rotations meant they were losing utilization."* Now, a new system has been introduced whereby *"for your first three years you're in a broad pool and not assigned to particular group. There's a non-attorney assignment manager who coordinates all the schedules."* A source noted that *"toward the end of the second year you do start hedging toward one group."* The New York litigation department has an assigning partner, though *"in truth it's a little more organic. If you're interested in a specific case or working with a partner, then the open door policy means you can express interest."*

See firm profile on p.619

Rankings in *Chambers USA*

Capital Markets	Litigation
Corporate/M&A	REITs
Insurance	Transportation
Latin American Investment	

For detail on ranking tiers and ranking locations, visit www.chambersandpartners.com

Recent work highlights

- Advised Hearst Corporation on its $82 million joint acquisition with Dreamworks of a 25% stake in Awesomeness TV
- Defending a British former Alstom executive against FCPA violation charges relating to alleged bribery of Indonesian government officials
- Acting for Credit Suisse in connection with parallel US and UK litigations relating to a cross-border debt financing deal

Sources in capital markets explained that *"generally the group deals with securitization. A lot of the clients are large financial funds,"* and noted that *"it's pretty impressive – these are people at the top of the market. Initially it's a little intimidating because you're playing with the big boys!"* Juniors handle *"the actual mechanics of closing a deal – making sure you have the signature pages and inputting comments on the purchase agreement."* As rookies progress, they'll often *"get more drafting opportunities on prospectus supplements and resolutions for companies."* Over in corporate, young associates *"sit in on meetings or conference calls and take the first stab at modifying an agreement to match our discussion."* Common tasks also include *"taking firsts drafts of memos and ancillary documents."*

"I've gotten to do a lot of pretty cool things."

Meanwhile, litigators told us that they'd been staffed on white-collar investigations, civil litigation and international arbitrations. *"I've gotten to do a lot of pretty cool things. Obviously doc review has been part of my work and will be in future, but I've had the chance to write memos, do legal research and meet the clients with a mid-level associate. I've also been involved with witness preparation and the logistics of trial preparation."* Like transactional associates, litigators get the chance to work on cross-border matters: *"I've dealt with leftover litigation from the UK Libor scandal and done some work supporting the London office with that."*

Training & Development

Incoming associates have a couple of days of orientation in New York, after which *"the training is a little different for transactional and litigation attorneys."* The former have *"a lot of sessions throughout the year like lunchtime seminars from partners giving us an overview of different transactions."* In addition, *"we also have quarterly or semi-annual training on legal writing."* One source explained that *"transactional associates have more training because they're not assigned to a group yet, so they can get a bit of everything."* On the other hand, litigators have more intensive trainings less frequently. *"We're still transitioning from a time when the firm was primarily corporate to now having a bigger litigation presence, so there aren't so many trainings geared towards litigation."*

"The reward for good work is more work!"

An interviewee in DC emphasized that *"there's a strong system of informal feedback. Partners are very interested and invested in training the associates. They'll take five minutes to say 'this is why or how we do this' and create a lot of teachable moments."* Not all sources agreed. *"It's pretty sink or swim,"* declared a New Yorker. *"You don't get much feedback unless it's negative and you've done something wrong. There's not a ton of 'oh you did a really good job!' although I've had some commendations from clients by email. A partner tells me regularly that the reward for good work is more work!"*

Offices

There are far too many CC offices to rattle off here, but the list includes everywhere from Jakarta to Bucharest, Seoul to Perth. Stateside, associates' reports on their digs was mixed: *"It's certainly not swanky – Davis Polk's office it is not!"* First and second-years share internal offices which means that *"we struggle a lot with the fact that there's not a lot of natural light. We spend so much time in them and it can feel a bit cave-like!"* As one put it: *"Anyone who's looked for an apartment here knows that windows are hard to find in Manhattan!"* Despite these gripes, *"there is an excellent cafeteria, which is the biggest perk."* Over in DC, *"the offices are a little tired although the lobby and client areas are impressive. It could certainly use an update. We have these old, gray carpets..."* Others looked on the bright side: *"I have a big window and my own office, which New Yorkers do not!"* Plus, *"we asked for standing desks and they quickly obliged."*

"Windows are hard to find in Manhattan!"

See firm profile on p.619

Hours & Compensation

Instead of a set billing requirement there's an unofficial target of 2,000 hours, which is the bonus threshold. Some transactional interviewees mentioned that they *"had concerns about not meeting it, because of a downtick in deal volume."* However, *"there's an understanding that first and second-years don't really control their hours because they're pulled from a pool onto deals. Lots of people in my class didn't make it but it's not held against them."*

"They want us to work as much as we can."

Some litigators had a different story to tell. *"They want us to work as much as we can and that means you're 'on' 24 hours a day and at weekends. I don't know anyone who's ever hit below 2,000 hours,"* revealed a source. *"We were told by a senior that we should be billing ten hours a day, six days a week. During that period, a lot of juniors were unhappy. The partners have made an effort to cut back on it and that's helped with morale. At the moment the hours are manageable, although there have been times when it wasn't at all."* Big Apple litigators commented that *"we have a lot of face time. Working from home is not generally encouraged. I'd be uncomfortable leaving before 6.45pm. I find that part of the culture unpleasant. Some people are more open-minded though and are fine with you working from home."*

According to a litigator in DC, *"I feel comfortable about taking vacation now, although I didn't at first. On a week to week basis, the unpredictability is a little difficult and your plans can be affected at the last minute, but people are good team players and will try to cover for you if they can. On average I leave about 8.30pm, but the latest I've stayed is 2am."* It's up and down for transactional folks too (*"I can go for a week leaving at 6pm every day or at midnight every day"*) although a source in DC asserted that *"they're protective of our work/life balance because they want to build a team that will keep working for them. That said, in November and December I didn't have any work/life balance at all..."*

Pro Bono

There's no cap on pro bono hours, which can all be counted towards the billable total. According to interviewees, *"they encourage you to do about 50 hours."* Juniors had *"helped young homeless people to fill out forms for benefits"* and worked with My Sisters' Place, a charity for victims of domestic violence. Others had taken on tax matters and *"IP licensing issues for non-governmental organizations."*

Pro bono hours

- For all attorneys across all US offices: undisclosed
- Average per US attorney: undisclosed (minimum 50 encouraged)

Culture

Firm culture is *"driven by the partners in each department,"* reckoned associates. *"In litigation, a lot of partners are personable and chummy – they'll stop by your office and tell you about their vacation."* The open door setup *"fosters a collaborative environment and you don't feel like anyone is off limits."* Another added that *"we work hard for sure, and work comes first, but there's a strong sense of camaraderie. I've become close with a lot of people I work with and consider them good friends which is wonderful. On the other hand when there's a bad egg or two, it's difficult because you're always around them – there's not a lot of space and not a lot of people as a buffer."*

"A lot of partners are personable and chummy."

When it comes to socializing, *"we have a wonderful holiday party and organize welcome lunches or drinks for new associates and laterals. Sometimes partners will say 'hey let's go have some drinks.'"* Sources in DC mentioned that *"we recently had an all-day office retreat during which no billing was allowed. We went into the countryside in Virginia for a day of hiking, horse-riding, clay shooting, zip lining and cooking."* During the week it's common for *"someone to send an email asking if anyone wants to grab a beer, but more often than not it falls through because of schedules. The thought is there though."*

Diversity

"It would be wonderful if we had some non-white partners and female partners – there are no female partners in litigation," said a junior ruefully. However, *"the firm is definitely trying to improve diversity – the managing partner Evan Cohen is very active in promoting it."* CC has a women's initiative, along with an LGBT committee, black and Latino lawyers' group and a Pacific Islander group. All of these host events, such as ethnic dance lessons and exhibitions for LGBT artists.

Get Hired

Hiring partner Nick Williams says that CC looks for *"team players. We're a traditional lockstep compensation firm, because that engenders a high level of cooperation between and amongst partners, and that means partners treat other partners with the greatest level of*

See firm profile on p.619

respect. This ethos permeates the entire firm and informs how partners treat associates and how associates treat other associates. So that's the single most important factor." Successful candidates also need *"a willingness to work hard, to be friendly, to be supportive, to have sense of humor – that's all critical. We know the people that we're hiring are very bright, that's a given, so things like the quality of their attitude are of critical importance."*

Strategy & Future

Managing partner for the Americas Evan Cohen tells us that *"we're expanding in a number of practices."* The flourishing LatAm projects practice *"not only continues to grow and be profitable, but it also helps us to increase our diversity in the office. We now have 25 to 30 fluent Spanish speaking attorneys."* Cohen cites US asset finance, structured finance and white-collar investigations as areas of growth. Restructuring work in Texas and Mexico will also boom as a result of the low price of oil: *"We'll see a lot of oil related companies going bust, and we're well positioned to get that work."*

"You get a small-practice, hands-on feel, along with all the benefits of being at a firm with an enormous network."

See firm profile on p.619

Cooley LLP

Lawyers per state

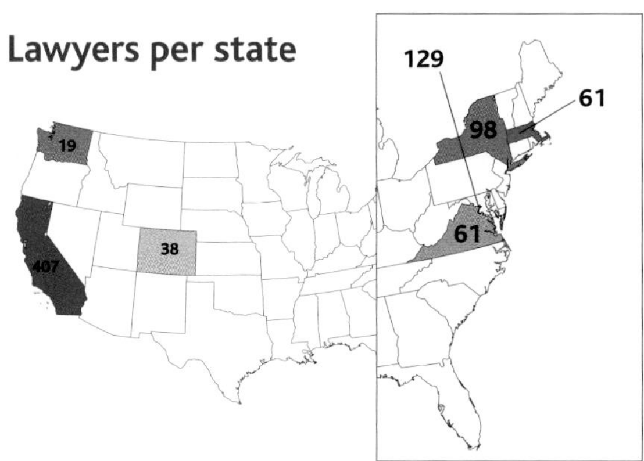

Largest US office: Palo Alto
US offices: 10
International offices: 2
First-year salary: $160,000
Billable hours: 1,950 target
Summers 2016: 65 (61 2Ls, 3 1Ls, 1 other)
Revenue 2015: $912 million (+13.7%)
Partners made 2016: 12 (all US)
Famous for: Cali cool; Silicon Valley clients

For associates at this tech whiz there are plenty of opportunities to get ahead without needing to scrap the vacation.

BEST known for advising promising startups and venture capitalists in Silicon Valley, Cooley's forte lies in all things technology, life sciences, venture capital, emerging companies and IP. Palo Alto is the nerve center of the firm's ten US offices, flanked by international offices in Shanghai and London, the latter celebrating its first birthday in 2016. *"It's allowed us to work on transactions that otherwise we wouldn't have,"* says a cheerful Joe Conroy, Cooley's CEO. *"It's been a long held aspiration of ours to be a truly global firm, and setting up in London was a big step towards achieving that."* There's a lot of positivity about Cooley right now, as a quick search of the legal press over the past year or two will reveal.

The aim for Cooley's 900-odd lawyers now is to crack into the global elite, a market position in which Conroy feels there's a Cooley-shaped gap. He elaborates: *"We can distinguish ourselves by being the only top 30 firm that can boast expertise in tech, life sciences, and representing high-growth companies of all stripes."* Key in driving this ambition will be a 50:50 balance between transactional and litigious work, a platform that has already been *"fundamental in successfully weathering economic climate variations."* Such a dual offering also means *"we're better positioned to drive our revenue by cross-selling our services across our core client base,"* and with giants like eBay, Facebook and Google all on the books, it's probably a smart move.

On chambers-associate.com...

- Interview with CEO Joe Conroy

Perhaps most encouraging for law students is that Cooley's summer hiring is now looking healthier than ever. This year the summer class has leapt up to 65, from 42 in 2015. Director of legal talent Carrie Wagner says *"like many firms, Cooley has a demand for junior level associates across a variety of practice areas."*

ASSOCIATES SAY...

The Work

Litigation and 'business' (corporate) are big takers, so usually just a few associates are divided between specialty groups such as real estate, healthcare, IP lit, and employment. Traditionally starting as generalists within their designated group, newbies are free to explore different areas, and felt *"encouraged to forge working relationships with a number of different associates and partners."* For litigators this means a mix of antitrust, commercial disputes, IP and white-collar crime cases, whereas transactional hopefuls keep busy in subgroups like corporate/M&A, emerging or public companies, technology, and venture capital. All have access to an assignment partner, who is supposed to help keep track of who's doing what. In practice, *"nothing much tends to come from it,"* with interviewees finding *"work comes more organically, so it's important to make an effort with partners whose work interests you."* Palo Alto has re-

The Inside View

See firm profile on p.620

Rankings in *Chambers USA*

Antitrust	Litigation
Capital Markets	Media & Entertainment
Corporate/Commercial	Privacy & Data Security
Corporate/M&A	Private Equity
Intellectual Property	Real Estate
Investment Funds	Startups & Emerging Companies
IT & Outsourcing	Telecommunications
Life Sciences	

For detail on ranking tiers and ranking locations, visit www.chambersandpartners.com

cently tried to improve the allocation process by placing associates into groups for weekly catch-ups, a development that sources noted *"has helped everyone to get a better sense of each other's workload."*

"Three years here is like six elsewhere"

"It's important to stress that in terms of client interaction and experience, three years here is like six elsewhere" asserted one associate. Early on, business juniors are expected to work for a mix of public and private company clients. *"It makes your client advice that bit more rounded,"* opined one deal-doer, as *"you really appreciate what private companies have to do to become a successful public company."* Providing better value for money that their more senior colleagues, rookies in business also do a lot of work with startups. *"I'm only a third-year,"* boasted one, *"but I'm the firm's go-to for numerous clients. Working on big IPOs provides a great insight into partners' case management techniques, but working on startups provides you with a platform to develop and try out your own."*

Litigators begin by ploughing through their fair share of doc review and research tasks, though *"partners do take your successes into account,"* so doors open for those who are ready. *"I started on a lot of internal investigations,"* remembered one caller, *"and mainly took notes on interviews. After a few months I felt confident enough to suggest subjects to cover and key documents to look at. Soon after the partner I was working for encouraged me to try interviewing, myself."*

"It's a very challenging but rewarding environment to be in."

"We need associates who can step up quickly, be smart about what they can do on their own, and grasp the nettle," concluded a Boston-based source. *"We are very well supported by our senior colleagues, but are expected to take ownership of our work and make decisions earlier than you'd probably expect. It's a very challenging but rewarding environment to be in."*

Recent work highlights

- Guided Axovant Sciences, a producer of dementia pharmaceuticals, through its $362.3 million IPO
- Won a motion to dismiss over 20 class actions filed against Facebook. Claims worth $15 billion had been mounted against the company for unlawfully tracking users' browsing activity
- Helped Patheon fend off an antitrust suit raised by rival pharmaceutical company Procaps. The claim, valued at $380 million, stemmed from Patheon's acquisition of one of Procaps' key rivals
- Acted for mobile email app Acompli in its $200 million sale to Microsoft. The app has been rebranded and now functions as Outlook Mobile for iOS and Android

Offices & Training

A cornerstone of Cooley's associate training program, Cooley College sees all first-years and junior laterals flown out to Palo Alto for a jam-packed week of training and networking. The main objectives are threefold: to further educate juniors about the firm's identity and modus operandi, to provide initial practice-specific training, and to encourage greenhorns from across Cooley's ten US offices to make ties that'll stick with them.

Foundations are laid during the course of the summer program, where newbies break the ice over a long weekend in Palo Alto. *"The first two days are spent in the HQ doing training exercises, and the other two focus on team building in a resort outside of San Francisco."* A year on, associates head back to the Bay for a full week, and Cooley College opens its doors.

To facilitate a smooth integration, things like happy hours, an assault course challenge and formal dinners are staged. The latter are *"well attended by partners from across the firm,"* providing *"a great opportunity to get talking and hear more about their practices."* Despite such a busy schedule, interviewees were grateful to have had *"plenty of free time at the end of the day to plan our own activities and get together for drinks."*

"Bonds are strong because of the efforts Cooley makes to support cross-office integration."

The training sees juniors divided into transactional and litigious streams, with each organizing partner-led talks on specific practice groups. There are also skills workshops covering areas such as effective writing, discovery and time management. Such gatherings not only *"make it much easier to reach out for advice in the future,"* but also play an important part in decentralizing the balance of power between offices. *"The relationships formed*

See firm profile on p.620

have helped us to set up cross office-training sessions with the Reston office," said one DC Cooleyite. *"There's no sense that we have to sign anything off in California. The value and expertise in each office is well appreciated, and those bonds are strong because of the efforts Cooley makes to support cross-office integration."*

Pro Bono

With no cap on the amount of pro bono hours attorneys can bill, *"hitting your hours while giving a little back is definitely achievable."* Do-gooders who rack up a half century receive an award recognizing their efforts, though *"we're under no pressure either way."* Associates are *"encouraged to seek out causes that inspire us,"* but a pro bono coordinator *"regularly sends out emails relating to immigration, clemency, and domestic violence cases,"* for those who need a pointer. *"There are corporate opportunities available"* too, *"but the firm has been really supportive of my desire to try out some litigation. Having that variation has been fun."* Pro bono is also a good way to dip your toes into more senior responsibility, as one litigator had discovered: *"I got to make my first court appearance on a pro bono case. It was nerve-racking, but I was glad to have had that early opportunity."*

"It was nerve-racking."

Pro bono hours

- For all attorneys across all US offices: 38,667
- Average per US attorney: 48

Culture & Hours

Pro bono hours

"I feel that we are a little misunderstood," states CEO Joe Conroy. *"Cooley isn't a lifestyle firm. We put a lot of effort into being a great place to work, but in our eyes a good workplace is not measured by how many Fitbits you can give out or parties you can stage, but by how much you can help people to realize their ambitions."* Key to this is a trickle-down belief that rookies will help to form the partnership of the future, so *"creating opportunities for associates is key to the firm's continued success."*

From Boston to Broomfield, insiders largely corroborated this view, with one New Yorker chiming: *"It's very collaborative here. Everyone works extremely hard on their own work, but is willing to spend time helping others. Partners and more senior associates take this responsibility particularly seriously."* That's fortunate, because associates have plenty to be getting on with, with billable targets recently increased from 1,900 to 1,950 hours to match a rise in bonus compensation. *"Meeting that goal hasn't been an issue,"* several confessed. *"It's been a busy year across the board, and it seems fair considering our salary."* As an additional sweetener, *"the firm hands out appreciation dinners after particularly busy months."* According to one Bostonian, *"they'll say 'bring us the bill' and they generally expect it to be pretty high."*

"Cooley's new age vibe ditches any unnecessary stresses."

"Cooley is pretty chilled when it comes to managing your work," so associates tend to leave at around 7pm, putting in an hour or two at home later in the evening. The odd weekend stint was mentioned, but *"it's rarely more than a few hours."* When vacation comes around, however, *"people unplug,"* and associates are *"definitely encouraged to take and enjoy it as a way of keeping our outside lives in check."* In fact, *"Cooley's new age vibe ditches any unnecessary stresses,"* so associates are welcome to scrap their neckties, should they wish. *"The real focus here is on getting results for clients and training our younger associates,"* beamed one. *"Most people wear slacks and a button-down."*

"It's been a long held aspiration of ours to be a truly global firm, and setting up in London was a big step towards achieving that."

Diversity

"Our talent pipeline is incredibly diverse," Carrie Wagner says. *"One reason for this is our 1L Diversity Fellowship program, which provides high-performing diverse law students with summer placements after both their first and second year of law school, as well as a financial award to assist with the cost of tuition."* Further up the ladder, *"diverse associates are exiting Big Law at higher rates than the overall associate population, and Cooley is committed to finding ways to increase the retention of diverse associates. Inclusion is imperative."* To lead this cross-office drive, Cooley brought in a diversity and inclusion manager in early 2015, and since then *"the firm has been making tremendous strides toward inclusion and retention."*

"The firm has been making tremendous strides towards inclusion and retention."

One of the key focuses has been to encourage more associates to take on leadership roles in affinity groups. When asked, juniors found the rise in sponsored diversity receptions *"an effective way of getting our colleagues*

The Inside View

See firm profile on p.620

and clients to engage with the industry's shortcomings." DC and San Fran callers also applauded Cooley's participation in the OnRamp Fellowship program. The scheme helps experienced female lawyers who've left the workforce – often to raise children or manage other family obligations – to return to action for six-month and one-year paid positions. *"I've never felt that Cooley avoids promoting female senior associates to partner,"* someone reasoned. *"It's just that like many other law firms, a little more flexibility is needed to work around family commitments. It's really positive to see that program in action."*

Get Hired

To get in on the action, applicants will have to be ready to tackle Cooley's behavioral interviewing techniques, designed to uncover evidence of the core competencies the firm values. Commitment, initiative, intelligence and teamwork are all prized, and Carrie Wagner advises hopefuls to *"be familiar with the behavioral interviewing technique so that they are prepared for these types of questions, which often begin 'Tell me about a time when...' We coach our interviewers to utilize this technique because we believe previous behavior is the best predictor of future behavior, and we are focused on identifying students who display the competencies we have determined are critical to success for an attorney at Cooley."* While self-reflection is important, applicants should make no secret of their ambitions: *"Do not be afraid to make clear your goals and priorities,"* Carrie Wagner implores. *"Students who can articulate how their prior work or academic experiences have led them to an interest in a certain practice area are of particular interest to Cooley."*

"Students who can articulate how their prior work or academic experiences have led them to an interest in a certain practice."

Strategy & Future

Setting up shop in the English capital was *"a big step"* toward becoming a truly global firm, though CEO Joe Conroy insists that *"London can't be it for us in Europe."* Boasting a *"strong economy and hotbed of life sciences, medical tech and IP opportunities,"* a waltz into Germany is *"a medium-term inevitability."* Far East, Conroy would *"also like to one day expand our presence in China"* to better service the firm's *"very robust client base there."*

"London can't be it for us in Europe."

Geographical ambitions form just part of Cooley's overarching strategy, identified by Conroy as obtaining *"as much high-end work as possible."* For that to happen, *"you need to be elite in every sense of the word: we need elite finances; elite practice capabilities; elite results; elite clients; and an elite brand."* Upholding the firm's rep as a go-to for emerging companies will also be key, and in the past year Cooley has *"added an impressive number of emerging companies into our pipeline."*

The Inside View

"A good workplace is not measured by how many Fitbits you can give out or parties you can stage, but by how much you can help people to realize their ambitions."

CEO Joe Conroy

See firm profile on p.620

Cozen O'Connor

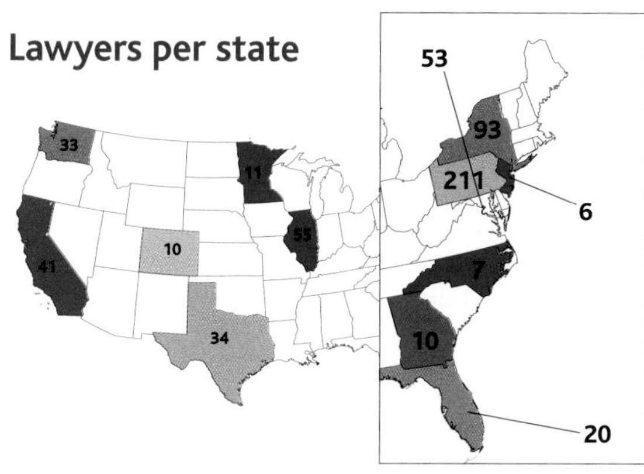

Largest US office: Philadelphia

US offices: 22

International offices: 2

First-year salary: $125,000 - $155,000

Billable hours: vary by practice area, between 1,800 and 2,000

Summers 2016: 19 (14 2Ls, 5 1Ls)

Revenue 2015: $341.5million (+9.1%)

Partners made in 2016: 15 (14 in USA)

Famous for: birthing subrogation; its name partners still walk the corridors; a cozy atmosphere for a big player

Ever-growing Philadelphian Cozen O'Connor offers associates mentorship, fancy new architecture, and "*high-level exposure.*"

WHAT'S new with Cozen? Where to begin? Over the past twelve months it has relocated six of its 24 offices to brand new digs, not least its Philadelphia HQ where attorneys have settled in to the new Center City building. Meanwhile, the 46 year-old acquired a labor and employment litigation team in Chicago by incorporating local firm Meckler Bulger Tilson. The maneuver also landed Cozen a new office in San Francisco, with 15 new attorneys. Over in DC, meanwhile, Cozen launched a new State Attorneys General practice made up of former Dickstein Shapiro partners.

Associates told us they chose Cozen over other firms *"because of the sense of camaraderie that permeates the corridors, where people are clearly focused on more than just their book of business, and where you're trusted and encouraged to strike a healthy work/life balance."* They singled out mentoring as one of the aspects of life at Cozen that confirmed *"they want us here for the long term."* Along with what some characterized as a *"small firm feel,"* comes top dog expertise.

On chambers-associate.com...

- Interview with managing partner Vince McGuinness
- Subrogation: Cozen's insurance specialty

ASSOCIATES SAY...

The Work

Cozen O'Connor – both of whose namesakes, by the way, are still around as chairman and vice chairman – sweeps up *Chambers USA* rankings for real estate, labor & employment, construction, transportation, litigation, corporate/M&A, bankruptcy, government and insurance. If you're wondering what the deal is with the firm's specialty area of subrogation, check out our website.

During their summer, interns in Philly get to spend half their time in litigation and half on the transactional side. At the end they express a preference, and sources reassured us that *"they're always willing to find the best fit for you."* When associates arrive as first-years, they're split between one of the transactional practices – such as corporate, real estate, energy or IP – and the so-called litigation pool. Litigators enter the pool for up to 18 months, rotating between different sub-groups, like commercial litigation, global insurance or subrogation. *"It's really interesting and it helps you find your niche; they're invested in that search because they want you to build a career here."*

"At mega New York firms, aren't associates just doing due diligence?"

"At mega New York firms, aren't associates just doing due diligence? I don't know of any other firms where first and second-years get the sort of high-level exposure that

See firm profile on p.621

Rankings in *Chambers USA*

Construction	Labor & Employment
Corporate/M&A	Litigation
Government	Real Estate
Healthcare	Transportation
Insurance	

For detail on ranking tiers and ranking locations, visit www.chambersandpartners.com

I've experienced," a content corporate junior confided. *"I've been asked to draft purchase agreements, and have taken the lead on some smaller deals, where I was the primary client contact."* Litigators were similarly satisfied, one tallying up: *"By the end of first year I had taken ten to 15 depositions and been to federal court. I was genuinely surprised by how much hands-on experience of case management and drafting we got. I'm loving it."* While a couple of litigation interviewees hadn't been to court yet, all concurred that levels of responsibility were high *"beyond expectation."* The consensus view was: *"I feel like I'm not replaceable, and that's empowering."*

Training & Development

A litigator felt that *"the sense that the firm wants you to succeed, and that they're investing in you, is palpable."* Summers are assigned a partner mentor, an associate mentor and a writing tutor to check over assignments. When fresh-faced lawyers arrive as junior associates, they're still matched up to formal mentors, but they also *"naturally find other mentors too. I have lunch (on the firm!) every month with my partner mentor, and she takes her role very seriously. She doesn't always give me the 'friend answer': she tells me what I need to hear, which is helpful."*

"I have lunch (on the firm!) every month with my partner mentor."

Last year we reported that Cozen was in the process of revamping its training scheme, and this year's insiders confirmed *"the new curriculum is excellent. It's rare that there's training I think I won't benefit from."* A source reflected that *"training and mentorship were two things I didn't consider when I was making a decision, but I've used Cozen's so much. Training is ongoing, which keeps it fresh."* The firm offers COTA, Cozen O'Connor's Trial Academy, and CODEP, a Deposition Program. If something is going on in Philadelphia, rookies from other offices can tune in via video conference, but *"once a year we're all flown out to the HQ for a firmwide associate training session."*

Recent work highlights

- Obtained summary judgment for ACE insurers based on 'pollution exclusion', meaning they didn't need to pay out a liability claim brought by an energy company (Catalyst) whose fracking operations contaminated some well waters
- Renewed its involvement in post 9/11 disputes by interviewing an imprisoned former Al Qaeda operative regarding the lawsuit against Saudi Arabia. Cozen represents the Executive Committee for Commercial Claims in the wrongful death and personal injury multidistrict litigation
- Served as counsel to health insurance company Blue Cross of Norheastern Pennsylvania in its $100 million merger with Highmark

Hours & Compensation

"My friend works at another big law firm in Philadelphia," a participant shared, *"where the hours requirement is 2,400. That pressure would stop me from concentrating."* While Cozen introduced billable targets a couple of years ago, all sources agreed *"they won't beat you up on it, and the targets are totally reasonable. The corporate group has a 1,600 minimum, but we all exceeded it by several hundreds of hours."* In real estate it's 1,650, and litigators should shoot for 1,800. Relaxed associates were quick to point out that *"we do work really hard."* Litigators cited 11-hour days as standard, and others confirmed that *"logging on from home at night is often necessary just to keep a deal moving."* Weekend work was rare: *"They know no one wants to be in the office on Saturday morning."*

"We're a meritocracy, not a lockstep."

Cozen's associate salary has been a slightly contentious topic in the past, mainly because the firm pays under market rate. This year it has upped its first and second-year salaries, to $145,000 in Philadelphia and $155,000 in New York and DC. Third-years were sitting tight and waiting for the end-of-year bonuses to be announced, *"which will reflect a pay rise retroactively."* Managing partner Vince McGuinness confirms this, adding *"we're a meritocracy, not a lockstep. We didn't want to increase everyone's salary without doing performance reviews first."*

Sources certainly didn't feel like Cozen was counting its pennies: *"The resources the firm's willing to give are second to none. If you say you'd like to buy a table's worth of seats at a fundraising event, they write you a check. They're beyond generous, particularly from a philanthropic perspective."*

See firm profile on p.621

Pro Bono

"There's a sense that you'd struggle to get your bonus if you didn't use up your 60 hours of billable pro bono." A designated director of pro bono circulates wide-ranging opportunities: *"We work for Wills for Heroes, helping police officers and firefighters with their wills. We take part in a mock trial program at a local high school, and we have a scheme with the Federal court in Philadelphia taking their pro se clients. Someone did a social security case from start to finish. Others hosted a divorce clinic, wrote clemency petitions, and worked at a legal clinic for the blind."*

Pro bono hours:

- For all attorneys across all offices: 11,247
- Average per US attorney: 17

Culture

Sources had only nice things to say about Cozen's culture. They pointed to *"how relatable people are, how partners' attitudes create a collaborative environment, and what a good job they do at encouraging a healthy work/life balance"* as contributing factors. *"When I interviewed, people talked to me about their schedule, not just their work,"* one recalled, while another explained that *"sure, there's a hierarchy, but it doesn't permeate the atmosphere, which is more results-oriented. I worked on a weekend once but it was only because the partner on the team was also working. Shareholders ask me for my opinion in front of clients."*

"Bowling, pizza and beers."

And how better to end a productive day of solid team work than by celebrating in style? *"I love all the social occasions they put together. They understand how beneficial it is to have people interacting."* These included *"random happy hours, practice group gatherings, and bowling, pizza and beers."* The highlight was undoubtedly the firm's retreat: *"Every couple of years everyone gets together and goes to Florida. It's so much fun."*

Diversity

Diverse attorneys across the entire law firm, from shareholders to associates, were asked to arrive at the latest retreat a day early. *"I chatted to an LGBT partner from Texas,"* a Philadelphian enthused, *"and at the end they gave you a little brochure with everyone's names in it, so you can use that network forever. Everyone was in such high spirits by the time the others arrived."*

Overall, most associates agreed that *"Cozen is committed, and does particularly well at hiring women,"* but some felt that *"it could do better, especially with regards to ethnic minorities."* Diverse sources spoke with conviction about *"never having felt excluded,"* however, and were enthusiastic about the firm's chair of diversity and about the various collaborations in place.

Offices

When we spoke to Philly Cozenites last year they were buzzing in anticipation of their new HQ. Can reality ever meet such high expectations? *"Absolutely. It's light years away from our previous office."* The space analogy is especially apt given that Cozen's starship has also risen from *"the ground floor of our previous building,"* to occupying the 21st to 28th floors of One Liberty Place. *"When clients get off the elevator to go to our 28th floor conference room, they're taken aback by the views."* When they're not admiring the outside world, associates can admire each other: *"All the offices have glass walls, which takes the open-door policy to the next level."* Crystal clear walls weren't the only feature of the new digs to be deemed conducive to a friendlier atmosphere: *"In the old office, we were spread across three enormous floors, but here we're on eight floors, so we can be organized by practice group. It makes us more efficient and collaborative. The new office has fostered a team feeling."*

"We can be organized by practice group."

The cherry on the cake? *"Excellent shrimp and grits in the cafeteria."* It's not only always sunny in Philadelphia though: we heard from DC rookies, also enjoying a *"modern"* new crib, that like Philly they *"have cupboards that are also white boards; it's like writing on the walls, kind of crazy."* At the time of our calls 14 of our interviewee list were in Philadelphia, five in DC, three in each of Seattle and New York, one in Houston, and one in Cherry Hill, NJ.

"Shareholders ask me for my opinion in front of clients."

Get Hired

A team of Cozen attorneys visits 16 university campuses for OCIs each year, while also accepting direct resumes. Hiring partner Matt Siegel says he looks for *"an entrepreneurial spirit. It's a cliché but it does make someone stand out. Also someone who is proud of their accomplishments but not cocky."* What kind of questions are asked in order to test candidates? *"If we see something on their resume about prior mock trial experience, we'll ask them to briefly describe the case. If someone has included an interest outside of law at the bottom of their resume, we'll ask about that to open things up a little bit."*

See firm profile on p.621

And finally, how important is a link to Philadelphia? The vast majority of participants based in the HQ had either grown up in the region or attended law school there. *"If there's no obvious connection, we always ask about it,"* says Matt Siegel. *"It's an important question to us."*

Strategy & Future

"The four practice areas we targeted – and continue to target – for growth are real estate, IP, labor and employment, and regulatory and government affairs. Litigation practices have been steady, and energy has experienced some growth, but nothing huge," comes the year's round-up from managing partner Vince McGuinness.

He confirms that the firm's previous strategy of *"slow and steady growth"* still holds true, but adds more excitingly: *"Although I said that last year and then we brought in two large groups."* He concludes that on balance *"we want thoughtful and steady growth in key areas, but we're also going to be opportunistic, for example by growing in California and achieving full coverage of that area."*

"We want thoughtful and steady growth in key areas, but we're also going to be opportunistic."

Vince McGuinness, managing partner

See firm profile on p.621

Cravath, Swaine & Moore LLP

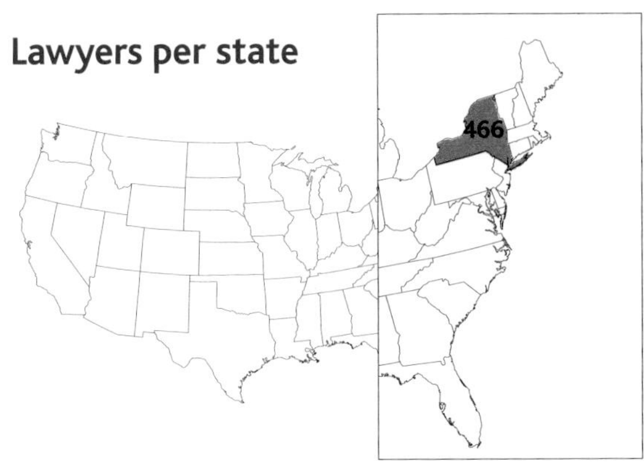

Largest US office: New York
US offices: 1
International offices: 1
First-year salary: $160,000
Billable hours: no requirement
Summers 2016: 116 (110 2Ls, 4 1Ls, 2 others)
Revenue 2015: $666.5 million (+2.9%)
Partners made 2016: 2
Famous for: mega M&A; the century-old Cravath System

When it comes to scaling the peaks of Big Law, you can't get much higher than Cravath.

MOUNT Everest, K2, the Matterhorn, Cravath... you have to be among the best to ascend these towering icons. For almost two centuries Cravath itself has been a pioneer among law firms, with many following in its footsteps by implementing the famed Cravath System. This series of business management principles shapes everything from hiring, training, and tenure to bonuses and compensation.

It takes more than just hiring and training policies to earn Cravath its almost mythical reputation. Just take a look at *Chambers USA*, which awards Cravath more best-of-the-best Band 1 rankings than Band 2 or below, the upshot being: if Cravath does something, it does it extremely well. The New Yorker's litigation and corporate teams are particularly well endowed with accolades, and attorneys here are known for handling some of the hugest M&A deals around. One such recent mega-merger saw Cravath represent Heinz in a tasty $60 billion combination with Kraft to create the third largest food and drinks company in the USA. Cravath is also assisting Shell in its fuel-injected $70 billion acquisition of BG Group – the biggest oil & gas merger of all time.

On chambers-associate.com...

- Cravath's rotation system
- We chat with hiring partners Karen DeMasi and Eric Schiele
- The Cravath System

ASSOCIATES SAY...

The Work

Juniors have long flocked to Cravath for its reputation for giving associates *"the most challenging and developmental work possible at an early stage."* Sources *"expecting to be thrown into demanding matters"* weren't disappointed by Cravath's rotation system: corporate juniors switch practice group around every 12 to 15 months while litigators aim to rotate every 15 to 18 months. *"Your responsibility level grows every time you move but you may know less on the subject than your juniors, who have been in the group for longer. It's exciting."* Check out our website for more associate thoughts on shifting groups.

Around 50 new first-years tend to join the corporate department each year. Half that number go into litigation and the remaining few head into tax or trusts & estates. Corporate juniors are attached to between three and five partners who dole out work, while litigators usually receive assignments from one partner.

"You're going to do it all."

Banking, M&A and securities are the three main corporate rotations and cover *"the main competencies you need."* Other rotations like real estate and corporate governance follow on from these. Banking juniors tackle *"finance and credit work for both borrowers and lenders. We handle credit agreements and facilities, and ac-*

See firm profile on p.622

Rankings in *Chambers USA*

Antitrust	Environment
Banking & Finance	Intellectual Property
Capital Markets	Litigation
Corporate Crime & Investigations	Media & Entertainment
	Securities
Corporate/M&A	Tax
Employee Benefits & Executive Compensation	

For detail on ranking tiers and ranking locations, visit www.chambersandpartners.com

quisitions financings for companies and banks." By their third year, interviewees were often *"the lead associate on deals, working on primary transaction documents"* – like credit agreements – *"and overseeing juniors drafting ancillary documents, and helping out with due diligence."* Concerning the latter: *"It's rare for anyone past their first twelve months at the firm to be doing this"* in any practice group. The *"main input of second and third-years within M&A is drafting a lot of ancillary documents, like guarantees, and taking a shot at the main purchase agreements"* for public and private transactions. Debt, equity, IPO and corporate bond offerings are regular assignments in securities.

Litigators' tasks *"can span the entire life cycle of the litigation as there are so many types of cases at so many stages. At the moment I'm working on a first draft of a motion to dismiss. We do some discovery but many of the juniors have the opportunity to take ownership of their cases so there is a fair bit of deposition preparation with expert and fact witnesses."*

Training & Development

When asked about training opportunities, nearly all of our interviewees were quick to point out *"the best way to train is to get involved. Participating on a matter with a group is the most informative experience you can have."* Another elaborated: *"A lot of the important stuff comes from being in the room with a partner on a big call and hearing how they handle questions and situations where you would not have known the answer."*

"The most informative experience."

Cravath's online database features heaps of CLEs and training sessions presented by the firm's partners. Deal and case-led study luncheons talk attorneys through recent significant matters, such as the firm's representation of orange juice giant Cutrale and investment fund Safra Group in their unsolicited offer to acquire banana seller Chiquita. Workshops on negotiations, depositions, legal writing and oral arguments feature mock exercises, and

Recent work highlights

- Assisted global pharmaceutical company Mylan in a $5.6 billion inversion acquisition of US healthcare company Abbott Laboratories' non-US specialty and generic business
- Represented Johnson & Johnson in a $4 billion sale of its Ortho-Clinical Diagnostics unit to private equity firm Carlyle
- Acted for British American Tobacco in several class action lawsuits relating to BAT's involvement in Reynolds American's $27.4 billion acquisition of fellow cigarette makers Lorillard
- Represented Credit Suisse in a lawsuit brought by wounded US soldiers and estates of deceased US soldiers that it, along with other European banks, violated US regulations to conduct financial transactions for Iranian banks. These funds were then purportedly used to fund terrorist groups in Iraq which attacked US forces

litigators can go one further and prepare for trial in Cravath's own mock court room.

Offices

Cravath's décor matches that of its realistic mock courtroom. *"Dark wood and earthy colors"* make this a *"very traditional office,"* associates told us. One source reasoned: *"We're not going to have 'look through' offices. That's not how we get down. The design is definitely conservative. More* Mad Men *than Apple."*

"More Mad Men than Apple."

Junior associates usually share an office until their third year. *"It's one of the best things the firm does."* Senior office mates *"will have already handled tasks you come across and you can bounce issues around working relationships off of them."* The only apparent bugbear is speaker phone limitations: *"Because of how much responsibility we're given at an early vintage, we're expected to be on the phone with clients from a very early stage. Often you both end up on the phone and it can be distracting."*

Culture

Office sharing isn't the only element at Cravath that promotes collaboration. *"I've been pleasantly surprised by the ancillary benefits to the rotation system. I ring people I don't know who have worked on a deal before to ask if they can help. They go out of their way to chat about it and dig through archived emails and documents."* Others were surprised by the general attitude of their colleagues. *"I thought people would be stuffy and it would feel like a white shoe firm where people were very driven and fo-*

See firm profile on p.622

cused on work, but unable to joke around and didn't have any sense of humor. People here are good at getting the job done efficiently and taking work seriously, but they're humorous and down to earth."

"The work ethic here is incredible."

That said, juniors still felt Cravath had a formal feel. *"We all have to wear suits,"* one interviewee pointed out, while another stressed *"our standards are high. We are not going to cut corners or be sloppy. We check every box."* That's partly because *"the work ethic here is incredible."* Cravath has *"a tradition of doing good work and people want to feel they live up to it."* One acknowledged that the firm does *"have a reputation as a difficult place to work, with demanding people. The work is demanding but people here are supportive."* So while attorneys have high expectations of both themselves and each other, it leads to a sense of being *"all in the trenches together."*

One word we heard time and again was *"perfection."* Cravath attorneys put *"client service above all. Everyone cares so much about doing an excellent job that they focus much more on completing a job flawlessly than keeping employees happy day to day. It's never a question of whether or not someone should stay up all night doing something perfectly for a client."*

Hours & Compensation

With client needs taking center stage, heading home tends to slip down the to-do list. *"You have to adjust what you expect in terms of work/life balance and be open to pushing back or altering plans,"* sources conceded. But we were told the firm is pretty good at leaving associates alone during vacation. One junior mentioned that *"there is not a face time requirement, so we can go home to work. I'm not saying I haven't had to cancel plans; recently it has been all-consuming. I've not seen anyone for a month!"* How consuming is all-consuming? *"On a relatively busy day I'll be at the office until around 9pm,"* another source professed. *"On really busy days I'll leave at two or three in the morning."* Busy periods can either fall in chunks – *"I've had months where I could leave at 6pm and others where I billed well over 200 hours"* – or unexpectedly blow in like freak blizzards: *"Last week I left at 7pm and worked from home but last night I stayed till 4am and then was back in at 8am."*

"You don't have to feel guilty."

Luckily there is no billable hours target and as all matters stem from the few partners juniors work with, *"if things are slow there is no burden on you to go out and find stuff to do. You don't have to feel guilty and can enjoy the slow days."* The other benefit to a lack of a target comes in the form of reduced competitiveness: *"With plenty of work to go around, no one is jockeying for that extra hour to receive their end of year bonus."*

The firm has long been known for setting the market rate for bonuses (nicknamed the Cravath scale) and nearly always declares them before everyone else. In 2014 Simpson Thacher announced first, and Davis Polk then set higher bonus rates, causing Cravath (and others) to revise up. Order was restored in 2015 when Cravath reasserted its place as the first announcer and everyone else fell in line.

Pro Bono

As they're kept so busy on client matters, juniors *"don't have that much time"* to take on pro bono. Many admitted: *"It's not at the forefront. The focus tends to be more on the client work we're doing."* Matters are *"not hard at all to pick up"* for those that want to. *"The pro bono department does a good job at keeping people aware of what is going on."* And what can juniors jump on? *"Anything. Immigration assistance, dealing with custody matters or helping someone with medical benefits or malpractice claims."* Cravath also collaborates with Montefiore Children's Hospital and Morgan Stanley Children's Hospital in New York in providing legal help related to medical care, such as assisting an immunosuppressed child with appropriate housing upon discharge from hospital.

"Cravath attorneys have been high achievers at every academic step of their life and are looking for a firm which embodies that ethic."

Pro bono hours

- For all attorneys across in US: 24,584
- Average per US attorney: 51

Diversity

Like pro bono, several sources felt that diversity at Cravath wasn't front of mind: *"I think they're continuing to work on it but I do feel other firms are more focused on it than us."* Others disagreed: *"I think they're very keyed in to issues of recruiting and fostering a diverse set of associates. The affinity groups are very active. We're making strides but it's always a process."*

The Inside View

See firm profile on p.622

"It's always a process."

The firm's diversity statistics are pretty much in line with the rest of the industry and Cravath runs affinity groups for ethnic minority, female, LGBT and parent attorneys. *"It's good to know there are other people at the firm who look like you and may face the same challenges that you face as a minority lawyer."*

Get Hired

Litigation hiring partner Karin DeMasi tells us: *"When people start at Cravath they are lawyers from day one. We look for people who are excited to be a contributing member of a team."* What does that person look like? One junior reckoned: *"Highly motivated, driven and intelligent. Most people here have gone to elite institutions. Cravath attorneys have been high achievers at every academic step of their life and are looking for a firm which embodies that ethic."*

A word of warning though: *"People get caught up in their credentials but the practice of law is different from the study. It's important to listen more than you speak."* So juniors involved in hiring want to see candidates *"exude confidence in their work without being arrogant. I want to be sure someone will work hard and master things fast but don't think they know everything because otherwise they won't learn."* Go online for more hiring tips.

"People who are comfortable being challenged."

Strategy & Future

Associates noted that Cravath is *"probably one of the more conservative firms at expanding into new offices and practices. We'll continue to follow a similar approach, which is one of the reasons the firm is so strong."* Corporate hiring partner Eric Schiele confirms: *"We tend to evolve rather than make wholesale changes to strategy on a short term basis. We're not looking to open any more practices or offices and we will continue to focus on what we're good at."* Not everything is static though, Schiele adds: *"We're continuing to grow in the investigations and white-collar areas."* Visit our website to see what else Schiele and litigation hiring partner Karin DeMasi have to say about the firm's strategy.

"The most challenging and developmental work possible at an early stage."

See firm profile on p.622

Crowell & Moring LLP

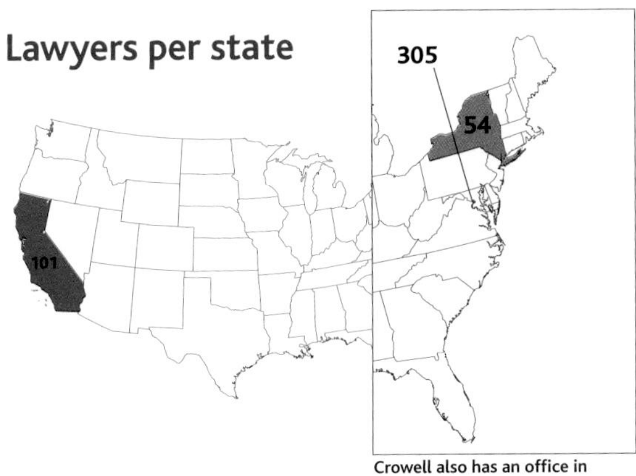

Crowell also has an office in Alaska with four attorneys

Largest US office: Washington, DC
US offices: 7
International offices: 3
First year salary: $160,000
Billable hours: 1,900 target
Summers 2016: 26 (23 2Ls, 3 1Ls)
Revenue 2015: $363 million (-1.4%)
Partners made in 2016: 9 (all US)
Famous for: government contracts; rubber ducks; lighthearted yet hard-working culture

As Washingtonian as House of Cards, and almost as much fun, Crowell & Moring offers the chance to do cutting-edge work in a place that doesn't take itself too seriously.

BEING a little different has long been a part of Crowell & Moring's DNA. The firm was founded in the 1970s by a splinter group from Jones Day who wanted to create *"a different kind of law firm."* This doesn't just refer to the firm's slightly quirky, duck-loving culture – the fountain in the DC HQ's lobby is famously home to a diverse collection of rubber duckies, as are other offices – but also to the way it does business.

Crowell was one of the first firms to bring in 'value-based billing', which in a world frustrated by law firms' insistence on charging by the hour, is a big deal. It's also looking to take advantage of the new practice areas opened up by big data, adding practices like cyber security & privacy to its traditional strengths of government contracts, litigation and healthcare, which are among those highly rated by *Chambers USA*. On the topic of ducks, real live versions actually nest from time to time outside the ninth floor conference room in DC, no doubt attracted here by their plastic cousins...

On chambers-associate.com...

- A brief history of the Crowell & Moring ducks

ASSOCIATES SAY...

The Work

On arrival, associates are assigned to two departments from their list of preferences. *"This allows you to work with a larger number of people, and get much broader experience than you otherwise would,"* explained a New Yorker. Associates generally specialize eventually in one of the two departments, although the firm is in no hurry to make them choose. We heard of some associates who didn't pick until their sixth year, and others who opted to join another department entirely. Junior associates are found in groups including commercial litigation, corporate, government contracts, intellectual property, energy, healthcare and international trade.

Some offices have particular specialisms; in antitrust, for example, the East Coast offices tend to represent corporate defendants, while the offices in California specialize in plaintiffs' recovery work. The firm's government contracts group and those with a regulatory focus like advertising are centered on DC, thanks to the *"sheer proximity to the contract, or the regulator."* The department primarily focuses on bid protests, where aggrieved contractors challenge the outcome of federal procurement process before the Government Accountability Office or Court of Federal Claims. The department offers a fascinating peek into the murky world intersection of the public and private sectors, and sees lawyers grappling with a multitude of rules. To resolve bids in a timely

See firm profile on p.623

Rankings in *Chambers USA*

Antitrust	Healthcare
Climate Change	Insurance
Corporate/M&A	Intellectual Property
Energy & Natural Resources	International Trade
Environment	Litigation
Government	Transportation

For detail on ranking tiers and ranking locations, visit www.chambersandpartners.com

Recent work highlights

- Defended the Army against a bid protest by Raytheon that it should have been awarded two contracts, worth $366 million and $414 million, for night vision equipment
- Represented telephone company SUFI Network Services in a breach of contract claim against the Air Force
- Representing Hewlett-Packard, which is alleging that manufacturers of optical drives are fixing prices
- Securing dismissal of claim on summary judgment of a False Claims Act allegation against ACDEMI, the private security company formerly known as Blackwater
- Acting as Court Appointed Monitor of the New York City District Council of Carpenters as a condition of a RICO settlement

manner, the GAO operates strict timetables, so good time keeping is a must.

"Crowell is much less wedded to the idea of giving all the tedious tasks to the new associates."

Many of the more specialized departments do mix contentious and non contentious work, allowing associates to try their hands at both. For example, the firm's burgeoning advertising & product risk management group grapple with both litigation and regulatory compliance. *"I will review product packing to ensure that clients adhere to FDA regulations and best practices,"* explained a lawyer in this department, *"and on the litigation front I get to take the first stab at all the major papers in a case."* A lot of cases and deals are quite leanly staffed, particularly in the more specialized departments, which means that associates can get a lot of responsibility very quickly. *"Crowell is much less wedded to the idea of giving all the tedious tasks to the new associates,"* said one source, adding that *"you're as likely to help a partner put together a memo as you are to do doc review."*

Offices

Several juniors were struck by the *"impressive"* DC building, with a few affectionately terming it *"the mothership,"* although the firm stressed that there is no official HQ. It's a stone's throw from the White House, and across the road from the FBI and Department of Justice buildings. Los Angeles is *"gorgeous, with floor-to-ceiling windows and a view of the mountains."* If the other California offices are *"a bit lacking architecturally"* by comparison, they also make up for it with fantastic views. San Fran *"is a little cuter and a little quainter than the other offices,"* said an associate based there. *"We have things like a pizza day once a month."*

"It's never a good sign when your office serves dinner," said a DC associate ominously. *"Fortunately, ours doesn't."* It does, however, have a cafeteria that serves breakfast and lunch. The office's other amenities include a gym. The smaller New York office has fewer perks, which associates there felt impacted on its social scene. *"It's a friendly place, and people talk in the corridors, but it can be a little quiet,"* explained an associate in the Big Apple.

"It's never a good sign when your office serves dinner. Fortunately, ours doesn't."

Training & Development

"The partners' willingness to mentor young associates really makes Crowell stand out," enthused a DC junior. *"They view it as an investment, rather than a cursory exercise like some firms."* New associates get both an associate and a partner mentor. Partner mentors also act as *"advocates"* for their mentees. *"They'll stick their necks out for you, help you get work and help you navigate the partnership,"* explained one associate. On arrival, new associates are treated to three days of orientation and then whisked off to 'bootcamp'. Don't worry, Gunnery Sergeant Hartman doesn't make an appearance: Crowell's bootcamps are a series of monthly training sessions. *"The courses cover things like writing motions or interviewing clients,"* explained a source.

"Not giving us cookie cutter objectives."

At the time of writing the evaluation system was undergoing something of an overhaul, and nobody we spoke to had experienced the entire thing. The new system has three stages. In the first, associates submit a written evaluation of their own work and receive the same from the fee-earners they worked with. Following this, they meet a partner from their practice group for an informal discussion. *"It's not like an interview,"* said an associate who'd been through this part of the new process, *"more of a chat."* They discuss things like what types of work they'd like to do more of and how their practice area is performing. After this, the partner liaises with the firm's Lawyer Development Committee, and the associate is

See firm profile on p.623

given a list of objectives. Our sources appreciated this part of the process, saying *"they make a point of not giving us cookie cutter objectives, but tangible goals."* The final stage is a meeting between the assessed associate, their partner mentor and the committee.

Pro Bono

Associates are required to bill 50 pro bono hours each year, and associates aren't short of different ways to help them bill those hours. Asylum and immigration, criminal appeals and landord and tenant cases all make an appearance. *"I'm doing a lot of pro bono trademark work,"* said one lawyer, *"but you don't get pigeonholed."* A dedicated pro bono partner is on hand to take requests: *"You can email and let her know what you're interested in doing, and she'll find you work in that area,"* reported one source. *"They don't look down on you for doing pro bono,"* said an associate in DC. *"At other firms management worries that it's taking time away from billable work."*

Pro Bono Hours

- For all attorneys across all US offices: 33,117
- Average per US attorney: 72

Hours & Compensation

Associates are paid in lockstep through to their sixth year, which helps eliminate competition between attorneys. The firm pays market rate, which associates were generally happy with, although some noted that legal salaries in general haven't kept pace with inflation. *"The salary for lawyers hasn't changed since 2006, but places keep getting more expensive,"* noted one.

> *"Does work interfere with my life to the point where it's not manageable? No way."*

Officially Crowell's billing target is 1,900 hours, but when you include the mandatory 50 hours' pro bono *"it's really 1,850, which is great, particularly in DC."* The firm has its ducks in a row when it comes to work allocation: there's a formal system run by an assigning partner who tracks everyone's hours, but it often functions as more of a backstop. *"In my experience, partners reach out to me,"* said a junior in DC. A New York litigator agreed: *"Most of the time, partners come by and say 'I have something for you.' Besides, the coordinators are all in DC."* This system keeps Crowell's attorneys busy with work, but it also leads to some late nights. *"I think because of the ducks and the quirky culture, people think we're all play and no work,"* said one source, *"but it isn't true. I regularly work 12 hour days."* Associates tend to get in around 9am and leave at 7pm or 8pm, but *"there's no pressure for face time, and a lot of flexibility. Does work interfere with my life to the point where it's not manageable? No way."*

Culture

"If I could describe Crowell's culture in a word, it would be 'forgiving'," said an antitrust lawyer on the West Coast. *"I refuse to say we're laid back, because we work hard, but it's a forgiving, encouraging and positive place to work."* Consider the following anecdote from a misty-eyed associate on the other side of the country: *"When I was a fresh attorney, I was given a massive task to do, and in my opinion did a terrible job."* Instead of slamming the hapless newbie, *"my supervisor wrote that I was the hardest worker she'd ever seen."*

> *"Every office has at least one duck."*

A quirky sense of humor runs through all the offices. The Agri, a less-than-picturesque sculpture in the front lobby of the San Francisco office, is a frequent butt of the office jokes. *"People send around emails claiming to be from the Agri,"* explained a San Franciscan, *"and someone did a mock 'New Yorker'-style cartoon starring the Agri. It's funny when you see it."* Then there are the ubiquitous ducks. Back in the depths of time, someone dropped a rubber duck into the fountain in the DC office's lobby. Others soon joined them, and the ducks became a symbol of the firm, to the point where *"every office has at least one duck."* All the offices have regular happy hours, which have names like 'lowering the bar' and 'cheap booze' (the booze is actually free), and, yes, the ducks make an appearance. *"Sometimes the cheap booze is themed, and they'll dress a duck up to match the theme,"* a Washingtonian told us.

> ***"I refuse to say we're laid back, because we work hard, but it's a forgiving, encouraging and positive place to work."***

Diversity

Once again, Crowell got top marks from associates for its gender diversity, although there was still a long way to go. *"I think we have two male and a dozen female associates, and more than half the counsel are female,"* remarked one source, *"but at partner level it still isn't great."* Some associates felt that the firm could do better when it came to ethnic diversity. *"We're no more or less diverse than our peer firms,"* explained a source in DC. Similarly, *"the New York office needs to be more diverse,"* although our sources there conceded that *"that's*

See firm profile on p.623

weighing heavily on everybody's mind." There are signs that Crowell is making inroads, however: *"Now that you mention it, I think there were only two white guys in my incoming class,"* recalled one source vaguely.

"We're no more or less diverse than our peer firms."

Get Hired & Strategy

Crowell was founded by some breakaway Jones Day lawyers who wanted to create a more interesting place to work, so it places a premium on hiring interesting people. *"I won't say they're looking for people who 'fit in,' because that sounds quite hostile,"* said an associate familiar with the hiring process, *"but Crowell wants people who want Crowell."* Sources recommend familiarizing yourself with not only recent cases, but also working out who's who at the firm. *"If you're interested in a certain practice area, find out who the big shots in that group are and mention them in the interview,"* they suggested. The firm's hiring process follows a fairly typical OCI then callback structure, and nobody recalled being thrown any curveballs. *"They tend to adopt a conversational style of interview,"* said one. Don't make the mistake of thinking getting into Crowell will be a cakewalk, though. *"Be smart, articulate and confident"* suggested one, *"but don't be arrogant."*

"Crowell wants people who want Crowell."

Crowell has *"no immediate plans to open any additional US offices,"* according to managing partner Ellen Dwyer. Instead, the firm is looking to build on its existing locations. Dwyer mentions an *"Internet of Things initiative"* and a big push to *"grow the Washington office as a regulatory hub,"* while sources in California identified a drive to increase name recognition. *"On the East Coast, everyone knows who Crowell is,"* explained a Californian, *"the big point is to let the West Coast know that we're a great firm."* To that end, Crowell is looking to bring in lawyers *"who are excited about building the firm and building our new practices."*

"If you're interested in a certain practice area, find out who the big shots in that group are and mention them in the interview."

See firm profile on p.623

Curtis, Mallet-Prevost, Colt & Mosle LLP

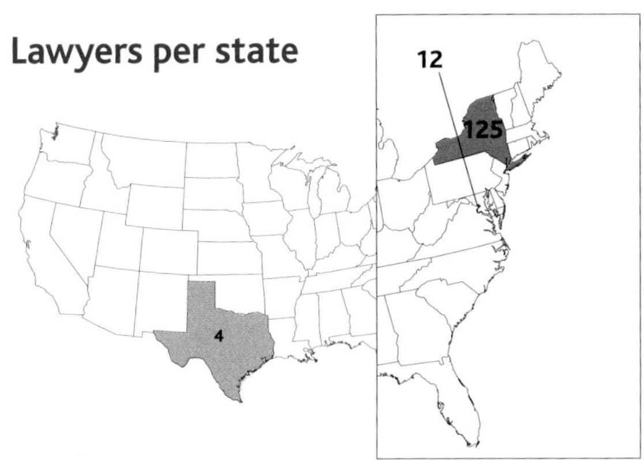

Largest US office: New York
US offices: 3
International offices: 14
First-year salary: $160,000
Billable hours: 2,000 target
Summers 2016: 10 (9 2Ls, 1 1L)
Revenue 2015: $151.5 million (-23.4%)
Partners made 2016: 9 globally (4 in US)
Famous for: expertise in international arbitration work

With over four times as many international offices as at home, Curtis welcomes worldly-wise wunderkinds to its select annual intake.

FOUNDED as long ago as 1830, Curtis grew from New York to become a blueprint for modern day BigLaw firms in terms of global expansion. One of the first to go overseas, this arbitration kingpin now hosts a 14-strong international office network, as well as domestic hubs in the Big Apple, DC and Houston. It's little surprise that hiring partner Carl Ruggiero informs us: *"We have our traditions, and are looking for people who'll buy into our culture. Many of our lawyers speak two or three languages, and a worldly sophistication and ease in working across different jurisdictions will set you in good stead."* That said, languages aren't a prerequisite (see the Get Hired section below for which practices seek what).

Despite boasting offices in locations as far-flung as Turkmenistan, Kazakhstan and Dubai, Curtis' smallish intake cuts its teeth in a New York office that *"is small enough so that everything is pretty flexible."* As one rookie continued, *"we're not quite big enough to need to bureaucratize and formalize everything, so if you know what you want to try out then it's just a question of going out and finding it."* Unusually for Curtis, revenue in 2015 took a dive from $187 million to just over $151 million.

On chambers-associate.com...

- Some recruitment tips from hiring partner Carl Ruggiero

ASSOCIATES SAY...

The Work

Curtis takes around ten new first-year associates per year. Although opportunities do occasionally crop up in groups like trusts & estates and restructuring & insolvency, the vast majority of Curtis' fresh faces splits between the 'corporate international' and litigation teams. Rookies' destinations are usually predetermined based on preferences expressed when applying. Nevertheless, *"there's no iron-clad rule pinning you down once you're there."*

Interviewees rated the *"wide range of different practices"* offered in each stream. Corporate newbies are *"encouraged to be proactive from the off,"* approaching partners to find work catering to their interests. An assigning partner is on hand for those who need steering in the right direction, but *"after providing you with openings for certain partners, they become more of a last resort."* Signing up as members of a pooled corporate department exposes associates to a varied docket, with international arbitration, investment management, IP, M&A and private equity & funds all in the mix. Corporate are big on client contact from day one, and *"although it does feel like you're in at the deep end, partners are happy to walk you through everything beforehand."*

Significantly, Curtis' esteemed international arbitration practice falls under the corporate bracket. On smaller arbitrations, rookies *"work one-on-one with partners,"* and are kept busy writing memos and even drafting filings.

See firm profile on p.624

Rankings in *Chambers USA*

International Arbitration   International Trade

For detail on ranking tiers and ranking locations, visit www.chambersandpartners.com

"On larger cases, you're the go-to team member for all things factual," recounted one arbitrator. *"The mid-level associates take on more of the drafting responsibilities, so I'm down in the trenches, looking at received documents and seeing if I can piece them together."*

"Most partners are keen to include us."

In contrast to Curtis' corporate and international arbitration departments, the firm's litigation and restructuring groups' clients and concerns are largely homegrown. Litigators enrol into a system *"a little more centralized"* than their deal-striking contemporaries, working in correspondence with an assigning partner to fill up their schedules. *"Inevitably you'll end up developing working relationships with certain partners,"* reasoned one junior, *"so you just need to make sure you keep everyone updated."* The spectrum here is equally wide-ranging, encompassing anything from complex commercial litigation to antitrust class action conspiracy cases, and government investigations to bankruptcy litigation. Beginning with *"a lot of legal research, memo writing, and the occasional bit of doc review,"* associates progress to drafting court documents, court briefs and deposition guidelines as soon as they've proved they're ready. *"Most partners are keen to include us in strategic calls and phone calls with the rest of the team,"* which helps to facilitate such progression.

Training & Development

Litigators and deal-makers alike were delighted to report that *"there is the complete expectation that juniors have something to bring to the table from the beginning."* Curtis' staffing model gives weight to such claims, demonstrating *"a global approach"* that matches individual skill sets to specific cases. *"The firm's mentality is to make the best use of its lawyers around the world,"* elaborated one source. *"When a matter comes in and a team needs assembling, the top concern isn't geographic proximity, but whose experience best fits the client's needs."* Respondents found this *"a helpful way to push forward your professional development,"* adding *"if a junior associate possesses greater relevant industry knowledge or language skills than someone a few years their senior, it's likely that they'll be drafted in."*

"There is the complete expectation that juniors have something to bring to the table from the beginning."

Recent work highlights

- Represented Venezuela during an arbitration worth $18 billion, which was initiated by subsidiaries of Mobil after two of its petroleum exploration and development projects were expropriated by the state
- Acting for E.ON in a $13 million compensation claim raised against PPL. The claim arises from tax shortfalls following the $7.6 billion sale of an E.ON subsidiary in 2010
- Providing international trade counseling for LG, covering matters such as antidumping proceedings, NAFTA appeals, and court appeals of past AD-CVD cases
- Acting as conflicts counsel to Wilmington Trust: a successor trustee in the Chapter 11 bankruptcy cases of MPM Silicones

It's fortunate that juniors receive such great development opportunities on-the-job, as the annual review was judged to be *"somewhat of an afterthought."* Bi-annual check-ins would be preferred, although those we spoke with generally approved of partners' ability to voice their expectations. If associates wish to discuss their progress, they can always bend the ear of their assigned mentoring partner, though callers agreed that *"depending on which colleagues you hit it off with, you may choose to seek that support informally."*

Pro Bono

Pro bono work does count hour-for-hour toward associates' billable hours target. On average, attorneys racked up a decent 63 hours of pro bono in 2015. Some of our sources, however, had not done any at all. Why? Two main reasons: many of Curtis' young-guns found themselves themselves *"too busy with paying clients to fit it in with my workload,"* and those who had found that *"some partners – not all – have a bit of a 'Why aren't you billing hours?' attitude."* But *"many do encourage it,"* one source pointed out, *"though there aren't many incentives to get involved. If we're interested, then the onus is on us to ask about it."* In fact, there is a dedicated pro bono coordinator (a partner) who sends out opportunities to get involved.

Pro bono hours

- For all attorneys across all US offices: 4,606
- Average per US attorney: 63

Diversity

Interviewees were also somewhat critical of Curtis' efforts to promote diversity. *"It's fair to say that you do hear a lot of different languages spoken around the office."* However, they reckoned *"that says more about the*

See firm profile on p.624

international scope of our work than the scope of our recruitment."

They felt that the gender balance was fairly even at lower levels, and female interviewees were encouraged by the presence of a women's initiative, which *"holds monthly discussion groups, and two networking events every year."* Elsewhere, though, *"there's little in place to help promote a healthy mix."* There are no affinity groups for LGBT or ethnic minority lawyers, but this is hardly surprising considering *"you could count the number of African-American attorneys here on one hand."*

Offices

"It's the fanciest place I've ever worked in," gushed one associate when asked about the New York mothership, *"and it's very comfortable too."* The interior styling speaks to Curtis' history: *"Old school and fairly formal, decked out in hunter green marble."* Bringing it all up to date is *"a nice selection of modern paintings,"* though the real eye-catcher appeared to be the *"amazing view when the sun sets over the East River."* In recent years there have been whispers of a proposed office relocation, though juniors were delighted to announce that *"the firm recently signed a new seven-year lease, so we're here to stay! It's great news: the location just couldn't be beaten. We're two blocks from Grand Central station, so there isn't any part of the city that isn't easily accessible."*

"The location just couldn't be beaten."

Besides New York, Curtis houses domestic offices in DC and Houston. Further afield, the firm has 14 international offices, covering Europe, the Middle East, Central Asia, East Asia and Latin America.

Culture

In another nod to its vintage New Yorker status, Curtis' sharp-suited associates are expected to look the part on company time. *"It may come across as old fashioned, but none of us seems to complain."* In fact, they felt that *"putting the effort into dressing properly makes us feel more professional. We want our appearance to suggest a commitment to high standards, because that's true of our working lives. If you're a lawyer in a sweater and jeans, there's a chance clients won't want to put their trust in you straight away."* But don't burn those chinos and summer dresses just yet: *"We do dress down on Fridays."*

"People aren't afraid to show gratitude for your endeavors."

The New York office environment is friendly enough but lacking on after-hours socializing, associates said: *"Every once in a while we'll go for drinks, but that's pretty rare. When we do go out, it's more because we're conscious of the fact that we probably ought to."* This *"certainly isn't because we don't get on – people here are very thoughtful, respectful of your time, and aren't afraid to show gratitude for your endeavors. It's just that after work everyone prefers to do their own thing, and we're all pretty comfortable with that."*

"The firm's mentality is to make the best use of its lawyers around the world."

Juniors felt management could plug them in more to decision-making: *"When asked, most partners are pretty good at explaining why decisions have been made, but information isn't always volunteered as freely as we might like,"* grumbled one. *"There have been overseas office launches where the first I heard came on the opening day. Perhaps partners just assume that we know more about the business than we actually do."*

Hours & Compensation

For associates, the most frustrating aspect was the confusion at bonus time. *"People say that the billing target is 2,000 hours,"* reported more than one interviewee, *"but whether they're awarded on seniority or merit beats me."* Another added: *"Some people say pro bono work doesn't necessarily count. Others say it all does. A few centrally accessible guidelines would really help to put a lot of speculation to rest."* Fortunately, *"if you don't make your hours it's not make-or-break."* For the record, associates become bonus eligible when they hit 2,000 hours, and unlimited pro bono hours can count as billable. The firm told us it sends out a memo each year outlining bonus criteria, and that exceptional performance would warrant a market bonus.

"You may need to negotiate time-zones when scheduling."

Bonuses aside, juniors were broadly happy with the remuneration they receive. *"Our salary is in line with all the major New York firms and I've only stayed until midnight once or twice,"* said a second-year. If corporate or international arbitration work is your thing then be aware that *"you may need to negotiate time-zones when scheduling,"* meaning *"6am starts occasionally pop up."* The office usually starts clearing out at *"around seven,"* and *"there's no expectation that you'll unthinkingly sacrifice your weekend."* That's not to say that Saturdays are off-limits, but *"working weekends is very much the exception to the rule."*

See firm profile on p.624

Strategy & Future

"It's been another successful year for our international arbitration group," Curtis' CEO George Kahale tells us. *"We're representing more states and state-owned companies than ever before, and have once again fortified our reputation as true market leader in the field."* Kahale also expresses delight at the bankruptcy team's recent performance, and cites both areas as *"key to Curtis' future growth plans, alongside our litigation and corporate international practices."*

"We don't have any grand plans to double in size."

The firm's strategy as a whole is one of measured investment: *"BigLaw is a tough and competitive business, and we don't have any grand plans to double in size or make big lateral acquisitions,"* he declares. *"Our main focus is to maintain and strengthen our market position."* Putting its money where its mouth is, Curtis recently bumped four corporate and international corporate associates up to partner, as well as four more in international arbitration.

Get Hired

Sidestepping Curtis' polyglot rep, hiring partner Carl Ruggiero insists that *"foreign language skills certainly aren't a benchmark requirement. Sure, there can occasionally be international aspects to litigation, tax, trusts or bankruptcy, but it's very rare that anyone would be expected to deviate from English in these practices. The same goes for servicing US-based corporate clients."* However, those covering international arbitration or international corporate work had found that *"languages are important, and can open doors to new clients and new responsibilities."* Ruggiero adds that *"we're not talking high school French. We want native speakers: multilingual, multicultural associates who possess an intimate understanding of the jurisdictions we service. We've found that foreign-trained lawyers with a US LLM often do well here."*

"If you're slacking you'll be found out fairly quickly."

"The firm is also looking for applicants who understand the implications of being at a firm this size," believed one junior. *"People will know who you are and what you're working on, so there's no room to hide."* Curtis is not necessarily looking for extroverts, but *"you need to be willing to ask and answer questions to move in the right direction. If you're slacking you'll be found out fairly quickly."*

"Many of our lawyers speak two or three languages, and a worldly sophistication and ease in working across different jurisdictions will set you in good stead."

See firm profile on p.624

Davis Polk & Wardwell LLP

Lawyers per state

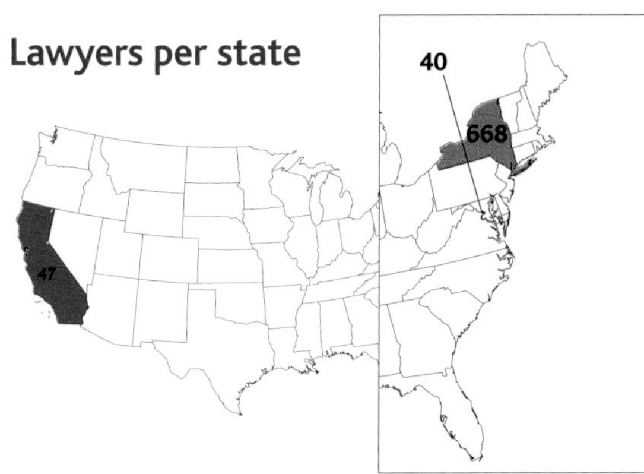

Largest US office: New York
US offices: 3
International offices: 7
First-year salary: $160,000
Billable hours: no requirement
Summers 2016: 159 (157 2Ls, 2 1Ls)
Revenue 2015: $1.1billion (+2.6%)
Partners made in 2016: 5 (all US, announced July 2015)
Famous for: over 150 years of New York heritage; polite culture; capital markets and M&A prowess

BigLaw has a stressful rep, but juniors here were keen to stress Davis Polk's *"relaxed"* and *"respectful"* ambience. Read on to discover the reality...

THIS veteran New York giant's glittering reputation for M&A, credit and capital markets wizardry attracts swathes of the Ivy League's finest year after year (and the best of the rest). *"In the past year the firm has been the beneficiary of a vibrant M&A market,"* acknowledges managing partner Tom Reid. In fact it was a record year for DP's dealmakers, who racked up the firm's highest ever market share of global M&A in 2015. However, there's more to DP than just deal-making, and the triumphant buzz of M&A has also spread to the firm's lawsuits fortress, which *Chambers USA* ranks among the Big Apple's elite. *"Our litigation team is having another incredibly busy year,"* Reid elaborates. *"Antitrust and enforcement work is up, and at one point in the last year or so, the market saw us lined up to try more than half a dozen major cases for clients across the country and in Hong Kong."* You can find out more about the booming lit practice in our Bonus Features online.

But these successes are only part of the rosy picture that Davis Polk's associates painted. Blue chip clients and DP's erstwhile white-shoe identity go hand-in-hand with a *"respectful and collaborative"* working environment, despite the sharp-suited appearances. Throw in a flexible work schedule and a 'try before you buy' approach to work specialization, and you can understand why the firm performed so well in our happiness survey. And, incredibly for the caliber of work they do, most sources told us they were only moderately stressed at work or not stressed at all. *"Demanding, not stressful,"* was the general verdict.

On chambers-associate.com...

- Lit it grow: litigation at Davis Polk

ASSOCIATES SAY...

The Work

Rookies who'd summered rated the summer program for its flexible structure, which allows them the chance to choose from a range of corporate, litigation and tax work on offer. At their exit interview, hopefuls are asked which of the three they'd prefer to move into permanently. Around two-thirds join the corporate department, which is split into subgroups including capital markets, financial institutions, M&A, credit transactions, insolvency & restructuring, and executive compensation. Corporate juniors get the opportunity to have a shot at one, two, or occasionally three different areas before settling down, thanks to a six month rotation system. It's a system that garnered widespread acclaim: *"Management wants you to be happy where you are and invested in work you're doing, so if the group you're in doesn't feel like the right fit, then it'll work with you to find one that does."*

Those in the M&A team had been busy prepping due diligence reports, and drafting documentation under the supervision of more senior lawyers for *"a good mix of private, public, blue chip and private equity clients."*

See firm profile on p.625

Rankings in *Chambers USA*

Antitrust	Financial Services Regulation
Banking & Finance	International Trade
Bankruptcy/Restructuring	Investment Funds
Capital Markets	Latin American Investment
Corporate Crime & Investigations	Litigation
Corporate/M&A	Media & Entertainment
Employee Benefits & Executive Compensation	Private Equity
Environment	Retail
FCPA	Securities
	Tax

For detail on ranking tiers and ranking locations, visit www.chambersandpartners.com

Recent work highlights

- Defended agrochemical manufacturer Syngenta against takeover proposals worth $46.5 billion, brought forward by arch rival Monsanto
- Defended RBS against $2.5 billion-worth of claims relating to the bank's involvement in a Forex-manipulating cartel
- Advised Aetna on its mammoth $37 billion acquisition of Humana, the health insurance industry's largest ever M&A deal
- Advised several underwriters on the $353 million public offering of common stock for Virgin America

Capital markets juniors *"regularly review documentation for deals going through,"* but also have a coordinating role, having *"devised strategies with senior associates and then managing an arsenal of paralegals to ensure that everyone is on board with the plan."*

"Not having to pigeonhole yourself is a big appeal."

M&A, credit and capital markets may be where the firm made its name, but with around 25% of beginners entering the litigation department, it's a bigger taker than any of the corporate subgroups. As you might expect, corporate and financial lit crops up regularly, though associates also have the opportunity to get involved in areas such as antitrust, white-collar crime, securities, bankruptcy and international arbitration. Much like their corporate colleagues, litigators felt that *"not having to pigeonhole yourself is a big appeal."*

Assigning coordinators are *"on hand if you ever need more work,"* though with time juniors tend to rely on more informal streams. *"Most people are receptive to discussing your workload,"* one junior added, *"so you can say 'no thank you but please keep me in mind' without fear they won't call you up next time."*

The Inside View

Training & Development

Regardless of where they end up, all starters congregate in the Big Apple for Lawyering 101: an initial week of orientation where new starters cover *"the office essentials such as computer training, document management training and billing."* Skills sessions also feature, honing in the fundamentals of good lawyering like time management, formatting and compliance matters. *"Leaving that week, I felt so much more confident,"* beamed one junior. *"Having a full briefing on something as trivial as email etiquette is really helpful when you're starting off."*

"Whenever I've sought support I've always received it."

Lawyering 101 is followed every second year by Lawyering 301 and Lawyering 501. Corporate juniors on rotation receive six-monthly partner reviews, and those more firmly rooted attend annual check-ups. Respondents were also thrilled with the opportunities they'd had to find their feet in the meantime: *"It's nerve-racking to know that hundreds of millions of dollars rest on your recommendation,"* one interviewee gulped. *"There's a certain art to knowing when it's appropriate to make a judgment call, and knowing when to go to a superior. The responsibility is on me to make that decision, and whenever I've sought support I've always received it."* When work is submitted, *"superiors try to find the time to go through it one-on-one to explain why changes were made,"* so all-in-all associates felt that *"our professional growth is really valued."*

Pro Bono

Pro bono is also a good way to notch up some valuable experience. In NYC, a slew of clemency petitions for federal prisoners is complemented by *"everything from helping small businesses and non-profits, to criminal defense cases, as well as plenty of immigration work."* The latter also crops up regularly in the Menlo Park office, where alongside eviction hearings, associates had knuckled down on plenty of U visa cases for juveniles and victims of domestic abuse.

Matters such as housing cases can last *"as little as two days,"* so although DP's PB program *"throws up more more litigious opportunities than transactional,"* corporate insiders viewed it as *"a fun way to complement our regular work."* Throw in a *"thorough pre-briefing and excellent supervision from senior attorneys,"* and it's no surprise that legal-eagles felt comfortable spreading their wings to file depositions and perform appellate arguments in court.

See firm profile on p.625

Pro bono hours

- For all attorneys across all US offices: 38,428
- Average per US attorney: 50

Offices

The firm's western spur can be found in California's Menlo Park. At the time of our calls the offshoot housed just eight juniors, and with *"a gym, walled gardens and a gorgeous patio with a big fountain,"* it's no surprise that respondents viewed the site as *"a very relaxed place to work."* Unlike their top-buttoned NY colleagues, associates noted *"it's rare to see people in a suit unless they're meeting clients. A lot of people will wear dark jeans and button down shirts."* The office takes on an even split of litigation and corporate recruits, with the latter group providing its associates with a broader spectrum of corporate dealings than their more specialized New York counterparts.

"Plenty of interesting artwork dotted about."

Focusing more on regulatory and litigation work, DC also takes on one or two first-years. However, the lion's share of Davis Polk's associates are in the Big Apple. Occupying 25 stories in midtown Manhattan, the full service HQ's 160-ish juniors are treated to *"a light and bright building with plenty of interesting artwork dotted about."* Each floor has a different theme, ranging from baseball to fish, and if browsing the associated paraphernalia doesn't whet your appetite, then the subsidized cafeteria just might. The eatery won plaudits for the *"well stocked fruit and veg selection,"* but can suffer from a lack of imagination, with one insider grumbling *"the pasta dishes all taste the same."* Juniors share an office for their first few years, and with the continued growth of DP's litigation offering, warned that *"the amount of space in the office is sufficient but not excessive."*

Elsewhere, the firm has attorneys in Beijing, Hong Kong, London, Madrid, Paris, São Paulo and Tokyo. Both summer associates and associates have the opportunity to spend time abroad.

Culture

"The day I leave Davis Polk is that day I leave BigLaw for good," asserted one insider. *"It really isn't your typical fratty, hyper-social BigLaw set-up. There's no expectation that you need to be engaged in informal networking to get ahead, as we're all busy people who appreciate spending our spare time with friends or family."* Instead, social events are arranged *"every four to six weeks,"* usually involving *"fancy cocktails somewhere nice. We don't go for dive bars."*

It's the summer program that truly unleashes the firm's social animal, with a *"generous budget"* propping up *"tons of events."* Interviewees cited performances of Shakespeare in Central Park and an enormous welcome dinner as particular highlights, and many raved about *"pitching a few balls on Citi Field. The firm has a good relationship with the Mets' owners."*

"We don't go for dive bars."

In our last few *Chambers Associate* features, DP has always been praised for it's collaborative and supportive internal environment. This continues to be the case, with one insider confirming: *"Usually I'm the most junior person on the team, so inevitably I make lots of mistakes. My learning and growth are valued, so there's never any finger pointing or yelling."* However, one litigator growled: *"That doesn't mean we're not ruthless externally! We treat our opponents with respect, but fight doggedly for our clients' interests, and are willing to play hardball if necessary."*

"Most people are receptive to discussing your workload, so you can say 'no thank you but please keep me in mind' without fear they won't call you up next time."

Hours & Compensation

With no billing target, bonuses are lockstep based on seniority. Sources commended this system for creating a working environment where *"no one is fighting for business, no one is killing themselves to hit an hours target, and people have strong incentives to work together. It's much better for your mental health."*

"Your time off really is sacred."

Eleven hour days in New York compare to Menlo Park's ten hour norm, though respondents from both offices conceded that *"when it's busy you could be here until 4am."* Face time *"isn't encouraged,"* so *"if it's a calm day you can leave at reasonable hour. The firm doesn't mind you working from home."* Bleary-eyed late-shifters can draw strength from the *"delicious bottomless free coffee"* provided on every floor of the NYC office, and gain comfort from the fact that *"your time off really is sacred. People respect your weekends, and we're encouraged to take our full four weeks of vacation every year."*

See firm profile on p.625

Get Hired

According to hiring partner Warren Motley, *"the firm takes in roughly 100 people a year in New York, and up to another ten or so in California and in DC."* There are a number of ways that you can get yourself a look-in, with previous work experience standing as one of the most revered: *"If someone has worked as an investment banker and wants to go into M&A then obviously that will put them in good stead."* However, Motley also looks for *"people who have taken on challenges, and made a success of difficult situations. Whether that's delivering legal services in South Africa, or working for Teach for America between college and law school, I like to hear about those experiences at the interview."* He also cautions that *"a bad interview is lacking in energy and engagement,"* so ditch the caffeine for camomile tea or hot milk to get a good night's sleep beforehand.

"We look for people who have taken on challenges, and made a success of difficult situations."

"While we do hire a significant percentage of our lawyers from the top 15 law schools, 28 schools from throughout the United States and Canada are represented in our 2016 summer associate class," Motley says. Associates touted word-of-mouth as a strong way to get yourself on the firm's radar, and are *"encouraged by partners to reach out to any promising law students that we know."*

Strategy & Future

With such a large New York intake, juniors got the impression that *"if you're gunning for partnership then you could end up being frustrated. The firm hires over 100 junior associates annually, whilst only four or five people make partner. The numbers speak for themselves."* Hiring partner Motley counters: *"We hire associates on the premise that they're capable of staying. But being an associate at Davis Polk means a lot of hard work for a sustained period, and people's ideas of how they want to spend their lives evolve. The caliber of our attorneys means that they're always surrounded by other opportunities."* One associate further elaborated, stating that *"no one really leaves under negative circumstances. Often people go elsewhere because a partnership opportunity has opened up there, or to spend more time with their family, or go in-house, or work for the government."*

"If you're gunning for partnership then you could end up being frustrated."

Diversity

"I can never imagine colleagues thinking less of someone because of their background," felt one interviewee. But *"when you look at our senior associates and partners, there's still some work to be done."* Fortunately *"the firm is really doing a lot to fight the headwinds, and foots the bill for affinity group events."* New Yorkers rated the LGBT network, who with *"around 160 members"* throw some *"very well-attended drinks and networking events with plenty of free food and alcohol."* Out west, one deal-doing Menlo Park minnow appreciated that *"around half of the corporate lawyers in this office are from an ethnically diverse background."*

"Another incredibly busy year."
Tom Reid, managing partner

See firm profile on p.625

Debevoise & Plimpton LLP

Lawyers per state

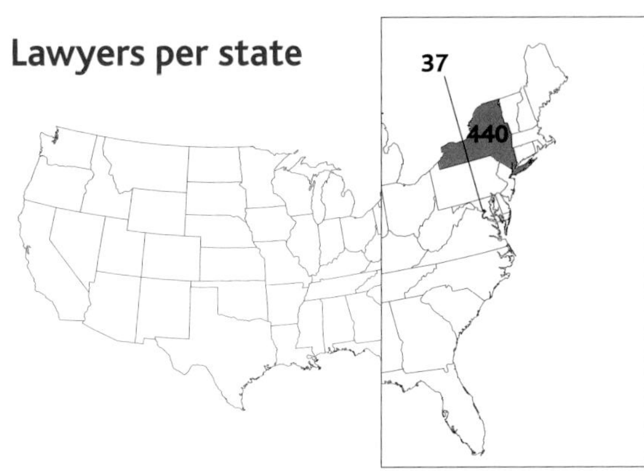

Largest US office: New York
US offices: 2
International offices: 6
First-year salary: $160,000
Billable hours: no requirement
Summers 2016: 75 (70 2Ls, 5 others)
Revenue 2015: $756.9 million (+6.6%)
Partners made in 2016: 6 globally (4 in US)
Famous for: polite culture (*"the nice firm"*); West Wing mentions

Stellar mentoring lays firm foundations for associates at this established New York institution.

DEBEVOISE'S towering reputation on the NYC legal scene was a major attraction to the associates we spoke to. Its name is so synonymous with the legal elite that even TV's *The West Wing* knows to name drop Debevoise. This former or current white shoe firm (depending on your point of view) carved out its reputation initially in the 1930s in funds-related work. These days you're just as likely to hear it mentioned in relation to a whole host of other transactional and litigation-related areas as well. White-collar crime, media & entertainment, FCPA [Foreign Corrupt Practices Act], intellectual property, insurance, and international arbitration are all considered top of the pile by *Chambers USA*, which also gives a nod to several of the firm's other practices.

"We're the proper white shoe firm filled with pride over the quality of our work," one source beamed. Juniors were just as eager to wax lyrical about the firm's reputation for politeness and collaborative teamwork: *"I got a good vibe when I interviewed,"* said one. *"I felt like these were my people. Given the strains and stress of BigLaw, we know we're all in it together."*

On chambers-associate.com...

- Interview with presiding partner Michael Blair
- Debevoise's white-collar and cybersecurity practices
- More on hiring

ASSOCIATES SAY...

The Work

The New York office takes nearly all the firm's first-years, though several start out in Debevoise's Washington, DC base. Most associates tend to head into corporate or litigation with a handful slotting into tax (which includes employee benefits). Both the larger groups offer a dual-track work allocation system which combines assignment by a staffing coordinator with the option to seek out or accept work directly from partners.

Corporate rookies head straight into one subgroup, which they switch for another at the end of their first year. Crunch time arrives at the start of third year when they must choose their permanent area from the two they've experienced, or head into a third they haven't tried. On offer are: M&A, real estate, capital markets, finance, bankruptcy, investment management, and insurance. Sources appreciated the chance to *"try working in different areas and get a feel for different people. If you find the first area is not for you then the rotation gives you a fresh start."*

"There are no artificial hurdles."

Diligence and disclosure are *"typical for corporate juniors but you also have multiple drafting opportunities. There are no artificial hurdles regarding roles and responsibility."* Deals tend to be staffed by *"relatively small teams so you get a lot of client contact. You're forced to*

See firm profile on p.626

Rankings in Chambers USA

Advertising	Intellectual Property
Banking & Finance	International Arbitration
Bankruptcy/Restructuring	Investment Funds
Capital Markets	Latin American Investment
Corporate Crime & Investigations	Litigation
	Media & Entertainment
Corporate/M&A	Private Equity
Employee Benefits & Executive Compensation	Projects
	Real Estate
Environment	Securities
FCPA	Sports Law
Financial Services Regulation	Tax
Insurance	Transportation

For detail on ranking tiers and ranking locations, visit www.chambersandpartners.com

learn and develop quickly." One source had even been the sole associate on a deal, telling us: *"I wrote my own purchase agreement and negotiated with opposing counsel – although I did also have to do all my own diligence and signature pages. Negotiations were hard and the opposing counsel were really mean but it was a terrific experience."*

Litigators start out as generalists for the first two years before specializing in one of the four following areas: general commercial, international dispute resolution, IP (including cybersecurity and data privacy), or white-collar crime. *"We have to choose a major and a minor as our focus areas"* – in DC the majority of litigators tend to go into white-collar – *"but we're not limited to only practicing those."* Sources here tended to stick with more junior tasks, as *"the bigger teams tend to be more hierarchical. If you can get on a smaller case you're able to do more,"* like drafting briefs. So, *"depending on the case, you can swing from doc review on one to interviewing a client's senior management members on the next."*

Training & Development

Newbies from offices around the world begin their time at the firm by flying into New York and attending a mini-MBA course to *"jump-start us into a business background."* Sources praised the course for *"helping you become more fluent in the terminology and in understanding where clients are coming from."* Come the second year, juniors attend thrice-monthly sessions within their practice area focusing on things like *"what every corporate lawyer should know about environmental law, tax and benefits or M&A. It orients you to what others in the group are doing and gives you an idea of when you need to call in a specialist."*

> *"It can be hard to get forthright feedback."*

Recent work highlights

- Advised The Carlyle Group in forming buyout fund Carlyle Europe Partners IV, which plans to invest €3.75 billion in midsize European companies
- Acted for Verizon in a $10.54 billion sale of its wireline operations in California, Florida and Texas to Frontier Communications
- Represented JPMorgan Chase in an investigation by the Consumer Financial Protection Bureau into JPMorgan's collection and sale of credit card data

Debevoise's reputation as a place full of polite lawyers has *"pros and cons,"* some sources told us, with one downside being *"it can be hard to get forthright feedback. Sometimes comments can be almost passive-aggressive."* That said, we came across plenty of interviewees who hadn't run across this problem. *"People are always willing to chat through things when I reach out."* Another interjected: *"I've even had people email and tell me they're hearing good things about my work."* One interviewee surmised that as the reputation for being indirect has been around for a while, *"maybe people are working to get around it."*

Culture

While some juniors admitted the firm's polite and genteel culture can sometimes result in a little *"passive-aggressiveness,"* the plus side is that people *"don't snap or yell and no-one degrades you. We have room to say what we want and people respect each other."*

> *"Charming, endearing nerds."*

One source summed up Debevoise as *"a place full of charming, endearing nerds."* That statement proved divisive when we put it to colleagues. While several disagreed with the word 'nerd,' others proudly embraced the label: *"That's why I came here! We have different interests and we can be ourselves around each other; if someone looked down on me for being into Lego I'd say get off your high horse, you're into Dungeons and Dragons,"* one source laughed. Regardless of whether they agreed with the generalization, juniors did concur that they felt comfortable around their colleagues. *"This is a place where people are good to each other as they'd want others to be good to them. We want to work well together; there's not an aggressive atmosphere."*

For the most part, partners are *"invested in your success and the advice and mentoring I've received has been so positive,"* one source praised. *"A high percentage of the partners have a strong EQ; they care about your development as a lawyer but they're also open to chatting*

See firm profile on p.626

about things outside of work – I can tell my mentor anything," one source claimed. *"Within the lines of what's appropriate to share!"* they quickly added. This supportive nature spills over from mentoring into daily life, where we're told *"supervisors give it their best shot to prevent pressure being passed down to associates. People here offer a human approach in a job where you're working less than human hours."*

Debevoise operates a lockstep compensation scheme, which juniors have long cited as contributing to the firm's collaborative nature. Some interviewees also felt it relieved the pressure of billing. *"Unless you well and truly deviate you won't miss your bonus. No-one likes a freeloader, but it's so busy you find very few of those."* The firm stipulates no official target but most sources aimed for around 2,000 hours.

Get Hired

"There are hardly any assholes here, which is awesome," one junior applauded. *"The people who come here tend to value good working relationships,"* another stressed. *"They enjoy working in a collaborative rather than competitive environment. If you want to prove you're better than your colleagues, this isn't the place for you."*

Any juniors involved in recruiting are asked to evaluate potential candidates on several factors, but especially personality. *"We see resumes but not grades so we take a holistic view. We're looking to see how well people can articulate and express their thoughts."* Another added: *"I ask myself would they have problems communicating with clients, are they easy to chat to and conscientious?"* Ideally *"we want people who are able to create a positive atmosphere even if we're working crazy hours."* Visit our website for more tips on getting hired.

"There are hardly any assholes here, which is awesome."

Hours & Compensation

Interviewees admitted that *"hours here can certainly be long"* but, one junior countered, *"I feel my seniors are working harder than me. If I'm here until midnight, counsel will be here until 2am rather than just pushing stuff onto juniors. We're a team and although I may get grumpy when I take on someone's workload while they're on vacation, I know they'll do the same for me."* They agreed that colleagues make an effort to respect vacation and *"recognize we all have lives outside work."* One elaborated: *"I'm gearing up for a busy few weeks but I'm still going away."* Don't get too confident your colleagues will always pick up the slack though, as one junior pointed out: *"It's not all roses: we still have to cancel things."* While clocking off at 6pm is rare, *"people won't burn the midnight oil from the office. This is an autonomous place. You can leave and work from home, so long as you're checking your phone."*

"I'm gearing up for a busy few weeks but I'm still going away."

Pro Bono

Pro bono hours all count toward billable hours. *"The only limitation is being able to find the time,"* one source reflected. A New York-based pro bono coordinator emails out opportunities, but juniors can also find themselves approached by colleagues looking for additional help.

"The only limitation is being able to find the time."

Among transactional associates, there's a *"strong need for people to assist small entrepreneurs and nonprofit groups,"* and helping people prepare bankruptcy petitions is also a common pro bono assignment. But dealdoers don't stick within transactional parameters, and we heard of plenty getting stuck in with their litigator counterparts on anything from climate change matters to immigration advice, asylum petitions and the Clemency Project. Debevoise also had a hand recently in overturning the West Virginia DMV's ban on transgender individuals using a photograph of themselves as they regularly appear on their driver's license.

"We want people who are able to create a positive atmosphere even if we're working crazy hours."

Pro bono hours

- For all attorneys across all US offices: 58,628
- Average per US attorney: 118

Diversity

Interviewees claimed there's *"room for improvement at the partner level"* where 89.7% are white and only 18.7% are women. *"The diversity is noticeably stronger the more you go down the ranks."*

"Our diversity coordinator is a champ."

Sources reckoned diversity was more than just about the figures though. *"Looking at the absolute numbers it's not*

See firm profile on p.626

very diverse, but as for the atmosphere, I'm diverse and I absolutely feel part of the firm. Our diversity coordinator is a champ and is always encouraging us to build up relationships" with partners and associates across the firm. Another added: *"Debevoise doesn't always get it 100% right but I chose to come here because I believed they considered diversity a high priority, especially when it comes to assisting parents."*

Offices

At the time of our calls, DC was in the process of moving into new offices. *"We're very excited; they gave associates a lot of input into the layout and what type of furniture we wanted."* Debevoise's New York office *"is not grand or gilded and there's no wild architecture; Debevoise tries to go for a cooler angle,"* one source told us. Each floor features *"amazing artwork"* like *"blurry city pictures"* or 1970s musicians. Juniors here usually share an office for the first two years, before bagging their own at some point in their third.

"Debevoise tries to go for a cooler angle."

While sources hadn't seen too much interaction between the firm's US offices, several had worked on projects staffed with attorneys from Debevoise's six international bases. There's even scope for a couple of summers to spend time in one of the firm's six overseas offices or to jet off on client secondments around the globe.

Strategy & Future

"There's an emphasis on 21st century issues like tech, privacy and cybersecurity," one associate told us. Several sources tipped Debevoise's cybersecurity practice as the focal point for growth; the team recently brought on Fannie Mae's former chief privacy officer Jeewon Kim Serrato and former head of the Department of Justice David O'Neil.

"An emphasis on 21st century issues like tech, privacy and cybersecurity."

O'Neil also straddles the firm's white-collar practice, which has seen *"a number of recent partner and counsel hires."* The white-collar team and Debevoise's financial institutions group were credited as two of the key drivers behind the firm's revenue rise. Growth in London, following a number of laterals hires in previous years, also contributed to the increase. *"Our 2015 performance was driven by continued success in our core practices: private equity, M&A, insurance and financial institutions on the corporate side; and white collar, international arbitration, complex litigation, IP and cybersecurity/data privacy on the litigation side,"* the firm tells us.

"I chose to come here because I believed they considered diversity a high priority, especially when it comes to assisting parents."

See firm profile on p.626

Dechert LLP

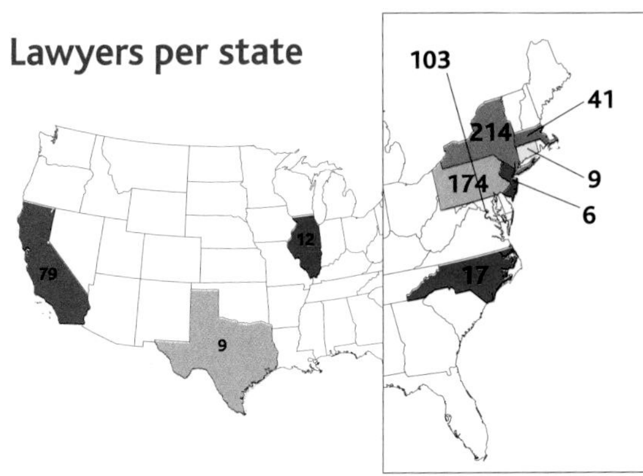

Largest US office: New York
US offices: 13
International offices: 14
First-year salary: $160,000
Billable hours: 1,950 target
Summers 2016: 75–76 (72 2Ls, 3–4 1Ls)
Revenue 2015: $890.2 million (+6.1%)
Partners made 2016: 14
Famous for: top practices including corporate and white-collar crime; global funds work; Philly origins

"*Dechert is an amazing line to have on your resume,*" boasted juniors who were glad to work at this "*corporate & securities powerhouse.*"

THE Big Apple outweighs scrapple (the Pennsylvania delicacy) at Dechert, for the New York office is the largest at this Philly-founded firm. Over the years, numerous notable lawyers have called the firm home. The primary American judge in the Nuremberg trials, Francis Biddle, was a partner from 1916 until 1939, for example. Arlen Specter practiced here for three years in the late 50s, before being tapped to serve on the Warren Commission, investigating the assassination of JFK. Norma Shapiro, who was Dechert's first female partner in 1973, still holds office as a US district court judge for the Eastern District of Pennsylvania. And you can read "The Big Interview" with Edward McDonald, the lawyer in *Goodfellas*, on our website.

High-profile attorneys attract high-profile clients. The list includes American Airlines, Pfizer and The Bank of New York Mellon. Associates felt that *"Dechert is the best place to work in Philadelphia because of the nature of our deals."* Similarly, the firm's reputation for giving juniors *"intellectually challenging work that isn't just cookie-cutter stuff"* is enhanced by strong *Chambers USA* rankings, especially for corporate/M&A, litigation, and investment funds expertise. A Philadelphia junior believed that from their point view *"finance & real estate and corporate & securities are our bread and butter, as they are the most profitable. The old perception was that Philly was a litigation powerhouse. Our business model has changed over the last ten years, so that the majority of litigation is in New York."*

On chambers-associate.com...

- Interview with CEO, Daniel O'Donnell

ASSOCIATES SAY...

The Work

We were given a list of 63 transactional associates to interview: 27 were in financial services; 19 in corporate & securities; 17 were in finance & real estate. Over in trial, 20 juniors were in general litigation, three in white-collar & securities litigation, and two in the complex commercial litigation group. IP claimed six, and there were three in antitrust/competition. Employee benefits, tax, business restructuring & reorganization, and labor each had one junior. Associates tend to get work initially through a formal assignment method and send weekly availability reports to their practice group coordinators. After that, it's much more informal. The corporate & securities group has the most formal assignment, and in the others *"it's primarily relationship-based."*

"Finance & real estate and corporate & securities are our bread and butter."

Typical first-year transactional work includes *"reading estoppel certificates and reviewing tenancy agreements."* As an associate matures so does the work. One junior had *"negotiated lots of SNDAs* [Subordination Non-Dis-

See firm profile on p.627

Rankings in Chambers USA

Antitrust	Life Sciences
Bankruptcy/Restructuring	Litigation
Capital Markets	Private Equity
Corporate/M&A	Products Liability
Financial Services Regulation	Real Estate
Intellectual Property	Securities
Investment Funds	Tax
Labor & Employment	

For detail on ranking tiers and ranking locations, visit www.chambersandpartners.com

turbance and Attornment Agreements, which detail the rights of tenants if the rented property is foreclosed]." Another had waded through *"pages and pages of due diligence, which is pretty much all you do for the first six months. But then you look at M&A alternative investment deals and SEC compliance by preparing information statements."* Manhattanites praised their ability to work on *"cutting-edge, hybrid entity mutual funds."*

Litigators had *"summarized the fiduciary case issues to get a real handle on the facts and law. You then draft briefs and prep witnesses."* For white-collar matters, work ranges from *"attending depositions, putting together witness kits, writing legal memos and participating in legal strategy."* Antitrust, as a hybrid of litigation and corporate work, encompasses *"HSR filings* [Hart-Scott-Rodino Antitrust Improvements Act 1976 documentation], *merger clearance and lots of discovery."*

Training & Development

First-years usually have monthly sessions on different topics per practice area. Litigators divulged that *"it's things like how to conduct and defend a deposition, how to do expert witness prep and how to write briefs. We also have a mock deposition program that's a whole day where you have to depose an actor who is defended by a partner. The partner is told to be bullish, so it's really fun."* Finance & real estate newbies told us that they had just started a private bootcamp that seniors run for two to three days. *"Day one is how to do doc review and update document checklists. Day two is learning how to use the firm technology specific to our group."* New Dechertites, in particular, can make use of the Critical Skills Institute. This monthly program helps develop communication, leadership, client relations and management skills. The Shadowing Program also allows juniors to explore personal interest areas by observing partners *"work on things you wouldn't normally get to see, and get credit for it* [25 hours]."

> "The partner is told to be bullish, so it's really fun."

The Inside View

Recent work highlights

- Representing AbbVie in the national product litigation surrounding its product Androgel, which is a testosterone replacement therapy
- Represented Bank of America Merrill Lynch Large Loan (BAMLL) as the issuer of a $1.25 billion single-asset securitization relating to a mortgage loan taken out by Saks Fifth Avenue in New York
- Obtained a summary judgment for Pfizer regarding 'apparent manufacturer' claims concerning the product Insulag which was created by a bankrupt former subsidiary. The issues relate to the product potentially causing mesothelioma

All this training doesn't go unnoticed. Senior associates who go the extra mile in helping rookies, can be nominated for the Exceptional Teacher Awards. Winners get a trophy and a handy $10,000 prize. *"Seniors have the most work and they not only help you out on assignments, but also explain to you how everything fits into the bigger picture."*

Six months in, associates face midyear *"informal check-ins, for general feedback."* Formal reviews happen six months later, when associates fill out forms that highlight what they've worked on for more than 15 hours and who with. Partners and seniors then send written evaluations for the practice group leader to walk the reviewee through.

Pro Bono

All attorneys, regardless of seniority, are required to devote at least 25 hours to pro bono projects. Juniors can count up to 200 hours toward their yearly billing target without asking anyone's permission. *"If you go over that you just talk to the partner in charge, then the rest of it can count too."* Juniors liked doing pro bono because *"you get to know the case better than everyone. It's the first time that I've been asked what I think. The partners listen to me."*

> "It's the first time as an associate that you get to run the show."

The full-time pro bono partner sends daily emails about latest opportunities. We heard of associates getting stuck into *"defending a Guantánamo Bay detainee, doing legal research and fact checking."* Others had *"worked on a criminal appeal and I'm in charge of drafting, submitting the brief and all of the oral arguments. It's the first time as an associate that you get to run the show."* Philly attorneys have worked in partnership with the University

See firm profile on p.627

of Pennsylvania Law School and their Transnational Legal Clinic, on immigration proceedings.

Pro bono hours

- For all attorneys across all US offices: 49,461
- Average per US attorney: 78

Hours & Compensation

Is it worth it? 1,950 hours makes you bonus-eligible. While most interviewees stressed that the firm was transparent about compensation, some felt that *"superstars who put in a lot of extra effort only get a small bonus, so it hasn't been financially worth it."* Philly newcomers, however, had something to shout about this year. Juniors used to have a salary of $145,000, whereas their New York and even Hartford counterparts were on $160,000. *"It didn't really matter at junior level when it's a difference of $15,000. But when you're a senior and it's about $60,000, then it's a problem."* Dechert now pays Philly associates the New York rate. *"We were all doing the same work and billing at the same rate. People were leaving purely because they were lured by better financial packages. But now we're the hotspot."*

"Now we're the hotspot."

Offices & Culture

Of our interviewee pool, 36 juniors were in New York; 25 in Philadelphia; 14 in DC; seven in Boston; three or four in each of Silicon Valley, San Francisco and Orange County; and one or two in Charlotte, LA, Princeton, Hartford and Chicago. With an expansive network of 27 worldwide offices (13 domestic and 14 international), one junior went as far as to say that *"if you're traveling and need to work, you're most likely to find an office wherever you are."* Closer to home, first-years normally get their own office, except New Yorkers, who must share for the first few months.

"Let's split the baby there, down the middle."

Sources told us about the close collaboration between offices. Philadelphia and New York, however, share a more symbiotic existence. So symbiotic in fact, that juniors couldn't agree which was the HQ. *"We're Philly-founded through and through. New York has a chip on its shoulder because there's more work, but our history is here!"* Others reasoned that *"our management structure and chairman are in New York. Our old CEO was in Philly. Our new CEO splits time between Philly and New York. So let's split the baby there, down the middle."*

Interviewees told us that, generally speaking, *"people work hard but are respectful of your life outside of work."* Among the social activities of offer, we heard that New York hosts an office pie-baking contest. The winning pastry delight then gets baked by chefs in Dechert's kitchens for all to enjoy. Californians have a Halloween costume contest that has caught on in Pennsylvania too: *"This year we had an inter-office contest per practice group. We all had different themes and because we are Philly, we all went as The Fresh Prince of Bel-Air."*

Diversity

"Since I've been here, you can definitely see it getting better. Even though there is still a way to go, Dechert is making a full-frontal effort." How? Like most firms, Dechert has an array of affinity groups that include Asian, Black, Latino and LGBT groups. Most visible, however, is the Global Women's Initiative. In DC, there's *"the occasional meeting where we discuss different topics like public speaking, or where new female partners speak to us about their journey."* Of the Diversity Committee-organized private performance of a 2012 off-Broadway play, *Disgraced*, one theater-goer said: *"The play centered around a Muslim American attorney and how he dealt with his identity post 9/11. We got to do a Q&A with the cast and crew afterward."*

"The changes have to trickle up."

Some sources pointed out that at partner level *"there's a big gender disparity, but attrition is part of it."* However, *"it takes time. We can't hire a diverse pool of associates and change everything instantly. It takes ten years to make partner and then you're partner for 40 years. The changes have to trickle up. But we all care about it."*

"Dechert is the best place to work in Philadelphia because of the nature of our deals."

Get Hired

Associates admitted that most firms will stress that it's all about personality. But juniors here were under few illusions about what counts first: *"Grades, grades, grades."* DC juniors praised the benefits of studying *"administrative or regulatory law because it gives you a lot of interview-talk fodder."* Hiring partner James Lebovitz further explains that *"if you come in and say you want to be a litigator because you watch 'Suits' and that's it, that's not all bad, but show how it feeds into what you've done to further your interest."* Philadelphians advised that *"when you're a second-year law student you don't know what you're talking about. Ask questions that articulate that*

See firm profile on p.627

you know you're thinking about the market and how you fit into it. Know who your interviewer is, because if you don't you're on a course for disaster."

Strategy & Future

"Saudi Arabia has been a natural development in the growth of the firm."

"Litigation is slammed," enthused one source. *"We have huge caseloads, which we haven't really had in the past few years."* On the corporate side, *"it's been incredibly busy, but all of the work was generated in 2015. It depends on the market. If it's good, finance & real estate, tax, and general corporate will be good. If it's bad, we know that litigation and bankruptcy will be fine."* CEO Daniel O'Donnell adds that Dechert entered into *"an association with the law firm of Hassan Mahassni in Saudi Arabia. It has been a great market for our core strength areas. For example, our capital markets and non-US M&A practices in particular are predominately run out of London and Dubai. So Saudi Arabia has been a natural development in the growth of the firm."* For Daniel O'Donnell's full interview, go online.

"Intellectually challenging work that isn't just cookie-cutter stuff."

See firm profile on p.627

DLA Piper LLP (US)

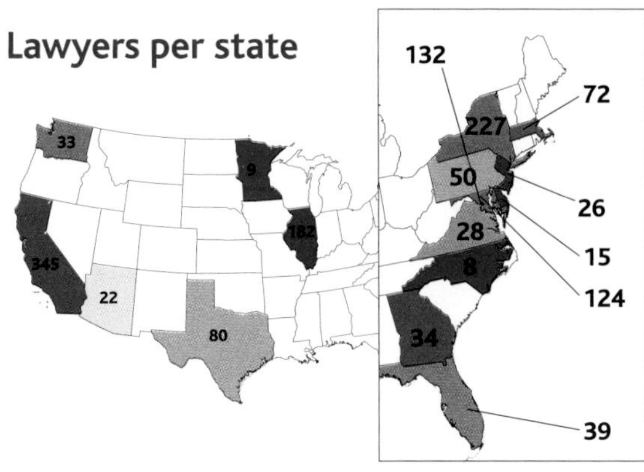

Largest US office: New York
US offices: 29
International offices: 63
First-year salary: $160,000 in major markets
Billable hours: 2,000 target
Summers 2016: 33 (all 2Ls; 1Ls tbd)
Revenue 2015: $2.543 billion (+2.5%)
Partners made in 2016: 48 globally (18 in US)
Famous for: being enormous; lots of partner promotions

Emerging from a massive transatlantic merger in the mid-noughties, DLA is one of the heftiest outfits there is.

IN 2005, things changed. YouTube was launched. Viewing habits, daily productivity and happiness levels were altered forever. But transformation was also afoot in the legal sphere. That same year, a three-way Anglo-American merger gave rise to a new colossus. Its name? DLA Piper.

Just over a decade since it thundered onto the scene, DLA Piper has amassed 29 Stateside bases and a further 63 around the world. Casablanca, Bratislava, Tbilisi... they're all on the location list. As such, it's no surprise that many of our sources cited the firm's *"global reach"* and *"the opportunity for international work"* as major draws. Looking closer to home, *"you get to work with people right across the country, which is pretty cool, especially when you start thinking about where you want to be in the future in terms of moving state. You're not trapped in one place."* The firm's US practice is highly regarded, with recognition from *Chambers USA* at national level for its corporate, IP, sports law, retail, product liability and real estate groups, among others.

But it's not just the promise of megadeals and billable bucks that attracts associates to DLA. *"I'd read about the firm's commitment to pro bono and the community,"* said one. *"And it's true in practice. I come from a relatively modest background and I wanted a firm that had a strong pro bono presence. Here the policy is geared toward incentivizing it for associates."* For more on these matters, read on.

On chambers-associate.com...

- We speak to hiring partner Ben Boyd

ASSOCIATES SAY...

The Work

You'll find junior associates spread all over the country, from Baltimore through to Sacramento and Seattle. New recruits are fairly even split between the corporate and litigation groups, but other areas that take juniors include government affairs, IP, real estate and employment. Interviewees described the work assignment setup as *"very much a free market,"* although *"there is a partner who collects a work forecast report from us every week and who fields requests from partners who need younger associates to work on particular matters."* Overall, sources thought that *"the system works well, although it can be an issue for a more reserved personality. You're encouraged to seek out people and teams you're interested in working with and grab your own career by the horns. Then, work begets work."*

> *"Not as much doc review as I thought there'd be."*

Litigators told us they'd tackled a wide range of areas, including FCPA [Foreign Corrupt Practices Act] matters, white-collar investigations, securities work, employment

See firm profile on p.628

Rankings in Chambers USA

Bankruptcy/Restructuring	Leisure & Hospitality
Chancery	Life Sciences
Construction	Litigation
Corporate/Commercial	Outsourcing
Corporate/M&A	Privacy & Data Security
Franchising	Products Liability
Government	Real Estate
Healthcare	REITs
Insurance	Retail
Intellectual Property	Sports Law
International Arbitration	Startups & Emerging Companies
International Trade	
IT & Outsourcing	Tax
Latin American Investment	Technology

For detail on ranking tiers and ranking locations, visit www.chambersandpartners.com

actions, antitrust, product liability and real estate cases, plus *"international investigations in the life sciences sector."* Apparently, *"there's not as much doc review as I thought there'd be. I'd say it takes up about a quarter of my time."* Another proudly declared that *"for the past six months I've been supervising other people on a doc review. There's a lot more analysis to it."* Research tasks are regularly called for (*"I often turn my research into a memo to give to a partner"*) and some seasoned second-years noted that *"I'm starting to draft more – motions to dismiss, portions of complaints, dispositive and nondispositive motions..."* As well as this, an interviewee mentioned that they'd *"participated in well over 100 witness interviews and traveled around a lot for them,"* while others were busy *"getting ready for trial in front of a DC governmental agency, which involves working on exhibit lists, a pre-trial submission and witness preparation."*

Meanwhile, transactional associates informed us that they *"generally work on different projects – anything that falls within the corporate category – rather than specializing,"* although some sources did flag up that they worked almost exclusively in smaller teams like sport and media. *"I've done several IPOs on the company and underwriter side,"* reported one, *"along with capital markets deals, work for startup companies and a lot of M&A."* The latter involves getting to grips with *"plenty of due diligence – I've gotten into the weeds like any junior!"* Drafting is also on the cards: *"I've worked on merger agreements and ancillary documents like resolutions and closing certificates."* All our sources were content with the sophistication of their work. *"I think it's challenging enough!"* chuckled a first-year.

"It really gets the blood pumping!"

Recent work highlights

- Representing British Airways in a putative class action brought by members of the airline's executive frequent flyers club relating to an alleged breach of contract over a fuel surcharge
- Acting for the Ministry of Transportation of the Republic of Turkey in an €800 million ICC arbitration concerning a major railway project that includes a new tunnel under the Bosphorus
- Represented the owners of the Atlanta Hawks on the $850 million sale of the NBA team to an investment group

Pro Bono

Associates emphasized that pro bono is *"a big focus at the firm. Everyone does it and it's not uncommon to do hundreds of hours."* Up to 400 hours of pro bono can go toward the billing target for first-years. From then on, associates can count 100 hours. DLA supports a number of 'Signature Projects' that address domestic violence, education and juvenile justice issues, among others. Lots of interviewees told us that they'd helped out with *"a world food program that needed temporary contracts drafted for various food vendors in developing countries"* and assisted on *"a program to help get businesses started that are owned by women or minorities, rather than Silicon Valley-type startups."* Others had taken on criminal cases, adoptions, immigration issues for victims of prostitution and compensation matters for veterans. *"It really gets the blood pumping!"*

Pro bono hours

- For all attorneys across all US offices: 110,000
- Average per US attorney: 79

Training & Development

In their first few months, new joiners converge in the Chicago office for an initial three days of training, followed by practice-specific sessions. *"They're interesting primers, but most training happens on the job,"* remarked an associate, while another characterized it as *"more of a social thing."* Other training opportunities are available throughout the year. *"Yesterday I attended an interesting discussion about persuasion in relation to the jury, using Daniel Kahneman's Thinking, Fast And Slow."*

"It depends on the partner."

Some sources were a little critical when asked if they felt well supported on a daily basis: *"I kind of get the feeling that you're thrown to the wolves and it's up to you to figure things out for yourself. There are a lot of stressful moments as a result of that philosophy. Everyone is so busy that there's not a lot of time for hands-on instruc-*

See firm profile on p.628

tion. Fortunately, I often work with a soon-to-be-partner who always takes time out of his day to teach me, but that's not a firmwide practice." Another commented that *"it depends on the partner. I know a few people who are very good about giving me feedback but frankly, people don't have time for that day to day. You turn in an assignment and don't hear from people – that's common to all BigLaw firms."* In addition to the annual review, associates can submit a request a written feedback form if they clock up 50 hours or more on a project.

Culture & Offices

DLA has tons of offices and we only have space here to give you a snapshot of some of them. *"It's demanding but not overbearing,"* said a source of the atmosphere in the DC office. *"There's a great respect for good work, but also for people's time and their lives outside of work. Overall, people don't exude a stressful attitude. It's a well-oiled machine."* Apparently, the office is *"stunning – it's very modern, comfortable and there's a gym."* Any aches and pains from the cross-trainer or all the fast-paced lawyering? *"You can have someone come and give you an in-office massage! It's just wonderful,"* purred an associate.

Over in the Big Apple, juniors were delighted with the *"open and energetic"* culture (despite the gym-less office). *"There's nothing worse than being around people who are always miserable, but you don't see that at DLA. No matter how busy people are they'll always crack a smile and make a joke. We're able to have fun."* Indeed, some New Yorkers mentioned that they indulge in games of wiffle ball in order to *"let loose and ease the stress when you're here super-late."* There are occasional happy hours, although *"not as many social events as people would like."*

"It's demanding but not overbearing."

In the Windy City, we heard that *"there's a silo culture. It's very disjointed, in my experience. There are a lot more partners than associates and people tend to keep to themselves. There isn't very much socializing, although the firm is making an effort to address that by organizing partner-associate events like dinners and a holiday party. The office is huge and lots of people have lateraled in from different places, so it's not like you have a group of people who've grown up together from their summer class."* The size of the Chicago base *"contributes to the disjointed atmosphere. There are so many offices and a lot of them are empty, so sometimes you'll be walking down the hall and see no-one. Sometimes you see no-one all day."* A silver lining is in sight though: *"We're moving to a new building in about a year, so that's gonna be great!"*

Hours & Compensation

"We get paid enough to be available whenever a client needs us: that's the reality," declared a junior. *"But the firm understands that we're humans too, with social and emotional needs. We need time away from work to be effective employees. They get that it's an endurance race, not a sprint."* Indeed, sources mentioned that they'd been able to take vacation and time off for family matters. Of course, *"working some weekends is unavoidable in a job like this,"* as are late nights, but overall *"it's pretty flexible – you can manage your own workload and work from home if you need to. You just have to let people know."*

"The firm understands that we're humans, with social and emotional needs."

Most associates thought that the 2,000 hour billing target was *"definitely achievable"* although *"you need to be pretty busy consistently. I didn't have a problem meeting it, but I know plenty don't come close. Partly it's out of an associate's control in terms of deal flow, but you have to be proactive and outgoing if your group gets slow."* Those who rack up the 2,000 hours are eligible for a bonus. *"A little more clarity on the bonus structure would be good. We know the process generally, but we could do with some more guidance on what goes into it,"* interviewees commented.

"I've gotten into the weeds like any junior!"

Diversity

"Diversity isn't swept under the rug at DLA," reckoned juniors. *"There are all kinds of initiatives, although at partnership level it's not equal – such is the legal environment."* The women's group provides *"a very good social opportunity for women"* with get-togethers and networking events scheduled *"at least every month."* Several interviewees mentioned that they were part of affinity groups for LGBT, African-American, Asian and Hispanic attorneys. *"They take pride in the work they do and connect minorities to established figures at the firm, helping them to build a successful practice."* There's a 1L scholarship program during the summer and a mentoring scheme.

Get Hired

"As a relatively young firm, we prize creativity and teamwork," hiring partner Ben Boyd tells us. In addition to an impressive academic track record and a penchant for doing copious amounts of high-quality work, the firm looks for *"indications of grit"* in candidates. *"We want*

See firm profile on p.628

people who can sustain interest in long-term goals and those who have the ability to respond positively to failure and adversity rather than just give up. We're interested in people who have experiences that show that when the headwinds get strong, they're going to lean forward a little harder, and keep moving forward."

"Indications of grit."

Associates added that *"the firm tries not to take on stuck-up types. Although pedigree is important, if you're a snob then people won't like you. Everyone tends to exude friendliness and have a sense of humor here. They don't want people who just want to punch the clock without interacting."*

Strategy & Future

Over the past twelve months *"the DLA Piper brand has continued to be built out in positive way,"* says co-managing partner for the Americas Mike Poulos. *"We're recognized as a unique kind of firm where creativity and entrepreneurship are valued."*

In April 2015, the firm combined with Vancouver-based firm Davis. Will DLA continue to spread across the globe? According to Americas co-managing partner Stasia Kelly, *"the Canadian firm merger is a good example of how we're remaining opportunistic in terms of expansion. We had been looking at Canada for a long time but we waited to find the right partner. It's been a very successful marriage already, and we've been impressed by the energy and enthusiasm of our Canadian colleagues. We've also had additional expansion in Mexico. We are always looking for opportunities that make sense for the firm."*

"We're remaining opportunistic in terms of expansion."

"You can have someone come and give you an in-office massage! It's just wonderful."

See firm profile on p.628

Duane Morris LLP

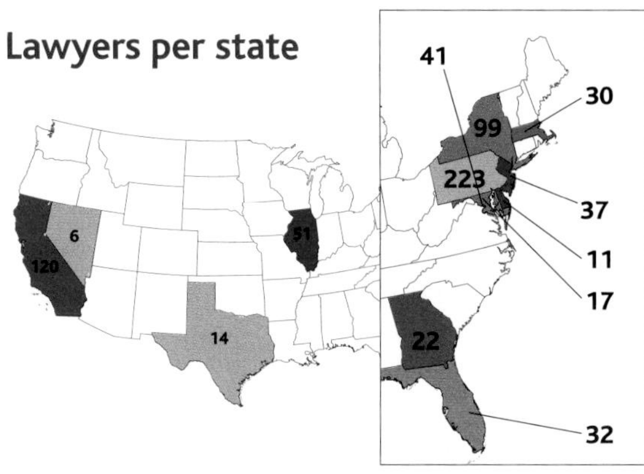

Largest US office: Philadelphia

US offices: 20

International offices: 7

First-year salary: $150,000 (NY, Philly and Baltimore only)

Billable hours: 1,950 required

Summers 2016: 17 (15 2Ls, 2 1Ls)

Revenue 2015: $434.5 million (+1.6%)

Partners made in 2016: 7

Famous for: identical offices, mid-Atlantic foundations, Harvard Business School case studies

A true Millennial, Duane Morris went global after Y2K and hasn't looked back.

'GO big or go home' is not a phrase generally associated with law firms, but we think it fits Duane Morris. Since 2000 this decent-sized stalwart of the Philadelphia legal scene has grown to 27 offices worldwide, adding global outposts from Hanoi to London on the way. It's not just litigation – or 'trial' as it's called at Duane Morris – these days, either. The firm gets top marks from *Chambers USA* for its bankruptcy, construction, corporate and IP practices. Compare this to its founding in 1904, when it had just four partners and was more likely to help you buy or sell farmland than defend a class action suit or restructure a company.

Much of this expansion has taken place since the turn of the century, and the firm doesn't plan to stop soon. *"We want to continue to grow our US platform,"* chairman and CEO John Soroko tells us, as well as seeking opportunities overseas. We hear a Taiwan foothold is in the offing. The approach seems to be working: 2014 saw *"all-time highs in firm revenue and partner profitability."* Even Harvard Business School's impressed: they have twice studied DM's rise from Philadelphian to citizen of the world.

On chambers-associate.com...

- Doing business with Cuba
- Interview with chief diversity and inclusion officer Joseph West

ASSOCIATES SAY...

The Work

In a process described as *"a bit like rush week,"* summer associates rank their three preferred practice areas. The firm then tries to match associates to practice areas, taking into account an applicant's preferences, their personality and the quality of their work product. Trial associates *"come with three official assigning partners"* but tend to get the bulk of their work by *"knocking on people's doors and figuring out what they need."* This, we're told, is *"stressful, but character-building."*

Duane Morris may have branched out but trial remains the largest department. It hosts *"the plurality of the associates"* and offers a practice range so broad that one associate told us that *"any dispute between two parties that might end up in court could land on my desk."* Associates described working on everything from construction, to product liability, to banking disputes. *"On cases with a lower dollar value, the partner might give me the file and tell me to run with it,"* said one courtroom brawler. Another praised the firm for *"doing a better job than most law firms in getting junior associates into the courtroom."* On the larger cases typical tasks fall under three broad headings: *"The first is doc review, the second is legal research covering a number of issues, and the third is motion drafting and brief writing."*

See firm profile on p.629

Rankings in Chambers USA

Banking & Finance	Insurance
Bankruptcy/Restructuring	Intellectual Property
Construction	Labor & Employment
Corporate/M&A	Litigation
Healthcare	Real Estate
Immigration	

For detail on ranking tiers and ranking locations, visit www.chambersandpartners.com

Recent work highlights

- Represented Brooklyn Law School in the $35 million disposal of a residential dorm
- Represented a contractor in a dispute with the City of Philadelphia over the construction of an airport terminal
- Representing the California Insurance Guarantee Association in asbestos litigation before the California courts
- Secured the dismissal of a breach of privacy class action against mobile video game developer Zynga

"They do a better job than most firms at getting junior associates into the courtroom."

Corporate associates *"start off as generalists and can work with anyone who needs assistance,"* which means *"when you specialize you'll know what sort of issues can arise."* A lot of the work falls under the heading of mergers and acquisitions, although it can include anything from equity financing to reinsurance. There's a lot of responsibility: *"I've been to more in-person closings than usual for a junior associate,"* said one. Corporate dealdoers *"often lend a hand"* to other departments *"when they need transactional work done."* If it all gets a little overwhelming, everyone we spoke to felt comfortable refusing work. *"After all,"* said one, *"they want you to give the project your full attention,"* and *"if you're getting too much work, you can talk to your practice group head and let them sort it out."*

Pro Bono

While *"there's no pressure"* on associates to do pro bono work, it's certainly encouraged. *"All the resources are all there,"* and all the right incentives are in place, too, with the chance to treat 100 pro bono hours as billable and the *"opportunity to do work that junior associates wouldn't be able to do for a paying client."* DM associates have worked on everything from *"veterans' benefits to forming nonprofits to helping the victims of sex trafficking expunge their criminal records."* As with paid work, pro bono cases are assigned through both formal and informal channels. *"Individual partners might ask you to join in on something they're doing,"* explained an associate, *"but the firm has a dedicated pro bono partner."*

Pro Bono hours

- For all attorneys across all US offices: 22,120
- Average per US attorney: 34

Offices

The fictional law firm Wolfram & Heart – villains of the TV show *Angel* – may not be the greatest legal role models in the world, but it does have one thing in common with Duane Morris. No, Duane Morris is not (to our knowledge) plotting to take over the world. In season 5, Angel and Spike travel to Wolfram & Heart's Rome office, only to find that it's identical to the one they've been dealing with back in LA. Similarly, Duane Morris's offices are deliberately set up to look alike. As a result, visiting different offices is *"both comforting and weird,"* we were told. However, each office is *"slightly different."* One associate quipped that this makes different offices *"feel like a familiar setting, even if you still can't figure out where the copy room is."*

"On New Year's Eve we gather in the boardroom and watch the ball drop in Times Square."

While the New York office's Times Square location is *"kinda horrible because of all the tourists,"* it is a great spot for the office New Year's Eve party. *"We gather in the boardroom and watch the ball drop,"* said an associate. On a more mundane note, it's also conveniently located for people commuting from outside the city, and only an hour and a half from the Philadelphia headquarters. Philadelphians raved about Morris' Cafe, which is named after the firm and resides in their building but is open to the public and run by Stephen Starr. *"It's so good that lawyers from other firms eat there,"* one informed us.

Diversity

In 2015, Philadelphia's newly elected mayor Jim Kenney picked head of diversity and inclusion Nolan Atkinson to head the city's diversity drive. The firm clearly has City Hall's approval, but what do the associates think? *"Our loss is Philly's gain,"* mused one. When it comes to recruitment our sources were impressed with DM's efforts at recruiting female attorneys, telling us that *"there are more women joining the firm than men,"* but thought that more could be done to attract top attorneys from ethnic minority backgrounds. *"I think we need to reach out to candidates earlier in the pipeline,"* one New Yorker opined.

See firm profile on p.629

The use of the word 'inclusion' in Nolan Anderson's title was deliberate, according to our sources. *"It's not enough to recruit a diverse workforce,"* explained someone in Philadelphia. *"You also need to make sure they feel like a part of the firm."* To that end, the firm focuses on *"reaching out to the diverse attorneys here and making sure they have the opportunity to build relationships with the firm's clients."* There are *"regular lunches and happy hours"* to make sure that attorneys of all backgrounds interact, and there is an annual diversity retreat which allows individuals *"to get to know people better,"* one informed us.

Hours & Compensation

"We work hard, within reason," explained one of our sources. There's a billable hours target of 1,950, *"and we can bill 100 hours of pro bono, so in reality it's more like 1,850."* Associates told us that the firm wants people *"who focus on producing the best work possible, rather than on billing 2,400 hours."* Not, we hasten to add, that the firm would object if attorneys did produce 2,400 hours – *"I'm sure they'd be delighted"* – but they'd rather attorneys didn't *"burn themselves out,"* not least because *"the quality of your work is likely to diminish."*

"Your work product has to be the best."

The flipside of this is that the firm won't settle for half-measures from attorneys. *"You can never just write up a memo, slap the word 'draft' on it and hand it in hoping it'll be OK,"* explained a New York associate, *"your work product has to be the best."* And, of course, sometimes when deadlines loom late nights are inevitable, although there was some disagreement about just how late is necessary. *"I've done a couple of all-nighters,"* claimed one, *"but that's because there was a deal that needed to close."* Another claimed *"never to have stayed in the office past ten o'clock,"* while a third thought that *"staying until 11.30pm or so is not unusual."*

Overall, though, hours tend to be pretty good and all-nighters relatively rare, with associates leaving at 6.30 or 7pm. *"If I need to work late I'd rather go home at a reasonable hour, have dinner with my family and remote in for a little while,"* stated one. There were some grumbles about the salary, $145,000 for first-years, which was described as *"a little below-market, whereas we do market work,"* but overall most of our interviewees thought that sacrificing a little salary for a better quality of life was a fair trade. *"Anyone can say they want more money,"* said one sanguine lawyer, *"but I'm convinced that my life is objectively better than my friends' at other firms."*

Culture

Those of a callous and mercenary disposition are unlikely to fit in at Duane Morris, which has a *"no jerk policy."* There's a close-knit atmosphere among associates, which is helped by the fact that the firm's incoming class is relatively small, which is like having *"a load of little families throughout the firm,"* in the words of one insider. *"I refuse to use the word 'collegial,' because it's only ever used in law firm marketing,"* a legal eagle told us, *"but there is a camaraderie and a sense that you're never alone."*

"There's a camaraderie and a sense that you're never alone."

More tangibly, we hear that associates are happy to *"decorate their offices in quirky ways"* and *"play pranks on one another."* Don't worry, it doesn't get too crazy: *"This is still a firm of sophisticated lawyers representing sophisticated clients,"* but one where people are happy to help each other out. Socially, *"Duane Morris is too big to have a firmwide social scene,"* but individual practice groups and offices are quite active on the social front.

"Sometimes I feel like I have too much responsibility, but that's no bad thing."

Training & Development

Respondents told us that *"law firm training is a hard thing to get right,"* but thought that DM was on the right track. *"I mean, there's some excruciating computer training at the start,"* recollected one, *"but they also provide us with enough CLEs that we never need to leave the firm."* The whole thing starts in Philadelphia and continues back at the individual offices. During the initial orientation period the firm stresses the importance of *"getting frequent feedback from all your projects,"* something the juniors we spoke to agreed with. *"Without feedback you can drive yourself crazy,"* they explained. *"You don't know if someone hasn't come back to you because your work was bad, or just because they're busy."*

"Candid but constructive."

In any event, there is a regular formal review process, which takes place twice (at six month intervals) during each attorney's first year of practice and once a year thereafter. Lawyers are asked to nominate their assessors from attorneys they have worked with. *"You can pick lawyers that you've done a lot of work for in one go, or those you've done lots of little bits of work for,"* one told

See firm profile on p.629

us. Assessees are provided with a copy of their feedback before meeting with the partners, which helps eliminate surprises. *"It's candid but constructive,"* one told us, and a good way for attorneys to learn where they need improvement.

Get Hired

While it participates in the usual OCI process, Duane Morris is also *"open to attorneys joining through other routes,"* such as write-ins for specific opportunities, law school resume books and, in one case, *"hounding them until they agreed to meet."* The OCIs themselves are conducted by partners rather than associates, and interviewing partners tended to be alums of the school in question.

At the callback stage, one interviewee noted that *"they had read my resume thoroughly,"* but that the interview was *"more like a chat,"* and there were *"no 'put them on the spot and see how they react' type questions."*

Chairman and CEO John Soroko tells us: *"One of the things that I always tell our summers is to take advantage of the opportunity while you're in law school to challenge yourself with the most interesting and, if you will, most difficult courses in the law school curriculum. Take courses in transactional law, taxation, antitrust... it's a wonderful opportunity to get that grounding."*

Strategy & Future

Associates identified booming Asia and rapidly thawing Cuba as two of the firm's key target markets. Newbies aren't just kept in the loop about the firm's future plans, they're also encouraged to bring them to fruition. The firm provides *"a lot of different business marketing and development courses,"* and also encourages associates to *"make connections with potential clients, even if they aren't in a position to give us business now, with a view to creating business down the line."*

"Challenge yourself with the most interesting and, if you will, most difficult courses in the law school curriculum."

See firm profile on p.629

Dykema Gossett PLLC

Lawyers per state

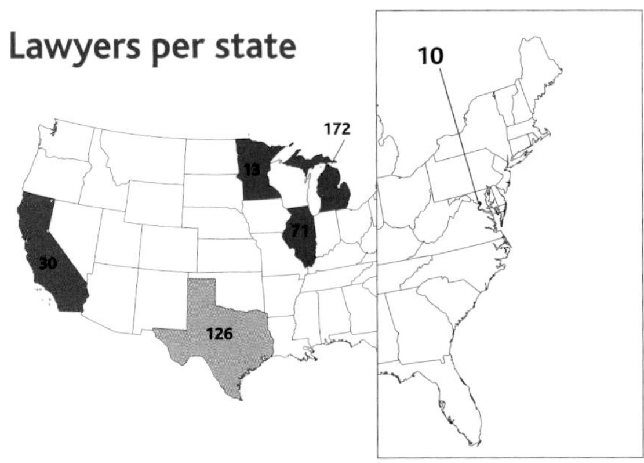

Largest US office: Chicago
US offices: 15
International offices: 0
First-year salary: $115,000–$145,000
Billable hours: 1,950 target
Summers 2016: 32 (27 2Ls, 5 1Ls)
Revenue 2015: $225 million (+26.4%)
Partners made in 2016: 13
Famous for: being big in Michigan; its steady expansion; long-term relationships with automotive clients

Detroit-born Dykema has blossomed further afield in recent years but hasn't forgotten its roots.

JUST to keep us all on our toes, when last year's *Chambers Associate* went to press in spring 2015, Dykema announced a combination with the Texas firm Cox Smith, which completed later that year. We managed to halt the printing presses just in time to add this key bit of late news, and this year chairman and CEO Peter Kellett is proud to tell us the move fulfills *"one of our strategic objectives."* Phew! Revenue for 2015 shot up by over 25%. Over the past ten years the firm's expansion has been steady and considered, gradually building up a roster of 15 offices across Michigan, where Dykema originated, Illinois and Texas, as well as bases in Minneapolis, DC and California. *"Last year I sensed we were getting close to a major opportunity,"* adds Peter Kellett, *"and we were. A year from now I hope to be talking to you about another similar move."* Watch this space.

Chambers USA recognizes Dykema's increasingly national strengths, with rankings in Texas and Illinois as well as Michigan. Ranked practices include M&A, litigation, employment, real estate, immigration, antitrust, restructuring and IP. At the time of our calls, five juniors in our interview pool were based in Detroit, three in Chicago, three in Bloomfield Hills, and one in Ann Arbor. Of these, seven were some kind of litigator, three were in real estate, and the others were in corporate finance, or taxation & estates.

On chambers-associate.com...

- Interview with chairman and CEO Peter Kellett
- Interview with hiring partner Lisa Brown
- The decline of Detroit

ASSOCIATES SAY...

The Work

Reputation – while *"excellent"* – wasn't the sole source of attraction to the firm for our interviewees: most expressed that the *"dedicated mentoring"* during the summer, or *"the good feeling during interviews, particularly when compared to the angry and stuffy attitudes of interviewers at the giant firms,"* sealed the deal. Some were drawn to Dykema's positioning as *"technically midsize with the work/life balance to match, but with clients just as sophisticated as its BigLaw peers."*

"They've really challenged me."

When new summer associates begin their ten-week experience (six in Texas), they're *"usually not assigned to a specific group but rather encouraged to rotate, initially using the free-market system."* A couple of sources in litigation expressed their passion for the practice area before summering, and were able to take on *"mostly litigation work and some research"* rather than experiencing the transactional side. At the end, future associates select their three top choices and all participants were pleased to be assigned to their preferred group. Once their associate life begins, juniors again *"go out and get work,"* a system experienced differently by different associates.

See firm profile on p.630

Rankings in Chambers USA

Bankruptcy/Restructuring	Insurance
Corporate/M&A	Labor & Employment
Employee Benefits & Executive Compensation	Litigation
Immigration	Real Estate

For detail on ranking tiers and ranking locations, visit www.chambersandpartners.com

A litigator offered this constructive criticism: *"While it gives you more control it can be unnerving and frustrating; we need an online workflow system."* On the other hand, colleagues commented that *"they do a good job of communicating and making sure associates have a good balance of work."*

Recent work highlights

- Successfully saved celebrity rescue pet Neville the Dog from death in a high-profile case involving a mauled 2-year-old and a petition signed 200,000 times
- Served as local counsel to Michigan software company Compuware in its sale to Thoma Bravo, valued at $2.5 billion
- Advised energy company ITC in the $512 million Thumb Loop Project – the construction of a 140 mile long electric transmission line in the Thumb peninsula of Michigan
- Successfully represented long-term client Ford in a class action where numerous plaintiffs from over 30 states alleged consumer fraud, based on cracked tailgate appliqués on vehicles

Real estaters were happy with the spread of work and responsibility levels. *"I'm getting a little more responsibility with each new matter,"* one reflected. *"At first, it was just whatever work needed doing. Now it's more focused."* Sources agreed that *"there's always due diligence, but as you go along you start to draft documents too, take on research, or coordinate a closing by preparing the relevant documents."* An interviewee spoke enthusiastically about *"being thrown into all the different strands of the practice, from amending leases, to lending transactions, to a buy/sell agreement. They've really challenged me."* Client contact came in the form of *"sitting in on conference calls."*

"Once in a while I'm given too much responsibility."

Litigators – assigned to subgroups such as class actions and product liability, commercial, business, or financial services – reckoned that *"the way we staff cases, in small teams of one partner and two associates, allows you to contribute quickly."* One recalled *"spending the first five months doing mostly research – there's a lot of that – and doc review, but after that I had my own cases and was working directly under a partner, drafting, coordinating discovery and interacting with clients."* While others didn't graduate into more substantive work quite as quickly as that, they confirmed that *"from second year onward I've been involved in the strategy and sit on case meetings, as well as working on a few small cases alone. I've taken two depositions and I go to court a lot. My friends at other firms are doing very basic stuff that's hardly even legal. Once in a while I'm given too much responsibility, but I always have partners I can talk to about it."*

Training & Development

While all newbies attend an orientation and there are practice group presentations on current issues, most interviewees found that *"we don't have a formal training process. It's learn-by-experience. Every partner has a different teaching style and works differently. It's not consistent but I've learnt a lot."* We heard this can be *"frustrating,"* depending on who you're working with and how busy they are: *"Sometimes it's hard to track people down and get a sense of what I should be doing. More partner involvement would be good because not getting enough feedback can be frustrating."* On the other hand, *"people are willing to talk to you about things: I've been able to go to my practice group leaders about anything."* Others confirmed they would cherish more consistency and concluded they *"wouldn't rave about training; sometimes we just have to learn by doing."*

Nevertheless, each associate is assigned a formal partner mentor. *"I worked a lot for a particular attorney during summer and still have dinner with her and her husband."* Like anywhere, some mentors prove more committed than others, leading one mentee to opine that *"they need to get someone who wants to mentor or scrap the program."* They also remembered *"having associate mentors during summer: they should carry that on, it's great!"* There's an annual formal *"individual sit-down meeting to discuss performance and any concerns."*

Hours & Compensation

"Yes, we do have time for a private life."

From the first year onward, hitting the hours target of 1,950 means eligibility for a *"merit-based"* bonus. Juniors confessed to being slightly unsure *"what happens if you don't hit the target,"* and suspected that *"occasionally everyone gets the bonus irrespective of billables."* The 1,950 was a source of stress for some, but not all. *"Perhaps there's not an over-abundance of legal work,"* one offered, *"but it can be really hard."* Others were more optimistic and asserted that *"considering how accepting the firm is of pro bono, you can make it."* *"Yes, we do have*

See firm profile on p.630

time for a private life," juniors told us. Starting the day *"at eightish and leaving by six or seven"* was standard, and while some did work regularly on weekends, most did not. Working from home when necessary *"is always an option."* One laughed and said: *"Partners tease me, saying I should go out more while I'm young."*

"My most substantive experience – such as depositions – has been in pro bono."

Pro Bono

"Pro bono is encouraged and it satisfies my need to help the community," a representative associate declared. *"We get a steady stream of emails and I've dealt with immigration issues, small business matters where I've worked directly with the client,"* and we even heard about an international child kidnapping case. Some cases *"lead to a hearing which I'll lead."* Another explained that *"my most substantive experience – such as depositions – has been in pro bono. I've worked on important prisoners' rights cases, racking up 300 hours, and it all counts toward my billable target. There's no problem with that."* Forty a year are compulsory, even for transactional lawyers, who admitted *"finding it much harder because our schedule is a lot more volatile."* A real estate attorney took it further: *"I don't partake because I don't see a benefit in my practice."*

Pro bono hours

- For all attorneys across all US offices: 10,030
- Average per US attorney: 43

Diversity

Pro bono hours

"They're certainly making an effort, particularly at associate level," was the consensus. *"At partner level, it's not great."* Still, while admitting that *"of course, like all firms it could always do a better job overall,"* sources felt *"really proud"* of Dykema's diversity effort in recruitment. They reckoned that supporting initiatives such as the Wolverine Bar Association demonstrates the firm's *"focus on creating a more diverse law firm."* One non-white female associate recalled *"looking around me during the summer and thinking it was incredibly diverse. You can add that as one of the assets that drew me to Dykema."* Overall, Chicago attorneys felt the results of the diversity efforts more strongly than those in other offices.

Offices

A proud Detroit deal-doer explained that *"because ours is the head office, it's got a more traditional feel. Think less glass and more wood paneling. We wear business casual whereas some of the other offices are more laid back in that respect. Still, it's open and you often see people walking around, strategizing. I know we're looking to make officewide lunches a more regular occurrence, and a nicer coffee machine would be great! It's currently not quite doing the trick."*

"A nicer coffee machine would be great!"

Chicago case-crackers had no beef with the coffee beans, but they didn't beat around the bush when it came to the office artwork: *"It's awful! It's a running joke. They're abstract and they look really old, as in dingy."* Other than that, *"everyone gets their own office and you can decorate it however you want. Some have better views than others. Overall the place is spacious and comfortable, and it gets the job done."* One did confess though: *"Sometimes I'm jealous because friends at other firms have beautiful offices. It's nice here, but it's not the nicest."* We also heard rumors of *"a rooftop terrace in Bloomfield Hills where they host socials once a month."*

Culture

Across all offices and practice groups, juniors agreed that *"partners are approachable and talk to us like we're colleagues. They're interested in our opinion and in our legal minds."* Generally speaking too, sources spoke of a *"friendly and relaxed"* atmosphere across the firm, *"where everyone from admin staff to equity partners respects one another and work together."* Beyond this, each location and department within it had different vibes. A real estate rookie in Detroit beamed: *"I've lucked out. I'm friends with all my co-workers. We don't just talk about work, we ask about each other's families."*

"Four days out of five we all have lunch together."

A source in Chicago found *"breaking into the social atmosphere quite difficult: there's not as much talking or joking among juniors here as I've seen in other groups."* A real estater commented instead that *"everyone is so close, at least four days out of five we all have lunch together."* The social scene, interviewees hoped, will soon see a ramp-up *"now that, since the combination with Cox Smith, we've introduced an associate committee. They had one so we wanted one firmwide."* For the moment, *"social events are mostly during summer; other than that there's not much."*

See firm profile on p.630

Strategy & Future

Speaking of Cox Smith: at the time of our research, Dykema associates had so far had limited time to experience the combined firm's new guise. But had they noticed any initial changes? *"Other than the associate committee, not really."* The evolution is far from complete, chairman and CEO Peter Kellett reminds us, affirming: *"We are not done growing. We will grow in each of the major markets we are in. In the long term, we will have a truly national platform, probably even global. We don't have an imminent plan but I'm always looking out for growth possibilities."*

Get Hired

Current juniors may not be feeling the effects of the merger yet, but future candidates surely will: *"We've expanded the number of law schools we visit in Texas,"* hiring partner Lisa Brown explains, adding that *"we went to the University of Wisconsin this year as well, which was new."* Although Dykema accepts direct applications, OCIs are typically its first point of contact with potential new associates. *"The first thing we do is study a candidate's resume for participation in journals, experience in leadership positions, and student organizations – activities that suggest they're able to develop client relationships. The quality of law school and a strong academic performance are important, but we don't have a grade cutoff."*

Lisa Brown also reveals that during interviews hopefuls are asked *"open-ended questions designed to elicit information about how they've made decisions and solved problems previously. They'll have more time to ask us questions in the callback."* The summer program is available in nine of the 15 offices.

"We are not done growing."
Peter Kellett, chairman and CEO

See firm profile on p.630

Epstein Becker & Green PC

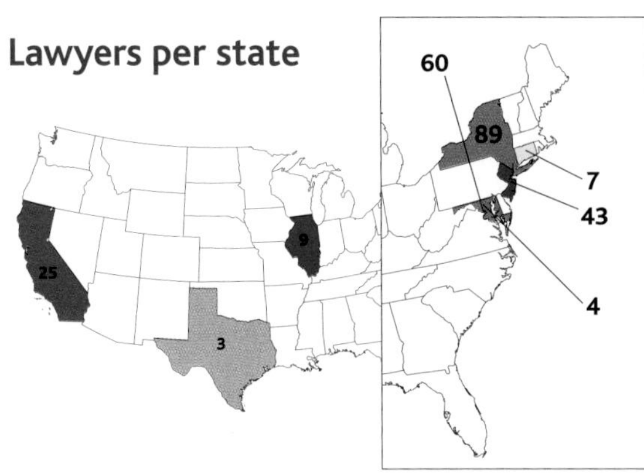

Largest US office: New York
US offices: 12
International offices: 0
First-year salary: varies by practice and location ($130,000 - $140,000)
Billable hours: 1,950 target
Summers 2016: 11 (9 2Ls, 2ILs)
Revenue 2015: undisclosed
Partners made in 2016: 3
Famous for: healthcare law; labor & employment law

Passionate about healthcare and labor law, Epstein seeks like-minded, entrepreneurial associates "*with a practical or educational background related to the industry.*"

KEEP reading if you're interested in going into labor. Labor law, that is, not medical labor. Speaking of medicine, if healthcare law is something that sets your pulse racing, then you should also read on. These two practices form the specialized heart of Epstein's work – and a quick glance at *Chambers USA* diagnoses it as an adroit performer in both labor & employment and healthcare. *"My background screamed healthcare,"* declared an interviewee, highlighting industry experience as a common factor among fellow attorneys in the department. This isn't prescriptive though – such experience can take many forms: *"There are people here who were nurses, or who have done policy work, or healthcare finance."* What's for sure, though, is that Epstein is a place for folk *"who want to be able to specialize from day one."*

Although some labor & employment associates had studied the subject at undergrad level, sources told us that this isn't mandatory. Others might have work experience in, say, human resources. *"You need to have a genuine interest in the topic, because the firm is so focused on its core practices."* So, if healthcare or labor & employment give you the heebie-jeebies, or you're just plain indifferent, then 'EeeBeeGee' probably isn't the firm for you.

On chambers-associate.com...

- The Affordable Care Act
- Interview with chair Mark Lutes

ASSOCIATES SAY...

The Work

First-year associates join the DC, New York or Newark office. In NYC, new recruits can be found in both core practices, though there tend to be a few more on the employment side. At the time of our calls, all the juniors in the capital were members of the healthcare department.

"I hear the word 'entrepreneurial' a lot."

There's no assigning partner, so juniors must be prepared to go out and find work for themselves, although *"they will try to line up a few projects in the beginning."* The system is *"challenging,"* we heard. *"I hear the word 'entrepreneurial' a lot, and that's accurate. As a first or second-year you're under pressure to try and build relationships with partners and not promise them more work than you can bill. It takes time to develop."* While some thought that *"it'd be nice to have a centralized system for a more even distribution of work,"* others insisted that *"it's great to have the freedom to touch on different areas and reach out to certain partners."*

Within the realm of healthcare law, juniors start out as generalists and appreciated the *"opportunity to dabble"* in a range of areas. *"I've been here a year and the work categories have been all over the place!"* exclaimed one, while another explained: *"I focus mostly on transactional and regulatory matters. On the transactional side*

See firm profile on p.631

The Inside View

Rankings in *Chambers USA*

Employee Benefits & Executive Compensation	Healthcare
	Labor & Employment

For detail on ranking tiers and ranking locations, visit www.chambersandpartners.com

Recent work highlights

- Acted for private equity firm General Atlantic on the sale of urgent care company MedExpress to health services company Optum for $1.5 billion
- Represented Children's and Women's Physicians of Westchester (a medical practice covering three states) in a transaction that affiliates it with the Boston Children's Hospital network
- Acted for Dolce & Gabbana in a class action for wages on behalf of interns

we represent a lot of private equity companies investing in healthcare companies, and that means a lot of due diligence. For someone who's junior, it's great to be able to dig into the heart of these companies, and see how they're structured and how they're trying to comply with the law."

Other areas tackled by new recruits include government investigations, along with fraud and abuse matters (to determine whether *"healthcare systems like hospitals are setting up inappropriate financial arrangements with physicians or submitting false claims."*) One noted that *"litigation isn't a big area for the firm, but there is a growing antitrust practice."* Day-to-day tasks range from *"simple things, like putting together binders of materials,"* to *"more complicated stuff like legal research and drafting memos and court filings."* There's plenty to keep associates on their toes, as one exhilarated associate proclaimed: *"The great thing about practicing health law at EBG is that the field is always changing. You're constantly having to learn and figure out how the client, and you personally, can adapt to changes in order to stay compliant."*

"Specialization happens over time."

Employment juniors also *"start out as generalists, and then specialization happens over time."* The department represents the management side of many big *Fortune 500*-esque companies across a range of industries including financial services, healthcare and telecom. Our sources had worked on discrimination cases relating to the Americans with Disabilities Act as well as wage and hour matters. *"I'm impressed with the amount of experience I've had within a short amount of time,"* said a junior. *"I've been doing things that I expected to do in the fifth year of practice."* Typical tasks include drafting mediation statements, subpoenas and memos, as well as research. *"I'm writing a motion this afternoon for an arbitration,"* reported one contentedly.

Training & Development

Rookies cover the basics like the email system and billing in their first few days. Then there are *"a number of lunchtime lectures as part of the 'EBG Academy', which starts in the summer, but not a whole lot of formal training."* However, *"health law is always changing so there are lots of webinars to participate in."* Also, fledgling healthcare lawyers are sent off to the annual American Health Lawyers Association conference.

"Health law is always changing..."

Some thought that a more substantial range of trainings *"might be helpful but difficult to implement, because every partner has a different style: partner A likes it this way, partner B likes it another way."* Others pointed out that *"you just have to learn organically,"* while certain interviewees thought that *"training is definitely a weak point for the firm. It would be nice to feel like there's more support."* However, we did hear that the firm has recently put a more formal training program in place.

What about feedback? *"It's an entrepreneurial culture here and it's incumbent on junior associates to reach out and solicit it, outside of the formal review,"* commented one. Another suggested that *"the level of informal feedback that you get day to day really depends on the partner. At any law firm, time is a valuable commodity and it's tough for people to be proactive about this, but partners tend to be responsive if you ask them directly."*

Offices

The DC, New York and Newark offices take on juniors, but Epstein has plenty more places in its national network: Baltimore, Boston, Chicago, Houston, LA, Princeton, San Diego, San Francisco and Stamford. Those in the capital and the Big Apple referred to their offices as *"a little dated in terms of décor, but comfortable."* Those in DC mentioned that a refurb or move is in the pipeline.

Hours & Compensation

We heard mixed reports about the hours. Some were cavalier about the 1,950 billing target: *"I'm someone who's definitely going to hit the hours,"* one assured us. *"It's very reasonable. You have to be active in seeking out work, rather than expecting it to turn up at your door."* However, for others in DC's healthcare department, racking up this amount *"is a big concern, espe-*

See firm profile on p.631

cially for juniors. There are times when it's very busy, but a lot of other times it's not busy at all and there's still the pressure to meet that target. It doesn't feel realistic given the flow and volume of work. So it's very challenging." One summarized: *"You don't have control over it – as a junior I can send emails and reach out, but I can't go out and get a client."* In terms of work/life balance, *"I'm either swamped or have nothing to do. It's difficult to enjoy the free time, because I feel uncomfortable with the fact I'm not busy."*

"Clients tend to be more cost-conscious and eyeball the bill."

Interviewees suggested that *"there isn't as steady a supply as there used to be of large projects on which juniors would traditionally build up their hours doing doc review. Now, clients tend to be more cost-conscious and eyeball the bill, so it's hard to justify putting 20 attorneys on a project when ten could do it, to keep the budget under control."* One thought that *"the problem could be fixed with a more coordinated system of work assignment. I don't think it's coming down the ranks."*

Apparently the firm's management is aware of this issue: *"Several juniors have raised the problem at an associate committee meeting, but I'm not sure how quickly the firm will figure out what to do about it."* Meanwhile, healthcare associates in New York didn't seem bothered by this problem. *"There's a broader scope of work to tap into, so while I do have slower months I'm not worried about hours."*

Epstein's salary falls below the market rate. Again, sources had mixed opinions. *"For me, the exposure to clients, the amount of responsibility and the type of work we do means more to me than an extra $30,000,"* declared one, while another mused that *"there's more work/life balance here, so that's the pay-off."* Others were less content: *"There's pressure to work very hard and perform at a high level, so it would be appropriate to be paid in line with the market."* Interviewees weren't sure about how the bonus system works *("it's a bit murky")*. This is because discretionary factors other than hours are taken into consideration, like 'firm citizenship'.

Culture

"*It's very congenial here,"* emphasized associates. *"People are calm and I genuinely enjoy working with them. Day-to-day life is pleasant and it's great to be surrounded by very smart colleagues who have a deep interest in health law."* However, *"some of the institutional issues, like workflow, mean that morale is affected. It's an added stress."*

This isn't a firm with a packed after-hours social calendar. *"It tends to be more family-oriented. Lots of people commute and have families they want to get back to, but there are some junior associates who make an effort to go out after work every once in a while."* That said, *"lots of associates go for lunch and coffee together during the day."* In addition to a big holiday bash, the firm organizes *"a handful of happy hours"* and monthly birthday celebrations.

Pro Bono

"Pro bono is encouraged, but it can be difficult to juggle it with billable work," remarked an associate, while another highlighted that *"it's not a huge priority because pro bono hours don't count until you meet the billable target. The firm would demonstrate more commitment if they counted it before that."* However, there is a pro bono committee and a *"dedicated member of staff who tracks opportunities."* Those that had taken on pro bono matters had tackled disability and landlord-tenant cases, as well as healthcare issues.

"You need to have a genuine interest...because the firm is so focused on its core practices."

Pro bono hours

- For all attorneys: 5,000
- Average per attorney: 20

Diversity

When it comes to diversity, interviewees agreed that *"the firm is making efforts. When I look at the juniors coming in, I see a diverse crowd that includes women and ethnic minority attorneys, rather than just white men."* A source in the Big Apple remarked happily that *"we have a lot of female partners, which is rare for a New York firm."* A women's initiative puts on regular events *("We recently held a comedy social and a fundraising event for a non-profit organization")* and there's a pipeline scheme for minority 1Ls.

Get Hired

"We recruit people in a practice-specific way," says Amy Simmons, director of legal recruitment and professional development. *"For healthcare we look for someone with a practical or educational background related to the industry, and we do the same for labor."*

See firm profile on p.631

"A practical or educational background related to the industry."

Besides this, what sort of personal qualities does the firm value? *"Associates have to be self-starters. We're not a firm to tuck juniors away doing research for their first three years, so from the beginning they'll be staffed on real projects with client interaction. We need people who are comfortable giving their opinion. From an early point they get a lot of responsibility. If that doesn't appeal, then they're not a good fit."* Associates added that *"they look for someone who's a nice person to be around. Everyone spends so much time at work, so they want to keep up the collegial atmosphere and open culture."*

"Exciting opportunities for associates."

Strategy & Future

Concentrating on the two core practice areas continues to be the Epstein ethos. *"We place emphasis on our brands in the healthcare industry and in labor & employment,"* chairman Mark Lutes tells us. *"Over the past year we've had conversations with many laterals across the country and have achieved a great deal of success in identifying those who realize that in a hyper-competitive legal market they need to develop their careers at a place with a strong brand in their specialty."* Looking to the future, Lutes predicts that the firm will probably expand its national presence and set up shop *"in another city or two."* However, *"we're not interested in growth for growth's sake. We only seek out additional opportunities that suit our specialties, where there's a hot healthcare or employment market."* Not that healthcare isn't busy to begin with. Lutes confirms that the Affordable Care Act is still making waves in the industry: *"It's going to have reverberations for years to come, with new sets of regulations reforming the way healthcare services are purchased and physicians are compensated by Medicare. All these economic and legal changes are creating exciting opportunities for associates."*

"It's great to be surrounded by very smart colleagues who have a deep interest in health law."

See firm profile on p.631

Fenwick & West LLP

Lawyers per state

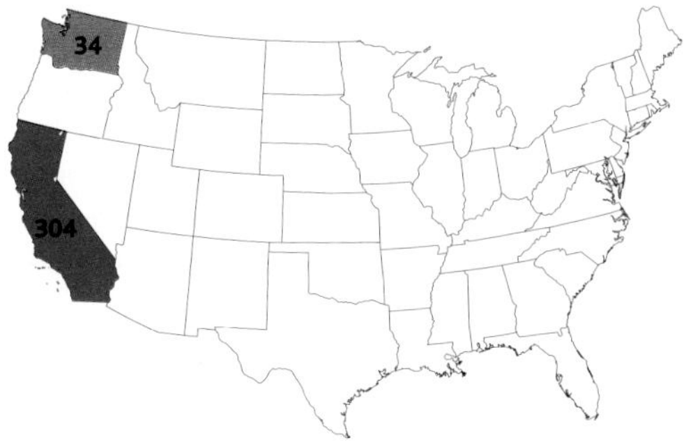

Largest US office: Mountain View
US offices: 3
International offices: 1
First-year salary: $160,000
Billable hours: two tracks: 1,950 or 1,800 target
Summers 2016: 34 (30 2Ls, 4 1Ls)
Revenue 2015: $363.6 million
Partners made in 2016: 6
Famous for: tech and life sciences clients; predicting the importance of technology in business

This tech-savvy West Coast firm encourages associates to make their own connections.

IF Fenwick & West told us that something as bizarre as computerized unicorns would be the next big thing, we'd sit up and take notice. After all, this is the firm with an uncanny ability to predict the future: back in 1972, four attorneys who realized the revolutionary potential of technology in the business world decided to up sticks from New York and head west to launch their own tech law firm in Palo Alto. This was at a time when Silicon Valley as we know it today didn't exist. Unicorns, by the way, as well as being mythical horse-like creatures, are the venture capitalists' nickname for startups worth over a billion dollars.

Today, Fenwick & West is seen as a pioneer in tech circles. Its lawyers, for example, invented the shrink wrap license agreement, which binds users to T&Cs just by opening a product. The firm has advised some of the biggest names in technology since its earliest days. Just two highlights: incorporating Apple, no less, in 1976 and representing WhatsApp from startup to its $22 billion sale to Facebook in more recent times. And while Fenwick is best known for its corporate work in the tech and life sciences sectors, it also has sizable litigation and IP practices. All these areas win rankings in *Chambers USA*, as do smaller departments like employee benefits and tax.

On chambers-associate.com...

- We chat with managing partner Kathryn Fritz
- Hiring tips from co-hiring partners Bill Hughes and Carolyn Chang

ASSOCIATES SAY...

The Work

Fenwick's free market system means associates *"can build the kind of practice and handle the kind of cases we want to."* Most sources felt the system *"works really well; getting enough work is not an issue."* One junior noted: *"There can be a tendency to get siloed into a sub-practice,"* but it's possible to avoid being pigeonholed *"as long as you're proactive."* At the time of our calls, most juniors were split fairly evenly between the firm's corporate and litigation groups. A couple head into IP to work on patent, trademark or tech transaction licensing.

"The chance to step up and shine."

The litigation practice is split into several subgroups, which include patent, employment, securities, IP and commercial. The final is *"a catch-all group and covers things like trademark, copyright, privacy, class actions and general commercial cases."* Although areas are clearly demarcated, *"it doesn't limit what work juniors might do,"* one source stressed. *"The groups are fluid; you can use the free market system to move between them."*

The Inside View

See firm profile on p.632

Rankings in *Chambers USA*

Capital Markets	IT & Outsourcing
Corporate/Commercial	Life Sciences
Corporate/M&A	Litigation
Employee Benefits & Executive Compensation	Startups & Emerging Companies
Intellectual Property	Tax

For detail on ranking tiers and ranking locations, visit www.chambersandpartners.com

Recent work highlights

- Represented Uber in two $1.2 billion venture capital financings
- Advised imaging satellite creators Skybox Imaging on its $500 million acquisition by Google
- Acted for games developer King Digital Entertainment in securing an injunction against Beijing game provider 6waves. King alleged that 6waves' 'Farm Epic' and 'Treasure Epic' games infringed on King's 'Farm Heroes Saga' and 'Pet Rescue Saga'
- Represented current and former directors and officers of Adobe in a shareholder derivative dispute arising out of allegations that Adobe violated antitrust regulations by entering into agreements with other technology companies concerning the recruitment of employees

Doc review is generally the preserve of staff attorneys. Instead sources were free to get stuck in on drafting anything from pleadings to appellate briefs or even taking depositions: *"Seven months in, I'd already taken three,"* one source recalled. *"I feel free to ask if I can take a deposition or argue a motion. Even if the answer is no, it's not considered a dumb thing to have asked."* Another emphasized: *"One of the toughest things about being a junior is being stuck in your box. Fenwick doesn't do that. It asks you to take control of your career and look for responsibility."*

Corporate is divided into several areas, including startups (handling venture financing for private companies), M&A, securities, employee benefits & executive compensation and private equity. *"People move fluidly between these. You don't really belong to one unless you self-select to be there."* Our sources had dabbled in each of these areas and by their third year could *"take the lead associate role on the majority of transactions. I'm negotiating the term sheet, drafting and negotiating agreements, managing due diligence and coordinating the closing. Fenwick has a lean and mean approach to staffing. It gives us the chance to step up and shine by tackling more substantive things but it does make for more stress."*

Training & Development

Juniors are allocated a 'confidential adviser' from among the junior associate ranks. The advisers are expected to *"be available at any time for questions or to help if you run into something difficult. They walk you through the process of certain tasks and sit in on your first client call."* After the first year, juniors are assigned a partner mentor who *"gives you advice on longer career building at Fenwick,"* but the free market system means there is plenty of room to find informal mentors too.

"Advice on longer career building."

New starters kick their first week off at the firm with training at the Fenwick University, which prepares juniors for the skills and tasks they need at this stage in their career. Regular lunchtime sessions on professional development and legal updates are all uploaded to the firm's virtual Fenwick Learning site.

Offices

Mountain View and San Francisco absorb most new starters but a couple swoop into Seattle. Interaction between the hubs is *"seamless; cases are not staffed on an office basis. Most of the largest matters consist of attorneys or paralegals from all three bases."*

"Developed relationships with partners in both offices.

Mountain View may be the firm's largest office by far – it houses around 220 attorneys compared to San Francisco's 85 while Seattle has half that – but we were told that popular demand to be in the San Fran hub has led to an unusual setup: *"More people wanted to work here than there was office space for. A couple of years ago someone decided to find a 'roommate'; there'd be one office in Mountain View and one in San Fran and they would alternate days at each base."* The trend caught on and now *"lots of juniors voluntarily office share"* between locations. While San Francisco is in the process of acquiring more office space, interviewees highlighted the benefits of the current make-do method. *"It's been good for my practice; I have developed relationships with partners in both offices."*

Culture

"Because people flow between our offices so frequently there is not much of a cultural division," one junior explained. Another went so far as to say: *"It's not fair to call them two offices; it's one office in two buildings."* Sourced reckoned Fenwick attorneys *"feel free to be*

See firm profile on p.632

themselves – this is not a formal working environment." One explained: *"Dealing with peer firms, I've seen grown men and women just sort of hush when their partners are talking or look to them to see if they're laughing at a joke. We don't behave that way. When something funny happens people just laugh."*

Interviewees credited *"living in the Bay Area"* with this straightforward attitude. *"It rubs off; there are not a lot of rules – like our free market system. If you have self-motivation you can run with things."* Navigating the system requires *"some backbone. You have to have some sort of agency to direct your career. If you're not given a road map to solve a problem, you have to be comfortable asking for help."* That's not to say that people are completely left to forge on alone. *"We're for the firm; that means if there is a task no one wants to do we don't have a situation where everyone waits to see who the partner will assign it to. Someone will volunteer because they know someone else handled a bunch of really boring tasks last time. However tough it is, or however many days you're working late, someone has your back."*

"When something funny happens people just laugh."

Fenwick sponsors events for associate morale and applies the terms pretty loosely. *"If more than a few people go for lunch on a Friday, a partner may tell us to put it under their name for associate morale. It's basically a hanging out together budget, I really like it."* Free lunch is just the tip of the iceberg as associates can also say 'Aloha' to a holiday in one of the firm's three Hawaiian condos. Priority is granted to those who've gone the longest without staying and partners aren't eligible to participate. Fenwick also pays for an airfare for two so *"it really feels like a free holiday! It's one of my favorite perks."*

Hours & Compensation

Those jetting off to Hawaii generally don't need to worry about being disturbed by those back in the office *"unless you say you're available to work."* We're told that for the most part someone volunteers *"to be point person for your responsibilities. Instead of constant interruptions you're only bothered if no one else can handle something."*

"Bonuses aren't the be-all and end-all."

Thanks to the ability to easily move between offices and the firm being *"so tech-friendly, face time is not a huge thing. As long as you're responsive, people don't care if you're sitting in your office or elsewhere."* Indeed, we even heard of several associates who predominantly work from home: *"The firm's flexible at allowing people to figure out the life they want at Fenwick. That's nice to see and I think it will only get better."* But don't let that fool you into thinking associates are switching off at 6pm every day: plenty reported working late into the evening either in the office or at home.

First-years aim for a billable target of 1,800 hours. Come the second year they can opt to stay on this reduced level or shoot for 1,950. Hitting targets affords juniors their end-of-year windfall but *"bonuses aren't the be-all and end-all here. People would be more concerned than impressed if you were billing 2,500 hours and the bonuses reflect that."* There is also the option to set lower targets and the firm is *"super accommodating"* for those who want to work a reduced schedule. One source praised Fenwick for *"doing a good job at keeping people on partnership track. I know of several women who have made partner while working on a reduced schedule!"*

"One of the toughest things about being a junior is being stuck in your box. Fenwick doesn't do that. It asks you to take control of your career."

Diversity

One junior reckoned the firm's flexible working policy aided diversity: *"It precludes the expectation that lawyers always have to work long hours, constantly be in the office and break their neck to support their team. It has meant Fenwick has brought in and retained more people"* such as working mothers.

"Retained more people."

Sources felt the firm's *"commitment to diversity is very clear."* Fenwick attorneys recently marched in the San Francisco Pride parade and various affinity groups host social and speaker events throughout the year. Several juniors believed Fenwick *"does a really good job, especially when it comes to women,"* although others were quick to point out *"most of the partnership is still white and male."* Racial diversity is *"more along the lines of our peer firms in California but it's not reflective of the population as a whole."*

Pro Bono

Up to 100 pro bono hours are automatically credited toward an attorney's annual billable hour target. *"After that they approve as many hours as you would like, as long as*

See firm profile on p.632

you request it." None of our sources had encountered any trouble getting additional hours signed off and we heard of associates crediting double the initial 100 allowance. *"Pro bono is definitely supported."*

All aboard the Justice Bus

Associates can go off traveling in the local Justice Bus, which transports attorneys to impoverished areas to provide legal advice. But they don't need to go far to get a pro bono fix: once a month the Mountain View office hosts Lawyers in the Library, where attorneys give virtual legal advice by video conference. Other projects we heard of included cases concerning violence against women, immigration, prisoners' rights, and assisting nonprofits with corporate affairs. The firm also does a virtual healthcare clinic in conjunction with Facebook.

Pro bono hours

- For all attorneys across all US offices: 17,580
- Average per US attorney: undisclosed

Get Hired

The firm's tech focus sees a large number of associates hailing from California law schools which specialize in tech law. Though by no means a requirement, there are also plenty of attorneys with science backgrounds, particularly among those who practice patent litigation: *"People who go to law school and say they're never touching math or science again would not do well here. We're a bit of a nerd firm; people here often discuss cool new gadgets."*

Recruiting committee cochair Bill Hughes tells us: *"We're looking for people who seem like they have entrepreneurial spirit and a self-starter mentality,"* as the firm is keen to recruit *"people who will operate independently."* Visit our website to read more from Hughes and fellow cochair Carolyn Chang.

Strategy & Future

"We'll continue focusing on being a full-service firm for tech and life sciences clients," interviewees told us. *"The strategy of focusing on tech really paid off during the last tech boom and Fenwick has every intention of continuing with that."*

"Constantly moving and evolving."

Managing partner Kathryn Fritz echoed this sentiment: *"Our focus is going to continue to be servicing the core need of tech and life sciences clients. The good thing about our particular focus is that our client base is the reverse of static; the technology and life sciences industries are constantly moving and evolving."* Go online to read our full interview with Fritz.

"I know of several women who have made partner while working on a reduced schedule!"

See firm profile on p.632

Finnegan, Henderson, Farabow, Garrett & Dunner LLP

Lawyers per state

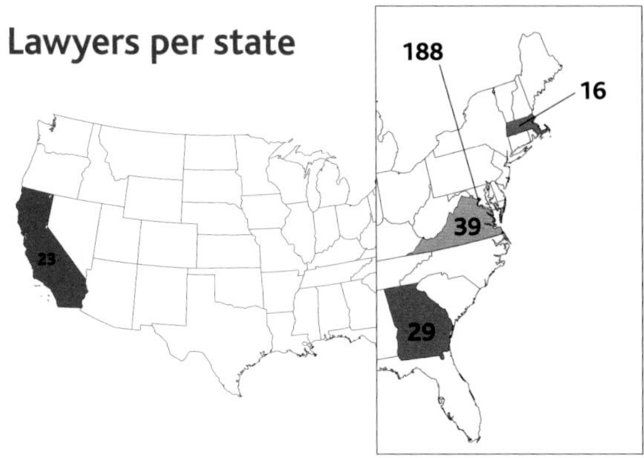

Largest US office: Washington, DC
US offices: 5
International offices: 5
First-year salary: $160,000
Billable hours: 2,000 target (or 1,920 plus 80 pro bono hours)
Summers 2016: 30 (24 2Ls, 6 1Ls)
Revenue 2015: $308.1 million (-0.3%)
Partners made 2016: 7 (all US)
Famous for: IP, especially patents

Clarity of focus and an arsenal of technical experts make Finnegan an obvious choice for all things IP.

STARTING off as a boutique IP firm in DC in 1965, Finnegan now comprises a host of domestic offices stretching from Boston to Palo Alto. Drawing in technical expertise in areas such as electronics, industrial manufacturing, biotechnology and pharmaceuticals, the firm's patent and trademark nous has earned it a reputation as BigLaw's go-to gang for all things IP. Long serving as a trailblazer for America's patent law firms, Finnegan was one of the first to break into Tokyo, setting up shop there in 1988. The firm's Asian presence further blossomed with the addition of offices in Shanghai and Taipei, and April 2015 saw the opening of an office in Seoul, making Finnegan the first IP boutique in Korea with expertise in US IP law. Such scale, focus and repute has attracted a catalog of A-list clients, with AOL, Caterpillar, LG, Sony and Toyota all on the books.

All luster aside, Finnegan proved an attractive bet for rookies thanks to the flexibility that the firm had afforded them. In a bid to attract industry's finest, the firm has a number of possible entry routes besides your standard summer program. Add to that a wealth of opportunities to try both patent lit and patent prosecution, as well as *"the ability to dabble in different practice groups should you fancy,"* and it's no wonder that the juniors we spoke to were struggling to find a reason to grumble.

On chambers-associate.com...

- Schools bout for summers: alternative routes into Finnegan

Finnegan's a good fit for tech types who're interested in life beyond the lab. As one junior regaled: *"I didn't know I wanted to be a patent litigator when I was at college, but I knew I wanted to try something a little different. Here you'll find personalities and a learning environment that'll suit anyone with an interest in scientific research, but unlike academia there's no pressure to specialize in a fixed area."* The level of academic achievement among Finnegan attorneys is *"definitely pretty advanced: you don't need a PhD to get an interview, but a lot of our biotechnology or pharmaceuticals patent prosecutors would argue that it would make your life a lot easier."*

ASSOCIATES SAY...

The Work

Most juniors are in DC, and the rest are sprinkled around Atlanta, Boston, Palo Alto and Reston. Based on their academic and technical backgrounds, new starters fall into one of the following practice groups: electrical, chemical, mechanical, biotechnology & pharmaceuticals, or trademark & copyright. When it comes to assigning work, *"most practice groups have a group director who will ask you to send a monthly workload report. They'll then pull some strings if your docket is looking a little empty, or if you're interested in trying something*

The Inside View

See firm profile on p.633

Rankings in *Chambers USA*

Intellectual Property
Life Sciences
International Trade

For detail on ranking tiers and ranking locations, visit www.chambersandpartners.com

specific." However, as time progresses *"you're expected to take a more informal approach, as you're bound to have struck up relationships with certain partners."* Juniors' technical knowledge is *"massively useful"* on complex litigation cases within their assigned practice groups, but *"it's not uncommon to approach members of other groups and ask to get involved. It makes you a more well-rounded attorney."*

"Handed the reins to develop strategies and even run your own files."

Depending on which groups they get involved with, Finnegan's associates can expect to work on matters relating to one or more of the following: electronics, computers, industrial manufacturing, consumer products, medical devices, biotechnology, pharmaceuticals, chemicals, or alternative energy. Within each practice, newbies' take on a mix of both patent prosecution and IP litigation work.

Patent prosecution work sees juniors guide clients through the patent application process. Alongside preparing drafts of claims for the initial filing, interviewees had frequently negotiated post-grant review proceedings, an area that has been *"particularly busy since the introduction of the America Invents Act in 2011."* There's also *"a lot of patent portfolio management to keep up-to-date with,"* to ensure that clients' patents remain valid. Patent prosecution work is *"quite heavily supervised at first,"* though with matters *"usually staffed with just a junior associate and a partner,"* rookies are *"soon handed the reins to develop strategies and even run your own files."*

"I like that we're thrown to the wolves every day."

IP lit tends to be a little more generously staffed, with *"three to six people assigned depending on the complexity of the case."* Juniors had begun by sitting in on strategy meetings, conducting research tasks and preparing memos, but were similarly pleased with the increased responsibilities afforded to them down the line, with several interviewees having drafted requests for instruction, motions and complaints within their first two years. Such a swift progression in responsibility *"can be tough,"* but associates weren't perturbed. *"I like that we're thrown to the wolves every day,"* relished one informer. *"We're well trained and well supported, so most of us thrive on that pressure."*

Recent work highlights

- Assisting Google with a portfolio of over 140 patent applications
- Defending tennis manufacturer Head against false advertising claims relating to its tennis rackets. It's alleged that the publicly-retailed models were marketed as the same ones used competitively by superstar professionals such as Roger Federer and Maria Sharapova
- Acting in two inter partes review proceedings for Biogen, which produces Tecfidera, a drug used to treat relapsing forms of multiple sclerosis
- Helped LG to settle a complaint at the International Trade Commission. The complaint centered on LG's importation of electronic items that infringed upon a number of asserted patents

Training & Development

"The firm doesn't provide much in terms of technical training, as it hires people on the basis that they have already developed that expertise," noted one respondent. Instead, much of Finnegan's training seems geared toward getting juniors up-to-scratch with the legal process. This begins with a week's orientation in DC, attended by all starters and focusing *"as much on developing interpersonal relationships as learning the legal ropes."* Crash courses in areas such as doc review, brief filing and patent prosecution are complemented by *"a lot of fun social offerings, such as bowling, tours of DC and even paint-balling."*

"No one will ever yell at you."

From then on, rookies are offered *"a ridiculously impressive amount of opportunities to develop on-the-go."* When mistakes are made, *"no one will ever yell at you, irrespective of how badly you've messed up. People will try to find the time to sit down and explain why they've made certain corrections."* One of the greatest tools at associates' disposal is Ed Good, a resident legal writing instructor, who *"is a great port-of-call if you want a second opinion on something before sending it off to a partner."* Ed's shiniest pearl of wisdom? *"Stay away from the passive voice. Scientific manuscripts use it all the time, but legal writing stays well clear."*

Diversity

At associate level, ethnic minorities are well represented at Finnegan. Standing tall at 25%, Finnegan's Asian American showing is particularly noteworthy among newbies. The playing field is pretty level when it comes to gender diversity too, with 43% female associates. *"The woman's forum is a fantastic resource when you're*

See firm profile on p.633

starting off," one female associate praised. *"I've attended dinners and seminars where you can bounce ideas off of one another, and it's great to learn and be inspired by female role models at the firm."*

Get Hired

"If you're a law student and looking to apply to Finnegan, you need to have demonstrated that you've committed to what you're doing," one source noted. *"Get involved in your school's IP law society, write a student paper with an IP professor, spend your 1L summer working on licensing matters at a uni tech transfer office – we want to hear how you've developed an understanding of the intricacies and requirements of patent law."*

"You need to have demonstrated that you've committed to what you're doing."

On the flipside, *"the day-to-day life of a patent lawyer is very different to that of an academic or researcher."* Again, it's all about familiarity with what you're getting into, so some legal work experience can really bolster your resume. Before heading to law school, many of Finnegan's future attorneys pull a shift as a technical specialist at the firm. It's a well-established route in, and you can find out more by heading to our Bonus Features online, with advice from chief recruitment & professional development officer Tim Henderson.

And then of course there's the beer test. Don't worry, this isn't some traumatic frat house-style initiation challenge. It stretches back to the firm's founder, Marc Finnegan, who according to insiders, *"would look to hire the kind of characters you'd want to have a beer with after work. That's not to say we're big drinkers, but that's not the point."*

Culture

The beer test has laid the way for a working atmosphere where *"if you're a prima donna you won't make it through the door."* Applied science and modesty are inextricably linked, one engineer theorized, because *"if you're not humble about what you can accomplish, then nature will humble you pretty quickly."* Respondents in all five US offices conceded that *"our work can be stressful, but putting in the odd late shift with a group that is so kind and gracious is a hell of a lot more pleasant."*

"You think you know someone and then you see them screaming at Pacman!"

Furthermore, *"the fact that many of us have a masters or PhD in our field means that people starting off here tend to have been out of college for quite some time. A lot of mid-level associates have families,"* spawning an after-work culture that *"is definitely more heavily weighted on the newer associates."* That being said, 2015 did mark the resurrection of Finnegan's much-fêted all-attorney retreat, which *"brought together lawyers from all of our US offices in a fancy hotel just outside of DC."* What did the weekend entail? *"There were fun activities in the morning such as golf, kayaking and crafts, which were followed by an afternoon of strategy-based presentations."* The evenings seemed to be the real highlight, with gala dinners proceeded by evenings of arcade or casino gaming. Finnegan's button-bashers loved having the opportunity to unleash their inner nerd, whooping *"you think you know someone and then you see them screaming at Pacman!"*

"Our work can be stressful, but putting in the odd late shift with a group that are so kind and gracious is a hell of a lot more pleasant."

Offices

"All of Finnegan's US offices are a microcosm of the DC office, so there's very little variation in the type of work offered between offices," one junior revealed. Under renovation at the time of our calls, the DC homestead had *"had a load of walls knocked down to allow in more natural light."* Nevertheless, the best place to catch a tan remains the HQ's roof garden, where *"a stunning view of the DC skyline"* makes for *"a great spot to have lunch, watch fireworks, or hold Friday happy hour."*

"A stunning view of the DC skyline."

Novices had the impression that satellite offices were perhaps a little more laid back than Finnegan central, because as one associate remembered: *"They got jeans Friday before us."* Living up to its Cali rep, *"Palo Alto is by all accounts the most chilled out office to work in. It's known as the office you can bring your dog into!"* Boston also received praise for its fine views. Waterside in the city's *"booming"* Seaport District, *"the engineers always get a kick seeing a ship longer than a sky scraper plough past at 15 knots!"* Seaport may be *"fast becoming Boston's young professional playground,"* but as one interviewee quipped: *"It's a great spot to watch a lot of people around you having fun. We're busy lawyers!"*

See firm profile on p.633

Hours & Compensation

Mind you, Finnegan's hours are far from titanic. *"It's rare to hit 12 hours in a day,"* and perhaps because of the firm's more mature intake *"people usually take off at a respectable hour to have dinner with their families."* Across offices nine till six seemed a pretty common day at the office, though most admitted that *"I'll often do an hour or two from home in the evening. The firm is pretty flexible on that front."*

Finnegan's billing target is 2,000 hours. To help rookies hit their billable benchmark, 80 hours of pro bono work can be counted toward it.

Pro Bono

"There's no pressure to do pro bono work," explained one source, *"but if you're interested in getting involved then there are plenty of opportunities."* Criminal defense representation, asylum cases and veterans appeals tend to flood the docket, with the latter particularly common. *"When a vet is entitled to a higher disability payment because an affliction has worsened, the Department of Veterans' Affairs tend to refuse it flat out,"* explained one legal volunteer. *"That's where we come in."* Besides helping out some of the country's bravest, associates found pro bono involvement to be a great way to earn new responsibilities, with one asking: *"Where else would you get the opportunity to write a brief to court all by yourself as a first-year?"* What's more, *"90% of the time our requests are successful. When that's the case we can submit a request to the court for a rebate on our legal fees, and every cent we claim back is donated to a local veterans fund."*

Pro bono hours

- For all attorneys across all US offices: 10,282.2
- Average per US attorney: 65.1

Strategy & Future

According to insiders, *"the retreat featured targeted strategy sessions that were particularly interesting. Breakout zones were set up for a bunch of different technical areas that the firm had determined as being of particular importance moving ahead."* Covering areas such as 3D printing, biological drugs and robotics, the sessions *"shed light on new developments in those fields, and the legal issues surrounding them."*

"You'll find personalities and a learning environment that'll suit anyone with an interest in scientific research, but unlike academia there's no pressure to specialize in a fixed area."

See firm profile on p.633

Fish & Richardson PC

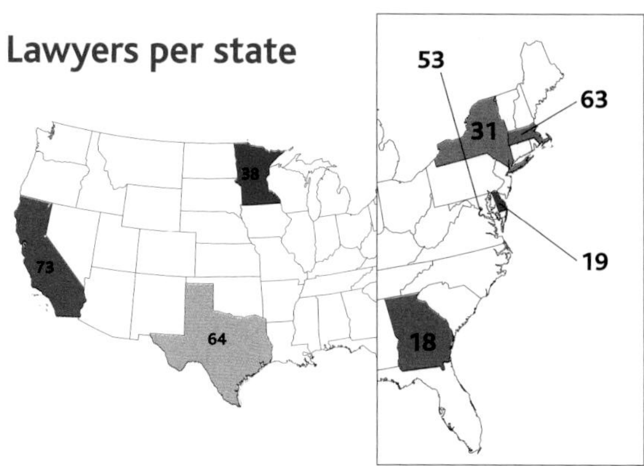

Largest US office: Boston
US offices: 11
International offices: 1
First-year salary: $160,000
Billable hours: 1,900 required
Summers 2016: 42 (32 2Ls and 10 1Ls)
Revenue 2015: $394.96 million (+10.6%)
Partners made in 2016: 14
Famous for: top-notch IP practice

A big Fish in a *"niche"* pond, this Bostonian filters the nutrient-rich waters of IP through its gills...

PLANES, trains and automobiles. You invent it, Fish will patent it. In the 130 years since its Boston inception, Fish has been instrumental in patents relating to a whole host of groundbreaking, everyday products, not least the airplane, steam turbine and car. Historic clients included the Wright brothers, Alexander Graham Bell and Thomas Edison, whose connections with Fish are honored daily as the names of the Atlanta office's conference rooms. Their modern-day counterparts are equally impressive: Google, Samsung and Microsoft, to name a few.

Chambers USA awards Fish the highest rankings for all things IP, including litigation and international trade. Associates appreciated the *"smorgasbord of responsibility"* and come here for the *"chance to work in a place where they change things."*

ASSOCIATES SAY...

The Work

New starters join either litigation or patent prosecution, and later *"we then subdivide into subpractice groups based on our interests."* Fish also has expertise in trademark, copyright, regulatory & government affairs, and post-grant review. According to one source, *"most summers go to litigation as the patent prosecution team looks for technical experience."* Juniors explained that *"most offices operate under the umbrella of litigation and prosecution."* Dallas litigators highlighted that *"we have a commercial practice that isn't as present elsewhere, but we don't have a construct where only Boston or some place does pharma."* Additionally, *"in Austin there's only a handful of litigators. It's mostly patent but it's not made that way by design."* Fish promotes collaboration between groups as *"almost every case naturally has someone from another office on it."* While many were happy to interconnect, others cautioned that *"it's difficult because you have to communicate through carefully worded emails so you don't convey the wrong tone or look like an idiot."*

> *"We'd be surprised if an associate didn't take a deposition in their first year."*

Newbies dubbed the assignment process an *"open market where you go and find work by talking to partners (formally called principals) as there is no centralized staffing system."* They reassured that *"there is one partner who helps workflow."* Nonetheless, *"partners will approach you primarily based on your expertise."* Though this may seem daunting, *"most have summered here so you already have relationships with partners."* Some juniors reflected that *"it can be tough because it leads to being responsive to too many bosses."*

On chambers-associate.com...

- Interview with president and CEO Peter Devlin
- Interview with former hiring principal Michael Headley

See firm profile on p.634

Rankings in *Chambers USA*

Intellectual Property	International Trade

For detail on ranking tiers and ranking locations, visit www.chambersandpartners.com

Recent work highlights

- Won a $28.9 million verdict for clients Paice and The Abell Foundation in a patent infringement case against Hyundai and its affiliate Kia Motors
- Successfully represented Microsoft in the Federal Circuit ruling that Microsoft did not infringe Walker Digital's online auction patent by selling ad space on its search engines, which is triggered instantaneously when a user enters a keyword
- Scored a high-profile jury trial win for Apple against GPNE, with the jury finding no infringement of two patents covering wireless data communication in pagers that GPNE claimed were infringed by Apple's iPhone5, iPad3 and iPad Mini
- Won a patent infringement jury verdict for Adobe, which found that the EveryScape patents in question were invalid in view of prior art

For patent prosecutors, technical backgrounds play a more pivotal role in assignment compared to litigation. Associates intimated that *"it's not a prerequisite to have a science degree but it helps enormously."* While all juniors can expect *"doc review to make up huge parts of assignments,"* most agreed that *"the smaller the team you work with the larger the workload."* One went as far as to say: *"With great power comes great responsibility."* Litigators typically undertake *"a lot of brief writing and mock crosses with witnesses. They throw you in right off the bat."* One recounted how *"on my third or fourth day I was left alone with an expert to go through their report with them."*

Others had *"dealt with both opposing counsel and clients," "mined discovery data looking for story evidence"* and *"argued motions and hearings in court. I wrote part of briefs for the federal circuit, and drafted settlement and license agreements."* This is the norm at Fish, as *"we'd be surprised if an associate didn't take a deposition in their first year."* Prosecutors are *"involved in patent office post-grant review matters. Inter partes review is something new that we are dealing with as well."* Generally, *"they throw you in. They say 'here is an office action, amend it,' or 'here is an application: go do it.'"*

Training & Development

"If you're the type of person that wants a lot of hand-holding to slowly develop your craft, Fish is not the place for that," warned one Dallas insider. Others elaborated that *"there isn't a regimented first-year plan where new hires will cycle through different training. It's much more 'throw you in the water and see if you can swim.' But there's good training which is optional."* Programs include *"30 to 60 minute webinars every other week using the firm's collective knowledge on specific aspects of litigation"* as part of the Fish Litigation University Program.

"A 360 review where associates review who they worked with."

Others spoke of *"weekly presentations on learned experience from trial victories or changes in procedure."* The National Institute for Trial Advocacy also *"comes in and trains you in trial practice and depositions."* New Yorkers avowed that *"it's doable, but if you're in the middle of a hot case you may not have the time. 'Lunch and Learn' where they feed and teach you is really useful."* Speaking of food, juniors praised the lunch mentor program where first-years dine informally with partners *"and the firm pays for one lunch a month."*

The formal review is "*a semiannual evaluation where we fill out a form that lists our supervisors, and our group leaders review it with us.*" Several liked that *"it's a 360 review where associates review who they worked with."*

Offices & Culture

Fish has 11 domestic offices and one in Munich, Germany. Fish works under a geographically *"distributed management structure so that there isn't one central office with satellite offices,"* former hiring principal Michael Headley (who passed on the baton to Betty Chen in March 2016) informed us. Despite Boston being the oldest office, associates stated that *"it's not Boston-centric. Each office isn't a sun; we work together as a constellation."* Astronomical analogies don't end there. Insiders revealed that *"we're like the Borg (in a nice way). We're all interconnected as we all love patent law."*

Speaking of *"geekiness,"* many interviewees retorted that *"of course it's geeky, it's full of PhDs and engineers!"* Nevertheless, *"nothing can compete with the 'nerddom' of doing a science degree with people who wore plaid and pocket protectors. In comparison, we are anything but nerdy."* At Fish, *"the average associate age is more mature. This affects the culture as there aren't a lot of socials because people want to get back to their families."*

"A conference room filled entirely with Batman memorabilia known as the 'Bat Cave'."

See firm profile on p.634

All associates have individual offices. New Yorkers approved of *"the premium space where people don't stay in their silos but share information."* Bostonians quipped that *"it's more spartan than most firms. It's more about the work."* Silicon Valley natives, however, recently competed in *"a miniature golf tournament. We turned a conference room and the third floor into a course. It was great."* 1,700 miles away in Dallas, associates are treated to *"a conference room filled entirely with Batman memorabilia known as the 'Bat Cave'."* Check out our Twitter page for photos. Apparently there are also Superman and Wonder Woman Roy Lichtenstein prints outside the offices of partners who have themselves *"been christened superheroes."*

Hours & Compensation

Associates found the 1,900 billable hour requirement is *"so achievable as I have more work than I have time for."* Across offices, juniors usually work around ten-hour days, with some *"logging back in and working from home each night."* One insider broke it down: *"It averages as 40 billables a week if you want two to four weeks vacation,"* although there's no official vacation policy for first-years. Others indicated that it's easier for litigators to attain as *"in prosecution, the clients put on pressure to keep the billing down because the patent doesn't exist yet so its value is unknown. You can't bill as high in that sense."*

"We want to reward our superstars."

Clocking in long days reaps rich rewards: *"People who work 2,200 hours almost always have bonuses that beat the market rate."* Others relied heavily on guesswork: *"I don't have a clue! The billable year is from October 1 to September 30 but our bonuses don't come out till January. It's a little annoying. I think it's largely driven by hours but it's a black box."* Michael Headley offers help: *"It's merit-based as opposed to a lockstep bonus system, which can be confusing to some people, but in reality it's higher than most places. Obviously we are not just throwing money around for people simply being in the building. We want to reward our superstars."* For our full interview with Headley, go online.

Pro Bono

Opinions varied about Fish's pro bono commitment. One newbie proclaimed that it's *"more committed than any firm that I've seen or heard of. There is a partner who oversees the program and then in each office there are separate partners who email out opportunities. We can also bill 200 hours of pro bono work to our billing total."* On the other hand, *"there are a couple partners who have causes to push, but firmwide we are kept so busy that it's hard to find the time."*

"With pro bono there is more responsibility earlier on."

Despite this, those who have dedicated more time have been paid back in kind. *"With pro bono there is more responsibility earlier on,"* insisted one associate. *"I've been running everything with the case."* Furthermore, associates aren't pigeonholed into solely working in IP. Fish has an active involvement with many pro bono organizations including the Advocates for Human Rights, Kids In Need of Defense (KIND) and Springboard for the Arts. One junior recounted that they were working on *"a clemency project preparing petitions for early release."* Others stated that *"there is a vast range, like helping political asylum seekers from Sudan become citizens."* Additionally, newcomers get to go to court very early on, which *"will help when I get to that point with my paying clients."*

Pro bono hours

- For attorneys across all US offices: 14,469
- Average per US attorney: 43

"We've bucked the trend across the industry."
Peter Devlin, president and CEO

Diversity

Bostonians admitted that it *"feels more male-centered here, but that's partly down to the sector."* Dallas sources also found *"there are a lot of white males, but we are engineers-turned-lawyers, so the hiring pool self-selects."* Yet those in DC believed that the sector had the reverse effect on diversity as *"tech and patent traditionally pull people together."* Austin associates hailed an *"active diversity scholarship program for incoming minority 1Ls that feeds into the hiring of summer associates."* Sources also praised Fish's participation in the OnRamp Fellowship, which launched in 2014 and helps women who have left the workforce for a number of years *"to reintegrate back into the legal profession."* (*The Good Wife*'s Alicia Florrick would have been a prime candidate had it existed in 2009.) There is also a flexible provision for those with families as one junior eulogized about the *"great childcare discounts. I've been able to bring my child to work and partners do it too."*

"We are engineers-turned-lawyers, so the hiring pool self-selects."

See firm profile on p.634

Although there are many affinity groups, women's initiative EMPOWER had the most presence among interviewees. The group promotes networking and career development opportunities for women. Recently, *"Fish's women flew out to a client office and participated in a mock arbitration with the client's female employees."* However, Silicon Valley sources stated that *"there are only four women associates here"* out of 15. This led interviewees to say that despite the firm's attempts *"there is more of a focus in the larger offices."* Nonetheless, all associates credited Fish with being *"better than other IP firms"* in this regard.

Get Hired

Juniors were united in their advice: *"We are looking for cordial people who fit in with the temperament of the firm, with high technical skills and the ability to work to deadlines."* Interestingly, *"if you have too many career changes before settling to become a lawyer it kind of looks bad,"* warned one source. Michael Headley similarly intimates that *"we are looking for people who are going to be exceptional but without an ego."* What else goes down well? *"We love science and math. We aren't lawyers because we failed at mathematics. We embrace it!"*

Strategy & Future

Commercial litigation is on the up at Fish. Michael Headley explains that *"there has been an explosion in interest for the issues surrounding white-collar crime with a tech focus, for example, privacy."* Although no sources polled could comment on any definitive expansion plans, most interviewees expressed that *"we have a robust practice, so we are selective about how it grows."* Others stated that *"it's still a focus, but it is slow. The people who grow this department are mainly in New York and Dallas."*

However, a common thread that employees proudly proclaimed is that they *"have a great litigation brand. Litigation is litigation no matter the area and we can use our trial experience for other cases."* President and CEO Peter Devlin confirms that *"there has also been a large surge in communications and software. We're getting stronger and we've bucked the trend across the industry."* For the full interview with Peter Devlin, go online.

"If you're the type of person that wants a lot of hand-holding to slowly develop your craft, Fish is not the place for that."

See firm profile on p.634

Fitzpatrick, Cella, Harper & Scinto

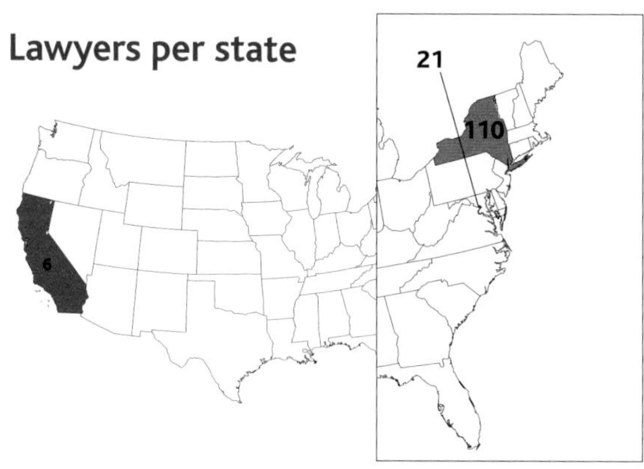

Largest US office: New York
US offices: 3
International offices: 0
First-year salary: $160,000
Billable hours: 2,160 target
Summers 2016: 8 (5 2Ls, 3 1Ls)
Revenue 2015: $98 million (-5.7%)
Partners made 2016: 3
Famous for: a leader in all things IP, especially pharma, gizmos and gadgets

With an increasingly balanced practice, this Big Apple IP boutique is making strides to address a tricky market for patent litigators.

ELECTRONICS has exploded at Fitzpatrick. *"This year,"* chair of the recruiting committee Ha Kung Wong tells us, *"we have experienced a lot of growth in certain areas, particularly in electronics."* A thriving electronics practice – serving the likes of Canon (a client for over 35 years) and IBM (for over 20 years) – has been one of the contributing factors that has helped Fitzpatrick bounce back after a slower year in 2014. IP litigation has taken a hit at firms around the country for various reasons, including the 2014 Supreme Court ruling in *Alice Corporation v CLS Bank International* that certain business methods are no longer patentable.

Nevertheless, Fitzpatrick's strong reputation and bench of high-profile clients are seeing it through. The firm is still synonymous with pharmaceuticals work, and associates proudly stated that *"all our clients are brand names, so when you start work you know it will be for them, which is exciting."* Others unabashedly proclaimed that *"if you take a step back and look at who your clients are, it's cool."* These include Sanofi, Novartis, AstraZeneca and Gilead Sciences. Non-pharma clients include Mars and SC Johnson. But it's not just the clientele that draws associates in: *"It's the fact that people are down to earth, and on top of that everyone is a fantastic attorney,"* believed one insider. And the rankings back this up, with Fitzpatrick scoring highly in *Chambers USA* for intellectual property nationwide and in New York.

On chambers-associate.com...

- Interview with chair of the recruiting committee Ha Kung Wong

ASSOCIATES SAY...

The Work

The firm's main practice is divided between litigation and prosecution. Most New Yorkers focus on litigation, while DC juniors normally take the prosecution route. Smaller groups including trademarks, copyrights, licensing & transactions, PTO contested proceedings, due diligence, e-discovery and ITC Section 337 litigation are also featured throughout all locations. Nevertheless, associates found more opportunities for exposure to these subgroups in the largest office, New York. Staffing requires associates to *"fill out availability reports every Friday which are reviewed by two assigning partners."* DC differs by forgoing the use of assigning partners but uses *"a docket"* – an assignment list that's emailed around. Additionally, associates recount that *"once you make relationships with partners they can assign you work."* Interviewees recalled that in the past year or two, slower business meant new associates weren't staffed on cases for several months, and did things like training and pro bono instead. However, one junior commended this year's efforts as *"now all first-years are staffed, which is telling of the caseload we are taking on."*

See firm profile on p.635

The Inside View

Rankings in *Chambers USA*

Intellectual Property

For detail on ranking tiers and ranking locations, visit www.chambersandpartners.com

For many associates *"it's a lot of doc review and management. We deal with interrogatory responses and objections, letters of discovery and preparing experts for deposition."* As a lawyer progresses, so does the nature of the work. Litigators who got to *"go to trial"* intimated: *"I learnt more in the days I was there than my entire first year at the firm. A couple nights I didn't sleep, but it was a lot of fun with a great team."* The substantive nature of the work varies according to team size, with greater responsibility awarded in the smaller teams. *"I've been second chair at depositions for smaller cases,"* stated one source.

"I've been second chair at depositions for smaller cases."

Patent prosecutors typically *"handle application paperwork, review disclosure statements, amend and respond to office actions and interview patent examiners and clients."* Associates explained that *"typically for patent litigation, company A sues B for infringement and B tries to defend it. Now there are new procedures. Essentially everyone can now challenge the validity of a patent in front of the Patent Office."* Juniors talked excitedly about new procedures including inter partes review (IPR), which took effect in 2012 under the America Invents Act. Basically, IPR operates under a lower burden of proof and faster timeframes, and is more cost-effective than traditional litigation. These *"new avenues of challenging patents"* offer a *"whole other side of work, so it's nice to get a mix."*

Training & Development

Newbies are initially enrolled in a two-week bootcamp in New York that is a *"crash course on the stuff they don't teach you in law school. It's about the day-to-day practice of the law. It's not pretty, but you need it to do a good job."* Patent prosecutors are additionally tutored in writing techniques for applications by *"expert writers in the field who train you in syntax."* Juniors are then given biannual coaching with the National Institute for Trial Advocacy (NITA) which focuses on *"the sexier part of the day-to-day stuff like interviewing witnesses, prepping experts and conducting depositions. You prepare exercises from a closed universe of fact. Actors then help you put into practice what you've learned and you get a critique."* Even summers *"take two NITA courses."*

"It's the sexier part of the day-to-day stuff."

Recent work highlights

- Successfully obtained a Final Written Decision in favor of clients Endo Pharmaceuticals and Grünenthal GmbH in an inter parties review relating to extended release gastric retentive dosage forms
- Successfully defended Novartis's patent relating to transdermal patches in the treatment of Alzheimer's disease
- Obtained an Initial Determination of a Section 337 violation on behalf of client Johnson Outdoors against Garmin in the use of side scan sonar patents
- Won General Exclusion Orders for Canon regarding its laser toner cartridge technology

After putting the training into action, associates receive *"end-of-year evaluations."* Evaluations are sent *"to partners that you have worked with and they review your work. Two partners that you haven't worked with then go over them with you, so that the process remains anonymous."* While many interviewees felt that the system was adequate, one New Yorker wished that *"there was something more concrete in place so that if there was an issue partners would tell you there and then what went wrong and how to fix it, otherwise it's left to the end of the year."* However, juniors appreciated that the review system operates under the constraints of time and circumstance as *"it's understandable why there is only one review per year because it takes a lot of work."*

Offices & Culture

Despite having three hubs in New York, DC and Orange County, the larger New York mothership sets the tone for all offices. Sandwiched between Rockefeller Center and Radio City Music Hall, associates mulled over the pros and cons of being *"right in the middle of everything."* One fledgling legal eagle intimated that *"it's just jam-packed. Sometimes there are concerts nearby and by the time you leave at night there is carnage everywhere and you feel like, oh I want to be a part of whatever that was!"* But on the upside, all associates are treated to individual offices, unlike many other firms in Manhattan. One insider speculated: *"I think window size is based on seniority. When you get to be a third or fourth year, the amount of windows you have goes up!"*

"By the time you leave at night there is carnage everywhere."

Rookies also suggested that Fitzpatrick felt like *"a boutique firm where I could learn more"* while *"catering to people from a whole range of positions in life both professionally and socially."* Socially speaking, in the summer months people in the Big Apple are treated to happy hours on the firm's onsite terrace. *"We hire a bartender*

See firm profile on p.635

to serve drinks and we play games like Cornhole. It's silly and fun but that's what makes it great because there are high levels of participation." The *"Fitzpatrick Olympics"* add to *"the palpable comradery,"* where attorneys compete in a combination of traditional and *"original"* games in *"teams made up of lawyers you haven't worked with before, so it is a great way to meet new people."* As IP specialists, however, *"the science plays a part in the culture."* Interviewees chuckled when asked if they felt *"nerdy."* Some explained: *"To a degree we are a bit nerdy. But people don't walk around in thick glasses or only talk about science. We do have 'sciencey' interests and people actually like to read science articles for fun and not just work."* The connecting thread throughout all offices, nevertheless, is that lawyers are *"personable and approachable who you can relate to."*

Hours & Compensation

Sources testified that *"we are in New York, so we are given a load of work to do with long hours."* The annual billable hours target of 2,160 is *"a 'soft' 2,160. The goal is 180 hours a month, but if we don't hit it it's okay."* Nonetheless, associates are far from taking it easy, with most clocking in at least ten-hour working days in the office, and some working late into the night from home. Conversely, one interviewee felt that taking work home was the firm's way of supporting its staff: *"As long as you get the work done on time there is a lot of flexibility."*

"We are still in New York, so we are given a load of work to do with long hours."

Compensation is lockstep, and bonuses are awarded based on hours plus other important things like quality of work, marketing activity, pro bono and recruiting support. The discretionary element left some sources *"confused."* In 2014, Fitzpatrick's revenue dropped 11.4% and partner profits fell, which impacted bonuses, associates believed. Some were disappointed to fall short of the perceived market rate by up to $10,000. However, Ha Kung Wong reasons that *"our bonus structure is merit-based and is determined on a year-by-year basis. We look at what occurs throughout the industry, but we make our own decisions."*

Pro Bono

Sources revealed that *"the firm is very committed to pro bono. We are offered help with our 50-hour requirement of non-billable work needed to pass the Bar."* Although there is no definitive pro bono target, a conscious effort is made by the pro bono partner to alert associates to multiple opportunities daily via emails and lunch events. Juniors have *"free rein to work in different practice areas"* with numerous pro bono organizations including the Pro Bono Partnership, the Federal Circuit Bar Association Pro Bono Program and Volunteer Lawyers for the Arts. Stellar efforts have earned a few associate awards for their individual contributions: *"The cases were pretty big wins with the Legal Aid Society so the organization gave them accolades for their work."*

"The cases were pretty big wins with the Legal Aid Society."

Pro bono hours

- For all attorneys across all US offices: 3,802
- Average per US attorney: 27

Diversity

Interviewees said Fitzpatrick's diversity is pretty much what you'd expect in BigLaw. *"It's not very diverse, especially in terms of partners, who are mostly white and male."* Associates blamed one factor in particular. *"It's not for lack of trying,"* mused one, *"but rather it's the product of the IP sector."* Others concurred, saying:

"We want creative thinkers because we have creative clients."

Ha Kung Wong, chair of the recruiting committee

"The IP sector makes the candidate pool shallower. There aren't a lot of female engineers who also go to law school." However, many insiders praised Fitzpatrick's efforts as *"there is an effort being made. The first-year class who have just joined are diverse and this is the beginning of them trying to put it into practice."*

"Epecially supportive of its women attorneys."

"One of the biggest incentives is that the firm is especially supportive of its women attorneys," exclaimed one New Yorker. Fitzpatrick prides itself with the Woman's Initiative Program, which regularly puts on events both exclusively for women and also firmwide to promote women in the sector. *"They hold an annual alumne event and also a benefit in November to which associates can invite industry contacts."* At least *"they are trying,"* which is a step in the right direction.

Get Hired

"We have a unique atmosphere here. We all have science backgrounds and scientists in all fields generally

See firm profile on p.635

like to collaborate," Ha Kung Wong suggests. But it isn't just the science that's important. Insiders insisted that it's equally important to have *"a personality that fits the firm's personality."* Wong likes candidates to be *"creative thinkers because we have creative clients."* Overwhelmingly, the firm is looking for *"team players."* One associate summarized that *"it's the airport test when it comes down to it: would you want to be stranded at an airport with this person?"* For more on hiring, read our interview with Ha Kung Wong online.

"It's the airport test when it comes down to it."

Strategy & Future

Referring to the growth of electronics in particular at Fitzpatrick, Ha Kung Wong says: *"We have brought on five lateral associates, from all levels of seniority, many of whom have joined us from large general practice firms. This is significant since it demonstrates that IP law firms, like ours, are continuing to grow and continue to be competitive with general practice firms."* Associates revealed that despite the huge focus on pharmaceuticals, *"our biggest client is Canon."* Therefore, savvy juniors recognized that *"we are trying to grow out from the model of the past and push the boundaries to the mechanical/electric side. We have a lot of PhDs but we want to push in the electrical direction."*

"We have a lot of PhDs but we want to push in the electrical direction."

The firm is *"healthy at the moment,"* with all departments reporting an increase in workflow as *"people seem busier firmwide."* This is comforting news for most juniors, who felt: *"We've had steady work this year. Because of the revenue drop, the firm was equilibrizing in terms of associate numbers, but now we balance. Long may it last."*

"We are trying to grow out from the model of the past and push the boundaries to the mechanical/electric side."

See firm profile on p.635

Foley & Lardner LLP

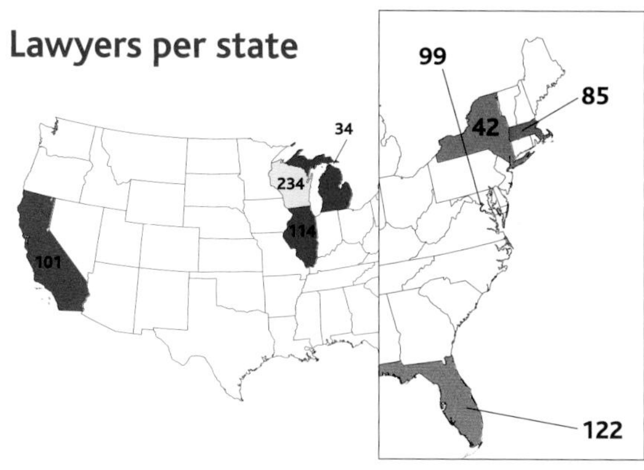

Largest US office: Milwaukee
US offices: 17
International offices: 3
First-year salary: $120,000 - $160,000
Billable hours: 1,850 required
Summers 2016: 61 (53 2Ls, 8 1Ls)
Revenue 2015: $683 million (+2.7%)
Partners made in 2016: 14 (all US)
Famous for: being the largest and oldest firm in Wisconsin

"*Foley is the preeminent firm in the state*" of Wisconsin, America's Dairyland. It's a big cheese further afield too...

"FOLEY is the best law firm in Wisconsin," enthused 'cheeseheads' here. More objectively, it is the oldest and largest law firm in the famously cheese-producing state. Since 1842, when Asahel Finch Jr (former Michigan state representative) and William Pitt Lynde (future Mayor of Milwaukee) founded the firm, Foley has spread across the rest of the USA, and internationally to Brussels, Shanghai and Tokyo.

Chambers USA's rankings provide substance to associates' assertions that *"Foley is the preeminent firm in the state,"* giving it top marks in Wisconsin for its work in corporate/M&A, IP, litigation, labor & employment, environmental law, and real estate. Outside Wisconsin, the firm has *Chambers*-ranked practices in California, DC, Florida, Illinois, Massachusetts and Michigan, as well as nationwide for franchising, healthcare and sports law. Clients include Citi and Major League Baseball. Interviewees also praised Foley's pleasingly refined culture: *"At other firms it's like 'I want to kill everyone I work with!' Not here. People are fantastic and incredibly smart."*

On chambers-associate.com...

- Interview with hiring partner Bob Scher
- Interview with chairman and CEO Jay Rothman
- The Big Interview with Major League Baseball Pro (lawyer) Bob Dupuy

ASSOCIATES SAY...

The Work

Junior associates are found in the IP (litigation and prosecution), litigation and business law departments. Business law is an umbrella practice that *"houses people who include typical general corporate attorneys, transactional M&A, healthcare, and government & public policy, which encompasses regulatory work like automotive and food & drug compliance."* Foley has both practice groups and industry teams. Industry teams focus on a specific area of law but can pull in people from other practice groups. For example, healthcare has both a practice group and an industry team that uses people from both litigation and other business law facets. Litigation, however, is generalist, where associates try out different types of work before they specialize. Work is predominantly assigned by relationships. Summers have a centralized portal where they can choose projects. However, *"day one as an associate is a grassroots campaign for work. It's challenging as there is no hand-holding."*

Office location plays a part in the type of work available. Litigation is strong in Wisconsin and Chicago, for example. Boston is viewed as a healthcare and IP base, with DC unsurprisingly making strides in both IP and government & public policy. Once staffed, private equity & venture capital business law associates had *"done a lot of diligence work. You then draft ancillary documents for the closing of the deal. For startup formations and financing, you come up with option plans for the com-*

See firm profile on p.637

Rankings in *Chambers USA*

Banking & Finance	IT & Outsourcing
Bankruptcy/Restructuring	Labor & Employment
Corporate/M&A	Life Sciences
Franchising	Litigation
Healthcare	Natural Resources
Insurance	Real Estate
Intellectual Property	Sports Law

For detail on ranking tiers and ranking locations, visit www.chambersandpartners.com

Recent work highlights

- Represented Fiserv Solutions (one of the leading providers of tech solutions to financial institutions) in its counter-claim for early termination fees owed by Wildfire Credit Union
- Represented Integrys Energy Group in its $9.1 billion sale to Wisconsin Energy
- Secured a complete summary judgment for Major League Baseball Advanced Media in a $20 million+ dispute with Baseball Quick. The case had been ongoing since 2010

pany's employees." Foley has a *"global reputation for traditional M&A work, specifically with large Midwestern manufacturing companies."* Government & public policy juniors had *"helped the clients prep for disclosure when they had compliance issues. You conduct client interviews and employee interviews. There is a little bit of doc review. I've drafted training presentations and internal company plans."*

"Foley is great for young litigators."

Litigation insiders had *"worked on large antitrust and ERISA class actions worth hundreds of millions of dollars, and also smaller cases. I've drafted briefs and taken six depositions. Fifty percent is devoted to the fun stuff and the other half is doc review and legal research memos. Foley is great for young litigators."*

IP lawyers stressed they were so busy they didn't have time to sit... literally: the standing desk craze has graced the department, with insiders joking that *"it has increased productivity, but my feet hurt at first."* Patent prosecutors warned their daily chores involve *"a lot of similar work."* A large part of their time is spent communicating with the US Patent Office and writing patents. But as a lawyer gets more experience, the range broadens to include writing opinions on the validity of patents, *"engaging with license agreements, assessing IP portfolios and writing responses to foreign jurisdictional instructions."* IP litigators had started out doing support research work but had progressed to *"drafting motions and depositions. If you demonstrate interest and aptitude they aren't going to hold you back just because you're a second-year."*

Training & Development

"They do a very good job of educating you." New starters have *"a week's crash course on the firm,"* dividing into practice groups to go over the basics. More substantive training comes later. *"Every month, first-years have mandatory training for an hour at lunchtime."* Business law newbies had a three-day training in November 2015 in Chicago: *"We were given a merger agreement in the summer and told to work on it. At the training we all went through the whole thing together. It's really helpful."*

"If you mess up, they know you're not a total idiot."

Litigators stressed that the informal trainings were the ones that had the most benefit. Rookies get guidance on drafting motions, briefs and practice negotiations and found that the best way to learn is just to have a go. *"At first you're like 'OMG I don't know what I'm doing' and you come back and find all your work is wrong, but you learn from your mistakes. If you mess up, they know you're not a total idiot."*

Biannual reviews happen at the six-month and one-year marks. *"If you've worked for senior counsel or a partner for over 15 hours, they're automatically added to your list of reviewers, but they can opt out."* A consensus evaluator (the person who has supervised you the most) will gather together all of the individual reviews and write a final review. Associates meet with their consensus evaluator, practice group leader and mentor to discuss what was said (all juniors have an associate and partner mentor which some felt *"was not utilized as much as the firm would like"*).

Diversity

New Yorkers reported: *"I think New York skews to the women: there are days when I have no interaction with men."* Ethnically, *"most BigLaw firms have work to do, but the chairs of the diversity committee go around to all the offices and roll out initiatives."* In its home state, juniors felt that *"Foley's strength is not in its diversity. That's not a reflection on effort, but the type of people Wisconsin attracts."* Hiring partner Bob Scher reasons that they are trying to remedy this at the recruitment stage, particularly through *"a diversity fellowship program for up to three summer associates who demonstrate a commitment to promoting diversity and inclusion. Each fellowship recipient receives $20,000 to help defray the costs of law school."* Scher also details that *"we recently created*

See firm profile on p.637

a Diversity & Inclusion Action Council, a new initiative made up of attorneys and staff in all practice groups to look at what we're doing and what we could be doing better. " In the 2016 summer class, 36% are ethnically diverse and 9% identify as LGBT – pretty good stats.

"Most BigLaw firms have work to do."

There are affinity groups, the most visible being the Women's Network, although different offices have varying levels of activity. In DC, *"there's a lot of effort to push it; we are still trying to get regular events. The group helped us advocate for higher bonuses like the men have."* While most groups host lunches and mentorship talks, the New York group recently ran an event where *"a clothing label for professional women hosted an event and all the catering was provided by other female-run organizations. We all brought our clients along with us and had a great evening networking and shopping."*

Offices & Culture

In the 17 domestic offices and three international hubs in Brussels, Shanghai and Tokyo, every associate has their own office. HQ is in the tallest building in Wisconsin, with some offices directly overlooking Lake Michigan. Rumors of potential renovation works taking place in 2017 were rife among associates. This is probably in response to the New York and Chicago centers having undergone the same transformation. Manhattanites in particular found that *"everything is glass. Most of us aren't fans as you can see through everyone's offices!"* Perhaps they were unaware that they do have the option to frost their glass if they want... *"But the benefits are that you can walk off the elevator and see the New York skyline."*

"Work hard but don't get too big for your britches."

Everyone concurred when asked about the culture: *"I really enjoy the people I work with, without exception."* While most offices have individual quirks, sources insisted that *"our national culture comes from the Midwest. We have a Midwestern vibe. Work hard but don't get too big for your britches."*

The average Foley associate has family commitments, so there isn't a big focus on socials. However, common occurrences are *"odd Fridays, where we have beer and wine every other week,"* and *"cactus club,"* where drinks and snacks are served in a New York partner's office (with a splendid collection of cacti, hence the name). In San Fran, drinks are served from a cool-looking SF cable car trolley. But, the crown goes to *"associate skip day"* in Milwaukee. All first-year Wisconsinites organize tickets for juniors to see a Milwaukee Brewers baseball game *"where we get to take the day off, tailgate and drink."*

Pro Bono

The first 100 hours of pro bono work can count toward billables, which can be extended with prior approval. As a participant in the Pro Bono Institute Challenge (a promotional program that aims to further pro bono in large firms with 50 or more lawyers), Foley devotes approximately 3 percent of total hours to pro bono. Most associates work on immigration cases. *"I've worked a lot with domestic violence victims seeking immigration relief. I get to go to court when it concerns children, as they need to have appointed guardians. It's taught me how to talk to clients, so these skills help my billable work."*

"Important work but difficult to do."

Milwaukeeans have a partner who is one of the appointed lawyers for the Seventh Circuit Court of Appeals. Associates had *"written briefs and argued cases before the Seventh Circuit. A partner helped me prep my arguments and I did two moot arguments in front of my colleagues beforehand, but it was intense."* Others described *"the darker side of pro bono,"* for example violence to children cases. *"The client is in jail, and because it's pro bono the problem is who is going to pay for new experts to come forward. It's important work but difficult to do."*

"We look for people who will fit into the bigger picture....There's no magic formula."

Bob Scher, hiring partner

Pro bono hours

- For all attorneys across all US offices: 42,144
- Average per US attorney: 49

Hours & Compensation

Big Apple interviewees told us that *"in the past three years, I haven't stayed in the office past 10pm."* Bonuses and billables, however, are slightly complicated. Foley operates under a tiered associate class system: tiers one and two, with the second tier housing six years. Officially the billable requirement is 1,850, which is the minimum needed to move up to the next class year. For bonus eligibility, you need to bill 1,950 (including pro bono) plus 150 'investment hours' (training, article-writing etc.). Bonuses are discretionary, but the assumption is that those billing 2,000 hours will receive at least 10%

See firm profile on p.637

of base salary as a bonus, and those hitting 2,200 will get at least 20%.

The discretionary element prompted some interviewees to say that they'd like *"more transparency on what type of bonus you'll get."*

"I haven't stayed in the office past 10pm."

Get Hired

The overall hiring goal at Foley is *"to hire summer associates who will spend their entire career here. It doesn't always happen. People leave law firms for all sorts of reasons, but this is our hope. A good indicator is that we made 15 new partners in 2015. That's a large number to make every year,"* states HP Bob Scher. Casting their nets beyond the T14, he explains: *"Our smaller locations recruit from a mix of national and regional schools, so it's a balance."* Grades and law school still play a part. But Scher insists that *"we do look at grades and academics, but certainly well beyond that. If all we looked at was grades, then we wouldn't even need to visit schools. "*

So what do they look at? *"There's no magic formula."* Like most firms they *"look for people who will fit into the bigger picture. We look at leadership abilities, great communication and interpersonal skills."* On top of that, insiders advised that candidates should research their interviewers, as the *"biggest issue is catering your questions to the interviewer. Show you've put in the effort."* For more on hiring, go online.

Strategy & Future

Insiders praised the firm for being *"very open about our financial state and the state of the market, and the chairman will regularly send out video emails to update and discuss this with us."* So much so that sources said there's been *"talk about expanding in the Southwest a little more."* CEO Jay Rothman tells us that while domestic US growth is always the first point of consideration, international expansion, as well as key practice area developments, are also considered. *"For example, how many clients were worried about cybersecurity ten years ago? Today, I don't think we have a client which isn't cognizant of the risks posed by cybersecurity breaches. In an ever-changing world, we need to be continuously focused on building expertise to serve the evolving needs of our clients."* Sources also felt that the energy and healthcare industry groups had had a strong 2015 too, while others explained that corporate M&A had been *"busier than it had in the past few years. No one's having trouble meeting their hours."* For the full interview with Jay Rothman, go online.

"People are fantastic and incredibly smart."

See firm profile on p.637

Fox Rothschild LLP

Lawyers per state

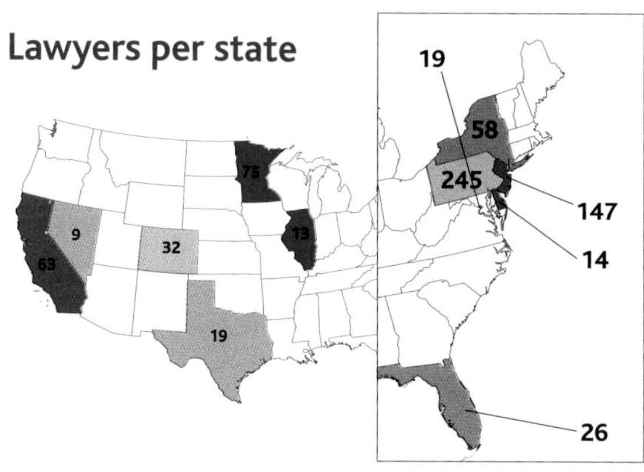

Largest US office: Philadelphia
US offices: 22
International offices: 0
First-year salary: $110,000 - $145,000
Billable hours: 1,850 required (litigation 1,900)
Summers 2016: 28 (22 2 Ls, 6 1Ls)
Revenue 2015: $364.5million (+10%)
Partners made in 2016: 21
Famous for: being entrepreneurial; several suburban locations

Full-service Fox Rothschild has an "*inviting*" atmosphere and a spread of 22 offices across the country.

AGILE Philly-born Fox has been building up territory pretty consistently of late, even collaborating with a Wolff to do so. Recently, it confirmed its expansion into the Upper Midwest by merging with Minneapolis firm Oppenheimer Wolff & Donnelly and boosting the overall attorney headcount to more than 700. Fox had also bolstered its numbers in Chicago earlier that year and added a Dallas branch to its collection by way of a merger in 2014. Financial growth has also been a pattern at Fox – in 2015 revenues grew by 10%, completing a decade of consecutive annual revenue growth.

Within its native state of Pennsylvania, *Chambers USA* recognizes Fox's real estate, healthcare, bankruptcy, and environment practices, while corporate and litigation receive nods in Eastern Pennsylvania. The firm also picks up rankings in DC, Minnesota and New Jersey.

ASSOCIATES SAY...

The Work

At the time of our calls, the largest cohorts of juniors were in Philly, Atlantic City and Princeton, with others spread across Miami, New York, Wilmington, Roseland, Exton, Warrington, Blue Bell and LA. Corporate and litigation take on the most juniors, followed by real estate. The tax, IP, entertainment, and labor departments also had a resident junior associate.

On chambers-associate.com...

- Interview with Mark Silow managing partner

"Benefit from watching someone really talented."

The litigation team handles a wide variety of matters. *"Within that the partners have certain niches but as juniors you go where you're called,"* associates informed us. *"It's good to see so many different things; you learn so much procedurally about the practice of law."* What do juniors get up to day to day? *"I don't spend that much time on doc review. I'd say it takes up less than 20% of my time,"* we were assured. *"I do a lot of research on case law and statutes as well as drafting a wide variety of filings, ranging from minor motions like discovery or motions to compel for extraordinary relief."* One associate reported: *"I'm a courtroom guy, and pleased to have been part of major cases where there are tens of millions of dollars at stake, but also I've been given much smaller cases that I can work on myself with some supervision. We can spend 50 hours a year on mentorship, so I've been to shadow another attorney, seen bits of trials and sat in on depositions. I'm not foolish enough to believe that I can't benefit from watching someone really talented."* On some matters, like contract disputes, associates get to "*handle things myself pretty much from start to finish. I've drafted the complaint, I communicate with the client, and then the partner looks over what I do. The firm likes people to get out there!"*

See firm profile on p.638

Rankings in *Chambers USA*

Bankruptcy/Restructuring	Healthcare
Construction	Labor & Employment
Corporate/M&A	Litigation
Environment	Real Estate
Gaming & Licensing	

For detail on ranking tiers and ranking locations, visit www.chambersandpartners.com

Recent work highlights

- Successfully defended Walmart against a claim regarding the fraudulent sale of concert tickets
- Represented Fidelity National Financial Ventures on the $200 million spinoff of restaurant company J. Alexander's Holdings
- Acting for Lions Gate Entertainment in a $55 million suit brought by actress Paz de la Huerta, alleging that she suffered injuries while shooting the sex horror film *Nurse 3D* and that her voice was dubbed without her consent

Similarly, juniors in the corporate department experience *"such a range of matters."* One noted: *"I do a lot of business purchases and sales, general corporate governance and formation work like filing with the state and drafting operating agreements, resolutions and bylaws."* As with litigators, sources were *"really proud of how much I've been able to take on. I've worked on a very small transaction that I ran myself, doing things like drafting the asset purchase agreement all the way through to helping the client to close it."* Of course, *"on a larger transaction I do more of the ancillary work like side agreements."*

The Atlantic City base is noted for its gaming expertise. Juniors get to grips with *"regulatory and compliance issues, representing manufacturers and distributors of gaming equipment or devices, like slot machine distributors. We represent them in their licensing proceedings in various jurisdictions across the world. The bulk of the work involves getting various clients licensed so they can operate legally. Day to day I research changes in the law, fill out applications, undertake due diligence and draft advisory memos on legal issues."*

"I don't spend that much time on doc review."

Over in real estate, *"one of the clients is a large bank that lends to a lot of multifamily housing owners, and the loans range from $1 million to $160 million. I've been able to travel in order to close a loan and then I've taken on some land use and zoning work, which involved preparing applications and preparing for a hearing."* Research tasks are also common.

Work assignment varies between offices and departments. Some have a supervising partner who channels work through to associates; others said that *"within my office it's informal – people just look in and ask if you have time to do something. But any work coming in from an outside office is filtered through the department chair."*

Training & Development

Interviewees praised the firm's *"robust formalized training program."* This kicks off with an initial orientation in Philly: *"It covers the basics like how to use the computer systems, your benefits and how to bill, through to more substantive workshops on legal writing and practice."* Following this, transactional associates and litigators have their own practice-specific training program, with the hours clocked up counting toward the overall billable total. There's mandatory writing training, a mock trial program and plenty of lunchtime seminars and CLEs available in-house. Associates in Atlantic City noted there's *"a good business development program that teaches you networking skills and how to pitch to clients."* One source murmured: *"I'm assuming it costs a lot of money, so it's nice that they're investing in us. It makes you feel like you actually mean something."*

"It's nice that they're investing in us."

The level of feedback *"really depends on the person. Some lawyers give you sparse written comments, but the bulk of attorneys are sincere about wanting to see you develop and their written comments are designed to help you learn to write more strategically."* One highlighted that *"I've developed mentoring, one-to-one teaching relationships with a handful of attorneys and they really take the time to break things down and explain why and what they're doing in terms of writing or motions practice."*

Offices

The Philly HQ offers *"beautiful views, especially at night when the city is lit up."* Is there any fancy décor? *"It's a law office, not an interior design firm!"* Meanwhile, the Princeton outpost is *"a typical corporate suburban office in a corporate park. Most of us have windows and our own offices, which is a pretty big thing."* Plus, there's a small cafeteria and gym. A couple of associates in Atlantic City flagged up its reputation as *"one of the ten most dangerous cities in the country. I've worked here for ten years so I'm more accustomed to it and I'll often be one of the last females here during the evening. I get a bit nervous but there is a guard who'll walk you to your car, although he's not armed. I haven't heard of any problems."* On the inside, *"it's fine, just like a stand-*

See firm profile on p.638

ard office – not impressive but not dilapidated, nothing that's gonna knock your socks off." Other Atlantic sources in Atlantic City said: *"We certainly have nice offices. They're clean and pretty modern. There's a kitchen and a pantry with coffee and teas and all that plus a small room with a TV."*

"It's a law office, not an interior design firm!"

Hours & Compensation

Litigators have a billing target of 1,900 hours, while it's 1,850 for everyone else. Most sources felt that *"it's a realistic figure because there's plenty of work to be done. The firm also encourages you to log non-billable hours for training and pro bono."* While some declared that *"it's a manageable workload that allows you to have a work/life balance,"* others flagged up that *"I do have concerns when I think about the lifestyle I want in the future. It is very time-consuming, especially because your billable time doesn't represent all the time you spend in the office."*

"It's pretty transparent."

Fox's starting salaries range from $110,000 to $145,000 depending on the market, although *"they just got readjusted to become more competitive."* Bonuses increase for every 25 hours associates clock up in excess of the billing target. *"It's pretty transparent: you pretty much know the dollar amount you're gonna get."* There's also discretionary bonus for those who bill over a certain threshold. *"I forget the figure but it's an outrageous amount of hours!"*

Culture

Philadelphia folk characterized Fox as *"an entrepreneurial place. They're open-minded about you bringing in business as an associate. This is a big town with a small-town feel and you're expected to be involved in the community, meeting people, networking – those relationships can translate into business. We're given a marketing budget to work with and encouraged to take friends from law school out to lunch. It's not a requirement to bring in business but they give you the resources to make it a reality."*

"Everybody is accessible."

Atlantic City is *"very laid back and everybody is accessible."* In Princeton, *"one of the great things is that everyone truly knows everyone, even though it's a larger office. Corporate partners know litigation partners and like each other, people know about one another's personal lives and ask about their families. You never see a closed door unless someone's on a conference call. Everyone's happy to help if you've got an issue."*

Socially, there are happy hours every fortnight in Philadelphia, although these sorts of get-togethers happen less frequently in suburban offices, as you might expect. There's also a national associates' weekend, most recently held in DC, in which lawyers from all over the country congregate for a weekend of *"seminars and awesome evening events. It's really cool to get to see colleagues in other offices. I met my best friend at a firmwide deposition training and we've built a relationship even though we're hundreds of miles apart."*

Pro Bono

Associates can count 50 hours of pro bono work toward the bonus program. While some sources had *"done very little,"* others had taken on *"a bunch of different things"* including prisoners' rights cases, family court matters and tax cases. Others had been involved in a project that *"helps people to get petty offenses and misdemeanors expunged from their records."*

"The firm has done a good job on gender equality issues."

Pro bono hours

- For all attorneys: 6,649
- Average per attorney: 10

Diversity

"We have diversity initiatives, but it's not the most diverse place," agreed interviewees. *"The firm has done a good job at gender equality issues. There's a policy for those with children to work on an adjusted part-time schedule. Some people are really satisfied with it; others think it's difficult because the full-time partners they're working for don't take into account that they have a day off."* In addition to the women's initiative (which holds meetings *"to address concerns unique to women, talk about what we're involved in and how we can support each other"*) there's a *"strong effort made to get people into the LGBT and racial minorities committee."*

"They're open-minded about you bringing in business as an associate."

See firm profile on p.638

Get Hired

Associates in Atlantic City reckoned that *"a candidate's tie to the local area is definitely considered because we're one of the few big firms down here. If they bring someone in from out of the area they may leave at the first opportunity."*

"We encourage young lawyers to attract and develop clients."

Managing partner Mark Silow tells us that the firm looks for candidates who are *"obviously very smart, bright and eager to succeed. We want someone who wants to take control of their career and do all the things required to have successful law practice like investing time in business development."* He adds that young lawyers must *"be prepared to make the necessary investment of time and effort to succeed. This is an excellent place to build a practice, and we have a very accommodative rate structure so we encourage young lawyers to attract and develop clients and practices. That's not something you find at a lot of large firms these days."*

Strategy & Future

"We're keeping our eyes out for new market opportunities."

Fox's most recent highlight is the merger with Oppenheimer Wolff & Donnelly in Minneapolis. What does the future hold for the firm? *"We continue to look for opportunities to grow,"* confirms MP Mark Silow. *"We're looking to grow our existing offices to make them all full service and we're keeping our eyes out for new market opportunities."* Where might these be? *"We're not really looking overseas, but within the US we're interested in Pacific Northwest areas like Portland and Seattle. Boston is also an attractive market to us."*

"You're expected to be involved in the community, meeting people, networking – those relationships can translate into business."

See firm profile on p.638

Freshfields Bruckhaus Deringer LLP

Lawyers per state

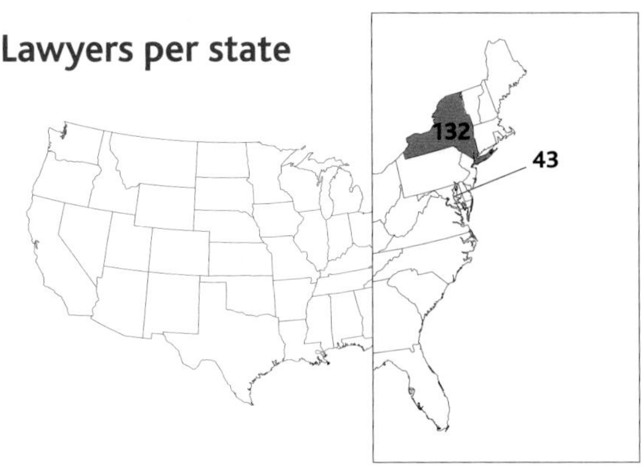

Largest US office: New York
US offices: 2
International offices: 24
First-year salary: $160,000
Billable hours: No requirement
Summers 2016: 27 (25 2Ls, 2 1Ls)
Revenue 2014/15: £1.245 billion
Partners made in 2016: 16 globally (3 in US)
Famous for: its global presence; magic circle history; penchant for dispute resolution

A lot of firms dip their toes in cross-border work; magic circle firm Freshfields is positively drenched in an "*international feel and culture.*"

WHEN Freshfields opened shop in London 273 years ago, Midtown New York was British-owned scrub land. This is the oldest of the five elite UK magic circle firms, but it took until 1977 to set up in Manhattan and then DC in 1998. The firm has 26 offices spread across Europe, Asia and the US. Adam Siegel, US managing partner, tells us: *"We're blessed to have an even balance in the world's financial centers, which is where clients see the biggest opportunities and also threats."* If this firm qualified for the *Am Law 100*, its revenue posting would place it comfortably at the top end, next door to the likes of Gibson Dunn, Morgan Lewis and Sullivan & Cromwell.

"Chambers Global ranks the firm in 6th position in its 'Global Top 30' firms"

An international rock star Freshfields may be – *Chambers Global* ranks the firm in 6th position in its 'Global Top 30' firms – but all magic circle firms' attempts at cracking the US market have been more Britpop than Adele's transatlantic splash. However, associates reminded us that *"the firm is trying to tone down the magic circle thing here."* And in a bid to raise its US profile, the Freshfields New York office has made several smart lateral partner hires over the past two years – and from top names like Fried Frank, Skadden, Shearman & Sterling, Wachtell and Cleary.

But we shouldn't overlook what the firm has already achieved. Between the New York and DC offices, *Chambers USA* ranks the firm for capital markets, tax, and antitrust. The lawyers we interviewed also did high-level work in trade finance, litigation and arbitration, corporate and projects. As is typical for Freshfields, clients are frequently huge banks like Bank of America Merrill Lynch, Goldman Sachs, Deutsche Bank and JPMorgan, and giant global companies like ConocoPhillips, Petrobas, Johnson & Johnson, GDF Suez, and Dubai Aerospace.

On chambers-associate.com...

- The magic circle explained.
- An interview with US managing partner Adam Siegel

ASSOCIATES SAY...

The Work

At the time of our calls juniors were stationed in tax, capital markets, finance, corporate and dispute resolution, with the latter being the most popular destination. Most join the NYC office, but a few join DC. Dispute resolution splits into three subgroups of international arbitration, investigations and white collar, but *"most associates start with general work and then specialize later on."* One associate told us: *"I don't think there is a specific day or year that demands you graduate to just one group. You do a little bit of everything when you start out."*

See firm profile on p.639

Rankings in *Chambers USA*

Antitrust
Capital Markets
Corporate/M&A
International Arbitration
Litigation

For detail on ranking tiers and ranking locations, visit www.chambersandpartners.com

Juniors in disputes had handled cases with financial institutions, pharmaceutical companies, universities, airlines and publishers: *"I'm currently working on a big investigation of a bank, a bankruptcy notification in NYC and an ICC arbitration,"* told one source. Juniors did *"a lot of legal research and analysis"* with the expectation that *"partners will ask you questions about something to do with the case."* Typical junior work also included *"drafting submissions, organizing document production, preparing hearings, writing and preparing witness statements and cross examinations for witnesses."*

"Opportunity to develop client skills."

Our sources in Freshfields' world-class arbitration practice (worldwide ranking first tier, *Chambers Global*) had been busy *"developing arguments and strategies with partners"* on giant cases like a $1.4 billion expropriation claim by ConocoPhillips against Ecuador, and an ensuing $2.6 billion counterclaim. *"You get a lot of client exposure in arbitration,"* a junior told us. *"There's a lot of responsibility and opportunity to develop client skills."*

The corporate practice splits into capital markets, finance, IP and corporate, *"which is basically M&A work."* Although this is a compact team it has benefited from the few big-name hires recently. *Chambers Global* also ranks Freshfields M&A department among the top four firms in the world, so deals are weighty and cosmopolitan, such as arranging a $5 billion acquisition for Japan Tobacco. *"It's hard to specialize in anything in the early days,"* associates said. *"You have to be ready to do a lot of different things."*

Typical rookie work in any corporate subgroup comprises *"reviewing contracts, identifying material issues, drafting agreements, preparing reports and,"* when you're a little more senior, *"being in charge of supervising whole projects."* The small size of team equals greater responsibility, but several grumbled that because of this, the more humdrum diligence tasks *"didn't go away"* in the third year.

"Everything that we touch is cross-border"

Several juniors get to go on client secondments, which sources agreed, *"was very, very, very useful once I was back at Freshfields."* Secondments out to the wider Freshfields network aren't uncommon – we heard of associate postings to Dubai, Frankfurt, London and Hong Kong. *"Everything that we touch is cross-border. All my cases have been cross-staffed – they bring in the London and Germany teams in more often than not,"* said a litigator. *"I was also in contact with my colleagues in Hong Kong on a daily basis; probably to their chagrin as it was me asking them to do things!"*

Recent work highlights

- Advised the London Stock Exchange on a proposed $1.15 billion sale of asset management business Russell Investments
- Acted for Dubai Aerospace Enterprise on its $2.1 billion disposal of its engine repair company StandardAero
- In an arbitration representing a Johnson & Johnson subsidiary, the firm defended claims in excess of $100 million from a Taiwanese pharma manufacturer
- Represented the former CEO of UBS Wealth Management Raoul Weil, who was accused of helping US taxpayers evade tax through Swiss bank accounts

Get Hired

We came across myths like *"I'm not sure you can get hired without a second language,"* and observations like *"most people have two or more languages"* and *"there are people here who have taught law at Chinese universities."* US MP Adam Siegel is quick to offer a more reasoned view: candidates must *"have the passion to work in a cross border context. That doesn't mean they have to speak six languages or have studied abroad."* And one associate reassured us: *"If you're a stellar candidate with impressive academic credentials, you'll get hired even if you only speak English!"*

"People make the decision to come to Freshfields; they don't just end up here."

Associates repeatedly told us how *"intellectual and academic"* their colleagues are. And again this year, a certain elitism came across when discussing the firm's candidate search. Freshfields can afford to be picky, but to be a megabrain is not enough: associates agreed candidates should score highly in *"emotional intelligence."* Pragmatism is also a must, insists Siegel: *"We're not a hierarchical office and we don't have the room for people who don't want to roll up their sleeves, or people who are, quite frankly, difficult."* Associates also stressed how the firm isn't just another BigLaw option: *"People make the decision to come to Freshfields; they don't just end up here."*

See firm profile on p.639

Culture

The office's cosmopolitan feel is no secret, and associates felt it sets Freshfields apart: *"The other international firms in New York are still very New York-centric,"* claimed one. *"There's a constant stream of British trainees and rotating German secondees, and there are Australian attorneys here permanently,"* juniors explained. *"It all adds to this international feel and culture that I really enjoy."*

"Everybody gets on the dance floor – even the partners!"

"People are generally very nice to each other," our sources chimed. *"Working relationships between the partners and the associates are great,"* and *"there are always people chit-chatting by the coffee machines."* This strays from the intimidating magic circle stereotype – *"there is definitely a more independent vibe in the New York office."* Reports of Freshfields do sound more sociable than a lot of BigLaw, too: there are *"frequent Friday drinks"* and firm-funded outings like *"an associate-only event where they took us to a Brooklyn brewery."* The summer party is a perennial hit: *"Everybody gets on the dance floor – even the partners!"* And on the summer program associates were treated to *"sunset sailing, bowling nights, karaoke, Shakespeare in the park"* and a 'design your own Converse' event.

Training & Development

With this size of office, practical on-the-job training works well. However, Freshfields uses a firmwide 'career milestones' training and assessment program, which wasn't so popular with interviewees. Opinions on this ranged from *"pretty confusing and hard to understand"* to *"arbitrary and ridiculous."* In theory the system – which forces associates to *"reflect on what you've concentrated on"* and to *"help you know where to aim"* – should be supportive, but in practice *"it's hard to evaluate yourself against eight different categories with ten sub-categories which all appear to overlap,"* one associate grumbled. *"I get why it exists in London. I know that it affects their compensation so they hate it! But it doesn't affect our compensation so it seems a little silly to have it at all."*

Pro Bono

"In order to compete here you have to take pro bono seriously," one associate said. *"They have a running top list of associates who've done the most pro bono and some get rewards,"* at special pro bono recognition events. However, *"there are people who do astonishingly little pro bono – read that as none – which I find surprising. It's not because the firm isn't committed to pro bono, it's just that clearly client work comes first."* That said, we found the firm to be accommodating: *"I'm on three pro bono cases right now and I think the firm has been very supportive of this decision."* Our associate interviewees found their work *"pretty invaluable."* They had run employment discrimination, sexual assault, and asylum cases, and they relished the opportunity to *"do your research, dig into the facts of the case and get your hands dirty."*

Pro bono hours

- For all attorneys across all US offices: 11,876
- Average per US attorney: 87.5

Hours & Compensation

The lockstep salary and bonus system was hailed as *"fair and transparent."* However, there's no billing target at Freshfields, which was a relief to some, but others found it *"actually quite stressful"* because expectations and transparency vary, partner-to-partner. *"Some partners have taken me aside and told me what they expect – many expect about 2,000 – but it's difficult to understand whether meeting that target is a must,"* said one interviewee. *"And some associates are told the numbers they're billing aren't enough, which I know is frustrating."* Despite uncertainty on this front, associates reported hours in line with the Big Apple norm: *"Usually I get home around 8 or 9pm,"* was typical, together with *"a few hours most weekends, and the occasional all-nighter"* at deadlines. Freshfields *"respects your personal life,"* associates stressed. If you're lucky enough to get married, *"they absolutely forbid you from doing any work on the days leading up to the wedding and then they let you take a long honeymoon!"*

"All my cases have been cross-staffed – they bring in the London and Germany teams in more often than not."

Offices

The *"light and airy"* 56th floor of the New York office made a very comfortable home to our interviewees. *"It's beautiful sitting here right now overlooking Central Park,"* rhapsodized one source, and another told of *"incredible 360 views of Central Park, the Chrysler Building, Long Island and Brooklyn."* The drawback of these exquisite views is *"it's very expensive, so we're stuck for floorspace."* All our sources shared an office, but none viewed this as a problem, because *"I like having an office mate,"* they concurred. It *"adds to the social vibe"*

The Inside View

See firm profile on p.639

and gives you someone to *"bounce ideas off."* Within this limited floorplan the firm does set aside space for 'wellness rooms', which are *"generally used for mothers who are breastfeeding."*

"It's beautiful sitting here right now overlooking Central Park."

Diversity

"That's an area I think every law firm wishes it could do better in," US MP Adam Siegel muses. But *"to make sure nobody slips through the cracks,"* the firm has in place a mentorship program. Siegel gives an example: *"Research shows that male associates are more likely to find informal mentors and forge close working relationships; we want our female associates to be given the same opportunities to succeed."* As a result the firm has *"a formal female mentorship program in place."* And according to associates, Freshfields is *"really trying to keep women associates here. On the junior level I can see that culture working – our latest batch of associates are overwhelmingly female."*

To learn about the firm's strategy, go online to read our full interview with Adam Siegel.

"We're never going to be all things to all people, but that's not what we want to be."
US managing partner Adam Siegel

See firm profile on p.639

Fried, Frank, Harris, Shriver & Jacobson LLP

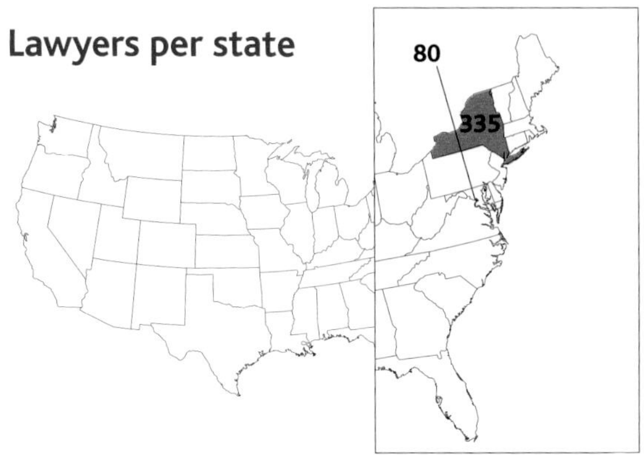

Largest US office: New York
US offices: 2
International offices: 5
First-year salary: $160,000
Billable hours: 2,000 target
Summers 2016: 74 (69 2Ls, 3 1Ls, 2 SEOs)
Revenue 2015: $504.3 million (+9.6%)
Partners made in 2016: 10 (all US)
Famous for: its triumvirate of expertise: corporate, real estate and litigation; being a bit *"New Yorky"*

Associates were pleasantly surprised by "*the people and the vibe*" at this longstanding Wall Street fixture.

FRIED Frank's name may read like the latest hipster diner chain, but its highly focused signature menu – no waffle – serves some of the world's biggest financial institutions and corporations. Top table for real estate work – top tier in *Chambers USA* in New York – the firm also wins rave reviews for its other main offerings of corporate/M&A, finance and litigation. After gnawing its way through sour-tasting times during the recession, Fried Frank today has around 450 lawyers overall, most based in New York. It also houses almost 100 lawyers in DC, and has branches abroad in Frankfurt, Hong Kong, London, Paris and Shanghai.

"I originally looked at Fried Frank because it's 'the' firm for real estate," one source revealed. *"I got a place on the summer program and tried real estate but didn't like it. By then I wanted to stay for the people and the vibe, so I chose another group."* Reputation was certainly a drawing point for wannabe Wall Streeters, and to discover whether Fried Frank's culture suited them some juniors had done internships, some had summered twice, and others had asked their law school contacts about what this 1890s-founded firm is like. Our pool of interviewees came from various law schools, most of which weren't in the current top ten lists, indicating that Fried Frank's recruitment scope is refreshingly broad for a top New York firm.

On chambers-associate.com...

- Fried Frank's summer program
- More on the firm's corporate, litigation and real estate teams

ASSOCIATES SAY...

The Work

At the time of our calls, 32 of 69 junior associates were part of the corporate group in New York. Real estate in the Big Apple claimed 11 junior lawyers, while litigation housed eight. The rest were in tax and bankruptcy. Fourteen of the 69 were in DC: most in corporate, a handful in litigation, and one in each of tax, antitrust, and executive compensation & employee benefits.

"The work assignment system is formal but the caveat is that it varies by group and by office," one explained. Staffing within the corporate department is controlled by an assigning partner, who mediates between partners and newbies. For the first six months or so (it can be flexible) new corporate associates rotate around the department. At the end, they rank their preferred subgroups and *"most people get the one they want."* Interviewees specified that within the framework of the formal system *"there are plenty of opportunities to get work in other*

The Inside View

See firm profile on p.640

Rankings in *Chambers USA*

Banking & Finance	Investment Funds
Capital Markets	Litigation
Corporate/M&A	Private Equity
Employee Benefits & Executive Compensation	Real Estate
Government	Tax

For detail on ranking tiers and ranking locations, visit www.chambersandpartners.com

Recent work highlights

- Acted for health insurer Humana in its $37 billion sale to Aetna, the largest ever deal in the health insurance industry
- Acted as counsel for private equity giant Permira and Canada Pension Plan Investment Board in connection with their $5.3 billion acquisition of software development company Informatica
- Represented Deutsche Bank, accused of aiding and abetting Dole CEO David Murdock's breaches of duty against the company's shareholders
- Advised longstanding client Brookfield Properties in connection with the development of Manhattan West, a proposed $20 billion development expected to include five acres of office space, hotels and homes in the Hudson Yards district

ways, like by talking to someone and expressing interest in a deal."

The so-called *"corporate umbrella"* finds seven subgroups huddled underneath it: asset management; capital markets & corporate governance; corporate real estate; finance; M&A & private equity; environmental; and IP transactional. Corporate real estate sources explained the group's job is *"to assist the real estate group on the corporate fractions of their projects."* For juniors, this involved *"lots of drafting of ancillary documents. We get feedback and then redraft."* Those working in asset management *"started with a lot of diligence but by the second and third year that falls by the wayside at a gratifying speed."* Diligence was replaced by *"so much drafting early on. They let you get your hands dirty by staffing leanly."* Third-years spoke of *"attending client pitches and kickoff meetings,"* being *"the most senior on a deal,"* and enjoying *"direct access to clients of huge caliber."* One added: *"We're on the cutting edge of so many deals, which means staying up late for something worthwhile."*

"They let you get your hands dirty by staffing leanly."

M&A & private equity sources explained that *"working on a public merger on the buy side is very different to the sell side, but we get to experience both."* Tasks depended on the type of deal, but *"typically here junior associates do due diligence and run the data room. If there's someone more junior than you doing that, you get to draft memos and other small documents such as purchase agreements."* A source who had worked at another firm commented that *"drafting is challenging and a lot of responsibility. At the other firm I was asked to do corporate support, but here associates play a big role and that helps you get through the day."*

"We're on the cutting edge of so many deals, which means staying up late for something worthwhile."

A practice group manager in New York handles the staffing of all litigation associates – DC included. While a period of rotation – *"floating,"* some juniors called it – still exists for litigators, *"you never actually have to specialize if you don't want to,"* although you can specialize if you do want to. If you prefer, *"you can be considered a generalist forever and they're always encouraging you to try different areas with different partners."* Junior litigators had gained experience of *"drafting motions, second chair depositions, and some exciting pro bono work."* Sources enthused that *"pro bono gives you the ability to do things you wouldn't do for regular clients,"* and one had worked on *"an appeal for which I wrote all the briefs and even did an oral argument myself. It truly exceeded my expectations."* Interviewees felt *"involved in the strategy of a case."*

"The firm supports you in wanting to branch out."

Pro Bono

Associates described the firm as *"aggressive in getting associates to take on pro bono."* A pro bono counsel circulates opportunities to associates, who must do at least 20 hours a year, *"but usually it's between 150 and 300 hours, which count toward your billable target."* Several felt rewarded by their work concerning *"U visas, specifically for domestic violence victims seeking resident status. It's part of the Violence Against Women Act."* Some corporate associates who retained an interest in litigation were able to take on contentious pro bono cases, *"which helps with writing and adversarial skills. The firm supports you in wanting to branch out."*

Pro bono hours

- For all attorneys across all US offices: 30,482
- Average per US attorney: 74

See firm profile on p.640

Training & Development

Support also comes in the form of *"excellent"* training, which includes a *"Fried Frank Academy for summers and Fried Frank University for new associates."* The former takes place over *"a day or two spent learning the essentials,"* while the latter is *"much more intensive."* Following 'graduation', new corporate recruits enjoyed *"weekly breakfast meetings with presentations from each corporate group."* Other training includes *"frequent lunches with presentations about developments in clients' sectors, a very beneficial accounting course, management skills training for midlevels, and a final stint at the FF University for seniors, who need to run entire matters alone."*

To make sure associates are prepared for and not caught out by their appraisals, a *"summary of the review points is sent to us 24 hours before."* While the formal reviews were described as *"generally painless"* and *"a chance for associates themselves to voice any concerns,"* most agreed that *"they're not as valuable as the informal feedback you can solicit and receive from partners and peers."* Some even ventured that *"the partners find the formal reviews a bureaucratic task and are working on improving them."*

Hours & Compensation

"There are periods when you're home for dinner every night and periods where you never make it out in time."

Everyone agreed: *"2,000 hours is very achievable, especially given 125 can be devoted to non-billables such as recruitment. And of course, 300 can be pro bono, and people even petition for more."* One admitted though that *"you do have to work pretty long hours to achieve it."* We heard of different schedules depending on what group people were in. Generally speaking, *"there's never a shortage of work, but there are periods when you're home for dinner every night and periods where you never make it out in time. Everyone's remotely accessible via a monitor and phone the firm provides, so you can choose to work from home when you need to."* Overall, interviewees felt they did have time for a private life away from work, one sharing: *"I asked the partner for a night off for my wife's birthday, and he said he'd cover me as long as I did the same for him a few weeks later!"*

Culture & Diversity

Understanding Fried Frank's culture means first of all acknowledging the implications of its location: *"At the end of the day, we're in New York at a Wall Street firm."* For some, this simply meant *"it's not a closed-door culture as such, but people's doors are closed because they're busy."* For others, it also engendered a *"bro-ey atmosphere."* At the same time, however, sources were keen to consider FF's *"great idiosyncrasies,"* embodied by *"everyone's personal uniqueness."* Several in New York acknowledged that *"the firm takes steps to be inclusive and welcome very different types of people. They also organize pizza parties, cocktail nights and beach retreats to get us all together."* One went as far as saying: *"If you insist on practicing BigLaw, do it here."* In DC sources were proud of *"the open communication between partners and associates."* One DC dweller recalled *"having a big pro bono court date and ten people showing up to help me prepare for it."*

"At the end of the day we're in New York at a Wall Street firm."

Associates reckoned that their peers' *"unique backgrounds and varied interests"* contributed to the firm's overall diversity, but how does Fried Frank actually fare when it comes to minorities? *"They do try. There are affinity groups, they take on diverse 1L interns, and they implemented a policy to support transgender lawyers,"* one junior highlighted. Having said this, most agreed that they do *"what all the other firms do."* While acknowledging its concrete efforts, another pointed out that *"there's an attitude of 'well we're not the only firm who is struggling with this,' instead of asking themselves 'what can we do differently?'"* Associates were particularly concerned with retention of diverse lawyers, pointing to the relative shortfall of female and black partners.

"Fried Frank Academy for summers and Fried Frank University for new associates..."

Offices

The New York office's location *"on the water"* was deemed as convenient as it is culturally significant. *"It's the southernmost skyscraper in Manhattan and really easy to get to."* The interiors are *"modern if a bit somber. There's dark wood everywhere,"* we heard, *"but other than that it's pleasant. There's a cafeteria which serves delicious sushi on a Thursday, and a free Starbucks machine on every floor. It grinds the beans there and then!"* The New York office recently opened an associate lounge – check out the *Chambers Associate* Twitter feed to see photos.

"It grinds the beans there and then!"

See firm profile on p.640

In DC we didn't hear of anyone bumping into Barack or Michelle on their way to the corner shop, even though the office is *"just across from the White House."* The dark wood is replaced by *"glass walls and doors which let a lot of light in."* Sources felt that being in DC is a perk: *"Corporate associates work on a lot of the same deals as the guys in New York, but we get to be in DC."* Sometimes, however, they felt like *"an afterthought, having to remind NY colleagues our meeting will have to be a conference call, not lunch, because I'm not in New York."* This speaks partly to how organically the two offices work together (in corporate, at least, *"litigation is more separate"*), but *"sometimes DC associates miss out on face time with partners."*

Get Hired

"You have to do more than look good on paper," said a source who had been involved in the callback process. *"It can detract a lot if you don't seem approachable."* From their albeit biased perspective, DC sources felt that *"there's a lot more emphasis here on finding people who are positive, enthusiastic and hard-working, demonstrating a willingness to assist others and be a team player."*

"It can detract a lot if you don't seem approachable."

Tips for summers included: *"Get experience in as many groups as possible, and you'll get a good idea of what the firm's like. The summer program isn't a disingenuous experience: by the end you know what you're getting into and there won't be surprises later."* A more general piece of advice was seconded by several sources: *"When you arrive as a junior your time is your main commodity and is therefore not your own. You can't control your schedule. If you can fly by the seat of your pants and be adaptable and spontaneous they'll support you, and help you become a leader."*

Strategy & Future

With a history at Fried Frank and a 20-year career at Goldman Sachs, David Greenwald returned as chairman in late 2014, and his presence is most definitely felt by juniors. *"He's pretty open about the strategy and keeps us in the loop with quarterly meetings."* During a *"town hall"* meeting twice yearly, Greenwald meets with the firm's younger members. We heard, for example, that *"the associate committee recently discussed with him why the route to become partner isn't clearer to us."*

Greenwald confirms: *"I met with them. We discussed the process and what to expect."* He also emphasizes that *"associates are the future of the firm, and we'll always listen to what they have to say. In this sense our strategy is tied to our culture."* So what's in the pipeline, strategically? *"A year ago we set out to increase, at the highest level, our bench in M&A, private equity, real estate, capital markets and finance. We've made huge progress and we believe the growth of those practices will lead to the growth of other areas. Another focus area is our London office, where we have a lot of important clients. We decided to focus our efforts on the US and Europe and downsize our presence in Asia."*

The Inside View

"Associates are the future of the firm, and we'll always listen to what they have to say."

See firm profile on p.640

Gibbons P.C.

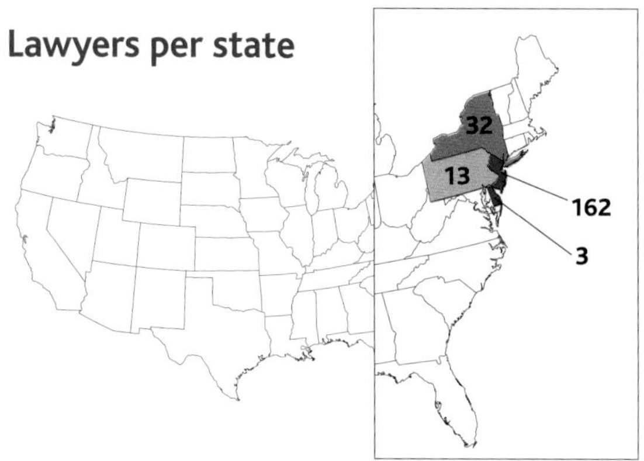

Largest US office: Newark

US offices: 5

International offices: 0

First-year salary: N/A. 2nd years: $135,000 plus clerkship bonus

Billable hours: 1,980 requirement

Summers 2016: no summer program

Revenue 2015: $108.05 million (-1.7%)

Directors made 2016: 6

Famous for: only hiring clerks; its focus on branding

New Jersey's finest seeks judicial clerks keen to "*work with some of the best people in the state.*"

GIBBONS is a big legal brand in New Jersey. *"New Jersey is my home,"* one associate proudly told us. *"I grew up here and I can't think of anywhere else I'd want to work and build my life."* It has offices in Newark and Trenton, but its network extends out of state to New York, Wilmington and Philadelphia, though almost all juniors are based in Newark.

Gibbons' roots in New Jersey sink deep: founded in 1926 by Andrew Crummy (his firm was known as 'Crummy lawyers'), Gibbons today boasts a former Chief Justice of the New Jersey Supreme Court among its ranks, for example, and some of its attorneys helped Governor Chris Christie's presidential campaign (before he pulled out of the race). Lifelong New Jersey resident Judge John J. Gibbons (who the firm is named after today) began his career here in 1950 and returned in 1990 following a stint as Chief Judge of the Third Circuit.

As Gibbons is a PC (professional corporation) rather than an LLP, partners are called 'directors' here (but associates called them partners anyway). Judge Gibbons and other distinguished directors are a big draw for newbies: *"There was no doubt in my mind which firm I wanted to join,"* enthused one associate. *"I knew it would be a challenge, but at Gibbons you've got the chance to work with some of the best people in the state."* Gibbons abandoned its traditional OCI and summer program well over a decade ago in favor of hiring worldly-wise judicial clerks. This makes sense as almost all junior associates work in Gibbons' top-ranked litigation team where they can put their experience with judges to good use. Other *Chambers USA*-ranked practices include corporate/M&A, intellectual property, healthcare, real estate and bankruptcy.

On chambers-associate.com...

- More on The Work and Get Hired
- Interview with director in charge of recruiting Pete Torcicollo
- We catch up with chairman and managing director Patrick Dunican

ASSOCIATES SAY...

The Work

Associates liked the *"informal"* assignment system at Gibbons: *"There are staffing partners but most of the work comes through particular partners and fostering relationships to get future work."* Although sometimes *"you've got to be outgoing and seek stuff out,"* Gibbons is far from a free-market free-for-all: *"I've never had to fight for anything I've wanted to do,"* one explained. *"The process ultimately depends on how many partners there are – in most practice groups they outnumber associates, and they do trust you with substantive work."* On quieter days partners *"want you to come and say 'Hey, I'm light on work right now.' That's seen as a good thing."*

See firm profile on p.641

Rankings in *Chambers USA*

Bankruptcy/Restructuring	Intellectual Property
Corporate/M&A	Labor & Employment
Environment	Litigation
Healthcare	Real Estate

For detail on ranking tiers and ranking locations, visit www.chambersandpartners.com

Recent work highlights

- Represented Hoffman – La Roche against approximately 4,000 cases of gastrointestinal problems caused by the prescription drug Accutane
- Represented music producer Ron Fusari against Lady Gaga over charges he withheld millions of dollars from her during the early stages of her career
- Conducted an investigation into Stockton University's botched $18 million purchase the former Showboat Casino. The transaction failed and left the New Jersey college expensive and unusable property
- Represented Mercedes-Benz USA against a suit alleging the use of defective rims that wouldn't cover repair costs within its warranty

Most juniors at the time of our calls were in the large business & commercial litigation (BCL) group, a few were in product liability; a couple each in criminal defense, real property & environmental, and corporate; and one in employment & labor law. Other options in past years have included IP, financial restructuring & creditors' rights, and government affairs.

"The opportunity to shine in front of clients."

Work in BCL *"really runs the gamut,"* according to sources here. *"There's a fair amount of class action defense in consumer protection work, but there are also lots of general business disputes, like breaches of contract. Cases are already in litigation but it's not until it gets really serious that we get involved."* If a company is accused of breaking federal or state laws, for example, typical junior associate tasks include *"research, which is getting a handle on the factual background, understanding the business and its position in the market, then weaving a potential defense."* Out of these labors comes *"a decent amount of doc review, case research, subpoenas, writing and redrafting."* Not everything is New Jersey-centered: *"Rarer things which are pretty interesting"* include *"foreign arbitration in different states."*

Over in the product liability team, clients include pharmaceuticals companies – of which there's a high concentration around Trenton and Newark – oil & gas, and telecommunications corporations. For big litigations, junior-level work includes *"a lot of research and writing. We'll do even more research if we're gearing up for hearings or filings – this is all about getting company materials ready, preparing for different outcomes. Everything needs to be perfect."* On smaller cases, 'to do' lists can change daily: *"If a client needs something done, I'll do it! This is stuff like reviewing letters or documents, covering depositions... It depends on the day."* Contact with large clients is less frequent than for small customers, who *"want to see me. They want to know about the people handling their cases. It's all about being engaged with who you're working for."* Luckily, senior Gibbons lawyers *"are great at giving me the opportunity to shine in front of clients. They really care about your career progression."*

In criminal defense, which is *"mostly federal and white-collar,"* in addition to government investigations, client meetings and court trips are common. Back in the office, work *"revolves around research and writing – the research is standard legal stuff but it depends on the statute and what the person is being charged with. We're always asked to come up with creative arguments – it's basically where your clerking background pays off."* For feedback on other practice groups, go online.

Offices

Gibbons has around 210 attorneys firmwide, with the vast majority of associates based in Newark. One admitted that *"Newark isn't the prettiest place in New Jersey, but better than Camden!"* Although there are *"not many bells and whistles,"* everyone we interviewed was *"happy with the space and location – it's a pretty easy commute."* The *"big office building"* is hard to miss as Gibbons' logo adorns its top in huge blue letters. Most (but not all) juniors share an office with another junior for their first few years, often someone from another department. *"When you're starting as a new associate it can be daunting, so while people may think it's utterly ludicrous to not have your own office, nobody here is unhappy about that. Sitting with other juniors means you get feedback that you might not have been comfortable asking a partner for."*

"Newark isn't the prettiest place in New Jersey, but better than Camden!"

Gibbons' other offices are much smaller than Newark's: New York, with just over 30 attorneys, and Philly (with around 15) have a similar spread of departments; Trenton handles a lot of lobbying and other government-related work; and the Delaware office focuses on bankruptcy.

See firm profile on p.641

Culture

"I think the level of job satisfaction comes from the people you're working with," one representative interviewee told us, *"and I like the associates I work with."* Another added: *"I'm sure some associates are competitive – you're bred to think that way in law school – but I don't get the impression anyone is gunning for anyone."* While we did hear the occasional grumble about *"difficult"* partners (*"They're lateral hires and from a different culture to me"*), sources were quick to clarify: *"Don't get me wrong, they're a nice bunch!"* So, in conclusion? *"Feedback and transparency"* could sometimes be better, but crucially *"everyone treats you with respect here, there aren't any tantrums, and nobody's screaming or yelling at you. There aren't any horror stories."* Culture varies by department but common feedback was that *"as far as my group goes, partners want us to succeed and put time into involving us in everything."*

"I don't get the impression anyone is gunning for anyone."

The firm holds annual events including a holiday gala for the whole family, Thanksgiving dinners, and recently celebrated *"90 years of Gibbons"* at the Hard Rock Cafe in New York. Saint Patrick's Day is big at Gibbons, and Irish-heritage managing partner Patrick Dunican acted as Grand Marshal of Newark's annual Parade in 2013.

Diversity

While some associates thought diversity *"is a priority,"* others found Gibbons *"supportive, but not that different from any other firm. I think they're making an effort."* Women's events in particular are *"well attended."* They include *"quarterly meetings and luncheons, events with clients and a book club. We're going to New York for shopping and dinner with other attorneys and potential clients. It should be really nice – we've done similar things in the past and they've been successful."* We frequently hear law firms explain that attorneys of color are underrepresented because there aren't enough diverse candidates applying for jobs. *"That's not a good enough excuse,"* one source felt strongly. *"They need to market themselves better, then I'm sure they'd see more diverse candidates apply."*

"Lots of events and discussions."

To its credit, Gibbons runs a diversity fellowship program in association with Prudential, where a diverse attorney works for Gibbons for two years then moves in-house to Prudential for a year. *"We also have awards and try to help individuals,"* an associate revealed. There are also *"lots of events and discussions with speakers about promoting diversity in the workplace."*

Pro Bono

"There is always lots of discussion between partners and associates about how important it is to be involved with your community," associates told us. *"We do all kinds of things: clinics, Hurricane Sandy relief, helping children with difficulty in school, victims of domestic violence, veterans, asylum cases. There are lots of options depending on what you're interested in."* While sources were pleased with the 50 hours pro bono which can count as billable (*"It's one of the things I love about Gibbons"*), many had exceeded this and some were concerned that *"any minute more than the 50 hours isn't counted toward your billable hours."*

"You've got to be outgoing and seek work out. If you don't go for it and put yourself out there you may not be busy."

Juniors valued the experience they get from pro bono work. For example, *"you run with the case, interview the client, do research, counsel them, let them know what to expect in court and then cross-examine the bad guys."* They also mentioned that as well as providing free legal advice, Gibbons supports local charities in other ways too.

Pro bono hours

- For all attorneys: 14,379
- Average per attorney: 68.5

Hours & Compensation

Most associates described the 1,980 billable target as *"achievable," "realistic"* and *"reasonable"* compared to elsewhere, *"particularly New York firms."* However, *"I know certain associates have a hard time. It depends how busy their group or project is."* We heard that, in smaller groups especially, newer juniors can struggle to hit their hours as *"partners take the phone calls"* and *"there aren't many tasks that can be delegated to me for the rate I'm billed at."* The repercussions of not making the target are *"you don't get a raise that year, but you can still get a bonus,"* which is determined by more than just hours. *"You have to be really slacking to get pulled up on it."*

"We're given flexible time if we need it."

Few interviewees regularly worked later than 7pm, with most clocking off at 6.30pm at the latest. Also, *"we're given flexible time if we need it and I'm glad of that."* Working late *"is a reality of the job"* at any law firm,

See firm profile on p.641

The Inside View

"but I don't work that late really. I have worked on weekends but it's been from home – if you're sitting in pajamas on your couch that's not too bad." Overall, associates felt that *"generally the partners are respectful of after-hours and vacation."*

Training & Development

Feedback on training and professional support ranged from *"incredible"* to *"it's there if you need it."* The Gibbons Academy is a series of presentations throughout the year which *"support your development and help you get your CLE. There are talks by various partners about different legal issues. For me as a junior associate trying to figure out whether this is the group for me, they're really helpful."* Past talks have included 'Corporate governance 101' and 'Protecting your license from litigation landmines.' *"The partners in my group also allow me to get involved in the industry associate task force; that brought me to a number of research institute programs and things to further my career."*

"No real goal-setting atmosphere here."

The appraisal system is *"okay but more of a 'here's what we've learned about you' situation than structured feedback. There is no real goal-setting atmosphere here – maybe there is later on. It's more about billing and pro bono."* However, others said that *"if you ask for feedback, it's there. The annual reviews are coming up and we get a lot of feedback from those. The partners you work the most with will submit write-ups on us and then the partners in our group will also give some feedback."* An *"associate achievement card"* is the place to log successes throughout the year like *"any publications, pro bono work, professional networking events, and marketing initiatives and achievements."*

Get Hired

Courting a firm with no OCI or summer program might be daunting for some, but Gibbons associates liked it. *"If you hire through OCIs then you're basing everything on one semester of grades, which doesn't show you the person who develops through law school."* As Gibbons almost exclusively hires those with clerking experience, sources were further up the learning curve when they applied: *"Knowing how things work and what the court expects is invaluable. You know when you draft something or revise something that it's what the court is looking for. It's what sets those who have clerked apart."* As a result, new starters join as second-years.

"They assume you're smart and can write."

Applying to Gibbons is similar to bagging a clerkship: you send off your resume, references and writing samples then *"wait for a phone call."* The next stage is an interview with a partner and senior associate. *"They assume you're smart and can write, the interview is more about working out whether you're a nice person to be around."* For our interview with director in charge of recruiting Pete Torcicollo, visit our website.

Strategy & Future

"We're very pleased with our position in the marketplace," chairman and managing director Patrick Dunican tells us. *"We've contracted a bit, so we're a little smaller, but we now feel that we're the right size to be poised for growth. We're in discussions with a number of teams from different firms who have seen what Gibbons has been doing in the marketplace and now want to be involved in that. When we talk next year, you'll see that Gibbons has grown in headcount and revenue."*

Readers should note that there isn't a summer program at Gibbons as it focuses its junior recruiting efforts on judicial clerks. Even at this level, entry opportunities are like gold dust as the firm does not hire huge classes. *"The work that's in the office dictates where we add junior attorneys,"* says Dunican. *"The business model has changed dramatically in the past few years. With that in mind, it becomes about the clients, and our clients want partners to do their work and not juniors, which is why we have focused on recruiting partner-level talent."* But there remain entry opportunities for those good enough to clerk and join Gibbons: *"Back in our heyday in the early 2000s, our classes were a dozen or more; this year, we had a starting class of four attorneys – which was the same as last year. We have specifically focused on reducing the headcount at the firm."* For the full interview, read our Bonus Features online.

"You've got the chance to work with some of the best people in the state."

See firm profile on p.641

Gibson, Dunn & Crutcher LLP

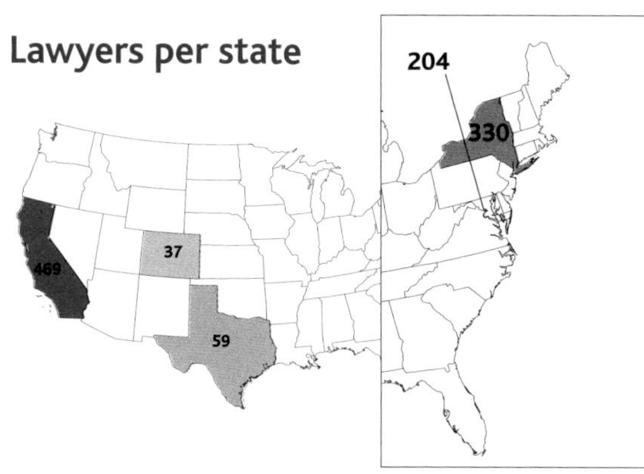

Largest US office: New York
US offices: 9
International offices: 9
First-year salary: $160,000
Billable hours: no requirement
Summers 2016: 126 (125 2Ls, 1 1L)
Revenue 2015: $1.54 billion (+4.8%)
Partners made 2016: 8 globally (all US)
Famous for: helping to overturn Proposition 8; huge presence on East and West Coast

Prepare to navigate a free market system at this prestigious international firm, which originated in LA nearly 126 years ago.

RED-bearded men have played some significant roles over the course of history: King Henry VIII (played by Damian Lewis in the TV adaptation of *Wolf Hall*), Vincent Van Gogh, Ulysses S. Grant, Brody from *Homeland* (also played by Damian Lewis...) and – though not quite so well known, we admit – corporate attorney John Dustin Bicknell. By 1890, Bicknell had created the legal outfit that was to become Gibson Dunn. Today the megafirm has over 1,200 lawyers across a network of 18 offices (half of which are in the USA) and a stockpile of nationwide rankings from *Chambers USA*, including top spots for antitrust, appellate law, securities litigation, corporate crime and FCPA [Foreign Corrupt Practices Act] work. On the transactional side, it's lauded for capital markets, M&A, and banking & finance brilliance, among others.

All the juniors we spoke to were adamant about why they'd joined Gibson: *"The firm's national spread and reputation stood out to me – the name is recognized from LA to New York."* An insider reported: *"When I was looking at firms, I liked Gibson best because it had a sort of swagger to it. Other places try and convince you about how good they are, but Gibson is confident about the fact that it offers great work and is full of great people to work with."* Others concurred, noting that it's *"a serious but social place. Obviously it's a prestigious, high-level practice but people are fairly relaxed and allow you to have a life."*

On chambers-associate.com...

- Interview with chairman Ken Doran

ASSOCIATES SAY...

The Work

First-year associates join Gibson's offices across the country, but the largest cohorts are based in New York, LA and DC. During their first two years, juniors have the opportunity to formally rotate between practice areas at six-month intervals. However, *"most people usually come in knowing that they want to be litigators, for example, and stick with that."*

"You need to take charge of your own destiny."

Thanks to the firm's free market system, *"you have the freedom to develop your own practice and build relationships with the people you want to build relationships with. You're not forced onto projects or at the mercy of an assigning partner."* As such, *"you need to take charge of your own destiny, figure out what you wanna do and go get it!"* Fortunately, newcomers aren't left to roam the halls in search of work on their first day: *"You're staffed on a matter to get you acclimated."* A rookie revealed: *"Coming in, I was worried that I might end up sitting around with nothing to do, but that hasn't been my experience at all. I reached out to people I'd worked with from the summer, but I also found that people I hadn't*

See firm profile on p.642

Rankings in *Chambers USA*

Antitrust	Intellectual Property
Appellate Law	International Trade
Banking & Finance	Investment Funds
Bankruptcy/Restructuring	IT & Outsourcing
Capital Markets	Labor & Employment
Corporate Crime & Investigations	Litigation
	Media & Entertainment
Corporate/M&A	Outsourcing
Employee Benefits & Executive Compensation	Private Equity
	Projects
Energy & Natural Resources	Real Estate
Environment	Retail
ERISA Litigation	Securities
FCPA	Tax
Government	Technology
Insurance	Transportation

For detail on ranking tiers and ranking locations, visit www.chambersandpartners.com

Recent work highlights

- Won a landmark education trial on behalf of nine plaintiffs relating to the tenure and dismissal of public school teachers in California
- Representing Uber in a series of putative class actions against the cab app company
- Representing Goldman Sachs as financial adviser to health insurance company Humana in its $37 billion acquisition by healthcare company Aetna
- Acted for the Governor of New Jersey, Chris Christie, in the investigation into the 'Bridgegate' scandal in which political staff schemed to close lanes without warning and create massive traffic jams in Fort Lee

worked with before were waiting to ask if I wanted to jump on board projects."

Although sources appreciated the flexibility and responsibility afforded by the free market system, they did emphasize that *"it's a big learning curve"* in terms of balancing workload. *"The only way to learn is trial and error!"* One warned that *"it demands an assertive personality type – you can't be afraid to say no to things."*

While some litigators told us that they do *"mostly appellate work"* or *"primarily white-collar investigations,"* others had sampled a whole host of subjects. *"My goal was to get a wide range of experience, because I didn't know what type of litigation I wanted to do ultimately."* We heard from juniors who'd tried their hand at employment cases, patent, fraud, oil & gas litigation, government investigations, antitrust work, entertainment, healthcare, and securities cases. Inevitably there's doc review to be done, but associates also get to grips with *"research, preparing for depositions, drafting briefs, dispositive motions and discovery motions."* Attending client meetings is also common. *"We work on matters of incredible substance, and even people at the very bottom take on real responsibilities."*

"Within a month of starting I was talking to clients."

Over in the corporate department, associates are able to try out a range of areas, including capital markets, M&A, finance, private equity and funds. An insider who'd got stuck into fund formation work explained that *"matters are staffed leanly, so a lot of the time I just work with a partner. I draft documents like limited partnership agreements and private placement memos, and then receive comments from the partner."* On M&A deals, rookies should brace themselves for due diligence and doc review but there's also scope for regular client contact: *"Within a month of starting I was talking to clients at least once a day."*

Training & Development

The firm offers weekly practice-specific training sessions for new associates that are beamed out via videolink across the offices. *"Each one covers a different topic like filing a complaint, or filing a motion to dismiss,"* explained a source. *"They're pretty helpful – it's good to cover the basics."* Of course, *"you learn the most from actually trying to do the job!"*

"It's a blast!"

There's also the annual New Lawyer Academy – a retreat in Tucson, Arizona, attended by all new starters, including laterals, from offices across the world. Although there are some panel events, *"it's weighted toward socializing and networking rather than training – it's a blast!"*

Interviewees tended to be pleased with the level of feedback received from seniors during the daily grind. *"I've been impressed with the partners here; they're concerned with how I'm developing and are good about taking the time to walk me through things."* Naturally, it's all *"personality-dependent."* While some folk have *"strong mentoring skills"* and readily offer advice, others are *"less proactive, but will give you red lines on your draft."*

Culture & Offices

"We're a West Coast firm at heart," reckoned an associate in Dallas. *"It's surprisingly laid back for BigLaw, but that shouldn't be misinterpreted – everyone here is ambi-*

See firm profile on p.642

tious and works very hard." A Denverite agreed: *"We're not that intense here, although our work is as good as anybody else's in the firm."* Some lawyers perceived that *"the New York office has a more traditional vibe."* An insider described the Big Apple base as *"very social – I get drinks and go to Mets games with my office mate – but also it's a 'work hard, play hard' culture with a high level of coffee consumption."*

"A high level of coffee consumption."

The DC base *"has a reputation for being a little more buttoned up,"* specifically when it comes to dress code. *"I'm eternally jealous of the Orange County office's Hawaiian shirt Fridays,"* noted a lawyer in the capital forlornly. Despite this *"superficial formality,"* DC juniors characterized the office as an *"excellent place to work, full of humble, hilarious and kind people. There's not a lot of ego here, despite the fact that there's probably justification for it. It's easy to work with people, and that's true for associates and partners. What with the free market system, work for jerks would dry up very quickly – both ways!"* An insider in LA concurred: *"Everyone is very intelligent but they don't act like it by sitting around talking pretentiously. People go hiking together and talk about bad TV and also happen to have excellent credentials!"*

"The firm's national spread and reputation stood out to me – the name is recognized from LA to New York."

When it comes to the social side of things, we heard that *"a large number of associates are good friends, so people often go for lunches together informally or see each other outside of work."* The firm also organizes a spread of get-togethers. As well as a big holiday bash, there are regular happy hours, weekly 'deli counter' lunches (*"I've found some of my best work just by plopping down next to someone at a table and striking up conversation!"*) practice-area-specific retreats and various sports teams, including softball and basketball. *"A lot of folk have families they want to get back to at the end of the day,"* noted associates. *"So while socializing is encouraged, it's not forced!"*

Hours & Compensation

The firm has a *"soft target"* of 1,950 hours for the year. All of our interviewees were relaxed about meeting this. *"I've never been concerned about it – there's more than enough work to go around."* Many mentioned that they'd *"surpassed the suggested target without any trouble."* However, it's understood that *"for first-years the hours might be difficult to meet when you're ramping up at the beginning."* Everyone we spoke to was pleased to confirm that pro bono hours *"count one-for-one toward the target, so there are a plenty of ways to make up the 1,950 hours."* Everyone is eligible for a merit-based bonus, even if hours are below 1,950.

"You're treated like an adult."

Sources also appreciated that *"there's no face time requirement. You're treated like an adult, so there's flexibility. People don't really care when you do the work as long as it gets done. I can work whenever I want – it's not a nine-to-five job – but then again, you're technically 'on' 24/7. So if you've got a motion due on Monday morning, you'd expect to be working on the weekend. But then you could take off early on Tuesday."* A junior trumpeted: *"The lack of face time matches my personality – I don't need someone to be nagging at me!"* As usual, attorneys emphasized that *"things really ebb and flow – sometimes I can come in at 10am and leave at 5pm with an hour for lunch, but if a case is going crazy then I'll be up late."* Associates also pointed out that *"if someone has important plans and informs ahead, that's really respected. My peer associates took a bullet for me when I planned to get engaged on a certain weekend and knew I wouldn't be replying to emails."*

Pro Bono

"We are very much a pro bono firm – we take pride in it and love doing it!" exclaimed an associate happily. As mentioned previously, the firm credits all pro bono hours and there isn't a formal cap. Every insider we talked to had at least one pro bono matter on the go – in fact, *"it would probably raise eyebrows if you didn't do any at all. It's the norm, culturally."* (Of course, this being BigLaw, *"the priority is still billable work."*)

"It's the norm, culturally."

Associates mentioned working on a wide range of cases – among others, immigration and asylum matters, people trafficking cases, disability benefits cases for veterans, domestic violence restraining orders, custody cases and matters for innocence projects and animal shelters.

Pro bono hours

- For all attorneys across all US offices: 130,005
- Average per US attorney: 120

See firm profile on p.642

Diversity

As with most BigLaw institutions, *"diversity isn't where it should be."* However, juniors thought that *"the firm is really focused on improving diversity."* Many mentioned that *"Gibson is very attentive to women's issues. They have regular lunches and events that encourage women to stay on track for partnership. There aren't as many women in senior leadership roles as men, so everyone agrees that this needs to be addressed."* There's also an all-women retreat *"to talk about retention and celebrate female lawyers."* Sources told us that they'd been involved in the LGBT affinity group, hosting events and helping with recruitment. *"I feel very strongly about how wonderful the firm has been. The firm recognizes that our world is very diverse, and shouldn't be full of curmudgeonly old white men."*

"Very attentive."

Get Hired

Insiders who'd been involved in recruiting remarked that *"Gibson is looking for students who show initiative, who come prepared with some knowledge of what the firm's known for and are able to ask questions about us."* Various lunches and dinners form part of the selection process (*"they put a lot of emphasis on seeing how you perform in a more casual setting*").

Associates noted that *"in terms of personality they tend to look for people who'll thrive in the free market system. I know some people here who are quiet, but everyone has a vibrant personality."* Academic credentials are obviously important, but *"they also want folks who are good at what they do without being that 'type A' aggressive law school type!"*

"A vibrant personality."

Strategy & Future

Chairman Ken Doran tells us: *"For us, growth areas would include white collar, antitrust, private equity and M&A, privacy, patent litigation, real estate, energy and infrastructure, restructuring, healthcare and life sciences. Our practice focus shifts with clients' needs."* Last year we heard that the firm was focused on building up the transactional team in London. Doran confirms that *"this remains the case. We're making great progress but we're not finished. Last year, we also brought on additional laterals in private equity and M&A. Similarly, we are continuing to grow in Asia and in the US."*

"When I was looking at firms, I liked Gibson best because it had a sort of swagger to it."

See firm profile on p.642

Goodwin Procter LLP

Lawyers per state

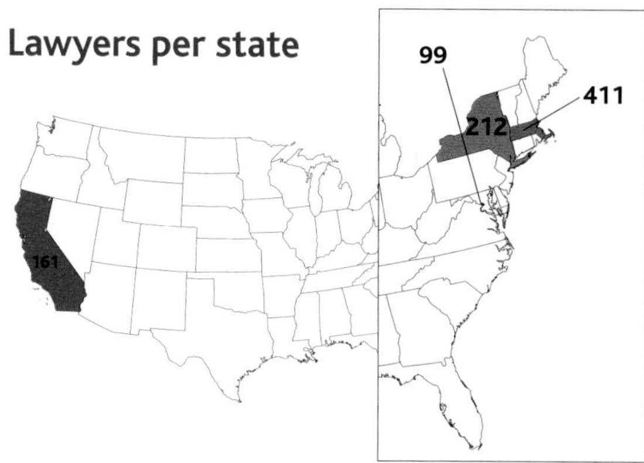

Largest US office: Boston
US offices: 6
International offices: 4
First-year salary: $160,000
Billable hours: 1,950 target
Summers 2016: 57 (55 2Ls, 2 1Ls)
Revenue 2015: $865.5 million (+10.2%)
Partners made in 2016: 19 globally (18 in US)
Famous for: tech and life sciences practice; small-firm friendliness with BigLaw responsibility

Associates win good at this Boston-founded firm which has entry-level openings on the East and West Coasts.

IN 1912, the year the Titanic sank (Goodwin represented one victim's family), two old law school classmates called Mr. Goodwin and Mr. Procter bumped into each other in the street and decided to go into business together. They split startup costs equally, with each man contributing the princely sum of $500. Their investment paid off handsomely, and in 2015 Goodwin Procter's revenue was up to $865.5 million. It now has ten offices worldwide (six of which are in the US) and picks up a slew of *Chambers USA* rankings for its work nationwide (including corporate/M&A, REITs, venture capital, life sciences, and financial services), and statewide expertise in Massachusetts, California, New York and DC.

Goodwin's as much a fixture of the Boston legal scene as TV's *Boston Legal*, but in the Nineties it spread along the East Coast to New York and DC, and in the Noughties opened three offices in California. There are also branches in London, Hong Kong and, most recently, Germany's financial capital, Frankfurt.

On chambers-associate.com...

- Read more about the Boston waterfront's Innovation District

ASSOCIATES SAY...

The Work

Incoming juniors join one of two big *"buckets,"* litigation or business law, and spend their first two years as general resources before specializing. The firm pushes partners to go through the central coordinator, which associates appreciated. *"It's easier to tell the coordinator what you do and don't like than a partner,"* admitted one. At the start, assignments trickle down from on high via the work coordinator (more officially called the attorney development manager). As legal eagles become more senior, the flow of work becomes more organic. *"I'll knock on partners' doors and they'll knock on mine,"* a source in the Los Angeles office explained.

> "They give you ownership of your career right off the bat."

"While I've heard stories where first-years are sent to a room full of documents and left there for days," said one associate; *"that doesn't happen here."* Associates told us that *"they give you ownership of your career right off the bat."* Depending on the size of the deal, associates in the corporate bucket can be responsible for anything from *"swapping out the names and updating dates on the ancillary documents"* to *"drafting most, if not all of the transactional documents"* with minimal partner involvement. As deal-doers get more senior, their tasks don't so much change as fill out. *"There's a lot of due diligence at the start, and that means a lot of documents,"* explained a

See firm profile on p.643

Rankings in *Chambers USA*

Banking & Finance	Labor & Employment
Bankruptcy/Restructuring	Leisure & Hospitality
Capital Markets	Life Sciences
Corporate Crime & Investigations	Litigation
Corporate/M&A	Private Equity
Employee Benefits & Executive Compensation	Products Liability
Environment	Real Estate
ERISA Litigation	REITs
Financial Services Regulation	Securities
Food & Beverages	Startups & Emerging Companies
Intellectual Property	Tax
Investment Funds	Technology

For detail on ranking tiers and ranking locations, visit www.chambersandpartners.com

third-year. *"When you get more senior, you're supervising the juniors going through them."*

The corporate cup runneth over, offering everything from *"large private equity deals to tech startups to a ton of real estate deals."* Over in litigation things are just as varied, with securities litigation, government investigations, product liability and general contractual disputes to get stuck into. *"I've done the standard doc review, of course,"* lamented one associate, *"but there's also been a significant amount of drafting."* Showing initiative is a great way to get early responsibility, litigators told us. *"I didn't want to just write the memos,"* said one litigator, *"and because I demonstrated ability I've already had the opportunity to draft motions for summary judgment and appellate briefs."*

Towards the end of their second year, associates pick a specific 'business unit' to officially specialize in. We say 'officially' because associates remain free to seek work from outside their chosen business unit. *"You're not forced to drop the cases you're already working on,"* an associate told us. Specialization is mostly an administrative matter, although it means that *"if you want to drill down into a practice area, you definitely can."*

The Inside View

Offices

"Oh my God, I can't wait, it's going to be a million times better," enthused an associate when asked about the Boston office's imminent move to an 'innovation hub' in the Seaport district. Our source acknowledges that there is *"some anxiety about the commute"* among the firm's lawyers, but is confident that *"we'll work the kinks out."* Boston is Goodwin's traditional hometown and largest office. *"Goodwin is largely run from here,"* a Bostonian believed, *"although the leadership is based in New York."* Goodwin's Big Apple branch is situated

Recent work highlights

- Representing the defendant, former hedge fund trader Mathew Matoma, in the largest ever insider trading case
- Advised Teva Pharmaceuticals, the largest generic drug manufacturer in the world, on its acquisition of Auspex Pharmaceuticals
- Advised TripAdvisor on a new $1 billion revolving credit facility
- Represented construction company Skanska on its construction of a new headquarters for PwC

in the New York Times Building, where lawyers share a cafeteria with the broadsheet's staff. With around 100 attorneys, Washington, DC is on the small side, so its attorneys regularly collaborate with Boston and New York. The office is centrally located, with easy access to important pieces of infrastructure like *"metro stations and the basketball arena."*

"We tend to represent the up-and-coming companies."

The Silicon Valley office is located in the 'burbs rather than in downtown Palo Alto, which makes the morning commute a bit less fraught. It mainly does corporate and IP work, and most of its clients are in the tech sector. *"We tend to represent the up-and-coming companies,"* explained an associate in this office, *"and leave the Facebooks and Googles to other firms."* This gives rookie lawyers unprecedented client exposure. *"As a junior, I get to work with a client's CEO or number-two guy,"* our spy told us, *"and I don't think I'd get that level of contact with a bigger company."* Just off Wilshire Boulevard, the Los Angeles office occupies a single floor opposite *"a brand-new hotel that will be the tallest building west of the Mississippi."*

Hours & Compensation

Our sources agreed that it's possible to have a private life away from the firm – so long as you plan ahead. *"It's easy to get sucked into cases,"* one explained, *"so you really have to be proactive about protecting your time."* The firm offers 20 days' vacation each year, and, provided you show a little hustle, our sources tell us it's possible to take it all. Once lawyers have managed to secure some downtime, the firm generally refrains from pestering them: *"Everyone values vacation time and everyone is willing to cover for you, so long as you return the favor."*

"I don't usually work on weekends."

The firm has a billable hours target of 1,950 hours. *"We're really busy,"* a source told us, *"so it's definitely*

See firm profile on p.643

doable," but hitting it will involve putting in the legwork. *"I don't usually work on weekends,"* one lawyer told us, *"but at the same time I work 11 or 12 hours a day."* The hours target really is just a target, however: *"You can get a very strong review and still get your bonus, even if you haven't quite hit your hours."* Salary follows the market, and *"Goodwin waits for the Cravath scale to come out,"* and adjusts its bonus accordingly.

Culture

Long hours are inevitable in BigLaw, so it's best if you don't spend that time *"sitting next to people who are going to yell at you."* Fortunately, that doesn't seem to be the case at GP. *"Lawyers are lawyers, and they're always going to be competitive,"* admitted a source, but at Goodwin *"you really can't be a jerk."* HR actively looks for *"people with personality who are fun to be around,"* and *"people understand that you have a life outside of work."* Overall, our impression was of a *"more laid back and cooperative"* firm than most. Each office had its little quirks: according to someone in LA, that office *"has a very teaching-centered culture,"* while those in DC thought that that branch was *"more geared toward work/life balance"* than the others.

"You really can't be a jerk."

"They try to be more sociable than the big-firm norm," said one source, *"but the billable hours model of business gets in the way."* As a result, *"you sometimes have to choose between spending your free time with co-workers and spending it with your family."* Others were more optimistic, with one lawyer describing the firm's social life as *"a happy medium,"* with regular lunches and happy hours serving to *"make sure people aren't just shut inside their offices working all the time."*

Diversity

Last year we said that, despite its best efforts, Goodwin still had a lot of work to do on the diversity front. Well, it seems like someone at the firm has taken notice, because our sources all told us that it's high on new chairman David Hashmall's list. Goodwin already has a long-running 1L diversity fellowship which provides a stipend for diverse law students to do public interest work over their 1L summer. Lately the firm has partnered with the Leadership Council on Legal Diversity on its 'pathfinder program,' and it also works with headhunters to bring in diverse candidates.

"Not just a bunch of white guys."

Sources on the West Coast were particularly impressed with their offices' diversity efforts. At a firmwide level *"diversity is something that comes up all the time,"* and there are both firmwide and office-specific diversity committees. Our interviewees thought that Goodwin did an OK job of attracting ethnically diverse talent, but that that there was a lot of work to do on the socio-economic diversity front. *"It's definitely not just a bunch of white guys,"* said a Bostonian, *"but I don't see many people from the less fortunate parts of Boston."* Sources also highlighted that Goodwin was one of the first firms to elect a female chair, but acknowledged that *"we still need to improve"* the number of women at the top. At the junior level the firm's intake is split roughly evenly between men and women.

"People understand that you have a life outside of work."

Pro Bono

"I had a prior commitment to pro bono work," one source told us, *"and at Goodwin I got to fulfill that commitment alongside my billable work."* Goodwin offers the usual panoply of pro bono projects, including immigration and asylum cases, landlord and tenant work, First Amendment matters and advising nonprofits on their corporate governance. *"A year or two ago, they changed the rules,"* a Goodwinian explained, *"and now every pro bono hour counts as billable."* This means that attorneys generally don't have to choose between paid and unpaid work, although one source acknowledged that *"you might raise a few eyebrows if you're only doing pro bono work!"* There's a perception among lawyers that pro bono is a litigator's game. *"They have a skill set that we don't,"* acknowledged a deal-doer, *"but the firm has been working hard to build up its business pro bono offering."*

"Working hard to build up its business pro bono offering."

Pro bono hours

- For all attorneys across all US offices: 65, 120
- Average per US attorney: 68

Hiring & Training

OCIs are a fairly traditional one-on-one affair, and Goodwin tries to make sure that *"litigators interview people who are interested in litigation and so on."* Callbacks involve meeting four to five interviewers, who are a mix of partners and associates. The latter *"were much more casual,"* recalled a survivor of the process; *"they said things like 'tell me about yourself.'"* From what our interviewees told us, the partners and senior associates didn't sound too much more awkward: *"They certainly didn't make us do some crazy business school-type logic*

See firm profile on p.643

puzzle." Instead, applicants fielded questions about resumes, prior experiences and law school.

"Convey a genuine interest in your chosen practice area."

While the old favorite 'why this firm?' made an appearance, our sources didn't recall being asked 'why here?' at any of the firm's different branches. *"It's more important to convey a genuine interest in your chosen practice area"* than demonstrate prior links to a particular locale, according to someone in San Francisco. This is especially important in the smaller offices which are, by their nature, specialized. Los Angeles has a heavy real estate emphasis, for example, so *"candidates should show evidence of a desire to do real estate work."* Across all offices, lawyers who had been involved in recruiting all agreed that they were looking for *"bright people who will work hard and people we'd want to be in a foxhole with."*

There's a week-long orientation at the firm's Boston HQ, and newbies take additional training sessions twice a week. After that, well, they're launched right into it, which our sources thought was *"the best way to learn."* New associates are reviewed midway through their first year, and once a year thereafter. Goodwin is a broad church, and hiring partner Ken Gordon tells us: *"If you asked ten people what makes a good Goodwin Procter lawyer, you'd get ten different answers,"* he admits. So long as you're willing to *"literally and figuratively roll up your sleeves and get stuck in,"* and *"can translate your intellect into practical advice for clients,"* you should be welcome here.

Strategy & Future

While the firm holds regular town hall meetings and *"tries to keep us abreast of the big picture,"* some thought Goodwin could do a better job at communicating with its employees. For example, in 2015 there were a number of layoffs in the litigation department as the firm repositioned itself toward transactional practices. *"That was very jarring,"* recalled someone at Goodwin HQ, *"and it might have been easier to manage if they'd given us some understanding of how things were going."* According to head of business law Mark Bettencourt, the firm's long-term goal is to be *"the preeminent global firm"* in six key practice areas: *"Technology & life sciences, private equity, real estate capital markets, financial institutions, securities & white-collar criminal litigation, and IP litigation."*

"If you asked ten people what makes a good Goodwin Procter lawyer, you'd get ten different answers."

See firm profile on p.643

Goulston & Storrs

Lawyers per state

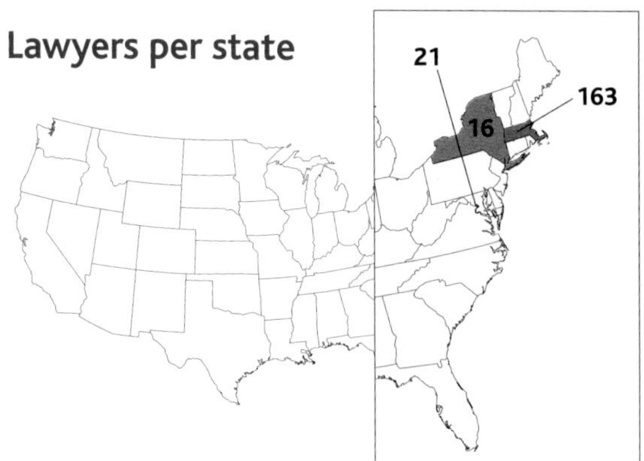

Largest US office: Boston
US offices: 3
International offices: 1
First-year salary: $160,000
Billable hours: no requirement
Summers 2016: 7 (6 2Ls, 1 1L)
Revenue 2014: $139 million (+7.8%)
Partners made in 2016: 6
Famous for: Boston roots and top real estate work

A waterfront view and harbor-side deck: Boston's Goulston & Storrs is a prime location for real estate-hungry associates.

PREMIER real estate firm Goulston & Storrs has nabbed itself some first-class Boston real estate with its harbor-side offices situated in a retrofitted warehouse. Goulston is one of three firms that have dominated the real estate landscape in Boston for over a decade (the other two are DLA Piper and Goodwin Procter). *"It feels like we've had a hand in most of the buildings in Massachusetts,"* one associate reckoned. *"Anytime I mention visiting a theater or restaurant, someone says 'we did the permitting on that!'"*

Real estate may be Goulston's best-known asset but the firm is also noted by *Chambers USA* for its banking & finance, bankruptcy & restructuring, environment, and general commercial litigation work in Massachusetts. The 160-strong Boston office serves as Goulston's HQ, but outside of its hometown Goulston has offices in Beijing, New York and DC. New York predominantly handles commercial real estate, construction and development, retail and corporate finance matters. Meanwhile DC, which also gets a nod from *Chambers USA* for real estate work, tackles all things real estate including historic preservation and military housing privatization.

On chambers-associate.com...

- We chat with co-managing partners Marty Fantozzi and Barry Green
- Hiring partner Bill Streuch talks us through hiring at Goulston & Storrs

ASSOCIATES SAY...

The Work

Real estate absorbs nearly all of Goulston's six or so annual new first-years, though the odd junior may sign up with another area like litigation, corporate or private client & trust. Each department has two work allocators who oversee the distribution of work, although we heard the system tends to be used less in smaller groups. Those teams that utilize allocators see associates fill out a roster every two weeks to *"provide updates on the projects you're doing but what tasks you're doing within them, so allocators know what experiences you're getting."* Sources reckoned the system *"works really well to ensure everyone gets a variety of work and has enough room on their plate."* Juniors can request repeat projects through the system, meaning *"you don't have the pressure of hunting for things but at the same time there is flexibility to work with particular partners if you want to."* Speaking of partners: as they outnumber associates by roughly two to one, juniors in all groups *"end up working directly with partners on basically everything."*

"You don't have the pressure of hunting for work."

Transactions, financing, and permit & development matters make up the lion's share of Goulston's real estate work. Juniors are encouraged to gain *"a high level of competency in all three areas"* before specializing later in their career. Permit & development work (aka zoning)

See firm profile on p.644

Rankings in *Chambers USA*

Banking & Finance	Litigation
Bankruptcy/Restructuring	Real Estate
Environment	Retail
Leisure & Hospitality	

For detail on ranking tiers and ranking locations, visit www.chambersandpartners.com

encompasses *"large-scale commercial and mixed-use development projects both inside and outside Boston. We guide our clients"* – local and national real estate developers and investors – *"from the initial process of securing the land all the way through to helping them to secure city, state or federal approval on a building permit."* Research projects on land plots, drafting contracts and initial filings, and preparing clients for and attending community agency meetings all fill the days of juniors here. *"I got to meet with city officials and attended hearings designed to promote projects and persuade officials to approve them,"* recalled one source.

On the transactional side juniors *"tend to work on leases and property acquisitions and sales"* for both residential and commercial developments. *"I've tackled everything from the initial drafting of purchase agreements to negotiating the exhibits, maintaining the checklist and taking care of closing,"* one source outlined. Other interviewees had conducted due diligence and reviewed land surveys and title deeds. Goulston's financing attorneys predominantly represent developers, though you may find the odd lender here. Tasks are similar to those working on acquisitions; due diligence, checklists and drafting ancillary documents all fall within a junior's remit.

Pro Bono

"The firm wants us to work on pro bono within our area of practice," said one real estater. *"Instead of being assigned to an immigration matter I may assist a real estate nonprofit in Boston with an affordable housing project."* Matters are assigned the same way as client billable work so *"you might not even know the work is pro bono unless someone mentions it,"* sources told us. *"Typically we're doing the exact same stuff we would do for a paying client."* As all pro bono hours count as billable, there is little need to keep track of which is which.

"You might not even know the work is pro bono."

Continuity may be encouraged but no barrier exists to practicing outside your practice area. Once a month juniors in all groups can swing on down by a local homeless shelter clinic to advise residents on issues like housing or benefits. The firm's diversity committee also invites associates to take on pro bono cases which deal with minority issues and communities in Boston.

Recent work highlights

- Advised commercial real estate investors CrossHarbor Capital Partners on the financing of a 13,600-acre private residential community in Montana
- Acted for WS Developments in its acquisition and redevelopment of the Royal Poinciana in Palm Beach, Florida
- Represented Harvard University in its development and leasing of properties of the university's Allston Campus
- Advised MS Boston Seaport – a joint venture between Morgan Stanley and Boston Global Investors – on the acquisition, financing, development and sale of numerous properties in Boston's Seaport district

Pro bono hours

- For all attorneys across all US offices: 11,823
- Average per US attorney: 62

Diversity

There is more to Goulston's diversity committee than organizing pro bono matters; a speakers' program, social events and community outreach projects are all on the cards. The firm also brings in diversity educators Facing History and Ourselves for *"cool training sessions; we watch a video and discuss the stereotypes assumed in it."*

"We're representative of Boston's culture."

Despite all this sources did feel the firm was *"not the most diverse. But Boston is not the most diverse place and we're representative of Boston's culture."* Interviewees reckoned LGBT and female attorneys were well represented but *"the firm knows it needs to work on diversity when it comes to racial minorities."* Improvements have been spied in junior classes: *"This year's summer class was six women, four of whom were diverse and they all got hired."*

Training & Development

Newbies are assigned a midlevel associate sibling – *"We're very touchy feely here,"* one source joked of the name – and a partner mentor. *"Your sibling is more for your day-to-day 'hey what's the difference between a mortgage and a deed of a trust 'cos I'm a clueless first-year?' questions. Whereas your mentor is more likely to ask you, 'hey, you've not handled any zoning, where do you see yourself developing in the team long term?'"*

See firm profile on p.644

"Your sibling is more for your day-to-day."

Goulston & Storrs University offers partner-led presentations on *"specific areas of practice, insights on things to watch out for or issues which are distinct to the state of Massachusetts."* Business development topics such as generating new clients also fall under the GSU heading. Boston associates are often joined by their counterparts from New York or Washington, DC during trainee sessions as non-Beantown attorneys *"try to get up every couple of months"* for training or other events.

Offices

Boston's been home to Goulston & Storrs since its founding in 1900, and the firm moved into its current waterfront haven in 1985. The converted warehouse *"is all exposed beams and bricks, it's very Boston chic"* and also rather *"mazelike: it takes new people a few days to figure out where they're going."* Hopefully those lost souls eventually find themselves occasionally on the firm's rear deck overlooking the harbour, where Goulston hosts summer associate and client events – DC and NY attorneys are all invited to these – including a lobster bake and games nights. We're assured it's also not bad for a spot of lunch in the summer either.

"It's very Boston chic."

The firm is so enamored of its real estate that instead of relocating the entire office when it outgrew current digs, Goulston took over the seventh floor in a neighboring building. *"The running joke is that they're two separate law firms"* as there is not a historical feature in sight in the overflow office, which is decked out *"with frosted glass and clean white marble."* Practically all Goulston's first-years are hired into Boston but as work allocators staff matters across offices, attorneys may find themselves sometimes working with colleagues in DC and New York.

Strategy & Future

Goulston's pretty happy with its national footprint so you won't be seeing new offices pop up any time soon. Washington, DC and New York bases are in for some development though as the firm tries to increase headcount here. *"We're trying to expand our core practice of real estate but also other areas like corporate and tax,"* associates understood. The firm's also expecting to see an increase in medical institutions and educational clients.

Culture

Associates are kept in the loop on firm happenings through a monthly associate lunch with the firm's managing partners. An *"edited version"* of the monthly partner meeting is relayed to associates here: *"We discuss everything from new hires to new clients and the firm's financials."* Associates also get the chance to *"discuss anything on our mind or ask questions about the state of the firm"* which haven't already been covered. *"It's very democratic here,"* one interviewee deduced. *"Our various committees are always run by a pair,"* another explained, *"so people have to collaborate to make decisions rather than have one person dictating their ideas."*

"It's not cool to be a jerk."

"Management does a very good job to instill in associates an understanding of the firm's culture and how it ties in with strategy," one associate stressed. *"They're very concerned to preserve the ethic of our culture."* For example, *"the partnership is not cut-throat or competitive as we don't have a system where people get more credit for bringing in more clients. Compensation is based on subjective factors. Partners ask how helpful other partners are, whether or not they've trained associates, and are they responsive when people ask them for help. I've found that when I send out a firmwide email I get back a whole lot of helpful responses rather than a few, flippant replies,"* one junior told us.

"Anytime I mention visiting a theater or restaurant, someone says 'we did the permitting on that!'"

Throughout the firm *"you can see the people who might be jerks have to check themselves, as they know it's not cool to be a jerk at Goulston,"* one source reckoned. *"People take a vested interest in our development and care about your wellbeing as a person and an attorney,"* felt another. *"This is the kind of place where the highest-earning partners walk into the kitchen and ask the dude behind the counter about his kids."*

Hours & Compensation

Goulston doesn't stipulate a billable requirement. Sources reported being encouraged to aim for around 1,800 billable hours but felt the lack of a prescribed figure was genuine. Bonuses are also nonexistent at Goulston. *"Years ago they made the decision that bonuses might advocate over billing or lead to a different culture where people were protective over matters. We don't get a bo-*

See firm profile on p.644

nus but that comes with the understanding that hours will be reasonable. If you're looking for a large bonus this is not the place for you," a source stressed.

"The understanding that hours will be reasonable."

Most interviewees reported leaving the office at around 7pm and put in a few hours from home if they have to. *"The hours here are conducive to having a good quality of life,"* one associate told us. *"People are focused on the idea of families and lives outside of work."* Vacations tend to be uninterrupted, but even those who had received the odd email claimed this was down to people forgetting they were on vacation.

Get Hired

Associates involved in the recruiting process told us: *"We want people who are friendly and appreciate the firm's culture. We'd rather hire someone we'd want to work with at 1am than someone who was number one in their class at Harvard."* Goulston's on-campus hiring tends to concentrate on the Massachusetts area though it also attends OCIs at Columbia, NYU and Georgetown.

Demonstrating a commitment to the law through work experience and extra curricular activities is a plus, but hiring partner Bill Streuch tells us, *"we hire people with very diverse backgrounds. We have lawyers who have previously been writers or musicians. Some of our most successful attorneys have had very different career paths."*

"Management does a very good job to instill in associates an understanding of the firm's culture and how it ties in with strategy."

See firm profile on p.644

Greenberg Traurig, LLP

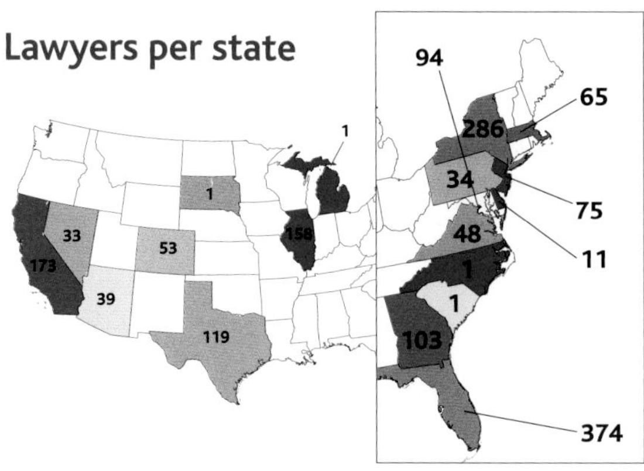

Largest US office: New York
US offices: 29
International offices: 9
First-year salary: $160,000
Billable hours: no official target
Summers 2016: 46 (44 2Ls, 2 1Ls)
Revenue 2015: $1.32 billion (+4%)
Partners made in 2016: 28 US
Famous for: megafirm with a flair for real estate work

Miami mammoth Greenberg Traurig continues to "*strike while the iron is hot,*" and has been eyeing up a major merger across the pond....

MIAMI-born in 1967, Greenberg Traurig's largest office these days is in New York. Founded by Jewish lawyers Mel Greenberg, Robert Traurig and Larry J. Hoffman, the firm remained exclusively Floridian for 24 years. It wasn't until 1991 that GT started to expand in the States and overseas. It has a strong international reputation for *"stellar real estate work,"* and partly because of this it was attracted to merger talks with UK property powerhouse Berwin Leighton Paisner (BLP) in early 2016. These talks eventually came to nothing, which isn't wholly surprising as Greenberg isn't known for growing through mergers.

Greenberg reported rosy financials for 2015 – a healthy 4% rise in revenue in 2015 to $1.32 billion. *Chambers USA* confirms the quality of GT's work all over the country. Top practices include real estate, corporate/M&A, banking & finance, litigation, immigration, retail, Latin American investment, and bankruptcy/restructuring. It's not just the work that appeals to potential recruits, though, as many interviewees were attracted here by *"clicking with the people more than anything"* and perceiving during interviews *"a friendlier environment than other places."*

On chambers-associate.com...

- Interview with Brad Kaufman, global chair of associate professional development

ASSOCIATES SAY...

The Work

Insiders confirmed GT's *"longstanding reputation"* for real estate work. Starting out as the founding practice in Miami, the department has grown into a 200-lawyer heavyweight. However, sources insisted that *"litigation is by far the biggest group, as it houses roughly 40% of all attorneys."* Corporate work is also prominent, especially in matters that have a Latin American link. Much of this latter work is done in the Miami hub. Out of the nearly 80 names that comprised the 2013 and 2014 associate classes at the time of our calls, most were in New York, followed by Miami. Corporate and litigation had 22 juniors each, with the latter comprising both general litigation and IP litigation. Real estate had 16, followed by immigration, labor, and business reorganization & financial restructuring with three apiece. Health & FDA business had two. IP prosecution, government contracts, trade customs and public finance all had one.

Most associates tend to start off as generalists regardless of their groups, with the option to specialize later. But depending on how strong your interest is in specific subpractices, *"the firm allows you to specialize immediately if you want."* For example, real estate can be divided into different groups that include condominium law, general leasing, financing transactions and sale purchasing. Litigation can encompass white-collar work, mass tort, IP, product liability, securities, civil rights, real estate, and business litigation. Assignment is based on informal

See firm profile on p.645

Rankings in *Chambers USA*

Banking & Finance	Latin American Investment
Bankruptcy/Restructuring	Leisure & Hospitality
Construction	Litigation
Corporate/Commercial	Media & Entertainment
Corporate/M&A	Native American Law
Energy & Natural Resources	Natural Resources
Environment	Products Liability
Franchising	Real Estate
Gaming & Licensing	REITs
Healthcare	Retail
Immigration	Tax
Intellectual Property	Wealth Management
Labor & Employment	

For detail on ranking tiers and ranking locations, visit www.chambersandpartners.com

Recent work highlights

- Represented Atkins North America (formally known as The PBSJ Corporation) against an SEC and DoJ investigation into the company's bids on engineering contracts in Qatar and Morocco (valued at approximately $100 million)
- Represented Platform Specialty Products (a producer of hi-tech specialty chemical products and tech services) in its $3.51 billion acquisition of Dublin-based Arysta LifeScience
- Advised Albertson's LLC on its $9 billion acquisition of the Safeway grocery store chain

relationships where partners (formally known as shareholders) reach out to juniors. However, there is a catch-all system to get more work, where *"you submit a report to your practice group leader every week, estimating your projected workload and when you're free."*

Once staffed, real estate newbies had worked *"on purchase transactions representing developers who want to purchase land. I've had to draft the purchase, sale and acquisition financing documents. I've also negotiated documents for condominium management agreements."* Other work has included doing the due diligence for title and loan documents. Leasing work required juniors to *"represent tenants who are opening restaurants in the Design District in Miami. Hopefully when they open, they'll call us."*

"The partner lets you argue in court."

Litigators had *"drafted document discovery reviews, prepped witnesses for depositions, written deposition outlines and motions to dismiss."* Responsibility varies depending on case size. *"In smaller cases the partner lets you argue in court and take depositions, but on larger matters, naturally the client is more willing to pay for partners as there is more at stake."* Conversely, transactional rookies actually like doing the due diligence *"as it gives you exposure to the types of documents that you then move on to draft."* Documents that associates get the first stab at writing have been some of the core transactional documents, like share purchase agreements and corporate resolutions. Most insiders had been working in the M&A sphere with some *"conducting run of the mill acquisitions of assets in the gaming industry."*

Pro Bono

"We do a fair amount of pro bono," associates told us. Others added that *"no one dissuades you from doing it, but it's easier to get involved if you're in litigation as it lends itself to it more."* Generally, *"they promote it but at the same time they limit your hours."* We heard from associates that the allowance is pretty generous, although the firm did not confirm the figure: *"Typically 100 hours count toward billables, but a lot of the time you're going over 200."* Juniors particularly praised the efforts of the Manhattan office, as there's a firmwide pro bono partner *"who is really invested and tries to get us all involved. She knows all of us by name and comes to us personally."*

"It's only helped my other work."

Some interviewees had worked with KIND [Kids in Need of Defense], an organization which GT works a lot with, particularly on immigration issues. Associates had *"researched and drafted various motions, talked to the clients to get all the facts and then gone to court"* for legal status hearings. Some pointed out that not all cases generate the publicity that a few have in recent years: *"I mean, we turned over the gay adoption ban, but now they're not as newsworthy! But we can always do more. It's never hurt anyone to get involved, and it's only helped my other work."* The firm is also a sponsor of the Holly Skolnick Fellowship in partnership with Equal Justice Works, which allows recent law school grads to work in various nonprofit organizations.

Pro bono hours
- For all attorneys across all US offices: undisclosed
- Average per US attorney: undisclosed

Training & Development

After an initial orientation, training is department-led. Litigators, for example, are enrolled into the GT Skills Academy, which offers roughly six two-to-three-day seminars on different topics. Different offices host different sessions that have included *"practicing drafting motions, depositions, mediation and trial skills. It's like a NITA* [National Institute for Trial Advocacy] *type*

See firm profile on p.645

thing." Additionally, GT provides regular lunch and CLE sessions. This is usually a lecture from a senior attorney, who discusses both developments in the field and experiences from their own career.

Transactional newbies have a corporate boot camp which tends to focus more on the specific needs of individual deals. This complements the other professional development schemes on offer at the firm, such as regular webinars and live presentations dealing with things like negotiation skills.

"It's great to see how all your feedback pieces together."

There are two reviews per year. For some, the first informal review meant being *"taken out to lunch with a partner to discuss where you're at as an associate."* The formal review focuses more on *"partners assessing your work performance, cross-comparing it to how you assess yourself and what you've done."* Two partners then take juniors through an anonymized, conglomerated evaluation from the different attorneys that have submitted assessments. While most were happy with this, one said: *"It's frustrating if you find out a specific partner hasn't liked something, because it's anonymous."* However, others felt that *"it's great to see how all your feedback pieces together into a bigger picture, and I've always been able to open up a dialog with partners to help me learn."*

Offices & Culture

Thirty-eight offices make up GT's global network. Nine overseas outposts include Shanghai, Tel Aviv and London, with additional strategic alliances in Milan and Rome. Back home, GT doesn't designate any office as the official headquarters, although one junior felt that *"New York is sort of the HQ, but there are a lot of higher-ups across the offices."* Others were adamant: *"Miami is still the staple."* The CEO is actually based in Denver. Either way, juniors described the Big Apple office décor as *"old school with dark wood. It could be updated; it seems old compared to the others."* The location is *"basically right on top of Grand Central Station, so there are really great options for lunch."*

The Miami base takes up five floors in the Wells Fargo building; each floor has soda fountains and specialized coffee machines that embrace the local Cuban culture. *"The views look over all of Miami, so you can see it raining in some places and not in others."* Unlike their Manhattan counterparts, newbies get their own offices straight away, with most New Yorkers having to wait until their third year.

"Bagpipe players to go round all of the floors to celebrate St Patrick's Day."

The firm's culture is centered around the GT slogan 'Built for change' that is emblazoned on its website. When asked what this means, interviewees mused that *"it goes to the big emphasis on entrepreneurial spirit. For example, the firm lets partners create their own practice groups in areas that aren't usually available elsewhere."* Within this, *"everyone collaborates across offices and it's very easygoing, which is not what I expected from this type of firm."* This is helped by regular happy hours and monthly associate lunches. In the New York office, *"the firm hires professional bagpipe players to go round all of the floors to celebrate St. Patrick's Day."* A Miami source remembered a recent regional business retreat where lawyers were given limited materials and

"I've always been able to open up a dialog with partners to help me learn."

told to make catapults. *"We got piping, bungee cords and duct tape. It was crazy, but everyone got really into it! Believe it or not they actually worked and we had contests to see who could go the farthest."*

Hours & Compensation

There isn't an official billable target; however, most associates explained that the firm operates under the understanding that 1,800 hours makes you bonus-eligible *"and you should shoot for at least between 2,000 and 2,200 for a significant bonus."* To reach the 2,000 hours mark, this breaks down roughly to eight hours a day. As always, work can fluctuate depending on what's on, and one litigator recalled that *"most associates leave around 7.30pm, but I've been here till 5.20am before."*

Others were keen to highlight bonuses, which operate under an 'eat what you kill' structure. Insiders thought that this *"promotes collegiality because it's on you alone to hit those numbers;"* in other words, those who perform exceptionally get rewarded. However, apart from the hours component, rookies said that bonuses are assessed *"in a black box. I'd love more transparency."*

Strategy & Future

Greenberg Traurig hasn't historically grown through big combinations with other firms, *"preferring to acquire small teams of attorneys, instead of full-scale mergers."* If the BLP merger had gone ahead it would have created a new firm with approximately 2,500 attorneys,

See firm profile on p.645

up from GT's current 1,950ish. Merger talks aren't the only thing the firm has explored recently. New York, for example, has acquired *"a few litigation partners to expand our practice."* The firm hit the legal headlines too in the New Year when it hired former New York Mayor Rudy Giuliani (and team) from Bracewell & Giuliani (which has been renamed Bracewell). When asked why such big changes were afoot, associates responded that *"we always look for people at that level to increase the firm's visibility and bring business. GT is not afraid to take these types of risks to develop practice areas. It's an exciting time to strike while the iron is hot."*

"Not afraid to take these types of risks to develop practice areas."

Diversity

A glance at the firm's diversity figures places it in line with *"corporate America, but GT is still pushing to be more diverse."* How? In Miami, for example, GT takes part in a 'minority mentoring picnic', which allows minority students to network with both associates and partners. Others recounted GT's support for new parents. One mother had been *"nervous about taking maternity, but people were just happy for me."* Although some thought that the maternity package could be better, others felt that the provision for three months paid and a further three months unpaid leave was, *"compared to other firms, really up there."* Global chairman of associate professional development Brad Kaufman explains that *"one of our previous CEOs, Cesar Alvarez, who was born in Cuba, put it best when he used to say that we didn't just have a diversity program, we have diversity! Our co-presidents are Hilarie Bass, a woman and the president elect of the ABA and the other is Ernest Greer, an African-American attorney and former managing shareholder of our Atlanta office."* For the full interview, go online.

"Speed networking evening."

The GT Women's Initiative hosts regular networking and development events throughout the year, to promote career progression. Events have included negotiation seminars led by partners, cocktail parties and a *"speed networking evening. We had to bring friends that were in other professions – not law – and we were then split between tables. Every five minutes a bell would ring and we'd rotate. It's been the most effective event, but it was very much a push to get business contacts, which I think should come about more naturally."* Nevertheless, rookies relayed that *"they're moving in the right direction, but it takes time."*

Get Hired

Interviewees stressed the importance of asking questions at interview. *"If you have personal questions about the firm,"* one advised, *"like what life's really like and what work you'll be doing, the juniors are the best people to ask and not the partners."*

While law school is good at teaching theory, but it's not so hot on teaching about the practical side. To combat this, GT operates a residency program for new associates not recruited through the OCI process. Juniors work for a year on a reduced salary and billables requirement, *"as the expectation is more on learning, before becoming a normal associate."* Additionally, associates suggested *"working as a clerk, or doing pro bono to get a sense of what practicing law is all about to give you an edge over others."*

"one of our previous CEOs, Cesar Alvarez, who was born in Cuba, put it best when he used to say that we didn't just have a diversity program, we have diversity! "

See firm profile on p.645

Hangley Aronchick Segal Pudlin & Schiller

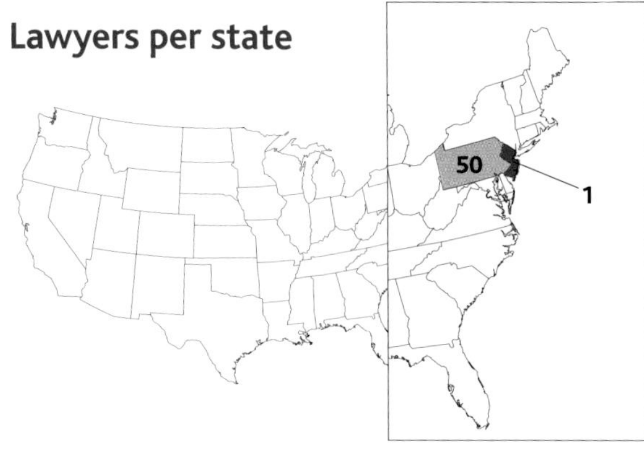

Largest US office: Philadelphia
US offices: 4
International Offices: 0
First-year salary: $135,000
Billable hours: no requirement
Summers 2016: no summer program
Revenue 2015: undisclosed
Partners made in 2016: 2
Famous for: its sense of humor; a life-sized model cow in the HQ

They may be young and fun, but don't mistake Hangley for a fool when it comes to litigation...

LIKE the renowned Philly cheese steak in its home city, Hangley's full name (see above) is something of a mouthful. And Hangley's connection to the classic Philadelphia dish doesn't end there, as there's a great big model cow somewhere in its headquarters. It used to stand pride of place in the lobby for all to see, but associates this year told us it's wandered off to a quieter corner in a conference area. A brief look at the firm's website highlights that making (and taking) a joke is a huge part of this firm's culture. As CEO David Pudlin tells us, *"we're just a fun group of people with a great sense of humor, and we enjoy each other's company – when you come to work we want you to enjoy it."*

But while Hangley attorneys may not take themselves too seriously, the same cannot be said for their work. For its relatively small size, this 21-year-old has racked up an impressive number of *Chambers USA* rankings within Pennsylvania, particularly for its insurance and general commercial litigation work. David Pudlin enthusiastically reports a *"fourth consecutive fabulous performance financially."* A busy year unsurprisingly requires more attorneys, and Hangley took on a total of five associates in 2015, marking a boom period for a firm which usually only takes on one or two newbies per year.

On chambers-associate.com...

- Interview with president and CEO David Pudlin
- The Lighter Side of Hangley

ASSOCIATES SAY...

The Work

The overwhelming majority of new associates begin Hangley life as litigators, and there's a very broad range of litigation work on offer, including antitrust, bankruptcy, business/corporate, environmental law, insurance coverage and real estate. *"I couldn't define the work as any kind, other than to say it's litigation,"* one associate told us. *"We do everything under the sun."* The generalist nature of the work is emphasized by the small size of the firm, as when a case gets particularly busy, *"they sometimes send out an email asking for help, so you can push for something more interesting."*

"There's a real effort to make sure associates get a diversity of experience."

Although *"there's a real effort to make sure associates get a diversity of experience,"* focusing in on one area isn't out of the question. Insurance coverage, for instance, is *"the largest subgroup,"* and has its own dedicated litigators (which also means newbies can expect a fair amount of work in this area). Similarly, *"we have some folks who are very focused on antitrust and environmental work, and they do that exclusively."* As one junior explained, *"I don't think they're against people specializing, but nobody is forced to; it depends on how your career unfolds and what issues you get into."* If associates do have a particular interest, they can express

The Inside View

See firm profile on p.646

Rankings in *Chambers USA*

Bankruptcy/Restructuring	Litigation
Insurance	Real Estate

For detail on ranking tiers and ranking locations, visit www.chambersandpartners.com

this via the assigning shareholder: *"There's definitely room for input on the type of work you want to be doing."*

A wide array of practice areas unsurprisingly means a wide array of clients, from banks to *"really big commercial insurers,"* to *"a number of municipalities on the environmental side. It really runs the spectrum."* As does the size of the cases: *"I've had cases in county courts in Pennsylvania, I've done international arbitrations, and had matters in federal and state courts all over the country."* Hangley's more petite proportions mean that these cases are leanly staffed, *"often just one shareholder and an associate."* As a result, responsibility levels are *"high. Disconcertingly high at times. You're trusted with a lot, and if you demonstrate good judgment you're trusted with more."* Our interviewees described tasks such as drafting motions for summary judgment and motions to compel, as well as discovery matters. That said, legal research is fairly common at the junior level, as is doc review, although *"if you do the doc review you'll also ultimately help write the brief."*

Training & Development

Another aspect of having fewer associates is that, aside from a few days of computer training, *"there's not really a formal training program"* at Hangley, although there are occasional training bootcamps. This means juniors are mostly expected – with help from others – to figure things out by themselves: *"When you get assigned to a matter, you need to have a good head on your shoulders and ask the right follow-up questions."* With allocated shareholder and associate mentors, however, there's no shortage of people to ask for advice. The associate mentors in particular are described as *"wonderful for asking stupid questions to like 'Hey what's going on?' or 'I have no idea what this means...'"*

"There's not really a formal training program."

Although formal training within the firm is minimal, *"we have lunches, and we'll have lunchtime talks on topics like changes in federal rules or how to use LinkedIn to network."* More substantive legal training is generally done outside the firm. It's the job of the associate development committee to *"keep an eye on training opportunities in the area, and it's down to the associate to organize doing that."* The firm pays for any outside CLEs that juniors need to do, with one example given being a two-day deposition training.

Recent work highlights

- Representing around 2,400 juveniles and their parents who were victims of a conspiracy involving two judges of the Luzerne County Court of Common Pleas. The judges were paid approximately $2.6 million to maximize the number of children committed to two new juvenile detention facilities
- Serving as real estate counsel to Aldi, one of the fastest growing supermarket chains in the USA, in connection with numerous development projects
- Successfully defended insurers Executive Risk Indemnity and Nutmeg Insurance Company in defense of a $135 million lawsuit brought by health insurance organization Cigna, related to coverage and bad faith allegations

Get Hired

There are no OCIs or summer program and the number of junior-level associates hired each year is is usually only one or two. As such, Hangley can afford to be scrupulous in its selection process. High academic achievement is of course a must, and almost all of the juniors we interviewed had clerked for at least a year. Although clerking *"isn't a formal prerequisite,"* the firm *"places considerable value on having that prior experience."* Potential applicants need to apply directly to Hangley: *"I contacted them and was pretty persistent! Then I did a screening interview with the hiring committee, then at my callback I spoke to about ten attorneys and got the good news a couple of weeks later!"* Quite often, judges will refer potential candidates to Hangley. Very occasionally the firm may take on one exceptional person as a summer associate.

"They hire people with an eye to keeping them on."

Fewer attorneys means the firm *"looks for people who are interested in getting a more hands-on experience. It's a place where people are genuinely interested in – and talk about – what they're doing."* It also means that *"each person they take on is an investment, so they hire people with an eye to keeping them on."* There's a fair amount of transparency: *"They're pretty good at telling people what they need to work on in general. Then at around your seventh or eighth year you'll get indications about what to work on in order to make shareholder."*

See firm profile on p.646

Offices

Most on our associate list were in the Philadelphia HQ, which houses 42 of the firm's attorneys. The other offices are in Harrisburg, Norristown and Cherry Hill. The recently renovated Philly hub, found in the town's business district, is *"beautiful"* and *"light-filled"* thanks to large windows in all the attorney offices. Associates are given a $500 budget to furnish their offices and *"to make it feel homey. I got some plants and a couple of prints framed."*

While orange ampersands (Hangley's logo) are still abundant around the office, the huge model cow – once the legen-dairy focal point of the lobby – has been mooved to a more discreet location: *"Before the renovation it was pretty front and center, now it's more tucked back. I'm sure the clients still see it though!"* Although the office *"doesn't have the same bells and whistles that a big firm would have"* (it lacks a gym, for example), it's nonetheless *"perfectly comfortable and serviceable."*

"People here nerd out on the law!"

Culture

Does Hangley's fun-filled website (go to 'The Lighter Side' section to see what we mean) match up to the reality? *"When I was doing my research, Hangley's friendliness seemed too good to be true. But there's not a big difference between how they present themselves and how they are."* That's a yes, then. But it's certainly not all fun and games, as *"there's a lot of very, very hardworking people here, and I don't want to diminish that at all. We work very hard and are very thorough."* Indeed, the word *"nerdy"* was frequently adopted by our interviewees: *"People here nerd out on the law!"* One interviewee laughed, adding that *"because there's no official training and things are staffed so leanly, you really need to get into it."*

"You're trusted with a lot, and if you demonstrate good judgment you're trusted with more."

The fact that Hangley doesn't have all the events usually associated with a summer program certainly doesn't deter its attorneys from socializing. There is a firmwide lunch every Friday, as well as the 'Rule of Four' scheme: *"Four or more people can get together and go out on the firm. It's a way of encouraging people to get together and discuss their cases."* Other events include the odd happy hour or more family friendly trips to the zoo, and there was even a mural tour: *"The Mural Arts Program is a big organization in Pennsylvania, and one of the firm's board members* [chair David Pudlin] *is a board member for them. He helped us arrange a walking tour of Philly to look at the murals here."*

"There's nobody I wouldn't have a drink with."

One associate enthused: *"During my first two weeks here, there wasn't a day when someone didn't come to my office and say 'Hey let's go get lunch!' It really is a positive place where people try to enjoy each others' company."* The social atmosphere is no doubt encouraged by the fact that *"the firm does a good job of hiring people that have a range of interests, be it pro bono or community work or general life experience. There's nobody I wouldn't have a drink with."*

Hours & Compensation

There's no official billing requirement at Hangley, although billables are connected to the budget: associates are budgeted for 1,800 billable hours a year. The general feeling was that *"most people reach their hours,"* and *"people don't stress too much,"* about hitting this number. Rather, *"everybody just does their work and does it well."* Because of Hangley's lockstep compensation system, *"there's no bonus incentive to do more than 1,800 hours, which does away with any competitive mentality."*

"Everybody just does their work and does it well."

Our sources reported that at Hangley *"people are pretty transparent about hours; they get shared every month."* A few admitted that this *"quite freaky"* system caused some anxiety, although others felt it was a good way to *"demystify what everyone's doing. It also makes it very clear if there are imbalances, and it lets partners know who has the capacity to take on more."* Although the Hangley salary is below market rates, juniors seemed happy with the trade-off for a better work-life balance: *"The shareholders here could be making more money if they changed the culture of this place and made it more demanding, but that's not the model they've set out to follow."* Recently, junior associates salaries went up – $135,000 for first-years, up from $125,000.

Pro Bono

"Everyone always wishes we could do more pro bono because the cases are so compelling!" Examples include working for the ACLU [American Civil Liberties Union] as well as for The Innocence Project, a nonprofit legal organization working to acquit people who were wrongly jailed: *"It's been a really meaningful."* Others had been involved in prisoner civil rights litigation, and volunteered legal advice at a homeless shelter.

See firm profile on p.646

Although there is a pro bono coordinator, it's up to the associates to take the initiative and arrange pro bono around their schedules. *"It's pretty self-directed. We have relationships with a number of organizations, but it's up to you to reach out and figure out what you want to do."* Take note, though: pro bono hours here don't count as billable.

Pro bono hours

- For all attorneys: undisclosed
- Average per attorney: undisclosed

"The cases are so compelling!"

Diversity

As far as the male to female ratio goes, *"it feels pretty equal in the associate pool. In the shareholder pool it's more lopsided, but there are a fair number of female shareholders."* In fact, there are 41% female associates and 29% female partners at Hangley. But interviewees noted that Hangley *"does not feel diverse"* when it comes to ethnic minorities. *"If I was going to fault the firm for one thing, it would be that. I think the interest is there, but part of the problem is that we don't hire that often."* As such, the lack of ethnic diversity at the firm is unlikely to change drastically in the near future.

Strategy & Future

"I think in the short term I see more of the same," CEO David Pudlin tells us. *"I don't see us developing any new practice areas, but we'll probably grow a little bit more, especially as we're attracting new business and new clients."* The firm's busy year in 2015 means *"we'll bring in more young new lawyers, and if we're approached by a lateral, we're always open to consider them."*

"Things are going well and we control our own destiny."

This doesn't mean that expansion is on the cards, however: *"We have no interest in any kind of merger."* The CEO continues: *"We're happy, things are going well and we control our own destiny."*

"Hangley's friendliness seemed too good to be true. But there's not a big difference between how they present themselves and how they are."

See firm profile on p.646

Harris, Wiltshire & Grannis LLP

Lawyers per state

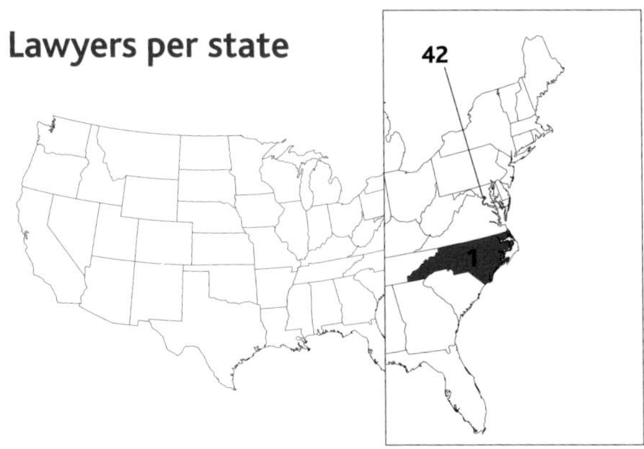

Largest US office: Washington, DC
US offices: 2
International offices: 0
First-year salary: $168,000
Billable hours: no requirement
Summers 2016: 3 (all 2Ls)
Revenue 2015: undisclosed
Partners made in 2016: 1
Famous for: boutique BigLaw telecoms masters; firm gong

With its boutique charm and mastery of the telecommunications market, HWG continues to prove that size doesn't always matter in BigLaw.

WHEN a firm pays the highest first-year salary in the *Chambers Associate* guide, the other hallmarks of a prestigious firm – like multiple locations and international ubiquity – become superficial details. Such is the case at pint-sized HWG: now entering the twilight of its teenage years, the firm is in rude health and bucking all the BigLaw trends. Unlike some teenagers, growing pains are not an issue, as the firm looks to increase recruitment into its tight-knit team, while maintaining its egalitarian principles. Managing partner Bill Wiltshire tells us: *"We've been attracting an enormous amount of business. We just have so much work we need people here to do it."*

This DC firm is renowned for its work in the telecommunications arena – *Chambers USA* awards the firm a coveted top-tier ranking in this area – but incoming associates should not consider this inhibiting. *"If you are an HWG associate, you are going to do some telecoms,"* although there is scope to explore other avenues. One source was keen to assure doubters: *"I don't want to give the impression that you can't come here and focus on litigation and white-collar – we have partners and associates who spend most of their time doing that."*

On chambers-associate.com...

- Net Neutrality

ASSOCIATES SAY...

The Work

The firm's boutique size is evident in the way business is run. Even so, you might be surprised at exactly how casual the firm is at times. If its assignment system were a dress code, well, it would be a 'no shirts' type of policy: a *"pretty unique system"* of *"self-assignment."* Partners *"will send an email with a general request. We then pull the partner off the chain and divvy up the work between whoever's interested."* That said, there is an *"expectation that you will accept a project"* when offered. This DIY system was universally lauded as *"really helpful for new attorneys"* because *"it gives you the opportunity to break out of your practice if it's not exactly what you want to be in."* Hours are logged, but in our interview with management, the partners were at pains to stress that this information is rarely – if ever – used to assess productivity.

Clients are typically high profile and international, and most partners specialize in telecoms. However, this does not mean that there isn't a diverse variety of work on offer. A glance at the firm's client list reveals big names like Google, T-Mobile, Comcast, and Iridium Satellite. One source explained: *"One thing you will learn at HWG is that even in the telecoms arena, work is highly specialized. I do telecoms work that I'm sure some partners here don't even know about."* Being on the *"cutting edge of different sharing technologies"* clearly has its benefits: *"The nature of the work is varied and interesting; it's a very broad umbrella."*

The Inside View

See firm profile on p.647

Rankings in *Chambers USA*

Telecommunications

For detail on ranking tiers and ranking locations, visit www.chambersandpartners.com

Recent work highlights

- Acted for Google, Microsoft, and Broadcom on a number of FCC wireless auction proceedings
- Advised DIRECTV in its $67 billion merger with AT&T
- Represented Comcast in large-scale FCC proceedings over wifi spectrum expansion, and by extension, successfully blocking Marriott's bid to stop the use of personal wifi in its hotels

"I was given an almost frightening level of responsibility when I started."

HWG has obviously learnt a lot from its clients. Communication is key and management's expectations are made clear from the start. An erudite attorney told us, *"I was given an almost frightening level of responsibility when I started. I say 'almost' because that is what I wanted."* Tales abounded of *"relatively junior associates being told to argue in front of a court."* Another excitedly divulged that *"my first week I was on a conference call with government officials and was the primary drafter on court documents."* This mature treatment was attributed to the fact that *"partners here are very concerned with career development."*

Training & Development

Perhaps these high responsibility levels are a reflection of the fact that the firm *"doesn't have a lot in the way of formalized training."* The firm's relaxed approach appears to work because attorneys are expected to be capable and to learn through being challenged rather than hand-held: *"The HWG approach to teaching someone how to work on a transaction is to put them to work on a transaction."* This lack of formal training is also perhaps down to the high number of lateral hires at the junior end. There is, however, a *"training CLE budget,"* and all hungry attorneys have access to an *"all-you-can-eat membership"* to the PLI [Practising Law Institute]. Being leaders in a niche field reaps dividends for the curriculum – *"the current president of the Federal Communications Bar is an HWG partner, which means that communications classes are usually geared toward things the firm is interested in, and we often host the classes."*

"How to make the perfect bagel..."

You can't profile HWG without mentioning their famous 'Anything But Law' and 'Nothing But Law' talks. Those adamant that training can't be fun should look away now. These sessions occur regularly and alternate between the two extremes. The former involve *"a partner, associate or guest speaker coming in and sharing their personal interests with the group."* Notable presentations have included: *"How to make the perfect bagel, the pleasures of Colombian cuisine, and how to enjoy a night at the craps table."* 'Nothing But Law' is quite the opposite and usually entails a partner or guest speaker talking about case law or something legal. This can include anything from *"a law clerk who worked on a famous amendment case at the Supreme Court,"* to *"an in-depth look at privacy law."*

Like the firm's assignment system, appraisals include an exercise in *"self-assessment."* Every year one partner runs the review process and they start by *"sending out requests for feedback and discussing it with you."* Associates will also receive a questionnaire in which they are asked about the cases they have worked on, whether or not they enjoyed them and what they learned. Partners then use this feedback for future work assignment.

Offices

"We have big conference rooms now!"

As HWG approaches the big 2-0, it can definitely boast digs to match its coming of age. It has been over a year since the firm moved into the Federal Communications Commission's old office and their new home *"feels more like a big law firm."* Most sources described it as *"a lot more formal"* and one source excitedly exclaimed: *"We have big conference rooms now!"* Crucially, the new office is in *"the best food area of DC,"* just south of Dupont Circle. Attorneys can offset burrito-induced guilt at the office's gym, to which all HWG employees have access.

Hours, bonuses and culture

High responsibility and a close-knit community mean that *"all the associates are together in a hierarchy-less mass,"* with only *"one or two who are conspicuously senior."* Though there are clear perks to this collaborative culture, some juniors did suggest that *"it might take a little longer to integrate here because there isn't much of a structure."*

"A lot of firms say they have a collegial culture but you can't not have that with a firm this size."

Nevertheless, most agreed with one enthusiastic source who said: *"A lot of firms say they have a collegial culture but you can't not have that with a firm this size."* Because of the layout of the office, *"in the morning, when you go*

See firm profile on p.647

to the kitchen for a cup of coffee, you'll always end up having a ten-minute chat with somebody." For those who see the law as a stepping-stone to another career, *"the partners are very good about maintaining a relationship if you move on elsewhere; alumni regularly join us for drinks. It's a family vibe."*

No surprises that HWG is decidedly chill about billables. *"They don't have an hours requirement. You work on as many cases as you feel you are capable of."* Although in some firms this can mean that lawyers are overworked, associates assured us, *"nobody here is billing BigLaw hours."* Most agreed that *"not having a target hanging over your head is empowering for an associate."* The bonus system complements this perfectly, which *"allocates tracking points and bonuses are then paid out quarterly."* All employees including legal assistants accrue tracking points based on the firm's profits. The system gives all employees *"an interest in the firm's success"* – *"sort of like being a partner."* As an associate, *"your salary stays the same but tracking points increase with seniority."*

"The firm is the proud owner of a large gong."

"The firm is the proud owner of a large gong, which we now sound to herald significant victories or the start of happy hour" every Friday at 5 o'clock. There are also *"monthly pizza lunches,"* which one gourmet assured us involve *"good pizza, not Domino's."* A unique innovation – and handy for washing down all that stodgy pizza – is the *"office kegerator"* presided over by a keg guardian *"whose job it is to keep it stocked with beer that is good enough for the keg guardian to drink."* So that's pizza and beer – what happens next? You guessed it: bowling. *"Mark Grannis takes bowling pretty seriously,"* and every few months there is a *"firm bowling night."* Apart from the obvious exercise benefits that these provide they are also the perfect opportunity for attorneys to sport their *"HWG bowling shirts."* These are given out to every new lawyer emblazoned with the year they joined: *"We now have 18 years of bowling shirts."*

Pro Bono and diversity

Because of the lack of billing targets, HWG treats pro bono hours *"the same as your billables."* Nonetheless, associates we spoke to were unsure about how committed the firm actually is to pro bono work. If associates are interested in something they can, by all means, bring it in. And certainly at the start of their HWG careers, if partners feel an associate is lacking experience, they will put them on some pro bono; an exercise one junior described as a *"mix of the altruistic and educational."* However, many of those that we spoke to had had a similar experience to the source who told us *"I haven't done any pro bono yet."*

As one associate put it: "*We are committed to diversity, though I'm not sure you'd know that looking at our website." But change is afoot. Jonathan Mirsky – HWG's head of hiring – mentions the work done by the firm's new 'diversity partner', Breta Strandberg, as evidence that they are moving in the right direction. This includes more flexible working hours used to appeal to women with families. As one proud attorney explained, "there are a lot of women. I feel like retention of women is something the big firms struggle with. I don't think they have that issue here."*

Pro bono hours

- For all attorneys across all offices: 1,779
- Average per attorney: 40

Get Hired

"Judicial clerking experience is a big plus."

Most attorneys are involved in some way in the recruitment process. The firm has a ten-person hiring committee, of which three are associates. In order to be hired, a candidate must be unanimously approved under a 'one person, one vote' system. Jonathan Mirsky explains it thus: *"As we try to form our consensus, associates are able to suss out information about our applicants because they are closer to that process."*

One member of this committee had these words of encouragement for potential recruits: *"I think it might frighten people off that we have a heavy focus in one area of law. I would encourage people to go ahead and apply; those criteria have nothing to do with your background or interest."* Since *"a good majority of folks"* join the firm as laterals, *"judicial clerking experience is a big plus."*

"The HWG approach to teaching someone how to work on a transaction is to put them to work on a transaction."

Applicants should be under no illusion that the interview process is a walk in the park – it is several walks. Since the firm hires so few people, sometimes candidates are interviewed four times before being offered a position. *"I think that says something about the firm. They are careful with who they hire,"* they thought. Associates were quick to stress that the interviews *"were never un-*

The Inside View

See firm profile on p.647

comfortable." Most agreed that suitability came down to this: HWG has *"two main hiring criteria: you have to have the potential to be a superstar attorney and you have to not be a jerk."*

Strategy & Future

The firm places a priority on foresight, and management is very keen to hire lawyers it sees as having *"partnership potential."* Through the points-based bonus system, associates are given an early taste of what it means to be a partner in the firm's success. But even earlier than that, expectations are made clear: *"When you get your offer letter it has a bit about your partnership class."*

HWG is on the up and up, with the firm – among other things – *"expanding into professional ethics."* New clients means more work, and the firm is *"busier now than it historically has ever been."* When pressed on whether this success would lead to geographical expansion, Bill Wiltshire replies: *"We've actually just opened a new office in Raleigh, North Carolina. Its very small right now, just one partner in fact but we're open to growing it."*

"We've been attracting an enormous amount of business. We just have so much work we need people here to do it."

See firm profile on p.647

Haynes and Boone, LLP

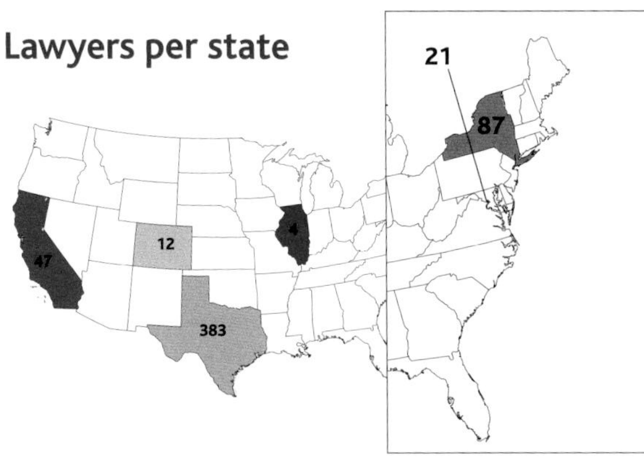

Largest US office: Dallas
US offices: 12
International offices: 2
First-year salary: $160,000
Billable hours: 2,000 target in Texas, 1,800 in NY
Summers 2016: 49 (38 2Ls, 11 1Ls)
Revenue 2015: $362 million (+6.8%)
Partners made in 2016: 13 globally (12 in US)
Famous for: a good work/life balance despite growth; Texan charm

This Texan's sociable nature and go-getting attitude continue to deliver in the Lone Star State and elsewhere.

HAYNES and Boone may not be the biggest bucking bull in Texas, but 46 years after its founding the firm is a major player in its home state and, increasingly, beyond. The Texan economy has over the years attracted new competition in the form of several big out-of-state law firms opening an office here too, but under the leadership of previous managing partner Terry Conner and, since January 2015, Tim Powers, Haynes and Boone has continued to offer something different to grow here and nationally. The New York branch (launched in 2004) is a big focus these days, while new offices in Denver and Chicago further power the firm's national ambitions. Chicago, it's worth mentioning, came from the August 2015 addition of an IP boutique, Mavrakakis Law Group, located in the Windy City and Palo Alto. A Shanghai base established in 2013 is *"focused on outbound investment from China into the US and South American markets, particularly in the energy technology, private equity and real estate sectors,"* Tim Powers tells us. *"Our China strategy is very different compared to most other firms."* The 20 year-old Mexico City office has also expanded with lateral hires recently. There's been a lot going on at HayBoo, in other words.

While energy is inevitably a major industry for the Texan, Haynes and Boone's *Chambers USA* rankings indicate the diverse spread of work on offer for associates: capital markets, M&A, IP, insurance, bankruptcy/restructuring, real estate, antitrust, general litigation, and Latin American investment, among others. Getting bigger doesn't necessarily mean getting more BigLaw, however, and the firm still places high importance on letting associates have a life of their own. *"I think the work/life balance is as good as it gets for a larger firm,"* one third-year told us. Revenue in 2015 rose nearly 7% to $362 million – another year of impressive revenue growth.

On chambers-associate.com...

- Interview with managing partner Tim Powers

ASSOCIATES SAY...

The Work & Offices

From our interview pool of 60 junior associates, almost half were in litigation, the bulk in Dallas and others in Forth Worth, Houston, San Antonio, DC, Orange County, Silicon Valley, and New York. Juniors involved in corporate work were more or less entirely located in the Dallas and Houston offices, and they constituted about a third of our sample. The remaining associates were spread around finance, IP transactional, IP litigation, real estate, and business planning, taxation & benefits.

Summer associates can try a range of areas during their summer program, after which the firm *"assigns you based on preference forms at the end."* Particularly in corporate, new junior associates can pick up a variety of work: *"I was in all transactional groups, and after a year they asked me if I wanted to focus on just one,"* one

The Inside View

See firm profile on p.648

Rankings in *Chambers USA*

Antitrust	Insurance
Banking & Finance	Intellectual Property
Bankruptcy/Restructuring	Labor & Employment
Capital Markets	Latin American Investment
Corporate/M&A	Litigation
Energy & Natural Resources	Real Estate
Environment	Tax
Franchising	Technology
Healthcare	

For detail on ranking tiers and ranking locations, visit www.chambersandpartners.com

Recent work highlights

- Advised American Electric Power in $550 million sale of barge operations subsidiary AEP River Operations
- Assisted WhiteWave Foods in its $550 million acquisition of Vega, a Canada-based producer of nutritional foods
- Acted as counsel to a group of leading Mexican institutional investors in their $2.1 billion joint venture with Canadian pension fund manager Caisse de dépôt et placement du Québec, for investments in Mexican infrastructure
- Represented Bank of America in connection with a $1 billion senior term loan facility for Prologis

told us. Another added: *"Here in the corporate group they let you dabble in what you want for the first year or so, then naturally you gravitate toward one discipline."* Although new starters are assigned a supervising partner who's in charge of workflow over the first few months, a few talked of knocking on doors, even simply because *"some people forget there's a new associate, so it was good to just go and say hello and remind them I'm here."*

Day-to-day responsibility levels vary. One associate in litigation spoke of how *"during my first month I got pulled in on an appeal on the Sixth Circuit, and I got to write an entire section for that."* Corporate sources described handling closing calls and drafting purchase agreements, although there is still *"a fair amount of due diligence and document review."* Deal size usually dictates the amount of responsibility offered: *"I've been given small deals in the $10-15 million range to work through on my own, while on the bigger deals I'm a cog in the machine."* Associates described a lot of M&A work and a fair amount of private equity cases. There is also overlap with other areas including energy, financing transactions and bankruptcy. *"We work a lot between practice groups."* The litigation group has a similarly broad range of focus, as well as a fair amount of crossover with other areas including white-collar, government investigations, and healthcare regulatory matters.

"I'm the client's first point of contact."

Those working in IP had lots of contact with their clients, *"regularly interviewing inventors,"* and other tasks include *"drafting patent applications and communicating with the Patent Office to get the patent allowed."* In finance, the focus tends to be on lending. One of the group's juniors described recent work with a smaller bank: *"I've taken on that entire process; I don't think anybody else even gets copied on their emails. I'm the client's first point of contact."*

Just as overlap in the work is the norm, matters are handled between offices fairly regularly, too. All of the sources we spoke to had worked with teams in other parts of the country. A Dallas associate noted that *"the first big project I did was with a partner from DC. I worked on that probably 70% of the time for the first six months."* And the interconnected nature of the firm extends to the international level, as *"every month we have telecom section meetings with our offices across the world."* A New Yorker described *"doing work for the transactional guys in Dallas,"* another adding, *"I've worked with offices in Houston and Washington, DC. We're really well connected."* After all, it must be hard to feel excluded from the action when you're working in the Rockefeller Center and sharing an elevator with NBC. *"I can see what's going on in the Today Show out the window, so that's kind of cool."*

Training & Development

The introductory 'HayBoo U' training program consists of a week's worth of general orientation, during which *"they teach you about how to use your secretary, how to make connections with partners in the office: all the tangible things."* After this, training varies according to practice area. For those in IP, for example, *"the firm has a patent boot camp for new associates,"* while corporate juniors are given an introduction to their practice: *"They walked us through the documents, orienting us for the different transactions that we'd encounter."* Other areas seemed to have a less structured training process, with one litigator noting that *"there is nothing that's comparable to HayBoo U going forward. That's fine with me: I prefer to learn on the job."*

"I can ask the dumbest of the dumb questions like, 'How do I respond to this email?'"

All juniors are assigned a mentor, usually a mid-level associate: *"I talk to her all the time. I can ask the dumbest of the dumb questions like, 'How do I respond to this email?' Or more sensitive questions about strategy."* Others mentioned regular workshops that all juniors are

The Inside View

See firm profile on p.648

encouraged to attend, in areas like public speaking and negotiation.

Culture

"It's hard not to be in the loop," revealed one junior. The powers that be *"send emails out all the time telling us about new offices and lateral hires, and they have a state of the firm meeting with us every year."* Most interviewees liked this approach. *"I'm in a place that's investing in me and I can see myself here for the rest of my career."* Another reflected: *"As the firm is expanding it's great for people to grow a legal career here. You get to know everyone and learn how things work, and all of a sudden you're part of the process, and that makes me want to stay."*

"I'm in a place that's investing in me and I can see myself here for the rest of my career."

Many of our interviewees were keen to highlight their decent (for BigLaw) work/life balance: *"After a really busy week, I was worried about whether I would be able to take a planned vacation, but they were literally pushing me out the door!"* Someone in Richardson reported: *"Here people get together and do stuff. We'll go to concerts and rock climbing together. It makes work a lot easier."* Nevertheless, some felt the firm could organize more official social events: *"I would give them a C in that respect,"* a New Yorker grumbled.

Does this sociable environment extend to the offices outside Texas? While one junior thought *"they do try to keep that friendly Texas vibe in the New York office,"* another pointed out that *"each office alters its culture to make it more appropriate to their location. New York is more BigLaw, for instance."* They were quick to add that *"ultimately it's still Haynes and Boone. As it gets bigger, I think that we're maintaining that mentality."*

Hours & Compensation

"In Texas, there's a billing target of 2,000 hours, and depending on whether you hit it or not, you're put on high base or low base. The gap between high and low depends what year you are, and the difference between bases expands as you've been there longer." But while some associates seemed clear on exactly how their billed hours impacted their compensation, others were a little confused: *"I don't feel like they tell us a set number. My understanding is if you hit 2,000 then you're going to get a bonus, but maybe they should be clearer."* One junior even mentioned, *"I've asked three or four times and they don't really want to talk about it."*

"They don't want it to become about just hitting the hours."

Interviewees in Texas found the 2,000 target more than achievable: *"I hit about 2,200 in my first year,"* said one. In New York, however, associates faced more of a struggle to hit their 1,800 target. Associates who are close to hitting their target will still receive a reduced bonus. There was a strong sense from some juniors that the hours were more of a guideline, and that quality over quantity was still important, as *"they don't want it to become about just hitting the hours."*

"I forget they're pro bono cases at times, as we treat them like any other client."

Pro Bono

While pro bono isn't mandatory, juniors can count up to 100 pro bono hours toward their billables (and more with approval). Assignments in Dallas we heard about included wills, taxes and divorces, and working with the organization ACT to help disadvantaged members of the community take a stand against drug houses. In New York, many pro bono cases are related to immigration: *"We do a lot of work with situations where illegal immigrants are subject to domestic violence."* Houston associates talked about tax cases as well as *"lots of people working on family law matters like divorce cases."* One junior told us how *"I forget they're pro bono cases at times, which is good as we treat them like any other client."*

"I think the work/life balance is as good as it gets for a larger firm."

Pro bono hours

- For all attorneys across all US offices: 13,090
- Average per US attorney: 33

Diversity

Many associates mentioned the high proportion of female attorneys, both among junior associates and in leadership roles. *"In my group, all of the associates above me are women except for one. And only two people below me are male."* Others spoke of regular lunches for female associates with discussion topics like the problems faced by women in the workforce.

What about racial diversity? *"I don't think we've totally figured that out, but I don't know that any firm has,"* admitted one associate, *"but they're actively working toward it."* The firm does have a diversity committee and is making the effort to recruit more diverse candidates,

See firm profile on p.648

with a range of programs in place in Dallas, Houston, New York and California which bring in diverse 1L students for six-week scholarship programs.

"In my group, all of the associates above me are women except for one."

Get Hired

At OCIs, interviewers look for *"students who are excited about the opportunity to interview with the firm,"* felt one who'd been through them. Make sure you do your homework because successful candidates must *"demonstrate genuine interest in us: ask specific questions about the firm, its clients and practice areas."*

"Ask specific questions about the firm, its clients and practice areas."

Candidates who show initiative over and above academic performance do well, too, and involvement in law journals and law school organizations is a definite plus. But make sure you can back up everything you put on paper. One had *"put on my resume that I spoke French, and when the interview began, it was in French – not at my request obviously! So they will call you on it."*

Strategy & Future

"In the short term we are focused on growing in the depth and breadth of the markets that we're in," managing partner Tim Powers tells us. The firm is focusing its attention on three core areas of energy, technology and financial services, although the recent acquisition of an IP boutique and resultant new offices in Palo Alto and Chicago demonstrates commitment to IP too.

"We may at some point expand into London."

And what about expansion geographically? *"In the long term, we want to continue to grow in New York and California, and we believe that we should have English law capabilities, so I think so we may at some point expand into London."* Read our full interview with Powers online.

"All of a sudden you're part of the process, and that makes me want to stay."

See firm profile on p.648

Hogan Lovells

Lawyers per state

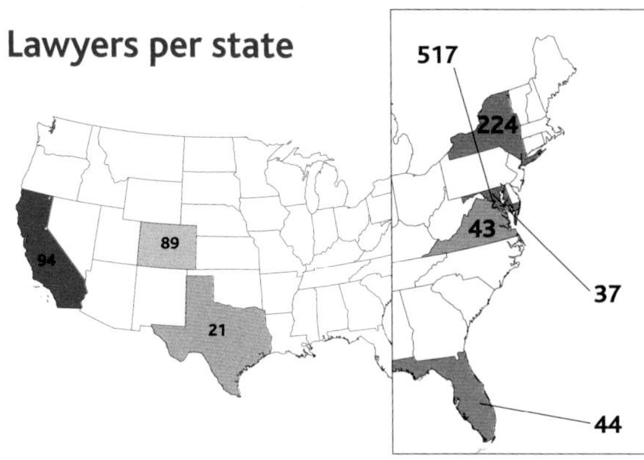

Largest US office: Washington DC
US offices: 13
International offices: 36
First-year salary: $160,000 in most markets
Billable hours: 2,000 target
Summers 2016: 102-107 (87 2Ls, 15-20 1Ls)
Revenue 2015: $1.82 billion (+2.2%)
Partners made in 2016: 24 globally (10 in US)
Famous for: its game-changing transatlantic merger in 2010

International heavyweight Hogan has a whole lotta' heart.

SIX years into its huge merger and Hogan Lovells is coming together in all the right places. You might assume that a beast as big as this wouldn't have the heart to match, but our sources insisted there's been a *"flawless synthesis"* of growth and care since the 2010 merger. Understandably, its 13 US offices still retain some of their distinctive pre-merger cultures and practices; but as Alice Valder Curran, a regional managing partner at the firm, puts it: *"I feel like now more than ever we are seeing the benefits of that collaboration and the formation of a universal image."* This image, she adds, incorporates a strong commitment to diversity both in practice area and recruitment.

With one arm Hogan welcomes juniors and with the other it educates; the firm offers a number of comprehensive training programs for its lawyers and, as this interviewee declared, *"is always encouraging us to expand our knowledge."* The CEO Steve Immelt also recently announced that the cap on billable pro bono hours would be lifted, a move that *"sent out a strong message, firmwide, that Hogan cares."* In April, the firm received favorable press when it was reported that it is introducing a single, nationwide bonus scale for associates.

On chambers-associate.com...

- Interview with Tim Lloyd, hiring partner
- Interview with Alice Valder Curran, managing partner

ASSOCIATES SAY...

The Work

Incoming juniors join five main groups: litigation, arbitration and employment (LEA); corporate; government regulatory; finance; and IP. The majority of juniors in our sample were fairly evenly spread between Hogan's LEA, corporate and finance groups. Only a handful had made either IP or finance their home.

In DC – the flagship office – new recruits are given the opportunity to do four-month rotations in different practice areas to get a feel for where they might best fit. The rotation system is by no means compulsory but juniors were grateful for the opportunity to sample. Despite this, most of our DC sources confirmed that many people end up opting to stay where they were first placed: *"It's less freewheelin' than they want it to sound, but it's nice because you have that 'out'."* Another junior enthused: *"I went to a happy hour with some lawyers from another firm. They said they did energy law. I asked 'Why?' They said, 'because we got put there.' It's not like that here."*

> *"Take ownership of what we are working on."*

In other offices, there isn't quite as much flexibility. Most juniors are *"recruited directly into a practice area,"* while those less sure *"have to decide whether you go the transactional route or go into litigation."* The approach to work assignment within groups is more uniform, we were told. *"Each week an associate turns in a report listing their current assignments, then you list the number*

See firm profile on p.649

The Inside View

Rankings in *Chambers USA*

Antitrust	Insurance
Appellate Law	Intellectual Property
Bankruptcy/Restructuring	International Arbitration
Climate Change	International Trade
Corporate Crime & Investigations	Latin American Investment
Corporate/M&A	Leisure & Hospitality
Employee Benefits & Executive Compensation	Life Sciences
Energy & Natural Resources	Litigation
Environment	Media & Entertainment
Financial Services Regulation	Privacy & Data Security
Food & Beverages	Real Estate
Government	REITs
Healthcare	Securities
Immigration	Telecommunications
	Transportation

For detail on ranking tiers and ranking locations, visit www.chambersandpartners.com

of hours you are able to work that week." This reflects management's desire for associates to *"take ownership of what we are working on."*

Rather than a top-down approach, juniors felt a healthy, collegial respect permeates the firm. *"Sometimes people will assume that you know more than you know,"* but a more relaxed hierarchy means that associates can always speak up and clarify: *"If you ask and you're proactive, its not a problem."* Overall, the workload throughout Hogan's offices mirrors that of other international behemoths. Most attorneys agreed that *"it's not so much that you have a lot of work, it's the unpredictability."*

Relative newbs are given pretty *"substantive work."* Litigators boasted of being involved in *"witness prep and drafting statements"* almost from week one. While a Virginia-based corporate associate told of drafting an array of ancillary documents while balancing *"a great deal of diligence memoranda."* Over in government regulatory, sources were especially pleased: *"The teams can be quite lean – just me and a partner and sometimes just one other associate. It means I've had the chance to interact with clients early on."*

Training & Development

Sources largely echoed the view that *"training opportunities at Hogan are phenomenal!"* One excited attorney divulged: *"Not only do they have internally-led training programs, they also make it easy for you to go out of the firm and complete the training you need to succeed."* Every year associates undergo one extensive program. *"First-years attend a general one, while second-years join a practice area-specific one."* Third-year associates are whisked away to Colorado for an intensive three-day

Recent work highlights

- Represented long-time client General Electric during the $9 billion sale of its financial services division to Capital One
- Advised TSB Bank on its £3.3 billion acquisition of former Northern Rock mortgages and loans
- Secured an asylum victory for a young gay man fleeing persecution in Belarus

program that includes *"courtroom scenarios with real actors."* So realistic are these exercises that *"things can get pretty heated,"* one lawyer revealed. *"You get to really grill these guys!"* Yet there's grilling of a more positive kind as well: *"Afterwards we take them out for dinner and help wipe the spittle from their faces,"* another joked.

"Training opportunities are phenomenal."

Once a year it's the associates' turn to be cross-examined: *"Around early September you're given a list of every matter that you've billed more than 20 hours on and you choose which hours you want to be reviewed on."* This approach allows lawyers to share with their superiors work that they are especially proud of. For juniors, assessment takes the form of a *"rating system based on stuff like 'firm-mindedness' and 'adaptation to the culture.'"* The latter category was deemed *"a bit too abstract really – no one pays it much attention."* Most juniors agreed that the reviews were *"pretty consistent,"* but a few did complain that *"sometimes it takes a while to receive the feedback."*

New starters are assigned two mentors: *"A partner and a senior associate."* Highlighting the tight bonds that are formed at Hogan, many told us that *"people tend to create their own relationships. The senior associate and partner ease you into starting at Hogan. Then, over time, you develop other connections."* Strong connections are also forged at the firm's famous summer retreat which takes place in DC for all summering associates. *"The retreat includes a lot of social stuff, a lot of ice-breakers, you make friends for life – we went zip-lining!"*

Hours & Compensation

From 2016, the billing target for associates in all offices is 2,000 hours. Before this new policy came into effect, associates in some offices said lawyers can choose to do *"1,800 hours at a reduced, below-market salary."* Those that choose the reduced target are compensated if they do reach the higher target. Most juniors agreed that *"not many go for the reduced target: it's mainly people with families and even then, they often end up hitting*

See firm profile on p.649

the higher target." Associates had varying takes on the levels of pressure they felt to achieve their billing target. Nonetheless, most concurred with a DC lawyer, who said: *"In DC, as a first-year, it's almost expected that you won't hit your hours."*

"Relative to other NYC law firms, my work/life balance is incredible."

The bonus system was deemed slightly opaque when we interviewed associates before the announcement in April 2016 of a single national scale. In New York, *"bonuses were market-rate"* but elsewhere sources were unclear about whether they needed to hit or exceed their hours in order to receive one. Another added: *"Laterals say that if you are even remotely close to your billing target at other firms you get a bonus, but at Hogan you have to exceed your target."* Now, regional differences have been ironed out as 2,000 hours is the target for associates wherever they are located.

The firm is very clear about its desire for lawyers to have a healthy social life. *"On a Friday, if you're working late, a partner will tell you to 'go home and do something fun'."* One New York attorney was especially thrilled: *"Relative to other NYC law firms, my work/life balance is incredible."* The firm recently ditched its mandatory four weeks for an unlimited vacation allowance: *"As long as you're billing your hours, there's no pressure not to take vacation,"* said one source.

Pro Bono

"Hogan has a heart. It has a live and beating heart," one source declared, rather intensely. It is, they added, reflected in the firm's recently introduced 'Citizenship Program'. The community outreach program is nationwide and requires every employee – *"even the janitor"* – to do at least 25 'citizenship hours' every year. The firm's commitment to pro bono is something that has drawn many attorneys to the firm. *"You go to a top firm's website and they all look the same. One of the things that stands out on Hogan's is the practice group especially dedicated to pro bono."* Facilitating this in both DC and New York there's *"one senior associate on an 18-month rotation,"* and in the former at least two other associates on four-month stints. There's also a nationwide pro bono coordinator who regularly circulates opportunities: *"We do good things for the Innocence Project, as well as stuff for homeless and veterans' organizations."*

Pro bono hours

- For all attorneys across all US offices: 77,199
- Average per US attorney: 79

Culture

"Hogan does a great job of marketing itself as a friendly place," and in reality *"people actually are friendly, engaging and a little more laid back."* The hours may be demanding, but *"at 2am, these are the people you want to be around,"* one attorney reflected. Again, geographical location can affect culture: we heard, for example, that the *"DC office is a bit more academic"* while the *"NY office is more frenetic."* Along with its hectic pace, the New York office has a nice tradition: *"When you get married the firm gives you a Tiffany vase. When you have a baby, you get a Tiffany rattle."*

The other offices conform somewhat to regional stereotypes; the Virginia office is *"homely and tight-knit,"* while an LA associate gushed over their office's *"SoCal culture: casual, relatable, tight and relaxed."*

"If you come to Hogan, you are not only going to be a very good lawyer, you are going to develop expertise."

Alice Valder Curran, regional managing partner

The desire to recruit the right kind of *"people-person"* applies to lateral hires as much as juniors. One source revealed that during the recruitment of a partner in their office, *"the head sent out an email detailing the candidate's attributes, flagging that they were 'a good person and a lot of fun.' I don't know anywhere else where this would've been taken into consideration."*

"We can go to a soul concert and get down."

Diversity

From the DC office, Hogan directs its diversity initiatives across the land via its array of committees. These include: *"An African-American committee, Latin-American committee, LGBT committee and many more."* Once a year the firm hosts its 'Pathways to Success' conference: the firm's African-American associates are invited to the capital, where they meet with diverse law students and offer advice on their career paths. One associate gushed about the firm's desire to celebrate diversity among its clients as well as its lawyers: *"The other day we rented out a suite in the Verizon Center and networked with diverse clients... maybe we don't know how to play golf, but we can go to a soul concert and get down."* Bucking

See firm profile on p.649

the trend across the country is Hogan's Virginia office, where *"most of the corporate partners are female."*

Offices

Most associates were keen to stress the leaps and bounds the firm had made with regards to inter-office cooperation. *"When this firm says it's one firm, it means it. I just got off a really high-profile deal and my team was made up of attorneys based in five different cities."* The 2010 merger between Hogan & Hartson and Lovells was designed to maximize the combined firm's international presence, but domestic space has been augmented too: *"Every attorney has their own office, they are very nice and of an adequate size."* At the moment, junior associates in DC are given windowless offices – *"which can be stifling."* However, after its planned renovation *"everyone will be given a portal to the outside world."*

Get Hired

An interest in the outside world is always a plus for those looking to become part of the Hogan family. *"Law school geniuses aren't necessarily what they are looking for. First and foremost, they want people who are well rounded. People with a bit of work experience are sought after too, as they can bring that to the table when dealing with and advising clients."* When it comes to the summer retreats in DC, associates are encouraged to organize activities and get thoroughly stuck into the social side of things. One associate raved about *"a microbrewery tour for the summers: there weren't any partners there judging them and everybody had a whale of a time!"*

Strategy & Future

Regional managing partner Alice Valder Curran believes that after six years, Hogan is finally able to move forward after consolidating post-merger: *"It takes time to get to know people in different offices and we have done that."* Though there are no plans to open more offices in the USA, the firm's international presence is flourishing. Fans of barbecues and marsupials will be glad to hear that management is looking at expansion Down Under: *"We are working on our Australian offices; we have good people down there,"* Curran tells us. For the full interview, go online.

"People with a bit of work experience are sought after."

"The teams can be quite lean – just me and a partner and sometimes just one other associate. It means I've had the chance to interact with clients early on."

See firm profile on p.649

Holland & Knight LLP

Lawyers per state

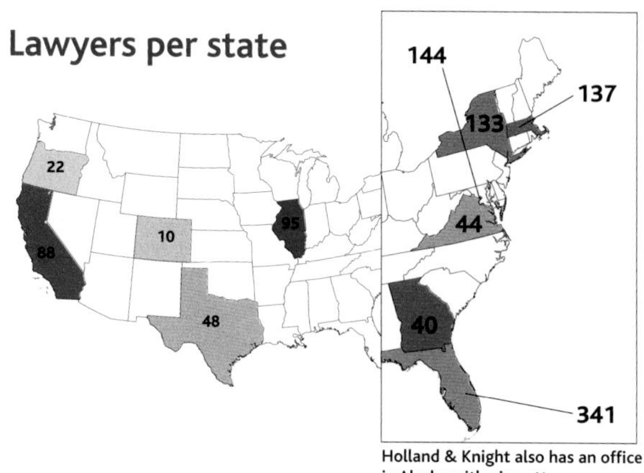

Holland & Knight also has an office in Alaska with nine attorneys

Largest US office: Washington, DC
US offices: 24
International offices: 2
First-year salary: $160,000 in major markets
Billable hours: 1,900 target
Summers 2016: 45 (42 2Ls, 3 1Ls)
Revenue 2015: $743.8 million (+8%)
Partners made in 2016: 31 (30 in US)
Famous for: big presence in Florida; national capabilities

Founded in the lightning capital of the USA, Holland & Knight has sparky associates who appreciate the "*good work/life balance.*"

THERE must be a special energy in Floridian air. Not only is it the state that experiences more lightning strikes than anywhere else in the country, but it was also the place that sparked the 1968 merger to create Holland & Knight, now a global heavyweight with 24 offices spread across the USA, and a further two in Bogotá and Mexico City. And, as the firm's recent expansion proves, lightning bolts aren't the only source of energy on offer, with the oil, gas and electricity industries providing H&K with an ever-expanding energy practice. The firm opened an office in Houston in 2015 to bolster its energy work, having only just set up shop in Denver, Austin and Anchorage in 2014. More recently, H&K announced offices in Stamford and Charlotte, opened in January and February 2016 respectively.

When it comes to *Chambers USA* rankings, it's hard to know where to begin. This Sunshine State's legal leader takes the top spot for real estate: zoning/land use in California and Florida, and ranks highly in an array of areas in the latter state, notably banking & finance, corporate/M&A, healthcare, environment, general commercial litigation, and tax. Go to the chambersandpartners.com website for the detailed rankings breakdown with commentary.

On chambers-associate.com...

- More on the work
- More on the offices
- We catch up with managing partner Steven Sonberg

ASSOCIATES SAY...

The Work

While some associates we spoke to had applied to the firm to work in a specific practice area, others hadn't, and therefore sampled different areas over their summer before choosing a preference when they joined as first-years (occasionally, those who are still unsure which practice area they prefer receive an 'open offer'). The firm is also *"definitely flexible"* if you change your mind further down the line, and we heard of juniors who had switched groups. Work at H&K is split into four sections, which are then divided into different groups. The business section, which comprises about 60% of new starters, is made up of the following groups: corporate finance, corporate/M&A, financial services, international & cross border transactions, private wealth services, public companies & securities, structured finance, and syndication.

In the corporate/M&A group, juniors were *"very pleased"* with the levels of responsibility they'd been given, as one second-year enthused: *"There is still some basic regulatory research, but I'm also playing a very active role dealing with all parts of discovery, as well as motion drafting. The work is available to you as long as you show you can handle it."* Over in financial services,

See firm profile on p.650

Rankings in *Chambers USA*

Banking & Finance	Leisure & Hospitality
Bankruptcy/Restructuring	Litigation
Construction	Media & Entertainment
Corporate/M&A	Native American Law
Environment	Products Liability
Food & Beverages	Real Estate
Government	Retail
Healthcare	Tax
Labor & Employment	Transportation
Latin American Investment	Wealth Management

For detail on ranking tiers and ranking locations, visit www.chambersandpartners.com

Recent work highlights

- Helped guide HFZ Capital Group's $870 million deal to buy a city block near New York City's High Line park
- Advised Mexican real estate investment trust Fibra UNO in launching a 6-billion-peso ($387 million) fund, which will invest in large-scale development projects
- Advised Corvias Campus Living in securing $548.3 million in private financing, to fund the initial phase of a partnership with the Board of Regents of the University System of Georgia
- Represented Banco Latinoamericano de Comercio Exterior, (Bladex) in the offer and sale of $350 million senior notes, due in 2020

juniors can expect a little less excitement, with *"lots of statutory research, drafting and editing documents, and due diligence."* The clients can be anyone from state and local governments to *"large multinational banks and regional, publicly-traded companies."* Tasks for newbies in public companies & securities involve *"mostly drafting agreements,"* as well as *"a lot of contracts and reviewing documents,"* plus the occasional research component for certain matters.

"The work is available to you as long as you show you can handle it."

Within the real estate section, most juniors do commercial real estate work within their region, although a few were specialized in areas such as transactions or land use & government. In the litigation section, most were in general commercial litigation, although there were two in IP and one focused on bankruptcy & creditors rights. Finally, the government section – the smallest with only four associates – was evenly split between public policy & regulation, and West Coast land use & environmental work. For more about the work in these three sections, read the Bonus Features on chambers-associate.com.

Although practice leaders monitor attorney hours, finding work at H&K is generally left down to the associates. *"You're encouraged to walk around and make yourself available, and to help out other associates if you see someone is overwhelmed."* Most of our interviewees had no problem with this free market system, although some pointed out that working on several matters at once can cause time management issues: *"There are times when I've had more work than I could deal with."*

Training & Development

Like finding work, *"associates are responsible for their own development. If you feel like a partner isn't helping you enough, you need to raise your hand and talk to your practice group leader."* That's not to say there aren't training sessions on offer, just that juniors need to be proactive in signing up to them: *"They're always emailing out different CLE opportunities. The firm has subscriptions to all the major legal training websites, so they definitely have the resources."*

"Associates are responsible for their own development."

Corporate newcomers have talks on legal developments such as *"any new SEC interpretive releases that come up, or any court cases that might have an impact on M&A deals."* Other sessions might be on structuring or closing a deal. Litigators, meanwhile, had taken part in more hands-on training, on topics such as oral arguments and depositions, with *"partners volunteering to participate so we could get feedback."* A few insiders did highlight that a more formalized training system would be useful, as *"it can be hard to find time to fit the sessions in."* All are, however, recorded and put online for associates to watch at their leisure. Juniors are assigned an associate (peer) and partner mentor, and while most had found theirs helpful, others were less convinced: *"I haven't spoken to my partner very much – often people are pressed for time."*

Offices

The firm doesn't have an official HQ, something that managing partner Steven Sonberg explains is *"a historical fact that we grew up primarily with mid-sized offices in a number of jurisdictions."* He goes on to add that *"important things happen in all our offices,"* making for *"a very collegial and collaborative environment."* Our list showed that Boston had the largest number of second and third-years (12), closely followed by Miami, New York, Chicago and Washington, DC. There were fewer newbies in the Tampa, Dallas, LA, Jacksonville, San Francisco, Orlando and Northern Virginia offices, and

See firm profile on p.650

there was just a single newcomer to the posts in Atlanta, Denver, Fort Lauderdale and Portland.

"I absolutely love the space here."

"I absolutely love the space here," gushed one associate of the Boston office, which is located in the heart of Back Bay. The firm is spread between the 11th and 15th floors of the building, and *"on the 11th floor there are two giant outdoor spaces. I have a door to the outside, and during the summer people tend to congregate out there during lunch."* Other amenities include coffee machines and *"a fantastic restaurant in the lobby of the building."* We even heard about a putting green on the outdoor terrace (although none of our interviewees had used it). For more on some of H&K's other offices, go online.

Culture

Overall, interviewees described a fairly relaxed, no-drama environment with *"none of the stereotypical BigLaw firm yelling or belittling of associates."* Another recurring theme about H&K's culture was associates' ability to balance work with a social life. *"They aren't operating with unobtainable expectations,"* one litigator told us eagerly. *"They're very upfront and realistic about the work, but they avoid burnout by also understanding that we have a life."* Juniors were able to keep to outside commitments such as community work, musical interests and family responsibilities: *"They've acknowledged and encouraged me to have an alternative interest."*

"They aren't operating with unobtainable expectations."

Another way the firm supports the work/life balance is by being a little more relaxed when it comes to face time at the office: *"Some people come in later and stay later, others leave earlier and work from home; the work schedule is very flexible."* In addition, *"there is a huge respect for weekends. You will sometimes get something on Friday that has to be done by Monday, but they appreciate that you'll be working at the weekend."* One junior added, *"we encourage taking vacation and protecting family time. As long as it doesn't impinge on your work, there's no problem with taking a day off to decompress."* That said, the high standard of work required at H&K means that *"when there are hard deadlines, they have high expectations. And I think that's a fair trade-off."*

When it comes to socializing, it tended to vary according to office and practice area. A New Yorker told us: *"I had a coworker come over for Thanksgiving. We've also been meaning to try and host a house party; a couple of people have unofficially been allocated as social organizers."* For most, though, the odd happy hour or dinner was more or less the extent of their out-of-hours get togethers.

Hours & Compensation

Associates felt that the 1,900 billing target was *"a fair number, and people are OK with meeting it."* While a few told us that they hadn't hit it in their first year, *"it wasn't the end of the world, and I still got a bonus."* As associates progress, however, there's more pressure to reach the requirement: *"We have monthly meetings about where we should be, and if we're below that we can talk to someone."* There seemed to be some general confusion as to exactly how associates are compensated, because although the base salary is lockstep, the bonus is calculated though *"a combination of subjective and objective factors. What those are and how they're presented have been a black box."* Discretionary elements include things like commitment to the community and diversity.

First-year salary now $160,000...

Good news: in spring 2016, H&K increased first-year associate salaries in the major markets to $160,000. This was after we'd interviewed associates, who at that time were slightly *"disgruntled"* with the previous figure of $145,000: *"I think we're worthy of market rates,"* one source had grumbled. *"I feel like our work is completely on the same plane as other firms."* And it's now rewarded thus...

"They're very upfront and realistic about the work, but they avoid burnout by also understanding that we have a life."

Pro Bono

Pro bono work is *"baked into the culture"* at H&K, and 100 PB hours count toward billables, assuming you hit the 1,900 target (including pro bono). Beyond this, *"if it's a big project you really care about, you can petition to have more count."* Most of the associates we interviewed had reached around 100 hours, with some exceeding this number. We heard of various activities, including working on veterans' claims and compensation, helping large nonprofits set up in a new state or country, volunteering at a homeless shelter and working for Kids In Need of Defense (KIND). The latter organization represents immigrant and refugee children: *"We help to get special immigration status or asylum for the children, based on their background, so they aren't automatically*

See firm profile on p.650

deported." Offices around the firm also have a community service day each year around 9/11.

Pro bono hours

- For all attorneys across all US offices: 60,375
- Average per US attorney: 55

Diversity

When it comes to ethnic minorities, *"the offices that are in more diverse markets match that,"* and those in Florida reported a more diverse group compared to Boston, for example. *"It's not the most diverse office in the world,"* one Boston-based associate remarked. *"There are a lot of white male partners."*

"Help them develop a more fine-tuned practice with an eye to becoming partner."

The firm fares better with female employment, at least at associate level. An attorney in Tampa commented that *"when I started, there weren't many female associates, but two years later, females outnumber males!"* A New York newbie added that the women's initiative *"has lunch once a month within the office, and we'll discuss articles and talk about some of the accomplishments that the women here have had."* Holland & Knight also has the 'Rising Star' program, aimed at female associates, to *"help them develop a more fine-tuned practice with an eye to becoming partner."*

Get Hired

Taking ownership of your work is a valuable skill at Holland & Knight, as *"partners are looking to be the passengers and let us drive; they'll just correct us when we get too close to one side!"* Considering that associates are largely responsible for finding their own work, a self-starting attitude does well too: *"You thrive here if you're going to step outside the box, find the work you want to do and focus on that. Nobody is going to guide you the whole way."*

"Partners are looking to be the passengers and let us drive."

Personality-wise, recruiters look for *"the individual that shows he or she is part of the team and demonstrates camaraderie. I don't think the stereotypical Type A personality is very accepted in a social sense."* Intellectual curiosity gets you a long way, too, as *"they appreciate a passion for your subject."* And before your interview, make sure to *"research the partners and understand what each practice area does, and be prepared to demonstrate that knowledge."*

Strategy & Future

MP Steven Sonberg tells us that the firm's hefty growth in recent months is part of a geographic strategy *"to focus on the US as well as Latin America, and that's really where we've targeted our geographic expansion."* He adds that *"while we don't have any additional offices we're ready to talk about, we're seeing a continuing number of opportunities."* As far as practice areas go, *"in litigation, we have expanded our practices in white collar defense and IP. In the corporate area, private equity and finance are two core areas we've strengthened."* Sonberg continues, *"we've identified six industries that are particularly important to us and strong: real estate, healthcare, financial services, technology, transportation, and energy & natural resources."* Go online to read his full interview.

"You're encouraged to walk around and make yourself available, and to help out other associates if you see someone is overwhelmed."

See firm profile on p.650

Hughes Hubbard & Reed LLP

Lawyers per state

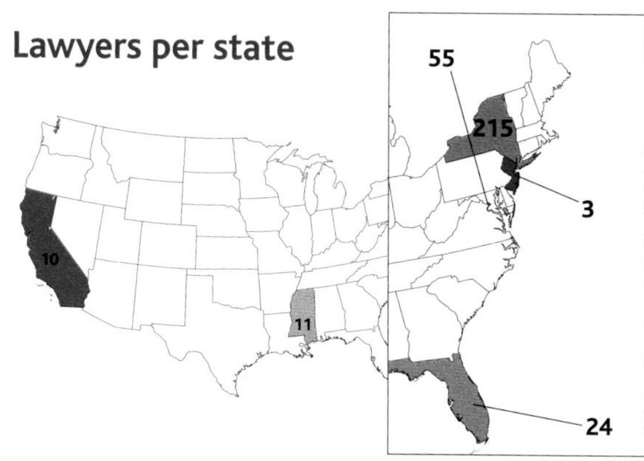

Largest US office: New York
US offices: 6
International offices: 2
First-year salary: $160,000
Billable hours: 1,950 target (1,750 billable)
Summers 2016: 22 (20 2Ls, 1 1L, 1 other)
Revenue 2015: $361.5million (-8.3%)
Partners made in 2016: 2
Famous for: founded by statesman Charles Evans Hughes; historic diversity achievements

Litigation is the largest practice at this New Yorker, which combines international scope with a small-firm feel.

THE 'Hughes' part of Hughes Hubbard's name is pretty significant. You've hopefully heard of Charles Evans Hughes, the statesman, Republican politician and jurist who, in 1888, joined the firm that would later become Hughes Hubbard & Reed. While Hughes himself had ambitions beyond Wall Street (he narrowly lost the 1916 presidential election to Woodrow Wilson), his firm went from strength to strength. Nowadays, it has six US offices, two international bases, in Tokyo and Paris, and a clutch of national-level *Chambers USA* rankings for product liability, aviation finance, international trade and international arbitration. Indeed, interviewees cited the firm's *"strong international practices"* as a major draw, while also praising its accommodating size.

ASSOCIATES SAY...

The Work

Most new juniors head to New York. DC also takes on newcomers and at the time of our calls there were a couple in Miami as well. Most are litigators, although there are some corporate juniors and a sprinkling in tax and IP. For those in New York and DC, the process of getting staffed on matters is fairly formalized. *"We have traffic managers and partners in charge of making sure that people are assigned work in the beginning and that it's evenly distributed between associates."* However, *"you do have the ability to shape your practice. After you've been here for a while, you get a sense of who you like to work with and build up relationships with them."* According to one litigator, *"when I came in I was doing a bit of everything. Last year I worked exclusively on an insurance matter, but I knew I wanted to do white-collar work and reached out to a partner."*

On chambers-associate.com...

- Interview with DC managing partner Bill Stein

Lots of our sources were involved in anticorruption and white-collar investigations. *"We're generally working for pretty large multinational corporations, occasionally individuals, doing internal investigations and compliance work,"* explained an interviewee. *"Some clients have been sanctioned by The World Bank, the DOJ or some regulator. As part of settlement there's a compliance program and we help them to strengthen their FCPA compliance and successfully meet the goals set by the enforcement agency."* Sources informed us that *"in this practice area there's not a lot of legal research, because most cases don't get to trial. Typically I'm reading emails, contracts and files. A lot of doc review is inevitable, then I can draft a chronology, put together a report and drafting emails and memos."* Also, *"there's a lot of client time and traveling to interview witnesses."*

"When I came in I was doing a bit of everything."

Over in securities, juniors had delved into class actions and spent their time *"preparing for depositions, developing questions to ask, reviewing documents, researching and drafting."* One declared proudly: *"My input is sought constantly. I do a lot more than just mundane stuff."*

See firm profile on p.651

Rankings in *Chambers USA*

Bankruptcy/Restructuring	Latin American Investment
Corporate/M&A	Media & Entertainment
International Arbitration	Products Liability
International Trade	Transportation

For detail on ranking tiers and ranking locations, visit www.chambersandpartners.com

Meanwhile, in the corporate department, interviewees reported *"working on a variety of matters from M&A to bank finance to securities, mostly M&A. I've been on very large deals and midmarket deals, both public and private."* Daily fare includes *"a lot of due diligence and coordinating diligence with more junior associates, as well as drafting some pretty substantive stuff like merger agreements, loan agreements and ancillary documents."* Client contact is also on the cards.

Training & Development

Incoming juniors attend an initial training week in the Big Apple, known as The Hughes Institute. *"There are a lot of lectures and panel discussions on life as an associate, including tips on how to survive. The rest of the week is litigation-focused; we're given an overview of every stage of the process and our responsibilities."* Corporate folk attend their own sessions. Juniors highlighted that *"it's a great program and an excellent way to get to know your colleagues."*

There's also *"substantive trial advocacy training"* for first-years in the form of an *"intensive"* three-day mock trial. *"It's fun but a little scary because you're performing in front of your peers. High school students come in to be the jurors and a Harvard professor was the judge,"* recalled an associate. In addition, the firm offers a range lunchtime trainings (*"sometimes put on by partners, sometimes by outside folk. Often they give you CLE credit"*). Sources appreciated that *"on the firm's internal web page you can seek training on any number of topics and there's an extensive list of video seminars."*

"We're given an overview of every stage of the process and our responsibilities."

Of course, a lot of learning happens on the job. *"We have a formal mentoring program which is a great resource but really subject to what sort of relationship you have – it can be hit or miss. I've got the best substantive support from people that I've sought out myself."* One added that *"I always feel comfortable asking questions."* Formal reviews happen annually.

Recent work highlights

- Representing former J.P. Morgan derivatives trader Julien Grout in connection with criminal and civil charges arising from the $6.2 billion loss caused by Grout's boss, Bruno Iksil, known as 'the London whale'
- Acted for the Federal Deposit Insurance Corporation (FDIC) during the investigation into claims of gross negligence brought against the former directors and officers of BankUnited, the largest independent bank headquartered in Florida before it failed
- Acted for Merck in its acquisition of antibiotics maker Cubist Pharmaceuticals for $9.5 billion

Hours & Compensation

In order to be eligible for a bonus, associates must clock up 1,950 hours, of which 1,750 must be billable (the rest can be pro bono etc.). Beyond that, *"it's a tiered system and pretty transparent."* There's also a nonbillable discretionary component, which is *"a little less transparent."* Associate reckoned that the 1,950 figure is *"definitely a realistic target for BigLaw. People make their hours pretty easily, we're super-busy."* Some sources mentioned that *"as a first-year it may be a little hard to meet, but the firm understands that it takes a little while to ramp up and they don't hold it against you."*

"I'm master of my own schedule."

When it comes to work/life balance, *"I find that seniors and partners are very considerate of your life outside the firm. I've been grateful for that since I've gotten here. People are respectful if you're on vacation. When you work late it's because there's actually work to be done – people don't give you stuff just to keep you here."* Of course, it ebbs and flows. A litigator revealed that *"last summer was the busiest time. I worked 250 or 300 hours a month. I had no balance: I was either working or sleeping. That was a crazy time! But then things died down a bit and I was able to catch up with friends and family."*

A certain amount of flexibility is granted and it's possible to work from home: *"I'm master of my own schedule, although obviously that changes if there's a filing or a short turnaround. In general, I'm treated as a grown-up and not micro-managed. My bosses are more interested in me getting my work done than where I do it."* Associates spend an average of around ten to 12 hours in the office on a typical day.

Offices

Asked about the office, the first thing a New Yorker flagged up was that *"there's a Starbucks on the site, which is helpful!"* Whether they're caffeinated or not, as-

See firm profile on p.651

sociates enjoy *"great views – we're quite near the Statue of Liberty."* The New York base is currently in the final phase of a renovation. *"We now have standing desks in every office and they've put an emphasis on light, so there's a lot of glass."* This transparency proved distasteful to some. *"My wall is made of glass and I have no privacy,"* one shared. *"I spend so many hours in this office and I can't change my clothes!"* Though obviously *"you can close your door."*

In DC, an office upgrade is in the pipeline. *"It's good that we don't share offices and we all have windows."* Although some described it as *"a little dated,"* one mused that *"it has more of a classic feel. The firm takes pride in its history and you'll see a lot of tributes to our founder Charles Hughes, as he's such a big figure in American political and judicial history."*

Culture

"It doesn't feel super-uptight. Everyone is impressive but not condescending," said associates. *"There's a saying around here that perfection is a standard for our work. The partners are committed to that, but not inconsiderate of your life outside work."*

The size of the DC office means *"you get to know everybody pretty well,"* though business travel schedules can mean *"there are fewer people around."* Generally, *"people have a sense of humor and don't take themselves too seriously."* The social calendar doesn't contain a whole lot of firm-sponsored events, but there are monthly attorney lunches. *"It takes a special kind of person to get a group together on top of a busy schedule but we do try to get together. Last year we had a big happy hour when the partners went away on retreat."* Sources also appreciated the business casual dress code.

"It takes a special kind of person to get a group together on top of a busy schedule."

Over in New York, there are *"pizza Thursdays and a breakfast every Tuesday morning where you can catch up with other attorneys and talk about your cases or life in general."* Plus *"there are good mentoring events which you can get reimbursed. Usually we have lunches or dinner, but I've also been to a spa and got my nails done."*

Pro Bono

Associates told us that the firm has recently become *"much more encouraging"* of pro bono by changing its hours policy *"in response to a lot of complaints."* Now, after 50 pro bono hours, hour-by-hour credit is given toward the bonus, up to 200 hours. Interviewees had worked on family and immigration cases, among others. The firm also works with nonprofit organization Human Rights First, which is currently campaigning to close Guantánamo. Lawyers also take on arts litigation, prisoner rights and HIV/AIDS issues.

Pro bono hours

- For all attorneys across all US offices: 50,922
- Average per US attorney: 131

Diversity

Historically, Hughes Hubbard has been known for its commitment to diversity – out of all the Wall Street firms, it hired the first female associate and made the first black female partner. Nowadays the firm is led by a female chair, Candace Beinecke.

"There's a saying around here that perfection is a standard for our work. The partners are committed to that, but not inconsiderate of your life outside work."

"History only goes so far," conceded associates, *"but I feel that the firm is very welcoming to people of all backgrounds. Hughes Hubbard is very international in its practice so there are people here from all over the world."* There are affinity groups for ethnic groups and LGBT lawyers as well as a women's group which organizes roundtable lunches with speakers and networking events. Despite the firm's *"huge, deep commitment to diversity,"* associates highlighted that there's still the *"frustrating structural problem in society that's reflected in the make-up of most big law firms."* Just under half (48%) of associates are female, and at partner level the figure is 23%. Among partners, 92% are white, and 70% of associates are white.

"There are people here from all over the world."

Get Hired

Hiring partner George Tsougarakis tells us that *"the ability to do well in a law school exam is the beginning and end point for a lot of law firms, but we're looking for people who can do that and in addition bring something else to the table, whether that's a skill or interest or something compelling about their background."* At interview, *"what impresses me the most is a candidate's ability to take the conversation any way it goes, whatever the*

See firm profile on p.651

tenor. People who can actually engage with you – that's the key indicator of success."

"What impresses me the most is a candidate's ability to take the conversation any way it goes."

Strategy & Future

DC managing partner Bill Stein tells us that *"we are not a huge firm and that's by design. We decided many years ago to focus our practice in areas where we could bring the most value to our clients in terms of high-quality legal service. We are not trying to be all things to all people. Our strategy is to grow in our areas of strength, or in adjacent areas, through organic growth from within the firm and through the strategic acquisition of laterals."* Bill Stein identifies antitrust, IP litigation, securities enforcement, and international arbitration as some of the areas currently being bolstered by the firm. *"We continue to look for this kind of careful, strategic growth in other areas of strength, such as in our anticorruption and investigations practice, arbitration, litigation and M&A,"* he adds. For the full interview, read our Bonus Features on Hughes Hubbard online.

"We continue to look for this kind of careful, strategic growth in other areas of strength, such as in our anticorruption and investigations practice, arbitration, litigation and M&A."

See firm profile on p.651

Hunton & Williams LLP

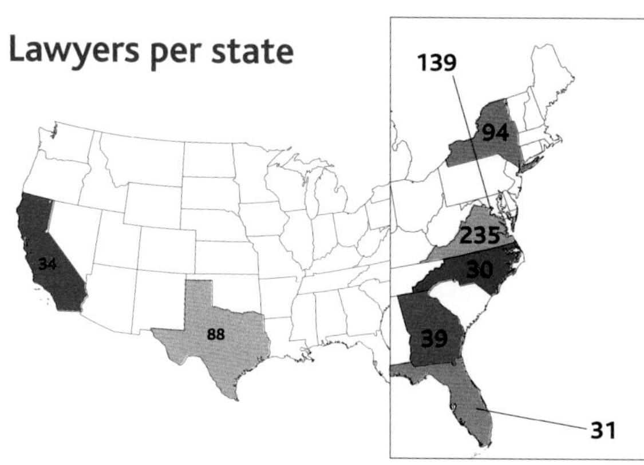

Largest US office: Richmond
US offices: 14
International offices: 5
First-year salary: $145,000 - $160,000
Billable hours: 2,000 target
Summers 2016: 35 (30 2Ls, 5 1Ls)
Revenue 2015: $528million (-7%)
Partners made in 2015: 6 (all US)
Famous for: modern Southern charm; global data security and environmental practices

Home overlooks the James River, downstream from the stunning Blue Ridge Mountains; one of this eminent Virginian's fortes is all things environmental.

MONSTER blue catfish, frisky otters and the nation's symbol – bald eagles – are just some of the curious creatures who make their home in and around Virginia's majestic James River. Of the human variety, you'll find the banks populated by those eager to partake in activities like fishing, white-water rafting and kayaking. There are also plenty of lawyers to be spotted – especially those displaying Hunton & Williams's colors. The firm's largest base, rising from Richmond's Riverfront Plaza, houses nearly 250 attorneys in all, who beaver away across the firm's full range of practices. Founded back in 1901, Hunton has since expanded beyond its native River City and nowadays comprises 19 offices across the US, Europe and Asia.

Recently the firm fine-tuned its strategic plan and decided to play to traditional strengths in four industries: financial services, consumer products, real estate and energy. When it comes to climate change work, Hunton holds the legal barometer, as it's recognized by Chambers USA nationally as a first-rate adviser in weather-related regulation. It is also among the nation's elite for providing environmental advice (e.g. Clean Air Act) to utilities, energy, chemical and manufacturing clients.

On chambers-associate.com...

- Interview with the hiring partners
- Interview with managing partner Wally Martinez

ASSOCIATES SAY...

The Work

Rookie Huntonians join one of eight teams: administrative law; capital finance & real estate; competition; corporate; energy & infrastructure; labor & employment; litigation; or tax & ERISA. New associates are assigned to a particular practice within their designated team. For instance, a litigator could join the retail and consumer products litigation practice, while a corporate junior could get stuck into corporate finance and M&A. As you'd expect, the Richmond base takes on the largest number of juniors, followed by the DC and New York branches. Atlanta, Dallas and LA also welcome newcomers, with a sprinkling in Miami and Charlotte. Generally, the corporate and litigation teams take the majority of newbies.

Sources were pleased to report that assignment is a *"relationship-driven"* process. *"After you've been here a while, you start to have specific partners you work with repeatedly. It's very organic."* Although *"people usually settle into a subject area,"* some interviewees noted that *"I occasionally work with partners on other teams as well. It's not a strict structure."*

"The doc review provides some respite!"

Corporate juniors commented that *"our clients are from a range of industries; it's not so much banks and financial institutions. A fair amount of them are energy com-*

See firm profile on p.652

Rankings in *Chambers USA*

Antitrust	Labor & Employment
Banking & Finance	Latin American Investment
Bankruptcy/Restructuring	Litigation
Capital Markets	Outsourcing
Climate Change	Privacy & Data Security
Corporate/M&A	Projects
Energy & Natural Resources	Real Estate
Environment	REITs
Intellectual Property	

For detail on ranking tiers and ranking locations, visit www.chambersandpartners.com

Recent work highlights

- Acting for pulp and paper company Georgia-Pacific in a case involving more than $100 million of cleanup costs for contamination in the Kalamazoo River
- Representing Chevron in an environmental cleanup case relating to alleged toxic contamination from underground storage tanks
- Acted for utility company Cleco Corporation on its $4.7 billion sale to an investors' consortium

panies." Clients also come from the pharma, technology, manufacturing and project management consultancy sectors. *"In the beginning, a big part of your role is due diligence,"* confirmed a source. *"But now I've been here a year I get to take the first draft of main documents like the purchase agreement, although obviously there are changes made before it's ultimately signed. I also take responsibility for smaller ancillary documents and side agreements that come up depending on the complexity of the transaction."*

Over in public finance, juniors get to grips with a variety of transactions, whether it's a *"simple financing like a school's water system or a sewer project"* or a *"more complicated public-private partnership to finance transportation and infrastructure."* Juniors draft purchase agreements, finance agreements, leases and supplemental certificates required to authorize the transaction. *"One of the things that makes me happiest about the firm is that associates are trusted at a really junior level to handle a lot of substantive work and interface with the client,"* declared one, sentiment echoed by those on other teams.

Meanwhile, a young litigator reflected that *"there's certainly doc review to get done, but if anything it's kind of refreshing. Sometimes you've been working so much on brief writing and putting together case theories that the doc review provides some respite! People think it's drudgery, but it's part of the practice."* Another source added that *"I've not taken a deposition as a second-year, but I've helped partners to prepare and have been second chair at a hearing in the Second Circuit Court of Appeals."*

"It's great that there's tons of training."

Training & Development

All new associates congregate in DC for a couple of days of orientation to cover *"the firm's systems and practices."* Throughout the first year, juniors can attend 'foundations for success' sessions that focus on *"skills a young associate should have, like interacting with partners, time management and working with support staff."* As well as this, partners hold practice-specific trainings. For litigators, *"there's everything from drafting a brief, conducting a deposition to cross-examining an expert and case management."* Overall, interviewees reckoned that *"it's great that there's tons of training – you could have one every single week if you wanted,"* but repeated the refrain that *"the best training comes informally from people you work with on a regular basis."*

"We're not Google."

One emphasized that *"the feedback loop is really good and ongoing. Partners have always been happy to give it to me. Although everyone's busy, it's never a bother."* The annual formal review involves associates *"putting together an 'I Love Me' memo that relates to what you've done over the year and how you made a contribution. You go into the review session with written feedback from partners and seniors you've worked with; there's a name attached to every comment so it's all transparent."*

Offices

Although the hometown office contains the most lawyers, the chairman is in DC and the managing partner is in New York, so it's hard to say which is the HQ. Domestically, Hunton has another 11 offices in its collection, as well as outposts in London, Brussels, Beijing, Bangkok and Tokyo. *"In terms of being a modern office space, we're not Google, but it's very light and bright,"* commented a Richmond source, while another proclaimed that *"it's lovely to overlook the James River and from the top floor you see so much nature, rather than a barren cityscape."* Over in Washington, lawyers reveled in *"gorgeous views of the cathedral"* and the White House. *"I still have to pinch myself when I come here!"* trilled one.

Culture

Given the firm's Virginian roots, we wondered if a Southern culture is discernible in day-to-day life at the

See firm profile on p.652

firm. *"There is some of that for sure,"* associates told us. *"Some old-timers prefer to be called 'Mr.' and insist that staff call them that."* A female associate pointed out that *"obviously the 'good ol' boy' Southern law firm thing is disappearing, and I haven't experienced anything that would constrain me because of my gender, but there is a definitely a kind of pride in the fact that it's not a like New York firm, it's a little more collegial. It's a congenial place."*

"The 'good ol' boy' Southern law firm thing is disappearing."

Another interviewee explained that *"engagement in the community is something that a lot of the older partners cherish and the opportunity to make an impact in the community attracts a lot of associates. It's not full of Southern stereotypes like seersucker suits and bow ties but historically this has been a traditional place. The firm has been slow to embrace a more casual workplace setting. That plays out in terms of policies – nonprimary caregivers are entitled to two weeks of leave and most men here do not take that, or even a full week. There's no pressure not to use the time, but it's reflective of different roles and expectations that are a holdover from a different era."* Those in the capital thought that *"the Richmond office is much more 'Southern' – here we're moving toward a large DC firm dynamic."* However, *"it's not a verbally brutal place. The lean staffing means you don't have to fight for attention or work."*

"After you've been here a while, you start to have specific partners you work with repeatedly."

The Richmond social calendar includes a Friday happy hour, which is *"lightly attended – people tend go home to their families."* That said, *"there are a lot of opportunities to socialize. People get together for special occasions. Recently the firm rented out a restaurant for the day to celebrate the World Bike Championships. You can only imagine how much that cost!"* Over in DC, a source listed team coffee mornings, a chilli cook-off and practice group pizza extravaganzas as social highlights.

Hours & Compensation

"This is a large firm with sophisticated practices, so it's a good thing to be busy and billing a lot," intoned an interviewee. Sources tended to have mixed opinions about Hunton's 2,000 hour billing target. *"It's realistic but it depends on how busy your group is. In some ways it's beyond your control because you're not the one bringing in work."* According to a junior, *"I have concerns about not meeting the target but as long as it's a team issue and not just you then you're not penalized. You're ineligible for a bonus, but it's not like there's a black mark on your record."* Speaking of the bonus system, *"it invites attention because it's so opaque,"* agreed sources. On the bright side, the salary has recently been raised by $10,000 in Richmond.

"I can make plans for Saturday afternoon and feel pretty confident that I won't have to cancel."

On average, associates spend about ten hours a day at the office and *"more often than not I hop back online in the evening after dinner because that's the only way to make your hours."* Those in Richmond praised the firm's attitude to work/life balance. *"There's a different attitude than in New York. People here are a little more focused on family and not being in the office seven days a week. That's not to say I don't work on weekends, but generally I can make plans for Saturday afternoon and feel pretty confident that I won't have to cancel."*

Pro Bono

All of our sources had taken on some pro bono work, confirming that *"the firm is very supportive of pro bono. It's never been a problem for me to leave for a client meeting, even though it's not billable."* Associates can count 50 hours toward the billable target *("it's not very much, frankly, but I've done 200 hours because the cases really interest me")* and emails frequently go out detailing opportunities. Interviewees had sought protective orders for victims of domestic abuse, worked with veterans on disability claims, and handled immigration cases and First Amendment issues, as well as corporate matters for nonprofit organizations. After vacationing on the Greek island of Lesbos recently, DC lawyer Adam Rosser witnessed the Syrian refugee crisis and decided to set up with colleagues a nonprofit organization, Sea of Solidarity, to help.

Pro bono hours

- For all attorneys across all US offices: 40,891
- Average per US attorney: 64

"It's never been a problem for me to leave for a client meeting."

Diversity

A female source commented that *"like any BigLaw firm, there's a lot of work to be done in terms of diversity. It's full of white men. I'd say it is a good place for women to work, and there are some women in leadership positions, but I did notice that in my review I was being evaluated*

See firm profile on p.652

by eight white men!" Most sources thought that *"diversity is a big priority for the firm"* and noted that there are affinity groups for ethnic minority and gay attorneys as well as a women's initiative. The Richmond and Dallas offices run 1L diversity schemes.

Get Hired

"We look for motivated self-starters who welcome a challenging learning curve and who have the drive to become fully engaged lawyers. Things move fast here. We encourage client interaction from the first day," co-hiring partner Tom Hiner tells us. Fellow hiring partner Kim MacLeod advises candidates to *"avoid focusing too narrowly when they interview. We have many national and global practices, and our hope is that candidates will have the interest and desire to explore as many of these as possible. I think it is also critical that people do their homework – while our teams and practices are nationally organized, we don't necessarily have all practices operating out of all offices. The important point is not to shut the door on opportunities and to demonstrate a desire to participate, a desire to learn and a desire to grow."*

"Being too specific and dead-set on a practice area can sometimes be damaging."

Strategy & Future

It's all about industry focus at Hunton. *"We're committed to our four leading industry sectors – financial services, real estate, energy and consumer products. In addition to those, we have a terrific emerging life sciences practice that includes healthcare,"* says managing partner Wally Martinez. *"Our real estate practice continues to grow and we continue to have success with energy and infrastructure work in Africa, Eastern Europe and Latin America; we're happy about those areas. Our public-private partnerships (PPP) practice is also doing well. Given the crumbling state of US infrastructure, and the fact that state and local governments are under tremendous pressure financially, we're increasingly seeing PPPs used to meet these needs and do it in a way that minimizes the burden on government treasuries. We're well positioned to play a role in that space."*

***"Things move fast here. We encourage client interaction from the first day."* – Tom Hiner, co-hiring partner**

See firm profile on p.652

Irell & Manella LLP

Lawyers per state

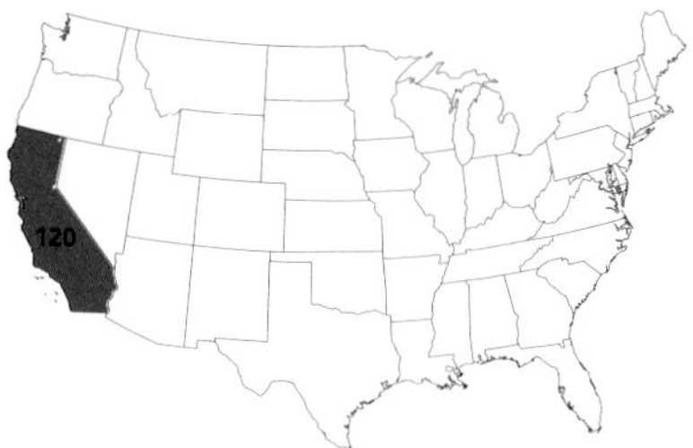

Largest US office: LA
US offices: 2
International offices: 0
First-year salary: $160,000
Billable hours: 2,000 target
Summers 2016: 20 (all 2Ls)
Revenue 2015: $199.9 million (–19.2%)
Partners made in 2016: 1
Famous for: legendary IP litigator Morgan Chu; its patent litigation practice generally; its intellectual vibe

Based in the City of Angels, this firm is heaven for would-be litigators...

ESTABLISHED as a two-lawyer tax firm during WWI, Irell & Manella's client base was originally the big names of television's youth. Since then, this Californian superstar has blossomed into an outfit of nearly 150 lawyers. The firm has kept to its media roots, nowadays representing film production companies such as Warner Bros. and Metro-Goldwyn-Mayer. However, Irell's golden touch extends to a range of practice areas, including securities litigation, bankruptcy, tax and – notable in particular for the fabled work of Morgan Chu – IP. The firm ranks highly in *Chambers USA* nationwide (and top within California), for its IP work, and is similarly well ranked within the state for areas including litigation (particularly in securities), and media & entertainment.

It will come as no surprise, therefore, that the firm is highly selective. As hiring partner Jon Kagan tells us, *"Irell is a platform for the best and brightest lawyers in the country."* And thanks to its smaller size, it is able to offer associates work that many consider beyond their years: *"Even in my first year, I've been able to do things you think of as 'being a lawyer.' I've been involved in how the case is going to progress rather than just being a supporting character."* Despite some instability at the firm at the beginning of 2015, when heavyweight partners John Hueston and Brian Hennigan took over 30 of Irell's lawyers to form their own firm, everybody we spoke to was positive about the future. *"The one thing that has remained the same is that Irell has continued to be successful,"* Jon Kagan points out.

On chambers-associate.com...

- Interview with hiring partner Jon Kagan

ASSOCIATES SAY...

The Work

The vast majority of new associates go into litigation, and only a few on the corporate side of things. The latter do a mix of M&A, licensing work and a lot of finance – mostly for venture funds. Their clients include a lot of early to midstage technology companies, and they can also expect many entertainment transactions. Within litigation there is an array of work, including entertainment, class action defense and securities, as well as copyright, trademark and patent matters within the IP group. As one associate told us, *"Irell has no formal practice areas; I would say about one-third of the work is IP, one-third is general litigation, and a third is transactional."* The firm uses a free-market system, meaning associates are able to try a mix of these or focus on one area: *"A lot of people come in knowing right away that they want to do one area, usually patents or securities. But there's also a sizable group of people who want to try different things."* All juniors are put on a case or matter to get them started off, often something they've worked on in the summer, and for many *"it just steamrolled from there."* Although there is a coordinator *"in the background,"* most associates hadn't needed to use this formal system.

"You're going to get early responsibility whether you want it or not!"

The Inside View

See firm profile on p.653

Rankings in *Chambers USA*

Bankruptcy/Restructuring	Litigation
Intellectual Property	Media & Entertainment
Life Sciences	Tax

For detail on ranking tiers and ranking locations, visit www.chambersandpartners.com

Everyone we spoke to agreed that Irell offers *"unbelievable"* levels of early responsibility. *"They're very trusting. If you want to hide out at a big law firm, this is not the place to do it. You're going to get early responsibility whether you want it or not!"* First-years spoke of tasks such as writing the first and second draft complaint for a *Fortune 500* company, as well as *"single-handedly writing a motion to dismiss for an entertainment matter."* One second-year added that *"there's really no typical day here in my experience. I've done a lot of writing, drafting motions and discovery responses, preparing for depositions and taking depositions."* Of course it's not all as glamorous as this, and there is some doc review, although *"by the time it comes around people are actually grateful for it because you can turn off for a bit!"*

Some spoke to us about being pulled onto high-profile cases when first joining the firm. *"I started in the discovery process, drafting parts of discovery motions. The bulk of what I did prior to trial was working with expert witnesses on reports, and testing products with them. It went from there into preparing the expert witnesses for trial."* When it got to trial, *"I did opening and closing presentations, and I took one of our witnesses and defended their deposition."*

Training & Development

Newbies have a week-long orientation which teaches them *"how to use the computer and other systems, what different departments such as the paralegals and document support team do, and where to direct requests for certain things."* Associates found this particularly helpful as *"we have a lot of different support organizations within the firm that can be hard to navigate."* As the first year progresses, there are various training sessions on aspects such as *"how to draft a discovery request, how to respond to a request, and how to cross-examine someone."* Newbies are also taken on a three-day retreat to a Palm Springs hotel. Afterwards, *"we had to prepare a deposition and they hired actors to make it as real as possible,"* while a partner sits in the room and gives feedback.

Juniors are assigned an older associate mentor each and share a partner mentor: *"We go to lunch once a month"* on the firm's dime. Feedback consists of a twice-yearly review, which provides *"very useful constructive criticism, things such as 'these are the experiences we'd like you to get in order to raise your profile in the firm.'"*

Recent work highlights

- Won a $234 million jury verdict for WARF [Wisconsin Alumni Research Foundation] against Apple, about patent infringement relating to chips used in most iPhones and iPads
- Served as corporate counsel for the Academy of Motion Picture Arts & Sciences, presenter of the Academy Awards, and its related foundations in connection with the issuance of $341 million of "Oscar Bonds"
- Representing Warner Bros. in a class action lawsuit challenging the way in which WB and other studios receive home-video royalties
- Won the dismissal of a putative shareholder class action over Tesla's $6.5 billion stock drop in the wake of highly publicized battery fires in the company's electric cars

Offices

All but one of the associates on our list of junior interviewees headed to the firm's HQ in Century City, *"a mini downtown."* There is *"a mall across the street with a bunch of restaurants, and a farmers' market once a week."* When describing the building itself, newbies told us that *"it's one of the less flashy buildings in Century City but it's perfectly comfortable."* Another pointed out that *"we have a really nice in-house coffee machine."* Associates have their own office and are allocated two small budgets for furnishing and technology.

> *"I have three pieces of art on my wall that I certainly didn't buy! It gives my office more character."*

The firm also has its own used furniture and accessories room *"which you can go into and pick from; I have three pieces of art on my wall that I certainly didn't buy! It gives my office more character."* The Century City office is currently undergoing a partial refurb. The Newport office was described as *"fantastic. I have a full-ocean view and because of the downsizing* [referring to the Hueston–Hennigan split] *anyone who wants this view can have one!"* Another added: *"It was remodeled in 2012, and everyone who comes down to visit is very jealous."* This office is located across the street from Fashion Island shopping center, where there are *"plenty of places to eat."*

See firm profile on p.653

Culture

"The culture here is intellectual and very friendly," one associate enthused, another more bluntly remarking: *"The stereotype of Irell is that we're a bunch of nerds, which works for me because I am one!"* A nerdy colleague added that *"going into a major law firm, I definitely expected more aggressive Type A lawyers who put themselves first, but here you see more helpful, thoughtful characters."* As a consequence, the firm has a *"quirky vibe,"* accentuated by the fact that *"there's a lot of people who have had a variety of experiences,"* from ex-military to people who have worked as agents in the entertainment industry.

"I come in to work to see other people because I genuinely like them."

Our interviewees spoke of a fair amount of socializing, many highlighting firm-organized events like the weekly happy hour, sponsored trips to concerts at the Hollywood Bowl, and the firmwide yearly retreat *"in the Newport Beach area during the summer. It's an overnight stay at a nice hotel, with dinner and casino games."* Associates also enjoyed coming together of their own volition; we heard of juniors hosting dinner parties and having meals with partners. Despite the option to work remotely, *"I come in to work to see other people because I genuinely like them."*

That said, because of the firm's flexibility for working at home, *"the offices can be somewhat empty"* come the day's end and many people *"want separate lives."* Over in Newport Beach, we heard there were also vacant workstations, although for a different reason: around half the office's attorneys left early in 2015 due to the Hueston–Hennigan split. *"It definitely feels different because a lot of the offices are empty, and a lot of people who I was very good friends with left,"* one associate remarked. However, *"there are so many fewer associates and roughly the same number of partners, so there's a tremendous opportunity to get lots of responsibility."*

Hours & Compensation

Most of our interviewees reported having no problems reaching the 2,000 hours needed in order to receive a bonus. They didn't feel huge pressure to reach this number, and *"if you don't you're not automatically in trouble – it's a target. They take into account the year, and whether you've done other things. That's another good thing about our size: people know where you are and whether you've been on a committee or something."*

"People will disappear for two or three weeks and nobody bats an eye."

Face time at the office is not a must, unusually even during usual work hours: *"I'm at home right now but I'll go into the office later for a meeting,"* one associate told us. The vacation policy is equally flexible, and *"if things aren't busy, and your case is settled, people will disappear for two or three weeks and nobody bats an eye,"* another revealed.

Pro Bono

"Irell is really great about pro bono," evidenced in part by the fact that *"every hour you do is billable."* So while associates are encouraged to do 60 pro bono hours in their first year, many reported billing far above this amount: *"I was in the multiple hundreds last year."* Pro bono commitments are kick-started in the summer, as the firm has a partnership with The Alliance for Children's Rights: *"They set up an adoption day where they schedule cases for associates to handle."*

"I've been involved in how the case is going to progress rather than just being a supporting character."

"On a pro bono case you are essentially the partner."

Once full-time at the firm, juniors described matters ranging from veterans' benefits rights cases, helping immigrant families get authorization to work, and aiding victims of mortgage fraud. Many juniors saw pro bono as a great way to gain more experience, as *"on a pro bono case you are essentially the partner,"* although partners are there to provide a safety net.

Pro bono hours

- For all attorneys across all offices: 19,196
- Average per attorney: 150

Diversity

Unlike pro bono, our interviewees didn't have a huge amount to say about diversity, and associates admitted: *"Honestly, it doesn't feel quite as diverse as it could."* The consensus was that the firm is aware of this, and initiatives like a diversity committee and a new diversity scholarship are steps in the right direction. Another junior told us that *"I'm part of a women's network which is working to create women-only events. We're planning talks on subjects like implicit bias."*

See firm profile on p.653

Get Hired

"The number-one thing is grades," one source declared. *"People here are universally very, very smart."* Irell has a lot of associates who have had careers in non law-related sectors. Hiring partner Jon Kagan explains the intention behind this: *"We have people who have been passionate about teaching children, or about pursuing an acting career. We want someone who can demonstrate that, once they get in here, they will transfer that passion over to the work they're doing."*

"Irell is a platform for the best and brightest lawyers in the country."

A proactive attitude is also important, as you need to be able to *"take control of your career, find your own work and partners to work with,"* according to an associate. In Jon Kagan's words, *"there are two main features that I really look for in a candidate: creativity and passion."* To find out what he means by this, go online.

Strategy & Future

Irell is certainly not adverse to expansion: *"Over this past year, we've added partners to our practice, and we're open to adding more. For us, it's really about finding the right people,"* HP Jon Kagan informs us. That said, the firm generally focuses on *"promoting from within,"* and will continue doing so. *"As far as firmwide expansion goes, our growth has always been organic."*

"Irell has no formal practice areas; I would say about one-third of the work is IP, one-third is general litigation, and a third is transactional."

See firm profile on p.653

Jackson Walker LLP

Lawyers per state

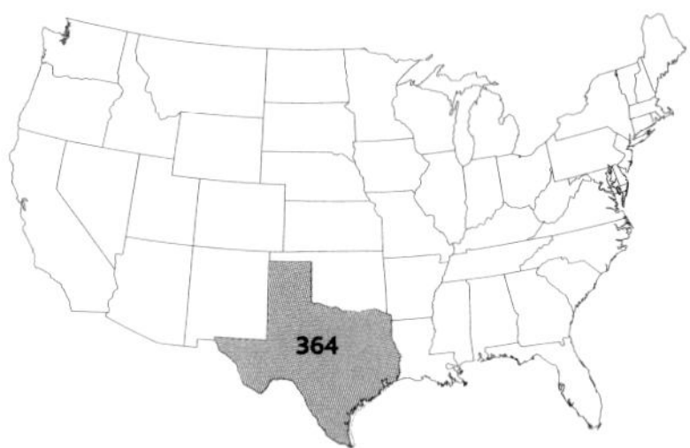

Largest US office: Dallas
US offices: 7
International offices: 0
First-year salary: $160,000
Billable hours: 1,950 target
Summers 2016: 26 (19 2Ls, 7 1Ls)
Revenue 2015: $221.54 million (+3.3%)
Partners made in 2016: 9
Famous for: being a Texan stalwart; having many partners who started here as associates

Texas favorite Jackson Walker offers a tasty draft of varied work, decent responsibility and culture that bestows a pleasant afterglow.

COULD Jackson Walker be the perfect Texas Tea cocktail? Mix one unit of *"very strong Texas presence"* with two units of *"genuine, salt of the earth people,"* incorporate a generous spoonful of *"family-friendly vibe,"* and shake well. Serve with a *"boutique feel"* and a *"sense of financial stability,"* but not 'on the rocks.' Known for serving a loyal clientele of *Fortune 500* companies, multinationals and leading financial institutions, this spirited Texan is one of the largest law firms in the state, but it doesn't abstain from national and international work. *Chambers USA* raises its glass to JW's achievements in the energy sector and real estate in particular, and hands it a round of celebratory shots for practices including construction, environment and healthcare.

Associates we spoke to had joined this Lone Star State fixture for its strengths in these and other areas. A labor & employment junior explained: *"There are boutique labor firms, but at Jackson Walker there's the potential to connect labor work to other legal issues across a broad spectrum, rather than be pigeonholed forever."* It's worth noting that most interviewees were either born and bred Texan denizens, or had some strong connection to the area.

On chambers-associate.com...

- Wave your right

ASSOCIATES SAY...

The Work

"One of the best things about Jackson Walker is that you get to try up to three practice areas during summer before picking one." Most interviewees had taken up this opportunity, and a few who already had an area in mind were able to spend the full summer in that department. In these cases, *"some experience showing commitment to this type of work"* was helpful. Most admitted that *"while they take your preference seriously, it's ultimately down to business need."* At the time of our calls, 14 of our list of second and third-year interviewees were in litigation, ten in corporate, a handful in real estate, and half a dozen dotted in energy, IP, labor, finance and wealth planning.

Once they get started, new juniors must contend with the *"entrepreneurial"* free-market system in order to get work. Some sources warned that this could be stressful: *"You find yourself working for several partners at once. They don't always communicate with each other, they all think their work is the most important, and there's no online system to monitor work."* But others found it empowered them and gave good early experience: *"The system is a great way of controlling your own destiny and not getting stuck repeatedly working for the same person."* It's worth noting that not all offices or sections use the free-market system; in labor in Dallas for example, associates are *"simply handed work."*

See firm profile on p.654

Rankings in *Chambers USA*

Bankruptcy/Restructuring	Healthcare
Construction	Labor & Employment
Corporate/M&A	Litigation
Energy & Natural Resources	Real Estate
Environment	

For detail on ranking tiers and ranking locations, visit www.chambersandpartners.com

Some insiders had the impression that JW experienced an *"exodus of litigation associates"* in past months (though the firm points out that attrition was low in 2015). They put this down to *"general attrition in the profession,"* and pointed out that *"hardly any have gone to competing firms."* One ventured that *"perhaps there's a frustration with the ups and downs of that kind of work."* Those who stuck it out in litigation concurred that *"the work is varied: eminent domain work, condemnation matters, defamation, personal injury work, oil and gas disputes, and partnership disputes."* On certain cases sources were able to *"draft and occasionally even argue motions,"* but even when they were *"mainly in charge of doc review, you become the person who knows the facts of a case better than anyone else, making you indispensable. Sometimes you're the only associate working with a partner so you really get your hands dirty. That kind of dynamic and exposure are priceless."* One reckoned that *"it's a sink or swim mentality here, which is daunting at first. They say that by your second or third year they want you to be able to handle a case from start to finish."*

"It's a sink or swim mentality here, which is daunting at first."

Corporate rookies were pleased that *"there's been a lot of activity recently – we've done well financially."* They put this down, in part, to the fact that *"we focus on mid-sized deals. We're a large firm but don't charge New York rates because we're not in New York."* Because *"we have a lot of M&A where we're working with the owner, we have to do handholding but get direct contact with the client."* Lean staffing on Jackson Walker's side, often just *"a partner and one or two associates,"* also increases responsibility for juniors. Tasks include *"drafting all the purchase agreements, ancillary documents and due diligence. You never sit around feeling frustrated that you're not doing meaningful assignments."* One proudly told of *"becoming the resident firm expert on a certain type of agreement after spending a few months on one as a first-year."* Clients can vary: *"Occasionally we have really big institutional clients, where we'll be the local counsel."*

Recent work highlights

- Represented Texan engineering company ZEC in the sale of energy company Precision Resource to Pittsburgh-based System One
- Media litigation attorneys successfully lifted a gag order against Dallas TV channel WFAA-TV (Channel 8) issued by the presiding judge in a high-profile murder case
- Successfully represented real estate company Virtus in the financing and development of two assisted living and memory care facilities in Illinois
- Represented private manufacturing company JB Pondexter in its acquisition of truck makers Reading

Pro Bono

"It's encouraged until it starts becoming too time-consuming."

While all interviewees conceded that *"the firm does encourage pro bono,"* most nonlitigators had *"found it hard to find time."* Associates are required to complete *"50 citizenship hours, but these can include things such as shadowing a partner at trial."* Transactional attorneys did find time to *"do some finance for Habitat for Humanity on behalf of a banking client,"* and a source in labor *"got to do an actual labor case where the client's employees were unionizing."* Litigators were more effusive, having *"handled a divorce alone from start to finish,"* an international adoption, contract disputes and a guardianship case. Still, a number of disputes respondents noted that *"the push for pro bono is more driven by certain individuals than by the firm as a whole. It's encouraged until it starts becoming too time-consuming."*

Pro bono hours

- For all attorneys across all offices: 6,930
- Average per attorney: 20

Hours & Compensation

That's not to say that the vital importance of racking up billable hours is inculcated into associates as the be-all and end-all of their life at JW: *"One of the best things the firm does is to not count your hours in first year. It takes the stress away and acknowledges that your workflow can be out of your control. All first-years get the same bonus."* From the second year onwards, the target to be bonus-eligible is 1,950 and all agreed that *"if the work is there, it's definitely achievable."*

"They want you fresh, with your batteries charged."

See firm profile on p.654

The typical day of a Jackson Walker junior starts around 9am and finishes *"either around 6pm, plus a few hours at home, or at 8pm at the office. They say there's no face time requirement but there kind of is. They also say that they value our work/life balance and that's true: we don't usually work on weekends, unless it's an extremely busy period. They want you fresh, with your batteries charged."*

Culture

Most interviewees chose the same words to describe the culture of Jackson Walker: *"It's Texas-focused, and the people don't take themselves too seriously."* One added: *"We take pride in being laid back, but that's not at the expense of sharpness. JW isn't one of those firms known for being friendly but doing subpar work."* Insiders also spoke of a *"lack of tension or negative energy"* in the offices, and observed that *"we're the kind of lawyers that clients actually want to have lunch with after a meeting: they've told us!"*

"It's not like I expected it to be like a sitcom..."

This didn't detract from a focus on hard work, and some did admit that *"it can be a stressful environment. It's not like I expected it to be like a sitcom, where I come in, put my feet on the desk and say something witty. Even so, workload issues and the attitude of certain longstanding individuals can get frustrating."* Still, associates admitted that *"longevity is a measure of the health of a firm, and you definitely see longevity here."* Fun things include weekly happy hours *"with hors d'oeuvres, a holiday party at the George Bush Presidential Library in Dallas, an attorney retreat every two years, a hired-out sailboat on a lake, and a family party at the Arboretum Botanical Gardens."*

Offices

The brand new Dallas HQ, taken over by the firm in 2015, is *"more modern, bright and tech-friendly than our previous digs. The location is also much more up-and-coming, closer to cultural events and restaurants, and there's a parking garage."* Associates get their own offices *"with the option of standing desks."* Houstonites were happy with their *"amazing views and nice chairs,"* until they *"saw Dallas's new space, so it's hard not to be a little jealous!"* Apparently Austin is next for an upgrade (though the office isn't moving). Austin attorneys were actually pretty pleased with their current setup, praising *"the beautiful downtown location overlooking the water, right in the thick of it, and the limestone building. Everyone has their own office with outside-facing windows, and we have a gym downstairs."* JW also has lodgings in Fort Worth, Texarkana, San Angelo and San Antonio.

"It's hard not to be a little jealous!"

Training & Development

There will be plentiful opportunities for upcoming rookie cohorts to check out Dallas's new crib: everyone is flown to the HQ for an initial training bootcamp, but they also return throughout their junior years for specific sessions like *"making ejections and authenticating documents for litigators."* On top of this, JW offers CLEs and NITA sessions, but many felt that *"you can't rival on-the-job training, and the onus is on you to seek that out."*

"We're not renting associates, we're investing in them for the long term."
Wade Cooper, managing partner

Similarly, while the JW junior calendar does feature a six-month and twelve-month review, participants commented that *"when you've done a piece of work, and you could have done it better, it's useful to know right away. Informal feedback is the best way to learn, and partners usually oblige."*

"Partners and senior associates we've naturally bonded with."

Relationships with their assigned partner mentors tend to vary from individual to individual, from someone who *"goes to lunch with my mentor all the time,"* to another more temperate account of *"an interesting relationship, where some things are better left unsaid."* Generally, though, *"we can all depend on one another when we're stressed, and on other partners and senior associates we've naturally bonded with."*

Diversity

Texas-based juniors usually comment on the region's overall struggle with diversity, so how does Jackson Walker fare? *"They don't do a great job, but not through lack of trying,"* came the consensus opinion. Most female respondents hadn't felt ostracized, and enjoyed taking part in *"tons of women's initiatives such as JW^2."* The majority of sources however pointed to the *"firm's poor retention of female lawyers, and its failure so far to come up with a flexible arrangement for mothers that actually works."* The firm has both salaried partners and equity partners, and one added: *"The women who do stay often fail to make equity partner. I want to see that the time I*

See firm profile on p.654

sacrifice will result in a payout." An associate in Austin observed that *"everyone I work with is white,"* and another in Dallas more leniently explained that *"there were no African-American students at my college in Texas either, so the firm does what it can given those circumstances."*

"I want to see that the time I sacrifice will result in a payout."

The firm comes back with some hard facts: *"In 2015, nine lawyers were made equity partners – five of those were women, all mothers. One of those women, Debbie Robinowitz, was not only promoted to equity partner but also named the head of our finance practice group, all while on the firm's Alternative Work Schedule. Over the past five years, our new associate classes were split evenly between men and women and were nearly 30 percent diverse. Of those new associate classes, more than 70 percent are still with the firm today."*

Get Hired

Jackson Walker visits ten schools for OCIs, asking questions *"aimed at identifying independence, intelligence, motivation, engagement and other characteristics that translate into performing well with our firm and our clients,"* hiring partner Jim Ryan says. Additionally, the firm visits *"some minority job fairs, consistent with our emphasis on diversity."*

"You can be confident without being arrogant."

After this initial round, shortlisted hopefuls are invited to their office of interest for *"an in-office interview that lasts roughly three hours, with eight to ten associates and partners."* HP Jim Ryan elaborates: *"Most students who visit our offices are highly qualified but we keep our summer program fairly small so we have to identify candidates who are our top targets. What ultimately sets people apart is academic performance, the ability to interact in a confident and mature way, the knowledge of the firm that they are able to demonstrate, and cultural fit. We have a no-jerk rule, so we automatically eliminate someone who is abrasive or difficult to get along with. You can be confident without being arrogant."*

Strategy & Future

"In the short term," managing partner Wade Cooper tells us, *"we will continue to be a firm that is financially conservative and that invests in its people. While continuing to be responsive to the marketplace, we will also hold on to our way of doing business, which emphasizes the hiring of small classes. We're not renting associates, we're investing in them for the long term."* And what can future partners expect in the long term? *"We see changes in the legal markets taking place and new client demands and we'll have to respond to them. We see the opportunity for growth within Texas and nationally, but we have no immediate plans to expand to New York or LA, or try to become different."*

"Longevity is a measure of the health of a firm, and you definitely see longevity here."

See firm profile on p.654

Jenner & Block LLP

Lawyers per state

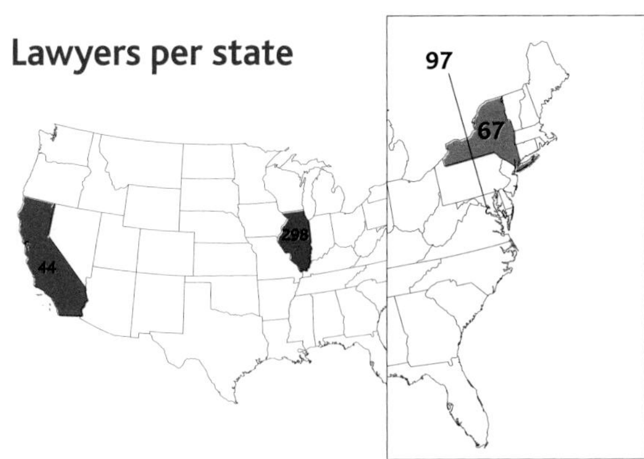

Largest US office: Chicago
US offices: 4
International offices: 1
First-year salary: $160,000
Billable hours: 2,100 target
Summers 2016: 39 (37 2Ls, 2 3Ls)
Revenue 2015: $464.89 million (+13.9%)
Partners made in 2016: 18 globally (all US)
Famous for: being a top pro bono player; its litigation reputation in Chicago; LGBT-friendliness

Its HQ rises like a green shoot from Chicago's concrete jungle, watered by Jenner's passion for public service, fertilized by its longstanding reputation for litigation, and blooming with new ideas.

IF Benjamin Button syndrome involved getting larger as well as younger (and fresher, fitter and more fanciable), it might be the perfect way of describing Jenner & Block. Once you free it from the image of Brad Pitt as a giant baby, wrap your head around this: Jenner recently turned 100, and while it retains a firm grip on its age-old reputation as Chicago's litigation hotshot, it is also growing dynamically. Inside sources repeatedly describe their employer as *"progressive"* for its pro bono prowess and diversity efforts, and its headcount and revenue are continually on the up. Add that its Windy City digs are in a state of the art, environmentally certified building, and further factor in that Jenner recently spawned its first international office, in London.

Its established prestige is as much of a reality as its passion for progress. *Chambers USA* awards Jenner top rankings in all kinds of litigation, from media and entertainment to insurance, and white-collar and government investigations. Its attorneys also distinguish themselves for their work in areas including corporate/M&A, tax, bankruptcy & restructuring and real estate. What's in the water at Jenner? *"Terry is big on innovation,"* chief talent officer Charlotte Wager says of fairly new managing partner Terrence Truax, *"and he has pushed us all to think about ways we can be innovative in our practice. We're also focusing more than ever on technology and how to leverage our tech to enhance client service. We've upgraded all our internal computer systems."*

On chambers-associate.com...

- Interview with chief talent officer Charlotte Wager
- Doing M&A in the middle market: Jenner & Block's perspective

Associates were open about their motivations for joining Jenner, and one reason in particular kept coming up: *"I was interested in pro bono work."* They agreed that *"Jenner blunts the edges of joining a big law firm."*

ASSOCIATES SAY...

The Work

In keeping with Jenner's pie chart of prowess, the overwhelming majority of associates can be found in the litigation department. Many litigators had gone through the firm's summer program, during which summers can try transactional work or focus purely on contentious. Seasoned summers then *"apply to the firm in general, not a specific department, but we never hear of someone who wants to be a litigator being put in corporate."* Once accepted into the ranks, junior litigators *"don't have to specialize until the fourth year,"* and even then many still pick up work from various practices. Participants appreciated the system: *"It would be intimidating to have to pick straight away. This way you get a chance to build relationships first."* First and second-years were involved

See firm profile on p.655

Rankings in *Chambers USA*

Appellate Law	Leisure & Hospitality
Bankruptcy/Restructuring	Litigation
Corporate/M&A	Media & Entertainment
Environment	Real Estate
Insurance	Tax
Intellectual Property	Telecommunications
International Arbitration	

For detail on ranking tiers and ranking locations, visit www.chambersandpartners.com

Recent work highlights

- Successfully defended Jay Z in an IP row after the father-of-one was accused of copyright infringement with his song 'Big Pimpin'
- Secured victory in a pro bono case for a freelance New York journalist seeking a video from the DEA of a drug interdiction operation in Honduras in which four people died
- Secured a win in a civil False Claims Act suit accusing a subsidiary of its client L-3 Communications of overbilling the US Army for helicopter maintenance when its mechanics were called to Iraq and Afghanistan
- Obtained over $17 million for its major record company clients when a counterfeit online music service was found guilty of willful infringement, trademark counterfeiting and cybersquatting

in criminal and government investigations, media work, white-collar matters and civil litigation, among other cases.

"There's none of the subordinate hand holding I expected."

From the get-go, litigators get work via *"a free market system with a back-up: there is an assignment coordinator but generally speaking you shouldn't need them."* Referring to the work, one put it frankly: *"There's none of the subordinate hand holding I expected. Most cases are leanly staffed which means you can get stuck with a lot of work, but a lot of it is substantive."* Doing your share of doc review initially is to be expected, but *"the documents become more complicated and you're able to have a hand in drafting motions at critical stages of litigation."* Others had been *"supervising discovery, taking part in strategy sessions, getting in contact with clients, attending a two-day arbitration and preparing witnesses."*

"Jenner is a sweet spot to be a corporate associate," one reckoned, *"because the department size means you work directly with partners. We've got some major clients as well: we're General Motors' primary lawyers. You're trained as a generalist, which means you don't get pigeon-holed and it makes you a better candidate to go in-house if that's what you want to do."*

Some felt differently. A disgruntled insider whispered that *"associates essentially get sponsored by certain partners and it makes it hard if you're not in one of those circles. It's not unheard of after a year for associates in the same class to have vastly different levels of experience. Sometimes if there's a big litigation case it's all hands on deck and corporate associates are asked to step in. Some people are protected from that by their partner mentors and others aren't. It's a crapshoot."* Ultimately though *"the experience you get from pro bono makes it a worthwhile trade off, and the corporate department is growing. There is possibility for development here."* Charlotte Wager adds that Jenner is growing its corporate practice and *"it can be challenging in the smaller departments like corporate to ensure that everyone is getting the same experience. In the end, we are a team here. Sometimes we need to pitch in to help others – we do what we need to do to serve the client."*

Culture

Sources brought their courtroom aspirations to their description of Jenner's culture. Exhibit A: *"I summered at other big firms and Jenner stood out for being more inclusive and transparent; they showed us stats and figures that other firms would consider confidential."* Worthy points for consideration, backed up by hard proof: *"It's clearly a firm that values your personal life. Recently several women were made partner while working reduced hours."* Concrete evidence: *"Huge value is placed on respect, to the point where if certain partners aren't living that out, other partners step in to fix these situations."*

"There's no Wolf of Wall Street *happening here."*

Interviewees also commented that *"we all share the same values, which doesn't necessarily mean similar personalities or political views, but rather similar priorities, like pro bono. Also, we're not flashy."* Not being *"flashy"* extended to the social scene, which stood out from the usual fancy BigLaw calendars. *"We have happy hour in the upstairs conference room,"* Windy City wanderers explained, adding quite cheerfully that *"it's rather subdued though. There's no* Wolf of Wall Street *happening here."*

Pro Bono

"There's no question that Jenner is committed to pro bono," came the consensus. *"It's expected of everyone, it's a huge part of why people join the firm, and they re-*

See firm profile on p.655

ally don't put a limit on hours." Sources also reckoned that because of its rep, Jenner gets the juiciest public interest gigs. They reeled off their experiences so far: *"I'm on an asylum case and an innocence case, and I'm driving both. Partners let you do that."* Another *"was the primary drafter on a huge lawsuit involving a number of citizens who were being sued under the Administrative Review Act in Illinois."* A third rookie wowed: *"I worked on a murder case."*

"I'm on an asylum case and an innocence case, and I'm driving both."

Interviewees explained that *"Jenner pays attention to associates hitting the benchmarks necessary to get on the Trial Bar in Illinois – skills such as drafting major discovery, taking depositions, drafting motions for summary judgment – and pro bono work allows you to work through those, so it's critical."* While all pro bono counts as billable, *"you can get over-involved in it: they won't be happy if you're turning down real work for pro bono work. If you're on a death penalty case and it takes 500 hours that's absolutely fine, but they don't want people taking lots of small projects to avoid doing billable work."*

Pro bono hours

- For all associates across all US offices: 54,455
- Average per US attorney: 108

Hours & Compensation

The 2,100 bonus eligibility target wasn't a source of concern for most associates. *"There's some leniency anyway. You're meant to roughly bill 2,000 and have 100 hours of pro bono or other firm-approved activities on top of that, but sometimes you can have more pro bono and still get a bonus."* The working day of a Jennerite *"starts on average at 8.30am and ends around 7pm,"* but most *"log back on at night for a few hours."* Some weekend work from home was frequent. Even so, all responded that *"yes, we do have time for a private life away from work, and the firm has been accepting of that."*

"It's a prima donna attitude."

At the time of our research last year, associates were still slightly miffed after the unveiling of what they considered disappointing bonuses. *"This year we got a memo explaining what the bonus would be for each class year. They clearly listened and made an effort to be more transparent."* All agreed that *"we are compensated generously for what we do here."* The point though, according to one, is that *"we are not Davis Polk, so complaining you didn't get a Davis Polk bonus is like complaining your Acura isn't as flashy as a Rolls Royce. It's a prima donna attitude."*

Offices

The Chicago HQ certainly sounded diva-worthy. We heard tales of a *"beautiful building with insane views,"* that sources *"couldn't say enough nice things about."* Every attorney gets their own office, *"there's a kitchen on every floor stocked with coffee and tea, and there's a gym you can join."* A chirpy foodie was a fan of the *"in-building cafeteria which sets up an amazing omelet station in the morning."* The firm also has bases in LA, New York, and DC.

"A commitment to growing our transactional side is key."
Charlotte Wager, chief talent officer

Diversity

While not all saw things quite as positively as the interviewee who exclaimed *"is it diverse? Up to your eyeballs,"* all sources had praise to dish out. *"Jenner is a liberal place, more open than other law firms. It's apparent from the interview process all the way up the firm. There are a lot of powerful women to look up to, and generally there's a robust program focused on gender."*

"Jenner is a liberal place, more open than other law firms."

Jenner is also known for doing a sterling job with hiring and retaining LGBT attorneys, and is consistently at the top of our charts for its success in this area. With regards to ethnic minorities though, interviewees were more phlegmatic: *"It's an area they can work on. It's less apparent."* Still, all in all Jenner juniors had faith in the firm's commitment to diversity, and frequently described it as a *"progressive"* place.

Get Hired

One source did feel the need to specify that diversity also means diversity of backgrounds, and they were hoping to see more schools represented in future associate classes. We spoke with chief talent officer Charlotte Wager, who said: "*We've stuck with the same law schools, but we've expanded our outreach a bit in order to target students more interested in transactional work. The strategy was very successful. Our 2016 summer program is a little*

See firm profile on p.655

bigger, and more of the summer associates have expressed an interest in transactional work."

"If you don't talk about pro bono in your interview with us, it shows you don't know us."

Wager also shares some tips on how to succeed at interview: "*We're looking for people who understand what Jenner & Block is about – who understand and believe in our core values. Not everyone is truly driven by the opportunity to do pro bono, engage in public service, and give back. We know some law schools discourage students from talking too much about pro bono because it sends the wrong message, but if you don't talk about pro bono in your interview with us, it shows you don't know us. On the other hand, we're not trying to attract people who only want to do pro bono. We'd all like that, but it's not how it works."*

Training & Development

Jenner offers *"orientation at the beginning, plenty of weekly CLEs, and some very helpful NITA deposition training,"* but on-the-job training and *"the experience you get doing pro bono,"* were equally if not further appreciated by sources. Six-month and 12-month reviews were another way for juniors to be confronted with their progress. Most felt these were useful, although several commented that feedback was a bit hit and miss: *"I don't always know how I've done after a task. Some partners give you a call after your review too, to talk things over, but others leave it up to you."* On the other hand participants spoke positively about their relationships with associate and partner mentors: *"I feel I can ask them anything."*

"I don't always know how I've done after a task."

Strategy & Future

Is Jenner on the road to change, or is it holding on to its old identity? "*I would say it's a combination. Our success comes from our commitment to core values, which are client service, pro bono and growing our people. Those things won't change. But to achieve success, we have to be nimble, to be open to change, and to find new ways to execute those core values. But we hold firm to our core values. We don't grow for growth's sake; we look at opportunities to see if they fit with our overall strategy. A commitment to growing our transactional side is key. We had ten lateral partners join us in 2015 and half were transactional, and we've added a further two there in 2016. We want law students and clients to recognize us not just as a litigation powerhouse, but also as a premier firm for transactional work."*

"Jenner blunts the edges of joining a big law firm."

See firm profile on p.655

Jones Day

Lawyers per state

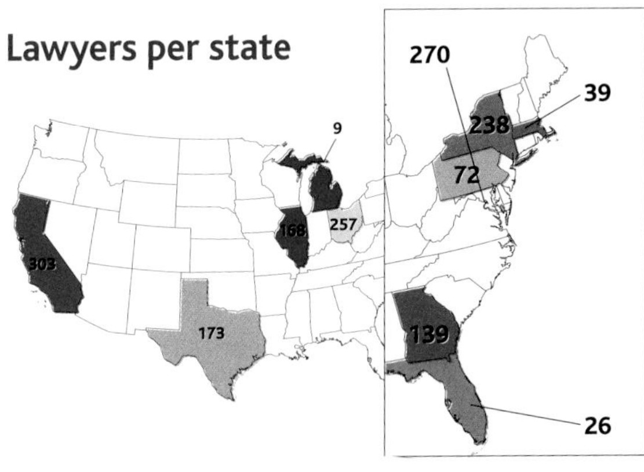

Largest US office: New York

US offices: 17

International offices: 26

First-year salary: $145,000–$160,000 depending on the city

Billable hours: 2,000 target

Summers 2016: 164 (131 2Ls, 23 1Ls, 2 3Ls, 8 SEOs)

Revenue 2015: $1.941billion (+4.9%)

Partners made in 2016: 47 globally (35 in US)

Famous for: being one of the world's biggest, most prestigious firms; representing Detroit in its bankruptcy

Like this globe-straddler's grand old age, associates' reasons for joining Jones Day were as easy as 1, 2, 3...

TURNING a respectable 123 in 2016, Cleveland-born Jones Day has had ample time to hone its great many practice areas. The firm is the cream of the crop nationwide in *Chambers USA* for its antitrust, bankruptcy & restructuring, retail, and labor & employment practices, to name but a few. Understandably then, *"prestige"* was among the top reasons why associates had chosen to join this global Goliath. The second frequently mentioned aspect was the flexibility of the first-year program: perfect for newcomers who appreciated *"the opportunity to try different areas."*

As for reason number three, the clue's in the slogan. Indeed, despite JD's impressive age, the firm is refreshingly outward-looking in its perspective – as its 'One firm worldwide' branding indicates. Associates told us that they were *"attracted to the collaborative opportunities that exist at the firm."* Sharyl Reisman, Jones Day's chair of recruiting, points out: *"For a firm of our size with our global presence – with 43 offices in 19 countries and five continents – that is trying to run an institution that does top-quality work, you need to have a unity of purpose. We have that at Jones Day, which I think makes us unique."*

On chambers-associate.com...

- We discuss strategy and recruitment with chair of recruiting Sharyl Reisman
- More on the work

In March 2016, Jones Day hit the headlines when it was reported that Donald Trump had hired its DC-based partner Don McGahn as his presidential campaign counsel.

ASSOCIATES SAY...

The Work

First-years join the New Lawyers Group (NLG) when they start out, meaning they can try work from any of JD's wide range of practice areas over the course of around seven to nine months. Business & tort litigation, M&A, IP, banking & finance, real estate and labor & employment are the groups with the largest number of newbies. Juniors sang the praises of the NLG: *"I wasn't even sure after the summer if I wanted to do transactional or litigation work,"* one told us, *"so it's good to explore and try different areas before settling on one."* Others did point out that handling several different matters at once can get tricky, although *"once you're in your chosen practice group it's a lot easier to manage your caseload."*

"It's good to explore and try different areas before settling on one."

In business & tort litigation – the group with the largest number of newcomers – we were told of a wide-ranging practice, as well as *"a lot of overlap"* with other groups. *"If there was a big labor class action that needed more*

The Inside View

See firm profile on p.656

Rankings in *Chambers USA*

Antitrust	FCPA
Appellate Law	Government
Banking & Finance	Healthcare
Bankruptcy/Restructuring	Insurance
Capital Markets	Intellectual Property
Construction	Labor & Employment
Corporate Crime & Investigations	Latin American Investment
	Life Sciences
Corporate/M&A	Litigation
Employee Benefits & Executive Compensation	Natural Resources
	Products Liability
Energy & Natural Resources	Retail
ERISA Litigation	Tax

For detail on ranking tiers and ranking locations, visit www.chambersandpartners.com

Recent work highlights

- Advised P&G on its agreement to merge its 43 beauty brands of hair care, cosmetics and fragrances with beauty products manufacturer Coty, for $12.5 billion
- Represented satellite TV provider DIRECTV on the antitrust aspects of its $67 billion acquisition by AT&T
- Acted for American Apparel as lead debtors' counsel in its Chapter 11 cases, filing for bankruptcy in October 2015
- Currently carrying out an internal probe for Volkswagen, following the emissions scandal in 2015. Jones Day is working to identify who ordered engineers to develop and install software designed to cheat US diesel emissions tests

litigation associates, for instance, it would be no issue for them to reach across. I've also worked on antitrust and bankruptcy litigation matters." Other juniors mentioned securities litigation and product liability cases. Responsibility levels are generally dependent on case size, but overall our interviewees were happy with the tasks on offer. *"On the bigger matters there is some doc review, but with smaller cases you get to do things like drafting subpoenas and various motions."* Another added that *"at trial I've had the opportunity to argue motions."* Read more about various other Jones Day practice areas online.

When it comes to actually getting work, sources described a system that is a mix of formal and informal elements: *"When you come in as a new lawyer, they have coordinators to help you find work that you're interested in,"* one junior explained. *"But you're encouraged to go and let people know that you're available and that you have an interest too."* There is a similar system in place once associates join a specific group; each practice has at least one coordinator that newbies can discuss their availability with, particularly *"if you have a slow month and need something to do."*

The Inside View

Training & Development

First-years are offered an array of training opportunities at Jones Day. After an initial week in their separate offices, newbies are taken to the New Lawyer Academy, *"when all associates from across the world come to DC for group presentations and activities."* After this, there are weekly training sessions which are *"initially very broad, based on general topics like professionalism, but as you get more senior they become more specialized."* Transactional juniors had sessions on topics such as the basics of contract drafting, while litigators have training specific to depositions and discovery. *"We had a deposition school which was good – it was not what I wanted to be doing on the weekend but it was a fun and helpful,"* one associate remarked.

"...patient teachers who will go over your work with you."

Almost everyone we spoke to noted however that *"the best form of training is on the job. A lot of the partners are very patient teachers who will go over your work with you."* A similar sentiment was expressed when it comes to mentoring. Although there is a formal system offering juniors an associate and a partner mentor, most felt that *"informal mentoring plays a big role. People give a lot of feedback and I feel comfortable asking questions and bouncing ideas off people."*

Offices

The New York and DC offices took the largest number of newbies on our list (around 15% each), with slightly smaller numbers going into the Cleveland, Atlanta, Dallas and Chicago offices. JD's other domestic offices are in LA, Miami, Irvine, Pittsburgh, San Diego, Silicon Valley, Houston, Columbus, Detroit, San Francisco and Boston. Big Applers were looking forward to a move from Midtown NYC to Brookfield Place in downtown in summer 2016. *"I saw a model office and it's pretty nice – there are going to be ergonomic desks,"* one junior informed us, while another remarked that the glassy layout will mean *"a lot of light and better views."*

Change is also afoot in the Cleveland HQ, which is currently undergoing renovations: *"They do a floor at a time, so everyone has to temporarily move. I think it's going to take a couple of years."* Sources reported that the newly updated spaces have a *"much more modern look,"* with new, convertible desks in associate offices. We heard great things too about the views overlooking the Rock and Roll Hall of Fame and also Lake Erie. Over

See firm profile on p.656

in DC, the office (within spitting distance of the Capitol) is formed of two buildings connected by an atrium, *"and the older building is pretty full while the newer one isn't."* One associate pointed out: *"I'm in the newer one, which is frustrating at times because sometimes I see almost nobody all day!"* That said, juniors in DC were glad of the two on-site gyms, cafeteria, *"floor-to-ceiling windows,"* and rooftop bocce court.

Culture

In past years, the interconnected nature of JD's offices has been frequently highlighted by associates, and this year was no exception. *"I've found the 'One firm worldwide' slogan to be very true,"* one junior told us, pointing to the New Lawyer Academy, where *"you meet associates from all the US and international offices."* Others cited the ease with which they can work with attorneys in different offices: *"We have a five-digit dial system, so you can call anyone worldwide – it's pretty seamless."* One junior noted that *"I never feel uncomfortable picking up the phone and talking to anyone across the firm, even if I've never met them before."*

"Whenever you call someone, they're willing to help."

The words 'respectful' and 'professional' were regularly used to describe the atmosphere within the firm. One DC junior mentioned that *"it's suits every day, which is pretty uncommon in DC,"* and while associate-partner communications were described by many as *"very comfortable,"* others reported a more deferential attitude. As one associate pointed out, *"the firm is not particularly kooky or idiosyncratic, it's pretty much by the numbers."* Nonetheless, juniors agreed that it is an *"open, friendly place to work,"* with *"very intelligent, helpful and resourceful people. Whenever you call someone, they're willing to help."*

"We're trying to hire the smartest person in the room who can go out and have a beer with the client."

Interviewees had differing opinions when it comes to socializing. Some felt that the number of events is *"less than other firms – it's not a crazy party culture. We have some nice office parties, but they respect that people have personal lives."* Others meanwhile had a more active social calendar. *"The firm organizes a lot of extracurricular activities for associates; I'm on the basketball team, and there's also a volleyball and baseball team,"* one sporty source mentioned. *"Associates take advantage of them and it's a good way to meet people."* A few also noted that regular office happy hours, as well as officewide holiday and summer events, were a good way to mingle. *"They often put events on for the NLG group,"* another junior added, *"and they have an associates' committee where people can go and bitch about things. If people complain enough about the same thing it gets changed..."*

Hours & Compensation

Most of our sources had had no difficulty in reaching Jones Day's 2,000 hour target, although there is less pressure to hit this in your first year, and for those that don't, *"you don't get in trouble. I know of people who were a few hundred hours below the 2,000 hour mark, and I haven't heard them receiving any backlash for it."*

"It removes any competitive aspect."

When it comes to compensation, a fairly unique aspect at JD is the *"black box model,"* whereby a *"confidential and holistic"* approach is taken to calculating salaries after the first year. It means that *"there isn't the bonus incentive that there is at other firms,"* so although *"you'll make plenty of money, it's not the most you could make anywhere else."* While there is no actual annual 'bonus,' additional sums are factored into each individual salary for second-years and above. In spite of this, associates were fully aware of the system before they joined the firm, so we heard few complaints about it. *"Overall I feel it's beneficial because it removes any competitive aspect,"* one source mused. *"I don't feel undervalued because I don't know if others are making more than me. I don't know so I don't worry!"*

Pro Bono

"A lot of associates like doing pro bono because you can lead case strategy and teams, so it's a good way to get that kind of experience," we were told. An added incentive is that juniors can count an unlimited number of pro bono toward their billables. The result was that everyone we spoke to had participated; the pro bono figure for first-years in particular was around 100–200 hours (although there were definite outliers: *"I was in the area of, like, 500 hours my first year!"*).

"You can lead case strategy and teams."

Among the broad range of examples given, those that were most frequently mentioned were police brutality cases, veterans' affairs and landlord-tenant disputes. Immigration work was also common: *"We work for an organization here in New York that sends us lists of avail-*

See firm profile on p.656

able cases. I do a lot of immigration work for women who have been victims of domestic violence." Another big program is the 'unaccompanied minors project' which helps refugees from Central America.

Pro bono hours

- For all attorneys across all US offices: 104,566
- Average per US attorney: undisclosed

Diversity

Interviewees told us that *"they're very into promoting diversity"* at the firm. The stats show us that 23% of partners are female and 10% are nonwhite, which is fairly average in BigLaw. Associates were nonetheless positive about the firm's initiatives: *"Every year they host a diversity panel here at the firm, and they'll bring in diverse partners from other law firms and the heads of our clients' diversity panels,"* one associate informed us. We spoke to juniors who had joined the firm through diversity fellowships: *"My program goes to schools that aren't usually targeted by law firms. The 1Ls come as summers and then the firm can decide to invite you back."*

"You see people from all different walks of life."

Nonetheless, the age-old mantra of *"we have a way to go,"* was repeated by several sources. One junior noted that JD's *"reputation for being more conservative perhaps hinders how we're viewed by diverse candidates."* In April, the firm held its first ever diversity conference for 1Ls in the Northeast. Jones Day also has a partner in charge of 'diversity, inclusion & advancement,' Yvette McGee Brown.

Get Hired

Interviewees felt that intelligence mixed with an affable nature is the winning mix at Jones Day: *"I think we're trying to hire the smartest person in the room who can go out and have a beer with the client."* One newbie pointed out that, *"at the end of the day, this job is about working with people, be it the clients, judge, jury, counsel, co-counsel, or your colleagues. So demonstrating that you're likable and can relate your ideas well is very important."* Others also highlighted that *"loyalty here is a big thing – they're looking for people who are in it for the long run and have looked into what this firm is all about."* Do your homework, in other words.

"Loyalty here is a big thing."

Strategy & Future

Recruiting chair Sharyl Reisman tells us that 2015 *"was a great year in terms of growth of the firm and client representation,"* pointing to the firm's involvement in several high-profile matters such as American Apparel's bankruptcy and the Volkswagen fuel emissions scandal. Reisman adds that while the firm's traditional strengths in areas such as M&A and private equity *"will always be a focus,"* there are more niche practices that Jones Day is looking to grow, including energy, cybersecurity & privacy, and global disputes.

As far as geographical expansion goes, JD opened up shop in Detroit in the summer of 2015, *"on the heels of representing the city through bankruptcy,"* and early in 2016 opened an office in Brisbane – the firm's third Australian office. According to Reisman, *"the work in the Brisbane office, in addition to focusing on energy, which is big in that area, will also be focusing on litigation, projects and infrastructure, and transactional work in IP and restructuring, as well as M&A, insolvency and energy industry projects."* Read our full interview with Reisman online.

"At the end of the day, this job is about working with people, be it the clients, judge, jury, counsel, co-counsel, or your colleagues. So demonstrating that you're likable and can relate your ideas well is very important."

See firm profile on p.656

K&L Gates

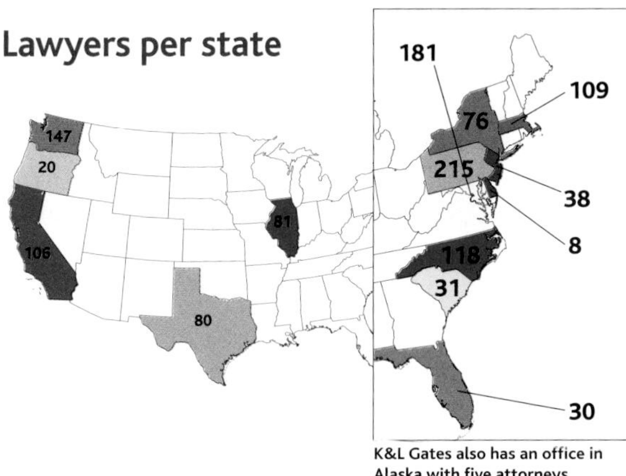

K&L Gates also has an office in Alaska with five attorneys

Largest US office: Washington, DC
US offices: 24
International offices: 21
First-year salary: $115,000 - $160,000
Billable hours: 1,950 target
Summers 2016: 81 (75 2Ls, 6 1Ls)
Revenue 2015: $1.065 billion (-6.9%)
Partners made in 2016: 47 globally (33 in US)
Famous for: rapid growth; merger history

Some people have left, many have joined global K&L Gates, which overall has been bolstering its US presence.

JUST over a decade ago K&L Gates opened up the merger gates and ushered a cascade of attorneys into the firm, quintupling its headcount in the process. 2005 first kicked off the drive for growth with a union between predecessor firms Kirkpatrick & Lockhart (headquartered in Pittsburgh) and London's Nicholas Graham Johnson. Just two years later the firm got its shortened name when Kirkpatrick & Lockhart Nicholson Graham merged with Seattle's Preston Gates. Throw another four mergers into the mix and K&L Gates now stands at 2,000 lawyers with offices in 16 countries.

Expansion may have been the mode du jour for a while but right now the firm is *"figuring out what it means to be as large and international as we are,"* sources told us. *"We expanded very quickly so now we're looking to better establish ourselves."* US managing partner Chuck Miller tells us: *"We will look at a couple of new markets but we really want to try to bolster and strengthen some of the places where we already are."* Throughout 2015, he continues, *"we particularly enhanced our offering in New York."* Going forward, the Big Apple's going to remain a focus for growth, alongside Chicago and the firm's California bases.

On chambers-associate.com...

- We check in with US managing partner Chuck Miller
- K&L Gates and revenge porn pro bono

You've probably seen reports that K&L has recently been hit by a number of partner defections. Despite the headlines, the firm maintains most of these moves were planned departures following productivity evaluations. Chuck Miller confirms: *"We lose and gain partners every year. Some of those are planned departures that we haven't discouraged. Of course we do lose some people we would like to keep but that's the nature of the profession. We're very active in the lateral market and see new laterals coming in every year."* Almost 70 partners have arrived at the firm since January 2015, over half of whom have joined the firm's US offices. Visit our website for more from Chuck Miller.

ASSOCIATES SAY...

The Work

Juniors join one of nine umbrella practice groups upon arrival: corporate & transactional; energy, infrastructure & resources; finance; financial services; IP; labor, employment & workplace safety; litigation & dispute resolution; policy & regulatory; and real estate. Commercial disputes and corporate/M&A take on the most newbies with investment management, energy, IP litigation, and financial services also absorbing ample cohorts.

"You're the keeper of the facts."

Litigators can dabble in areas like consumer finance, contract disputes, insurance coverage, white-collar crime

See firm profile on p.657

Rankings in *Chambers USA*

Banking & Finance	Insurance
Bankruptcy/Restructuring	Intellectual Property
Corporate/Commercial	Investment Funds
Corporate/M&A	Labor & Employment
Energy & Natural Resources	Litigation
Environment	Outsourcing
Financial Services Regulation	Real Estate
Government	Technology
Healthcare	Transportation

For detail on ranking tiers and ranking locations, visit www.chambersandpartners.com

and labor & employment, to name a few. Starting out in commercial disputes, newbies undertake their fair share of *"reviewing discovery documents and conducting research. As I'm still fairly junior I handle more discrete research assignments rather than sticking with one case."* Sources who'd established themselves were more likely to end up *"running an internal doc review team and doing the first draft of all discovery motions; you're the keeper of the facts."* Others had prepared witnesses and partners for, respectively, depositions and arguing motions.

One typical corporate associate told us: *"I've done due diligence and now I'm managing both the process and the reports. I work on schedules, creating new entities, work directly with clients or third parties for third party consent documents, and draft a lot of ancillary documents. I've also worked on the primary agreements but haven't drafted one by myself yet."* Among other areas, venture capitalist financing, securities and *"pure M&A deal work that gets everybody paid"* are all sampled by corporate/M&A rookies.

Once out the starting gate it's generally up to juniors to seek out their own work. *"You're responsible for selling yourself and seeking out your own niche, which really appeals to me,"* one source found. Another lauded the ability to *"go after the partners you like to work with."* Ad hoc safeguards are in place to stop associates from falling at any hurdles; mentors *"typically have an assignment lined up to get you started"* on your first project. Some departments send out monthly emails *"just to check in and see if anyone is low on work"* while the Seattle office recently *"placed an emphasis on trying to protect associates and ensure work allocation is smooth."* Workflow coordinators are now in place here but associates can still seek out matters by themselves.

Recent work highlights

- Assisted West Virginia headquartered WesBanco in its $324.4 million merger with ESB Financial Corporation
- Represented World Wrestling Entertainment (WWE) in lawsuits which allege that WWE is liable for brain injuries in past wrestling performers
- Advised Goldman Sachs and other lender and purchases of non-qualified mortgages on compliance with 'ability to repay' requirements
- Acted for US silver and gold producer Hecla Mining Company in its $20 million merger with Revett Mining Company

Offices

Matching décor may be one way to link all of K&L's bases but less superficial initiatives include *"a definite drive to cross-sell and collaborate between offices."* Most interaction appears to take place within the USA. One Pittsburgher reckoned *"almost every team I've been on has been split across two locations."* K&L's largest US office is in Washington, DC although Pittsburgh's base is considered the firm's epicenter. Other larger bases are Seattle, Boston and Chicago.

"A definite drive to cross-sell."

But what about the lure of the global platform that had enticed so many of our sources to the firm? Transactional matters were most likely to contain an international aspect, with one junior estimating that *"a third of the deals I've handled have some international element."* Despite this juniors see *"not nearly as much as expected. We work with international companies but usually we're just responsible for the US portion of it. The international platform brings in large, interesting, multinational clients but we often reach out to our own international offices who work on the foreign aspects in their own country."*

Culture

The *"patchwork of mergers and acquisitions"* that make up K&L has resulted in various opinions about the firm's culture. Seattle – which came aboard with Preston Gates in 2007 – appears to have remained staunchly committed to its pre-merger culture, leading associates here to describe the firm as *"a bunch of legacy firms staying true to the culture of the office that started there."* Another agreed, elaborating: *"We still have a significant number of people from Preston Gates so the Seattle culture has remained largely intact. I think that's probably true for a lot of our large offices; the creep of Pittsburgh hasn't affected them yet."*

See firm profile on p.657

"Patchwork of mergers and acquisitions."

Other offices had noticed more of a change. Chicago is *"six years on from the merger* [between K&L and Chicago's Bell, Boyd & Lloyd] *and with lateral hires from larger law firms coming in we're losing the midsize feel we once had. It has a Midwest vibe at the moment but I think that's also changing as we're becoming more integrated into a global platform."* Regardless of location we found a few commonalities: *"People are receptive to office visitors because of the free market system; they know people will be coming in and talking to them,"* one Pittsburgh source told us. A Boston associate agreed, adding: *"Because of the way we solicit work I rarely feel uncomfortable having to knock on someone's door."* The same source noted that Beantown attorneys are *"very work-focused. There is not a ton of water cooler chat, not because people don't want to but because the occasions don't always arise."*

Across offices juniors also noted a lack of competitiveness among the lower ranks. *"We like and help each other,"* one Chicagoan offered, while a DC source expressed relief at *"not having to worry someone is going to stab me in the back. People are relaxed and friendly."* Pittsburgh juniors also touched upon that latter point, saying: *"Everyone is kind of pushing you to pay attention to personal matters. It's incredibly flexible,"* while others pointed to the slacks and button-down shirt dress code.

Get Hired

Associates deemed local connections were important to all of K&L's offices so expect to find bases dominated by juniors from local schools. Those who'd applied to offices outside of a region they had a connection to recalled *"having to do a fair bit of convincing"* about their reasons for the move.

"Confidence to knock on doors."

Sources said that the free market system requires *"very personable people; you need to be friendly and have confidence to knock on doors."* Introverts are not excluded from this. *"We're not all necessarily outgoing but we're all team players."* Otherwise, juniors concluded, there doesn't appear to be a common trait among attorneys. Seattle proves the exception to this: juniors perceived *"an outdoorsy bent to people; we're usually proud of an activity or hobby outside of work."* Hikers, skiers and mountain climbers, get your applications in here.

Hours & Compensation

Maybe it's all that fresh air that makes Seattle attorneys a flock of early birds – *"people come in at 7am or 8am"* – but wherever they were in the States, juniors appeared to be pulling ten-hour days in the office. *"People work pretty hard but it's sure not a sweatshop,"* one source thought of their hours. *"On occasion I have to put in time at home. There is an expectation you're available but that doesn't necessarily translate into having to work."*

"More of an incentive than a target."

Associates become bonus-eligible once they hit 1,950 hours; reaching this figure really depends on your practice, we were told, but it's *"not an issue"* if you fail to achieve it and plenty of our sources were yet to do so. *"The bonus is more of an incentive than a target,"* one interviewee felt. *"It is really not a huge driver at the firm; we are never featured in the press throwing money to associates."* And that point is where we started to hear conflicting opinions. *"The only gripe from associates is that the bonus structure is lower than at other large law firms,"* one acknowledged. Another source stressed: *"I worked a lot of weekends. I met my hours and the bonuses weren't even close to market. It's frustrating."* Others accepted that bonuses were *"just not that exciting"* with people *"happy to make less money and have more of a life."*

"We expanded very quickly so now we're looking to better establish ourselves."

Pro Bono

All pro bono hours count as billable and every hour counts toward the bonus threshold. Alongside the usual milieu of asylum claims, landlord/tenant disputes and assisting nonprofits with corporate governance, associates can also work with the firm's Cyber Civil Rights Legal Project on revenge porn cases. *"A lot of young associates work on these matters; I think we have a better understanding of the things you can do on a smartphone."* See our website for more on this hot issue.

"A nice version of 'Shark Tank'."

Pittsburgh juniors handled Protection from Abuse Orders (Pennslyvania's version of a restraining order) where they *"shepherd a packet of cases through the process."* Attorneys in Washington, DC collaborated with a pro bono client to sponsor and coordinate a 'Dolphin Tank' event. *"It was a nice version of 'Shark Tank' where a panel of business experts came in and gave feedback to entrepreneurs."*

See firm profile on p.657

Pro bono hours

- For all attorneys across all US offices: 55,243
- Average per US attorney: 45

Training & Development

Most interviewees were happy that people would take the time to offer feedback if asked, but a few juniors noted that it can be difficult to get constructive feedback. *"People don't like to criticize. They tend to forget what it's like to be a first or second-year so a lot of times you have to seek out that critique."*

"Seek out that critique."

Larger offices like Pittsburgh and DC host training sessions which are broadcast firmwide. Transactional associates can sit in on merger workshops, negotiation training or sessions on compiling documents like audit response letters. The firm doesn't skimp on litigation training either. *"Oh my gosh, in the first year we have a ton of sessions,"* one source proclaimed. Skills coaching such as *"brief writing, how to give a compelling oral presentation, the fundamentals of research"* taper off after six or seven months.

Diversity

Pittsburgh juniors reckoned K&L was making an attempt to increase diversity *"but it's still a lot of white people"* in the Pennsylvania base. The firm's just launched a diversity fellowship with the University of Pittsburgh, and a women in the profession (WIP) group hosts a number of happy hours and networking events, including welcome dinners for new associates.

"Dominated by female participation."

In Boston *"there really isn't that much racial diversity"* but the WIP group is *"very active. We hosted a panel event for first-year female law students to talk about OCIs. I think that resulted in us having more female applicants when recruiting season came around."* It's a similar picture in Seattle where diversity initiatives are *"dominated by female participation. LGBT initiatives aren't lacking either,"* but aside from *"a lot of Asian Americans, we're struggling with underrepresented minorities."* DC associates, however, thought their office was *"pretty diverse."*

Strategy & Future

K&L's global platform seems to be having an increasing impact on the work passing across the desks of K&L's lawyers. US managing partner Chuck Miller explains: *"We're continuing to see an increase in regulation in various sectors of the world and it's having an interesting effect; for one thing we're seeing a lot more combined regulatory and transactional work."* The firm's also continuing to increase interaction between its offices. *"Around 30% of our work is interoffice,"* Miller tells us. *"The percentage of interoffice work has been increasing internationally, especially as our most recent combination in Australia* [K&L Gates merged with Australian firm Middletons in 2013] *gets fully online."* Go online to read more from Miller on the firm's global network.

"Around 30% of our work is interoffice."

See firm profile on p.657

Kasowitz, Benson, Torres & Friedman LLP

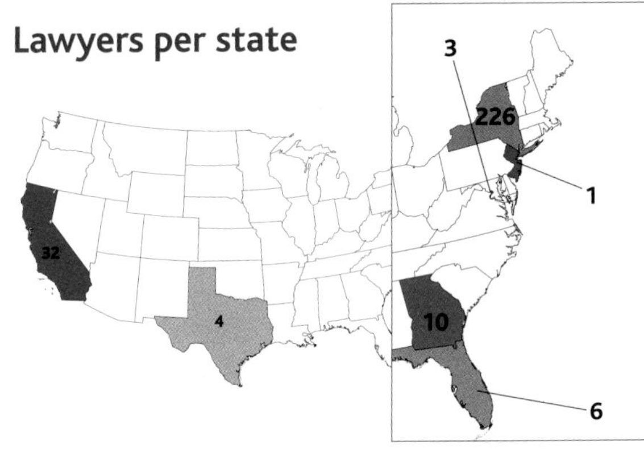

Largest US office: New York
US offices: 9
International offices: 0
First-year salary: $160,000
Billable hours: varies (unofficially 2,150)
Summers 2016: 9 (7 2Ls, 1 1L, 1 other)
Revenue 2015: $234.5 million (-10.8%)
Partners made in 2016: 2
Famous for: its eponymous hero and aggressive litigating style

Kasowitz's *"aggressive"* litigators are as formidable as ever.

READERS should be in no doubt about this New York-headquartered firm's raison d'être: *"Kasowitz is first and foremost a litigation shop."* Led by Marc Kasowitz – dubbed 'Kas' by his attorneys – the firm has maintained its tough reputation in the courtroom while navigating a challenging period. Kasowitz has seen its headcount drop in recent years: it conducted layoffs in both 2014 and 2015. A few lawyers also left to join DLA Piper and McKool Smith.

However, juniors were keen to point out that the firm has worked from *"the top down"* to improve associates' lives. An associates' committee was created and (to universal approval) bonuses were set firmly at market rate in 2015. This certainly put a spring in our sources' step, and in their opinion, Kasowitz has weathered the storm and emerged as a leaner and more productive outfit.

Chambers USA regards Kasowitz as part of 'The Elite' for its general commercial litigation prowess in New York. *Fortune 500* companies like Ford, Comcast and News Corporation fill the books, and high-stakes cases can roll into the billions. The department is especially well known for its successful defense of insurer MBIA against 19 of the world's largest financial institutions in the wake of the financial crisis. Elsewhere, Kasowitz boasts some transactional capabilities in the form of small corporate and real estate practices.

"I've worked on cases where I've prepped Marc himself."

Be warned: Kasowitz is not for the faint-hearted. *"You need to be aggressive,"* juniors agreed, highlighting the extent to which newbies have to be proactive and self-assured in order to thrive. *"It's the kind of place where if you seek out more responsibility you'll be rewarded for it."*

ASSOCIATES SAY...

The Work

The vast majority of juniors join Kasowitz's commercial litigation practice in New York. This may sound restrictive, but there's plenty of scope to diversify one's practice. As a source explained, *"when you sign up to do litigation, you're exposed to around 20 niches,"* including product liability, securities and antitrust. A tiny handful of juniors join smaller practice areas – like IP and transactional real estate – but are usually put there because of prior work experience or educational background.

In commercial litigation, an informal assignment system (*"based on the relationships you made as a summer associate"*) has been scrapped in favor of a more structured one. *"Every Monday morning there is a pop-up*

On chambers-associate.com...
- Interview with Aaron Marks, Kasowitz hiring partner

See firm profile on p.658

The Inside View

Rankings in *Chambers USA*

Bankruptcy/Restructuring Litigation
Insurance

For detail on ranking tiers and ranking locations, visit www.chambersandpartners.com

Recent work highlights

- Represented TPG – one of the world's largest private equity firms – during bankruptcy proceedings associated with portfolio company Caesars Entertainment
- Defended AMC and its affiliates against a lawsuit claiming the network withheld compensation rightfully owed to those involved in television series 'The Walking Dead'
- Acted for fashion mogul Peter Nygard in a multimillion-dollar defamation suit brought by his neighbor and hedge fund billionaire Louis Bacon

you have to fill out before your computer will function;" in this associates explain what they're working on and their future availability. A slightly paternalist approach it may be, but it replaced an *"inequitable system"* that often meant *"some people were slammed"* while others *"slipped under the radar."*

Despite a fairly rigid hierarchy, Kasowitz's associates are given responsibility early on. Newbies proudly declared that they'd drafted a mix of *"discovery requests, motions and reviews,"* attributing their success to the fact they showed willingness to tackle more substantive tasks. One source even boasted: *"I've worked on cases where I've prepped Marc himself."* On smaller cases, *"you have a lot more opportunity to work directly with partners and senior associates."* The likelihood of assisting with depositions also increases on these more modest gems. The bigger cases, meanwhile, are run *"from the top with partners delegating – there are many layers between juniors and seniors."* For those just starting out, this can mean working through a pile of doc review.

Training & Development

New starters enroll at 'Kasowitz University', but don't fear: you won't have to cram for exams or join a sorority. It involves *"mandatory CLE training via a series of workshops that take you through how a case works. They get everyone familiarized with the litigation process."* After graduating from Kasowitz University, on-site training becomes scarce. However, all lawyers are given *"free membership to the Practising Law Institute"* which is *"a five-minute walk away"* from Kasowitz's HQ.

Due to gripes over bonuses and how they're worked out, Kasowitz's review process has recently been revamped. Juniors now complete an online form and submit it to partners they've worked with. After their feedback has been collated, usually *"a partner you haven't worked with delivers your review."* This *"more regimented"* system has been designed to ensure that those who don't receive full bonuses are given clear reasons why. We also heard that several juniors received above market rate bonuses this year.

Culture

Many Big Apple firms try to water down their hard-nosed image but Kasowitz has always celebrated its more aggressive reputation. But what's it really like on the inside? Associates described it as a *"top-down culture, with Marc K as the face and head of the firm."* While some name partners take a hands-off approach, Kas *"really sets the tone in terms of collegiality"* and holds meetings with associates to discuss planned changes. Given that Kasowitz is *"geared toward litigation, it appeals to confident, outgoing types."* Many mentioned that it's also a firm *"that values independence,"* attracting those with an *"entrepreneurial spirit: if you work hard and take on responsibility, you will advance."*

"Appeals to confident, outgoing types."

The layoffs put paid to the weekly happy hours partly out of sensitivity for those who lost their jobs; *"there's a couple of things now and again, but nothing on a formal weekly or monthly basis."* Every year there's a firm outing which *"traditionally involved Marc renting a country club for a day"* with breakfast, lunch and dinner interspersed with *"free golf and massages."* Last year the firm eschewed convention and the whole office spent an evening at Chelsea Pier *"in this big restaurant on the waterfront."* There was still a lavish spread and lawyers were up till the wee hours *"laughing and dancing to the band."*

Offices

"It's shinier, it's prettier, it's a much nicer office."

Like the firm as a whole, Kasowitz's Midtown HQ has also undergone something of a transformation –*"it's shinier, it's prettier, it's a much nicer office generally."* Claustrophobics beware: this renovation also entailed a change in the office allocation system. Rather than giving all new lawyers their own window office, they now *"share for a year and a half."* Next they're given their own windowless office, and then *"it takes another two years to move back to an exterior one."* Those who had experienced the change admitted *"it was hard losing the*

See firm profile on p.658

natural light" but they weren't too vitamin D-deprived: *"The hallways are well lit because the exterior offices' doors are always open."*

Kasowitz has built up a national network of offices over the years, spanning California, Texas, Florida, Georgia, New Jersey and Washington, DC. However, these offices are significantly smaller than the New York mothership, and only a couple of associates on our list were based outside of the Big Apple.

Hours & Compensation

Reforms have also shed light on the firm's billing system. *"There used to be a vague figure; people said it was 2,100 but no one really knew,"* a junior explained. As part of the change-up *"they decided to come up with clear criteria – it's now 2,150."* This target includes *"pro bono, business development and recruiting hours."* Formalizing a target has helped to combat an opaque bonus system: *"Historically bonuses were a black box. We heard a lot of things about them but most of it wasn't true."* The newly-formed associates' committee raised this issue and *"worked with the partners to put together a bonus matrix."* Even for those without Morpheus-like levels of intelligence, the matrix is pretty simple: *"On one side they have your reviews and on the other side they have your hours."* Associates must perform well on both fronts to get a full bonus: *"If you hit your hours but get bad reviews, you won't get the full payout."* Those who are deserving always come out on top, we were assured: *"I've never come across someone I thought would be entitled to a full bonus and then heard they didn't get it."*

"Very good about face time."

After the reduction in staff, associates' workloads increased. This, coupled with the fact that most Kasowitz attorneys *"never say no to work,"* meant that a lot of our sources had a very frenetic first few months at the firm. This has since improved and many were happy to report that Kasowitz is *"very good about FaceTime,"* so working from home has become more popular. Associates are given 20 days of vacation a year, although those hoping for a work-free break shouldn't get their hopes up. One diligent attorney told us: *"I still take my BlackBerry with me on vacation."*

Pro Bono

Pro bono is *"always available"* but associates aren't *"pushed to do it."* Though officially pro bono hours count toward billables, juniors were unclear on how the system worked: *"They say it counts but I never know how much to trust that."* There is a pro bono coordinator but insiders advised future newbies to make the first move: *"He'll help out if you come to him."* The few sources that had done pro bono had mostly been involved in *"asylum work,"* though one attorney spoke glowingly of the help Kasowitz had given to the Hudson River Park Trust. Other potential avenues for pro bono assignments include Her Justice, Human Rights First and Volunteer Lawyers for the Arts.

Pro bono hours

- For all attorneys: 9,741
- Average per attorney: 35

"Marc said this – if there are two candidates and one has a higher GPA but the other is a nicer person, they will take the latter."

Diversity

Diversity is an area in which progress has been fairly moot, according to juniors. While the firm supports minority organizations (such as the Cuban American Bar Association) and sponsors a variety of networking events, many sources wanted to see more robust initiatives established internally. Aaron Marks insists that *"diversity from our perspective starts with leadership"* and pointed to the fact that Hector Torres – a Hispanic lawyer – is a name partner. On the gender front, sources were hopeful that a recent *"mostly female"* class will provide the firm with more senior women lawyers in the future.

Get Hired

Just to make it crystal clear: *"It's important to know that Kasowitz, unlike other New York firms, is a litigation shop. You're not going to get through the interviews if you don't have a strong reason why you want to do litigation."* If you tick that box it's important to note that the firm also *"really focuses on a candidate's personality."* For anecdotal evidence: *"Marc said this – if there are two candidates and one has a higher GPA but the other is a nicer person, they will take the latter."*

"Really focuses on a candidate's personality."

In 2015 – after two years of reduced class sizes – the firm hired more summer associates: a sign, our sources hoped, that the days of layoffs are far behind Kasowitz.

See firm profile on p.658

Strategy & Future

Aaron Marks had this to say about the firm's future: *"I think in ten years' time we'll still largely be doing what we're currently doing. Maybe we'll be a little bigger but not much. We'll still be litigation-focused and New York-centered."* In terms of practice areas, he added: *"I can imagine that the ever-expanding world of privacy litigation will only continue to grow. Otherwise IP and banking will continue to be fertile ground."*

"The ever-expanding world of privacy litigation will only continue to grow."

We did have to mention that elephant in the room though. Here's Marks' take on those layoffs: *"From our perspective we were looking at what we thought the future held for us. We acted smartly to keep our headcount at a manageable level."*

"I think in ten years' time we'll still largely be doing what we're currently doing. Maybe we'll be a little bigger but not much. We'll still be litigation-focused and New York-centered." – Aaron Marks, hiring partner

The Inside View

See firm profile on p.658

Katten Muchin Rosenman LLP

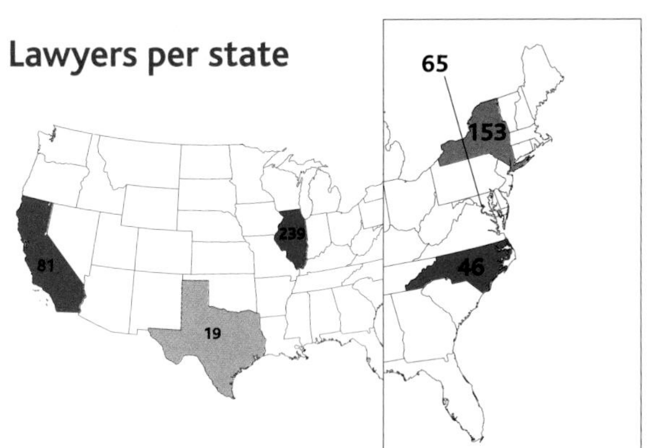

Largest US office: Chicago
US offices: 11
International offices: 2
First-year salary: $160,000 ($140,000 in Charlotte)
Billable hours: 2,000 target (1,950 in Charlotte)
Summers 2016: 24 (18 2Ls, 6 1Ls)
Revenue 2015: $561.5 million (+4.5%)
Partners made in 2016: 19 globally (18 in US)
Famous for: entrepreneurial spirit

This entrepreneurial Katten got the cream.

IF you want proof that you can still look the cat's whiskers at 42 then look no further than Penelope Cruz, Christian Bale, Leonardo Di Caprio or Katten Muchin Rosenman. It's not expensive dentistry or lucky genes that got the last of these looking so alluring but a healthy bottom line and careful growth: revenue was up 6.2% in 2014 and 4.5% in 2015. So what's behind this steady expansion? Chairman Vince Sergi replies: *"Corporate deals and private equity were up significantly and our particular expertise in environmental and workplace safety was booming last year. Our structured finance and securitization group has had a phenomenal year,"* says Sergi. *"We're doing very well; we're growing carefully and deliberately and we're very excited about it."*

The Chicago-born firm built its name servicing growing, entrepreneurial clients, but as the (relatively young) law firm matured, an increasing number of larger, institutional clients joined the books. We've wondered in the past whether the firm's shift toward larger clients will dampen some of its famed entrepreneurial spirit; a few associates we spoke to are pondering too: *"Katten seemed like a more nimble firm when I applied. Now I don't know what will happen with these feathers in the institutional basket."* However, Vince Sergi assures us: *"We're still very entrepreneurial. Any juniors who join us are not going to be on a low track, they will be on whatever track they can handle."* This, at least, still rings true for associates: *"I interpret our entrepreneurial spirit as 'if you have an idea, go for it, and we'll support you',"* one told us.

On chambers-associate.com...

- Chairman Vince Sergi chats to us about Katten's past year and its future plans
- We speak with Katten's new national hiring partner Howard Rubin

ASSOCIATES SAY...

The Work

Litigation takes in the largest proportion of Katten's 30-odd new first-years, followed by real estate and corporate. The remaining quarter are littered through areas like insolvency, financial services, commercial finance, trusts & estates, and environmental.

The size of each department (and office) typically determines work allocation. Larger groups, like Chicago's litigation, real estate or corporate practices, tend to have an assigning attorney: *"For the first couple of years it gets you through the system,"* but juniors felt the best work to be had was found by *"expressing an interest to partners who will think of you when a project comes up."* Another added: *"I found only the worst work goes through the system; if there is any interesting work, partners approach associates directly."* Without an assigning attorney acting as a back stop in smaller groups, the onus is very much on being *"entrepreneurial"* with the spoils often going to *"those whose hunt things down."*

"Hunt things down."

See firm profile on p.659

Rankings in *Chambers USA*

Banking & Finance	Litigation
Bankruptcy/Restructuring	Media & Entertainment
Capital Markets	Real Estate
Climate Change	Sports Law
Corporate/M&A	Tax
Environment	Transportation
Healthcare	Wealth Management
Intellectual Property	

For detail on ranking tiers and ranking locations, visit www.chambersandpartners.com

Recent work highlights

- Assisted German logistics company Schenker AG in filing a lawsuit which alleges antitrust violations were committed by numerous air freight carriers who colluded to fix air freight shipping prices paid by Schenker
- Represented the Chicago Transit Authority Retiree Health Care Trust in a dispute over whether unions and municipal/state employers can, by agreement, modify healthcare benefits for retirees
- Advised global real estate company Ivanhoe Cambridge and real estate private equity group Callahan Capital Properties in their $2.2 billion acquisition of Three Bryant Park in Manhattan. This is the second most expensive sale of an office building in US history
- Represnted Ardent Health Service in its $1.75 billion sale to real estate investment trust Ventas

Bankruptcy, healthcare, white-collar, consumer disputes, class actions and general commercial litigation are just some of the areas junior litigators can get their paws into. Interviewees were generally pleased with their responsibility, with one clarifying: *"I've slowly been getting more and more. It evens out to an appropriate third-year level. There are still times when I'm doing basic first-year stuff but I've had opportunities to do more senior tasks. It's a function of being a midlevel law firm; the distribution of work is not as regimented as it might be elsewhere. We fill in and do what's necessary on a case."* This can range from doc review – *"I'm definitely still at that stage for general projects,"* one third-year told us – to writing substantive briefs or drafting mediation statements.

Real estate rookies also start off as generalists, touching on *"joint ventures, financing, straight acquisitions. We do a bit of everything for the first few years. After that there is no formal specialization but people might veer toward one area."* Katten's juniors take the lead on smaller sales and acquisitions but slip further down the responsibility ladder for larger transactions: *"On financing, for instance, I work with the partner, draft the first take of loan documents, push the transaction forward but don't negotiate anything."*

Training & Development

Formal training sessions are department-specific, resulting in mixed opinions from our interviewees. A corporate source revealed: *"There are lunchtime trainings or presentations. We've not had those in a while and they aren't tremendously useful. It's an area we could definitely improve."* Real estate fared slightly better. Although we heard *"there is not a lot of formal training"* here, associates can clock up monthly CLE sessions and those in Chicago *"typically attend the practice area orientation for first-years to refresh everything."*

"Not a lot of formal training."

Litigators were the happiest with their lot, citing *"ongoing sessions which are specific to the type of work we're doing during the first three years."* Tasks such as brief writing, answering depositions or responding to subpoenas are all covered. All junior litigators convene in Chicago every other year for deposition training and every year for a mock trial.

Hours & Compensation

Putting in ten to twelve-hour shifts a day was the norm among most of our interviewees. *"Katten talks about being a lifestyle firm but I don't think it's like that,"* one source reflected. *"The reality is BigLaw always requires extensive hours and it can be difficult."*

"Anyone working at a big firm has to juggle."

Generally, sources accepted this lifestyle as *"something anyone working at a big firm has to juggle. Katten is definitely a place which emphasizes being able to work at home. No one has an issue if you're not here at night."* Or sometimes the afternoon: *"If there is nothing on I have no problem leaving at 3pm,"* but before you start dreaming of regular early exits take note that this same source had notched up numerous 10pm finishes.

Katten doesn't stipulate a billable requirement but 2,000 hours earns rookies a class level bonus (1,950 in Charlotte), although they need to bill more to get a market-level bonus or more. *"It's definitely achievable,"* sources agreed. *"But many people feel it's not exactly competitive with the market."* Hitting 2,100 gets you market rate, and bonus amounts increase every 100 hours beyond that. *"There is a large swing between the class and market bonus,"* but a smaller step up for every increase beyond the 2,100 to emphasize that *"we're not driving for those crazy hours of 2,300."*

See firm profile on p.659

Culture

Chicago rookies detected a *"genuine Midwestern niceness"* among their colleagues, with one telling us: *"People genuinely enjoy being around each other."* Juniors had no concerns about approaching partners for advice or taking time to shoot the breeze. *"I don't feel uncomfortable laughing in the hallway; what brought me here was the feeling I wouldn't need to censor myself."*

"It's not a small dog either, it's a German Shepherd!"

The DC office *"struck me as very friendly,"* offered one out-of-towner, with a DC native confirming: *"It's very communal and relaxed. We wear jeans on a Friday and a partner sometimes brings their dog into the office. It's not a small dog either, it's a German Shepherd!"* A similar atmosphere permeates LA. *"I've heard this office is much more laid back than the Chicago HQ; the dress code and personal interactions are a bit more relaxed."* Non-New Yorkers suggested the firm's second largest office, in NYC, swung the other way: *"Maybe it's just my Midwestern bias. The people are nice but something feels different; New York is more fast-paced than Chicago."* A Big Apple junior maintained that although *"people here understand the work needs to get done and we're going to do whatever it takes to do that, I don't see a lot of the unrealistic expectations or silly timing issues I see with peers at other firms."*

Anyone for ping pong?

And what about juniors' thoughts on the firm's famed buzzword, 'entrepreneurial'? *"I think it's true. Everyone is encouraged and urged to find their own work and develop their own clients."* Others reckoned the reputation had attracted *"a certain type of person looking to work hard and get ahead."* But that drive doesn't come at the expense of their colleagues. Although the firm is *"scrappy because people fight for what they want, it's not ultra competitive. Fellow associates will help you if you have a problem."*

Offices

The Chicago HQ was recently revamped to make it *"more modern; it's not a dramatic update."* Plans for glass office walls were nixed by associates, but the *"browny-green"* color scheme has been replaced by a *"lighter, cleaner, greyish look."* The *"word on the street"* is that an associates' lounge may be on the cards, so now's the time for people to put in their request for that ping pong or fussball table.

Katten's Chicago office is full-service (just like its cousins in Century City, New York and Washington, DC) but several of the firm's smaller bases have more of a specific bent: Austin serves clients in the energy and chemical sectors. Fellow Texas base Houston tackles environmental compliance and workplace safety matters. Environmental clients can also be found in abundance in San Francisco while Charlotte, which overlooks the Carolina Panthers stadium, focuses heavily on real estate and litigation.

Strategy & Future

The East Coast is where the action's currently at. *"We've added some new people in Washington, DC and are on the verge of adding more; I think that office is really poised for some very good growth,"* chairman Vince Sergi tells us. *"We're also really targeting New York for this fiscal year for more lateral growth and more bottom-up growth from law schools. We need more help as our New York business expands and we're very excited about that."* Visit our website for more from Sergi on Katten's future plans.

"We are a firm that's built on entrepreneurial spirit and a commitment to being true business counselors to our clients."

National hiring partner
Howard Rubin

Pro Bono

Juniors had worked on a variety of pro bono matters from aiding domestic violence victims to assisting on asylum applications or helping *"low-income youth who end up in court on truancy charges; we provide representation otherwise they'd be in a courtroom by themselves not knowing what's going on."*

"...end up in court on truancy charges."

Once a month, Chicago attorneys hold a legal clinic *"which meets at a school. Parents and locals can come and run their legal problems past us, and we'll give them an assessment of whether we can help."* And while not strictly legal work, attorneys can also bill pro bono hours for teaching lessons on law and the Constitution to students of the same school. A hundred pro bono hours are automatically credited as billable. *"After that you have to request permission for more, but from what I've heard it is pretty much always approved."*

See firm profile on p.659

Diversity

Sources believed that like most of BigLaw Katten *"doesn't feel that diverse. I think they could be better at retaining women and recruiting and retaining minority attorneys."* One interviewee added: *"I've heard from women in litigation that it's hard for them not to have as many equity partners to look up to as role models."* Things might be about to start changing, though, as we heard the Women's Leadership Forum (WLF) has been *"relaunched with a new emphasis on attracting and retaining women."*

"New emphasis on attracting and retaining women."

An LGBT coalition, a Minority Associates Committee and a Committee on Racial and Ethnic Diversity are also active at Katten, but does their reach extend beyond the firm's headquarters? *"The WLF is pretty big in New York and holds regular meetings,"* but as other affinity groups *"are generally run out of Chicago, New York associates don't participate so much."* Elsewhere, juniors were aware that affinity groups existed at the firm but not always entirely sure *"what they do."*

Get Hired

Time and again when we asked about interview tips, juniors told us *"the firm really likes personality."* Any kind in particular? *"An interesting personality."* Suffice to say, recruiters will probably *"ask a lot about your interests outside of work and see if people are willing to engage on a variety of topics,"* so ensure you demonstrate that your life doesn't completely revolve around the law.

"Collaborative successes the student has had."

National hiring partner Howard Rubin offers a bit more detail: *"We don't practice law individually so our interviews are trying to capture who is going to be a great teammate. We want to gain an insight into collaborative successes the student has had, either in prior work experience or in the law school setting. We're trying to gauge whether the student is someone who anticipates issues and has a confidence which will help them thrive in such an entrepreneurial environment."* See our website for more hiring tips from Rubin.

"I don't feel uncomfortable laughing in the hallway; what brought me here was the feeling I wouldn't need to censor myself."

See firm profile on p.659

Kaye Scholer LLP

Lawyers per state

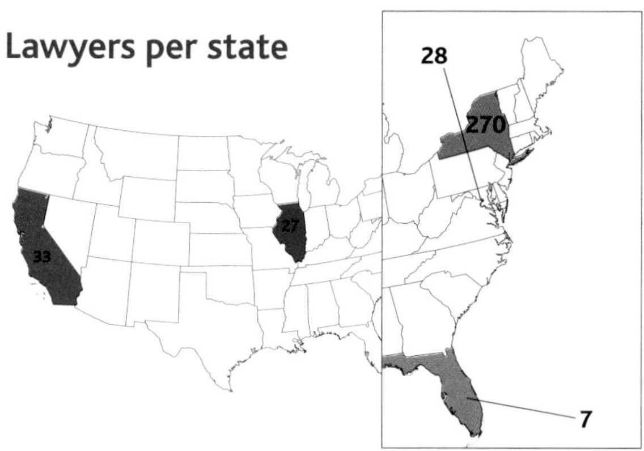

Largest US office: New York
US offices: 7 (including operations center)
International offices: 3
First-year salary: $160,000
Billable hours: 1,800 target
Summers 2016: 25 (21 2Ls, 4 1Ls)
Revenue 2015: $360 million (-4%)
Partners made 2016: 4 (all US)
Famous for: litigation prowess

Fierce in the courtroom but easygoing behind the scenes, this 99 year-old allows attorneys a degree of flexibility that bodes well for long-term development.

REVERED for its commercial litigation practice and strong in financial services, life sciences, real estate and technology, this Big Apple old-timer gives rookies plenty of high-stakes matters to sink their teeth into. And with centenary Champagne corks scheduled to pop in 2017, Kaye Scholer attorneys will have plenty to toast. This good news comes after a tricky period when Kaye Scholer has been in the news for unfortunate reasons. A gender discrimination case filed by a former associate was settled out of court in late 2015, and further controversy was stirred up when former partner Evan Greebel, who'd been with the firm for a relatively short time, was arrested for alleged dirty dealings with super-villain-of-the-moment Martin Shkreli, the hedge fund and pharmaceuticals entrepreneur.

Associates weren't bothered by this attention. *"I knew it was a great firm,"* said one representatively. *"It has definitely lived up to my expectations."* Interviewees highlighted the *"decent amount of control over our work and our schedule,"* as well as the *"laid back and respectful"* internal atmosphere that the firm promotes. *"It really inspires confidence in the long run."*

On chambers-associate.com...

- Interview with hiring partners Jeff Fuisz and Kate Schumacher

As we went to press, rumors of a possible merger with Arnold & Porter started doing the rounds.

ASSOCIATES SAY...

The Work

The bulk of Kaye Scholer's entry level-hiring takes place in New York. The real estate, IP, corporate, tax & private client, and finance teams all take on their fair share of rookies, but topping them all is complex commercial litigation, where around a third of the firm's freshmen end up. DC, LA, Chicago and Palo Alto also take on a tiny proportion of new entrants each year, though DC doesn't run a summer program.

"They'll throw you in there as soon as they see you can handle more responsibility."

Work is dished out by assigning partners, who *"do a very good job of making sure workloads are democratically spread."* Contacting partners directly can also work in your favor, because *"although assigning partners do their best to expose you to a range of work, they won't cherry-pick opportunities for you."* More organic workstreams eventually form as working relationships begin to blossom, and these often stretch across the firm's US network. A Californian told us: *"We work very closely with New York and Chicago, so I get a lot of work from*

The Inside View

See firm profile on p.660

Rankings in *Chambers USA*

Bankruptcy/Restructuring
Capital Markets
Corporate/M&A
Intellectual Property
Life Sciences
Litigation
Products Liability
Real Estate
Transportation

For detail on ranking tiers and ranking locations, visit www.chambersandpartners.com

there too. So many firms try to talk up their national presence, but here it really feels interconnected. Every day I'll be on the phone to DC, Chicago or New York."

Complex commercial litigators don't specialize when they first arrive, so take on a mix of white-collar, antitrust, products liability and labor cases. *"For the first year or so the focus is more on variety than depth of experience,"* so expect to start off with a hearty portion of targeted research and coordinative admin tasks. Our second and third-year sources had moved on to draft briefs, pen scripts for witness examinations, and even interview clients themselves, so juniors' impression was that *"they'll throw you in there as soon as they see you can handle more responsibility."*

Meanwhile, over in IP juniors cover patent litigation, trademark, copyright and trade secrets work for large pharmaceutical, technology and biotech clients, among others. *"About a year ago I'd had less than a year's experience,"* reflected one respondent, *"but was asked to assist in co-writing a brief for a relatively high-profile case."* With the likes of Pfizer, Novartis, Google and Nintendo on the cards, it's no wonder that same source happily continued *"it was amazing to have such a hands-on involvement at that early stage."*

The real estate team represent buyers and sellers from a client pool that boasts some of the world's largest financial institutions, institutional investors and real estate owners. *"The responsibilities you receive here are way higher than you'd expect,"* one rookie bragged. *"I've had senior associates put me in charge of entire deals, leaving themselves with just the loan agreement to tie up. They helped me whenever I needed it, but being responsible for managing a deal and a team of paralegals was so important in developing my leadership skills."*

"The most useful training comes through working alongside more senior attorneys."

Training & Development

In their first week associates kick-off with an orientation 101, covering areas such as billing and internal computer systems, as well as introductions to the firm's practices.

Recent work highlights

- Disputing product liability claims on behalf of Bayer. The claims relate to the German multinational pharma company's anticoagulant drug Xarelto, which plaintiffs argue caused unwarned bleeding as a side effect
- Guided drybulk shipping company Baltic Trading through its merger with parent company Genco Shipping & Trading
- Successfully shunned over $900 million of consumer class action claims filed against Avon, whose anti-ageing products were alleged to be deceptively marketed and ultimately ineffective
- Advised Deutsche Bank on the mezzanine financing of two deluxe rental apartment buildings in Tribeca, with combined mortgages worth $360 million

Over the next few months, new starters receive more substantive weekly run-throughs. *"Having that initial awareness of how to write a memo, file a brief or conduct discovery means you're really ready to hit the ground running,"* said one junior. But of course, *"the most useful training comes through working alongside more senior attorneys,"* in part because *"most are forthcoming with suggestions for improvement."* One relieved associate reported that *"feedback is usually along the lines of: 'You did a great job; here's one thing you could change next time, but you did a great job!'"* Such off-the-cuff feedback is *"predominantly verbal,"* though *"supervisors do cc you on emails to explain any changes or ask for your opinion. It's nice to be considered in that way."*

Formal assessment comes through annual reviews, and six-month reviews for first-years and laterals. Those who wish to talk things over in the meantime can draw from their monthly mentoring stipend to head for lunch with either their partner or associate mentor.

"It's a relaxing place to be."

Offices

"The office was completely renovated a couple of years ago," reported a New Yorker, *"so it's a well-oiled machine. All the tech is reliable and up-to-date, which is one less stress!"* The mothership's outdoor terrace overlooks Eighth Avenue and *"in the summer everyone has their lunch out there. There are even trees with fairy lights in so you feel separate from the street. It's a relaxing place to be."* During colder months, the cafeteria proved a cozier option for informal catch-ups. Well-subsidized, it caters to a range of different appetites. *"The fried chicken and mac & cheese are particularly good,"* laughed one gastronomist, *"but there are plenty of healthy dishes on offer too."*

See firm profile on p.660

Juniors get the opportunity to mix with other offices through videocon training sessions, usually broadcast from the New York office. *"It's actually really conscientiously managed,"* nodded one Cali caller. *"Everyone gets their chance to talk, so you don't feel you're watching people get trained. The vast majority of our associates are in New York, so it makes sense."*

Culture

"If you like parties then Kaye Scholer is a good place to be," one New Yorker was happy to relate. Whether it's watching Billy Joel at Madison Square Gardens, designing custom sneakers at Niketown or scoffing burgers at PJ Clarke's, *"there's an after-party pretty much every day of the summer program."* Things calm down a little from then on, though *"junior associates often meet for breakfast or lunch in the cafeteria."*

"If you like parties then Kaye Scholer is a good place to be."

Weekly cocktail hours every Friday are an opportunity to nourish partner-associate relations. *"It's always well-catered, and well-attended by a mix of partners, associates and support staff,"* said one rookie. *"People sometimes bring their partners, family members or friends along too, so often we won't talk about work at all."* Following a move to 55th street a few years ago, it's top buttons undone at the Big Apple hub. Most of the time, that is. *"Reinstating Jeans Friday was a popular move,"* grinned one New Yorker, *"but if clients are coming in then we'll be in suits."* Elsewhere, it's similarly laid back, with one DC caller adding *"we're expected to be presentable, but that doesn't have to mean suits and ties. Management realizes that if we're comfortable we're more likely to enjoy our work."*

Overall, *"the provisions made for us, the flexibility we're afforded and the respect that we're shown makes it easier to handle the stresses of working in a high-hours profession,"* reviewed one happy source. *"Counsel are always saying 'it's a marathon, not a sprint,' which shows that they don't want us burning out, and care about our long-term progress."*

"No pressure on you to drown yourself in work."

Hours & Compensation

To make their bonus, juniors must rack up at least 1,800 billable hours, plus 200 hours of things like pro bono, firm citizenship, client development and writing articles. Most of our sources hadn't struggled to hit their targets, and one or two had even raked in an 'extraordinary bonus' for amazing work. That said, *"there's no pressure on you to drown yourself in work,"* and *"if the work's not there then you'll still have your job."*

Though subject to fluctuations, rookies' days average out at about ten hours, and grafters were pleased to report that *"we're well set-up to work remotely."* As one DC slicker added, *"there's an awareness that facetime culture isn't always accepting of the realistic demands of 21st Century living. If you need to go to the doctors, or want to head home early to spend time with your family, that's fine as long as you keep people in the loop."*

"Feedback is usually along the lines of: 'You did a great job; here's one thing you could change next time, but you did a great job!'"

Many of our interviewees put in an extra hour or two from home in the evening, but *"no one will bother you at the weekend unless it's really important."*

Pro Bono

Pro bono take-up went one of two ways among our callers, who were either striking up some 200 hours each year or *"unable to take on much thanks to an already full plate."* Opportunities are circulated by a dedicated pro bono counsel and manager based in New York, and even those out west had found that *"they're always reaching out to let us know of local opportunities."* Whether wading their way through death penalty cases, asylum proceedings or transgender name-change applications, juniors in all offices have the support of a supervising attorney. Probably for the best, as our charitable interviewees had been lucky enough to cross-examine witnesses, write and coauthor motions before independent city commissions, and defend several depositions, all on pro bono matters.

Pro bono hours

- For all attorneys across all US offices: 20,662
- Average per US attorney: 56

"Our network of affinity groups is helping give a voice to minority attorneys at the firm."

Diversity

In October 2015 the firm settled a $20 million lawsuit filed by former senior associate Bari Zahn. Ms Zahn

See firm profile on p.660

claimed to have been inadequately compensated in relation to her male peers due to her gender and sexual orientation, and unfairly dismissed after expressing her concerns to management. When questioned on the scandal, juniors conceded that *"the higher levels are male and caucasian-dominated,"* but felt that *"under-representation of minorities is a problem industry-wide, and efforts have been made to bring that conversation to the floor."* A network of 'attorney resource groups' – African American, Asian, Latino, LGBT, women, and working parents are all represented – is *"helping give a voice to minority attorneys at the firm,"* and the introduction of a new director of diversity and inclusion, Satra Sampson-Arokium, has also helped. Negotiating the provision of activities, specific training and other resources for diverse attorneys, *"Satra helps put the needs of those groups on the firm's agenda."*

Get Hired

Beyond stellar academics, *"we're really looking for self-starters who can both lead and work collaboratively in a team environment,"* says co-hiring partner Kate Schumacher. *"A lot of our questioning centers on those qualities."* A varied resume can really court you some favour in this respect, but it's imperative that your experiences are relevant to your own career goals. As fellow hiring partner Jeff Fuisz hints, *"judicial clerkships are a good way to prove that you're invested in practicing law. It gives students an excellent insight into how different lawyers work, as well as a clearer perspective as to how judges approach cases."* But as Schumacher follows: *"Some of the best interviewees are the ones who'll have waited tables whilst at college, but can explain what they learned from that experience and how that'll translate to them becoming a good lawyer."*

Not only do interviewers want to know why hopefuls will be an asset to the firm, they also want to see a degree of oratorical ability and composure that'll cut them out as future success stories. *"So much of what we do is communicating with clients, courts and colleagues,"* nods Schumacher, *"so juniors really need to be able to articulate their own story convincingly and comfortably."*

Strategy & Future

Despite registering a 4% drop in revenue in 2015, co-HP Jeff Fuisz assures us that *"Kaye Scholer will continue to invest cautiously in the coming years."* As one rookie elaborated, *"litigation and transactional work in the life sciences, financial services, technology and real estate spheres will continue to reign supreme,"* and *"it's unlikely that there'll be any drastic deviations from these core target areas."*

"Juniors really need to be able to articulate their own story convincingly and comfortably."

Recent cost-cutting moves – the firm's decision to shift all back-office admin functions from New York to Tallahassee being a good example – have landed Kaye Scholer a little extra pocket change, and all of this bodes well for future employment opportunities. One area that has particularly benefited is entry-level hiring. As Jeff Fuisz recalls, *"in the past few years we've been recruiting between 18 and 20 summer associates, whereas now we're talking more than 20."*

"Counsel are always saying 'it's a marathon, not a sprint,' which shows that they don't want us burning out, and care about our long-term progress."

See firm profile on p.660

Kilpatrick Townsend & Stockton LLP

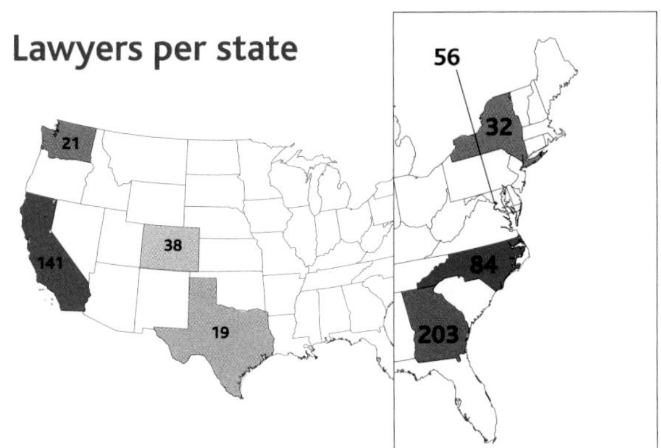

Largest US office: Atlanta
US offices: 15
International offices: 3
First-year salary: $135,000 – $160,000
Billable hours: 1,900 target (1,850 for first-years)
Summers 2016: 32 (23 2Ls, 9 1Ls)
Revenue 2015: $411.5 million
Partners made in 2016: 12 globally (11 in US)
Famous for: strong IP practice; Atlanta HQ

"*Entrepreneurial*" Kilpatrick is a lot more than just an IP firm.

BACK in 1893, when the inventors of a sickly-sweet morphine substitute felt they were probably onto something, they turned to an IP firm to register their new brand. And thus the Coca-Cola trademark was born, registered by a firm that was to become Kilpatrick Townsend. Since then, the firm has been busy growing through mergers, and 2015 saw the launch of the firm's first Texas office after it merged with Dallas-based litigation boutique Crouch & Ramey. This new addition brings the firm's US office roster to 15 (it also has attorneys in Shanghai, Stockholm and Tokyo).

The firm's broad geographic spread – spanning both coasts and states in between – is largely thanks to the 2011 merger between California-based Townsend and Crew and Atlanta fixture Kilpatrick Stockton. Both legacy firms were themselves products of historic mergers. Both had long been known for their stellar IP capabilities and the IP practice remains highly respected today. But, as one junior rightly pointed out, *"we're a full-service firm with an incredibly strong IP base."* Other robust practices where juniors can get involved include corporate, construction, labor, litigation and real estate, to name a few.

On chambers-associate.com...

- We check in with managing partner Susan Spaeth
- Recruitment committee chairman Charlie Henn talks us through Kilpatrick's unusual recruitment process
- More on diversity

ASSOCIATES SAY...

The Work

After rotating through three practice groups during the summer program, rookies rank them in order of preference. Around three-quarters of juniors tend to head into the various subgroups within IP. The remainder are split between Kilpatrick's litigation and CFRE (corporate, finance & real estate) departments. Although each group has access to a formal workload system where juniors can indicate their availability, some teams *"don't seem to use it too much."* Most assignments come from senior attorneys *"reaching out to those they're interested in working with."* But juniors needn't just wait to see what comes through the door as *"we're an entrepreneurial firm. If you want to reach out to partners they appreciate the initiative and find something for you."*

IP associates join one of five subgroups: patent litigation; trademark & copyright; medical & mechanical devices; chemistry & life sciences; and electronics & software. Attorneys in the last three groups tend to predominantly work on patent prosecution (applying for patent status), though they're not restricted from working on patent litigation matters. Trademark & copyright juniors are required to work on both sides. *"Depending on the complexity of the case, I could run the litigation or just be one of the hands,"* one patent litigator outlined. Regardless of complexity, technical and legal research is

The Inside View

See firm profile on p.661

Rankings in *Chambers USA*

Bankruptcy/Restructuring	Franchising
Construction	Intellectual Property
Corporate/M&A	Labor & Employment
Employee Benefits & Executive Compensation	Litigation
Environment	Native American Law
Financial Services Regulation	Real Estate
	Tax

For detail on ranking tiers and ranking locations, visit www.chambersandpartners.com

Recent work highlights

- Represented Fox in a trademark lawsuit after ExxonMobil alleged the interlocking Xs in Fox's 'FXX' logo infringed on the style of Exxon's trademark
- Acted for Belgian firearms and weapons manufacturer FN Herstal in bringing a trademark infringement case against Georgia firearms store Clyde Armory relating to FN Herstal's SCAR mark
- Represented Newell Rubbermaid subsidiary DYMO against allegations of patent infringement surrounding printer hardware and software
- Acted for lighting fixture providers Acuity on patent protection matters, including securing patent applications and averting patent infringement

almost a given. Interviewees had also drafted discovery requests, reviewed deposition transcripts and prepared senior attorneys for depositions. Over on the patent prosecution side, juniors *"meet with inventors or in-house attorneys to learn about the invention and draft patent applications complete with technical drawings. We file it and then work back and forth with the patent office to make revisions to the claims."*

"It's a bit of a chess game."

Sources acknowledged that even though tasks on offer *"can appear repetitive, we're always looking at different technologies. Someone may make one claim about the science involved; our job is to say 'we view it another way' and prove our point is valid. It's a bit of a chess game and I really like that aspect."* Others pointed out that the firm *"gives you responsibility so that you can become an expert. The partners are interested in developing a specialist area for each associate but it does pigeonhole you. Only one or two people here know more about my niche than I do, which is great but it can't be the only thing I do. It's a double-edged sword."*

Culture

In Atlanta *"the atmosphere depends on the level you're on."* The IP floor, for instance, has *"a very laid-back atmosphere. It's just very collaborative,"* with chairs being dragged into partners' offices for team meetings. *"If someone new walks by, people pop their heads out of their office to ask who they are."* The greetings don't stop once you become a familiar face: *"I always get a good morning when people walk past my office."*

"They have a magnetic aura."

One interviewee felt this attitude might surprise some people, as *"I don't know if you'd describe most lawyers as fun, and patent law is the most nerdy and esoteric area of law, but everyone is extremely friendly. People crack jokes that are not just nerdy, they're actual jokes."* Another IP junior put this ambience down to the teams *"attracting people who others want to be around; they're charismatic. They don't have to be chatty or funny but they have a magnetic aura about them."* Beyond the IP pale, *"if you go up a couple of levels it doesn't have the same feel. The litigation floor is a bit more intense."*

Compared to the IP boutiques in town, Kilpatrick's Seattle base is *"probably more buttoned up."* But associates here felt *"people are really friendly and easy to talk to. I've known a lot of attorneys and there is not a lot of ego here."* Although lawyers *"get intensely into their work, it doesn't get super intense."* If someone becomes overloaded colleagues are generally up for *"transferring off matters. People are willing to help out."* Down in San Francisco, *"people ring each other with questions. It's not competitive at all."* Just like in Atlanta, the patent prosecutors are *"a little quieter than those on the litigation floor where four people are working on one document."*

Offices

Atlanta welcomes the largest concentration of Kilpatrick rookies, followed by Seattle and San Francisco. The rest are spread sparsely around most of the firm's 15 offices. At the time of our calls we also found juniors in Charlotte, Denver, Los Angeles, Raleigh, San Diego, Silicon Valley, Walnut Creek and Winston-Salem.

"We have two nerve centers."

Atlanta is also considered Kilpatrick's de facto headquarters although management is split between here and San Francisco. *"We have two nerve centers due to the merger. Currently our chairman is in Atlanta and our managing partner in Silicon Valley; it used to be the other way round."* Our sources tended to work most closely with offices in their region: *"Typically I'll be working with the East Coast,"* articulated one Atlantan. *"Lots of people spend time in another office to interact more with other*

The Inside View

See firm profile on p.661

teams." Cross-office interaction appears visible early on but opportunities *"grow as your career progresses."*

"Dealing with difficult clients."

Training & Development

New starters are all flown to one location for practice group boot camps. The *"three-day intensive training session"* covers things like *"what's needed to respond to an office action or conduct an interview."* This is topped up around the fourth year for *"more advanced topics."* Litigators additionally attend a two-day mock trial where they *"prepare and present to partners"* and can also take advantage of a three-day deposition training. A professional development series brings in speakers to *"chat about improving and tightening legal writing or client development."* It also, handily, covers *"dealing with difficult clients."*

First-years are assigned a senior associate as mentor (mid or senior-level attorneys are paired with counsel or partners). But there are plenty of informal mentors around as *"lawyers are funny; they love to talk and feel important. If you ask someone to mentor you they get really excited about it."*

Pro Bono

In the Bay Area *"there's quite a lot of immigration"* matters helping children gain visas and asylum. *"Some are fleeing drug cartels and violence; their family members may have been killed. All kinds of horrible things happen to them. It's rewarding to do something for someone with a very tangible result."*

"Fleeing drug cartels and violence."

Kilpatrick's Atlanta office has *"a whole program devoted to grandparent adoptions."* Come Saturday, some juniors here can be found hanging around the Atlanta Volunteer Lawyers Foundation, *"interviewing people who need help. It's a pretty good way to pick up pro bono."*

Domestic abuse and landlord/tenant matters or advising indigent inventors on IP rights were popular assignments across the firm. Attorneys are required to complete 30 hours of pro bono a year and can credit up to 50 hours toward their annual billable target.

Pro Bono hours

- For all attorneys across all US offices: 39,733
- Average per US attorney: 57

Hours & Compensation

Entry-level associates are required to bill at least 1,850 hours a year. Second-years and up shoot for an annual target of 1,900. *"It's achievable but easier for attorneys in certain practices."* Patent prosecutors, for example, may struggle more than litigators. That being said, one interviewee felt: *"This isn't the kind of place that looks at an associate and blames them if they're not hitting the hours. It's a team effort and partners take personal responsibility if not enough work is going around."*

"Achieving just the minimum is not going to get you an A+ review."

For those able to meet the target, it's worth bearing in mind that *"achieving just the minimum is not going to get you an A+ review. There's an understanding you should strive to go above it,"* especially if you want to be seeing dollar signs in front of your eyes: *"If you don't exceed the target by a good amount, don't expect a bonus."*

"We're a full-service firm with an incredibly strong IP base."

Although *"lots of people are early birds"* and in by 8.30am, how associates notch up their hours is generally up to them. *"They don't insist we stay here for 60 hours a week. I may have to do 60 hours' worth of work but if I'm only in the office 40 hours a week, I can go home and be a decent parent."*

Diversity

Sources praised the firm's supportive attitude toward parent attorneys: *"It's one of the biggest things I love about this firm."* Juniors in Atlanta judged that *"compared to most firms, especially in the IP area, we have a much higher percentage of female partners and associates."*

"It compares favorably."

Females are *"still under-represented"* in Seattle. It's also *"pretty homogeneous in terms of race. The Atlanta office is more racially diverse, but it's in a city with a large African-American population."* The Bay Area *"seems fairly diverse. I think it compares favorably to others."* See our website for more associate thoughts on diversity at Kilpatrick.

Get Hired

Kilpatrick scrapped the traditional callback interview format a couple of years ago. *"We felt we weren't getting a full picture of how the candidates would perform in*

See firm profile on p.661

real-world circumstances at a law firm," hiring committee chairman Charlie Henn explains. *"We weren't getting good information on teamwork, collaboration and creativity in trying to solve client problems in a group."*

Instead, the firm devised 'Super Call-Back Weekend'. Dinner and drinks with the firm's attorneys on a Friday are followed by a task-filled Saturday. Aspiring attorneys are put through their paces in a one-on-one interview, a writing exercise and group tasks including a treasure hunt. Read our online interview with Charlie Henn to find out more.

"See if people are fake or genuine."

Current juniors were on board with the changes: *"I think it's better. Some people don't interview well, or they interview well but can't work in groups. The assessments get at things which wouldn't come out in interviews."* And dinner the night before allows attorneys to *"see if people are fake or genuine. So much of this job is not academic as much as tolerating the people around you."*

Strategy & Future

2015 saw the opening of Kilpatrick's Dallas office to *"better support our Texas client base,"* managing partner Susan Spaeth tells us. *"We are looking to have our office footprint better match our national and international client base."* Spaeth is keeping tight-lipped about the possibility of additional offices to service this commitment but explains: *"Our firm is team-centric. When we look at strategic growth it's more around what growth we need to have in different practice offerings and where that affects a particular geographic region. We are very interested in further growing our corporate offering in California, for example."*

While IP will continue to be the firm's front runner, Kilpatrick will *"further expand and support our corporate and commercial litigation depth and breadth"* across the USA. Go online to read our full interview with Spaeth.

"People crack jokes that are not just nerdy, they're actual jokes."

See firm profile on p.661

King & Spalding LLP

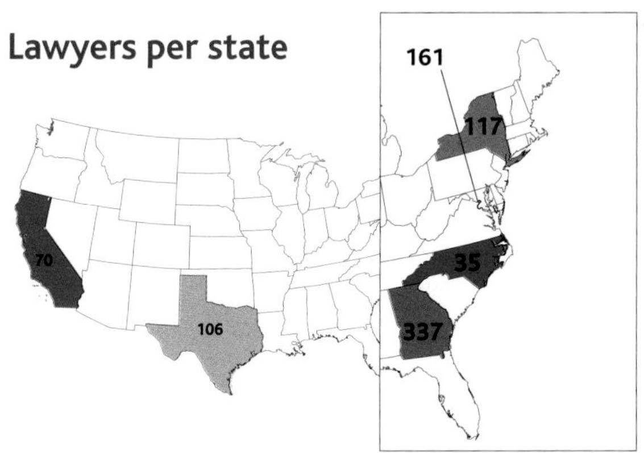

Largest US office: Atlanta
US offices: 8
International offices: 10
First-year salary: $160,000 ($135,000 in Charlotte and Atlanta)
Billable hours: no requirement
Summers 2016: 56 (51 2Ls, 5 1Ls)
Revenue 2015: $1.018 billion (+9%)
Partners made in 2016: 24 (18 in US)
Famous for: its standing in Atlanta; its recent expansion

Becoming a King & Spalding associate has long been a hot gig. But today there are one billion reasons to try and nab it...

A LOT has happened since 2007: presidential elections that made history, financial crises, Beyoncé and Jay Z's wedding... But even the perspective afforded by these major events can't diminish the magnitude of King & Spalding's expansion. Over the last decade the Georgian VIP went from a respectable five offices to a globetrotting 18, across the USA, Europe, the Middle East and Asia. The most recent addition, following strong hints from chairman Robert Hays in our 2015 interview with him, is Tokyo. Oh, and the firm hit the $1 billion revenue mark for the first time.

With regard to its practice areas, though, Robert Hays confirms that the K&S approach is to build upward rather than outward: *"We'll continue to broaden that handful of things that the firm is world-class at: energy, life sciences and healthcare, financial institutions, technology and IP, financial institutions, global disputes, and government investigations."* Its *Chambers USA* profile confirms the veracity of this list and presents a staggering catalog of top marks for K&S's outstanding work, particularly in Georgia.

"There's only one firm in Atlanta that does New York-caliber work, and that's King & Spalding," championed one, adding that *"coming here was a simple decision when valuing top-quality work coupled with Atlanta's lifestyle."* Others agreed, nonchalantly informing us: *"It's known as being the most prestigious firm in the area."* One coyly confessed: *"I shot for the stars,"* while another set the record straight: *"There's a perception that non-New York firms' practices aren't as vast and sophisticated but that's not the case. Just look at the work K&S does."*

On chambers-associate.com...

- Interview with chairman Robert Hays
- From the K&S hall of fame: Griffin Bell

ASSOCIATES SAY...

The Work

During summer, Atlanta hopefuls rotate between different practice areas before expressing a preference. If they know they're keen on litigation over corporate, for example, they can hop across different contentious teams and bypass the transactional side. In New York and DC summers don't rotate but are recruited into single groups. Most K&S associates work in business litigation, but a significant number can be found in corporate, as well as 'special matters'. About the latter, one explained: *"It's essentially white-collar crime. It's good for merging litigation with political interests."*

"There's not a lot of doc review because we have a 'discovery center'."

Business litigators in Atlanta worked *"on a variety of matters including professional liability, security and de-*

See firm profile on p.662

The Inside View

Rankings in *Chambers USA*

Antitrust	Intellectual Property
Appellate Law	International Arbitration
Banking & Finance	International Trade
Bankruptcy/Restructuring	Labor & Employment
Construction	Latin American Investment
Corporate Crime & Investigations	Litigation
	Products Liability
Corporate/M&A	Projects
Energy & Natural Resources	Real Estate
Environment	REITs
Food & Beverages	Securities
Government	Tax
Healthcare	

For detail on ranking tiers and ranking locations, visit www.chambersandpartners.com

Recent work highlights

- Atlanta lawyers advised Carmike Cinemas in its $1.1 billion merger agreement with AMC Entertainment Holdings
- DC litigators successfully represented two acute-care hospitals that had been denied $700,000 in Medicare bad debt claims by the Health and Human Services department
- LA lawyers advised real estate company Douglas Emmett on the acquisition of four office buildings in West LA worth $1.34 billion
- In Austin attorneys were victorious for ATP Oil & Gas by obtaining a dismissal of claims brought by purchasers of $1.5 billion in notes from the company, who claimed that ATP had falsely projected better prospects

rivatives, class actions, malpractice, and data privacy." They explained that *"an eight-person team is considered large here, so you get substantive tasks. There's not a lot of doc review because we have a 'discovery center'."* One's highlight was *"being involved in deposition prep just a few weeks into joining, and even doing one deposition by myself. It's exciting for a first-year. I also had a role in drafting a summary judgment brief."* A DC litigator couldn't hide their pride: *"They let me appear in court on behalf of a client, I got to attend a four-day trial where I was the only chair. The partner was there but wasn't even sat at the table!"*

Another popular destination for litigator types was tort and environmental litigation. *"It's divided into tobacco, pharmaceutical, toxic tort, and automotive, among others. With tobacco, teams are of two attorneys. Work includes drafting motions to compel, taking depositions of fact witnesses, and some research when it comes to trial."* One bragged: *"I've been to trial four times. It's an awesome experience."* In LA it's *"mostly public liability work in the pharmaceuticals sector, with either small cases where one guy gets sick and sues, or mass tort with hundreds of plaintiffs."*

"Some of my best friends in my life are on my team."

Corporate associates also told of *"leanly staffed teams"* where you *"get thrown into drafting quickly."* And even though *"in the first year there's a lot of diligence, it's not uncommon for a second-year to take the first cut at drafting a purchase agreement. Then of course there's things like disclosure schedules."* Insiders had been *"working mostly on M&A transactions, recently on the sell side of public matters, as well as some private equity acquisitions."*

Culture

Associates happily admitted that, particularly in the firm's Atlanta HQ, *"K&S is a bit more traditional than some other firms: everyone is very academic and polite, and people present themselves well, where other offices might be more casual."* They were just as confident, however, in dispelling any suspicion that with being *"academic"* and *"traditional"* comes stuffiness or uncomfortable silence. *"It's just professional, but that doesn't mean people don't take an interest in you as a person. Some of my best friends in my life are on my team,"* one said heart-meltingly, *"and I wouldn't think twice about going to talk to a partner, even if the doors are sometimes closed."* Sources across other offices agreed wholeheartedly, describing the atmosphere as *"collaborative, where even partners ask my opinion and are receptive to my needs,"* and characterized by *"camaraderie among associates."*

Beyond the working day, K&S clearly values its social scene. Atlanta antics included *"a large Christmas party downtown with a band and a lot of senior partners dancing hilariously, whiskey and wine tastings, and watching a game in our lounge area. It has a big TV, couches, and a fridge with beer in it."* New Yorkers enjoyed *"happy hours with hors d'oeuvres, and frequent impromptu drinks."*

Hours & Compensation

"Atlanta is a traditional workhorse," said a stoic source, *"and our hours reflect that."* Logging on after dinner and weekend work (from home) were common. While there's no minimum hours requirement, a *"flat bonus"* is awarded once associates hit the 2,050 mark. Anything above this number, which all participants in the HQ had vastly exceeded, *"is recognized"* with more cash. Most reported billing between 2,200 and 2,700, *"which is higher than anyone wants it to be, but is a product of the firm performing so well."*

See firm profile on p.662

Sources didn't feel the firm was pushing them beyond the limit, however, and added that *"the people who know I'm working a lot try and get me some relief where possible."* They also stated that *"the firm shows folks that billables aren't everything: there are other bonuses you can get for pro bono, or for attracting new clients to the firm."* Generally rookies agreed that *"it's hard to be anything but grateful"* for their kind of compensation but some would have appreciated *"a bit more transparency"* with regard to bonus amounts.

"The firm shows folks that billables aren't everything."

Pro Bono

"I'm the poster child for pro bono," one junior joked. *"I did 250 hours in my first year when a case went to trial and the firm credited every single hour."* For mere mortals, the billable limit is supposed to be 100 (up from 50 a few years back). Insiders thought this was fair and agreed that *"the firm does an excellent job of promoting pro bono through a specially appointed counsel, but the onus is on the individual if they want to give back, and some people don't do any."* Those who had spoke with verve about their do-gooding endeavors so far, citing *"going to trial for a neighbor dispute that got out of control, working on a clemency petition, getting restraining orders for domestic violence cases, defending a prisoner who was sexually assaulted by her doctor, and representing seven plaintiffs in a sexual assault case against their karate instructor."*

"Some people don't do any."

Pro bono hours

- For all attorneys across all US offices: 22,365
- Average per US attorney: 29

Diversity

With 91% of KSLAW partners and 84% of associates being white, it was no surprise that some ethnically diverse respondents felt tangibly outnumbered. At the same time, insiders unanimously agreed that the firm was *"committed to and supportive of diversity"* and is *"working on it."* Turning to gender, sources felt results were more evident, explaining that *"they're promoting maternity leave and other part-time opportunities for women, while trying to look at different ways they can level the playing field."* A female associate in New York did lament that *"there aren't as many female partners as I'd like,"* but in Atlanta *"there are a lot of women, and we're certainly diverse for the region."*

Training & Development

"On-the-job learning is part of the training, sure, but if I was a surgeon I wouldn't practice on my boyfriend." While the stakes are thankfully slightly lower when, say, writing a brief for the first time, this source's analogy cut through what others were feeling: *"I think the firm struggles with training,"* one ventured. *"There's a two-day orientation when you arrive but it's not as helpful as you'd hope. Then there are formal academies every year but they're organized by class and aren't tailored to the individual."*

"If I was a surgeon I wouldn't practice on my boyfriend."

Another agreed that *"we don't do a whole lot. There's a NITA program but other than that the firm itself doesn't formally take you through that day-to-day, hands-on stuff you don't learn at law school."* On the other hand, juniors appreciated their mentoring system, internally called 'Link'. Each new starter is appointed an associate and a partner 'link', and while *"everyone has a different experience,"* most had felt supported by their mentors. *"My partner link taught me to be a realist about things, and she expresses her own troubles to me too."* The style, dynamic and frequency of formal and informal feedback were also popular.

"There's no hubris in what we're trying to do."

Robert Hays, chairman

Offices

Atlanta housed 27 of 68 juniors on our list at the time of our calls, DC claimed 14, and 12 were in New York. *"New York has an excellent litigation department and the antitrust practice is based in DC."* The rest were scattered across Houston, Charlotte, Austin, LA, San Francisco, Silicon Valley and Sacramento.

"I'm in the background of most of the tourist photos!"

A Big Apple caterpillar felt similarly about the tech offering, stating that *"IT support has been lacking, but the space is nice with great views."* DC deal-doers bragged about their *"hilariously idyllic walk to work: I'm in the background of most of the tourist photos! We also have this crazy amazing rooftop where we watch fireworks on the fourth of July. The only downside is when you're trying to do a conference call and the White House motorcades go off."*

See firm profile on p.662

Get Hired

King & Spalding travels to 26 campuses and a dozen or so other events as part of its recruitment effort. *"We mainly go to the same schools every year, but add or subtract based on how well we feel K&S connects to those schools,"* chief recruiting officer Kate Ferguson shares. At this stage *"most candidates express an interest in one particular office, but some do keep it open to more."* There's no set percentage that gets invited for a callback, it's decided on an ad hoc basis. *"The second interview is an extended version of the first, we're looking for the same key traits: intellectual capability, but more importantly intellectual curiosity, collegiality, a collaborative spirit, resilience and good judgment. We're looking for people who want to keep learning and developing themselves, who are goal-oriented, and who can translate that into good client service."* The callback is usually with five or six people, and while there are no oral or written assessments, there's sometimes a lunch.

Strategy & Future

"There's no hubris in what we're trying to do," asserts chairman Robert Hays. *"We're mindful of where we're succeeding and where we're not, but we have not decided to make any identifiable changes in our strategy. We're not currently planning to leave any practices behind, or move into new ones. Our growth has been organic, we promoted more partners last year than in the history of the firm, and we've increased our focus on associate development and promotion. Some firms have expanded at the expense of their culture, but we're mindful of that."*

"Coming here was a simple decision when valuing top-quality work coupled with Atlanta's lifestyle."

See firm profile on p.662

Kirkland & Ellis LLP

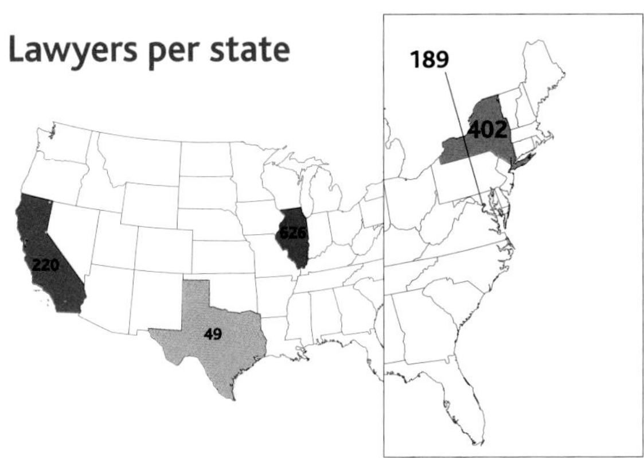

Largest US office: Chicago
US offices: 7
International offices: 5
First-year salary: $160,000
Billable hours: no requirement
Summers 2016: 165 (146 2Ls, 18 1Ls, 1 3L)
Revenue 2015: $2.305 billion (+7.2%)
Partners made in 2016: 93 globally (80 in US)
Famous for: eye-popping deals and tricky litigation

Driven associates thrive in this Midwest behemoth's entrepreneurial atmosphere: "*It's Kirkland at its best.*"

YOU'RE a huge corporation facing a highly publicized multibillion-dollar lawsuit and federal prosecutors are gunning for you. You're going to need a firm with a formidable courtroom pedigree. Step up, Kirkland & Ellis – the *"litigation juggernauts,"* maintained one associate – one of BigLaw's most recognizable brands. The firm has been immersed in some of the biggest, headline-grabbing lawsuits in recent years. Kirkland has represented BP since the fallout from the disastrous Deepwater Horizon oil spill in 2010, for example, and acted for General Motors after a faulty ignition switch prompted a colossal recall of 2.6 million cars back in 2013.

It's unsurprising, then, that Kirkland earns top-tier *Chambers USA* rankings for litigation in its home city of Chicago, but the firm is far from a one-practice wonder. Its corporate team dominates Chicago's legal landscape – for over a decade it has earned the highest ranking *Chambers USA* can bestow on a firm – and Kirkland's antitrust, bankruptcy, IP, insurance, real estate and tax offerings are all among the cream of the crop too. Outside Illinois, Kirkland notches up a raft of nationwide *Chambers USA* rankings, alongside a whole host more for its work in California, New York and DC. Visit chambersandpartners.com for the full rundown.

On chambers-associate.com...

- We speak with firmwide recruiting committee vice chairs Beth Deeley and Jason Kanner
- Kirkland's taste for formidable litigation

ASSOCIATES SAY...

The Work

Kirkland's free market system was recently deemed too *"scary sounding,"* so to calm the fraying nerves of incoming associates *"they've rebranded it as an open assignment system."* The rebrand hasn't changed the process, but juniors reassured us that *"although people arrive and think they will have to knock on doors, there is so much work going around that people tend to call you. Juggling projects can take some getting used to"* but the open assignment system found favor with most of our interviewees: *"I work hard enough, I don't need someone telling me who to work for,"* one source stressed. *"If I don't like working with someone or our styles don't click then I can avoid that option in the future,"* another elaborated. *"I can shape my career and the kind of work I want to do. It really works to your advantage."* Over half of Kirkland's 100-plus first-years head into transactional departments, and around a quarter slot into litigation. The remainder are divided between restructuring and IP.

> *"Juggling projects can take some getting used to."*

Although some transactional subgroups – like funds formation – hire several newbies directly into their area,

See firm profile on p.663

Rankings in *Chambers USA*

Advertising	Intellectual Property
Antitrust	International Trade
Appellate Law	Investment Funds
Banking & Finance	Life Sciences
Bankruptcy/Restructuring	Litigation
Capital Markets	Media & Entertainment
Climate Change	Outsourcing
Corporate Crime & Investigations	Private Equity
	Products Liability
Corporate/M&A	Real Estate
Energy & Natural Resources	Securities
Environment	Tax
FCPA	Technology
Insurance	Wealth Management

For detail on ranking tiers and ranking locations, visit www.chambersandpartners.com

Recent work highlights

- Represented General Motors in over 190 class action lawsuits surrounding the mass recall of 2.6 million cars due to defective ignition switches
- Acted for Chicago Cubs owner Tom Ricketts in a breach of contract dispute after two rooftop businesses alleged that expansion and renovation of the Cubs' stadium would harm their businesses
- Assisted Teva Pharmaceuticals with antitrust aspects of its $40.5 billion acquisition of Allergan's generics business
- Acted for Brazilian investment group 3G Capital and Heinz in the $46 billion merger of Heinz and Kraft Foods

most deal-doing juniors begin life as generalists. *"We're expected to take on one or two matters in every subset,"* and sources had dabbled in M&A, debt finance, capital markets, private equity and funds formation. *"My experience as a third-year is drastically different to when I first walked in the door. Back then I was just trying to get my head around what a transaction entails, conducting basic due diligence and handling very straightforward ancillary documents like certificates for closing. It picked up very quickly; by the fifth month I was running diligence and negotiating and drafting ancillary documents. Today I'm running deals, drafting and negotiating the main agreements and managing client expectations."*

Litigators tend to remain as generalists throughout their career. *"The partners do a bit of everything,"* so juniors don't have to move around much to experience areas such as antitrust, bankruptcy, trade secrets, securities, general commercial litigation and white-collar crime. One litigator told us: *"Matters like the BP litigation require a small army of associates on doc review, but I've had only a very small number of cases where I've just sat behind a screen and done that. Most caseloads allow us to get involved with every aspect, from attending and leading depositions to managing the discovery process,"* to legal research and brief writing.

Hours & Compensation

Kirkland routinely pays bonuses *"significantly over market,"* with juniors avowedly *"pretty happy"* with their windfall. All those dollars aren't for nothing though: *"There are three levels of busy. If it's quiet, I'm not here after 4pm. Normally it's relatively busy and I'm out by 7pm. If we're slammed I'll be here until 10pm when they turn out the lights in the hallway."* Even if that energy-saving measure seems like a good sign that associates might want to vacate the building, there can be little relief in the sanctuary of their own home. *"It's hard to shut your brain off,"* one source admitted. *"It's easy to get sucked into working more than you would like; we're all hard workers so it can be a challenge to switch off."* Technology proves *"a blessing and a curse; in a sense, unless I'm asleep I'm always on call. I get emails at all hours of the night until I go to bed and see more when I get up."* Even taking vacation *"is sort of at your own risk."* While colleagues *"try to be respectful of it, when you have knowledge people need they will email you questions."*

"Significantly over market."

Relief may come in the lack of a formal billing target. *"Kirkland is as hard-working or intense as people are willing to make it; if you want to work lots of hours you can but if you don't, that's fine too."* Interviewees put the *"sweet spot for maximizing a bonus and your work/life balance"* at around 2,000-2,200 hours, but we spoke to several juniors billing well into the mid 2,000s. *"I'm knackered,"* one admitted. Other high-billers were quick to point out: *"We went to top law schools and all strive to be the best. I feel no external pressure to work certain hours but everyone has an internal drive to work as much as possible."*

Culture

High-billing, super-motivated... sources admitted that Kirkland can *"sound daunting to some people. Inevitably you will find champions, mentors and people you click with and they'll help you through. People work hard when they have to, but the firm knows we cannot go 100 miles an hour 24/7."*

"You can find your niche."

Several interviewees noted their surprise at finding the firm *"very different from its cut-throat reputation. There is a lot of team-based cooperation and so much work go-*

See firm profile on p.663

ing around that we have to turn it down, not fight for it!" Another pointed out: *"We may have a reputation for being tough-edged but I've found everyone very friendly."* The open assignment system *"acts as a check on people treating each other the right way; if you're not nice, no one will work with you."*

While the drive to work hard seemed pretty consistent across the offices – *"this place is made up of a lot of workaholics"* – juniors did point out the difficulty of identifying other defining Kirkland characteristics. *"There are 200 to 300 corporate attorneys in Chicago; you can find your niche in terms of the culture you like."* Those in smaller offices found it easier to spot trends. One junior reckoned DC is made up of attorneys *"very much doing their own thing,"* while over in San Francisco *"we hang out together outside of work and the partners know everyone. People take my work for a week if I'm really slammed. The job can be very demanding but people don't express that in a negative way."*

Training & Development

"Kirkland puts its money where its mouth is when it comes to training; it's not something they just whack in the marketing brochure." New starters are all flown to one office to spend several days learning *"about tech, time entry systems and all that stuff,"* followed by practice area orientations.

"It's a love/hate relationship."

Ongoing practice area training sessions are delivered through the firm's Kirkland Institute program. The Kirkland Institute of Corporate Practice (KICP) covers *"most of the different practice areas and deals you see in first and second year."* By the third year, sessions include topics such as *"how to run a deal; it's less substantive legal training and more how to be a better associate."*

At the time of our calls, third-year litigators were about to get stuck in to their annual Kirkland Institute for Trial Advocacy program (KITA): first-years conduct cross and direct examinations while second-years stage a bench trial and third and fourth-years participate in a mock jury trial. *"It's a love/hate relationship. They're really fun and we look back on them with fond memories but in the weeks leading up to it we're wishing we didn't have all this fake work when there is so much real work on our plates."*

Offices

HQ and mega office Chicago houses almost 600 attorneys in an *"amazing office. There is no comparison."* New York is currently undergoing *"mass renovations; we're turning the conference floor into two floors interconnected by a grand staircase."* DC has a few more years to wait before moving to new, smarter digs in 2019. In San Francisco it's all about what's outside the window: *"The view is incredible. It's the best out of any of the offices,"* and overlooks San Francisco Bay.

"There is no comparison."

Despite the miles between them, juniors reckoned their offices were well integrated into Kirkland's US network. Although most cross-office interaction happens among the higher echelons, many interviewees still had the chance to work *"pretty seamlessly"* with other bases on cross-border deals or call upon remote specialists, such as DC's employment team.

"Kirkland is as hard-working or intense as people are willing to make it it."

Pro Bono

All pro bono hours are counted as billable and Kirkland expects every attorney to reach at least 20 hours a year: *"Come October or November and the pro bono coordinators start hounding people who haven't hit the minimum."* Many in fact do much more than the 20.

"Act fast."

Assisting startups and nonprofits to incorporate, revise charters or draw up employment agreements proved popular among associates in the Windy City. San Franciscans have to *"act fast"* before the pro bono cases they want are snapped up by others. *"We do a lot of work to assist veterans who have health or criminal issues or whose disability filings have been denied,"* and the firm also sends some attorneys down to the local housing court twice a week. DC associates also have a hand in helping veterans or working on landlord/tenant matters, while in the Big Apple *"the firm does a lot of asylum applications for LGBT individuals,"* among other things.

Pro Bono hours

- For all attorneys across all US offices: 103,846
- Average per US attorney: 72

Diversity

"Diversity isn't our strongest point but I think they're prioritizing it heavily," one East Coast source ruminated. *"We hold diversity events such as dinners or happy*

See firm profile on p.663

hours, and the Women's Leadership Initiative (WLI) held a retreat to a country club for a day to chat about issues unique to women." Over on the West Coast *"the attrition rate for women in some groups seems to be steep but the firm has made several accommodations to women; they've introduced a mothers' room"* in San Francisco and the office has an active WLI group.

"They've introduced a mothers' room."

In Chicago, *"the WLI and LGBT subcommittee are big here,"* but associates did note that like most of BigLaw the firm *"does skew toward white males. I think it's changing in the younger classes where there is a lot more gender and ethnic diversity."*

Get Hired

Several sources felt that *"the people who do well at Kirkland are self-starters."* Recruiters *"try to hire people who are driven. The open assignment system treats you like an adult, so you need to be self-motivated to do well and succeed."* Others reckoned that assertiveness would make it easier for associates *"to thrive"* when seeking out work.

"Being wishy-washy about practice groups is a bad idea."

One junior found that *"associates here tend to be more outgoing than at other firms we come across; you don't need to be an extrovert, just demonstrate that you have a personality rather than being stoic."* Another associate told us that when it comes to interviews: *"Being wishy-washy about practice groups is a bad idea. It's better to be clear and say 'this is my goal, I have an interest in this and it's demonstrated by my resume'."* Go online to read our interview with recruiting committee vice chairs Beth Deeley and Jason Kanner.

"No more splashy hires."

Strategy & Future

"We're in a conservative, slow-growth mode right now," juniors believed, with sources predicting *"no more splashy hires or new office openings."* (Back in 2014 the firm launched an office in Houston and hired so-called '$9 Million Man' (per year) IP partner Jim Hurst into Chicago.)

But Kirkland isn't standing still. Big Apple associates had noticed a steady *"shift away from our focus on litigation"* in the sense that corporate in particular (and public company within that) is going great guns right now (litigation is growing too). One junior confirmed: *"Over the last couple of years there has been strong growth in our corporate group."*

"If you're not nice, no one will work with you."

See firm profile on p.663

Kramer Levin Naftalis & Frankel LLP

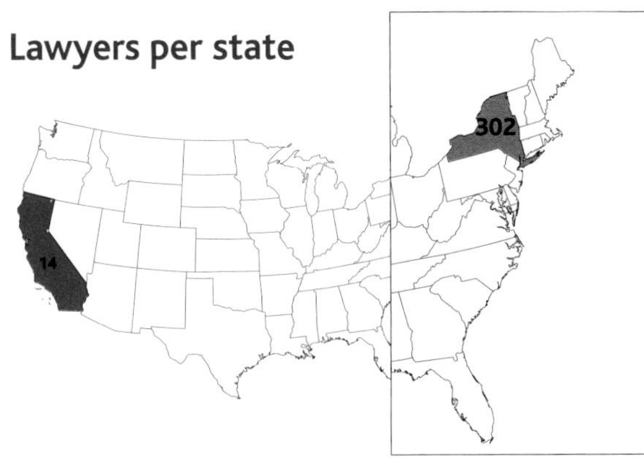

Largest US office: New York
US offices: 2
International offices: 1
First-year salary: $160,000
Billable hours: 2,000 target for 60% bonus (2,150 for full bonus)
Summers 2016: 15 (13 2Ls, 1 1L, 1 SEO)
Revenue 2015: $332 million (+3.6%)
Partners made in 2016: tbd
Famous for: friendly work environment; LGBT and pro bono commitments

A midsized Big Appler, Kramer Levin's *"nice normal people"* make it *"a place where associates are generally very happy."*

KRAMER Levin has seen a spread of lateral hires recently: *"Two IP partners in the life sciences area, a real estate partner, a corporate partner, a fund formation partner and a commercial litigation partner,"* managing partner Paul Pearlman tells us. Such a number of additions is fairly uncommon at the firm, although he highlights that it isn't part of any particular growth plan, but rather a mix of opportunistic hires and gap-filling. Even so, Kramer has certainly expanded since it was founded nearly 50 years ago, with just six partners and eight associates to its name. The Manhattanite now has over 300 lawyers across nearly 30 practice areas in two offices. With advertising litigation being the apple of Kramer's eye – ranked number one nationwide in *Chambers USA* – the firm also takes the top spot statewide for its bankruptcy & restructuring and immigration work.

But while, as one junior enthused, the firm *"works on cutting-edge, sophisticated deals and cases,"* associates were also eager to highlight Kramer's pleasant working environment, and how much they *"enjoy each other's company."* In the words of Paul Pearlman, *"one of the things we try to do is maintain the best of both worlds: the collegiality and collaboration of a small firm, while practicing against and with the major firms out there."*

On chambers-associate.com...

- Kramer's crews: more on the practice areas
- Interview with Paul Pearlman, managing partner

ASSOCIATES SAY...

The Work

On the summer program, *"you can do as much or as little of any department's work as you like."* Some cautioned that the firm *"does not give department-specific offers at the end of the summer, because they can't always know what their needs are going to be two years in advance."* Incoming junior associates find out what department they're in just before they join, and their preferences are taken into consideration. Around 20% of our interviewee list this year were lateral hires, reflecting junior-level opportunities for those wishing to switch from other employers. Kramer's litigation and corporate groups take the most juniors overall, while most of the rest go to intellectual property, real estate and creditors' rights (bankruptcy) teams. The remainder are spread around tax, immigration, environment, financial services, and the individual client group.

"Older associates and partners would reach out to us."

Most departments have a *"hybrid system"* of work allocation with an assigning partner coupled with the expectation that juniors do some door-knocking to get onto interesting cases. IP doesn't have an assigning partner, but *"older associates and partners would reach out to us according to their needs."* In litigation, the work can be *"very varied,"* with a big focus on general commercial disputes, government investigations, white-collar

See firm profile on p.664

Rankings in *Chambers USA*

Advertising	Immigration
Bankruptcy/Restructuring	Litigation
Capital Markets	Real Estate
Corporate/M&A	Tax

For detail on ranking tiers and ranking locations, visit www.chambersandpartners.com

Recent work highlights

- Obtained a $250 million settlement in an antitrust class action of consumer goods companies including Kraft Heinz, against News Corporation and co-defendants, alleging that News Corporation monopolized the third party in-store promotions market
- Represented the issuer, HERO Funding Trust 2015-1, and the transaction sponsor, Renovate America, in the issuance of $240 million of asset-backed notes
- Represented the official committee of unsecured creditors of NII Holdings in a Chapter 11 case worth $4.35 billion
- Successfully defended Procter & Gamble in a challenge by Kimberly-Clark over the absorbency of a brand of diapers

defense, and false advertising cases (for example leaky diapers, 'odorless' deodorant and '99% natural' toothpaste...). Clients range from consumer products giants and big banks to small business owners. Litigators are also often brought in to *"work on certain slices"* of bankruptcy assignments and banking & finance matters. First and second-years get *"a lot of doc review – it's just the way the legal world works at this level,"* although by their third year, associates had *"noticed the difference"* in responsibility levels. *"Now I'm doing an arbitration and attending hearings – generally getting very involved in the case."*

"As a first-year there was a lot of getting into the weeds."

Corporate deal-doers similarly discovered that *"as a first-year there was a lot of getting into the weeds, reading contracts and doing due diligence. That has grown into leading the process more, like drafting the memo that goes to the client."* Associates reported doing much M&A work, mainly for private equity funds. Mid-market deals (those under a billion dollars) are *"Kramer Levin's sweet spot."* Capital markets also features (including securities and public offerings), and cross-over with other groups includes restructuring: *"Bankruptcy generates a lot of work for the corporate group."* Go online for info about the bankruptcy, real estate and IP departments.

Training & Development

New associates take part in an orientation week, which includes anything from *"going over benefits and paperwork to computer training."* After this, the learning process is fairly informal, particularly in the smaller groups like IP and real estate, where it's more *"learn by doing,"* although there are regular practice group presentations. This doesn't mean newbies are just thrown to the lions, however. They're allocated mentors to guide them through the initial stages, and one real estate junior highlighted that *"if I'm working with a partner on something, they'll definitely go out of their way to teach me how things work."* First-year litigation and corporate associates also mentioned *"constant CLEs and presentations on practice-specific areas."*

"Go out of their way to teach me how things work."

The assessment process consists of a yearly review (biannual for first-years), during which two partners *"go over evaluations that people have submitted about you. They tell you their impressions of you and give you the opportunity to ask questions."*

Offices

The vast majority of juniors are based in Kramer's New York HQ, where they share an office for their first two years. *"I don't know who I would talk to if I was here by myself all day!"* one junior laughed. Associates dig the building's convenient Midtown location, *"basically across the street from the Rockefeller Center,"* even if *"on the downside it's close to Times Square."* There's a *"nice art collection: it's amazing, super weird, sort of modernist. It's definitely, like, got a flair to it!"* Sources were less complimentary about the old cafeteria, but excited about its refurb: *"We had kind of a crappy cafeteria and they just replaced that. It's really good!"* Sandwich, soup, pizza, yoghurt, salads...the choice is yours. One attorney mentioned that the offices are located within the lower half of Manhattan's Americas Tower, so associates *"don't get jaw-dropping views. You're not going to get a 66th floor office that takes your breath away."*

"I don't know who I would talk to if I was here by myself all day!"

The firm's only other domestic office, in Silicon Valley, has around 15 lawyers and specializes in IP litigation, particularly involving tech and life sciences. Kramer's single international outpost, in Paris, was acquired in 1999 as the unexpected result of Clifford Chance's merger with Roger & Wells. The Paris office of the latter firm decided not to participate in the transaction, so Kramer saw their chance: *"We were looking to do something in Europe at that time to better service our clients,"* explained managing partner Paul Pearlman.

See firm profile on p.664

Culture

Almost all of our interviewees mentioned that Kramer's culture was one of the main draws for them. *"For me it was important to be in an environment where it's more down to earth, and the people are personable,"* one revealed. Has it lived up to expectations? *"Definitely,"* was the emphatic reply. *"Obviously there are exceptions, but they hire people who you want to work with, grab lunch or a drink with."* A third answered: *"You can walk into any partner's office and ask a question or get advice."* Talking of partners, one newbie bravely confided that *"they're not gods! I know every one of the top partners in my group. You don't have to go through three levels of partners to get access to those guys."*

"People need to have realistic expectations."

Some felt that the firm's smaller size was part of the reason for this cordial environment. *"I think Kramer Levin is right on the edge,"* one associate mused. *"If they put in another 100 attorneys it would feel a lot bigger, but as it is you don't feel like you're working for a giant corporation. You get to know people within your group."* But while getting along is important, socializing isn't necessarily a priority, as *"people have lives, families, friends; we recognize the value of going home at the end of the day. If you need to run out early nobody's going to question it."* But don't fall into the trap of assuming the culture is laid back: *"A lot of people think that it's some version of BigLaw but also a lifestyle firm, and it's definitely not,"* warned one associate. *"It's probably not as cut-throat as a lot of big law firms, but it is nonetheless a big law firm, and people need to have realistic expectations about that."* Another added: *"People work until midnight. Someone canceled a vacation recently and was reimbursed – that sort of thing happens."*

Hours & Compensation

Associates need to rack up 2,000 hours to get 60% of their bonus, and 2,150 for the full sum. While many felt that this was too high, and that the firm is *"off the market with that,"* others thought it doable, particularly as *"all pro bono and CLEs count toward it,"* as well as things like recruiting and helping promote diversity. Associates were also quick to highlight that *"the firm doesn't penalize you if you don't meet the threshold. I was under last year and they acknowledged that my group had been slow."*

"The category of what's included in billables is much broader than at other firms."

Interviewees generally reported working around ten hours a day, and a few hours at weekends. All-nighters aren't unknown, and we heard of one or two marathon 100-hour weeks. *"That's as bad as it gets though,"* we were promptly assured. *"The partner I was working with said that was one of the worst deals he's been on – a normal week would be 50 to 60 billable hours."*

"Our strategy continues to be the same: to remain independent and grow organically through selective lateral transitions."
Paul Pearlman, managing partner

Pro Bono

There's no cap on pro bono at Kramer. It all counts toward the bonus. Real estate associates reported (unsurprisingly) working on landlord and tenant disputes, while the litigation group does a lot of work with the South Brooklyn Legal Services program (which also offers an externship). In another departure from the BigLaw norm, Kramer provides associates to work here on secondment: *"They send someone to work for four months full-time,"* one explained. Other initiatives include helping domestic abuse charity Her Justice, with which Kramer *"has a longstanding relationship"* supporting women who've been victims of violence, and offering child custody assistance.

"They send someone to work for four months full-time."

Meanwhile, others had worked on *"assisting with an application for special juvenile immigration status,"* and we heard of lawyers setting up an organization for children from low-income backgrounds, teaching them computer skills in a summer school-style environment.

Pro bono hours

- For all attorneys across all US offices: 23,254
- Average per US attorney: 82

Diversity

"The firm is really well known for its LGBT support, and you feel that. Some of the partners submitted amicus briefs for all the Supreme Court matters for the gay marriage proceedings, and some very interesting speakers came in to talk about that." Elsewhere, led by the diversity committee *"they're making an effort. We have*

The Inside View

See firm profile on p.664

an attorneys of color group, and we do events to promote diversity in recruitment."

"The firm is really well known for its LGBT support."

In litigation, juniors felt that the male to female ratio *"seems pretty even,"* while over in the corporate and real estate groups, *"there are definitely more men than women."* One corporate associate added that *"for the last few months, there has been one female lawyer on my floor."* The firm is trying to change this, however: *"There are almost too many women's initiatives!"* one junior joked. *"I keep getting emails about meetings and I'm like, 'I can't go to another one!'"* Overall, Kramer currently has 46% female associates.

Get Hired

According to Kerri Ann Law, Kramer's hiring committee chair, *"people who are willing to seize the opportunities that they're given do well here. We want someone who we can put in front of a client, court or adversary, and know that they are able to handle themselves; someone who's going to thrive where they're a bit uncomfortable."* And make sure you do your homework before the interview, as *"we want people who are as interested in us as we are in them."* This means coming prepared with thoughtful questions: *"What they shouldn't say is: 'I've learned everything I can learn from your website, so I don't have any questions.'"*

Most sources acknowledged that *"the partner prospects are not great"* at Kramer. One corporate junior added that *"in my group it seems like there's more fluidity, compared to a traditional firm, with respect to where you are in the hierarchy,"* due largely to the fact that Kramer *"doesn't have an up or out system of promotion. A lot of people have come from in-house, or are laterals."* To counter this, however, *"they are encouraging to people who want to leave to go to a smaller firm, in-house, or to the US Attorney's office, for instance. A lot of associates do leave, and we often hear about what they've been doing."*

Strategy & Future

"Our strategy continues to be the same: to remain independent and grow organically through selective lateral transitions. Depending on the year, we may be taking more or fewer laterals; it just depends on our needs and if laterals meet our requirements," MP Paul Pearlman informs us. When asked about specific areas, he responds that *"we're always looking to expand some of the core practice areas, but again we don't simply look to expand for expansion's sake; we don't necessarily think bigger is better."* Read our full interview with Pearlman online.

"We don't necessarily think bigger is better."

"One of the things we try to do is maintain the best of both worlds: the collegiality and collaboration of a small firm, while practicing against and with the major firms out there."

See firm profile on p.664

Latham & Watkins LLP

Lawyers per state

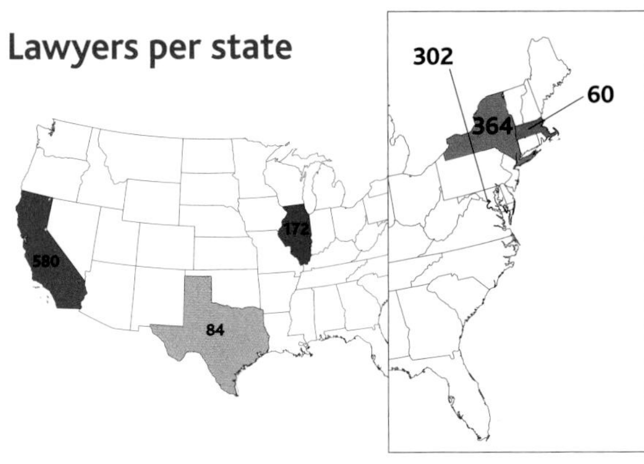

Largest US office: New York
US offices: 10
International offices: 20
First-year salary: $160,000
Billable hours: 1,900 target
Summers 2016: 202 (193 2Ls, 7 1Ls, 2 others)
Revenue 2015: $2.65 billion (+1.5%)
Partners made in 2016: 34 globally (22 in US)
Famous for: *Am Law* #1; unassigned junior associates; global reach

Am Law-topping and practice area-hopping make this a prime destination for high-reaching associates.

WHAT'S better than hitting number one on the *Am Law* 100? How about achieving number one on *Am Law*'s global 100 in the same year? Latham beat repeat winners Baker & McKenzie and DLA Piper to the global top spot in 2015 after its 2014 revenue increased by 14% on the previous year. In doing so it became the first US firm to record revenue of $2.6 billion, but has this success come at the price of sacrificing some of its reputation for laid-back California cool? *"We're ambitious but not aggressively ambitious. You never feel like anyone's trying to climb over you."* associates claimed.

Almost a third of the California-founded firm's 32 global offices are found in the States, where the full-service firm earns a wealth of top-tier *Chambers USA* rankings in areas ranging from corporate, life sciences, and real estate matters to white-collar crime. Visit chambersandpartners.com to see the rest of Latham's rankings both at home and around the world.

"Ambitious but not aggressively ambitious."

On chambers-associate.com...

- We check in with Latham's global chair of recruiting Manu Gayatrinath
- Latham in Asia

ASSOCIATES SAY...

The Work

Associates begin life at the firm as 'unassigned' so they can experience different areas, whether that's a variety of corporate assignments or figuring out whether you want to be a deal-doer or litigator. Rookies needn't worry about being forced to sample the whole menu if you arrive with more definite ideas of what you want to do. One source stressed: *"Although I've tried a handful of other areas, the firm was terrific at understanding I wanted to concentrate on one specific field."* After two years, associates are encouraged to formally align with one of the firm's five core practices: corporate; finance; litigation & trial; tax; and environment, land & resources.

Newbies can make use of Latham's formal assigning system, 'The Book', to pick up work. Juniors are staffed on projects based on their availability but *"as you move through the firm and build up relationships with people you'll rely on it less and less."* Subgroups within the wider practice areas vary in their allocation process; some employ a staffing partner while others require associates to find matters themselves.

"I appreciate the mix as practically running deals is stressful!"

Deal-doers told us that by the third year, *"you'll be the most senior associate on half your deals and then at the bottom of the pile on the rest. On larger matters I'll be*

The Inside View

See firm profile on p.665

Rankings in *Chambers USA*

Antitrust	IT & Outsourcing
Appellate Law	Latin American Investment
Banking & Finance	Leisure & Hospitality
Bankruptcy/Restructuring	Life Sciences
Capital Markets	Litigation
Climate Change	Media & Entertainment
Corporate Crime & Investigations	Outsourcing
	Private Equity
Corporate/M&A	Projects
Employee Benefits & Executive Compensation	Real Estate
	REITs
Energy & Natural Resources	Retail
Environment	Securities
FCPA	Sports Law
Financial Services Regulation	Startups & Emerging Companies
Healthcare	
Insurance	Tax
Intellectual Property	Technology
International Trade	Telecommunications
Investment Funds	

For detail on ranking tiers and ranking locations, visit www.chambersandpartners.com

doing the grunt work and checking nothing's slipped through the cracks but I'll do almost everything on the smaller transactions. I appreciate the mix as practically running deals is stressful!" Another associate explained: *"The firm is pretty good at letting you take a shot at what you'd like to work on. My responsibility is driven by how far I want to stick my neck out."* Another felt their rising capability was motivated by their supervisors who *"are very deliberate in giving out tasks to push people."*

Litigators were similarly pleased with their ascent. *"I did doc review for two months and then moved onto helping with deposition preparation. We're not overstaffed so you can find responsibility early on. The partners I've worked with know it benefits them if I develop my skills on harder tasks"* like drafting, taking or defending depositions. One source even told us: *"I know third-years who are conducting direct and cross-examinations and it's not considered atypical."*

The Inside View

Training & Development

"If you never wanted to buy lunch you could go to a session everyday – although they may not all be relevant to you." Practice groups hosts talks on anything from recent court cases to legal updates in specific areas like leveraged finance. In their first year juniors attend 'core curriculum' sessions every few weeks featuring presentations from partners and associates on different practice areas and key skills such as drafting and negotiation.

Recent work highlights

- Advised Goldman Sachs as underwriters on multiple senior note offerings totaling $825 million by holding company CNO Financial Group
- Represented Pacific Gas and Electric against allegations the company violated the Pipeline Safety Act, resulting in a pipeline explosion which killed eight people and destroyed 38 homes in California in 2010. Latham also advised PG&E in related litigation including regulatory investigations and insurance arbitrations
- Acted for supermarket Safeway in its $9 billion sale to Albertsons
- Assisted Union Bank, BNP Paribas, Citibank and GE Capital as lenders in financing the Moxie Freedom Generation Plant in Pennsylvania

"If you never wanted to buy lunch you could go to a session everyday."

Latham's formal academy program sees associates flown out to one location for *"very condensed training and conferences"* in their first, third and fifth year (summers and partners also attend academies). These bring associates up to speed with *"what's expected of us in that year and give you the skills you need to develop into that role."* For example: *"Our third year academy talked us through how to supervize more junior associates and give feedback."* Attorneys also make the most of all being in one place to meet people from the firm's other offices. Some of the dinners have seating plans *"so you'll be thrown together with lawyers from all over the world. The social aspect is the best part; everyone goes out and has fun."*

Culture and Hours

"I've met very few people who are tightly wound. There is pressure to work hard but not to kill yourself," one associate claimed. Another added: *"People take pride in their work but it doesn't come along with an ego or stuffiness and senior associates won't take credit for your contribution. We're ambitious but not aggressive. This is not an intimidating environment."*

Juniors are treated by partners as *"colleagues not resources who only handle basic tasks,"* with one source even revealing, *"I'll play tennis with the partners on weekends."* But partners aren't just good for a game of doubles. *"There is no avoiding hard work and tight client deadlines but people try to make it humane; the partners will push back on clients if they're being unreasonable. I've had people check to make sure I'm not overwhelmed or relieve me from their deal when something else I was working on blew up. Everyone will pitch in and if I'm here til 4am I'll be thanked."*

See firm profile on p.665

One interviewee told us: *"A lot of people here have families and the partners and senior associates set the tone by not remaining chained to their desks late into the night. It's okay to go and see your kids and then bill from home later. No-one's ever asked 'where the hell were you?!'"* The firm recently rolled out the option for everyone to have an office phone installed in their home and *"makes it easy to get your hands on whatever you need to work remotely."* All that connectivity means it can be difficult to step away from work. *"My work/life balance isn't the greatest but I don't blame Latham, I blame the world! Everyone expects you to be accessible."* That being said, another junior reckoned: *"It's up to you to say no and put down your parameters. People do try to respect them."*

"It's up to you to say no."

To be bonus eligible associates must reach a target of 1,900 hours, but most of our sources had hit at least the 2,000 mark, with some billing several hundred hours above that. If you just slip past the 1,900 *"that's fine. I don't want to bill 2,500 because my family commitments are my priority and no-one's called me out for under billing."* Not meeting the 1,900 means *"you just won't get a bonus. If you only hit 1,700 and everyone else in your group was in the 2,000s, then they'd be asking questions."*

Pro Bono

Pro bono hours all count toward the billable target with some juniors racking up three figures. Everyone's expected to do at least 20 hours and if you're looking a little low *"the pro bono coordinators will personally call you to try and bring those up."* Sounds like the firm takes it seriously. *"I've never had a supervisor tell me, 'drop your pro bono, my work comes first'. The firm understands it counts just as much as client billables,"* one junior confirmed.

"I can't emphasize enough how many emails I receive."

Transactional associates can get stuck in helping low-income entrepreneurs or assisting with a business clinic. For a more litigious slant there are *"projects representing veterans, assisting the homeless or domestic violence victims, or working with the children's court. There are loads of opportunities. I can't emphasize enough how many emails I receive."*

Pro bono hours

- For all attorneys across all US offices: 127,200
- Average per US attorney: 85

Diversity

Houston's association with the oil and gas industry means the office here is *"a very male driven environment but the firm is making huge strides,"* one source claimed. *"As a relatively new office we've only recently seen female attorneys returning from maternity leave but Latham's been very accommodating toward their transition."* One LA associate told us: *"We're looking at retention rather than just recruitment. There are a lot of discussions right now about the importance of diverse mentors,"* while DC juniors proudly proclaimed: *"We've got a number of strong female partners, like former White House counsel Kathy Ruemmler"* [read our interview with her online]. Despite the high profile figures, several sources across the firm pointed out that *"the number of female partners is still low and we could definitely improve the racial mix. Sometimes it feels like a bunch of old white men talking about diversity but their intent is in the right place."*

"The firm is pretty good at letting you take a shot at what you'd like to work on; my responsibility is driven by how far I want to stick my neck out."

Firmwide, juniors were quick to highlight that new global chair Bill Voge had highlighted the topic of diversity as *"one of his top priorities"* while in office, so we'll have to see whether initiatives soon start kicking into overdrive. Current resources include a three-day Diversity Leadership Academy for law students and mid-level associates, the Women's Leadership Academy and the associate-led Multicultural Promotion & Attainment Coalition (MPAC).

Strategy & Future

Improving diversity may be on the chairman's list, but what else is the firm going to be focusing on in coming years? Plans are in the pipeline to open an office in Seoul, South Korea; this will become the firm's sixth office in Asia.

Korea on the cards?

The firm's also bolstering its established footholds in Asia, including Hong Kong, whose private equity practice saw the addition of three new partners in 2016. Latham also has strong practices in China more broadly, Singapore and Indonesia – check out *Chambers Global* for more info. New York's litigation offering is also getting a boost with the addition of former Chief Judge

See firm profile on p.665

of the New York Court of Appeals Jonathan Lippman, among others.

Offices

Interaction between the firm's 12 domestic and 20 international offices is fairly well oiled. *"I can't remember a deal when I didn't liaise with another office,"* one interviewee mused. The phone may be their best friend on cross-office deals but popping between bases and working out of the firm's 'guest offices' is *"seamless. You can even make use of them if you're going to be in the area for personal reasons."*

"Our patio terrace is being turned into the showpiece."

Juniors reckoned the New York office was *"the least impressive."* Renovations are under way so those stuck with *"stained carpets"* will soon be sitting in swanky digs *"done out in a dark espresso and light gray color scheme."* Remodeling in DC is being undertaken on a grander scale: *"Our patio terrace is being turned into the showpiece."* Work-wise, corporate and finance are the show-stopping practices here, although DC also does a considerable amount of regulatory work. Full service LA often works with emerging companies and has just opened a *"Latham lounge; it's got a pool table, games console and dartboard. They understand we need to take a break,"* while energy-focused Houston was praised for *"free snacks and gorgeous views."*

Get Hired

"Anyone extremely difficult or too intense won't get far," one source posited. *"Everybody here has lots of accomplishments and impressive backgrounds but they don't wear it on their sleeve; we're easy to get on with."* So if you stick to this associate's preferred interview routine you may be in with a good shot: *"I want to spend five minutes on your resume and then fill the rest of the interview with a chat about something, anything, else."* Others involved in the recruiting game mark you down for *"awkward silences and only chatting about law"* or *"sharp elbows."* Global recruiting chair Manu Gayatrinath elaborates: *"People who can demonstrate they have past teamwork experience"* can catch the eye of interviewers. Go online to read our full interview with Gayatrinath.

"We need colleagues we're happy putting in front of a client."

Confident and engaged associates are in demand as *"we need colleagues we're happy putting in front of a client. Someone who's trustworthy, laid back and can roll with the punches"* also ticks this box.

"We're ambitious but not aggressively ambitious. You never feel like anyone's trying to climb over you."

See firm profile on p.665

Linklaters

Lawyers per state

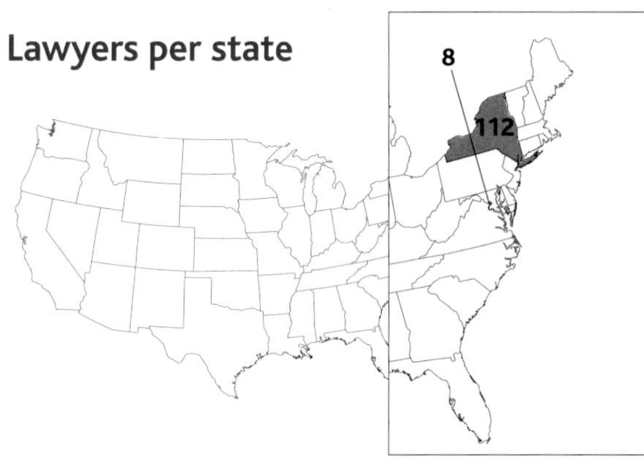

Largest US office: New York
US offices: 2
International offices: 27
First-year salary: $160,000
Billable hours: no requirement
Summers 2016: 20 (15 2Ls, 3 1Ls, 2 SEOs)
Revenue 2015: £1.27 billion (April 2015)
Partners made in 2016: 24 globally (1 in US)
Famous for: magic circle status and international outlook

International interconnection is the name of the game at this British-born magic circle giant.

ASSOCIATES didn't have to pause for thought when asked why they chose Linklaters. *"The international character of the firm was hugely appealing,"* they chorused. *"Linklaters is spread across so many countries, cities and cultures, yet it works together as one. Coming here is a genuine opportunity to work abroad and to work with people abroad. If you're only interested in domestic deals then this isn't the place for you."*

Sources emphasized the interconnection between offices in different jurisdictions: *"In my interview I asked a partner how Linklaters distinguishes itself among all the many so-called international firms. He told me that a lot of other firms just have foreign offices in different countries, whereas here we actually work with those offices. Two years into the job I can confirm that that's the case."* In fact, juniors concurred that *"almost everything I've done has some sort of cross-border aspect to it."* Some associates head abroad to ply their trade. At the time of our calls, there were US juniors stationed in London, Frankfurt, Paris, Hong Kong and Seoul as well as the New York base. The summer program also allows students to spend half their time at an overseas office, usually either Hong Kong or London, although some opt to stay in the Big Apple.

On chambers-associate.com...
- Interview with hiring partner Justin Storms

Hiring partner Justin Storms tells us that the New York office *"has only been a growth story for the last ten years. For young attorneys it offers a unique opportunity to be part of a sophisticated 175-year-old firm while still having exposure to growth. It's like being in a small startup firm with the backup of an enormous pool of resources."* This pool comprises 29 offices, a total of 2,600 lawyers and a horde of mega clients like AT&T, Credit Suisse, investment multinational BlackRock and pharma giant Novartis.

ASSOCIATES SAY...

The Work

The majority of New York newcomers are to be found in investment management, tax, banking, dispute resolution and corporate, with a few lone rangers scattered across antitrust, financial regulation and capital markets (LatAm). Work assignment tends to be *"quite informal. You can volunteer for some work if you're excited about it, or partners will directly assign things depending on capacity."* Overall, it's a system that *"seems to work."*

"It's not just vanilla deal after vanilla deal."

A junior litigator described the range of matters they'd taken on: *"I started with a breach of contract case for a bank. Now I've done a couple of antitrust cases and several internal investigations. Clients also come to us*

See firm profile on p.666

Rankings in *Chambers USA*

Investment Funds	Latin American Investment

For detail on ranking tiers and ranking locations, visit www.chambersandpartners.com

with concerns about US sanctions." Day to day *"there's a lot of research, talking to the client and drafting. I've drafted motions to dismiss, motions in limine. When I first started I drafted half a motion for summary judgment, which was crazy. It's a steep learning curve, but you quickly get up to speed."* Apparently, *"I've never been overrun just with doc review. Investigations usually have tight timelines so I haven't had to do months and months of it. In most cases, I prefer to get doc review done from my couch after work, and take on substantive work during the day."*

Over in corporate, associates were happy to note that *"it's not just vanilla deal after vanilla deal – a lot of the stuff we do is bespoke."* For juniors that requires *"researching random questions of law involved in transactions. There are often unique little concerns to do with other jurisdictions, so I need to be able to figure those out or determine who to talk to."* We heard that *"there's certainly the standard due diligence"* to contend with, but *"honestly, for the bulk of the past year I've been working on a large pharmaceutical transaction. I've not been locked in a room looking at documents. I've been running calls, getting tons of exposure to clients and liaising with people in other offices, like London, Stockholm and Brussels. I've also worked across multiple jurisdictions on private equity deals."* In addition, juniors get the chance to draft *"standard-issue formations, resolutions and share purchase agreements."*

Pro Bono

"Pro bono is emphasized here and the firm really encourages you to figure out how to fit it into your workload," we heard. In fact, the firm recently started counting pro bono hours toward overall billing totals. *"There are two pro bono partners and a manager who sends out frequent emails with different opportunities,"* said interviewees, all of whom had taken on significant amounts. Juniors had, among other things, handled Uvisa cases, worked on human trafficking and housing issues and helped nonprofits to *"get 501(c)(3) status to make them non-taxable entities."*

Pro bono hours

- For all attorneys across all US offices: 8,685
- Average per US attorney: 79

Recent work highlights

- Represented AT&T on various transactions including a $9 billion unsecured syndicated credit facility
- Acted for Novartis on the sale of its flu vaccines business to biotherapeutics company CSL for $275 million
- Representing Air France and Dutch airlines KLM and Martinair in a suit filed by logistics company DB Schenker alleging that the defendants conspired to fix the prices of air freight services

Training & Development

Rookies from offices all over the world descend on the firm's London HQ for a week of training. *"It's most valuable for networking and socializing,"* reckoned associates. *"There are lawyers from so many jurisdictions there at the same time so it tends to lose focus in terms of substantive training. For example, as a US attorney I don't deal with EU directives, and there was a session on that."* Others noted that *"it was really good to get an overview of what the other departments do. As a litigator it was helpful to attend courses going over the sort of work that different departments do, like M&A and banking, because my work touches on these things."*

> *"There's a collaborative, flat kind of structure."*

Back home, there are practice-specific training sessions available *"every week or two."* For tax attorneys, the changing complexities of their practice area means that there are *"lots of CLEs to go to and we have weekly meetings where we discuss what's gone on in the tax world."* Outside of the formal feedback given in yearly appraisals, *"partners are generally good at backing up and explaining things."* According to juniors, *"there's a collaborative, flat kind of structure. The people I work with are pleasant and give feedback in a supportive, growth-oriented way, rather than lashing out at you and pointing out your shortcomings."*

Hours & Compensation

Sources appreciated that the firm doesn't impose a billable target. *"I think the goal is to be as busy as the rest of your group,"* mused one, while another stated: *"There's enough work to be done and I take the time that I need to. I don't worry about my number for the day. I don't feel pressured by that."* The bonus and salary are lockstep, although some thought that *"they might be about to implement a metric for the bonus, based on contribution to the firm like pro bono and marketing, not just billable hours."*

See firm profile on p.666

A standard shift at the office tends to last about 12 hours. *"If it's a light day I can get out by 7.30pm, but if I'm slammed with a ton of work I'll be here until 3am or 4am. Fortunately, those nights don't happen that often."* Associates repeated the refrain that *"there are peaks and valleys: I've had a month of working late almost every night, getting out between 10pm and 2am. Then the following month was much quieter. Anybody who gets into this business is aware that work/life balance means something different than it would if you were a surf instructor in Malibu."* Apparently, *"partners really respect your weekends, unless there's something truly urgent."*

"Work/life balance means something different than it would if you were a surf instructor in Malibu."

Culture

"The culture is one of the best things about Linklaters!" exclaimed a source eagerly. *"The office isn't huge like at a lot of US-based firms, so you get to know most people. I've made very close friends here."* Fortunately, *"the partners are generally approachable and aren't scary – although there are exceptions of course!"* Asked whether the firm's British identity is apparent in New York, sources told us that *"there are certain 'British-isms'. We have a drinks cart on Fridays, the closing book is called a 'bible' and meetings are called 'prayers' – it's funny because no one knows what they are at first and nobody shows up!"* One junior was delighted by the fact that *"when I call IT support or voicemail it's a British recording."* Plus it's not uncommon to come across documents in which *"'color' has a 'u' in."*

"People have an international outlook."

However, it would be wrong to assume that Links' NY base is all cups of tea and bowler hats. *"You hear English accents in the hallways and when all the partners come to visit you remember it's a British-based firm, but if anything it stands out as being very international,"* interviewees agreed. *"There are obviously a lot of Americans and people from all over the world in this office. People have an international outlook; we're connected to the wider world."*

Juniors described it as a *"very social office"* although *"we're not necessarily going out for drinks every night. I go out for lunch or have coffee with colleagues."* As well as a *"standard office holiday party"* there are also fortnightly *"popcorn socials in the middle of the afternoon and Wednesday afternoon cakes."*

Diversity

Associates thought that *"it's more diverse here than at many New York firms because a lot of people grew up elsewhere or have international backgrounds. It's not only white males."* Sources praised the women's committee, which *"holds a monthly breakfast and a book club where women can gather to talk about how to advance within the firm."* There are also affinity groups for LGBT and ethnic minority lawyers. Linklaters offers a scholarship for 1Ls.

"It's not only white males."

Offices

The New York office is located in a convenient spot Midtown *"along with a lot of other law firms. It's a nice area and it's easy to grab a drink after work – if you wanna pay $15 for a martini!"* Inside, *"there's nothing spectacular or extraordinary. It's comfortable enough for me to work in for 12 hours straight,"* tittered an associate, although we did hear that *"sporadic walls are painted in the Linklaters pink,"* which sounds cheery.

"It's comfortable enough for me to work in for 12 hours straight."

Last year we heard of a shrine to Will and Kate in the antitrust department; this time around, no royal tributes. But that's not to say attorneys don't add a personal touch to their work space, and some had even spotted *"a whiteboard decorated with a pig making facial expressions, and the bottom of an elephant."* Incomers share an office for their first couple of years at the firm. There's also an outpost in DC, which usually has at least one junior associate.

"Almost everything I've done has some sort of cross-border aspect to it."

Get Hired

Hiring partner Justin Storms tells us that *"we look for students who are outward facing and open to new and different cultures and ways of working – the idea being that this isn't a parochial US practice but an international law firm."* He continues: *"Language skills are a plus, and may be necessary in certain offices. What's needed throughout the firm, though, is top notch intellectual and analytical skills."* Comparing Linklaters to a typical 'white shoe' firm, Storms insists that *"elbows are less sharp here. We still demand a very high volume of*

See firm profile on p.666

quality work from associates, but our environment is one of mutual respect and collaboration."

"You need to have a self-starting spark."

Successful candidates are those who *"have a willingness to take initiative and move the ball as far as they can. There's an entrepreneurial spirit here, so we look for that self-starting spark."* A final word of advice from Justin Storms: *"At interview some students say, 'I'm interested in practicing international law,' which means practicing at the Hague or the UN! Here, we practice law internationally: for example New York law, English law and Hong Kong law being practiced in transactions across borders."*

Strategy & Future

US managing partner Conrado Tenaglia tells us that *"over the past year we've continued to grow and develop our global US practice. We've hired laterals but most of the partners we elect are homegrown."* The focus will continue to be on building up the New York and DC offices. Tenaglia cites antitrust and FCPA [Foreign Corrupt Practices Act] work as expanding areas for the firm, while *"restructuring and insolvency is another area where we are taking a bold approach."*

"It's like being in a small startup firm with the backup of an enormous pool of resources."

See firm profile on p.666

Lowenstein Sandler LLP

Lawyers per state

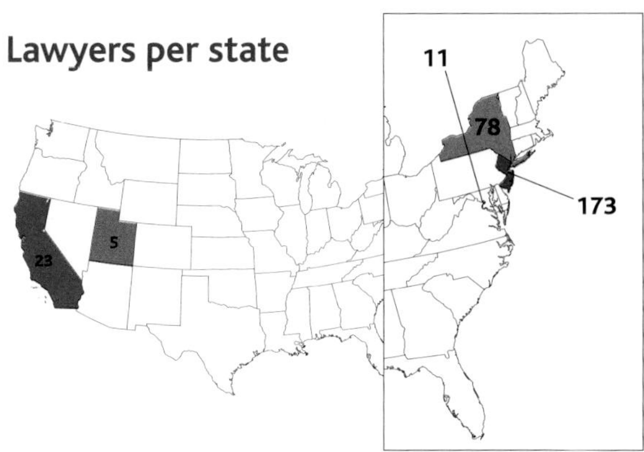

Largest US office: Rosewood, NJ
US offices: 5
International offices: 0
First-year salary: $160,000
Billable hours: 1,850 target
Summers 2016: 24 (19 2Ls, 5 1Ls)
Revenue 2015: undisclosed
Partners made in 2016: 2
Famous for: BigLaw work, New Jersey heritage, entrepreneurial spirit, pro bono clinic

Firm founder Alan Lowenstein was something of an innovator in New Jersey legal circles, and his firm encourages *"attorneys to think differently about problems."*

"IF you want to practice law in New Jersey, and you want the BigLaw experience, there are only one or two firms that you should look at," one associate here told us. But Lowenstein reaches far beyond the Garden State, with offices in locations as close as Manhattan and DC, as distant as Palo Alto, and as remote as Centerville, Utah (20 miles from Salt Lake City) – Lowenstein's newest office. *Chambers USA* recognizes the firm's hedge funds work on a national level, and bestows top or excellent rankings in New Jersey for areas including corporate/M&A, general litigation, insurance litigation, white collar crime, bankruptcy/restructuring, labor & employment, and real estate.

The late Alan Lowenstein shook up Newark's municipal charter, grew the state philharmonic into a cultural treasure, and came up with a new form of corporate structure that would allow employees to buy up distressed companies. So it's no surprise that the firm he founded places a premium on entrepreneurial hustle. This can manifest itself in a range of ways, according to chairman and managing partner Gary Wingens, from *"encouraging attorneys to think differently about problems"* to *"connecting clients to opportunities in the marketplace"* all the way to *"turning the traditional pro bono model on its head."*

On chambers-associate.com...

- More on the Lowenstein Center for the Public Interest

ASSOCIATES SAY...

The Work

"It's kind of a double-edged sword," mused one associate, *"but one of the benefits and burdens of working here is how leanly staffed we are."* On the one hand, newbies get a great deal of responsibility very early on. That said, *"there's never a sense that we're drowning in work."* The firm is good at *"ensuring that there are enough people on a deal to get it done if everyone pulls their weight."* In general *"it's a knock-on-doors-to-get-work kind of place."* While some sources thought they could benefit from a more formalized system, they suspected that it might be *"too much of a departure from the entrepreneurial culture that they're trying to create."* Head hiring honcho Ray Thek agrees: *"I tell every incoming class, 'if you're getting your work from an assignment system, you're doing it wrong!'"*

"It's a knock-on-doors-to-get-work kind of place."

On arrival, most associates are split between corporate and litigation, with the former taking slightly more. One or two go into bankruptcy or tax. Both deal-doers and courtroom pugilists spend their first two years as gener-

The Inside View

See firm profile on p.667

Rankings in *Chambers USA*

Bankruptcy/Restructuring	Labor & Employment
Corporate/M&A	Litigation
Employee Benefits & Executive Compensation	Real Estate
Environment	Startups & Emerging Companies
Intellectual Property	

For detail on ranking tiers and ranking locations, visit www.chambersandpartners.com

alists, hustling up work from different partners. *"In your first year you're kind of bombarded with work from all sides,"* said one transactional attorney. *"At times you can feel uncomfortable saying no."* Even the freest of markets needs some intervention to protect against market failures. According to Ray Thek, Lowenstein has created the JADE program to avoid things like an associate *"getting trapped in a big room stamping documents for three years."* More than just a snappy acronym, the Junior Associate Development program exists to *"make sure there's an even spread of hours and opportunities"* among new associates.

New corporate attorneys bounce between M&A, finance, securities and corporate governance work. We heard of attorneys working on *"nuts and bolts deals where smaller businesses are selling or leasing something"* and *"large-scale transactions, often involving the pharma industry,"* which is booming. Unsurprisingly, in Palo Alto much of the work has a startup or tech focus, *"although once in a while, we'll work with an outlier like the food industry."* Clients here are either newly-formed private companies or venture capitalists looking for investment. *"In my time here, my tasks have run the gamut,"* said one transactional attorney, *"everything from diligence and other junior associate tasks"* to *"drafting the primary acquisition and sale documents."*

"Opportunity to gain management skills."

In litigation, *"the primary assignments for junior associates tend to be research and writing tasks,"* a third-year reported. *"You'll get a research question, spend hours looking into it, and then draft a memo or an email with legal analysis."* There's also the discovery process, which offers Lowensteinians more than mere doc review – *"discovery opens opportunities to draft pleadings, interrogatories and document production requests,"* said another litigator. As people get more senior they take on more of a managerial role, *"managing junior attorneys, working with documents and prepping deposition binders."* This *"can be tedious,"* our source admitted, *"but it's a good opportunity to gain management skills."*

Recent work highlights

- Represented the creditors of Borders in the national bookseller's liquidation
- Represents the United Mine Workers of America in its negotiations with the beleaguered Patriot Coal
- Represented Tesla Motors in two disputes with the New Jersey state government
- Representing a Taiwanese government agency in a dispute with the trustee in a case relating to the Bernard Madoff scandal

Pro Bono

"We literally do tons of pro bono," enthused one associate, figuratively. There's no doubting the firm's commitment to pro bono work. Both contentious and transactional work is on offer, with associates representing the victims of domestic violence, helping set up nonprofits and 'educational equity litigation', among other things. Associates can treat up to 200 pro bono hours as billable, so *"there's no reason not to do pro bono."* All told, sources were impressed by the firm's commitment, but there was one slight gripe: *"Pro bono work counts toward your annual billable targets, but not your monthly ones."*

"We literally do tons of pro bono."

Firm founder Alan Lowenstein was a big advocate of pro bono. The firm's efforts are organized through the Lowenstein Center for the Public Interest. According to MP Gary Wingens, lawyers here aren't interested in *"waiting until the phone rings"* and *"taking pro bono cases if we have lawyers free."* Instead the Center is staffed with people who *"strategically think about the kind of work our lawyers are best suited to."*

Pro bono hours

- For all attorneys across all US offices: 27,279
- Average per attorney: 84

Diversity

"It doesn't feel like a bunch of white men at the associate level," said a source, adding: *"At the partnership level, more so."* Sources in Washington and Palo Alto claimed that their offices were more diverse than the larger New Jersey HQ. *"New Jersey doesn't feel very diverse and as it's the HQ, this can trickle down,"* lamented an associate. There are diversity initiatives in New Jersey and elsewhere, and recruiting-wise the firm has dispatched delegations to various minority law fairs and law schools to market the firm to diverse candidates.

"We're one of the few firms that has 1L summer associates," HP Ray Thek tells us, *"and each summer we*

See firm profile on p.667

reserve two slots for the Lowenstein scholars." These receive a $10,000 stipend to help them with law school tuition, plus a further $15,000 if they return for a second summer, in addition to two summer associate salaries.

"A visitor would struggle to pick the first-years from the partners."

Culture

Lowenstein *"prefers people who knock on doors and drum up work to those who stay in the office and let it come to them,"* explained an informant. While the firm expects a certain proactivity from its attorneys – it has *"that sort of culture for people to develop and push themselves in the direction they want to go in"* – it's by no means a Darwinian, dog-eat-dog place. Indeed, *"laterals always say how nice the place is."* No law firm is without hierarchy, but at Lowenstein *"a visitor would struggle to pick the first-years from the partners."* While this might be a slight exaggeration, *"people are comfortable picking up phones and talking to partners without senior associates or counsels interceding."*

Hours & Compensation

There's a target of 1,850 hours, including 250 hours of non-billable work such as pro bono. *"I hit it every year,"* relayed an associate in the corporate department, *"but I think people in some of the smaller groups like trusts and estates can have a tougher time."*

"I've never pulled an all-nighter."

"I don't know if anyone in corporate can say this, but I've never pulled an all-nighter," boasted a litigator. While all-nighters may be rare, late nights do come with the territory. *"My day is normally 9am to 6.30pm,"* a transactional attorney told us, *"but I might have a spurt of late nights once or twice each quarter."* A source in litigation agreed: *"I've definitely had my share of nights that ended at midnight, 1am or even 2am."* Lowenstein *"treats you like an adult,"* and *"if you need to leave in the middle of the day for some emergency, you can leave in the middle of the day."* For those with families, leaving at 5pm and working remotely is also an option.

Training & Development

Newbies *"spend a few days"* learning how to use the firm's resources and technology. The whole thing is *"pretty comprehensive, and sets you up to use what's around you to the best of your abilities."* Perhaps unsurprisingly, continued training is *"free-flowing"* and *"what you make of it."* Much of what our sources learned wasn't gleaned from CLEs or courses – although there are CLEs and other courses aplenty – but from seeking out individuals they've worked with and getting feedback. This can be a bit hit or miss, one explained: *"If you seek out the right people you can get terrific training, but if not you might find yourself working for people who don't provide much depth."*

Offices

Home is famously where the heart is, and Lowenstein's heart remains in Roseland, New Jersey, where it moved from Newark in the 1980s. It's a half-hour commute from the firm's office in Manhattan, but couldn't be more different. While New York occupies the 17th through 19th floors of a high-rise *"smack in the middle of Midtown,"* associates described Rosewood as *"suburban, bordering on rural,"* and associates burning the midnight oil can occasionally see *"deer or other wildlife walking around."* The New Jersey office is currently spread over two low-rise buildings, although plans are afoot to consolidate the office into a new, shiny building by 2017.

"Laterals always say how nice the place is."

Different as they are, collaboration between New Jersey and New York is the rule, rather than the exception. *"I work with New York every day,"* said someone in the Jersey mothership, *"and many people are admitted to both the New York and New Jersey Bars."*

"I work with New York every day."

Further West, the California office is located in the heart of downtown Palo Alto, which in the words of MP Gary Wingens *"puts it close to the most amazing coffee of any office."* Californian associates agree that the downtown location is *"awesome"* and considerably preferable to that of rival Silicon Valley firms, which tend to be based in uninspiring office parks. With five lawyers, the firm's newest office, in Utah, is by far the smallest, and supplies the Palo Altans with IP know-how.

Get Hired

According to hiring partner Ray Thek, Lowenstein is eager to *"meet law students in a different way"* from rival firms. That said, sources told us Lowenstein has a *"pretty standard OCI process,"* with questions on things like *"my work experience, the classes I was taking at law school, and why I was interested in Lowenstein."* Interviewers were interested in candidates' career plans, our sources told us. *"I was asked 'why this department,'"* recollected a Californian, while a Jerseyean said: *"They definitely wanted to know if I was interested in corporate*

See firm profile on p.667

or litigation." Be prepared for the occasional tough existential question: *"The question 'why are you here' kind of surprises some people."* Applicants can expect to see four or five interviewers during callbacks, and are likely to field questions on *"intelligence, communication and leadership."*

"Open to additional locations."

Strategy & Future

Twice a year the managing partner holds a town hall meeting which *"everyone is expected to attend,"* according to juniors. This gathering lasts about an hour and *"goes into a very detailed assessment"* of *"what the firm has been doing and how we can improve."* Reports from the most recent roundup tell us that the managing partner *"was very excited about opening the Utah office."* And what of the future? We'll let the managing partner himself, Gary Wingens, tell you. He describes Lowenstein's strategy as *"continuing moderate growth while deepening relationships with core industries."* He singles out New York and Washington, DC as particular sites for this growth, but he tells us that Lowenstein's *"open to additional locations in Northern and Southern California, beyond Silicon Valley."*

"A culture for people to develop and push themselves in the direction they want to go in."

See firm profile on p.667

Marshall, Gerstein & Borun LLP

Lawyers per state

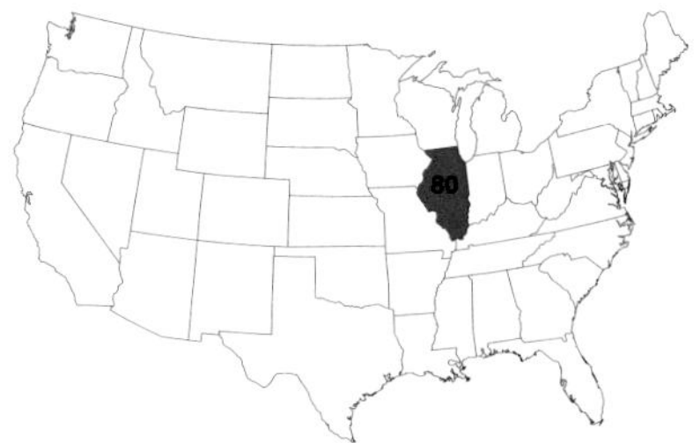

Largest US office: Chicago
US offices: 1
International offices: 0
First-year salary: $160,000
Billable hours: 1,950 required
Summers 2016: 3–4 (2 2Ls, 1–2 1Ls)
Revenue 2015: undisclosed
Partners made in 2016: 3
Famous for: being an IP boutique specializing in the science and engineering industries

Despite being home to many self-described "*nerdy*" associates, Marshall Gerstein is patently a sociable, vibrant place to work.

THE year 1955 was an important one for technology. Not only did it see the birth of both Microsoft cofounder Bill Gates and World Wide Web creator Tim Berners-Lee, but it was also the year that IP whiz firm Marshall Gerstein came into being. Managing partner Jeff Sharp describes Marshall as *"a diversified, full-service IP firm"* that practices *"across all areas of technology."* He goes on to add that while *"traditionally the firm would have been described as a patent firm,"* it has since diversified to include trademark, copyright and transactional work.

Regardless of its petite proportions of around 80 lawyers, this wunderkind of the IP world is not to be messed with. Lawyers here were once given samurai armor by a client to thank them for their fierce and loyal representation (a samurai sword wasn't permitted into the building, alas). With its high ranking in *Chambers USA* in Illinois for IP, associates echoed that MGB's *"well-established practice"* in Chicago and *"sophisticated matters"* were the biggest draws to the firm.

On chambers-associate.com...

- Interview with managing partner Jeff Sharp
- Interview with hiring partner Julianne Hartzell
- IPRs - what are they, and what do they mean for IP?

ASSOCIATES SAY...

The Work & Get Hired

MP Jeff Sharp tells us that *"over 90 percent of our attorneys have a technical degree or a technical background, and most of us did something else before we attended law school, so that's one of the things we look for."* Unsurprisingly then, many of our interviewees had come from highly specialized scientific backgrounds; PhDs and work experience at the Patent & Trademark Office were oft-cited examples. This wasn't the case for everybody, however; as one junior pointed out, the firm has much smaller – yet significant – trademark and copyright practices *"for which the science background isn't necessary at all."* Professional credentials aside, the firm is also looking for *"the ability to interact with clients. We're put in front of clients right away, so we look for people who are personable and comfortable with that."* Go online to read what hiring partner Julianne Hartzell has to say on the matter.

"The ability to interact with clients."

On the patent side of things, the work is divided according to industry, and includes areas such as chemical sciences, mechanical engineering, medical devices and biotechnology. The main focus of the associates in these groups is patent prosecution. *"I prepare applications, I do some freedom to operate opinion work, and I work with clients directly to discuss their strategies for filing applications,"* one junior summarized. *"I also work*

See firm profile on p.668

Rankings in *Chambers USA*

Intellectual Property

For detail on ranking tiers and ranking locations, visit www.chambersandpartners.com

Recent work highlights

- Worked with BioMarin Pharmaceutical to build a worldwide patent portfolio relating to Vimizim, a drug designed to treat Morquio syndrome
- Handled the IP due diligence relating to InterMune's acquisition by a global pharmaceutical company for $8.3 billion
- Currently acting for Amgen, which has filed a lawsuit against Hospira for allegedly violating the provisions of the Biologics Price Competition and Innovation Act

directly with inventors to figure out their research and what can be filed and when and where to file it." In litigation, there is a separate group involved in patent litigation, copyright and trademarks, and while *"there's not a great deal of overlap,"* those in prosecution did mention doing *"a bit of litigation."* One junior also pointed out that *"there are some opportunities to do IPR* [inter partes reviews], *which is akin to doing litigation."* Read more online about IPR online. Associates reported clients ranging from big corporate companies to small startups, with consumer products, manufacturing, heavy-duty machinery and pharmaceuticals being some of the industries mentioned.

Those in the nonlitigious trademarks and copyrights group spoke of trademark prosecution and enforcement, the latter including *"Trademark Trial & Appeal Board proceedings, sending and responding to cease and desist letters, that type of thing."* Another junior added: *"I also do trademark availability, running clearance searches and writing search opinions."* On the copyright side, *"we do copyright registration and analysis, and things like UDRP* [Uniform Domain-Name Dispute-Resolution Policy] *complaints."* In general for this group, *"anything that's not patent-related I've probably handled!"*

"At this point I'm pretty much handling projects by myself."

Generally speaking, *"when a matter comes in that matches my technical background, it usually comes to me."* That said, there is certainly an element of door-knocking when it comes to getting work. One newcomer noted that *"I can seek out work from any of the partners, and they can in turn get me work. It's a fairly free agent system here."* When it comes to responsibility levels, *"as soon as the partners realize they can trust you, you get a lot of responsibility very quickly."* One junior told us that *"I had client contact very early on, and at this point I'm pretty much handling projects by myself, with minimal partner oversight."*

Training & Development

Upon joining the firm, associates are taken through 'MGB Academy.' This involves a few days of training to cover the basics of the firm's legal areas, as well as more general training on topics such as *"the expectations, professionalism, and how to use your administrative assistant efficiently."* After this, the firm offers a range of online CLEs, *"and partners with particular expertise present on various topics, from patent prosecution – particularly current issues – to licensing and nondisclosure agreements."* That said, associates felt that most of the training was on the job, as *"the partners and senior associates are excellent at providing the patience and time to develop your skills."*

"Time to develop your skills."

Associates are paired with partner mentors: "*You can ask them anything you want,"* gushed one source, while others mentioned that *"they're a wonderful resource for career advice."* Feedback is offered in the form of a formal summer review, and a six-month winter review. *"All the partners with whom you've worked answer a questionnaire, which are then anonymously compiled. Then a member of the executive committee talks you through them, and discusses the steps to make improvements."* On an informal basis, *"feedback depends on the person; some people are very forthcoming and with some people you have to seek it out."*

Offices

The Willis Tower location of MGB's Chicago office is the second tallest building in the US, so we weren't surprised to hear that associates *"have a lovely view of the city and the lake."* And juniors quite literally go through the motions when it comes to settling in: *"We had terrible storms about a week ago and my office swayed in the wind, which was interesting!"* Being on the 62nd and 63rd floors means *"you definitely notice the movement"* if the weather in the Windy City gets a little, er, blowy. Turbulence aside, the interior was described as *"a really nice, comfortable space, and we have nice facilities like a kitchen."* The building also has onsite restaurants and a gym, and *"if you have to stay late – that means beyond about 7pm – the firm buys dinner for you, and they'll pay for a taxi."*

"My office swayed in the wind...!"

See firm profile on p.668

Culture

The sentiment expressed by our interviewees about the overall atmosphere at MGB was that *"things are relaxed. I can ask any partner any questions at any time and they're very receptive. And people are social, they joke around; it's not an intensive environment."* Another newbie added: *"Everyone seems to be interested in engaging people beyond just the work that's being done – we know each other on a more personal level."*

"It's not an intensive environment."

We kept hearing the phrase 'work/life balance', and when we delved further juniors informed us that *"within reason you can set your own hours; as long as the work is getting done there's no issue if you have to leave early for some reason."* Others noted that the two-tier billable hour requirement was another way of promoting a more balanced lifestyle. *"It's the most explicit way the firm says, 'If you don't think you can do this work at this level, then just do less.' There's really no negative stigma associated with doing the lower tier."*

The stereotype of science and technology whizzes being somewhat unsociable is not one that applies to Marshall Gerstein. As one mechanical engineering junior remarked, *"engineers are known to be nerdy – and there's no exception to that! But the ones here are extremely social, which is a rarity..."* A range of firm-organized events doubtlessly helps this attitude: *"Lawyers who pass the bar host a party."* Then there's *"a casino night and a holiday party. There's also a bowling night that everyone gets really excited about – people make team T-shirts and talk a lot of smack to each other!"* Others mentioned a firmwide picnic and kayaking day during the summer, while the different practice groups also put on their own *"impromptu happy hours."*

"People make team T-shirts..."

Hours & Compensation

"For your first two years, you have to hit 1,950 hours, because the learning curve is huge. After that, associates can choose to drop down to 1,800 hours for a lesser salary; people do that if they need more time for things like families." To be considered for a bonus, associates need to bill 50 hours above their billing target – although this does not guarantee that they will receive one. Bonuses are discretionary, taking into account work quality as well as hours, and while some interviewees felt it would be good to know more about how they're calculated, others didn't mind: *"I don't view bonuses as a guarantee, so it doesn't bother me."*

"My schedule is really what I make it."

On a day-to-day basis, sources appreciated a more flexible approach to the hours. One newbie reported that *"my schedule is really what I make it, keeping in mind my billable hour requirements."* Those who do a lot of prosecution added that *"rarely will something come up that I didn't know about,"* so as a result, *"I usually come in at 8am and leave at 6pm."* That said, *"if a client wants advice quickly I will work weekends and stay late."* For the ones who had been involved in litigation, the hours were understandably less predictable: *"In the last few months I would come in at 9am and leave after 7pm. On a really long night I would stay until ten, and bring work home after that."*

"We're put in front of clients right away, so we look for people who are personable and comfortable with that."

Pro Bono

Interviewees agreed that the firm strongly encourages pro bono. A distinctive feature at Marshall Gerstein (and a big incentive for associates) is that for the first 50 pro bono hours billed, the firm counts double that number toward billables. As a result, all of our interviewees had completed at least 25 hours of pro bono in the past year. One keen associate told us: *"I've probably billed over 200 hours this year, and I've never been pressured to curtail my pro bono time. It really seems like the firm is dedicated to offering these types of services."*

"I've never been pressured to curtail my pro bono time."

Examples of matters that juniors had participated in include working with organizations such as the Wills For Heroes Foundation, Lawyers for the Creative Arts, and the Cabrini Green Legal Aid Clinic, which provides legal aid to low-income residents of Chicago. One newbie added that *"the firm is really open to new pro bono clients; they recently brought in training so you can work with victims of domestic violence, for instance."*

Pro bono hours

- For all attorneys across all offices: 2281
- Average per attorney: 32

Diversity

The general feeling toward the firm's diversity efforts was positive across the board. MGB has a Committee on Diversity and Inclusion, and associates reported getting

See firm profile on p.668

"emails all the time about the different diversity events that are happening. Last Friday, for instance, we had a lunch to celebrate Black History Month." Others pointed to the firm's efforts in supporting outside organizations: *"The firm contributes money to help Girls 4 Science, which provides programs for inner-city girls ages ten to 18 to help promote the scientific disciplines."*

As far as male-female ratio goes, associates told us that despite the world of IP being known as traditionally male-dominated, they felt it to be pretty even. *"There's a women's group that gets together once every couple of months to discuss different topics,"* one junior told us. *"And there are also a few attorney women's groups in Chicago. There are members of the firm on those boards so they can give us information about the activities they're doing."* That said, certain groups such as mechanical engineering did report a fairly *"male heavy"* practice.

Strategy & Future

MP Jeff Sharp informs us that *"despite headwinds in the overall economy in 2015, we had a strong year, and litigation looks like it will be taking off in 2016 – we're anticipating good things to come."* He adds that *"electrical engineering and computer science have been the fastest growing areas since the recession,"* while mechanical engineering has also seen *"huge growth"* in recent years. *"It's now possible to construct and operate things that you could only imagine but not build ten years ago, so there's a huge amount of innovation going on."*

"Litigation looks like it will be taking off in 2016."

On the topic of geographical expansion, Jeff Sharp says *"we're always thinking about the possibility of opening new offices, but I think it has to be under the right circumstances. As it is, it's easy to get on a plane in Chicago and be in California by the afternoon!"* Read his full interview online.

"Within reason you can set your own hours; as long as the work is getting done there's no issue if you have to leave early for some reason."

See firm profile on p.668

Mayer Brown LLP

Lawyers per state

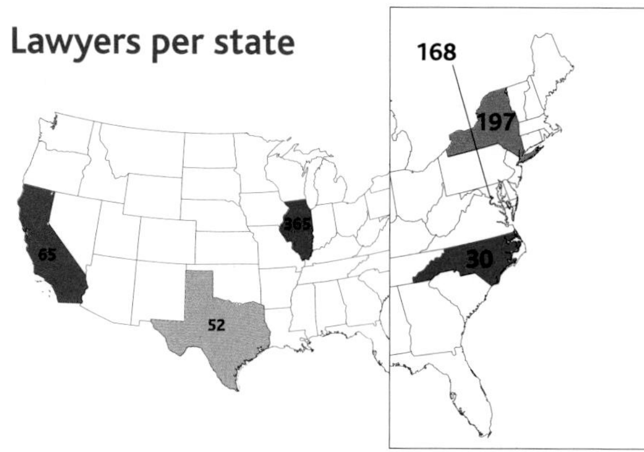

Largest US office: Chicago
US offices: 7
International offices: 14
First-year salary: $160,000
Billable hours: 2,000 required (2,100 to be bonus-eligible)
Summers 2016: 67 (62 2Ls, 1 1L, 4 3Ls)
Revenue 2015: $1.257 billion (+2.8%)
Partners made in 2016: 27 (20 in US)
Famous for: Chicago institution; intellectual culture; recent boosts in profits

Associates at this Windy City institution were blown away by the "*really interesting group of individuals*" and "*broad spectrum*" of work on offer.

IN 2013 and 2014 Mayer Brown had big success, posting a double-digit rise in profits per partner, as well as surges in gross revenue. But is the wind still blowing in the right direction for this international juggernaut? It sounds like it: *"2015 was another excellent year from a financial standpoint, in a difficult legal market,"* enthuses managing partner Ken Geller. *"We had great success in our financial results, great achievements in terms of awards and rankings, and great results in lateral recruiting."* The firm's 2015 revenue rose 2.8% on 2014 to $1.257 billion. It seems like it's all go for Mayer Brown: the firm opened new digs in Mexico City in 2015 to bolster its energy practice, and was due to set up shop in Dubai in summer 2016, which will be its first Middle Eastern outpost.

Fortunately, this Chicagoan's recent prosperity doesn't come with an overly aggressive culture, according to junior associates here. *"Generally everyone is very helpful,"* one enthused. *"Your first year can be a daunting experience, and the clients we work with are very high-profile, but generally people take the time to work with you and help you learn the ropes."*

On chambers-associate.com...

- Interview with hiring partner Brad Keck

ASSOCIATES SAY...

The Work

The largest proportion of associates on our interviewee list – around a third – was in finance, with the corporate & securities and litigation groups each accounting for around a quarter. The remaining few were dotted across employment & securities, financial services regulation, government and global trade, IP, tax controversy, real estate, bankruptcy & insolvency, wealth management, and tax transactions & consulting. During their summer program, newbies can try work from any of these groups, after which they make a decision on which practice area to join full-time. One associate assured us: *"I haven't heard of anybody not getting an offer in the group they selected."*

"I was able to express my preferences and get a variety of work."

Most of our interviewees accessed work through a free-market system, which worked reasonably well for the majority: *"I was able to express my preferences and get a variety of work."* Several, however, pointed out that working for multiple partners can sometimes cause matters to pile up, and *"some partners aren't particularly organized."* That said, juniors appreciated that there are *"partner-associate liaisons who do a good job of helping associates to balance their work schedule."* Finance associates described a broad-ranging practice: *"We do everything from leveraged and structured finance to se-*

See firm profile on p.669

The Inside View

Rankings in *Chambers USA*

Antitrust	Insurance
Appellate Law	Intellectual Property
Banking & Finance	International Trade
Bankruptcy/Restructuring	Labor & Employment
Capital Markets	Latin American Investment
Communications	Litigation
Corporate/M&A	Outsourcing
Employee Benefits & Executive Compensation	Products Liability
	Projects
Environment	Real Estate
Financial Services Regulation	Tax
Government	Technology
Immigration	Transportation

For detail on ranking tiers and ranking locations, visit www.chambersandpartners.com

Recent work highlights

- Advised Wells Fargo in its $32 billion acquisition of GE Capital's Commercial Distribution Finance and Vendor Finance platforms, as well as a portion of its Corporate Finance business
- Representing Nestlé Purina PetCare in a false advertising action against Blue Buffalo, alleging that Blue Buffalo makes false claims regarding its products
- Acts as US brand management counsel for Lindt in the US involving significant prosecution, enforcement and related advertising counsel
- Represented Whirlpool Corporation, as borrower, in both a $2 billion loan under a long-term agreement, and a shorter-term $1 billion loan

curitization and project finance, and we have a couple of people who do exclusively derivatives." One junior added: *"We represent a lot of banks, both as lenders and in terms of securitization, and we also do a lot of insurance."* When it comes to the daily grind, tasks include preparing for client calls, drafting agreements and negotiating the smaller points of a deal.

Over in litigation, the work can be anything from mortgage-backed securities cases and fraud to breach of contract, antitrust and environmental matters. We heard that travel opportunities have been abundant for New York litigators of late: *"I was on an internal investigation where I was staffed out of the country for a few months. We have a lot of junior associates in the Caribbean and Paris right now."* It's not all glamorous jet-setting, of course, and newbies aren't unfamiliar with doc review, although other more exciting tasks include writing motions and prepping witnesses for depositions. Corporate associates also get *"a pretty broad spectrum. I've done a number of equity and debt offerings on the securities side, and I was staffed on a few large transactions on the M&A side."* Other subgroups that corporate juniors can get work from include business and technology sourcing. Client secondments are also available.

Training & Development

Mayer Brown splits its attorneys into three groups: starting level, midlevel and upper level, *"so they gear the training programs toward each of those levels. Once you're a fourth-year, your goals change, and you get more training on aspects like business development."* Associates start life at the firm with an initial first-year 'Fast Track' training series, which takes place every Monday for their first six months at the firm, covering topics such as time management, career planning and maximizing feedback.

A range of more substantive legal training sessions are also on offer: *"We did a large interoffice negotiation exercise,"* one finance newbie reported. *"We split into teams to negotiate legal opinions, and we were critiqued by senior-level associates."* Litigators, meanwhile, are taught *"how to draft a motion, how to do discovery responses – we get actual practical training that I've found very helpful."* Newcomers are assigned an associate and a partner mentor, although the general feeling was that *"in reality you go to the people you work with when you have questions. I think informal mentoring is more successful because you're drawn to certain people, and you can't change that."*

Offices & Strategy

Our list of junior associates showed that nearly half of them had joined the firm's original – and largest – office in Chicago, while around a third were in the New York digs. The rest were spread between posts in Charlotte, DC, Palo Alto, LA and Houston. The Chicago office is undergoing *"a bunch of renovations. I don't know what it's going to look like, but a lot of the space will be changing."* Remaining unaltered, however, is the onsite gym and cafeteria, and its location *"downtown right near the Willis Tower"* is still as convenient as ever.

"A lot of the space will be changing."

Big Applers meanwhile moved into 1221 Avenue of the Americas in early 2015, *"so this office is very modern, with lots of glass."* As far as amenities go, *"in the basement there's a gym,"* as well as restaurants on the first floor and basement of the building. Some of our sources felt that the new space was almost too big, and at times impeded contact with others: *"The floors are huge, so you may not always see people on the other end of the floor."* First and second-years in New York share an office, while those in Chicago get their own from the start.

See firm profile on p.669

But renovations to existing digs aren't the only changes happening at Mayer Brown's offices, with the opening of a Mexico City outpost in 2015, and Dubai in 2016. *"In late 2015 we brought over two corporate partners from Baker & McKenzie, who have a large practice representing Western companies who do business in the Middle East,"* MP Ken Geller explains. *"So we've decided to open a small office in Dubai, largely to help with that inbound work but also to service Middle Eastern clients."* And which practice areas are doing particularly well at Mayer Brown right now? *"We did a significant amount of lateral recruiting during 2015 to build out our global M&A platform, including laterals from Davis Polk, Cleary Gottlieb and Baker & McKenzie,"* Geller informs us, adding that *"we had record-setting years in finance and real estate."* In addition, litigation – the firm's largest group – has had *"a very strong and consistent practice in 2015."*

Culture

While strong academics are a common trait among Mayer Brown's attorneys, the firm makes an effort to hire an eclectic mix of characters. From the *"classic nerd"* to the secretly intellectual *"frat guy, it's a really interesting group of individuals; I like that there's no dominating group."* Others mentioned that quite a few colleagues had had previous careers in sectors including engineering, consulting and journalism: *"It brings all kinds of perspectives to a problem; the more voices you have in the room the better."* When it comes to partners, *"there are some who are significantly more laid back, but there are also those who are quite highly strung and more like the stereotypical New York partner."*

"A really interesting group of individuals."

By and large, socializing isn't at the top of the agenda for the majority of Mayerites. *"I appreciate that, though,"* one junior was quick to add. *"I have other social outlets in my life, and there's nobody here that I don't get along with."* Others appreciated the firm's more flexible approach to time spent in the office: *"They expect that when you do your work, you do it well. After that you have leeway; if you want to go home, you can."* Another second-year confided: *"If you're not busy, there's no weird face time issue where you're just sitting there doing nothing, which is the worst. My advice to first-years would be: if you're not busy, go home!"*

Hours & Compensation

Compensation is calculated using a rather complex system. In order to remain in good standing at the firm and advance to the next level in the pay scale, associates need to bill 2,000 working hours. These consist of not only billables, but also matters such as pro bono, business development work and training sessions – *"it's a pretty broad bucket."* However, there is a subset of the working hours – which the firm refers to as 'creditable hours' – which only includes billables and up to 200 pro bono hours, as well as *"some limited quantities of other things, for instance if we received a subpoena."* To get a bonus, associates need to bill at least 2,100 creditable hours. In general, our sources hadn't had any problems hitting this target: *"We've all been pretty busy!"*

"Went back to the lockstep system."

Last year we were told that the bonuses were calculated using a mixture of lockstep and discretionary factors. *"They shifted to that system for exactly one year, but there was a bit of an outcry, so they went back to the lockstep system."* Salaries are also lockstep. When it comes to vacation, *"you can take as much time as you want, there's no set number of days."* Although this sounds like a dream, *"it's really a blessing and a curse – some people are better about taking vacation than others. Most people take a couple of weeks."*

"I think informal mentoring is more successful because you're drawn to certain people, and you can't change that."

Pro Bono

Mayer Brown is signed up to the 'Law Firm Pro Bono Challenge,' which means it dedicates at least 3% of its total billable hours to pro bono. Junior associates are expected to bill at least 60 hours, although *"you can go up to 200 hours."* In general, our interviewees had billed between 60 and 100 hours, with one source noting *"I would take more on if I had more time!"*

"I would take more on if I had more time!"

Mayer associates can get involved in a wide variety of matters, from representing inmates and working on appellate briefs for criminal defendants, to asylum cases and helping senior citizens access medical benefits. *"We probably get an email every week from our pro bono director with new opportunities."* We also heard of associates who had been able to bring in their own cases.

Pro bono hours

- For all attorneys across all US offices: 42,024
- Average per US attorney: 53

The Inside View

See firm profile on p.669

Diversity

"In my group in New York we don't have very many female partners, and that is a concern for me as a female associate," one junior confessed. Our figures show that Mayer Brown has only 39% female associates, and 18% female partners. That said, steps are definitely being made in the right direction. Each office has its own Women's Forum, for instance, *"and those meetings are great! Although I do think that the female associates would benefit from having female partner and associate mentors, too."*

"They are putting more resources into these things."

Where racial diversity is concerned, most of our interviewees praised the firm's efforts: *"When I started, the firm hired a director of diversity* [Jerry DeBerry] *and he's created a lot of events; they are putting more resources into these things."* There is a three-day diversity retreat in Chicago, and those who had attended it agreed that *"it was good to network with other people in other offices that you normally wouldn't be exposed to. The firm is definitely making a very big push in terms of diversity."* Others felt that there is a lot of talk and little action, however: *"We have a lot of presentations where we're told the management is focused on diversity, but I've not actually seen that it is. And I'm not aware of any concrete structural changes here."*

Get Hired

Rather predictably, given the intellectual atmosphere at Mayer Brown, the firm is *"fairly choosy about academic performance,"* according to hiring partner Brad Keck. And at interview, don't be afraid to express your opinion: *"If you are truly interested in the firm, let us know!"* Keck tells us. *"That's important, because everyone wants to feel some mutuality; sometimes it's hard to know which candidates are sincerely interested."* Read Keck's full interview online.

"If you are truly interested in the firm, let us know!"

When we asked associates for their opinion on hiring criteria, several highlighted that *"it is very much free-market at Mayer Brown, so you have to be much more of a self-starter. You have to be willing to approach the partners; they prefer you to knock on their door and ask questions rather than just sit in your office and email them."*

"Your first year can be a daunting experience, and the clients we work with are very high-profile, but generally people take the time to work with you and help you learn the ropes."

See firm profile on p.669

McGuireWoods LLP

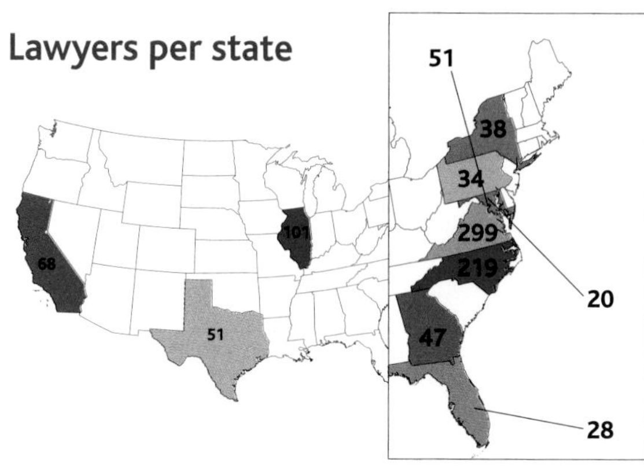

Largest US office: Richmond
US offices: 19
International offices: 2
First-year salary: $115,000 – $155,000
Billable hours: 1,950 required
Summers 2016: 18 (16 2Ls, 2 1Ls)
Revenue 2015: $653.5 million (+5.4%)
Partners made in 2016: 16 (all US)
Famous for: being a long-established litigation powerhouse

This Virginia native is all over the East Coast and further afield, and has global expansion firmly in its sights.

THE 'Old Dominion' is home to the oldest judicial system in America and the oldest legislature in the Western hemisphere. Another Virginian institution that has stood the test of time is Richmond-based McGuireWoods. Aging gracefully over the past 182 years, McGuire has grown into a firm with 19 offices all over the US and two overseas, and over 1,000 attorneys. The newest office to add to the collection is a strategic alliance with Shanghai-based FuJae Partners. Managing partner Tom Cabaniss explains that *"globalization is an important part of the market today. Therefore, concerning our new alliance with FuJae Partners, we had been waiting for an opportunity to find the right fit for a connection in Asia, and now that we have it we can fully realize our ability to serve our clients who have Asian ties. There will be opportunities to get fantastic experiences both here and there in terms of legal work and culture."*

Highly regarded practices include litigation and wealth management, to name a few, and are rewarded by top marks in *Chambers USA*. Top work is matched by top clients, who include the likes of Starbucks, Home Depot, Bank of America and Wells Fargo.

On chambers-associate.com...

- Interview with managing partner Tom Cabaniss
- More on The Work

ASSOCIATES SAY...

The Work

The 72 associates on our interviewee list worked in groups including: business & securities litigation; M&A & cross-border transactions; tax & employee benefits; complex commercial litigation; and real estate & land use. Insiders said that *"the main operations in DC are government investigations and white-collar crime."* Another stated that *"in Charlotte it's debt finance and finance litigation, as Bank of America is down the street."* Class breakdowns in Chicago show that *"there were six people in my class. One went to financial services litigation, one went to labor & employment, one to specialty corporate practices, one to debt finance and two chose healthcare."* In the Richmond HQ, *"restructuring & insolvency generates high revenue"* as does private wealth, *"which is unusual as most of those groups are drying up elsewhere."* The assignment system is *"pretty free flow. You're assigned a supervising attorney in your practice group to report to. You also get an associate mentor. But you show up and can take whatever work is available. It's great because it gives you a lot of autonomy."*

"I've been thankful that they've involved me."

Regulation & compliance juniors had typically done *"a lot of standard research on legal issues. I spent two days doing client interviews for an internal audit. I've also drafted briefs and a compliance manual."* In restructur-

See firm profile on p.670

Rankings in *Chambers USA*

Antitrust	Intellectual Property
Banking & Finance	Labor & Employment
Bankruptcy/Restructuring	Litigation
Corporate/M&A	Products Liability
Energy & Natural Resources	Real Estate
Environment	Technology
Food & Beverages	Wealth Management
Healthcare	

For detail on ranking tiers and ranking locations, visit www.chambersandpartners.com

ing & insolvency, *"we work all over the country, so I get tasked with finding out the law in different districts. I've been thankful that they've involved me in substantive pleadings, drafting responses to summary judgments and insurance protocol payments. I don't feel like it's just busy work."*

Associates in the specialty corporate group explained that *"we work in the energy space. It's different to typical stock or asset purchase work. It's intertwined with the production of energy products. There's a high level of drafting ancillary purchase agreements."* Financial services litigators had *"drafted complaints, written substantive motions to dismiss, attended hearings, and argued motions to dismiss on a $20,000 case. I've also drafted requests for discovery. I had my own caseload of 300 single-plaintiff cases for one client and I had to negotiate all the settlement agreements. It's been fantastic."* For more on The Work, go online.

Training & Development

An initial two-day orientation *"is on stuff like 'how do I turn on my computer and how do I get out of the building?'"* After this, *"the firm puts on weekly presentations on legal writing and how to be successful."* This is traditionally broadcast across all offices via video link and runs every Friday for the first six weeks of employment. Other training beyond first-year level has been implemented in *"response to people clamoring for it. So they now try and put on basic reviews in practices that you are not necessarily in. It's very rare to get an issue that only one practice group is engaged in. So it's good if everyone has a baseline of competence."*

"Each department has an associate committee liaison."

There's more informal opportunity to solicit feedback on work from partners. But once a year, attorneys *"list everyone we've worked with from seventh-year associates and above. They are all sent a copy of our self-assessment and asked to review you. Each department has an associate committee liaison go over it with you and your supervisor can be there too. For me it works."*

Recent work highlights

- Negotiated an immunity agreement for Jonnie Williams, CEO of Star Scientific, who was under investigation for allegedly bribing former Virginia Governor Robert McDonnell. The agreement granted immunity in exchange for testifying against the McDonnells
- Represented the Toronto-Dominion Bank in the $1 billion Rothstein Ponzi scheme fraud litigation and Chapter 11 bankruptcy proceedings
- Represented DuPont in a civil trade secrets litigation against Kolon Industries, for conspiring with former employees to steal information about the bulletproof fiber Kevlar

Diversity

"I wish it was more diverse because most people who are diverse don't stay," opined one junior. Others added that *"diversity is a relative term. Is it a representative sample of the USA? No. Is it a representative sample of law school graduates? No. But McGuireWoods is doing the same as other firms our size."* Many interviewees stated that this wasn't *"for lack of trying"* and that *"the firm is making the right moves to make it the norm."* McGuireWoods has various affinity groups, including the African American Lawyers Network, and the Asian Pacific Lawyers Network. The most visible is the Women's Lawyers Network. One associate mused that *"we have loads of events. We invited all our female clients to the Chicago Ballet to network. It's a really high-profile event."*

"Is it a representative sample of law school graduates?"

However, a few told a different story. *"Don't get me wrong, people are nice but since I've been here it's gone from about ten nonwhite associates to a grand total of two,"* said one of their particular surroundings. Another's view was that *"I don't want to be out in an affinity group spending the weekend in Richmond discussing problems: I just want to focus on my hours."* Others insisted that *"diversity and inclusion is one of our core values, so we have a diversity inclusion committee."* There's also a *"diversity program for 1Ls. I think we only take on 1Ls under the program. Everyone at law school knew about this, so it's very visible in the community."* Most interviewees felt that the firm was trying to *"cover all the bases to do more day-to-day things, so that it's not just focused on getting diverse people in positions of power, but at every level."*

See firm profile on p.670

Offices & Culture

The largest of McGuireWoods' 19 US offices is Richmond, followed by Charlotte then Chicago. Across all these locations, associates have their own offices. In Chicago, juniors joked that *"our views are amazing but the restaurants are garbage! I don't know what to do about that!"*

"We all went to watch them compete in a law firm battle of the bands."

In the summer of 2015, Richmond moved into an 18-story, purpose-built building. *"It's beautiful. All offices are the same size with floor to ceiling windows. There is a great view of the Court of Appeal."* In downtown Charlotte (known as *"Uptown"* to locals) the firm uses *"ten stories of a 30-story building, with great places to grab lunch,"* making up for the *"slightly austere décor."*

Newbies stressed that regardless of geography, *"one of the best things we do is that we don't let the work consume our lives."* Many continued that *"it's not cut-throat and you can ask questions of anyone."* Interestingly, some Richmond residents felt that *"it's a Southern law firm so it's a little more formal. I've read before that people say it's more relaxed, but if you look at those who are on the partner track, it's all suits five days a week. But I was incredibly impressed by the fact that on the first day, everyone knew my name. It makes it an environment where I'm happy to work. That goes to a Southern thing as well, everyone is treated well."*

On the social side, most associates *"wished there were more opportunities to independently get together outside of work."* However, Charlotte sources praised the holiday party *"hosted in a baseball field."* Juniors told us that *"we had a Thanksgiving competition against all the other offices* [including international], *seeing who could make the most sandwiches for soup kitchens. One of our partners is also in a band, so we all went to watch them compete in a law firm battle of the bands."*

Pro Bono

"I think the firm is committed to pro bono," one junior began. They then qualified the statement, intimating that *"objectively speaking, I know our hours can seem a little lower than other firms, but we're not terribly behind. The partners are trying to correct this as we all value it here."*

"Everyone cares about it. It's not only the right, moral thing to do, but it builds skills."

Juniors unanimously declared that *"everyone cares about it. It's not only the right, moral thing to do, but it builds skills."* McGuireWoods allows 50 hours to count toward billing targets (but not bonus eligibility). Additionally, the firm selects a *"handful of associates who have gone above and beyond, gives them awards and brings them to the annual partners' meeting."*

Associates described pro bono examples including work with *"a not-for-profit organization looking at their employee benefits plan. I've had to review, draft and file documents with the IRS. I've done everything that I would do for a paying client and it's given me greater confidence."* Those in Richmond gave vivid accounts of their work setting up *"a pretty sophisticated tax vehicle called 'Conservation Easements.' If you have real property, you can place the easement on it and get an income deduction. It's easy to mess up and the IRS thinks that it's too tax-friendly. I did this for a museum and I drafted deeds and negotiated contracts with the charity that was the beneficiary."*

"I was incredibly impressed by the fact that on the first day, everyone knew my name."

Chicago natives said they'd *"devoted a large amount of time to a housing administrative hearing. I did the opening statement and the questioning. Every opportunity in front of any judicial officer is good."* Other new starters applauded the fact that *"we now have a pro bono head in each office."*

Pro bono hours

- For all attorneys across all US offices: 27,749
- Average per US attorney: 44

Hours & Compensation

On average, insiders work between *"ten to 12 hours a day."* Unsurprisingly, *"every once in a while there is a really late night, but other than that I usually go home and relax and then do another hour of work."*

As recompense for toiling away, newbies divulged the firm's approach to bonuses. With a yearly billing target of 1,950 hours a year, when associates reach 2,000 hours, they become bonus-eligible. At this point juniors *"get a $5,000 bonus. You get $5,000 for each 100 hours over until you hit 2,200 hours. This is because the firm wants to promote a healthier life balance. But additionally we have a performance-based bonus if you have been truly exceptional. I think 12% of attorneys got it"* in 2015.

See firm profile on p.670

Get Hired

McGuireWoods' litigation team has a strong tradition of either hiring associates with past clerkship experience, or alternatively helping to give clerkship opportunities to their new hires. Charlotte newbies suggested that, when interviewing, McGuire wants *"people who have really good resumes, so that it sounds good on the website. But more importantly than that, the firm seeks out people who are fun to work with."* Others praised the firm's investment in its employees, and for example it was *"instrumental in getting me a Federal District Court clerkship."*

"You get a $25,000 clerkship bonus."

Hiring partner and cochair of the recruiting committee, John Adams explains that *"this is because a year or two of clerking with a federal judge is an unparalleled training ground. You enter the real world of law in a courthouse, so that when you come to us, you can hit the ground running."* Insiders agreed and reasoned that a clerkship is valuable because *"first-year lawyers are the least profitable, so it's a good way to get up to speed. Secondly, it's really good experience to see how the sausage gets made! Third, I think it's the prestige, as we have a lot of ex-clerks here. Plus you get a $25,000 clerkship bonus"* [for district courts, and $35,000 for appeals court clerks].

Additionally, Washingtonians advised that other practical experiences were viewed favorably. *"Law Journal Review experience is a bonus, as is moot court. I worked at a federal agency in the summer, so I could demonstrate my interest in the area I was interviewing in."*

Strategy & Future

Juniors agreed that *"private wealth, energy and debt practices are busy"* and *"healthcare is always booming."* A large proportion of our interviewees were lateral hires. Sources explained that *"we are definitely busy due to the legal market picking up since the low point in 2008. More hands are needed, so we lateral a lot."*

"Asia is a big player."

Regarding the international alliance with FuJae Partners, associates intimated that *"it seems like most firms recognize that Asia is a big player. We are about strategic partnerships, which is why the firm has grown so quickly."* Managing partner Tom Cabaniss goes further and tells us that this *"will help us meet our clients' needs in China more effectively and provide us with access to Chinese clients doing business in the US, Europe and around the world. It's been a busy and satisfying year."* For the full interview with Tom Cabaniss, go online.

"We had been waiting for an opportunity to find the right fit for a connection in Asia, and now that we have it we can fully realize our ability to serve our clients who have Asian ties. There will be opportunities to get fantastic experiences both here and there in terms of legal work and culture."

See firm profile on p.670

Milbank, Tweed, Hadley & McCloy LLP

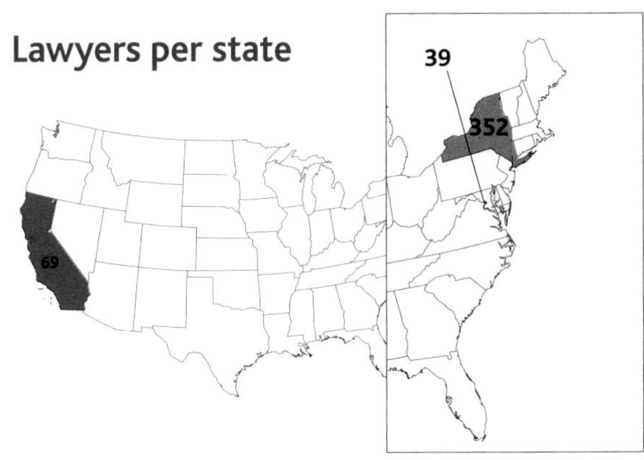

Largest US office: New York
US offices: 3
International offices: 9
First-year salary: $160,000
Billable hours: no requirement
Summers 2016: 67 (65 2Ls, 2 others)
Revenue 2015: $771.1 million (+1.3%)
Partners made in 2016: 5 globally (4 in USA)
Famous for: early clients were the Rockefellers and Vanderbilts; financial services expertise

This grand old man of the New York legal scene has shed its fusty image and offers today's generation of lawyers a wealth of opportunities.

MILBANK was founded in 1866, in the age of steam and top hats, and when the telegraph was considered 'disruptive technology'. In the old days it was a white shoe firm whose attorneys rubbed shoulders with the likes of the Vanderbilts and Rockefellers, and this pedigree led to its 'white shoe' moniker sticking somewhat as the modern Milbank evolved. Chairman Scott Edelman reminds us that, far from being stuck in the past, Milbank is *"a very young firm, and the sort of place where a young lawyer can get an enormous amount of responsibility."* These days it's well known in particular for operating in the dynamic worlds of hedge funds, investment banking and Chapter 11 bankruptcy, often on a global scale.

The firm gets top marks from *Chambers USA* in practice areas including bankruptcy & restructuring, Latin American investment, project finance and aviation finance, and gets nods for others like tax, securitization and wealth management. In addition, the firm has 12 offices worldwide, in financial hubs both traditional – like London, New York and Frankfurt – and new – such as São Paulo and Seoul.

On chambers-associate.com...

- Milbank and the Rockefellers

ASSOCIATES SAY...

The Work

Litigation takes the lion's share of the firm's first years, with the next largest chunk of newbies being scattered among the various finance-themed sub-groups, followed closely by corporate. In the course of our research, we heard of juniors running their own finance deals, drafting pleadings and even, in one case, arguing in court. *"You can get whiplash sometimes,"* cautioned a New Yorker. *"We're at the bottom of the totem pole, but we're getting real responsibility."* Of course, there's no escaping the drudgery of doc review or due diligence, but sources told us that *"even seemingly mundane tasks are vitally important."* Furthermore, *"when a client wants something done cheaper [than partners' rates], it can be a great opportunity for a junior associate."*

> *"If you're willing to have more responsibility, they're happy to give it to you."*

This is particularly true in the firm's highly regarded bankruptcy and restructuring group, which our sources described as *"the firm's only hybrid department – we're the only department that has both transactional and litigious elements."* Juniors are exposed to both of sides of the bankruptcy coin, with some focusing on the contentious side of things, for example, before switching to transactional tasks once they have enough experience of the business side of things. *"This is a product of the fact that law school doesn't always give you an under-*

See firm profile on p.671

Rankings in *Chambers USA*

Banking & Finance	Litigation
Bankruptcy/Restructuring	Projects
Capital Markets	Tax
Corporate/M&A	Telecommunications
Intellectual Property	Transportation
Latin American Investment	Wealth Management

For detail on ranking tiers and ranking locations, visit www.chambersandpartners.com

standing of the business issues," explained an associate in New York. Milbank's traditionally a creditor shop, but will do debtor work on occasion. *"Creditor cases are more leanly staffed, so they take up less manpower. On creditor cases it will be you, a senior associate and a partner, while there can be ten people working on a debtor matter."*

Restructuring may be the firm's *"engine room,"* but project finance also commands a hefty amount of prestige, particularly on the West Coast. This is another department where *"if you're willing to have more responsibility, they're happy to give it to you."* Junior associates see their fair share of *"diligence, checklists and drafting smaller documents,"* but there are also opportunities to *"negotiate and draft the main financing and security documents."* Given California's expertise in this area, it's no surprise that the West Coast branch of this department handles its fair share of renewable energy work, and it also does a healthy slice of business for clients in Latin America.

Pro Bono

A lot of the firms we profile have a fairly impressive commitment to pro bono, but few take it quite as seriously as Milbank. Incoming associates have the opportunity to spend up to four months of their career with the firm working full time at a pro bono organization of their choice, for full pay without having to do any billable work for the firm. *"We went to orientation in October and then jumped right into pro bono,"* reminisced one neophyte, *"I didn't actually get started in Milbank until January."* In a given year, *"anywhere between half and two thirds of new associates take part,"* says hiring partner Jay Grushkin. Sources who had completed the program came back to the firm with *"a rich experience that you can talk about with partners and associates."*

"Encourage us to do around 100 each year."

But that's not all, folks. Not only can pro bono fellows bring their work back to the firm, but there's an obligation to do at least 20 hours of pro bono work and *"they try to encourage us to do around 100 each year."* If you're not getting at least your 20 in, expect to be *"pinged"* with emails around the middle of the year reminding you to get stuck in. On the litigious front, there are asylum, wrongful conviction and LGBT discrimination cases, while transactional lawyers can help set up nonprofit schools or perform research for NGOs.

Recent work highlights

- Advising Ambac Financing, which insures $10 billion worth of Puerto Rican government bonds, in relation to debt negotiations with the Commonwealth of Puerto Rico
- Helped Seaborn Networks finance a fiber-optic cable between the US and Brazil
- Represented the Government of Canada on its largest ever US denominated global debt offering
- Represented the unsecured creditors of Lehman Brothers in a series of mediations over disputed derivatives contracts.

Pro Bono hours

- For all attorneys across all US offices: 46,091
- Average per US attorney: 96

Culture & Offices

With 'tweed' in its name and a history dating back to the 1860s, you could be forgiven for thinking that Milbank was a little, well, old fashioned. Thankfully, we hear the opposite. In fact, one associate admitted *"I didn't actually know we were so historic until after I started working here."* Beyond that, culture tended to vary between offices and departments, making it tricky to pin down any kind of firmwide culture. *"Culturally, we're more like a compilation of many smaller firms than one big one,"* ventured a New Yorker. However, a lot of deals are cross-staffed, and with so much contact between the different offices, cultural quirks from one office frequently migrate to the others. A good example is jeans Friday, which began in LA and has recently taken off in the Big Apple.

"I didn't actually know we were so historic until I started working here."

One area in which Milbank can feel a little dated is the New York office, which our spies there thought needed to be spruced up. Even that's only a minor grumble next to the office's waterside location, and 360-degree views and besides, plans are afoot to overhaul the decor. And those tired of the wallpaper can always venture to Milbank Miami, a floor *"where everything's shiny and glass,"* and the only downside is *"everyone can see what you're doing."* New York's not the only place that's getting new digs; LA is going one better and moving to a brand new

See firm profile on p.671

office in Century City. Based in Washington's famous – or infamous – K Street, the DC office has no plans on going anywhere, our sources there told us.

Training & Development

Training begins on the summer program, with novices role playing a fictional transaction, completing a different stage each week. *"It helped me understand the breadth of what we do here, and what our colleagues do,"* admitted one. At the start of their associate-hood there's a week of orientation at New York, which is attended by all the newbies. And we do mean all the newbies; *"everyone, including from the offices overseas, is invited."* After an overview of the firm, everyone splits up and attends department specific training, which continues back at their own offices. *"They brought in this guy to teach us legal writing,"* recalled a Washingtonian, *"he was a total nerd who read Supreme Court cases for fun, but the training was very helpful."*

"They have to turn their BlackBerries, iPhones and Androids off and focus."

Once associates hit their third year, they're bundled off to Cambridge, MA for a week of learning at the Milbank@ Harvard program. This is run by the law and business schools at Harvard and is an intense week spent learning business, law and soft skills topics. *"They have to turn their BlackBerries, iPhones and Androids off and focus,"* says Jay Grushkin, *"it's a major commitment on our part and we want them to get the best from it."* Associates also learn on the job and have access to CLEs aplenty, but our sources found the relationships they'd built up with their colleagues. *"I think I've grown a lot as a professional,"* reflected a source, *"and a lot of that is down to the mentoring I got from partners and senior associates."*

Diversity

In previous years, insiders told us that Milbank talks the talk on diversity but *"doesn't necessarily walk the walk."* We asked our interviewees if that was still the case. *"I think if you look at the partners you can understand why people feel that way,"* answered one, *"but recent summer classes have been very diverse."* Sources generally gave the firm good marks for gender and LGBT diversity, but agreed that *"more could be done"* to attract strong candidates from ethnic minority backgrounds. Milbank's diversity scholars program offers a $25,000 scholarship and a summer place to 2Ls from traditionally under-represented groups.

"Recent summer classes have been very diverse"

There are a number of different affinity groups, including ones for African-American lawyers, Latino attorneys and female lawyers, which attend recruitment events and bring in speakers. Some are more active than others, and most are run out of the New York office; *"there's a limit to how much you can participate over the phone,"* sighed a Californian. Particularly highly regarded was the women's group, with associates praising its cross-practice liaisons, 'lean in' style bookclubs and *"the fact that we can hear about the experiences of more senior female lawyers."*

Hours & Compensation

Associates described Milbank as *"less about work-life balance and more about integrating work into your life."* Hours were generally reasonable, with no facetime requirement, but associates do find themselves taking their work home. *"My average day is nine am to six pm,"* said a litigator, *"and then I'll go home and do some more work."* Although all-nighters do happen, the firm's flexibility about remote working meant that they were kept to a minimum. *"I've stayed past 3am once in the last six months,"* recalled a source. Another had stayed *"until 1.30 or 2"* twice in the same timeframe. Court-mandated deadlines, demanding bankers and an impending insolvencies were all cited as causes of late nights, rather than unreasonable partners. *"Partners encourage us to take advantage of the time when we aren't busy,"* said a source, *"and if it's slow, you can leave at four."*

"Even seemingly mundane tasks are vitally important."

"Nobody gets punished if work is unexpectedly slow."

Pay is at market rate, which associates were generally content with. *"Whenever I do complain, my friends remind me that I still earn a lot of money,"* laughed one. There's no billable hours target or requirement, which *"creates a fair atmosphere and makes sure that nobody gets punished if work is unexpectedly slow."* It also removes the incentive to be sharp-elbowed, and keeps associates focused on work, and *"there's certainly no sense that people are competing to be staffed on deals and cases."*

Get Hired

The OCIs are usually conducted by one partner and one associate, while the callbacks feature a larger panel of five or six. Interviews, especially OCIs, can feel *"like a speed dating session where everybody looks more or*

See firm profile on p.671

The Inside View

less the same" – both are daunting, and both can involve making important decisions with very little information to guide you. Our sources found the interviewers from Milbank much warmer and more inviting than other potential suitors – indeed for one hopeful, it was the people on the other side of the desk who helped seal the deal. *"Everyone was so happy,"* they recalled. *"Take a look at the bios on the firm's website to get a feel for what the firm has done,"* counseled one. *"When I was applying, I got hold of some people who had summered at the firm, and they gave me a valuable insight into the experience,"* the source added.

"OCIs are like speed dating where everyone looks the same"

In addition to brushing up on your knowledge of the firm, insiders advised applicants to take courses that would help them understand their clients' businesses. *"Even litigators need to understand the commercial context that clients operate in,"* explains Jay Grushkin, *"so having studied subjects like the bankruptcy, tax, securities law or the Uniform Commercial Code will definitely help."* It's not all black letter stuff, interviewers are also on the lookout for people with the right personality. Grushkin recommends being *"confident but not cocky and assertive without being pushy. Essentially we're looking for people who can engage with clients from day one,"* he says, *"but also who we enjoy hanging out with."*

Strategy & Future

Chairman Scott Edelman makes it clear that the firm's *"global footprint"* is a key part of its strategy. Does this mean Milbank is looking to build an empire of Dentons-esque proportion? Not quite, he tells us; *"we'll continue to grow, but slowly and in a way that allows us to maintain a high quality of work and lawyers."* In a few years, Milbank *"will be basically the same firm, but a little bigger and a little more built up."*

"Confident but not cocky and assertive without being pushy. Essentially we're looking for people who can engage with clients from day one."

See firm profile on p.671

Mintz Levin Cohn Ferris Glovsky and Popeo PC

Lawyers per state

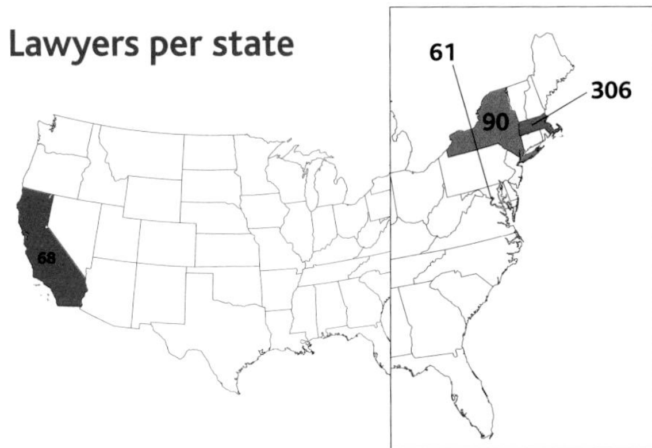

Largest US office: Boston
US offices: 7
International offices: 1
First-year salary: $160,000
Billable hours: 1,850 target
Summers 2016: 17 (12 2Ls, 5 1Ls)
Revenue 2015: $363.4 million (+17.7%)
Partners made 2016: 7
Famous for: life sciences, healthcare and technology focus

Boston-born Mintz Levin is rapidly building its "*21st Century*" practices.

"LIFE sciences are a core, and growing, area for us, along with our IP team," managing member Bob Bodian tells us while sipping camomile tea in a plush hotel lobby on a recent trip to London. *"If students are interested in these areas they should definitely take a look at our IP team as we've been a hiring a lot of associates into them recently."* Life sciences and intellectual property are two of what Bodian has called the *"21st Century"* practice areas that 82 year-old Mintz Levin is focusing on right now. The others are, broadly speaking, communications, technology, and healthcare. *"We formed a strategic planning committee about four years ago which came to the conclusion we should be focusing on areas where we had the most strengths, such as life sciences, bio tech, energy technology, healthcare, and privacy and data security. We're using those areas as drivers for the rest of the firm."*

In its home state of Massachusetts, Mintz Levin wins *Chambers USA* rankings for practices including public finance, bankruptcy/restructuring, environment, employee benefits, and real estate. Corporate/M&A, litigation and healthcare in particular are highly regarded here and also in New York. Health-related stuff – the whole gamut, including transactions, court cases, antitrust and regulation – is strong in DC too, which also boasts a *Chambers*-ranked telecommunications team. Many Mintz groups have been working at full throttle recently, resulting in an influx of senior and junior laterals. Nearly half of current third-years, for example, left other firms for greener pastures at Mintz with some experience under their belts. As for those who join straight from law school, one new recruit reasoned: *"So many people lateral into Mintz, I thought: well, why not start here from the beginning?"*

On chambers-associate.com...

- Interview with managing member Bob Bodian
- Interview with director of legal recruiting Shannon Davis
- More on Mintz Levin's US offices

ASSOCIATES SAY...

The Work

Boston absorbs most of the firm's newbies while the rest head to New York, Washington, DC or San Diego. Juniors are split pretty evenly between the corporate and securities, litigation and IP groups, although a handful go into other areas such as real estate, healthcare and employment. All departments employ a practice manager to oversee work allocation, but juniors are also free to *"seek out the projects and people you like."* While corporate sources felt this system worked well, litigators told us: *"The oversight of who is working on what could be better. Some people end up slammed while others are just sitting around."*

"I'm in over my head just enough."

The Inside View

See firm profile on p.672

Rankings in *Chambers USA*

Banking & Finance	Healthcare
Bankruptcy/Restructuring	Labor & Employment
Corporate/M&A	Life Sciences
Employee Benefits & Executive Compensation	Litigation
	Real Estate
Environment	Telecommunications

For detail on ranking tiers and ranking locations, visit www.chambersandpartners.com

Recent work highlights

- Advised Massachusetts-based biotech developer Anchor Therapeutics in its merger with Acer Therapeutics
- Acted for oncology company ARIAD Pharmaceuticals in a securities class action lawsuit after plaintiffs alleged the company misled investors over risks associated with a leukemia drug
- Represented graphics creation company ChyronHego in its acquisition by private equity firm Vector Capital
- Assisted Enterprise Systems Technologies, portfolio holders of patents developed by Siemens, who leveled patent infringement allegations against several respondents

Greater Boston is home to lots of tech companies, research institutions and universities, so IP juniors here see plenty of work involving things like *"medical devices, consumer electronics, mechanics, and pharmaceuticals."* Associates we spoke to had worked on patent litigation (suing or defending people) or patent prosecution (applying for patents). Sources practicing the latter reported: *"We're mostly working with local clients to develop products from the ground up,"* which can be *"fascinating."* One source told us: *"There's a lot of independence to draft things like applications, opinions and motions. I'll get the first, second and third draft. I'm in over my head just enough."*

Mintz's corporate and securities group predominantly works with clients in the tech, biotech, health and life sciences industries. Its tech slant sees corporate rookies tackle venture financing or investment funds, but as juniors here start off as generalists, deal-doers can also see the usual run of IPOs, M&A and securities matters. All our interviewees here had knuckled down with due diligence, but generally *"everyone's eager to make sure I'm not just doing grunt work."* Indeed, we heard of juniors drafting anything from ancillary documents and confidentiality agreements to revising partnership agreements. Working on venture financing matters sees *"plenty of client contact."*

The firm's core industries also feed into litigation, which tends to be high stakes rather than commoditized and so commands higher rates. Specialisms include licensing, class actions, insurance, securities and product liability disputes. *"Sometimes I'll do things way above my pay grade – motions or summary judgment, substantive heavy work – and then other times I'll be putting binders together."* Another source observed that, as they gained experience, *"I've really noticed a shift from doc review to more stimulating tasks like preparing expert reports and drafting pleadings."*

Strategy & Future

Associates pegged the corporate and IP departments as two areas to watch. The former is *"going gang-busters: we're having to hire loads of new people,"* while the IP department is experiencing *"huge growth."* The latter recently lured five attorneys away from Womble Carlyle and also bagged an 18-strong life sciences team from Edwards Wildman (now Locke Lord).

Corporate is "going gang-busters."

"We've increased our headcount by around 10% this last year. Our corporate and IP teams have been in great demand," managing member Bob Bodian confirms. *"We're going to continue to grow our main strengths in major areas such as corporate, IP, litigation and healthcare, and we'll be looking to increase the size of our California and New York offices."*

Offices

Boston is Mintz's largest office – go online for more on the firm's bases – with *"a spectacular view of downtown and the harbor. It's fantastic for commuting as we're opposite South Station."* Several sources were less enthusiastic about the *"dark, dull and dated"* décor, although others weren't too fussed, with one interviewee claiming, *"I don't mind dated! Modern, glass offices are sterile."* San Diego juniors liked their glass office, however, describing it as *"beautiful! All glass and hardwood floors."*

"People will bug you if you don't dress it up."

Mintz juniors all receive their own office, and woe betide DC-ers who don't make the effort to personalize theirs: *"People will bug you if you don't dress it up. Some folks have loads of stuff on their walls."* The firm's Big Apple base is set out in a helpful circle – *"you can just keep walking round until you find what you need"* – and has a whole corridor filled with kids' art. *"Once a year, everyone brings in their little ones for an ice cream party and children's art exhibition."* Other offices organize similar events.

See firm profile on p.672

Culture

Intellectual property attorneys in Boston recently let their creative juices flow onto canvas at this year's 'paint night' at a pub when an artist showed them how to paint the Boston skyline. *"Mine was awful,"* one source sheepishly admitted. *"I'm too embarrassed to show it to anyone."* Although most offices host a happy hour every Thursday or Friday, sources across the firm pointed out that *"there's a strong emphasis on billing so we're not always the most social, but everyone is friendly and welcoming. People are very receptive to helping each other and juniors don't throw each other under the bus."* Another elaborated: *"If anyone yelled at an assistant, people would look at them as though they had three heads. From top to bottom abrasive personalities are not tolerated."* Generally, *"there's not a barrier between partners and associates; you'll often be sitting in your superior's office planning out a deal with them."* And we even heard of one partner *"who thanked his associate for all their hard work with a bottle of Cognac."*

"There's a strong emphasis on billing."

While there's a fairly consistent culture between offices, interviewees mentioned a couple of differences. In Boston *"the culture differs between practice areas: IP seems more laid back than other groups – I feel overdressed whenever I visit – whereas litigation is full of different personalities so it's hard to put your finger on an overriding characteristic."* Over in DC, juniors were especially quick to point out that *"our time is respected, which is especially beneficial for those who have young families."*

Hours & Compensation

Several of our sources had gravitated to Mintz with one eye firmly on its family-friendly reputation, although they remained realistic: *"This is a law firm, but although it's busy and expectations are high I actually feel like I have a good amount of control over my life,"* one source divulged. *"Most people clear out of the office by 7pm, although depending on what stage a project is at, the deviation on a 7pm exit is massive!"* But unless a tight deadline rears its ugly head *"we can work to our own schedule and no-one's prowling around at 7pm to see who's gone."* Another junior added: *"I chose Mintz so I wouldn't have to work until 3am every night and bill 2,400 hours. I mean, I work at night and sometimes on weekends but if I need to take it off or have plans I can do that, it is totally manageable. It's easy to work around the expectations if you plan around them it's doable."*

"Life sciences are a core, and growing, area for us, along with our IP team."

Bob Bodian, managing member

"The deviation on a 7pm exit is massive."

Associates aim for a client billable target of 1,850 hours which affords them an automatic bonus. Once they've hit this any training, pro bono and special projects (like blog writing) count toward the hours-based bonus. Interviewees understood that reaching 1,500 hours was the expected minimum but as they reckoned the 1,850 was pretty achievable, this wasn't something they worried about missing.

Pro Bono

Pro bono hours used to count toward the 1,850 bonus target but a recent overhaul in policy which now sees them only count after the 1,850 has been met has caused a few grumbles. *"The change has discouraged pro bono. There are plenty of opportunities but the motive and desire has chilled,"* one interviewee felt. But others believed the change had made little difference: *"Mintz really rallies behind its domestic violence program,"* and we heard of several juniors who'd received support in bringing their own pro bono matters to the firm. Managing member Bob Bodian tells us: *"Pro bono hours have remained roughly consistent since we initiated the change. The firm is still hugely committed to it and associates can credit all the pro bono hours they put in."* For more clarification from Bob Bodian on pro bono and other things, read our Bonus Features.

Pro bono hours

- For all attorneys across all US offices: 19,668
- Average per US attorney: undisclosed

The firm's Domestic Violence Project is a pro bono staple, but you'll also find attorneys working on things like asylum and immigration cases, advising on affordable housing or assisting low-income entrepreneurs get up and running.

"Mintz really rallies behind its domestic violence program."

Training & Development

First-years are all flown out to Boston to participate in the firm's Base Camp to undertake general and practice area-specific orientations. After this, associates can attend training on anything from *"how to deal with the tsunami of emails we receive, to improving writing skills.*

See firm profile on p.672

There are also more detailed series on topics like venture capital."

"How to deal with the tsunami of emails."

Associates are subject to an annual review where they're able to see what senior attorneys have written about them. First-years also check in at an additional mid-year review. In between these evaluations juniors reported a mixed level of feedback from partners. *"A few will sit you down and chat you through the changes, while others will just return to you with more tasks. Partners don't have to return to you for future projects so that in itself indicates you've impressed them."*

Everyone's assigned a mentor when they start and Mintz also operates a sponsorship and retention program which pairs up associates of color with a partner to help them network within the firm.

"It's not an 'old white man' firm."

Diversity

"Law firms aren't a good yard stick for measuring diversity but as the profession goes, I think Mintz is fairly diverse," one junior reckoned. DC juniors felt their office was *"pretty good"* when it came to gender: *"It's not an 'old white man' firm and it feels like there are a lot of women here."* Across Mintz, juniors agreed that racial diversity, especially at partner level, needed improving. To combat this the firm offers a Richard Mintz Summer Associate Diversity Scholarship offering a place on the summer program and $10,000 toward third year law school tuition.

Mintz also operates MIATTY (its minority attorneys group), a Women's Initiative, and The LGBT Group. An annual diversity retreat rotates between offices, and involves socializing, *"presentations, and break out sessions topped off with a dinner."*

Get Hired

Director of legal recruiting Shannon Davis tells us: *"We want to see people who are competitive in a healthy, collaborative and team-oriented way. We also try to focus on people's previous experiences and what drives people as this is a profession that requires a lot of motivation."* Read our Bonus Features for the full interview with Shannon Davis.

"You don't have to be an extrovert."

Alongside the Loyala Patent and Boston Lawyers Group fairs, the firm conducts OCIs at 15 law schools; most of which are in the North East. We got the impression that a large proportion of Boston-based attorneys have some tie to the Massachusetts area, though local ties at other offices don't seem as marked. 10% of the firm's first year class arrived through its summer program (offered in San Diego, New York and Boston) though there's also a number of entry level juniors who've arrived through alternative routes.

"So many people lateral into Mintz, I thought: well, why not start here from the beginning?"

See firm profile on p.672

Morgan, Lewis & Bockius LLP

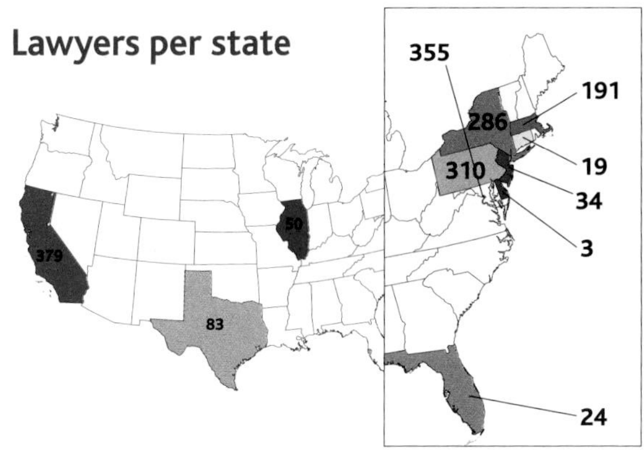

Largest US office: Philadelphia
US offices: 17
International offices: 11
First-year salary: $145,000 – $160,000
Billable hours: no requirement
Summers 2016: 62 (57 2Ls, 5 1Ls)
Revenue 2015: $1.844 billion (+40%)
Partners made in 2016: 24 globally (all US)
Famous for: being the biggest firm in the country, its labor and employment prowess.

This Philadelphian-by-birth recently became the biggest firm in the US (by headcount), and the world's largest to be led by a woman. Fancy getting in on the action?

"LAST year was transformative," chair Jami Wintz McKeon tells us, and it's almost an understatement. In a coup that monopolized legal news at the time, Morgan Lewis swallowed up over 700 lawyers and staff from the struggling Bingham McCutchen. At the same time *"we entered into Singapore through a first-of-its-kind combination with Stamford Law, and since then we've brought in hundreds of new clients who hadn't previously been clients of any of the three firms, but who recognize our expanded strength and breadth."* That strength consists of top-rated client service in areas like capital markets, energy, litigation, and labor & employment. The 17 US offices are carefully planted to ensure comprehensive coverage of the country. They include the head office in Philadelphia, plus bases in New York, Boston, DC, Chicago, Houston, Dallas, LA, and San Francisco.

The firm's largest offices offer summer programs (which exactly depends on need and it varies, we're told). During summer, future associates *"get to try as many different areas of work as you want. If you come in wanting to focus on one thing because you've got previous experience of it, they let you do that. If you're not sure, they let you explore."* Preferences are then expressed. In what initially sounds a bit like the contents of a spa brochure, Morgan Lewis offers summers the option of three different *"experiences: the client experience, the community experience, and the firm experience."* Participants can elect to spend four weeks in-house with a client, join a pro bono organization for a month, or spend the full ten weeks at the firm.

On chambers-associate.com...

- Interview with chair Jami Wintz McKeon
- From Bingham to Morgan Lewis: a timeline of events

ASSOCIATES SAY...

The Work

Labor & employment rookies described the practice area as *"people-oriented"* in explaining its appeal. One expanded: *"I picked it because I thought I'd never be bored, and it turned out to be absolutely true. Broadly speaking there are two types of cases: single plaintiff ones, and larger class action cases. The former type are always staffed leanly, often it's you and the partner, who lets you take the ball and lead the case, drafting briefs, taking depositions, and all sorts of discovery issues. With the latter, there might be four or five associates, and as a junior you're supporting the team but also learning how to manage a large litigation."*

"I picked it because I thought I'd never be bored."

See firm profile on p.673

Rankings in *Chambers USA*

Antitrust	Labor & Employment
Banking & Finance	Latin American Investment
Bankruptcy/Restructuring	Life Sciences
Capital Markets	Litigation
Corporate/M&A	Media & Entertainment
Employee Benefits & Executive Compensation	Outsourcing
	Products Liability
Energy & Natural Resources	Projects
Environment	Real Estate
ERISA Litigation	Retail
Financial Services Regulation	Securities
Healthcare	Startups & Emerging Companies
Immigration	
Insurance	Tax
Intellectual Property	Telecommunications
Investment Funds	Transportation

For detail on ranking tiers and ranking locations, visit www.chambersandpartners.com

Recent work highlights

- Philadelphia lawyers represented automotive retailer Pep Boys in its sale to Icahn Enterprises for $1.031 billion
- New York and DC attorneys represented healthcare services private investment firm Varsity Healthcare Partners (VHP) in its investment in South Carolina medical practice Colonial
- Advised biopharmaceutical company Acerta in its sale to AstraZeneca, for up to $7 billion
- After nine years of litigation West Coast lawyers secured a trial victory for Yusen Terminals when a marine clerk alleged she had been discriminated against during a training program, requesting millions in damages

We heard it wasn't uncommon for the firm to hire legal clerks into its litigation department. Regardless of how they got to the populous department though, junior litigators reported being thoroughly satisfied with their experience so far. *"Most of us work on white collar litigation, class actions, and general commercial litigation. There's also antitrust and IP but they're considered as a slightly separate world. If you work on those as well as the others, they call you a 'dual citizen'."* In the areas rookies did get to go into, they started off *"with doc review, but not always in the traditional sense. It's more about figuring out the story of a case, and when there's a trial coming up we prepare witness binders, timelines of events, and sometimes interview clients."* One was proud to have *"drafted a motion to dismiss early on,"* while another had even *"taken a deposition."*

A sure way of getting extra responsibility was to ask: *"I was vocal about wanting to do trial prep and they've been accommodating. It's the squeaky wheel that gets the grease, after all."* Several reported that *"your role as researcher means your knowledge of a case builds up, making you a useful resource in developing the strategy too."* Morgan Lewis is known for representing big pharmaceutical companies, especially in Philadelphia, as well as financial institutions, and big names in the automotive and tech sectors.

Offices

The Philadelphia HQ is handily located *"right above the train station, so if you're coming from the suburbs on the train, you don't even have to go outside to get to the office."* Sources were frank, though: *"Outside it's very ugly. Inside it's not super modern, but all attorneys have their own office with a window, and they've been renovating it floor-by-floor."* There's a free gym, a roof deck, and a cafeteria serves breakfast and lunch to hungry attorneys. *"I don't love the food, but it's adequate,"* one admitted. More importantly (arguably), *"there's a full law library. Some firms don't have that anymore but we do, it's useful when you're digging out a case from the 1800s!"*

"I don't love the food, but it's adequate."

Over in Boston, the office building was more kindly described as *"really nice and pretty modern."* The cafeteria – rumored to be nicknamed *"the spaceship"* – was particularly popular, and the art deemed *"interesting."* In San Francisco, *"we're right on the water, next to the Ferry Building. We have bay views from some offices. It's the most expensive rent in the whole city,"* one boasted. Binghamites who had to move across from their base to their new home allegedly *"considered their old office to be nicer than ours, so there was a bit of an issue, but it's OK now."* Phew.

Hours & Compensation

"There's no shortage of work," a busy employment associate assured us, *"so 2,000 hours is achievable."* The billable target is just that: a target, rather than a requirement, but *"it's understood that you need to reach it, or just under, to be bonus eligible."* We previously reported that while all the offices operated by a discretionary bonus system, Philadelphia had an additional *"standard bonus"* triggered by hours. This has now changed, at least for juniors, whereby first and second-year salaries have been increased and the standard bonus scrapped, leaving only the discretionary one. *"It came down to the same amount of money,"* one said nonchalantly, *"I think they were just trying to match market."* Bonuses and compensation in general didn't elicit bitterness or anxiety from participants, although one resigned source did reveal that *"I had great feedback during my review but I didn't get a discretionary bonus because my hours were just over*

See firm profile on p.673

1,800. Apparently as you get more senior hours have less leverage though."

"It hasn't seriously impacted my personal life."

What do 2,000 yearly hours look like day-to-day? *"You're looking at working nine to 11-hour days, but it varies. There's no face time at all here so you can work from home and you don't have to be here long days if you're having a slow period."* Weekend work wasn't unheard of, but neither was it a regular occurrence for most. *"I have less free time than someone who works a nine to five job, but I expected that. I've never had to cancel a vacation, and I work out regularly. It hasn't seriously impacted my personal life."*

Pro Bono

There wasn't a shadow of a doubt among associates, who chuckled knowingly: *"Are they committed to pro bono? Almost to the point of being annoying!"* Everyone's challenged to complete at least 20 hours a year, and from then on the sky's the limit: *"There's no cap and they can all count as billable, which is really helpful."* Some had completed over 100 hours, spent on cases they deemed not simply *"great experience,"* but also rewarding on a human level. One said of *"an LGBT asylum case: I can't believe what my client has gone through in their life."*

"I can't believe what my client has gone through in their life."

Another shared: *"I've been involved in a family court matter. I think I'm the person that's been on it the longest besides the judge."* A source *"worked with a women's homeless shelter where I went every two weeks and saw to their legal needs, helping with birth certificates and paperwork."* Other examples included *"a citizenship clinic, clemency projects, same sex marriage charges, and internal investigations for non profits."*

Pro bono hours

- For all attorneys across all US offices: 88,912
- Average per US attorney: 55

Diversity

Participants who identified as diverse were firm: *"I don't feel out of the loop as a minority."* Sources were positive overall; they admitted *"it's a pretty male Caucasian place"* but added it's *"not by design."* They remained vague, however, regarding the concrete actions to promote and secure a diverse workforce at Morgan Lewis: *"They're implementing some aggressive policies,"* one insisted, *"partly because clients are putting pressure on them,"* but associates were largely unable to give further detail. We did hear that *"there are plenty of female role models in the partnership, including in finance which is promising,"* and that *"non-diverse partners take an interest in what life is like for us as diverse lawyers."*

"We use behavioral interviewing."

Get Hired

In 2015, Morgan attended 42 law schools and 21 job fairs in its pursuit of the perfect associate cohort. At the earliest stages of recruitment, the firm considers candidates' resumes and is especially scouting for a propensity towards team work. OCI interviews are usually 20 minute conversations with a single representative from the firm, while callbacks last half an hour and can be with up to six interviewers. *"We use behavioral interviewing,"* hiring partner Christina Melendi explains. *"Looking at how a candidate reacted in past situations might indicate future behavior."*

"We view ourselves as a relationship firm."
Jami Wintz McKeon, chair

Training & Development

After initial firmwide training and orientation sessions, it's up to specific departments to rear their cattle. Finance sources appreciated that *"since the combination with Bingham the group's got a lot bigger, so they've formalized training and it happens once a week. It's helpful."* As well as *"periodic sessions throughout the year,"* litigation livestock went through *"two days of deposition training. You take an actual deposition of a fake witness at the end. Senior associates get a trial academy."* While formal training sessions left some awestruck (*"some partners are so good you sit there hoping you will be as good as them some day,"*) most agreed that *"the best training is on the job."*

"You take an actual deposition of a fake witness."

This includes constructive and ongoing feedback of course. Some partners performed better than others in this area: *"We're a small group, so they have a little more time,"* one explained, while another complained that *"they can sit on their criticisms and leave it all to the formal yearly review."* Another reflected that *"people are brought up being evaluated all the time in life, so it's weird that at Morgan Lewis if you want to know how you're doing you have to go and ask. They should set up*

See firm profile on p.673

more regular opportunities for partners to tell you you're doing a good job and give you a pat on the back. Evaluations can be self-fulfilling prophecies after all." We should point out that associates each get a mentor whose job is partly to provide feedback throughout the year.

Culture

"It's interesting to have your firm become huge and your day-to-day not change," mused a Philadelphian. First and second-years in the HQ all confirmed the transition had been *"seamless,"* but acknowledged it might be because Bingham didn't already have offices in Philly. Those in the likes of Boston, New York or San Fran, where the global firm did have bases, hadn't been too phased either: *"I get along with everyone that came over,"* said a New Yorker, *"and they've put on special events so we can get to know each other."* A proud Californian explained that *"here in San Francisco we were the first to combine under one roof, so we became a shining example of how to do it right. There were growing pains, sure, but it's much better now."*

"There were growing pains, sure, but it's much better now."

Having established then that – so far – it hasn't been adversely affected by the recent changes, how would associates describe the culture of Morgan Lewis? *"It's a hard-working environment, but the support of your talented peers and of approachable partners makes for a very friendly atmosphere."* Sources explained that the lack of value placed on face time prevented a *"big brother feeling,"* and gleefully told of *"bumping into important people in the halls who are extremely casual with you. How many junior associates can say they regularly have a drink with the managing partner?"* The social life was active, with *"weekly happy hours and excellent holiday parties,"* which ranged from *"a casino night at the University of Pennsylvania Museum of Archeology, and renting out a zoo for the day with everyone's partners and families."* We even heard of a *"wine and food pairing evening."*

Strategy & Future

What's next when you're already the biggest firm in your country? More combinations? Further geographic expansion? World domination? Not quite so fast. Chair Jami McKeon assures us the firm doesn't aspire to become a franchise, adding: *"We view ourselves as a relationship firm and go where clients need us to be. Morgan Lewis will continue to have strategic growth in key practice areas and geographies, and to focus on becoming a fully integrated organization: one firm, one vision.*

"If you come in wanting to focus on one thing because you've got previous experience of it, they let you do that. If you're not sure, they let you explore."

See firm profile on p.673

Morrison & Foerster LLP

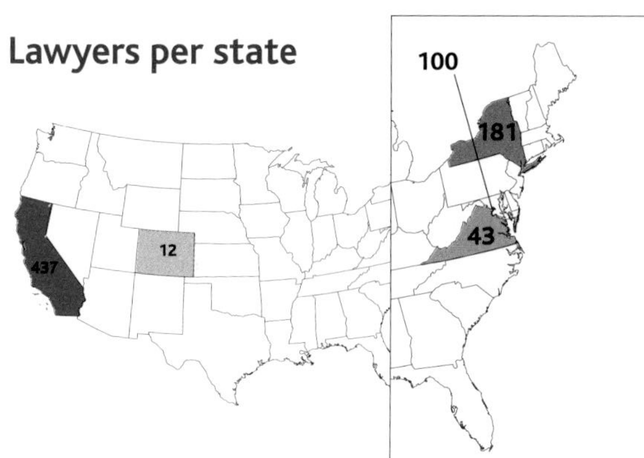

Largest US office: San Francisco
US offices: 9
International offices: 8
First-year salary: $160,000
Billable hours: undisclosed (associates spoke of 1,950 target)
Summers 2016: 100 (82 2Ls, 18 1Ls)
Revenue 2015: $979.3 million (+1.1%)
Partners made in 2016: 12 globally (9 in US)
Famous for: California-casual dress, unlimited pro bono hours and mega tech clients.

Beneath MoFo's relatively informal exterior lies a steely work ethic and a determination to succeed...

TO picture the kind of firm that MoFo strives to be, think of Apple, perhaps its most high-profile client. Like Apple, the firm's zeal for success is mixed with a commitment to its unstuffy Californian roots. *"MoFo is as laid back as you could possibly get in all of BigLaw,"* one associate highlighted to us (as did several others). *"Laid back"* is not a phrase law firms like to use to describe themselves, as they rarely are, so don't let this associate's words mislead you. MoFo is as hard-working and excellence-driven as any BigLaw firm out there, if not more.

MoFo's litigation expertise – especially in the intellectual property arena – has seen its portfolio of tech clients grow and grow. A star-studded client roster includes international heavyweights such as Fujitsu, Hitachi and Toshiba, alongside the jewel in its crown, Apple, which it represented in the so-called 'smartphone wars' against Samsung. Thanks to *"a lot of very large, well-established internet and software clients,"* MoFo's Palo Alto office continues to thrive, and is currently undergoing refurbishment of its three-building campus: a sure sign, if one was needed, that MoFo is changing and growing *"both literally and figuratively."*

On chambers-associate.com...

- Interview with firmwide managing partner Craig Martin
- Interview with MoFo's head of law school recruiting Nicole Wanzer

But litigation and tech are far from the only things happening at MoFo, as a glance at its *Chambers USA* rankings reveals. Other top or highly ranked practices in California and/or the East Coast include capital markets, corporate/M&A, climate change, restructuring, and financial services regulation.

ASSOCIATES SAY...

The Work

Many new junior associates join the litigation department, and a sizable chunk ends up in corporate. Smaller departments are tax and finance. Outside litigation, where juniors are generalists, associates are allocated to a specific practice group: for example, general corporate, patent, or capital markets.

"You need to be assertive..."

When it comes to assignments, MoFo likes to wear its casual heart on its short-sleeves. Assigning partners do exist, and – depending on which practice area you are in – they are either present, or not very, in your life. Generally, litigation associates take advantage of the assigning partners, with many echoing one newbie who said: *"It allowed me to reach out and do the work I want to be doing."* MoFo's massive litigation department is also unusually structured. One attorney explained: *"There are four subgroups of litigation: securities, litigation, enforcement and white-collar (SLEW)."* Although stressing

See firm profile on p.674

The Inside View

Rankings in *Chambers USA*

Antitrust	IT & Outsourcing
Appellate Law	Labor & Employment
Banking & Finance	Life Sciences
Bankruptcy/Restructuring	Litigation
Capital Markets	Outsourcing
Corporate Crime & Investigations	Privacy & Data Security
	Products Liability
Corporate/M&A	Projects
Employee Benefits & Executive Compensation	Real Estate
	Securities
Environment	Startups & Emerging Companies
FCPA	
Financial Services Regulation	Tax
Intellectual Property	Technology
International Trade	Transportation

For detail on ranking tiers and ranking locations, visit www.chambersandpartners.com

Recent work highlights

- Represented SoftBank in its $1 billion finance deal with SoFi Investment
- Represented VMware in connection with Dell's $67 billion acquisition of parent company EMC Corporation
- Secured a significant victory for Sandoz Inc. against rival Amgen which allowed it to launch its first biosimilar product in the US
- Won a case for Sotheby's regarding the payment of royalties for artists when their work was resold

the malleability of the groups, one source proffered that *"the distinction is more among partners than associates."* Blurred lines mean that associates are encouraged to craft their practice to suit their skills and interests, or to put it simply: *"You need to be assertive or you aren't going to get the kind of work you want."*

MoFo's corporate lawyers operate in much more niche teams – often with only one or two associates per practice area. There is less need for a formalized assignment system because *"partners sit next to you and know exactly what you're working on."* There is an online program that associates use to keep partners updated on their workload: *"You fill in client and other matters you're working on."*

Associate experience varies greatly depending on practice area and which partners are in charge. The kind of tasks juniors are set could be said to reflect the firm's egalitarian traditions, or simply the fact that they're a bit partner-heavy: *"I hate to throw out this caveat, but we're pretty leanly staffed so you're pretty much thrown in at the deep end."* Rather than balk at the extra responsibility, most MoFo lawyers revel in it: *"Compared to my law school friends, I'm doing much more advanced work. I've drafted depositions – they haven't even looked at one!"*

Training & Development

MoFo's San Francisco office – *"the mothership"* – is the venue for all new attorneys' induction into the firm. The two-day event is attended by new recruits from all 17 MoFo offices worldwide. The itinerary includes *"a bit of training, speeches from senior lawyers, dinner with the partners in the office, and a cocktail party."* Perhaps unsurprisingly, the educational bits were not attendees' favorite aspect of the event. A large proportion we spoke to agreed that *"some of the training was slightly redundant,"* but they enjoyed *"lots of opportunities for socializing."*

"Training from Harvard Business School teachers."

After this initial pooling of talents, training becomes far more ad hoc, and differs greatly based on location and practice area. In corporate, *"there is a series of required introductory trainings"* on everything up to and including *"'how to use a computer.'"* The non-stop litigation machine offers its lawyers weekly CLEs through which to hone their skills, or develop new ones. MoFo also gives incoming lawyers the opportunity to add a very distinguished feather to their caps through participation in the Fullbridge Program. The Program involves joining the firm *"a month early and receiving training from Harvard Business School teachers."* Classes include everything from *"accounting to IP law and PTO updates"* [Patent and Trademark Office].

Associates get a *"six-month review in their first year and then an annual one after that."* Before the review, *"you submit a list of matters and the hours you've spent on each. Then you sit down with two partners – one head of your group and one your mentor – and look through the feedback together."* Most divulged that it was *"really laid back."* However, some erudite associates found that this was an area in which MoFo's 'Cali-casual' vibe wasn't necessarily a good thing. A few of those we spoke to sympathized with the view that *"it's too informal."*

Hours & Compensation

One area on where there was no doubt is MoFo's billings target. Set at 1,950, it means firmwide parity and represents for many associates something *"absolutely hittable."* The target is *"probably about average,"* and especially welcome was the fact that it includes *"all pro bono hours, without a cap."* Some felt that *"it's not about hitting targets, its about learning."* Nevertheless, there's no

See firm profile on p.674

getting away from the fact that BigLaw hours are long. New York associates – with their office at the center of the financial world – felt they bore an especially heavy load. One Big Apple attorney believed that this was hitting retention in his office: *"I think NYC associates are working a lot. We've lost a few good people."*

"If you work over three hours on a vacation day, you get it back."

The subject of bonuses also provoked conjecture, with the firm having recently changed its policy. The story goes like this: *"Two years ago it was merit-based, tied in part to your review and to your hours. Now it is completely lockstep."* Most juniors were big fans of lockstep. Management apparently *"polled associates about keeping lockstep and there was overwhelming support for the policy."* Some hard workers, however, were aggrieved by what they saw as an attempt to clip their wings: *"That's one area that I don't see eye to eye with the partners. They follow the New York system, which is based on seniority."* Another added: *"There's no incentive to work harder."*

Vacation was another sore spot, proving that life isn't always a beach. MoFo follows a system whereby lawyers accrue holiday entitlement. *"You accrue ten hours a month, with eight hours meaning you can take a day off."* The outcome is that all first, second and third-year associates – except those in New York – can accrue a maximum of 15 vacation days a year. However, all Big Apple associates, and fourth-year associates and above, can accrue a maximum of 20 per year. Though vacation is earned, many lamented that it isn't always respected: *"If anything comes up, they are not hesitant to email."* However, one source pointed out that *"if you work over three hours on a vacation day, you get it back."*

Pro Bono

Pro bono is big at MoFo, evidenced by its lawyers clocking up an average of a whopping 114 hours each in 2015. There's no cap on the number of pro bono hours attorneys can bill, and they all count toward their billable target. One associate even admitted: *"I know a couple of lawyers who are billing more pro bono than paid hours."* Two partners coordinate pro bono work and both are keen to find associates stuff that is both stimulating and fulfilling.

"MoFo does a lot for LGBQT rights."

Many sources spoke of how they had expressed an interest in a specific cause when they first joined and had received great pro bono work in return. As one junior put it, *"a lot of firms say they care about pro bono, but MoFo makes sure you get real substantive work that actually makes a difference."* MoFo was the first major firm to have an openly gay chairman (read our Big Interview with Keith Wetmore online), so it was no surprise to hear *"MoFo does a lot for LGBQT rights."* This has included substantial support for organizations campaigning for gay marriage rights, which was *"celebrated in style"* at MoFo San Fran.

Pro bono hours

- For all attorneys across all US offices: 81,749
- Average per US attorney: 114

"A lot of very large, well-established internet and software clients."

Culture

Though most of the firm's lawyers were at pains to stress that MoFo's US operation is firmly focused on perpetuating a *"one-firm mentality,"* there is no doubt that its California base is the biggest influence on the firm's overall culture. This fact, coupled with its high number of tech clients, means *"there's not this 'banking culture' that permeates other firms."* Others put it down to *"the people they hire: not just attorneys, but staff, recruiters – everybody is down-to-earth, normal human beings."* This down-to-earth approach extends to all areas of the firm. As one elated attorney digressed, *"the managing partner of the firm, Craig Martin, is a great guy. The first time I met him, we talked about baseball. I think that that is indicative of the firm."*

"Take the work very seriously but don't take yourself too seriously."

Not all MoFo attorneys are baseball fans, but everyone we spoke to was a fan of *"casual Fridays."* Most agreed that this was not a particularly noteworthy tradition, however, since *"no one here is particularly buttoned-up."* The firm's tongue-in-cheek nickname, MoFo, is indicative of a universal refusal to take itself too seriously – *"it's the right balance. Take the work very seriously but don't take yourself too seriously."*

Perhaps it's this fun-lovin' attitude to work that has led to *"many partners turning down better money in order to stay at MoFo"* – as we were told by numerous sources. Some suggested that this might also be due to the firm's extremely understanding attitude toward employees with families. Tales of flexible work conditions abounded, with many concurring that *"the office is a ghost town come 6.30pm."* Nonetheless, the family feel of the firm

See firm profile on p.674

doesn't necessarily negate an active social environment – though extra-curricular activities do tend toward the wholesome. Litigators told us of *"litigation cooking competitions"* with special memories reserved for a *"particularly memorable guacamole-off."*

Diversity

Diversity is evident at both the partner and associate level at most of the firm's US offices – though sources in Denver and McLean admitted they *"get the feeling that in the bigger offices it is more of a focus."* Rather than stemming from any particular initiative – though there are a few – MoFo's diverse make-up is due to the fact that *"naturally the firm is concerned with taking on the best people, and usually those are very diverse."* Every two years the firm invites its diverse attorneys to either its San Fran or New York office for its 'Diversity Summit,' during which there are lectures and plenty of social opportunities.

Offices

With four of its nine US offices in the Golden State, MoFo can sometimes seem a little Cali-centric. One New York attorney stressed that *"even over here it's seen as a California firm and is a little more laid back than the white shoe firms."* Although Big Apple lawyers are *"told early on that if you want California, go to California."*

MoFo's smaller operations – in San Diego, McLean and Denver – are all expanding, and benefit from having *"the resources of a massive firm, but in a cozier environment,"* especially since there are not many other *"large, respected international law firms"* in those locations. These offices do still possess their own niches and the firm's Denver office has benefited from its proximity to the new United States Patent Office in the 'Wall Street of the West.'

Get Hired

MoFo fits a certain type of lawyer. Generally, this was someone described as *"personable, serious about work, but not completely serious about everything else."* Nicole Wanzer, MoFo's head of law school recruiting, insists the firm's recruiting efforts are focused *"on the top talent at the top 15 law schools."* But, as mentioned, their search is not purely grades-focused: *"Grades are one piece of the puzzle. Things that really stand out are moot court and journal experience, leadership roles, community involvement and, of course, relevant work experience is always helpful – especially in the IP sector!"*

"Personable, serious about work, but not completely serious about everything else."

Strategy & Future

When asked about what the future holds for the firm Craig Martin, MoFo's firmwide managing partner, replies: *"More of the same!"* Nonetheless, the recent hiring of Murray Indick as a partner and chair of MoFo's emerging companies and venture capital practice – *"a robust area of growth"* – shows the firm's desire to add exciting startups to its impressive roster of established clients, especially in the tech sector.

"The resources of a massive firm, but in a cozier environment."

"When I talk about the firm's values, I talk about commitment to excellence; a commitment to public service; and finally a commitment to contributing as a member of a team" – Craig Martin, firmwide managing partner

See firm profile on p.674

Munger, Tolles & Olson LLP

Lawyers per state

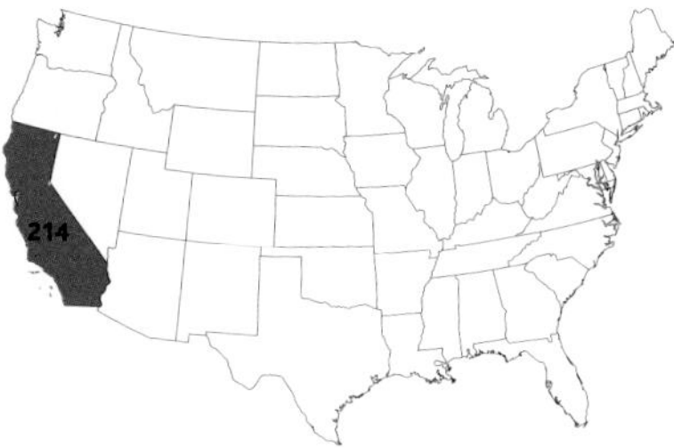

Largest US office: Los Angeles
US offices: 2
International offices: 0
First-year salary: $160,000
Billable hours: no requirement
Summers 2016: 22 (20 2Ls, 2 1Ls)
Revenue 2015: undisclosed
Partners made in 2016: 4
Famous for: a unique committee-based democratic structure and some superstar clients

With its egalitarian principles and plenty of perks, all's fun and fair in the Munger Games.

IF California-based Munger were a tribute in *The Hunger Games*, it would definitely be Katniss: a relatively small, highly-skilled operator that manages to regularly punch above its weight. Even discounting its close relationship with one of the world's largest and most famous investors – Warren Buffett's Berkshire Hathaway – Munger still brings in deals that would make other firms four-times its size green with envy. *Chambers USA* awards laurels to Munger in various litigation categories like media & entertainment, securities, general commercial disputes, and white-collar crime, as well as other practice areas including labor & employment, energy regulatory, corporate/M&A, real estate and tax.

Munger's warrior credentials don't end there, and one attorney boasted *"it is lean,"* meaning *"the ratio of partners to associates is low."* Its unique committee-based decision-making system gives every lawyer the same voting power and encourages them to decide on everything from office size to which new recruits to hire. All of this contributes to a *"highly, unusually democratic and transparent"* culture, with one proud associate exclaiming *"sometimes it takes interaction with people from other firms to realize how equal it is here."* Although the Munger Games might not be the most thrilling, they'd definitely be the most fair.

On chambers-associate.com...

- Interview with co-chair of the recruiting committee Bethany Kristovich
- Who is Charlie Munger?

ASSOCIATES SAY...

The Work

Unusually in BigLaw, Munger doesn't allocate its fee-earners to specific, named practice areas. *"One of the reasons I was drawn to Munger was because I heard they were more flexible in terms of practice area,"* more than one junior associate told us. This allows attorneys to be more adventurous with the kind of work they get involved in, though most admitted that once you are *"deep into litigation, it can be hard to switch."* However, *"if you really want to switch the firm is very accommodating."* Most new associates will get involved in the litigation side of things, though every year a few juniors can be found in corporate.

"I heard they were more flexible in terms of practice area."

Munger operates an informal work assignment system. For the first six months, *"you are given a work coordinator who will come to you with a list of cases and ask if any sound interesting,"* but after that *"it is totally up to you to get work."* There are a couple of main ways an associate can get involved in a case: either *"someone calls you on the phone and says: 'I need someone for a case,' or you reach out to them."* Help is also offered with

See firm profile on p.675

The Inside View

Rankings in *Chambers USA*

Antitrust	Media & Entertainment
Corporate/M&A	Real Estate
Energy & Natural Resources	Securities
Labor & Employment	Tax
Litigation	

For detail on ranking tiers and ranking locations, visit www.chambersandpartners.com

Recent work highlights

- Advised Berkshire Hathaway in $37 billion acquisition of Precision Castparts, the largest deal in its history
- Represented UCLA Health as it was cleared in a landmark patient privacy case
- Successfully defended Verizon in a patent infringement lawsuit
- Won an appellate victory for Facebook in a lawsuit brought by a proposed class of minors

the circulation of 'conflict checks' which arrive prior to a case and are seen by all lawyers. Most associates we spoke to were fans of the system: *"It forces partners to be reasonable people to work with, because I could just say 'no',"* one explained.

A lot of the work the firm does is for some of the biggest names in business. In Munger's *Chambers USA* Band 1-ranked media & entertainment practice, clients include all six of the major motion picture studios, all four of the major recorded music companies, and the trade associations of both industries. Over in corporate/M&A, the firm's relationship with Berkshire Hathaway – Charlie Munger is the company's vice chairman – continues to reap rewards. For example, co-managing partner Brad Brian highlights *"representing Berkshire in the $37 billion acquisition of Precision Castparts"* (the largest deal in Berkshire's history) as one of the most significant assignments of MTO's year.

Culture

Munger's own brand of egalitarianism permeates the firm, and attorneys told of an *"unspoken rule not to mention hierarchy."* Nearly all major decisions at the firm *"things like whether to move office, what kind of work we take on, who we hire"* are made by a vote: *"One lawyer, one vote – even new hires."* The firm administers the decision-making process through its many committees. *"There are lots of committees"* an associate admitted, ranging from a 'recruitment committee' to a 'sherry-sip committee' that organizes the firm's weekly get-togethers. One junior reckoned that *"if the firm's primary aim was to make money it would have a different structure;"* however, *"its short-term loss is its long-term gain."*

"We are people before lawyers."

The firm's focus is on being more *"family than frat-boy friendly."* This is evidenced by the subsidized on-site daycare facility at the LA office where *"at any time there are between ten to 15 attorneys' kids,"* a move that one associate says *"helps remind everyone that we are people before lawyers."* Co-chair of the recruiting committee Bethany Kristovich strongly agrees, claiming *"I don't think I would have made partner without onsite daycare."* She also admits that having a family is a plus when it comes to getting hired: *"At the end of the day, you want people who are healthy, well-balanced members of the community."*

MTO lays on weekly social events in the form of the 'sherry-sips' we mentioned earlier as well as an annual retreat, which usually takes place at a nice hotel somewhere in California. Unusually for a BigLaw firm, MTO encourages attorneys to bring their families for a long weekend that involves *"a mix of programming, including speakers and opportunities to socialize."* Retreat activities include *"anything from sitting by the pool and drinking to surfing."*

Pro Bono

One thing that Munger definitely does not retreat from is pro bono work. *"The firm treats pro bono like normal work,"* meaning there is no cap on the number of pro bono hours attorneys can bill. Rather than having cases foisted upon them, associates are encouraged to go out and find work or pursue causes that are close to their hearts.

"The firm treats pro bono like normal work."

This was certainly the case with the much-fêted work the firm did defending the First Amendment rights of protesters in Ferguson in 2014. An associate saw unlawful arrests on the news and approached a senior attorney; someone got in touch with the Missouri ACLU and senior partners circulated an email encouraging junior attorneys to get involved. Less famous, but equally important, is the work Munger does for groups like Kids In Need of Defense (KIND) – *"an organization that matches young asylum seekers with pro bono attorneys."*

Pro bono hours

- For all attorneys across all offices: 26,874
- Average per attorney: 133

See firm profile on p.675

Training & Development

Munger's desired recruits must be 'self-starters' and this is reflected in the provision of training and development. Unlike most rival firms with their comprehensive training programs, Munger favors learning on the job. This is apart from an initial retreat for new attorneys and a litigation training day. During this time, associates undergo fairly intense training – a process sources described as *"a lot at once – so you query how effective it is."*

"We have some fantastic writers here."

There are opportunities to hone skills and enhance knowledge, but the onus is very much on the lawyer to be proactive about exploiting these. One Friday every month there are writing workshops where *"attorneys are encouraged to bring a piece of writing which a senior partner will then go through with them."* Those who had attended these insisted *"writing workshops are fun because we have some fantastic writers here."* These workshops are complemented by weekly firm lunches where guest speakers have included *"inspirational lawyers and museum curators."*

Assessment at Munger takes the form of twice yearly reviews. Associates are assigned a reviewer – usually a partner they have never worked with – who then speaks to their mentor as well as partners who have worked with them. The process is described as *"pretty robust and mostly positive, not at all intimidating,"* though it is *"fairly intricate"* and also involves a written questionnaire as well as a presentation with the partnership and your personal reviewer.

All associates are assigned two mentors when they join: one a partner, and the other a more senior associate. *"Those mentors are supposed to be a resource for everything from 'how to get out of the parking lot' to more formal stuff like 'how to draft a witness statement.'"* After two years at the firm – by which time you will have hopefully mastered the skill of parallel parking – you are allowed to pick a new mentor from one of the senior partners.

Hours & Compensation

Munger's bonus system is holistic and is tied to the review process, though sources stressed it is less opaque than it might seem. Recruiting co-chair Bethany Kristovich describes it as *"both qualitative and quantitative."* In a similar vein, there is no official billing goal. There is *"an unspoken target of around 2,000 hours. But it's not something someone will chide you about."* Every month management will circulate a list of how many hours each attorney has billed and if they feel someone has exceeded what they deem to be a lot, *"someone will call you and check you are alright."*

"You can't help but realize that we are paid a lot of money."

Associates we spoke to felt that Munger's special brand of California-casual style targets set it apart from the more demanding New York firms: *"Part of the reason people choose this firm is because its not a big New York firm and our flexible bonus structure allows this."* Nonetheless, there is an unspoken understanding of the level of work expected from attorneys; as one source put it, *"you can't help but realize that we are paid a lot of money. I think you should bill enough to justify your salary."*

Offices

Munger has two offices, one in Los Angeles and one in San Francisco. Though LA is the home office, and it deals with the vast proportion of the firm's cases, efforts are made to promote a *"one-firm mentality."* This means every time there is a firm lunch or guest speaker, the other office is on video link and encouraged to participate in discussions. However, since most of these take place in LA, it can feel *"a little impersonal"* on the San Francisco side. Associates also confirmed that *"one of the challenges of being in SF is being visible in LA."*

"Sometimes it takes interaction with people from other firms to realize how equal it is here."

"Junior associates have the same size office as Ron Olson."

Unlike most big firm attorneys, Munger associates are given their own office as soon as they start work. There are two sizes of office, 'small' and 'big', and after two years all associates move to a 'big office'. This means that, *"relatively junior associates will have the same size office as Ron Olson – a name partner,"* a policy that will continue when the firm moves to new premises in LA.

Diversity

While a lack of diversity in office size is a positive, a lack of diversity in staff is not. Unfortunately, like most big US law firms, diversity at Munger is not great. *"It's something that the firm cares about. I've seen that in our voting and internal discussions,"* but *"the execution is often hard."* The MTO Fellows Program is a step in the right direction, a *"one-year initiative aimed at preparing*

See firm profile on p.675

20 to 30 aspiring diverse students for admission to and success in law school." And before you ask, yes it does have its own committee.

Get Hired

Munger's high standards are evident from its OCIs. One associate explained her reason for choosing the firm: *"They had one of the higher GPA requirements – high standards appeal to me."* Though this might not be everybody's yardstick, another source added *"life experience is valued a bit more here."* Bethany Kristovich notes that *"some sort of leadership experience is always a plus"* before reiterating *"I think we are generally looking for people who know what it means to lead."*

"Life experience is valued a bit more here."

Strategy & Future

There doesn't seem to be a clambering for the exits at Munger, and there is recognition that the hard work demanded by the firm is more than reflected in the ethic of its lawyers. Most sources generally agreed that *"people who leave usually don't go to another firm"* because *"coming to Munger opens many different doors."* On the whole, associates we spoke to saw their immediate future with the firm, most echoing the view that *"people know what it takes to make partner. I have a mentor, they will let me know if I'm on the right track."* Another said – referring to the partner/associate equilibrium – *"I think my odds of making partner here are better than at any other firm."*

In terms of the firm's long-term future, co-MP Brad Brian puts it like this: *"We are a national and international law firm based in LA and SF. Many years ago, we decided not to open ten offices, we decided to focus on our core offices in Los Angeles and San Francisco, and from here we handle cases all around the world."* When pressed on whether this left the door open for any more offices, he says: *"I would never say no to anything. We are definitely looking to expand our presence in Silicon Valley, and we are always on the look-out for special lawyers."*

"We are definitely looking to expand our presence in Silicon Valley."

"We're different in that we consider diversity to encompass a number of things including socio-economic background."

Bethany Kristovich, hiring partner

See firm profile on p.675

Nixon Peabody LLP

Lawyers per state

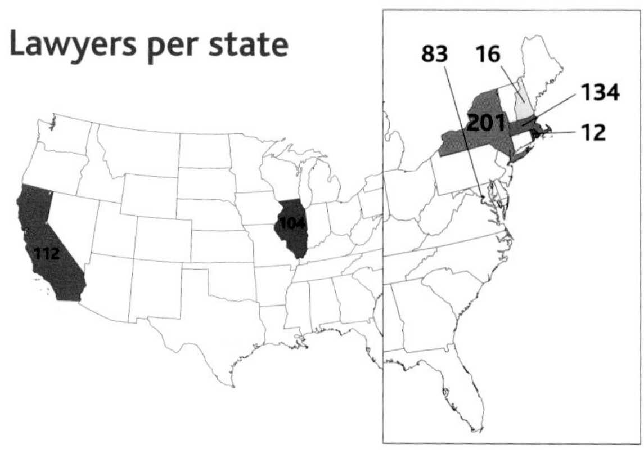

Largest US office: Boston
US offices: 13
International offices: 3
First-year salary: $160,000
Billable hours: 1,900 target
Summers 2016: 22 (20 2Ls, 2 1Ls)
Revenue 2015: $461 million (+13.3%)
Partners made in 2016: 11 (all US)
Famous for: a myriad of mergers; entrepreneurial culture

After years of mergers, Nixon Peabody is looking to consolidate its base and keep up the good work.

2015 was a bumper year for the ever-expanding Nixon Peabody. Fresh from adding Chicago outfit Ungaretti & Harris to its growing family, managing partner Andrew Glincher explains: *"Our strategic plan was to expand in Chicago, California and NYC, and we've achieved all three."* Expansionist moves have been accompanied by what Glincher describes as *"our best ever fiscal year."* Lateral hires included 22 associates. Further afield, he highlights growth in China.

He also singles out for special mention Nixon's work in food and beverages – for example, it recently advised on the largest craft beer acquisition, Ballast Point Brewing – and healthcare, which *Chambers USA* ranks highly in Massachusetts, Illinois and New York. Other highly regarded practices include corporate/M&A, litigation, banking & finance, energy, franchising and environment. Search for Nixon on chambersandpartners.com for the full rankings breakdown with commentary.

"Our best ever fiscal year."

On chambers-associate.com...

- Interviews with managing partner Andrew Glincher and John Snellings, hiring partner

ASSOCIATES SAY...

The Work

Nixon Peabody offers incoming associates a plethora of practice area possibilities. Summer associates are taken at eight offices (Boston, Rochester, LA, Chicago, Long Island, NYC, Rochester and San Fran). They have the opportunity to *"work generally throughout practices,"* after which they are asked to select their *"top three choices."* Many incoming first-years opt for the area into which they were first assigned, and *"if not your first, they definitely try and give you one of your top three."* Most juniors end up in one of the firm's beefy corporate or litigation teams, while others go to groups including healthcare, labor & employment, and real estate. Nixon continues to be hot on housing, with one associate declaring: *"The firm is known for having the best affordable housing practices in the country."*

After lower than normal recruitment in some key locations since the financial crash, Nixon is steadily increasing its associate pool. Nonetheless, a number of offices are still *"very partner-heavy"* and this can affect the way work is assigned. One junior opined: *"A lot of the time partners are super busy so they don't have time to explain it. Rather than explain it they will just do it themselves."* However, others insisted: *"You knock on doors, you get work."* Some groups, however, have a formal workflow assignment coordinator. In the smaller offices, like Long Island and Providence, assignment is very informal and

See firm profile on p.676

Rankings in *Chambers USA*

Banking & Finance	Healthcare
Corporate/Commercial	Labor & Employment
Corporate/M&A	Litigation
Energy & Natural Resources	Private Equity
Environment	Real Estate
Franchising	

For detail on ranking tiers and ranking locations, visit www.chambersandpartners.com

Recent work highlights

- Combined Hong Kong office with leading Asian business firm CWL Partners to form Nixon Peabody CWL
- Advised The Notorious B.I.G. estate and others in a copywright claim win
- Acted as counsel for Constellation Brands in its $1 billion acquisition of Ballast Point Brewing – the largest craft beer deal in history
- Won a victory for client Pla-Fit Franchise and a Planet Fitness franchisee obtaining the dismissal of a lawsuit attacking the company's transgender-friendly locker room policy

associates are often called upon to ease the workload of their colleagues in Boston or NYC.

"I'm doing due diligence and I'm barely a second year!"

One thing that locale does not affect is the responsibility juniors are given. All of those that we spoke to were given substantial work from the outset. Typical tasks included *"turning over documents and research assignments,"* while one associate excitedly exclaimed: *"I'm doing due diligence and I'm barely a second year!"* Associates are trusted early on: *"Even when I was a summer associate, I was doing really high-level work."*

Training & Development

There is, of course, orientation for new attorneys, and while all *"first-years go off to Boston and get trained on background,"* most early training comes through non-compulsory programs and conferences. Sources found *"one-on-one advice with a mix of encouragement"* was the most useful training they received.

In the first year, reviews take place in *"six-month cycles,"* then occur annually. *"You submit the partners and senior associates you want to review you. Then they send you what the partners wrote about you."* These assessments are preceded by a *"self-review,"* during which the reviewee is asked to rate their performance in different areas on a scale of one to five. They are then told to *"list some goals for the next year."* Most of those we spoke to echoed one source who described the process as *"mature and rewarding."*

The Inside View

"The firm is definitely behind the effort."

Pro Bono

Like the review process, pro bono is another firmwide policy on which Nixon's 13 offices sing from the same song sheet. Up to 60 pro bono hours can count toward the 1,850 billable requirement – *"a strong indication that the firm is definitely behind the effort,"* according to associates. The importance of pro bono is emphasized right from the start of your Nixon career: *"When I joined they asked me what I was interested in, then they gave me some similar work and put me in touch with like-minded people."* Most of the work is very region-specific as local pro bono is another way the firm strengthens its community ties; this has included land use cases in Rhode Island and property evictions in New York City. Nationwide, the firm's lawyers have worked on the 'Transgender Name Change Initiative.'

Pro bono hours
- For all attorneys across all US offices: approx. 34,000
- Average per US attorney: 61

Hours & Compensation

"I know some firms where they keep their financials closed," one associate reflected. *"Here, they're pretty forthright with the bonus info at present."* Nonetheless, this relative transparency does reveal a somewhat complicated system: *"There are two types of bonus – an hourly bonus and a percentage calculation."* Which in layman's terms means *"there's basically a weird percentage based on every 50 hours above 1,900 you bill. It stops at 2,400, when you get 15%."*

As well as the 1,850 requirement (and 1,900 target to be bonus-eligible), there's an additional 400-hour requirement for stuff like *"personal and client development."* The latter is officially mandatory but opinion differed from office-to-office on how strictly it was enforced. Of course, if you don't hit your billables you don't get a bonus but *"you won't be shouted at or shown the exit."* In Rochester, where the firm's roots date back over a century and there are strong ties with the local community, *"there is an effort made to make clear what the firm's expectations are – and that extends to the 400."*

"Technically you can take off as much time as you want."

See firm profile on p.676

Unlimited vacation means that *"technically you can take off as much time as you want."* But before you start stockpiling the tanning oil, most associates agreed that *"while it might seem liberal"* this policy is *"actually pretty constrictive."* We spoke to some who'd only taken a few days' annual leave. Those long months of work aren't without firm socials, though, including monthly *"wine and Martini tasting events."* Further perks are available via an *"internal shopping system"* called 'NPerks' that employees can use to get discounts from restaurants and stores.

Culture

With 13 locations spanning the US, it can be hard to ascribe Nixon Peabody a single culture. Nonetheless, a few things kept popping up when talking to associates. These included the *"organic approach to training and mentoring younger attorneys,"* rather than a rigid training program. This approach extends to the emphasis the firm puts on developing its lawyers. Partners often *"encourage you to get involved in your local area"* and *"push younger associates to get their names out there by writing in law journals."* One thing that is *"really frowned upon"* is *"internal competition."* And one source observed wryly that *"people here are humans. They work really hard but they are people. They have lives and they have families."*

Offices

The 13 US offices have their own idiosyncrasies and traditions that survive from their past lives belonging to legacy firms that merged with Nixon Peabody. Boston is very clearly *"Nixon HQ"* and lawyers there spoke of its *"pleasant Old World charm,"* a feeling enforced by its proximity to the city's historic harbor.

"When I called my grandma and told her I was going to Nixon, she whistled."

The Rochester office is *"particularly engaged in the local community"* where it has existed in one form or another for over a century. *"A large percentage of Rochester's attorneys sit on non-profit boards,"* and one proud Rochesterian told us how, *"when I called my grandma and told her I was going to Nixon, she whistled."* In the smaller offices of Providence and Long Island, juniors spoke of having *"the resources of the empire but with a small town feel."* Over in DC, excited attorneys could not stop telling us about their new *"very green home"* in which *"all the offices are see-through, because there's an emphasis on transparency.!"*

Diversity

When it comes to diversity, Nixon experiences similar issues to its BigLaw rivals. *"They definitely have groups,"* associates told us, mentioning the women's and LGBT initiatives, and an Asian group. We heard that some associates had met with the new diversity and inclusion specialist *"to talk about getting money for diverse events and opportunities. I've heard from associates who tried to get the funding that it's bureaucratic."* In 2008, the firm was one of the first to offer domestic partner benefits to same-sex couples. The LGBT affinity group regularly hosts 'Out and Equal' events and the firm attends the Lavender law fair each year. Over half of associates – 51% – are female, and at partner level this figure falls to 21%.

Get Hired

Generally, there was the view that recruiters *"look for people with a variety of experiences and viewpoints."* Hiring partner John Snellings gives his insight: *"This is a great generation, a generation that has traveled and done things. It is one thing to learn in a classroom but if an individual has learned building a house or helping with water irrigation in Africa, there is a different perspective when speaking to them."* In other words, it's important to show there's more on your resume than just good grades.

"Our strategic plan was to expand in Chicago, California and NYC, and we've achieved all three."
Andrew Glincher, managing partner

"We ask everyone to keep an eye out for talent."

Aside from law school hiring, which sees 22 summer associates and 21 first-years join in 2016, Nixon Peabody places great emphasis on informal lateral recruitment. According to John Snellings: *"I always say that every person at Nixon is deputized in our recruitment efforts. We ask everyone to keep an eye out for talent."* In terms of retention, managing partner Andrew Glincher is keen to stress that *"in this industry we have one of, if not the, lowest in unwanted departures."* For those definitely not looking to leave, he has these words of encouragement: *"We owe it to our people that if they do what they are supposed to do and have worked well for clients, they have the opportunity to take it further and become partner."*

See firm profile on p.676

Strategy & Future

When asked what's next for Nixon, Andrew Glincher replies that the firm's strategic plan for 2015 was fully achieved, and highlights growth in California: *"We've had a lot of growth in LA – in real estate, entertainment and IP,"* he says. After years of expanding its US operation, the firm is now setting its sights further afield. It recently combined its Hong Kong office with leading Asian business firm CWL Partners to form Nixon Peabody CWL and is now looking to increase its presence in the Chinese market, as well as helping its Chinese clients gain exposure worldwide.

"People here are humans. They work really hard but they are people."

See firm profile on p.676

Norton Rose Fulbright

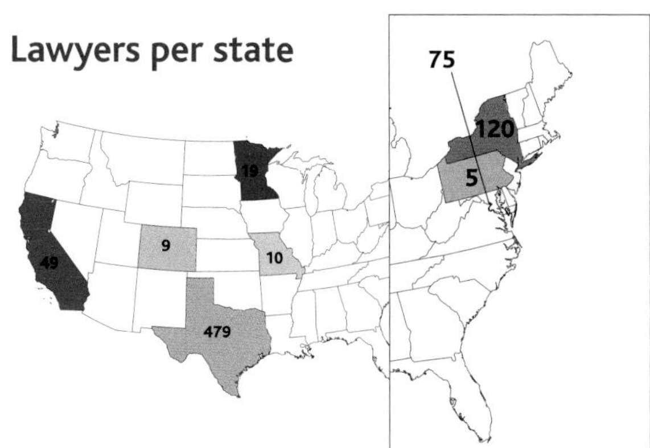

Largest US office: Houston
US offices: 11
International offices: 41
First-year salary: $160,000
Billable hours: 2,000 target (2nd year upward)
Summers 2016: 64 (52 2Ls, 12 1Ls)
Revenue 2015: $1.737 billion (-4.2%)
Partners made in 2016: 14 in US
Famous for: Texas vibe; giant international scope

A *"courteous, good-natured and calm"* Texan heart, global reach... what could be better? Not least work variety nor *'tons'* of responsibility, and a modern US HQ that *'rose'* high and is *'full'* of *'brightness.'*

"WE'RE on every single continent except Antarctica," Norton Rose Fulbright's US managing partner Linda Addison reminds us proudly, *"and that's only because our clients haven't expressed that need yet."* It's true: across all the major world capitals and business hubs there are over 50 offices with the NRF welcome mat outside their door. And each of these offices is pulling its weight, says *Chambers Global,* which puts the firm at seventh place in its 'Global Top 30' ranking.

Despite its huge size and expansion, current associates were keen to tell us about the firm's *"reputation for being family-friendly and for attracting salt-of-the-earth people, who aren't super buttoned-up."* One mentioned that *"disinterested recommendations from law school professors spoke volumes about the firm,"* while a diverse attorney *"appreciated they pair you up with a diverse mentor during summer, which was encouraging and meant the experience wasn't alienating."* Size doesn't have to mean impersonal, in other words.

In Texas, *Chambers USA* ranks Norton Rose Fulbright for areas including antitrust, bankruptcy & restructuring, healthcare, intellectual property, and labor & employment. Nationally, the firm wins plaudits for (among others) energy projects of all description, corporate/M&A, general litigation, product liability, retail, tax and aviation finance.

On chambers-associate.com...

- NRF's history so far
- More on recruitment
- Interview with US managing partner Linda Addison

Norton Rose Fulbright formed in 2013 when the UK's ancient Norton Rose merged with Texas-based Fulbright & Jaworski. The firm's global headquarters are in London, and its biggest US office is in Houston high up in the *"very modern"* Fulbright Tower where *"we all have window offices and can see views for miles and miles around."*

ASSOCIATES SAY...

The Work

Just over 60 junior associates on our list of interviewees were spread across as many as 21 practice areas. The corporate, M&A and securities group was the most populated with 12 novices. Before the summer program begins, prospective participants receive a form to indicate which types of work they'd like to experience. Some sources had used this as an opportunity *"to narrow down the broad umbrella of litigation."* Typically, associates experience two rotations. *"I wasn't sure between transactional and litigation and they let me try both,"* one recalled. *"At the end, you apply to your preferred department and I've never heard about anyone not getting what*

See firm profile on p.677

Rankings in *Chambers USA*

Antitrust	Labor & Employment
Banking & Finance	Litigation
Bankruptcy/Restructuring	Products Liability
Corporate/M&A	Projects
Energy & Natural Resources	Real Estate
Environment	Retail
Healthcare	Tax
Insurance	Technology
Intellectual Property	Transportation
International Arbitration	

For detail on ranking tiers and ranking locations, visit www.chambersandpartners.com

they wanted. They also show flexibility, though, and a few people changed their mind and switched."

"You might call our assignment system a managed market economy, whereby you get work by chasing it up yourself, but at the same time partners keep constant track of how busy you are." In offices other than Houston, these systems might be slightly different; in Dallas for example *"the summer allows for more than just two rotations."*

"The responsibility levels are really high, sometimes it's too much!"

All Houstonite corporate sources agreed that *"the responsibility levels are really high, sometimes it's too much!"* Examples of this substantive work include *"pretty much running deals worth up to $50 million, handling major drafting and even closing deals."* One recalled *"closing a deal with a fourth-year on the other side who couldn't believe I was a first-year. The firm helps you grow up, and provides you with skills such as dealing with clients, which will come in handy if, say, you then decide to go in-house."* Make no mistake though, at the very beginning, corporate newbies did get their fair share of *"due diligence, proofing, checklists and research, but it evolves and changes every month toward distinctly mid-level tasks."*

Aside from corporate, associates could also be found in areas including IP transactions and patent prosecution; other strands of IP; straight finance as well as financial institutions and insurance; and regulations, investigations, securities and compliance. There are various groups dedicated to the energy sector, such as energy and infrastructure, energy transactions, and power and alternative energy. Certain offices are best known for specific expertise, like Dallas with its litigation know-how. Insiders proudly observed that since the combination *"we've worked across offices a lot more, both nationally and internationally."*

Recent work highlights

- Representing San Antonio-based medical device company CeloNova in the sale of its radiology business to Boston Scientific for over $70 million
- Successfully represented insulation manufacturer Reflectix, accused of patent infringement by competitor Promethean
- Successfully defended Catholic health organization CHRISTUS in a wrongful death lawsuit brought by the deceased's widow and adult children requesting $1 million in damages
- Advised retailer Oxford Industries on the $63.7 million sale of Ben Sherman to Marquee Brands

Training & Development

"One of the most wonderful things the firm does is a program called 'shadowing,' which allows first, second and third-years to tag along to meetings or events juniors wouldn't normally see. It's billable." This is in addition to the New Lawyer Academy as part of *"a full training program that feels a bit like law school. As a result of the combination, we can take advantage of Norton Rose's well established training program called International Academies 1-5. One and two happen when you first start, and include the chance to do a mock client pitch. It shows they're investing in us, and it's fun!"* Senior associates attend the more advanced 'academies.'

Furthermore, litigation associates get *"put up in a swanky hotel for a week, during which we go through a whole mock trial, with seasoned partners as judges. I didn't do this at law school so it was eye-opening."* Corporate animals aren't left high and dry, with *"two hours a week for six weeks of formal M&A school when you start the second year, as well as monthly training with presentations."*

"It shows they're investing in us, and it's fun!"

As is frequently the case, interviewees found the formal review system to be *"fairly useful, but only in conjunction with frequent, timely and constructive on-the-job feedback."* Once a year, associates get a sit-down with their head of practice and a partner from the associate committee, who read out feedback from partners.

Along similar lines, insiders found that although a formal mentoring scheme is available, *"you can use it to the degree you want, and usually informal mentoring relationships arise in summer anyway. Mentoring in all its forms is very useful at the firm."*

See firm profile on p.677

Hours and Culture

Most sources hadn't felt the need to turn to mentors out of extreme stress, which they felt the firm's infrastructure did a good job of preventing. Juniors appreciated that during their first year there's no billable hours requirement: *"It's to help you focus on learning rather than hours, and they're not just saying that."* When first-years bloom into second-years, a target of 2,000 hours kicks in, on which hangs standard bonus eligibility. *"It's achievable,"* most agreed, although some in more specialist practice areas commented that *"it's more subject to the needs of larger groups, so it's not always easy."* Everyone agreed that *"you don't get in hot water here if you don't achieve that number."* There are also discretionary bonuses. *"People are understanding."*

"It's an organization that is clearly trying to correct the reasons why women leave the law."

"Family friendly" was a phrase that came up again and again in our interviews, corroborated by observations regarding *"the many women who work here who have multiple children. It's an organization that is clearly trying to correct the reasons why women leave the law."* Insiders were also keen to point out that the firm feels *"relaxed but business-like, whereby some of us wear suits and everyone is very professional, but it's not a quiet place, it's noisy, and everyone goes into each other's offices instead of calling."*

Many felt sure the atmosphere was down to Fulbright & Jaworksi's southern identity, which they felt had been *"retained"* and had *"integrated well with the Norton Rose culture."* Being *"courteous, good-natured and calm is our common thread; it's such a welcoming environment, which makes people want to invest back into the firm."* Regular events like *"floor lunches, happy hours, wine tastings, poker nights, fundraising events, rodeos, beer festivals, and dorky things like the Texas Renaissance Festival"* were greatly appreciated though *"never compulsory."* In Dallas, a source shared their *"favorite thing about working here: people walk down the corridor stopping by each office to ask who wants to go for lunch, so no one has to eat by themselves. We call it the lunch train!"*

"The majority is still white and male, especially in the partnership."

Diversity

While the individual experiences of diverse sources were characterized by positivity – *"it's great to come to work and see faces that look like mine"* – insiders also readily conceded that *"the majority is still white and male, especially in the partnership."* Still, everyone made the point of singing the praises of NRF's *"constant push"* to improve in this area, citing *"monthly firmwide meetings, a goal of making the partnership 30% female by 2020, and even extra bonuses for diversity efforts."* A Dallas rookie was impressed by *"a woman who was made partner while on maternity leave."*

"My most rewarding case so far."

Pro Bono

Interviewees responded positively when quizzed on the firm's commitment to pro bono, listing NRF's *"strong passion and commitment to this type of work"* as a key draw. Litigators were especially proud of their experiences. *"I've done a divorce case, and a death penalty appeal,"* said one, while another shared: *"I went to trial. It's been my most rewarding case so far. When I won, the partners sent an email out to the entire practice as if I'd won for a paying client."* Transactional lawyers found it *"a bit harder to translate pro bono to M&A but did help form entities for not-for-profits, and became part of the Houston Volunteer Lawyers program the firm has affiliations with."* 100 hours of pro bono can be counted toward the 2,000 target.

Pro bono hours

- For all attorneys across all US offices: undisclosed
- Average per US attorney: undislosed

"To provide the highest level of legal services, we must have specialists, not generalists."

Linda Addison,
US managing partner

Get Hired

Hiring partner Andrew Price sheds some light on how applicants can make the cut: Norton Rose Fulbright *"hired consultants to look at high performers at our firm and help us identify the distinguishing attributes common to those individuals, which we then use to recruit associates. Those attributes are: being committed to achieve, displaying entrepreneurship and leadership, as well as strong academics and communication skills."* Following OCIs, shortlisted candidates are flown to their desired office where they undergo a day of interviews, culminating with a presentation by lawyers at the office and a dinner or other networking event. From that, summer offers are made. Check out our website for more info on getting into NRF.

See firm profile on p.677

Offices

Houston is the firm's biggest US office by headcount, and houses far more junior associates than any other base. *"The firm takes over the top dozen floors of the Fulbright Tower, and you can see for miles and miles from up there. All partners and associates have their own window offices. We have soda fountains, nice coffee machines and loads of restaurants in the neighboring area."* One even whispered that *"the fact that the firm has naming rights over the tower gives me a great feeling as I walk through the door each day."* Dallas got a new space in March: like Houston, *"it's all white and very bright and airy."*

"You can see for miles and miles from up there."

Austin, New York and DC are the next three most junior associate-heavy offices, followed by San Antonio, Denver, LA, Pittsburgh and St. Louis, which claim only one or two each.

Strategy & Future

We asked US managing partner Linda Addison where she sees the firm in the near-ish future: *"As global markets become more regulated, we expect to see increasing demand from clients for regulation and investigations advice. When you combine that with increasing global market connectivity, that will result in more cross border activity. We are, and will be, well-positioned to meet this demand."* With its wings firmly spread across the globe, what major jurisdictions are left without the Norton Rose Fulbright flag? *"We are not yet in Mexico,"* Addison admits, *"but we expect to be there in the not too distant future."*

Regarding the future of its individual lawyers, she agrees with sources who felt they were being groomed to become *"more specialist than generalist."* Addison beams: *"Absolutely. That's what our clients expect and need. They want lawyers who have a deep knowledge of their industry. To provide the highest level of legal services, we must have specialists, not generalists."*

"Favorite thing about working here: people walk down the corridor stopping by each office to ask who wants to go for lunch, so no one has to eat by themselves. We call it the lunch train!"

See firm profile on p.677

Nutter McClennen & Fish LLP

Lawyers per state

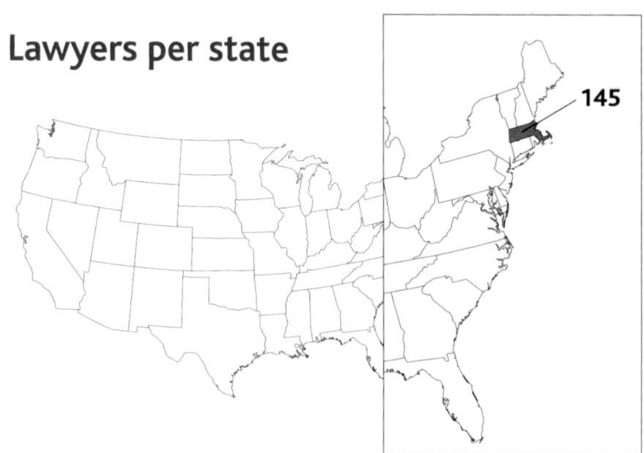

Largest US office: Boston
US offices: 2
International offices: 0
First-year salary: $145,000
Billable hours: 1,900 required
Summers 2016: 7 (4 2Ls, 3 1Ls)
Revenue 2015: $87 million (+3.6%)
Partners made 2016: 6
Famous for: one of Boston's finest mid-sizers; cofounded by legendary SCOTUS Justice Louis Brandeis

Associates here went nuts for "*a place that invests in its associates with the intention of wanting them to stay.*"

"ANY managing partner you talk to who isn't trying to figure out how to make the historic law firm model responsive to 21st century business needs won't be in their job much longer." Such is managing partner Deb Manus' response when asked about Nutter's extensive 2016 rebrand. *"We want to be sure that the market's view of Nutter is in alignment with who we are."* Associates too were clear about Nutter's identity as a strong smaller firm: *"I think that to law students all firms can look the same,"* said one, *"but Nutter has a unique history being founded by Louis Brandeis, and also commitment to public service. There are other firms outside the biggest names."*

Its makeover aside, Nutter – founded in 1879 by Supreme Court Justice Louis Brandeis and a pal – is one of New England's best law firms. Although it only has 150 lawyers, Nutter boasts *Chambers USA* rankings in banking & finance, environment, labor & employment, litigation and real estate. Clients include Johnson & Johnson, Boston Children's Hospital and Dunkin' Donuts. Nutter always does well in associate satisfaction surveys, and has a reputation for *"good people, good work and an office where everyone knows each other,"* juniors told us. *"I wanted to go to Nutter because it was a Boston firm without offices everywhere,"* a litigator shared. *"It's much easier to get things done when the entire office is physically in the same place."*

On chambers-associate.com...

- Interviews with managing partner Deb Manus and hiring partner Matt Bresette

ASSOCIATES SAY...

The Work

Juniors begin their career at Nutter in one of the following practices: real estate, trust & estates, tax, IP, litigation or business (Nutter's word for corporate). Associates must fill out weekly reports for an assigning partner to check their availability for work, but we were told the process is a little more *"organic"* as partners regularly contact associates they'd like to work with.

Litigation is Nutter's largest department and, at the time of our calls, housed the most juniors. Commercial litigation offers the chance to work nationally on matters such as *"implications of discovery in four different states."* International products liability – for example, work with faulty medical devices – is also a subgroup that provides opportunities to *"work with lawyers all over the country"* and overseas. Other litigation groups include securities, IP and labor & employment. Typical junior work in litigation tends to be standard *"researching legal issues"* and *"writing the first draft of a brief or any other legal document."* Cases vary, and we heard of government investigations into *"possible kickbacks"* as well as defending *"a bank in a supposed ponzi scheme."*

The Inside View

See firm profile on p.678

Rankings in *Chambers USA*

Banking & Finance
Environment
Labor & Employment
Litigation
Real Estate

For detail on ranking tiers and ranking locations, visit www.chambersandpartners.com

The generalists in trusts & estates are *"exposed to every stage of estate planning,"* including *"abstracting wills, powers of attorney, trust administrations, terminations of trusts, tax returns and court probate."* Typical junior tasks might be *"drafting documents, tax administrations and tax returns."* Trusts associates also work in the much smaller Hyenas office in Cape Cod on the *"third Friday of each month"* to cater to the wealthy *"Martha's Vineyard community."*

"A lot of deals take place in Boston, we have a national presence."

Real estate associates work in dual practices: commercial finance, which works with banks, borrowers and lenders; and land use, which focuses on zoning laws and representing cities. Commercial finance deals relate *"to refinancing, acquisitions and sales of property."* While *"a lot of deals take place in Boston, we have a national presence. We've done deals in Texas, California and Oregon. There aren't any typical clients here. It's developers, business entities, borrowers, supermarkets and municipalities."*

The smaller business department busies its associates with *"basic junior BigLaw tasks"* like *"forming different types of business entities, drafting regulatory compliance documents"* and *"drafting amendments to credit agreements for start up companies."* As one associate put it: *"I'm usually preparing something!"*

Culture & Offices

Associates said that Nutter's small headcount is *"part of our culture."* In fact, *"if we got bigger we'd lose that."* The Nutter spirit is exemplified in what associates dubbed a *"supportive culture"* where everyone *"is willing to help each other out."* MP Deb Manus pinpoints a *"culture of respect and friendship"* that *"people at every level appreciate."* On the social side, the summer months are busiest and happily include *"associates-only"* events for juniors and summers. Come late fall, Nutter hosts a networking event where *"you invite at least ten professional friends or classmates to a cocktail party overlooking Boston Harbor. It's a fun networking event for young lawyers and potential clients."* After this, firmwide events are scarcer, but associates did mention a weekly cheese and wine do in the cafeteria. *"Boston doesn't seem to have happy hours! It just doesn't seem to be a huge deal like it is in other cities."*

Recent work highlights

- Successfully represented a security company in arbitration proceedings relating to the termination of employee contracts and violations of work rules
- Advising clients Adams Community Bank, Greenfield Co-operative Bank and Granite Savings Bank in their various mergers and acquisitions
- Generating patents for an advertising tech publishing company
- Recently represented a company in a social media patent infringement case
- Won a landmark pro bono case that will grant better access to veterans suffering from service-related tinnitus

"Everyone here does important work."

From day one, *"each lawyer has his or her own office"* that's the same size as everyone else's. *"It's very egalitarian,"* one comrade enthused. *"It's not like partners have corner offices or one that's bigger."* Others believed that the office system was *"a testament to the fact that everyone here does important work. I wanted to be at a place where people know each other and I'm not just another cog in the wheel."*

Training & Development

Nutter's training development begins with the aptly titled Nuts and Bolts program which associates said *"struck the balance between giving formal instruction and recognizing the need to teach associates how to do things themselves."* The program is tailored to fit the different departments through *"presentations by partners on specific subjects they specialize in,"* such as *"how to conduct discovery in a case."* Litigators recalled learning *"information on federal practices, state practices, different steps of litigation, taking cases to trial and tackling ethical issues."*

"I can see myself being on track for partner."

According to interviewees: *"The firm invests in its associates with the intention of wanting them to stay."* Not only that, associates believe that making partner is a realistic target: *"They have been very clear to me about progress and how I've performed in comparison to associates historically to give me a sense of where I am in the pack."* Another confided: *"I'm committed for the long term. They'd have to drag me out! I can see myself being on track for partner."* Deb Manus insists that *"advanc-*

See firm profile on p.678

ing to partner is not a political process." She continues: *"I love our partner elections, because I look at the candidates and see individuals who have succeeded and I feel proud of the investment we've made in them."* She says that those *"who do leave Nutter don't typically go to work for competitor law firms."* Moreover, *"we have had a number of people leave and then return to the firm. I think that says something."*

Diversity & Get Hired

According to Deb Manus, Nutter is always *"looking to add great people who will join Nutter and really blossom."* We asked associates what blossoming at Nutter means. After *"good grades"* at law school, they said it's all about being *"invested in the Boston community and wanting to put roots down here."* The key to dazzling in an interview is *"knowing why you want to work at Nutter and what your life is going to be like. I know I was asked why I wanted to work here."* Go online for advice from hiring partner Matt Bresette.

"I know I was asked why I wanted to work here."

In 2015, Nutter recruited an outside diversity consultant to *"look at Nutter through the lens of diversity"* (in the words of Deb Manus) and implement a *"Diversity and Inclusion strategic plan."* Manus hopes that plan will create *"a culture of inclusion"* by talking *"about issues in a way that isn't about culpability or blame."*

"If we bring in the right "tigers," whether baby or mature, and nurture them well, then the firm and our clients win."

Deb Manus, managing partner

The firm is female friendly and most *"junior associates coming through are women,"* associates pointed out to us. There are also *"lots of female partners."* Female associates also told us about the women's mentoring circle which holds *"quarterly breakfasts and luncheons"* for *"partners and associates to talk and catch up."* But there are still *"hurdles to overcome,"* especially regarding ethnic diversity, and associates conceded that *"when you just look at the numbers it doesn't look like we've done a good job at being diverse."*

Pro Bono

Nutter has an historic connection to pro bono – the firm's cofounder Louis Brandeis was a big fan. Flash forward 130-odd years and pro bono is still very much *"part of the Nutter experience."* It *"counts toward your billable hours and there's no limit to how many you can bill."* To encourage associates to take it on, the firm holds *"an annual pro bono recognition ceremony"* in October where it *"recognizes associates who contribute a large bulk of their billable hours to pro bono."* Depending on their practice, juniors tackle things like *"immigration cases involving children, tax exempt forms for non profit organizations, and wills for people who don't have much money but want to leave certain things to certain people."*

Pro bono hours

- For all attorneys across all US offices: 6,142
- Average per US attorney: 42

Hours & Compensation

Interviewees sounded content with their lower salary than at bigger Boston firms – $145,000 as opposed to $160,000 – and better quality of life. One representative associate told us: *"I know it's under market rate but I knew there is a trade off between working at a big firm for big money and having a life. I didn't pick a firm based on the salary because it's way more than I've ever earned. Boston is an expensive city but it's plenty of money."*

"An annual pro bono recognition ceremony."

It can be tricky for newbies to reach the firm's 1,900 billing requirement as *"we have so much training in the first year and, unfortunately, many of those hours aren't billable."* A possible consequence of not meeting the billing target is missing out on the annual bonus. *"I've never gotten a bonus!"* one associate laughed. *"If I'm honest I'd rather work a little less hard and not get one."* On top of the required 1,900 hours are an extra 100 *"commitment to the firm hours"* which can include anything from *"CLE courses"* to *"community outreach programs."*

"I multi-task while watching box sets and doing emails!"

Speaking of having a life outside work, *"I don't know many people who work on the weekends,"* one trusts & estates source said. *"When I do it's always self-imposed and from home. Luckily, in this department there aren't a lot of hard deadlines so there isn't that psychological pressure. I multi-task while watching box sets and doing emails!"*

See firm profile on p.678

Strategy & Future

While associates would welcome *"a little bit more transparency"* over the firm's decision-making (what associate anywhere wouldn't?), they did feel more involved than they might be at larger firms. *"Partners are part of the business strategy,"* one explained, *"and because we're a small firm if you're working with a partner you know it's something important. Whereas at a large firm you could be working with a partner on something not to do with the overall strategy."*

Managing partner Deb Manus says the firm's strategy in a nutshell is *"about an emphasis on excellence, not just at lawyer levels – because that's the table stakes – but at all levels of the organization. I'm so proud of the strides that we've made in the last year through really thinking about how we develop our business and practices. We've been tackling every initiative in a team-driven and organized way. One of the great things about the younger people coming up is how they approach work: they are purpose driven, they want to work toward common goals. I think we do a good job with our junior lawyers. They are fantastic lawyers and their level of career satisfaction matters to us – it makes us a stronger organization."*

To read the full interview with Deb Manus, visit chambersandpartners.com.

"It's much easier to get things done when the entire office is physically in the same place."

See firm profile on p.678

O'Melveny & Myers LLP

Lawyers per state

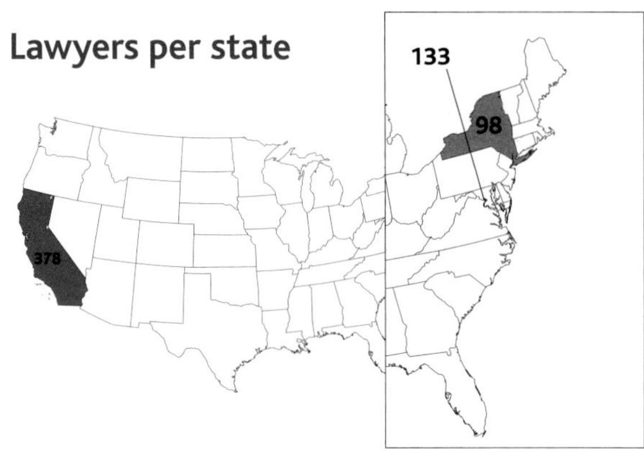

Largest US: Los Angeles
US offices: 7
International offices: 8
First-year salary: $160,000
Billable hours: no requirement
Summers 2016: 92 (91 2Ls, 1 1L)
Revenue 2015: $689.5million (+3.7%)
Partners made in 2016: 11 globally (9 in US)
Famous for: California heritage, global ambitions; strong pro bono offering; lack of billable hours target

It may sound like a family-run business in rural Ireland, but with 15 offices globally and a range of sophisticated practice areas, this LA-born superstar is anything but quaint.

O'MELVENY & Myers has been part of the Los Angeles business scene since 1885, well before Hollywood showed up. Like the movie industry, O'Melveny has created its own stars and exported its product around the world. It's got five offices in the Golden State alone, bases in New York and Washington, DC and a further eight in major Asian and European business centers like London, Seoul, Geneva and Hong Kong. *"I'm proud of our LA roots,"* chair Brad Butwin tells us, *"but I don't think people think of us as an LA firm anymore. We're an international firm."*

Litigation is a traditional O'Melveny strength, but it also wins Oscars – sorry, *Chambers USA* rankings – for antitrust, media and entertainment law, tax, bankruptcy, capital markets of both the debt and equity variety, labor and employment, IP, corporate and its federal appellate practice. Possibly more importantly, the firm's work got it name-dropped on *The Sopranos*. Away from the small screen, O'Melveny plans to keep on keeping on, according to Butwin: *"Focusing on existing clients and doing well is a better strategy than rebuilding from the top down,"* he tells us.

On chambers-associate.com...

- Becoming a lawyer in Cali

ASSOCIATES SAY...

The Work

Having experienced both transactional and litigation work as summer associates, new O'Melvenites join one of these two categories on starting with the firm. O'Melveny is keen to train 'all-round lawyers' rather than specialists. This isn't to say that the firm is dead-set against newbies knowing what they want to do. *"Technically, I was a generalist,"* recalled one of our sources, *"but I was working for my chosen group from the start, and everyone knew this was where I wanted to go."* What it does mean is associates spend the first two or three years at the firm as generalists. As you can imagine, this leads to a good deal of variety for both dispute-settlers and deal-doers.

On the litigation side this can mean the same lawyer can do *"antitrust matters, white collar investigations, insurance matters, bankruptcies and securities litigation"* before deciding where to end up. For all this variety *"there is always going to be some doc review,"* lamented one litigator. Happily *"we're not doing doc review for 12 hours every day."* Newbies start off by researching and drafting sections of motions and *"as you prove yourself, you gradually become responsible for drafting the entire thing."* And it's just as varied on the non-contentious side of the fence, with *"real estate transactions, bond deals, mergers and acquisitions and private equity fund formation,"* on offer. Responsibility also varies, we're

The Inside View

See firm profile on p.679

Rankings in *Chambers USA*

Antitrust	Intellectual Property
Appellate Law	International Trade
Bankruptcy/Restructuring	Labor & Employment
Capital Markets	Litigation
Corporate/M&A	Media & Entertainment
Employee Benefits & Executive Compensation	Products Liability
Environment	Projects
ERISA Litigation	Securities
Insurance	Tax

For detail on ranking tiers and ranking locations, visit www.chambersandpartners.com

Recent work highlights

- Representing boxing promoter Top Rank in an antitrust lawsuit accusing Floyd Mayweather's manager Al Haymon of abusing his dominance of the boxing market
- Secured the dismissal of a lawsuit against Ford alleging complicity with the apartheid government of South Africa
- Helped engineering giant Honeywell International acquire Aviaso, a Swiss company making fuel efficiency software for the airline industry
- Representing real estate broker Coldwell Banker in a class action over whether its sales agents should be classed as independent contractors or employees

told. *"On some deals it's just me and the partner,"* an Angeleno told us, *"and by the end of it I was doing the majority of the work."* Contrast this with the larger IPOs, which involve *"ten attorneys grinding on and getting it ready to go to market."*

"We're not doing doc review 12 hours a day..."

The impression we got from associates was that they originated a lot of their work organically through relationships, although the firm makes sure the whole system is overseen by work coordinators. Our sources found this *"a useful backup for when you're either too busy or not busy enough."* Of course, there's not too much of the latter; one New Yorker told us that the firm is *"very busy right now, so there isn't much time to sit around twiddling your thumbs."*

Hours, compensation and pro bono

While there's no official billable hours target, office chatter has it that there's an 'unofficial target' of between 1,850 hours and 1,950 hours that associates should aim for if they want to be bonus-eligible. *"I always thought it was 1,950, but I've heard others say 1,900,"* mused one associate. *"There is no formal hours cutoff,"* hiring partner Allen Burton tells us, *"and billable hours are just one of a number of different factors that we look at when calculating bonuses."* That said, he acknowledges that *"1,900 hours is colloquially understood as a general ballpark"* by associates.

In addition to billable and pro bono hours (which the firm treats as billable), associate involvement in recruiting, mentoring and business development are all taken into account when calculating bonuses. An average working day begins between 9 and 9.30am, and ends ten hours later between 7 and 7.30pm. Associates with young children can leave at 5pm and work remotely. There are late nights, of course, although remote working means that even the most diligent of attorneys can avoid spending too much time in the office. *"The latest I've stayed is probably 10pm,"* reported one informant *"but just because I'm not in the office doesn't mean I'm not still working."* Of course with *"clients based in Europe and Asia"* and tight court deadlines, some late nights are unavoidable, with a few associates reporting staying until 1 or even 2am.

"Just because I'm not in the office doesn't mean I'm not working."

O'Melveny, our sources told us, takes pro bono very seriously. *"This is an excellent BigLaw firm to work for if pro bono work is something you think is part of your obligations as a lawyer,"* enthused one source. The good news is there's no cap on the number of pro bono hours that associates can treat as billable. Every new O'Melvenian is given at least one pro bono case to work on in their first year. Work varies from *"advising the directors of a non-profit on corporate governance,"* to *"helping veterans with PTSD get discharge upgrades"* all the way to *"prosecuting misdemeanors at the Rodondo Beach DA's office."* According to chair Brad Butwin, the firm recently got involved in the Court Square Law Project, a 'low bono' organization that will operate out of the City University of New York law school and will provide discount legal services to low-to-mid income clients.

Pro bono hours

- For all attorneys across all US offices: 54,779
- Average per US attorney: 97

Culture

"'Welcoming' is the first buzzword that comes to mind when you mention O'Melveny & Myers," an Angeleno told us. Apparently the second is 'Californian,' but our sources suggested *"that might evoke a bit of a carefree attitude."* Of course, despite the surfer dude stereotypes, neither California nor O'Melveny are places for slackers. *"Because it was founded in California, the firm is a*

See firm profile on p.679

little more down-to-earth than others," a New Yorker told us, *"but like California it's also high achieving."* Others were struck by their colleagues' enthusiasm for their chosen fields; *"this seems like a strange thing to say,"* admitted one, *"but all the partners and senior associates seem to love their practice areas."*

Diversity

With the exception of Newport Beach, most of the folks we spoke to at O'Melveny thought the firm did *"fairly well"* on the diversity front. *"During the recruitment process, we keep an eye on diversity at all levels,"* an insider told us. *"This includes sex and gender, race, age and economic background."* The firm certainly makes an *"effort to reach out to all kinds of diverse attorneys."* It offers the usual range of affinity groups, and there's *"an associate group that can bring issues to the partners' attention."* There's also a program called CustOMMize that allows new parents and those looking after sick relatives to work on a reduced schedule.

"We keep an eye on diversity at all levels."

Get Hired

Applicants usually meet two lawyers at the OCI stage. According to a source who'd been one of those two lawyers, *"personality fit"* is *"98% of what we're looking for,"* with the remaining 2% dedicated to making sure the candidate's academics are up to scratch. Questions were described as *"fairly typical"* although occasionally an interviewer might put an applicant on the spot with something like *"what's the hardest decision you've ever had to make?"* Having *"a well thought out reason for wanting to be here,"* can only help an application to the California offices, but it isn't something the firm makes an issue of. *"We obviously don't want people using us for a free vacation to LA,"* explained someone from the city, *"but the bar isn't too high."*

According to insiders, interesting summer jobs, experiences of community work, mock trial and moot court experiences and having served on a journal are all things that can help wow interviewers. Hiring partner Allen Burton agrees, telling us: *"We look for candidates that have diverse life experiences that reflect a commitment to citizenship and leadership."* In particular, he cites people who have experience *"helping others, taking chances and taking ownership of any difficult situations they have encountered,"* as prime examples of those *"likely to succeed at O'Melveny & Myers."* Chair Brad Butwin adds that the ability to *"look a client in the eye and answer the question 'what do I do?'"* rather than simply quoting statute is something the firm really values.

Training & Development

An early orientation lasting a few days is followed by regular seminar talks across the first month, where various staff members *"tell us what we're getting into."* Apparently the orientation process is identical to that given to incoming summer associates, which led to some grumbles that it was *"redundant."* More helpful, we hear, is the firm's new associate mentoring program, which pairs neophytes with more senior members of the firm. *"You meet for coffees and lunches,"* said an associate, *"they'll ask how work's going and you can share any concerns you have."* Associate mentors are usually responsible for gathering and delivering feedback, something which newbies appreciated. *"It's nice to have a neutral third party giving you feedback,"* one told us, *"as they will pass negative feedback on in a way that doesn't sound too critical."*

"It's nice to have a neutral third party giving you feedback..."

The formal review process starts with attorneys filling out a report evaluating their strengths and weaknesses. *"Even the partners have to do it,"* whispered one insider. Any partner that the reviewee has spent more than 5% of their billable time with will have the opportunity to read a summary report and write a review. A partner collates all of this feedback into one large report which they then discuss with the individual at a face to face meeting. *"You don't know who has said what,"* someone who'd been through the process told us, which spares some awkward conversations. It's at this stage that attorneys find out whether they're bonus-eligible, but it's also a chance to get useful feedback on their performance to date.

"On some deals it's just me and the partner."

Offices

The firm avowedly has no official HQ, although headquarterly things like firm retreats, the first-year leadership academy and much of the admin do take place in Los Angeles. Sources in other offices were quick to tell us that the firm felt *"more like a well-connected network than a hub with satellite offices."* Where the center of gravity lies often depends on the individual practice area. DC is big on the appellate front, for example, while Century City hosts most of the firm's entertainment law practice, and San Fran associates are likely to encounter IP work.

See firm profile on p.679

Strategy & Future

Chair Brad Butwin tells us the plan is to focus on what he calls *"the double down strategy."* The goal, he says, is *"to focus on clients who already use our services and to deepen those relationships across geographies and departments."* In other words, O'Melveny plans to build on its existing relationships by doing more stuff in more locations for its existing clients. That's not to say that the firm doesn't have growth on the mind, but that it will be *"prudent, demand-driven growth,"* rather than growth for its own sake.

"Because it was founded in California, the firm is a little more down-to-earth."

See firm profile on p.679

Orrick, Herrington & Sutcliffe LLP

Lawyers per state

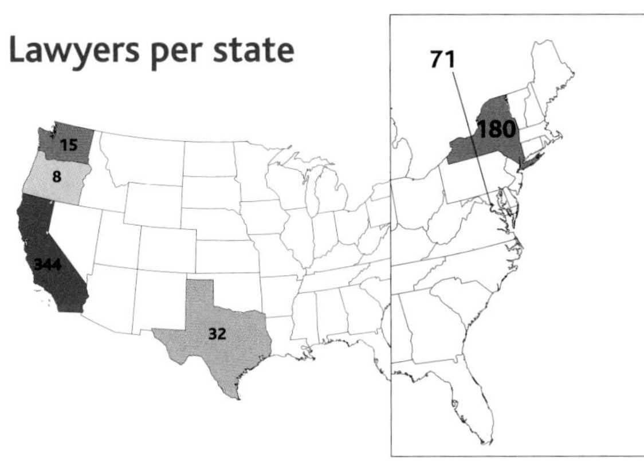

Largest US office: New York
US offices: 11
International offices: 14
First year salary: $160,000 ($145,000 in Portland, Sacramento and Seattle)
Billable hours: no requirement (1,950 encouraged)
Summers 2016: 50 (46 2Ls, 4 1Ls)
Revenue 2015: $913.4 million (+4.2%)
Partners made in 2016: 19 globally (15 in US)
Famous for: energy and infrastructure, technology and finance industries, global network; unicorns

Want to help bankroll the next Netflix or finance an African dam? Try this *"friendly but not fratty"* Californian globetrotter.

ORRICK has literally left its mark on California: since its founding in the 1860s, lawyers here helped finance major West Coast landmarks like Los Angeles International Airport (LAX) and the Golden Gate Bridge, no less. But just as generations of Americans flocked to the Golden State in search of a golden future, Orrick too has journeyed in search of opportunities, and in the last year opened offices in Houston and Geneva, Switzerland, and an affiliated office in Abidjan, Ivory Coast. These offices will build on the firm's expertise in energy and infrastructure, Latin America, litigation, IP and public finance, with Abidjan giving Orrick a foothold in the rapidly growing African market, and Geneva boosting its international arbitration practice.

Energy and infrastructure are one of Orrick's three core industry focuses, the other two being technology and financial services. *Chambers USA* ranks a glittering array of practices in the fields of capital markets, litigation, intellectual property and finance (plus more niche areas like Native American law) – explore the wealth of information about these at chambersandpartners.com. One area that always gets associates here talking excitedly to us is Silicon Valley-related work, especially when start-up clients have morphed seemingly overnight into 'unicorns' – worth over a billion. For more on Orrick's work with unicorns, read our Bonus Features.

On chambers-associate.com...

- What is a unicorn?

ASSOCIATES SAY...

Strategy & Future

This focus on the rapidly developing African infrastructure sector is no coincidence. According to Orrick chairman Mitch Zuklie, the firm's strategy for the next few years is to focus on its key specialisms while working to become *"the best firm to work for."* Instead of headline-grabbing gimmicks – *"we're not giving massages every Tuesday"* – he points to things like the firm's new parental leave policy. Orrick offers new parents of either gender *"22 weeks' paid leave and a guarantee of one's job for up to nine months,"* and a central liaison to keep them up-to-date with comings and goings at the firm, and help them transition back in. He's also keen to emphasize Orrick's personalized approach to business development, which sees each associate entrusted with a personal business development budget.

The Work

Energy and infrastructure are one of Orrick's three great strengths, along with technology and financial services. Within these three broad areas, Orrick offers incoming associates a range of corporate, litigious and specialist practice areas to get stuck into. The large litigation group has a more formal allocation system involving a central

See firm profile on p.680

Rankings in *Chambers USA*

Antitrust
Appellate Law
Banking & Finance
Bankruptcy/Restructuring
Capital Markets
Corporate/M&A
Employee Benefits & Executive Compensation
Energy & Natural Resources
Insurance
Intellectual Property
IT & Outsourcing
Labor & Employment
Litigation
Native American Law
Products Liability
Projects
Real Estate
Securities
Startups & Emerging Companies

For detail on ranking tiers and ranking locations, visit www.chambersandpartners.com

Recent work highlights

- Advised Pinterest on two rounds of venture capital financing
- Advised venture capital firm Andreessen Horowitz on its $50 million investment in Buzzfeed
- Defending Whole Foods in a false advertizing class action arising out of Whole Foods' sale of homeopathic remedies in its stores
- On behalf of Microsoft, filed a civil action to take down the 'Ramnit' botnet, a network of Trojans targeting US and European banks
- Represented Patern Energy group in relation to the consctruction of a wind farm being built to power one of Amazon's data centers

assigning partner. In the corporate group, associates tend to be immediately placed into specific subgroups. With fewer new associates to juggle, these smaller corporate teams can afford to be a bit less formal. Even where there is a centralized assignment system, some associates found themselves either reaching out to higher-ups or being sought out for work. *"It's on you to say 'no' if you're too busy,"* said one, *"which can feel uncomfortable at times."*

In addition to a *"heightened awareness of filing deadlines,"* new litigators should be prepared for a healthy degree of responsibility quite early on. In litigation, *"the partners really let you take ownership of cases,"* particularly on the smaller, more leanly staffed matters. *"You do as much of the legwork as you can,"* said one litigator. *"You're drafting requests, communicating with counsel and filing motions."* Associates can also get stuck into the deposition process. *"We need to come up with a series of questions in order to secure key admissions,"* a source in the Bay Area explained. *"Your questions have to be good."* On larger cases, associates find themselves doing more traditional junior tasks like doc review and research memoranda, and associates didn't mind: *"When you're a first-year, it's nice to have a buffer between you and the partners,"* admitted one.

"You do as much of the legwork as you can."

Corporate associates can get involved in a range of areas from emerging companies work to large-scale M&A. Lean staffing is the name of the game in all but the biggest deals in corporate, and *"depending on how ambitious you are, you can find yourself responsible for tasks so high level, you aren't sure how to do them!"* When working with startups – not an infrequent occurrence – *"you might even get to run the deals yourself,"* enthused a lawyer in Silicon Valley. *"You'll still have to bring the partner in on specific issues but it'll be your baby."* Where deals aren't so leanly staffed, associates can expect more traditional tasks like drafting ancillaries or undertaking due diligence.

"Got to appear in front of a judge."

Pro Bono

"I'm convinced that Orrick has the best pro bono offering in New York," enthused one associate rather hyperbolically. *"You can get any type of case you want,"* with everything from immigration cases to *"noise complaints arising out of life-saving medical equipment."* There's no limit to the number of pro bono hours you can treat as billable, although *"your billable work doesn't go down,"* so just how much pro bono each associate does *"depends on how important it is to you."* That said, most junior lawyers manage to fit in a good amount of pro bono. *"I did a few hundred hours' pro bono in my first year,"* recalled one. *"I was a little worried by how much I was doing, but the partner said that was normal for a first year."* It's also a great opportunity for juniors to get some hands-on experience managing and trying high-level work. *"I did the intake, the client interview, prepped for the hearing and got to appear in front of a judge,"* recalled a West Coast litigator.

Pro Bono hours

- For all attorneys across all US offices: 60,248
- Average per US attorney: 92

Offices

People tend to think of Orrick as a California firm, but while the bulk of its legal eagles still reside out west, the firm's largest single office is actually New York. *"Many people don't like it, but I think it's great"* said a New Yorker of that office's futuristic glass interiors. *"I hate feeling isolated in the office, but I can understand how others find the layout distracting."* The Los Angeles of-

See firm profile on p.680

fice occupies the 31st through 33rd floors of a centrally located office block. The office itself was described as *"oval-shaped,"* with the associates' offices situated in an outer ring giving them commanding views over either downtown LA or the construction work going on at the Staples Center, depending on which side of the building they're sitting in.

It may be smaller than NYC, but *"spiritual headquarters"* San Francisco is still a good size, occupying four floors in the Orrick Building. It's a steel and glass edifice in San Fran's financial district. Down the road in Menlo Park, the Silicon Valley office is a horse of a different color. It's set in a cluster of four low-rise buildings set in a park in the suburbs. *"There's a really nice campus feel to the place,"* we were told, and this is probably helped by the fact that it's a stone's throw from Stanford University.

Training & Development

A key part of Orrick's drive to become the best firm to work for is its Talent Model. This is not some attorney-run fashion show, but Orrick's name for its career development program. Attorneys opt to join one of two 'tracks,' the partner track and the career associate track. The partner track is by far the more popular of the two. It divides associates into three grades: associate, management associate and senior associate, and is *"a more tailored, individualized version of the lockstep model used by other law firms,"* sources informed us. *"At other firms, associates just slog away and then one day they either make partner or they don't,"* Mitch Zuklie explains, *"but we want to make sure that everyone has a clear sense of what they have to do in order to advance."*

"It's on you to say 'no' if you're too busy."

Under the Talent Model, Orrickians can get individual coaches, who they work with to identify and develop the skills they need to advance. *"Say you need to improve your deposition skills,"* explained a junior, *"you would reach out to your coach, explain what you needed to do and ask if you can do work in that area."* There's also more traditional training set up in the form of a few days' orientation at the start, which attorneys described as *"very administrative,"* and the usual array of practice-specific training sessions for the first couple of years. New lawyers are reviewed six months in and at the end of their first year, with subsequent reviews taking place annually. Not only is it *"nice to get feedback,"* it's a useful opportunity to let management know if there's a particular area you're interested in working in. *"It's your opportunity to say 'I haven't worked for this or that industry yet,'"* one told us.

Hours & Compensation

One of the more tangible ways the different tracks impact new attorneys is in the number of hours they work. While Orrick doesn't have a formal billing target, partner-track attorneys are encouraged to bill at least 1,950 hours, compared to the lower 1,600 to 1,800 hours for associates on the other tracks. *"Management understands that being a corporate lawyer is difficult,"* ruminated one partner-track associate, *"and you can bill less than the 1,950 and still get a bonus."* While billing a stupefying number of hours looks impressive on paper, *"it's important that you produce high quality work in that time,"* and the bonus system is calibrated to take into account quality and quantity of hours.

"Management understands that being a corporate lawyer is difficult."

Vacation is *"technically unlimited,"* but in reality most associates take two weeks a year. *"This depends on their circumstances,"* qualified an associate, explaining that *"if someone's just got married they might take three weeks for their honeymoon, and if work is slow they may take several little vacations."* Attorneys work long but not excessive hours (by BigLaw standards), with an average working day generally lasting between 9am and 7pm or 8pm plus remote working from home in the evenings.

Get Hired

It wants to be the best law firm to work for. What does Orrick ask for in return? *"We start at the same place as other firms,"* says hiring partner Lisa Simpson, referring to strong academic performance, and *"students who can write well are at a premium, particularly in litigation."* Attorneys agreed the firm *"cares a lot about your writing skills,"* and also stressed that *"beyond the normal metrics they want to see if you'll fit in with the other lawyers."* Orrick's also looking for folks with initiative, teamwork skills and *"the ability to power through when it's difficult,"* Simpson tells us. All well and good, we hear you say, but how can I show this? *"Inside or outside of law school, find something you have a passion for, and use that as an opportunity to show your skills."*

"There were no 'gotcha' questions"

OCIs are *"professional but not too formal or rigid,"* according to juniors. *"It was more like they were getting to know me,"* elaborated one. At the callback stage, questioning styles vary depending on individual interviewers, with some partners being *"tough questioners"* and others more conversational. Regardless, there were *"no 'gotcha' questions and the interviewers seemed genuinely interested in what I had to say."*

See firm profile on p.680

Diversity

Associates expressed disappointment on the diversity front, something we hear time and again at virtually all the firms in this guide. One litigator expressing surprise at *"how few women partners there are in my department."* Another junior was even blunter: *"The partnership's still mainly made up of white males."* One source described this as *"something left over from a previous era,"* and pointed out that the current crop of associates is split evenly between men and women. Furthermore, ten of the 19 recent promotions to partner were female – the first time more women than men have been promoted.

The situation was similarly mixed on the ethnic minority front, with associates from Silicon Valley to New York using phrases like *"it's quite ethnically diverse,"* and *"there's some ethnic diversity."* That said, no one we spoke to doubted the firm's commitment to improving diversity. There are active affinity groups and if diverse associates feel uncomfortable raising *"diversity issues"* with management they can bring them to their diversity mentors. In addition to actively recruiting from various diversity careers events, some Orrick partners recently clubbed together with Microsoft and Morgan Stanley to hold the first ever veterans' legal careers fair.

Culture

We're aware that the statement *"law firm culture is more relaxed in California"* is something of a cliché, but in Orrick's case it seems to be true. *"California lawyers have a different attitude than New York lawyers,"* explained one interviewee, *"and they aren't as obsessive about the hours."* This isn't to say that Orrick's lawyers aren't all *"serious attorneys with a lot expected of them,"* simply that they're *"friendly but not fratty."* It's a culture that seems to trickle down from up high, and associates are *"often struck by how approachable the partners are,"* with chairman Mitch Zuklie singled out as someone who is *"willing to sit down and talk about anything."*

"Even the chairman is willing to sit down and talk."

"Depending on how ambitious you are, you can find yourself responsible for tasks so high level, you aren't sure how to do them!"

See firm profile on p.680

Patterson Belknap Webb & Tyler LLP

Lawyers per state

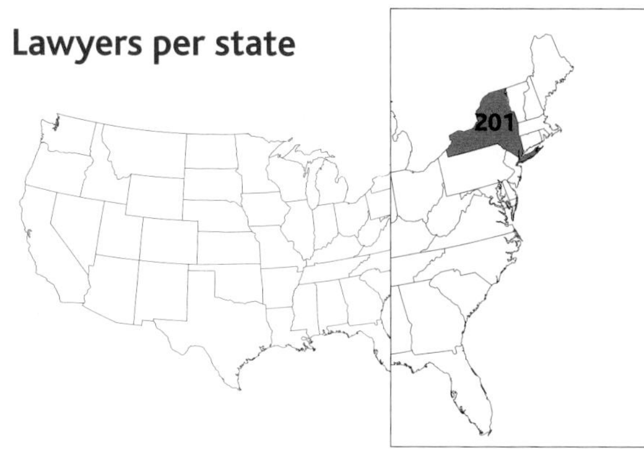

Largest US office: New York
US offices: 1
International offices: 0
First year salary: $160,000
Billable hours: 2,100 target (incl. 250 non-billable)
Summers 2016: no summer program
Revenue 2015: $187.9 million (-0.6%)
Partners made 2016: 0
Famous for: laser-focus on litigation; loves judicial clerks; regular check-ins with managing partner Lisa Cleary

This 200-lawyer, one-office litigation expert scrapped its summer program in favor of hiring judicial clerks and a few lucky 3Ls...

WE'D just watched the new *Star Wars* movie when we were researching Patterson this year, so forgive us for making a slightly unusual (but highly complimentary) comparison. It struck us that Patterson is a bit like Yoda: they're both smaller than their rivals yet pack a mean punch. They are both mighty duelists, Yoda with a lightsaber and (bear with us) Patterson in courtroom spars. While no one at the New York firm has ever lifted a starfighter with the power of their mind (as far as we know), like Yoda they boast formidable intellects. And finally, while Yoda's expertise comes from studying the Force for 900 years, Patterson takes the quick route and hires brilliant scholars straight from judicial clerkships. Refreshingly for BigLaw, not one of the associates we spoke to referred to the firm as the Death Star... quite the opposite, in fact.

Although mainly known as a litigation firm, Patterson also has a noncontentious offering. This includes a corporate department which does M&A work for small to medium sized companies, plus real estate, tax, employee benefits, trusts & estates, and a group serving tax-exempt organizations. Litigation takes the lion's share of new recruits, and 3Ls take note: the firm hires a handful each year into various practice groups.

On chambers-associate.com...

- More from hiring partner Bob Lehrburger

ASSOCIATES SAY...

The Work

Worried about getting pigeonholed early? Patterson takes the view that *"being a generalist is a good thing,"* and here you'll find everything from false advertising to contract disputes to residential backed mortgage securities work. Associates juggle several different cases at a time, dipping in and out as their schedule allows. *"When one case is quieter, there's another getting busy, so there's always something I can jump into."* The variety *"can make your head spin,"* admitted our sources, but everyone we spoke to found it preferable to *"working on a single case for two years."*

"You can do up to 20 depositions in a week."

Assigning partners are on hand to ensure that work is doled out fairly and associates are kept busy, and although one associate found that *"cases are usually staffed by people raising their hand,"* they still have to ultimately go through the assignment person. Associates *"meet with the assigning partners every couple of months to let them know how busy they are."* It's also possible to express an interest in a particular type of work at these meetings. Other than that, there's not much else to it – when work comes in, the partners send an email around the office to see who has capacity, and *"there's nothing stopping you finding your own work"* by contacting the assigning partners yourself.

See firm profile on p.681

Rankings in *Chambers USA*

Advertising	Media & Entertainment
Intellectual Property	Real Estate

For detail on ranking tiers and ranking locations, visit www.chambersandpartners.com

All attorneys are *"informally required"* to do a two-week externship with the City of New York's law department. Here, they generally handle personal injury work – New York's a big city, with a lot of sidewalks to trip over – and they find themselves conducting and defending depositions. *"We're kind of thrown in the deep end,"* recalled one former participant. Another added *"you can do up to 20 depositions in a week."*

Hours & Compensation

There's a billable hours target of 1,850, and a target of 250 hours' worth of relevant nonbillable work. The latter can include CLEs, marketing and all-important pro bono work. *"It works out as 35 billable hours a week,"* calculated one source, *"which is very reasonable for a New York firm."* Others agreed: *"There's no chance of missing it if you work five days a week."* The firm's position is that associates need to hit both the billable and non-billable hours targets to be eligible for a full bonus, but associates who fall short on one or other of those goals but who still hit 2,100 overall will be assessed on a case-by-case basis. Patterson is open to *"splitting the baby"* and *"giving half-bonuses and other percentages,"* or even full bonuses, depending on an individual's performance.

"On a dollar-per-hour basis, we probably make more than people at other firms."

In the legal world, 'work/life balance' is traditionally something that happens to other people, but Patterson's lawyers seem to do all right. Day-to-day, most Pattersonians show up around 9-9.30 am and finish at 7pm. *"95% of the time I've left the office before 8 o'clock,"* said a not untypical associate. When trials loom it's sometimes necessary to stay late or work over weekends. *"When I do work weekends, I'm usually only working for a few hours at a time,"* said one. *"Unless there's a pressing trial, I'm loathed to stay past 10pm,"* added another. We were told that at the senior associate level, salary is a little below market, but juniors are on a par with their counterparts in other firms. *"In fact, if you look at it on a dollar-per-hour basis, we probably make more than people other firms,"* said one, referencing the more humane working hours. And, for recent parents, it's possible to work flexibly – for example, working a reduced schedule for a reduced salary, although there are various different options.

Recent work highlights

- Defending Coca-Cola in a suit accusing the sugary drink maker of false advertising for claiming Coke has "no artificial flavors or preservatives"
- Representing the Alavi Foundation against claims that it performed unlawful services on behalf of the Iranian government
- Defended Hershey against claims that it had abandoned the Trademark "Maltesers" in the United States
- Representing Ambac Assurance, which alleges that EMC falsely induced Ambac to insure worthless Bear Stearns mortgage loans

Pro Bono

A lot of firms claim to take pro bono seriously, but few can match Patterson for pro bono bragging rights. 2016 is the twelfth year running that the firm has achieved a 100% participation rate. *"If you're falling short on your pro bono hours you can expect to receive a phone call,"* said one associate, *"because they really want to get 100% participation every year."* Opportunities range from *"individual cases where you represent someone who's about to be evicted,"* to big, time consuming projects, to representing clients at mediations. Not only are there *"lots of different opportunities,"* but *"the firm is open to you bringing stuff in."*

Pro bono hours

- For all attorneys: 25, 261
- Average per attorney: 135

Culture

While *"litigators are supposed to be aggressive,"* there's more of a *"gentle, bookish culture"* chez Patterson. This isn't to say that the firm's courtroom brawlers can't throw down with the best of them when their clients' interests are at stake – merely that people feel like *"respected professionals"* rather than *"billable hours machines."* Having all the firm's lawyers under one roof definitely helps the atmosphere. *"Partners are never walled off,"* said one, *"and everyone sees everyone in the cafeteria and in the hallways."*

"You literally just go and talk."

The firm's inviting culture is due, in part, to the efforts of cochair and managing partner Lisa Cleary. *"She really sets the tone,"* said one source, while another described her as a *"driver of the firm's culture."* Cleary personally meets every associate every two months to make sure they're happy and getting the work they want. *"There's no real agenda,"* a spy tells us, *"you literally just go and talk."* And she's not the only approachable bigshot; part-

See firm profile on p.681

ners aren't *"walled off,"* and the entire place is just *"a little less hierarchical"* than your average law firm.

"Near Times Square, not In Times Square..."

Offices

Associates raved about Patterson's location, saying *"any firm in Midtown is going to have a great view, but we're right by Times Square, Bryant Park and Grand Central station."* One source gave it top marks for being *"near Times Square, but not IN Times Square."* The firm seems to be wasting no time getting ready for the Internet of Things; a recently completed facelift has left *"iPads on meeting-room walls and teleconferencing technology everywhere."* It also means that *"all associates have window offices to themselves,"* allowing for some glorious views. For associates who can't face the lunchtime crowds, there's a subsidized cafeteria, as well as an associates' lounge with an assortment of snacks, coffee machine, TV and video games on offer. Plus, for those who haven't had time to grab breakfast on their way into the office, the firm provides a free bowl of fruit every morning.

Get Hired

"One of the main things we look for in a candidate is fire in the belly," hiring partner Bob Lehrburger tells us. This, of course, is in addition to the usual things like legal reasoning, leadership, and communication skills. Where might one go to find such a candidate? The firm thinks the ranks of the nation's judicial clerks is a good place to start. In fact, if Patterson made novelty mugs, they'd probably say *"you don't have to be a judicial clerk to work here – but it helps!"* Although it hires a few candidates straight out of law school, Patterson focuses most of its efforts on wooing judicial clerks. The seduction begins in January with clerks receiving an invite to a clerks' reception in Tribeca. The subsequent hiring process is refreshingly uncomplicated; applicants submit a resume, cover letter and transcript, and go through a single round of interviews. The interviews themselves run from January to June each year, but places are filled on a first come, first served basis.

"Why don't we hire them when they're done clerking?"

There are obvious advantages to hiring clerks: it guarantees a ready supply of clever people with inside knowledge of how the courts operate. But why focus almost exclusively on hiring clerks? *"People would summer here, work here for a year, and then go off to clerk,"* hypothesized one source, *"so the firm said 'why don't we hire them when they're done clerking?'"* Another thought the firm's motives might have been financial: *"I think it's because the summer program was expensive and unnecessary."* Hiring partner Lehrburger tells us that the truth is closer to the former. *"We were getting more and more of our associates from clerk ranks,"* he says. All of those recruited through this pipeline go into litigation, with noncontentious roles filled either by laterals or through special recruitment campaigns.

Training & Development

As is traditional, new Pattersonites are treated to a week of orientation, covering everything from *"filling out tax forms to setting up your email account."* Sources described it as *"sitting in a room being trained, which sounds annoying but was something I reallly appreciated."* Then there's a series of one to two hour long CLEs called 'nuts and bolts', which teaches lawyers how to manage a case from beginning to end. Associates praised the firm's willingness to pay for outside consultants and professional coaching. *"There's a writing coach who comes in once a week,"* one told us, *"and you can run any of your briefs or memos past her."* Most memorably, the firm helps associates prepare for hearings by staging a full moot, with partners *"playing the role of a hot bench"* and putting the associates through their paces, giving feedback at the end. It isn't just the high value, two week long jury trials either. Small oral arguments *"that aren't really a big deal"* and even pro bono cases get this treatment.

"One of the main things we look for in a candidate is fire in the belly."

Instead of pairing partners and newbies, associates join 'Associate Learning Groups' or ALGs. These are groups of six associates and one partner which meet three or four times a year for educational and team building outings, which can vary from *"going to a musical or the symphony"* to *"wine tastings and nice dinners."* There's also a more formal, and *"very thorough,"* review process. Every six months, partners collate feedback on associates' performance and present it to them. What's interesting about the process is the feedback is not anonymous. *"They tell you how each partner rated you,"* although our agents at the firm tell us that the first one is off the record.

See firm profile on p.681

Diversity

"Diversity is valued here," said one associate, *"but I wouldn't say our ethnic makeup is commensurate with our desire for diversity."* Another was less diplomatic: *"Everyone I work with seems to be white."* To improve the variety of backgrounds, the firm offers a $25,000 diversity fellowship each year. In addition to that tidy sum, the fellow, who must be a diverse judicial clerk, sits on the firm's diversity committee and gets to name a nonprofit as the beneficiary of a $5,000 donation. Happily, the firm does considerably better at recruiting female attorneys. *"More than half of our associates are women,"* boasted an attorney, *"and we're above the national average when it comes to hiring LGBT lawyers."* That said, we heard some grumbles that *"we haven't made a woman partner in a few years,"* although the firm did actually promote a female partner in 2015.

Strategy & Future

Residential mortgage-backed securities [RMBS] litigation has kept many of the firm's best and brightest busy in the last few years, but many of the insiders we spoke to thought that line of work was coming to a natural end. Hiring partner Bob Lehrburger agrees, telling us *"that team is doing extremely well; of course, RMBS work will start to wane as the cases go through their life cycle."* Patterson's not a one-trick pony though, and is already beefing up its expertise in other areas. The firm's false advertising practice has been *"going gangbusters"* according to Lehrburger, and Patterson has also expanded its cybersecurity offering.

"More than half our associates are women."

"We want people who can take ownership of their work. Identifying a problem or stumbling block is good, but proposing a solution is even better."

Bob Lehrburger, hiring partner

See firm profile on p.681

Paul Hastings LLP

Lawyers per state

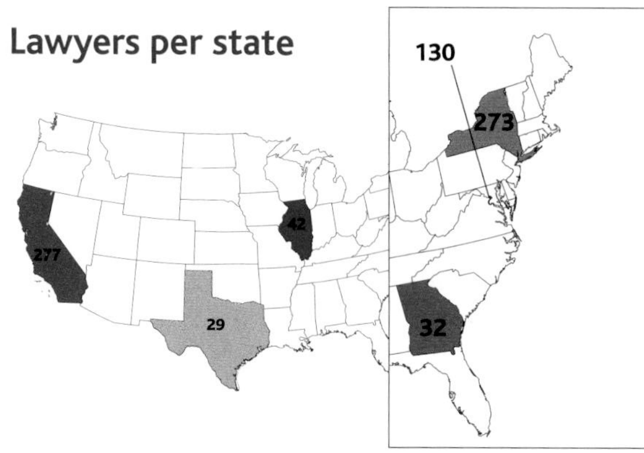

Largest US office: New York
US offices: 10
International offices: 10
First year salary: $160,000
Billable hours: 2,000 target
Summers 2016: 132 (126 2Ls, 4 1Ls, 2 3Ls)
Revenue 2015: $1.057 billion (+5.7%)
Partners made in 2016: 10
Famous for: its building's cameo in *Transformers*; international Californian whose biggest office is New York

70 years old but young at heart, this international firm has its eyes firmly on the future.

WITH 20 offices and 1000-plus attorneys, Paul Hastings may not be quite the *"scrappy young firm"* (as one associate put it) that was founded in Los Angeles back in 1951, but that go-getting spirit still exists. To managing partner Greg Nitzkowski, the firm's relative youth is an advantage: *"We don't have some golden age 150 years ago,"* he tells us, *"so we don't lament change."* Of course, change can sometimes cause some grumbling – the announcement that the New York branch would move to an open plan layout was met with *"some pushback,"* for example – but overall our sources liked working somewhere that didn't *"rest on its laurels."*

Paul Hastings was founded in LA, but these days it's New York that hosts the most associates. This is due in part to the fact that the firm sees New York along with Palo Alto and DC as the firm's key growth areas. This isn't to say that the other offices are falling by the wayside. According to Greg Nitzkowski, *"every office has its strength, which means that while every office is relevant, each office will offer students slightly different opportunities, and a lot of our offices are very focused on what they do best for clients."* Atlanta, for example, might attract students interested in M&A and banking regulatory work, while those inclined toward real estate should look at LA and San Francisco *"where there are a number of enormous, generational real estate developments going on."*

On chambers-associate.com...

- Interview with managing partner Greg Nitzkowski

ASSOCIATES SAY...

The Work

Applicants get to express their interests during OCIs, and rotate through a number of departments while summering with the firm at the larger offices. After this, *"you rank your preferences,"* explained a New Yorker, *"and they make every effort to put you in your chosen practice group."* There is some flexibility, with associates able to split their first year between two practice groups before transitioning to one full time. *"I certainly can't think of anyone who got stuck in a practice group they didn't want."* The biggest groups for junior associates are litigation and corporate, then real estate. Smaller groups include employment and tax.

Associates in the bigger offices usually fill in weekly status reports which are submitted to an assigning partner, who is particularly useful for making sure *"you have enough work, you have the sort of work you want to do, and you aren't overburdened."* Use of the system isn't mandatory, but our sources acknowledged its usefulness. *"The firm encourages us to approach partners and senior associates for work,"* one told us, *"but some people aren't comfortable doing that at first, so it's nice to have the assigning partner as well."*

The Inside View

See firm profile on p.682

Rankings in *Chambers USA*

Antitrust	Healthcare
Banking & Finance	Intellectual Property
Bankruptcy/Restructuring	Investment Funds
Capital Markets	Labor & Employment
Corporate/M&A	Latin American Investment
Employee Benefits & Executive Compensation	Leisure & Hospitality
Environment	Litigation
ERISA Litigation	Real Estate
FCPA	Tax

For detail on ranking tiers and ranking locations, visit www.chambersandpartners.com

Recent work highlights

- Represented data analytics firm Seed Scientific in its sale to Spotify
- Representing Airbnb on the development of its global payments systems
- Represented utility company Calpine on the implementation of Californian and Federal climate change regulations
- Advised Samsung on the launch of its mobile payment system

The larger departments, like corporate and litigation, are divided into sub-departments. *"In theory, you're a generalist,"* said a corporate attorney in M&A, *"but I found when I started that 90% of my work came from one department."* Corporate contains the usual stalwarts like M&A and equity capital markets, but other specialties like leveraged finance and project finance also fall under its umbrella. Although *"there's always a partner there to make sure I don't mess up too badly,"* associates across the corporate groups get a good helping of responsibility. *"I've drafted SPAs and ancillary documents, and I've walked clients through changes I've made,"* one corporate associate told us. Litigation subgroups include patent litigation, securities and white-collar crime. *"What's great about this group is that we don't do much doc review,"* a litigator revealed. *"That's normally done by contract attorneys."*

"There's always a partner there to make sure I don't mess up too badly."

A stint in real estate is likely to see juniors liaising with other offices, for example Chicago lawyers helping New York colleagues on the property aspects of their transactions. Real estate is a smaller department in most offices, which lends itself to leanly staffed assignments and greater responsibility: *"I was tasked with junior, mid-level and even senior work, and soon I was running the smaller deals."*

Culture

Law firms in general are fond of talking up their culture: *"A lot of the time it's a load of crap,"* reflected one associate. But at Paul Hastings, talk of an *"entrepreneurial"* culture means the firm is *"more practical and less burdened by ideas of what a law firm should be."* We were told there's a constant effort *"to be more innovative in how we approach clients, structure fees and staff deals."* This isn't to say that Paul Hastings leaps onto every bandwagon it sees: *"We don't follow the crowd. Management wants to make sure we only do stuff that makes sense."*

"Less burdened by ideas about what a law firm should be."

Paul Hastings may attract people who want to push the envelope and set trends, but *"you won't find any sharp elbows or crazy gunners here."* This came as a relief to associates. *"The work is tough, but it's that much easier when you're working with someone you get a long with,"* mused an Atlantan. *"There's a mutual respect between partners and associates, and everyone is treated equally,"* said an IP boffin, adding *"I certainly didn't expect it to be so egalitarian."* Socially there's *"less of a happy hour crowd in DC than in New York,"* whose associates admitted to *"multiple informal happy hours."*

Training & Development

Paul Hastings uses the catchy acronym PH DNA (it stands for Paul Hastings Developing New Associates) to describe its training program. It kicks off with the associates assembling at one location for a few days of *"symposia, business training and other general 'how to be a lawyer' things."* This includes training on the culture of the firm, followed by practice group-specific training, then there's informal mentoring throughout the year. Usefully the firm gives new associates 150 client readiness hours, giving them billable credit for *"sitting in on phone calls, accompanying partners to meetings and shadowing senior people in court."* These not only allow juniors to make mistakes and discover strengths and weaknesses, but they also give them exposure to much higher level work than they'd normally see. *"I've done all sorts of fascinating things with those hours,"* mused one.

"I've done all sorts of fascinating things."

The assessment process has recently been overhauled to make it less formal and more *"organic."* The associates

See firm profile on p.682

we spoke to approved of this, citing the age-old principle that *"less paperwork is better."* Under the newly de-paperworked regime, associates *"are encouraged to seek feedback throughout the year,"* which involves discussions with associates and partners and filling out a self-assessment. This is then reviewed by the partners, who sit down with the associate and discuss the latter's performance throughout the year. *"It's not unduly burdensome,"* thought our sources, *"and it gives you the right level of feedback and information."*

Strategy & Future and Offices

The New York office is *"currently a little dated, but that's all slated to change in April 2016 when we move."* The new digs will be above Grand Central Station in the MetLife Building which, in the words of one associate, *"will make it easier to get into work."* The move is likely to see attorneys swapping their offices for an open plan workspace, which ruffled a few feathers. *"The firm's definitely thinking about communal spaces,"* said one associate. *"Maybe it's a fad and maybe not."* No such worries in Atlanta, which is *"one of the smaller offices, but located in one of the biggest buildings in Midtown."* Paul Hastings's other domestic offices are in Chicago, Houston, LA, Orange County, Palo Alto, San Diego, San Fran and DC. It has a further ten offices overseas.

According to managing partner Greg Nitzkowski, the firm's key markets for growth are London, New York, Washington, DC and Palo Alto. *"Those are where the work we want to do is,"* he explains. *"For example, we've always been strong in real estate finance, and more and more of that sector is concentrated in London and New York."* Similarly, he sees the firm investing in *"intellectual property, Foreign Corrupt Practices Act investigations, white-collar criminal defense and equity capital markets,"* among other staples like M&A. This isn't to say that Paul Hastings is running down its other offices; he sees them becoming *"smaller and more focused"* on their own specialist areas.

"They're happy for us to keep our own hours as long as the work is done."

Hours, Compensation and Pro Bono

"When the deal is on and the deadline is looming...I usually go home," confessed one associate when asked whether late nights were necessary, though admittedly they continue working from the comfort of the couch. *"They're generally happy for us to keep our own hours as long as the work is done,"* said another. Sometimes tasks require attorneys to be physically present in the office, so late nights do ensue. *"I've had to stay until 2am or 2.30am a couple of times,"* recalled a source in M&A, *"but that was during a closing, when everyone was running around with their hair on fire."*

Of course, when the work requires it, attorneys did find themselves pulling all-nighters, but these were balanced by the opportunity to go home early when work is slow. *"Barring something crazy, you aren't expected to sit in your office all the time,"* said a source. What associates are expected to do, at least if they want to be bonus-eligible, is bill 2,000 hours a year. *"It's definitely manageable,"* said a non-plussed attorney. *"The firm makes sure you hit the target at a reasonable pace."* For first-years, this is helped by the presence of those 150 client readiness hours, and associates at all levels can bill as many pro bono hours as they like toward the target. All associates who hit that 2,000 hour mark get a bonus, although the amount varies depending on how many hours over the target associates are, as well as their performance review.

"The partners here take it extremely seriously."

There may not be any upper limit on the number of pro bono hours Paul Hastings lawyers can bill, but there is a minimum requirement of 20. *"Everyone does way more than that,"* said one associate, who had done so much pro bono work they had lost count. Additionally, a lot of the pro bono matters the firm gets involved with are *"discrete tasks that you can get involved in when you have the time,"* which helps harried associates fit them into their busy schedules. Pro bono offerings range from death row miscarriage of justice cases to helping independent filmmakers secure permits. *"You really get to run with the cases,"* enthused a third-year. *"It's a great way to get your feet wet."*

"Each office will offer students slightly different opportunities."
Greg Nitzkowski, managing partner

Pro bono hours

- For all attorneys across all US offices: 68,582
- Average per US attorney: 90

Diversity

"The legal profession hasn't been the greatest when it comes to diversity," admitted our sources, *"but the partners here take it extremely seriously."* Paul Hastings boasts all the usual affinity groups, which run a variety of *"speakers, mentoring programs, dinners, lunches,*

See firm profile on p.682

and roundtables." They also host certain "*less traditional activities, like happy hours,*" and, in the case of the women's group, produce an annual report on female representation on corporate boards. "*It's one of the most read items on the website,*" explained an associate who had taken part. To encourage diverse students to apply, the firm offers a couple of $10,000 scholarships, and looks to foster connections with diversity organizations on campus. "*We collaborate with leading diversity organizations, law schools, diverse student groups, and clients to host panel discussions, career workshops, receptions, and job fairs around the country,*" official sources at the firm tell us.

Get Hired

Paul Hastings currently asks 'behavioral questions' at the callback stage (although this may change as the firm is reviewing its recruiting processes). We heard that these can cover topics like how you deal with tricky situations. While such questions may have been a source of anxiety, associates who have sat on the other side of the table assured us there's nothing to worry about. "*Some people find them difficult to answer,*" one admitted, "*but ultimately all we're trying to do is get them talking about themselves.*" Interviewers generally confine themselves to one behavioral question per interview. "*They aren't the emphasis of the interview,*" recalled a DC source.

"Drive, intellect and interpersonal skills."

Instead questioning focuses on candidate competencies. These include things like achievement, drive, teamwork, leadership, strong written and oral communication and a knowledge of the business world. The associates we spoke to who had been involved in recruitment also stressed the importance of personality. "*Drive, intellect and interpersonal skills are important,*" one explained, "*but if you're mean spirited you won't fit in here.*"

"We don't follow the crowd. Management wants to make sure we only do stuff that makes sense."

See firm profile on p.682

Paul, Weiss, Rifkind, Wharton & Garrison LLP

Lawyers per state

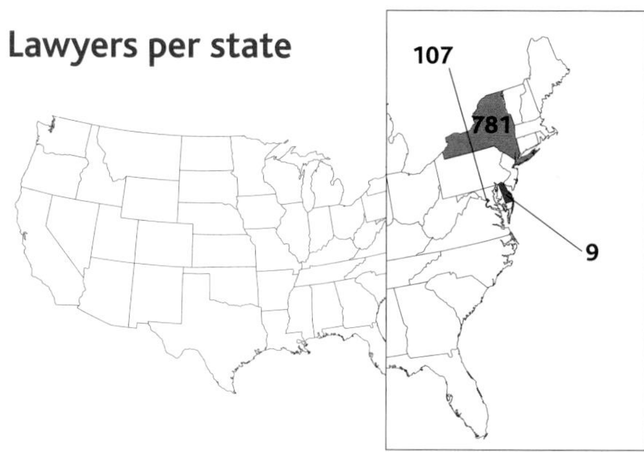

Largest US office: New York
US offices: 3
International offices: 5
First-year salary: $160,000
Billable hours: no requirement
Summers 2016: 144 (127 2Ls, 11 1Ls, 2 3Ls, 4 SEOs)
Revenue 2015: $1.11 billion (+7.1%)
Partners made 2016: 6 (all in US)
Famous for: star litigators; being one of New York's largest law firms; pro bono

Don't make the mistake of forgetting the comma in Paul, Weiss – attention to detail is as important as *"intelligence, poise and presentation skills."*

FROM assisting with the NFL in its investigation into the infamous Deflategate scandal to working on *US v Windsor* at the Supreme Court which legalized gay marriage, Paul, Weiss is the place to be for litigators who want to work on headline-grabbing cases. *"I knew that I wanted to be a litigator in New York,"* one associate told us, *"and everyone at law school told me 'go to Paul, Weiss: they're the best', so why would I want to go anywhere else?"* The firm boasts big name lawyers in its ranks, including legendary litigator Ted Wells; former head of the US attorney's criminal division in Manhattan, Lorin Reisner; and of more recent fame Roberta Kaplan, who led the marriage equality case.

It was a stellar 2015 for Paul, Weiss – it closed more multi-billion dollar cases than in any other year in its history. In lititgation, managing partner Brad Karp highlights the firm *"won approximately a dozen trials and arbitrations"* and successfully ended the Southern District United States Attorney's *"multi-year winning streak"* with the successful *"reversal on appeal of the insider trading convictions of Chiasson and Newman,"* two hedge fund managers.

On chambers-associate.com...

- More on media & entertainment
- Interview with managing partner Brad Karp and hiring partner Bob Zochowski

As well as litigation, Paul, Weiss has racked up multiple *Chambers USA* rankings in areas including corporate/M&A, capital markets, bankruptcy/restructuring, media & entertainment, IP, and financial services regulation. Brad Karp tells us that the *"M&A and private equity practices have been going like gangbusters for several years."* To aid growth *"the firm has deepened our talent base and expanded our relationships with our core institutional anchor clients."* Helped by the lateral hires, Paul, Weiss is *"focused on those practice areas and offices where we are market leaders; we do not try to be all things to all clients in all geographies,"* according to Karp. For the full interview, read our Bonus Features online.

ASSOCIATES SAY...

The Work

Although litigation is the firm's largest practice, many juniors join the corporate group and rotate through subgroups before specializing in their third year. A handful of juniors join the smaller practices of tax, real estate, personal representation, employee benefits, and bankruptcy. Assignment is a *"true hybrid system."* New starters are given *"a caseload database that you fill in with your responsibilities and interests each month."* An assigning partner then uses this to allocate junior work. After a few months associates can *"be proactive and seek out work or particular people."* However, *"I don't think*

See firm profile on p.683

Rankings in *Chambers USA*

Antitrust	Financial Services Regulation
Banking & Finance	Intellectual Property
Bankruptcy/Restructuring	Investment Funds
Capital Markets	Litigation
Corporate Crime & Investigations	Media & Entertainment
	Private Equity
Corporate/M&A	Real Estate
Employee Benefits & Executive Compensation	Retail
	Securities
ERISA Litigation	Tax
FCPA	Wealth Management

For detail on ranking tiers and ranking locations, visit www.chambersandpartners.com

Recent work highlights

- Represented Harlequin Enterprises, the largest publisher of women's e-books, in a dispute over royalties to authors
- Assisted Time Warner Cable with its $78.7 billion merger with Charter
- Conducted a report on behalf of the NFL, regarding the New England Patriots' involvement in the deflategate Super Bowl scandal
- Worked with Paramount Pictures regarding its SPV vehicle Melrose against plaintiff accusations of misleading information. The SPV invested in a string of movies including *Mean Girls* and *Mission Impossible 3*

there is the true anxiety of a free market because of the assigning partner," said one junior. *"I'm never worried that I won't have work to do."*

"I like that Paul, Weiss sees itself as a firm of litigation generalists," enthused one newbie. *"You never have to pick a specific group to devote your time to."* Fellow litigators agreed: *"Paul, Weiss thinks that if you're a true litigator it can throw any problem at you."* A wide range of litigation matters is up for grabs – juniors work on anything including *"IP, antitrust, securities, mass tort, white-collar, and FCPA* [Foreign Corruption Practices Act]." Over in the much smaller DC office, associates have the opportunity to sink their teeth into meaty matters such as *"assisting and analyzing financial documents, drafting interview outlines, prepping partners for witness interviews, presentations to the government and assisting companies with compliance programs."* Associates were pleased with the *"tremendous amount of responsibility and client contact the firm offers."*

"I'm never worried that I won't have work to do."

Corporate juniors are unassigned until their third year when they specialize in one of the subgroups, which include securities, M&A, finance, funds and IP. Some unassigned juniors had done *"a lot of structured finance and leverage deals."* While *"there is certainly some very simple junior work in corporate, Paul, Weiss gives you as much as it thinks you can handle,"* one busy associate told us. Another shared: *"I recently worked on a credit agreement involving a large public company's debt. That's a great example of high-level work between a partner and myself. The partner told me what to look through, what to focus on, and how to tackle all the options."* But responsibility in corporate is something of a mixed bag, and *"if you're the only the junior on a smaller matter then you'll be given more responsibility."* Some saw this as a double-edged sword: *"Sometimes it feels like too much responsibility. You're getting the opportunity to impress clients and people you work with. It's great, but there are always high risks attached."*

Training & Development

As only *"a small percentage of associates actually become partners,"* many associates will have thoughts at the back of their minds about future careers in government or in-house. Partners are aware of this and *"will help you get experience. They're pretty good at letting you start to shape your career as you go along."* However, we were told it's *"very rare to see people go from Paul, Weiss to another BigLaw firm."*

"Barrage of formal training."

In their first week, juniors can expect *a "barrage of formal training"* in *"everything from tech, substantive law, how to delegate work and how to manage time effectively."* Informal training programs run throughout the year, giving associates an introduction into the firm's different practices. Midlevel associates are also invited to *"a conference in New York where you meet other associates for a retraining session."*

Culture

Friendships that associates have made during the summer program have endured. One associate even revealed that *"I recently went to my third Paul, Weiss wedding!"* A litigation associate was more than happy to tell us about a firm that's *"a place of quirky individuals"* which allows *"me to be myself and not check my personality at the door."* Another added: *"There is no cookie cutter Paul, Weiss associate."* Associates here do crack the occasional joke at the expense of BigLaw culture. *"Most firms act like they're doing God's work and it's exhausting,"* one corporate lawyer quipped. *"Here, we're working for the man but we acknowledge it. We even joke about it!"*

"The Met Ball with lawyers."

See firm profile on p.683

Good working relationships lead to active social lives and *"there is always somebody organizing things"* in the New York office. *"We have a regular sushi Thursday in corporate and there are people who are constantly organizing karaoke nights,"* a junior relished. *"You wouldn't expect it's the nerdiest guys who get totally drunk!"* There's also a weekly cocktail party on Fridays. The firm's social pièce de résistance is its annual summer event, a sort of *"Met Ball with lawyers"* at MoMA. *"The coolest part is having the run of the museum,"* a previous attendee gushed. *"It's just you and The Starry Night."*

Hours & Compensation

There's no billing target at Paul, Weiss but associates assured us that *"as long as you're not actively avoiding work you'll hit a decent amount of hours."* Associates were keen to stress: *"We work a lot here. I don't think that's a surprise, and no one deceived me on that front."* The average 2,000 hours were generally seen as *"tolerable and sustainable,"* although not unusual *"are stretches where I've stayed past midnight several nights in a row."* For others, late nights are *"few and far between."* Juniors tend to start work at 9am and leave any time between 7.30pm and 10pm.

"We work a lot here. I don't think that's a surprise."

The definite con of the hours system is the effect it has on the firm's (market-rate) bonus system. *"It can seem unfair if you've been the person who went to trial three times and your bonus is the same as somebody with a lighter year,"* an associate grumbled. However, a very notable pro is the firm's generous flex time, officially called the 'alternative work program'. *"I take a pay cut and commit to 75% or 80% of the average billing hours,"* one mother told us. *"If you do end up working more at the end of the year they'll reimburse you for that amount. It works great for me because it enables me to tell people that I need to go home at a certain time."* Employees on reduced hours are provided with a *"home office,"* and an *"extra laptop and a printer."*

Offices

"Paul, Weiss may have eight offices but the vast majority of the people are in the New York office. Other offices service main New York clients operating elsewhere in the world," a corporate associate explained. *"Paul, Weiss is very New York centric. A few people go to work in London or Asia but they're mostly here."* The New York mothership is currently going through renovations and associates worried that *"we're growing faster than we are in floorspace."* As a result, waiting time for solo offices has increased, though the firm is buying up more space in the building. *"It's supposed to be that you share an office for the first year, then you get your own internal office without a window. The year after that you get an office with a window,"* one associate told us. Juniors appreciated the firm's art collection dotted around the place: *"I just go up and have a look at the art. It's pretty neat to go up there and see Annie Leibovitz."*

"I just go up and have a look at the art."

DC associates – several of whom had worked in New York – disagreed with the idea that working in New York was the be all and end all. *"When I moved to DC my cases didn't change. I remained on the same teams, just in a different office. None of my responsibilities changed."* On the whole, associates who'd worked in both offices could see the pros and cons of each office. *"In New York it's a typical BigLaw firm, there's lots of hustle and bustle and you meet a lot of people. In New York it's about the exposure the comes with the big office environment."* However, *"the DC office is great because it's attached to the New York office but it's a close knit environment – you won't get lost in the crowd here."*

"Everyone at law school told me 'go to Paul, Weiss: they're the best'."

Diversity

Paul, Weiss has a history of promoting diversity in its offices. In 1927, the firm was one of the first to allow Jews to practice with Gentiles; in 1949, it hired an African American associate, Harvard grad and ex-SCOTUS clerk William T. Coleman, at a time when few if any did; and in the early 1950s Carolyn Agger joined to become the first female partner at a major law firm. Juniors were quick to assure us that the firm stills strives to promote diversity in its offices: *"We speak about diversity a lot during the recruiting process,"* one associate revealed.

"We're also expanding the schools we're looking at – it's easy for firms to look at the same six schools over and over again." There are affinity groups for LGBT, ethnically diverse, female attorneys, and new parents. *"Do I think diversity is perfect here? Absolutely not!"* But most associates felt that *"in terms of sheer numbers, it's obvious BigLaw in general has a long way to go."*

"High schools in underprivileged areas put on mock trials."

See firm profile on p.683

Pro Bono

Pro bono hours are counted like any other hours and associates insisted that the number of hours they put in was never questioned. *"I'm not as involved as I'd like to be. If anything, I'm not being chased up as much as I should be."* Litigation rookies can take on *"criminal tasks like robberies, drug conspiracy allegations, landlord disputes and unemployment benefit appeals."* Corporate attorneys can *"help transgender people change their names, work on Iraqi refugee programs and working in family law clinics,"* among other things. Other associates were *"involved in a street law program with Georgetown,"* which sees *"high schools in underprivileged areas put on mock trials. Every week we choose a time to go to the school and teach students about the trial process."*

Pro bono hours:

- For all attorneys across all US offices: 55,151
- Average per US attorney: 63

Get Hired

"This a place of self starters," an associate warned. *"People who are just book smart but nothing else would have a hard time here."* Hiring partner Bob Zochowski sheds some light on the interview: *"In general, we try to talk about legal issues to get a sense of somebody's intelligence, poise and presentation skills. We try to imagine that they're a junior associate who is explaining something they've just researched for us."* However, he issues a word of caution for interviewees: *"At the end of the interview, we always ask whether you've got questions for us and not being able to ask anything says a lot about the candidate."* Go online for the full interview.

"A place of self starters."

Strategy & Future

"It's more of the same for us," hiring partner Bob Zochowski says of the firm's hiring plans. *"We're a steady state firm through good and bad. We didn't lay anyone off during the recession and we also didn't reduce our intake."* Although it weathered the 2008 recession, there are fresh challenges for the firm in the shape of a tough litigation market. However, managing partner Brad Karp is confident and tells us that *"the widely reported 'slow down' hasn't affected us. We're certainly aware of the current market dynamics, but we've been fortunate in that our litigation and white-collar practices have never been more active."* He continues: *"Our goal is to ensure that our brand remains pre-eminent in the litigation and white-collar areas."*

"We have fun working here and, from top to bottom, we pride ourselves on practicing law the right way. I feel so blessed to work here and to lead this firm."

Brad Karp, managing partner

See firm profile on p.683

Pepper Hamilton LLP

Lawyers per state

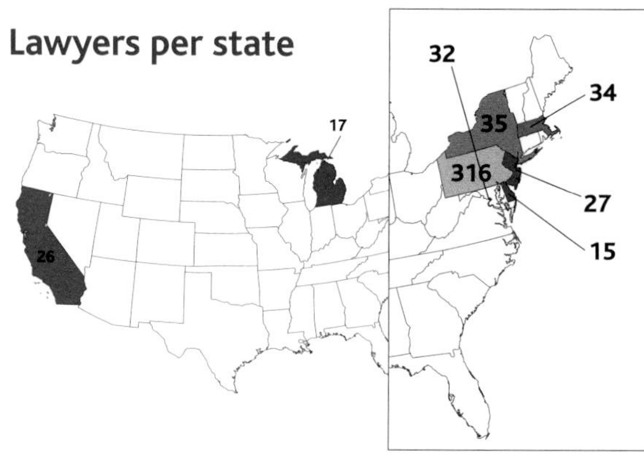

Largest US office: Philadelphia
US offices: 13
International offices: 0
First-year salary: $150,000 - $160,000
Billable hours: 1,940 target
Summers 2016: 23 (20 2Ls, 3 1Ls)
Revenue 2015: $389 million (+1%)
Partners made in 2016: 7
Famous for: life sciences know-how; Philadelphia institution

This healthy full service Philly firm is a heavy hitter in its home city and has a growing presence on both coasts.

IN law, as in life, change is a constant, and Pepper Hamilton didn't get to the sprightly age of 125 without moving with the times. The firm hasn't just developed new practices, grown to nearly 500 lawyers, or expanded out of its Philadelphia birthplace to offices on both coasts. It's innovated in other ways, and for example was one of the first law firms to offer value-based billing instead of rigid hourly rates. A focus on innovation is appropriate given that many of Pepper's clients come from the fast-moving pharmaceuticals industry, and shines through its snazzy website – one of the better law firm sites we've seen.

Thirteen offices countrywide include all the places you'd expect and a few that might surprise you. New York, Los Angeles, Boston and Washington, DC are all represented, but so too is Berwyn, a Philly suburb (population 3,631, a short drive from Villanova University). The firm is also one of the few in this guide that has an office in Princeton and Harrisburg. *"We do not have a plan to get to a certain size,"* managing partner Tom Cole explains, *"but we'll get as big as we need to in order to service our clients' needs."* However, most junior associates were based in Philadelphia at the time of our calls. As we went to press, it was reported that Pepper Hamilton had entered merger talks with Reed Smith, although these came to nothing.

On chambers-associate.com...

- We talk to managing partner Tom Cole
- Pepper Hamilton on Health Effects Litigation

ASSOCIATES SAY...

Offices

Pepper is organized by practice area rather than along office lines, which leads to a high degree of cooperation between offices. *"Philadelphia is the main office, so things often start here,"* said a health effects litigator at Pepper HQ, *"but I could be working with health effects lawyers in New York while my friends in commercial litigation work on stuff in California."* That said, some offices do have a geographical or sectoral focus. Princeton is full-service, but with a focus on the New Jersey market. Given their reputation as hotbeds of innovation, the offices in Boston and Silicon Valley have strong IP practices, while unsurprisingly DC hosts some government-centered groups, like government contracts and international trade litigation. The other offices we haven't mentioned so far are in Detroit, Orange County, Pittsburg, and Wilmington, DE.

"I could be working with health effects lawyers in New York while my friends in commercial litigation work on stuff in California."

The Inside View

See firm profile on p.684

Rankings in *Chambers USA*

Antitrust	Labor & Employment
Bankruptcy/Restructuring	Litigation
Construction	Products Liability
Corporate/M&A	Real Estate
Healthcare	Tax
Intellectual Property	

For detail on ranking tiers and ranking locations, visit www.chambersandpartners.com

Recent work highlights

- Advised Bojangles' Famous Chicken 'n' Biscuits on its $147 million IPO
- Defended health insurance provider Kaiser Permanente against a claim that its disciplinary processes violated physicians' due process rights
- Advised the Trump Organization on the preparation and negotiation of design and construction contracts for the re-construction of the Old Post Office in Washington, DC
- Represented electronics retailer GameStop in its acquisition of shares in novelty retailer Geeknet

The Work

Health effects litigation is probably Pepper's best known practice, and takes the most juniors. It's a product liability group with a focus on pharmaceutical companies and medical device manufacturers. Juniors are assigned to large teams focusing on litigation arising out of dodgy products, for example if they've injured someone. Within their 'product teams', they're then assigned to work on specific cases. Depending on the case's progress, tasks can include *"written discovery and drafting interrogatories, drafting and filing motions, and supporting memoranda,"* and *"writing outlines for expert depositions."* It's a science-y department and newbies can expect to grapple with some scientific as well as legal concepts: *"I've been working on some issues surrounding molecular biology,"* for example. But don't panic just yet: humanities and arts grads are actually well represented in this department.

The second highest number of juniors work in commercial litigation, which is research heavy and *"involves the ever glamorous document review"* but also offers the chance to depose witnesses and interview clients, among other things. Comm lit's appeal is the broad, almost eclectic mix of cases available: *"We're like the grabbag of what the other litigation groups don't do,"* joked one associate, *"so there's no such thing as a typical case."* Alongside the more traditional contractual disputes work, the group also handles data protection, white-collar and higher education internal investigations.

Litigation generally constitutes the bulk of Pepper's work, but the transactional side of things is big too and has been growing. The corporate & securities group offers a mix of capital markets, fund formation and M&A work, and deals can be national, regional and even international. *"I was amazed at how varied the work has been,"* enthused one here. *"I'll do the first draft of something, manage the checklist and the diligence process. I've never had an associate say 'next time I'll do the first cut'."* Corporate lawyers work closely with transactional IP experts, whose department *"covers all things patent, copyright, trademark and trade secrets-related."* In addition to doing specialist due diligence work for their corporate colleagues, there's also *"a lot of drafting work, preparing license agreements and doing markups."* This is a smaller group, *"which means I get exposed to more things at a quicker place,"* explained one associate. *"We're encouraged to be the clients' first point of contact."*

> *"We're encouraged to be the clients' first point of contact."*

Different departments have different ways of allocating work. In corporate & securities, associates report their availability, giving assigning partners an overview of who is available, enabling them to match partners who need help with free lawyers. In health effects, assignment is handled by team leader Nina Gussack, while in some of the smaller departments, juniors approach those higher up. Whatever system they used, there was no one left twiddling their thumbs. *"At a lot of firms, new associates worry about not having work to do,"* noted one health effects litigator, *"but that's not the case here."*

Training

The first week of training is the same for everyone, regardless of practice group or office. Associates from all over the firm converge on Philadelphia for such exciting topics as *"systems training and how to interact with support services."* Following this, there is *"ongoing orientation tailored to your particular practice area."* This isn't just about getting to grips with legal skills; it's also a chance to bone up on commercial awareness. *"It's all about understanding the industry,"* said a source in health effects. *"There's a big push for young associates to understand their client's business."*

> *"It could be more hands-on and less theoretical."*

Outside Philly, a lot of training is conducted by videoconference, which people had mixed feelings about. *"Some of it was helpful, some less so,"* admitted an associate in a smaller office. *"I think it could be more hands-on and less theoretical."* Associates enjoyed the two deposition

See firm profile on p.684

training events, one where Pepper partners with other law firms, and the other where local UPenn sciencey students (e.g. PhDs) will volunteer to play the witnesses. *"There was an attorney taking the deposition and one defending, and then the wild card: a PhD student acting as a witness,"* one junior experienced.

"I pulled an 18-hour day a couple of months back. It's rare for that to happen, but when it does, it's exciting."

Hours & Compensation

"I wasn't expecting New York hours," said one Philadelphian, *"but sometimes that was what I got."* Fear not, though: it's certainly not back-to-back late nights, and lawyers occasionally get to work nine to five when it's slow. *"When you're on a deal and you're working, you're really working, but when you're not, you can do what you want,"* summed up one associate. Even when the heat is on, lawyers admitted that the adrenaline rush more than compensated for the long hours. *"I pulled an 18-hour day a few months back,"* confided one source. *"It's rare for that to happen, but when it does, it's exciting."*

Everyone we spoke to thought the billable hours target of 1,940 was realistic. Associates described their salary as *"competitive,"* and felt that it adequately compensated for the times when they did have to work late. *"I remember how scary the economy was when I was in law school, so I'm happy to have a salary"* admitted one, *"and besides, we all just got a raise."*

Culture

"There isn't that much happening after work," admitted a Philly lawyer, *"but people are always getting together for lunch or a drink."* Much of the socializing is done in a *"nonstructured kind of way,"* but there are regular happy hours, and practice groups put on formal events from time to time. When we asked if it was possible to work at Pepper and have a life, interviewees answered with a collective 'yes.' For one thing, they get four weeks' vacation and partners allow them to use it all up. If that isn't possible, associates can roll one week of it to the first quarter of the following year.

"Someone who's only out for themselves wouldn't fit in here."

Pepperites insisted this isn't the sort of firm for those with sharpened elbows. *"There's no competition and nobody's trying to one-up their neighbor,"* said one. *"Someone who's only out for themselves wouldn't fit in here."* When the pressure's on and deadlines loom, lawyers *"are all rowing in concert."* Which is just as well, *"because there's a lot of work to do."*

Pro Bono

Pepper gets its associates involved in pro bono from the start. *"They really encourage you to get stuck in,"* explained a source. *"I was able to get involved immediately."* Others concurred: *"There's no limit on the number of pro bono hours you can do, and there's no distinction between pro bono clients and paying clients."* Depending on the office and practice group, there's a range of matters to sink your teeth into. In Philly, litigators can go to bat in Municipal Court for low-income tenants having difficulty with their landlords, while other sources reported working on *"guardianship matters, children's social security appeals and representing children in abuse cases."*

"I had my on-campus interview and thought: 'this is where I want to be'."

It's not just in the courtroom, either. On the transactional side, there's the opportunity to help startup businesses and nonprofits. Pepper also sponsors an annual essay writing competition named after former federal judge (and current firm bigwig) James T Giles. The idea is to get Philly's diverse public school students thinking (and writing) about hot-topic legal and policy issues. As part of its 125th anniversary celebrations, the firm organized a community service week, which included bussing Philly associates to a big park to give it a clean-up, helping at a homeless shelter, and assisting veterans.

Pro bono hours

- For all attorneys across all offices: 25,731
- Average per US attorney: 50

"...guard against unconscious bias and focus on the quality of the application."

Diversity

Diversity *"is definitely something that Pepper believes in,"* said one interviewee. *"It's not just for show."* The firm has affinity groups for ethnic minorities, LGBT attorneys and veterans and has a 'champion of diversity' award for someone prominent in business or academia who's worked to promote diversity. According to hiring partner Sean Fahy, the firm has also made a concerted effort to weed out unconscious bias. He tells us that *"we've made a big push to train everyone involved in the hiring process on implicit bias, and to guard against it*

See firm profile on p.684

we remove any reference to a candidate's name and law school from their writing sample." This not only removes the risk of unconscious bias but also *"allows us to focus on the quality of the application,"* ultimately leading to better recruitment decisions.

Get Hired

When it comes to a candidate's resume, Pepper tends to focus on what a candidate has done at law school. *"They aren't looking for anything in particular,"* explained an associate, *"but things like law review, mock trial or affinity groups certainly help."* While you'll need to show that you're committed to working in Philadelphia if you want to work here, Pepper isn't as picky as other firms in the neighborhood. *"Some firms are suspicious that people are planning to disappear off to New York or Washington, so they'll question you over and over about your motivation,"* we heard.

"The worst thing you can do is not be yourself."

"In some years, half our class is made up of people who have written to us directly, applying outside the OCI process," says hiring partner Sean Fahy. Associates told us the OCIs themselves aren't *"too wacky,"* and serve as a screening process for the main callback interview. At either the write-in or OCI stage, candidates submit a writing sample. At the callback, recruiters pick the applicant's brains about his or her writing style. Following that, *"you're given a hypothetical legal scenario to talk through with the interviewers,"* said one source familiar with the process. Although *"there's no right or wrong answer,"* sources involved with recruitment admitted that this part *"could feel a little wacky if you're on the other end."* Sean Fahy advises against panicking though: *"All of our interviewing is designed to to get to know you; the worst thing you can do is not be yourself."*

Strategy & Future

Speaking of recruitment, Pepper hires between 20 and 25 first-years each year, of which most tend to go to Philly. This formula isn't set in stone, according to HP Sean Fahy. *"Recruitment is driven by discussions with the partners in each office,"* he says. There's certainly a push to increase Pepper's presence outside Philadelphia. As the firm is *"already a strong player in Philadelphia and the mid-Atlantic, we're looking to grow our presence on the West Coast and, on the East Coast, in New York, Boston and Washington, DC,"* managing partner Tom Cole tells us. *"We want to be geographically balanced across the country."*

"We do not have some grand plan about what size we want to be, but we'll get as big as we need to in order to service our clients needs."
Tom Cole, managing partner

See firm profile on p.684

Perkins Coie LLP

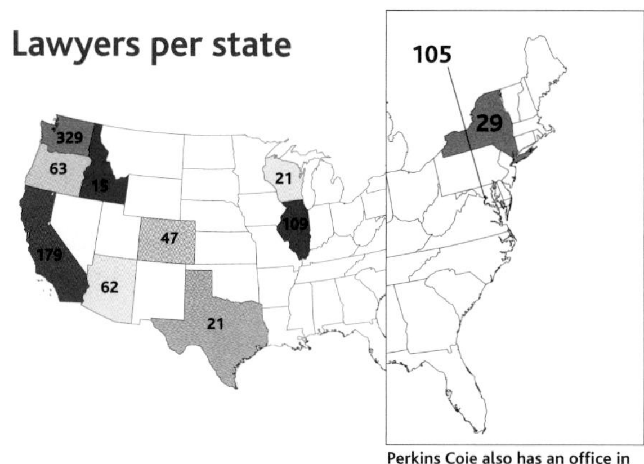

Perkins Coie also has an office in Alaska with nine attorneys

Largest US office: Seattle
US offices: 16
International offices: 3
First-year salary: $100,000 (Anchorage) - $160,000
Billable hours: 1,800 - 1,950 required
Summers 2016: 47 (all 2Ls)
Revenue 2015: $748.6 million (+5.4%)
Partners made 2016: 22 (all US)
Famous for: aviation; political law; lack of neckties

Rising in the West and settling in the East, this tech-savvy outfit has become a national star without losing its West Coast shine. Just don't call it a lifestyle firm...

GROWING out of Seattle and boasting a strong Bay Area presence, it's little surprise that Perkins Coie's tech credentials are long-established. The firm has made its name servicing some of the most cutting-edge companies going, and its client roster now reads like a who's who of social media and technology companies. Household names like Amazon, Facebook, Microsoft and Netflix are all on the books, and the high-flying aviation practice – top ranked in *Chambers USA* – has been servicing Boeing for a century. *Chambers* recognizes a dozen other practice areas too, including general commercial litigation, labor & employment, IP, retail, and political law. For more on the latter, read our interview with Hillary Clinton's campaign lawyer and Perkins Coie partner Marc Elias on page 60.

It's been a prosperous year for Perkins Coie (pronounced coo-ey). Revenue is up by 5.4% and there have been some significant triumphs for the firm's esteemed political law practice. In Florida there was a big victory for voters when Perkins successfully challenged the lawfulness of the Sunshine State's congressional voting map. Head to Illinois, and Highland Park's ban on assault weapons and large capacity magazines was upheld with Perkins Coie's help, a coup that rookies were *"extremely proud of due to the ripple effect it could have upon gun control laws nationwide."* We join them in firing our metaphorical guns in the air with glee.

On chambers-associate.com...

- We speak with Perkins' head recruiter Mike Gotham

Juniors were also highly complimentary about the firm's culture. Though now a national presence, *"Perkins' management has retained a considerate approach that many of our East Coast rivals lack."* Managerial transparency is pretty good, suits have made way for slacks, and weekends in the office are thankfully few and far between. *"We're all extremely hard working and there are late nights,"* reminded one interviewee, *"but we also care a lot about supporting one another and working together to make our clients' problems disappear. The firm's approach just helps to facilitate that end result."*

ASSOCIATES SAY...

The Work

On arrival, a handful of new recruits are snapped up by smaller teams such as energy & resources (EER), political law and product liability, but most go into the business, commercial litigation, or IP practice groups. Fledglings in these three practices are assigned to one of a number of subgroups. Business has subgroups including: corporate governance/transactions; emerging companies & venture capital; financial transactions/restructuring; international transactions & trade; private equity; and tech transactions & privacy. Within commer-

The Inside View

See firm profile on p.685

Rankings in *Chambers USA*

Bankruptcy/Restructuring	Litigation
Corporate/Commercial	Native American Law
Corporate/M&A	Natural Resources
Environment	Privacy & Data Security
Government	Products Liability
Insurance	Real Estate
Intellectual Property	Retail
Labor & Employment	Startups & Emerging Companies
Leisure & Hospitality	
Life Sciences	Transportation

For detail on ranking tiers and ranking locations, visit www.chambersandpartners.com

cial litigation, juniors join one of: antitrust; business litigation; construction; environment; insurance recovery; securities; or white-collar/investigations. IP folks choose to specialize in patent work or trademark & copyright.

"You feel increasingly integral with every month that goes by."

The subgroup allocation can be more a formality, because *"scheduling is quite fluid."* In fact, juniors are *"encouraged to scout out work from seniors and partners whose practices we find interesting. Once you've shown them what you can do, they'll usually keep you busy."* Associates fill in regular email surveys to help management keep an eye on utilization, and a career coach is on hand for those who feel they've got too much on their plate and to answer anything else related to career development. As one Seattlite chimed: *"She used to work here before becoming a counselor, so understands what it's like to practice at a BigLaw firm. Having that safe space to discuss any anxieties is a huge resource."*

Juniors' development is *"well managed,"* and the consensus was that *"they get you up to speed carefully."* To begin, rookies are accountable for more discrete responsibilities, which for litigators involves doc review and research, and for deal-doers includes diligence and disclosure. *"We're always told to ask questions, no matter how stupid they may seem. As your understanding and experience grow, people become more open to giving you new responsibilities. You feel increasingly integral with every month that goes by."* By their second year most young litigators had taken depositions or drafted motions, whereas on the transactional side our more experienced interviewees had negotiated on smaller deals and handled ancillary documents. Often offering the chance to work one-on-one with partners, smaller matters were touted as *"a good fast-track to higher responsibilities."*

Recent work highlights

- Serving as general counsel to Hillary Rodham Clinton's presidential campaign 'Hillary for America'
- Staged a successful patent challenge on behalf of pharmaceutical company Mylan. The appellate victory invalidated the patent of rival company Teva's 'Copaxone', a multiple sclerosis medication that sells in excess of $3 billion annually
- Helped Amazon to set up its $100 million Alexa Fund. Launching with investments in seven emerging companies, the fund's aim is to support developers whose products explore the boundaries of voice technology
- Represented analytics startup tenXer in it's takeover by Twitter. The brainchild of blackjack boffin Jeff Ma, who served as the inspiration for the film *21*, tenXer's sale was valued at roughly $50 million

Offices

"Whenever we've asked for improvements to be made, Perkins has really listened," was the experience of one happy junior. In Seattle, for example, *"there was recently some demand among associates for standing desks, and the firm happily obliged"* (though we should point out these don't come as standard in all offices). It's little surprise that those in the Emerald City like to be on their feet: whether they're dashing off to the *"generously subsidized"* cafeteria, hitting the free gym or taking in the *"spectacular"* view of Mount Rainier from their office, *"there are no expenses spared to create an exciting and inspiring work setting."* But when it comes to views, Perkins' Anchorage outpost really steals the show. Sources had heard that *"you can see Denali from your desk, and beluga-spotting emails circulate when a pod is spotted in the Turnagain Arm!"*

"There are no expenses spared to create an exciting and inspiring work setting."

Outside Seattle, Perkins Coie has 15 other offices spread around pretty much most of the country. With so many footholds nationwide, does Perkins feel like an integrated operation? *"I don't feel like the HQ bosses us around,"* non-Seattlites agreed. Each January the firm's new associate retreat serves as *"an invaluable tool"* for promoting cross-office interaction, welcoming all new starters to Seattle for *"breakout training zones, writing clinics, presentations on the firm's culture, and tutorials on how to reach out to other offices to get work. I've gotten work through contacts I made on that retreat."*

See firm profile on p.685

Training & Development

The new starter retreat is trailed by a succession of monthly CLEs and departmental training sessions, which are broadcast firmwide. The mini-MBA begun just over a year ago for deal-doers was just as popular in its second year, providing transactional hopefuls with tips on representing businesses over the course of six 90-minute sessions. *"When I began I didn't even know what an income statement was,"* sighed one rookie, *"so the mini-MBA helped to map out a lot of gray areas."*

"The onus is on us to consult partners."

Guided by biannual appraisals in their first year, and annual appraisals from then on, rookies' learning is bolstered on-the-job. *"We're busy folk, so the onus is on us to consult partners if we'd like feedback,"* elaborated one. *"If you ask partners to sit with you and talk through your progress they'd find a time to do it, without question."*

Diversity

There are two firmwide diversity retreats every other year: one for women, and one for all other minorities. *"It's not just a free vacation,"* explained one minority associate. *"The leadership comes out too, as there's a belief that these kinds of events can really help the firm to grow. When management asked us what the firm could improve upon, I really felt it was listening."*

On a more regular basis, *"the firm stages internal discussions focusing on nuanced discrepancies like the difference between working with introverts and extroverts,"* highlighted one Phoenix junior. Such considerations bleed into Perkins' hiring, where *"a far-reaching range of geographic locations and law schools is represented."*

"A far-reaching range of geographic locations and law schools is represented."

Furthermore, Perkins' 1L diversity fellowship scheme *"is also an important tool for recruiting students who ultimately become associates,"* says director of recruiting and retention Mike Gotham. *"The program offers a dozen or so paid summer associate positions per year, and recipients are also awarded a $7,500 scholarship to assist with their school tuition."*

Culture

"Around 35% of us are based in Seattle," one second-year explained, *"so the overall pulse of the firm really stems from here."* Interviewees in offices nationwide had felt the effect of this West Coast cultural lifeblood. They noted a relaxed dress code – *"we're not here in shorts, but ties are a rarity. We'll wear jeans on a Friday"* – a friendly working atmosphere, and the flexibility to dictate your own office hours as some of the key benefits. *"It's a really pleasant environment to be in,"* associates agreed. *"No one seems to take themselves too seriously. There's a recognition that we're all a team that comes together to get the job done."*

"We're not here in shorts, but ties are a rarity."

Perkins may boast a *"laid back West Coast feel,"* but it's not all country retreats and mountain-gazing. In the words of managing partner John Devaney: *"We manage with a real emphasis on collegiality, transparency and civility – we work hard for our clients, and we also work hard to make the firm a place where people want to come in each day, roll up their sleeves and do great work with people they enjoy. People here are extremely determined and devoted, and we want to reward that with a fulfilling work place."*

Hours & Compensation

Billing targets and salaries are linked to local markets, so whereas 1,800 hours will bag you $100,000 in Anchorage, for example, those in DC, Texas and California are among those expected to put in 1,950 to earn $160k. In Portland the figures are 1,850 for $120,000, the same hours as those in Seattle but for $30,000 less salary. *"Different markets command different rates,"* accepted one junior, *"but our pay is on par with most of the larger firms in our respective locations."*

"Our pay is on par."

Portland's rise to hipsterdom has pushed up rents significantly, prompting some calls for a salary increase. Following their Seattle neighbors' recent compensation and billing target raise, Portlandians *"couldn't have been more impressed with the way the firm handled it. Our managing partner held a lunch to inform us how our compensation would be reviewed, and let us know what we could do to assist the process."* Bonuses are awarded for every 50 additional hours that associates put in beyond their billing targets.

"People here are extremely determined and devoted, and we want to reward that with a fulfilling work place."

"The work/life balance is tremendous here," said one happy caller. *"Sure it's a lot of work, but people are incredibly considerate of your time. As long as you're get-*

The Inside View

See firm profile on p.685

ting everything done it doesn't matter where you are." Most of our sources put in an average of ten hours a day, but *"whether you clock in all your your hours in the office, or put in some at home is up to you."* Weekend work is *"somewhat of a rarity,"* thanks in part to partners' *"accepting attitude of the need for a life outside of work."* As one respondent delighted, *"if people send you an email on a Sunday, they'll often start it off with 'Sorry to bother you,' and 'Don't do anything until tomorrow!'"*

"Pretty much everyone has a pro bono matter on at all times."

Pro Bono

Whether it's acquitting Osama bin Laden's driver of supporting terrorism or overturning Arizona's same-sex marriage ban, Perkins has earned a real reputation for taking on headline-hitting pro bono cases. More than just a mere ploy to hit the front pages, the firm's *"dedicated approach to social justice"* brings in all sorts. All pro bono hours count toward associates' billable target, so whether it's prisoners' rights cases, immigration work, or landlord-tenant disputes, *"pretty much everyone has a pro bono matter on at all times."* One good Samaritan added: *"When it comes to skills such as case management, drafting, redrafting, and even advocacy, it can really open some doors early on."*

Pro bono hours

- For all attorneys across all US offices: 54,408
- Average per US attorney: 59

Strategy & Future

When we asked associates what's on the horizon, the answer was almost unanimous: *"Keep growing our national presence."* One elaborated: *"We've been labeled as a super-regional firm for too long, and when you consider the locations and clients we cover, we feel that 'regional' misses the mark."*

"We feel that 'regional' misses the mark."

As Perkins' first managing partner outside of Seattle in over a century, DC-based John Devaney's 2015 ascension *"marked a real turning point."* As the boss himself continues: *"Selecting a managing partner in DC shows that we're a firm with a national and global outlook."* Are there any further expansion plans in the pipeline? *"We intend to continue our growth by further strengthening in our major markets: the Bay Area, Chicago, DC and NY,"* he explains. *"We're still a bit weighted towards the western side of the Mississippi river, so though nothing is imminent, we are certainly interested in increasing our East Coast footprint."*

Get Hired

Like all top law firms Perkins is looking for intelligent hopefuls with a demonstrable interest in the legal world. Law review, moot court, or prior work experience were all cited as good resume-boosters, but *"what sets our hiring apart is the emphasis placed on also finding a good match,"* said a someone in a medium-sized office. *"A survival of the fittest mentality doesn't wash here. That's especially true if you're applying for a smaller office."*

"A survival of the fittest mentality doesn't wash here."

Recruiting chief Mike Gotham also shuns any sharp elbows, confirming *"we hire associates with the expectation that they'll be here for the long haul."* And though the day-to-day dress code may allow a little more breathing space than at some rival firms, when it comes to interviews, Gotham has *"never seen a student show up in less than a suit."* Read our full interview with him in the Bonus Features.

"In the Anchorage office you can see Denali from your desk, and beluga-spotting emails circulate when a pod is spotted in the Turnagain Arm!"

See firm profile on p.685

Pillsbury Winthrop Shaw Pittman LLP

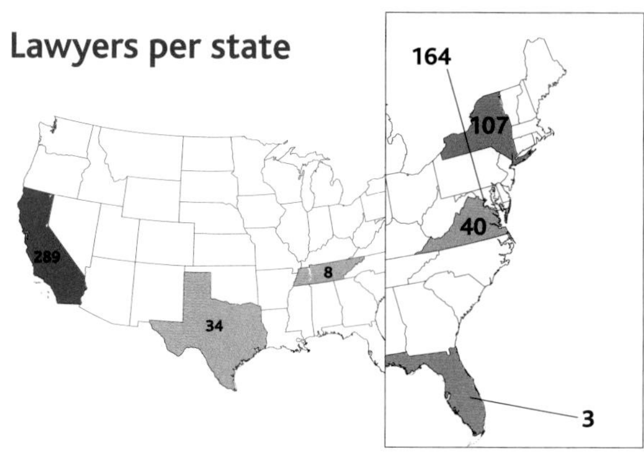

Largest office: Washington, DC

US offices: 13

International offices: 5

First year salary: $160,000

Billable hours: 1,950 target (bonus eligible at 1,900 and 2,000)

Summers 2016: 43 (42 2Ls, 1 1L)

Revenue 2015: $557 million (-0.5%)

Partners made 2016: 5 (all US)

Famous for: the urge to merge; California history

Thanks to the California sunshine and big-name clients, associates reckoned life at Pillsbury is *"as good as BigLaw gets."*

ESTABLISHED after the California Gold Rush, San Francisco-based Pillsbury is one of California's original powerhouse firms. It's been through four mergers since 1990, and has been a regular in the legal press over the past few years regarding a potential merger with the likes of Orrick and Norton Rose Fulbright. These came to nought, as did rumored talks with New York-based Chadbourne & Parke in late 2015. But it's worth googling Pillsbury before your OCI to see if any new suitors are being speculated about. *"Hopefully associates and others will see that any move we might make would be done to strengthen the firm and to thrive for years to come,"* Pillsbury's chair and CEO Jim Rishwain tells us. *"Any combination we would consider would be to meet strategic objectives and gain greater depth in our sectors and markets."*

Associates we interviewed highlighted the firm's roster of high profile clients, such as Chevron, Disney, VISA and Amazon. *Chambers USA* gives the thumbs up to a multitude of practices including construction, energy, environment, corporate/M&A, life sciences, tax, and real estate. Revenue in 2015 dipped slightly (0.5%) to $557 million but profits per partner rose 1.7% to $1.185 million. This was thanks in part to a drop in equity partners, though head count rose overall. In March 2015, Pillsbury lost a group of corporate, finance and private equity partners to Winston & Strawn, and in June three IP partners jumped ship to Sheppard Mullin. Despite this, Jim Rishwain says: *"We have had our most significant year for partner growth, despite some departures early in the year. We have added 30 partners in 2015, with more additions on the near horizon."* At the end of 2016, Rishwain will hand over the reins as firm chair to David Dekker, after a decade in the driving seat. Finally, in March 2016 it was reported that Pillsbury is launching a Hong Kong office.

On chambers-associate.com...

- Interviews with chair and CEO Jim Rishwain and hiring partner Mariah Brandt

ASSOCIATES SAY...

The Work

Associates explained that *"there is no formal assigning process"* but that it's not *"overtly competitive."* They believed that the free market encourages associates to be *"outgoing"* and to *"let partners know what you're working on, the kind of work you're interested in, and how many hours you can spare."* On the flip side, sources found that *"partners are pretty good at reaching out and doling work out fairly."* Corporate & securities was home to the most juniors at the time of our calls, but new associates are spread around a wide range of practices. These include litigation, global sourcing, environmental, public practices, IP, communications, real estate, insolvency, finance, and estates & trusts, and tax.

See firm profile on p.686

Rankings in *Chambers USA*

Capital Markets	International Trade
Construction	IT & Outsourcing
Corporate/M&A	Outsourcing
Employee Benefits & Executive Compensation	Real Estate
	Retail
Energy & Natural Resources	Tax
Environment	Technology
Food & Beverages	Telecommunications
Government	Transportation
Insurance	Wealth Management
Intellectual Property	

For detail on ranking tiers and ranking locations, visit www.chambersandpartners.com

Recent work highlights

- Won a $55 million jury verdict for Victaulic in a high-stakes insurance recovery case
- Continued to work on a complex dispute regarding the San Onofre nuclear power plant in California
- Involved in transactions totaling $12 billion for Deutsche Bank in Latin America
- Assisted Global Cash Access in its $1.2 billion acquisition of publicly traded slot machine company Multimedia Games
- Won a trademark suit for Facebook's virtual reality company Oculus

Corporate associates told us that *"the work is pretty much a 50/50 split between capital markets and M&A,"* but day-to-day tasks were *"a little bit of everything."* The Silicon Valley practice assists *"clients abroad – especially companies in Europe – that are looking to transition into that Silicon Valley model. As a result, they set up companies in Europe and they need our help, whether that's making a parent company in the US or a subsidiary."* Cross border work with *"big Asian companies"* is also up for grabs. Work for LA corporate attorneys *"includes specialized M&As, debt acquisitions, private equity,"* and *"some compliance regulatory work for aviation and real estate."* Over in New York, juniors had tasted *"underwriting, capital markets, private placements and lots of utility clients."* Associates also told us that *"we staff quite leanly here,"* and *"on the smaller side there are deals where I've been the only associate."*

"There are deals where I've been the only associate."

"One of the things that attracted me to litigation was that it's large enough to have its fingers in many different pies," an associate enthused. *"If somebody in real estate has a lease dispute or a construction problem they call us. If somebody is advising somebody and they get slapped with an incitement they'll call up the guys in white-collar."* Associates draft *"motions, brief memos, discovery and responses,"* and *"persuasive documents and filings of differing length and complexity"* make up the bulk of junior work. There is *"also a pretty solid amount of doc review and discovery requests."* Overall, litigators were happy with their workload and that *"partners give us responsibility early on. Everyone is patient and understanding; they've been here before."*

Real estate work *"revolves around large institutional real estate investment trusts,"* an associate explained. *"It's a lot of buying large office buildings, joint ventures to hold properties, and lease work on anywhere from Twitter HQ to small office buildings all around the country."* Newbies had been asked to *"review titles to see if there are any issues,"* and *"help revise and update agreements."* Associates also *"go through surveys and title documents with a client, negotiating deals and getting documents together for closure."*

"An office straight out of an HBO show."

Offices

With offices in San Francisco, Los Angeles, Silicon Valley, Sacramento and San Diego, it's not surprising the firm is known for its California footprint. However, offices in Texas, Nashville, Northern Virginia, Washington DC, New York and Florida ensure that the Pillsbury presence isn't limited to The Golden State. Over in the Big Apple, the Times Square location was seen *"as blessing and a curse,"* juniors bemoaning their *"minimal lunch options, tough commute"* and the unpleasant task of *"wading through tourists."* However, there are *"stunning views of the ball drop area."* The DC office recently moved from its HQ of 30 years to a sleeker build with *"great rooftop views of the city"* and *"a smaller floor plan, which means you can't get through the day without interacting with everyone."*

The LA outfit looks like *"an office straight out of an HBO show,"* thanks to enviable views of the Hollywood Sign and the ocean. Associates and their various entourages – friends, contacts and potential clients – can also rock up to to Lakers, Clippers and Dodgers games thanks to Pillsbury's complimentary seats. The San Francisco office can be found at the far end of the financial district *"near lots of shops, food stalls and a farmer's market that happens three times a week."* Like associates in LA and DC, juniors get their own *"office from day one."* As *"the last building before the water,"* it offers *"beautiful views of the Golden Gate and Bay Bridges."* Sports fans are in for a treat as Pillsbury has *"a box at the Giants Ball Stadium,"* where lucky associates can take *"clients to games to seal the deal."*

See firm profile on p.686

Culture

Associates generally described the *"vibe"* of their office as *"casual. Everyone is on a first name basis and there are social events to help departments interact."* In DC, *"regular ice cream socials get people away from their desks"* and there's a *"jeans Friday,"* which one junior told us they took *"1,000% advantage of."* Day-to-day, *"people with families tend to peace out at 6.30pm and then log on at home."* New Yorkers all agreed that Pillsbury is less *"OTT than other firms,"* adding: *"This isn't a party firm."*

"Mixers and scavenger hunts."

Similarly, Los Angeleans *"prioritize going home to their families and having lives outside of the Pillsbury bubble."* The office puts on *"mixers and scavenger hunts"* when summer associates are around. The LA culture is *"as good as BigLaw gets,"* and young partners in particular *"are interested in you as a person and not just an employee."* Associates in San Francisco are a sociable group – younger attorneys apparently take full advantage of the *"associate happy hours"* put on at local bars. The office's associate development committee runs *"training and mentoring programs to get associates out and interacting."* The committee puts on *"mixers"* and charity fundraising events such as *"a casino night where all the proceeds went to charity."*

Get Hired

According to associates, the ideal Pillsbury attorney is *"able to work well with others. People like that do better than quiet shy types who keep themselves to themselves."* One source even said they were *"praised for speaking my mind and being loud and boisterous!"* We wouldn't advise too loud and boisterous, though... Others were keen to stress that people *"with aggressive type A personalities won't succeed here. When you're billing long hours and everything is hitting the fan, that abrasive personality will start to wear on your co-workers."*

"Don't be afraid to knock on the door."

Associates who'd been through OCIs had some sage advice for nervous students: *"Relax a little! If you're interviewing at this level you've got amazing accomplishments, so be yourself."* Candidates who haven't received an offer should *"never underestimate the power of calling up the firm. Don't be afraid to knock on the door and say 'I really love this firm and I'd love you talk to you guys when you have a moment.' Interviewers remember people who do that."* For tips from hiring partner Mariah Brandt, read the Bonus Features in our web version of Pillsbury.

Diversity

Pillsbury has been consistently praised for its gender diversity and it's been named in the *Working Mother*'s 100 Best Companies list for ten consecutive years. The firm holds an attorneys of color diversity conference every three years which is *"a two day set-up with various diverse speakers and panels for diverse associates and partners."* Attorneys *"get together and brain storm ways we can improve diversity."* Fruits of these labors can be seen in the *"recent implicit bias training"* and a continued presence at diverse law fairs such as the LGBT Lavender Law Fair and National Black Law Student Association (NBLSA) career fairs. LA attorneys felt their office was the most diverse. One representative associate told us: *"I do think the firm could improve, but again, I've not got much to compare it to, and from what I understand it's an area all firms can improve in."*

"We have added 30 partners in 2015, with more additions on the near horizon."
Jim Rishwain, chair and CEO

Pro Bono

Associates are given a pro bono target of 60 hours – recently raised from 25 – but are allowed to bill as many pro bono hours as they want. We heard about various pro bono organizations the firm has relationships with. In LA, associates work *"with the center for gun violence,"* which is *"a nonprofit group that does a lot of research into fighting gun violence and gun law."* In San Francisco (home of sky high rents), associates *"co-sign negotiations to do with leaseholds,"* as *"unfair evictions are a major problem in San Francisco. A lot of people are being unlawfully evicted."* In DC, some people work pro bono for the Bread for the City clinic, which assists low-income clients with legal issues.

Pro bono hours:

- For all attorneys across all US offices: 31,132
- Average per US attorney: 56

"Make sure you've got the fundamentals down."

Training & Development

First-years are trained via Pillsbury University (PU), a system made up of *"video conferences"* tailored for specific practice areas. *"They're keen to make sure you've got the fundamentals down."* Corporate juniors were taught *"how to negotiate venture debt"* while litigators

The Inside View

See firm profile on p.686

are offered help in *"discovery motions and legal writing. They offer a variety of training options,"* a PU graduate told us. *"I'd advise first-years to take it."* However, other sources claimed: *"You could go through the entire year and ignore it,"* though this *"isn't the wisest decision you could make."* First-years are allowed to bill 150 hours of PU work, one of the scheme's more popular features.

Hours & Compensation

The 1,950 billing target can seem tough when *"there is a mountain of work to be done,"* but overall our sources were optimistic. *"It's about riding the wave of work,"* one corporate associate mused. *"When you're busy, you bill the crap out of your hours. But work is deal driven so it really depends on what's on."* Most associates weren't worried because *"if you're below your target they do make exceptions. I was at 95% of my hours last year and I still got a raise."* The firm offers a standard bonus and a second discretionary bonus *"if you hit 110% of your hours."* This bonus is *"not being transparent enough,"* some felt, and others were unsure *"whether I'm even going to get it."* Associates are eligible for bonuses if they hit 1,900 or 2,000 hours.

"Work is deal driven so it really depends on what's on."

Billing 110% may seem daunting, but associates in busier seats such as corporate were accustomed to staying till the early hours: *"There have been times when I've left at 3am and come back in at 6am to close the deal."* However, 3am finishes are rare and associates usually arrive at 9/9.30am and leave by 7.30pm.

Strategy & Future

Changes are afoot as decade-long chair Jim Rishwain prepares to hand over to chair-elect David Dekker on January 1, 2017, something that Pillsbury announced back in 2015. *"I am working with Dave very closely,"* says Rishwain. *"He is shadowing me both internally and externally with respect to all aspects of being the chair of the firm. I am absolutely committed to ensuring that we become a role model for firm leadership succession."*

Expanding regions in the past year include Texas and the South: *"We have not opened an office this year, but our Austin office has grown from four to 30 people since we opened in 2014, and we continue to grow our global operations center in Nashville. Overall, it has been a prosperous year for Pillsbury."* On the topic of a possible future merger, Rishwain tells us: *"Our strategy is not to merge just for the purpose of merging. Our strategy is to have the depth and breadth to best serve clients. We pursue that strategy through a variety of means, including internal talent development, lateral hiring, law school recruiting, and by being open minded to different groups. We would only merge with another firm from a position of strength and strategy."* For the full interview, visit our website.

"People with families tend to peace out at 6.30pm and then log on at home."

See firm profile on p.686

Proskauer Rose LLP

Lawyers per state

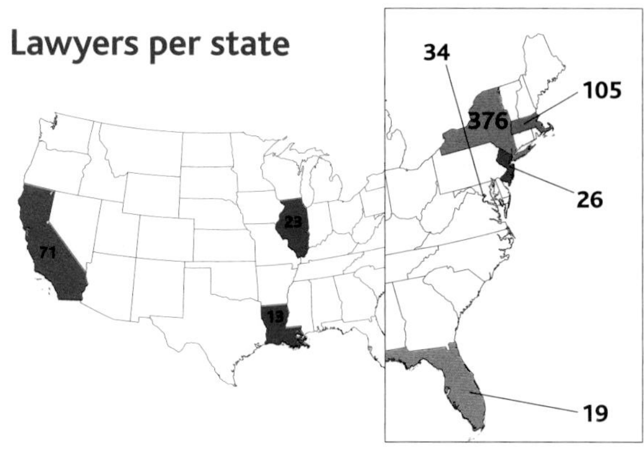

Largest US office: New York
US offices: 8
International offices: 5
First-year salary: $110,000 - $160,000
Billable hours: no requirement
Summers 2016: 77 (63 2Ls, 12 1Ls, 2 SEOs)
Revenue 2015: $822.3 million (+0.5%)
Partners made in 2016: 9 (8 in US)
Famous for: labor & employment work; sports practice; extensive alumni network

In the BigLaw league, Proskauer's hard to beat.

LOS Angeles' bid for the 2024 Olympic Games – LA 2024 – got an energy boost recently when it joined forces with elite legal athlete Proskauer. The sports law superstar (Band 1 in *Chambers USA*) serves as LA's legal counsel and strategic adviser in the race, and will do much of the running for the bid in the coming years. Before all the college jocks and jockettes among you rush to apply, we should point out that Proskauer's sporting prowess is a fairly niche activity among the far greater number of corporate and litigation teams which account for the largest proportion of the firm's 700-plus attorneys. That said, the Olympic bid will over time utilize the firm's expertise across multiple offices and departments.

But it's Proskauer's longstanding position atop the podium for its labor & employment work where the firm originally earned its esteemed reputation for greatness. *"If you're going to work in labor and employment in New York, there is no other place,"* one junior proclaimed. *"It's the gold standard."* The Big Apple houses the firm's HQ but it also operates a further seven bases at home – most of which are on the East Coast – and rounds these off with overseas offices in London, Paris, Hong Kong, Beijing and São Paulo.

On chambers-associate.com...

- Proskauer's training program
- More on offices

ASSOCIATES SAY...

The Work

Juniors can jump straight into the corporate, labor & employment, litigation, healthcare, real estate, tax, or private client services departments. Most newbies slot into the corporate group. Labor and litigation take in the next largest batches and a small handful are sprinkled among the remaining groups. Everyone begins life as a generalist and in each department a legal director coordinates work allocation. *"It's particularly helpful when you want to try a different area but don't know anyone within that team."* After two years juniors join a more focused practice area where work assignment tends to be allocated on an informal basis, though you're still able to reach out to the director if things run quiet.

> *"It's particularly helpful when you want to try a different area."*

Corporate rookies could find themselves working on the usual milieu of M&A, private equity, capital markets and bankruptcy matters for clients like banks, private equity funds and companies in the healthcare, real estate, retail and leisure industries. Sources spent most of their days on diligence or preparing signature and closing documents. Most also had a smattering of opportunities to tackle first drafts of ancillary documents or simple agreements. *"I've had more responsibility than I expected,"* one interviewee discovered. *"There's sufficient guidance to feel supported but enough rope to grow."*

See firm profile on p.687

Rankings in *Chambers USA*

Advertising	Labor & Employment
Banking & Finance	Latin American Investment
Bankruptcy/Restructuring	Leisure & Hospitality
Capital Markets	Litigation
Corporate/M&A	Media & Entertainment
Employee Benefits & Executive Compensation	Privacy & Data Security
	Private Equity
ERISA Litigation	Real Estate
Healthcare	REITs
Immigration	Sports Law
Insurance	Tax
Intellectual Property	Technology
Investment Funds	Wealth Management

For detail on ranking tiers and ranking locations, visit www.chambersandpartners.com

Recent work highlights

- Represented heart-rate monitor manufacturers Biosig Instruments in a dispute with home fitness equipment manufacturers Nautilus over a patent's validity
- Acted for Major League Baseball in a class action suit after plaintiffs alleged the MLB colluded with several member clubs, broadcasters and program distributors to create a monopoly on broadcasting of live MLB games
- Assisted biopharmaceutical company Celgene in its $7.2 billion acquisition of fellow biopharmaceutical company Receptos
- Advised Morgan Stanley as financial advisors to REIT Gramercy Property Trust in Gramcery's merger with Chambers Street Property

At the time of our calls, several litigators were specifically assigned to the patent team but most were part of the commercial litigation group. Here they undertake anything from insurance and securities disputes to false advertising or antitrust. Sources appreciated being able to pursue their own course: *"I'm developing a niche and no-one's stopped me if I've expressed an interest in doing something."* Topping up *"your standard big doc review projects"* is plenty of research and drafting sections of briefs and motions. *"There's never any hesitation about handing tasks to juniors,"* sources reckoned.

Labor & employment is split between those doing *"more traditional labor work"* and those handling employment matters. The former involves managing the relationship between labor unions and companies, and dealing with issues and litigation which may arise. Employment tends to cover things like writing employee handbooks, dealing with employee benefits and handling discrimination cases. *"Doc review doesn't subside until third year,"* sources conceded. But we're told the firm places *"a strong sense of trust in you once you've established your credibility,"* so working directly with clients or drafting sections of briefs all come around eventually.

Offices

Most juniors – around 40 – are in the New York office, and roughly 20 are in Boston. LA takes on the next largest group and at the time of our calls there were also a few rookies spread across New Orleans, Chicago and Newark. LA, New York, Washington, DC and Chicago offer a broad range of the firm's practices, while other offices have more specialized focuses. New Orleans and Newark, for instance, do all things labor & employment. An array of litigation, labor and corporate matters are offered in Boston but its banking and private equity teams are the real standout. Boca Raton, Florida, began life dedicated to private client services but has since branched out into other areas.

"It's quite common to be working with colleagues in Boston or LA."

Deal-doers and litigators had seen some cross-office interaction but it was in the labor group where geography most seemed to melt away. *"We have a national staffing model so it's quite common to be working with colleagues in Boston or LA,"* one New York source explained. All newbies meet at orientation in the Big Apple and use bonds gained there to *"help each other out. We email around to ask who's worked on certain matters before."* To make cross-office staffing easier, videophones were recently rolled out across the firm. Juniors approached these rather warily at first: *"It's weird,"* several shared. *"One time talking to senior counsel I rolled my eyes,"* another source admitted. But they now seem to be coming round to them. As for other mod cons, New York takes the biscuit for plush offices. Visit our website to find out why.

Strategy & Future

"It feels like every month there's a new partner in our London office," one interviewee found. Not quite, but London's certainly been bolstering its corporate and finance offerings with a number of recent partner hires into the firm's M&A, private equity and finance groups. Transactional growth forms the most imminent focus here, though eventually the firm hopes to continue building on its UK regulatory, tax and employment practices.

"We're trying to increase our international presence."

Juniors also anticipated the Hong Kong office could be next in line for expansion. *"Our associates are very*

See firm profile on p.687

perceptive people," chairman Joe Leccese hints. *"We've spent a lot of time on our London office and will continue to do that but we also need to become stronger in Asia."*

Culture

"People here have a sense of achievement, a drive for excellence and take the job seriously," but – another interjected – *"they don't take themselves too seriously. Even as the hours get late no-one's stressed and losing their mind."* Happily, senior associates understand burdens placed on juniors, newer associates told us, and help to alleviate them. The atmosphere is generally *"relaxed: you don't get a tense feeling. This is a respectful place – we don't have any yellers."* Another added: *"I've never felt that someone on my team was shortchanging me or that I was being used only for low-level work."*

In fact several sources were pleasantly surprised at how receptive partners were to juniors' opinions on whatever they're working on. *"If an associate drafts a brief and the clients push back the partner asks for that associate's opinion."*

"I've never felt that someone on my team was shortchanging me."

Others felt that Proskuaer was a place where *"instead of those at the top pushing work down to clear their plate, everyone's trying to clear everyone's plate."* This means that as far as is possible, *"everybody's trying to make sure you have your weekend. It's not always possible and there are emergencies but I feel people are pretty conscious of others' schedules."* One junior meditated: *"Proskauer understands you're a whole person, and not just an attorney."*

Perhaps the best example of this comes in the form of the firm's *Friday Focus* newsletter which lists events like weddings or births. Each week features a different associate outlining their interests and answering must-know questions like 'if you could have any superpower what would it be?' *"It's a great way to learn about other people. If I saw someone had a shared experience or traveled somewhere I was going to, I could shoot them an email."* There are also snippets on what the firm's alumni are getting up to.

Training & Development

Proskauer operates a pretty active alum network with an alumni bash in the fall and various talks led by former attorneys throughout the year. *"During the summer program our first lunch was about life after Proskauer and three alums"* – a restauranteur, a tech startup founder and a general counsel – *"came to chat to us about making connections and what they'd learned since moving on. Proskauer doesn't shun leavers. They're our future clients and we want to keep them close."*

"Proskauer doesn't shun leavers."

While the firm embraces its alumni, it's also striving to ensure more juniors remain with the firm long-term through increasing transparency and professional development training. *"It's a double edged sword,"* several interviewees deduced. *"We have such fascinating clients it's tough not to want to go in-house."* Another put attrition down to the fact that Proskauer *"trains us so well, it makes us more hire-able."* Visit our website for a rundown of Proskauer's training program.

Pro Bono

At the time of our calls, labor juniors had just started training to first chair New York City grievance arbitrations. Here they'll oversee things like claims of employment discrimination. *"It'll be scary but a good learning experience. They're always coming up with new ways to develop us."* Proskauer also works with the City to take depositions for *"a whole bunch of civil litigation for slip and falls or wrongful suing."*

"If you're going to work in labor and employment in New York, there is no other place."

"A whole bunch of civil litigation."

Juniors can tackle the usual run of advising on asylum, immigration, veteran and children-related matters or assisting nonprofits with tax exemption, corporate governance or employee handbooks. One interviewee stressed: *"You can pretty much work on anything you want."* So you'll also find attorneys doing anything from assisting Iraqi military translators as they settle in the US to helping Holocaust survivors apply for compensation. For several years Proskauer's also worked closely with the American Civil Liberties Union. Most recently the firm and ACLU represented the Wikimedia Foundation in a lawsuit against the NSA over claims of mass internet surveillance. In October 2015, Proskauer hired a partner, William Silverman, to lead pro bono efforts full time.

Pro Bono hours

- For all attorneys across all US offices: 33,233
- Average per US attorney: 51

See firm profile on p.687

Hours & Compensation

Proskauer has no billable requirement but most sources tended to aim for between 1,800 and 2,000 hours, which can include unlimited pro bono work. While interviewees considered this a reasonable target, several admitted they would struggle to reach it due to slow practice areas or undertaking *"a few hundred hours of non-billable work"* as first and second-years. *"It's reiterated to us that we don't have much control over our schedule early on."*

"The actual hours I work aren't crazy at all but it's unpredictable."

Proskauer's website proudly proclaims: *"Around the clock or around the world, we're there when you need us, because legal problems don't follow a schedule."* Plenty of associates could attest to that. Some had spent a month or so working *"every waking moment,"* before getting out early most days the next. Another mused: *"The actual hours I work aren't crazy at all but it's unpredictable."* Despite schedules sometimes being *"sporadic or brutal, or both,"* most juniors were pretty pleased with the respect afforded to life outside the firm. *"I'm not just satisfying the whims of another's timetable. When someone asks for work at an inconvenient time I feel it's because it needs to be done for reasons other than it's convenient for a partner to have it now."* When it comes to securing that well-earned vacation, *"people understand if you want to take one. You just have to be good at setting boundaries."*

Get Hired

"We're looking for high achievers but more importantly, we're looking for high achievers who work well in teams," hiring partner Michael Mervis reveals. The firm recently introduced new guidelines to help interviewers gauge information on candidates' strengths in areas like initiative, leadership and collaboration. But Mervis clarifies: *"We don't sit around with a scorecard ticking off who's a good leader. It's part of an effort to elicit more granular information during interviews."*

"We don't sit around with a scorecard ticking off who's a good leader."

Prior work experience, Mervis goes on to say, is *"a plus. For those interested in transactional work, for example, a background in finance can be attractive."* The firm's pretty open about what you've done, though. Among current junior associates we found former engineers, HR professionals, consultants, and financial and policy analysts. Mervis is keen to point out that although the firm values real world experience, it is by no means a prerequisite for candidates.

Diversity

"It could be more diverse," one representative source accepted. *"But there are efforts to make that happen and they recognize it's important."* Proskauer's Silver Scholar Program offers summer associate places to diverse 1L or 2L students. Associates are also matched up with someone from the Diverse Lawyer Mentoring Circle Program to *"increase the probability they will stay longer."*

"Increase the probability they will stay longer."

People can also reach out to affinity groups for ethnic minority attorneys, religious observers, women, LGBT and flex-time lawyers. The Women's Alliance meets monthly and *"everyone loves those events."* Get-togethers center *"around different topics like creating and making the best of a firm profile or networking. They also organize for different people to come and speak to us."*

"Everybody's trying to make sure you have your weekend. It's not always possible and there are emergencies but I feel people are pretty conscious of others' schedules."

See firm profile on p.687

Reed Smith LLP

Lawyers per state

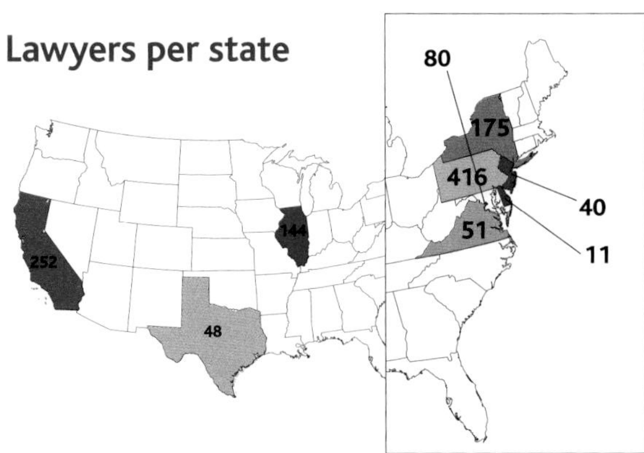

Largest US office: Pittsburgh
US offices: 15 (including global customer center)
International offices: 12
First-year salary: $140,000 - $160,000
Billable hours: 1,900 target (1,950 for profit sharing bonus)
Summers 2016: 47 (43 2Ls, 4 1Ls)
Revenue 2015: $1.123 billion (-2.5%)
Partners made in 2016: 24 globally (16 in US)
Famous for: international reach; being a Pittsburgh steelworker – helping to create US Steel, which is still a client

Now with nearly as many international as national offices, Reed Smith is one global Goliath that won't stop growing...

OPENING a new office in Frankfurt in 2015, vast Reed Smith has now cut the ribbon on seven new offices in as many years. The Pennsylvanian was founded in Pittsburgh in 1877, and today stretches across 27 offices, from London (the largest) to LA, and Athens to Abu Dhabi. The firm's founding partner, James H. Reed, thought big too when he assisted Andrew Carnegie in the establishment of US Steel – at one time the world's largest corporation – in 1901. To read more about Reed Smith and the Steel City's interconnected history, read our website Bonus Features.

Looking back on 2015, global managing partner Sandy Thomas highlights a particularly good year for the firm's corporate & transactional advisory group (CTAG), as well as insurance recovery: *"We're the largest firm with a policy-holder only practice, and that's a booming area for us."* The *Chambers USA* rankings confirm this, with Reed Smith ranking well nationwide and number one in Pennsylvania for insurance. It also takes the top spot in the Keystone State for its banking & finance and bankruptcy/restructuring practices. In January 2016, the firm announced some layoffs which affected 45 attorneys, plus staff globally. Reed Smith said at the time this was due to market changes while pointing out that 2015 revenue was over $1 billion for the fourth consecutive year and it had hired 40 lateral partners during the year. As we went to press, it was reported that Reed Smith had entered merger talks with Pepper Hamilton, although these came to nothing.

On chambers-associate.com...

- Reed Smith and Pittsburgh's productive partnership
- More on Reed Smith's practice areas
- Interview with Casey Ryan, global head of legal personnel

ASSOCIATES SAY...

The Work

Nearly a third of junior associates on our interview list were in complex litigation, while close to a quarter were in the corporate & securities group. The rest were spread across a wide range of departments, including global regulatory enforcement, insurance recovery, financial services litigation, life sciences & health, and energy & natural resources. Newbies are able to try work from any or all of the firm's practice areas over their summer, at the end of which they submit their top three groups. Preferences are taken into consideration (although not always satisfied), and *"it's not until the month before you start that you find out which group you're in."*

Associates in corporate & securities described *"a very busy year in M&A,"* although *"if you want more exposure in capital markets, private equity or securities you can reach out to the appropriate partners."* Day-to-day, *"as a junior your primary responsibility is the due diligence process."* This involves *"coordinating with differ-*

See firm profile on p.688

Rankings in *Chambers USA*

Advertising	Intellectual Property
Antitrust	Labor & Employment
Banking & Finance	Life Sciences
Bankruptcy/Restructuring	Litigation
Construction	Products Liability
Corporate/M&A	Real Estate
Healthcare	Tax
Insurance	

For detail on ranking tiers and ranking locations, visit www.chambersandpartners.com

Recent work highlights

- Successfully defended Kraft Heinz in a false advertising lawsuit. The plaintiff claimed that certain Heinz products contain trans fats, although their label indicates that they have "0% trans fat"
- Currently advising Microsoft on its acquisition of TouchType, the maker of 'Swiftkey', a predictive keyboard that is installed on hundreds of millions of smartphones
- Successfully defended Nintendo against a lawsuit filed by an inventor, who was seeking $350 million in damages. He claimed Nintendo infringed the key features of the Nintendo Wii handset
- Advised Kindred Healthcare in its $1.8 billion merger with Gentiva Healthcare
- Advised sports equipment company Vista Outdoor in its agreement with BRG Sports, to purchase Bell, Giro, C-Preme and Blackburn Brands for $400 million

ent specialists and the client, and organizing the schedules." Second-years spoke of meatier tasks: *"Right now it's just me and a partner on a deal, and I've done all the drafting."* There's no assigning partner, so *"if people aren't giving work to you, you can knock on doors – that reflects well on you."* Corporate juniors reported clients ranging from sports product companies and hospitals to the holding company of a fashion brand.

"If people aren't giving work to you, you can knock on doors – that reflects well on you."

Over in complex litigation, the work *"completely varies. Sometimes I feel bogged down in doc review; other times I will draft a motion and someone will review it."* We heard about about one particularly busy case when the team *"took about 60 depositions in five weeks. I was sent all over the country and I took or defended about ten depositions."* Juniors in this group reported trying work in other areas: *"I also do life sciences, some entertainment and media, and some financial industry work. It's very common and encouraged to try different things."* Clients for litigators tend to involve *"products you use every day: you see their adverts on the street and on TV."* As in the corporate group, *"the onus is on the associate to reach out to people,"* in order to get staffed on cases, and workflow is monitored by a complex litigation partner, or *"traffic cop,"* who has access to associates' weekly billed hours. Read more online about financial services litigation, global regulatory enforcement and the life sciences & health industry group.

Training & Development

Training is provided to associates via Reed Smith University, the firm's educational resource that is linked to CareeRS, the associate development initiative. Sessions come in the form of both online and live courses, which can be practice group-specific, or more generalized sessions and bootcamps on topics such as brief writing, trial skills, and external legal developments. The different courses are offered through a web portal: *"Every week we get notifications about the programs available. You can attend any subject you like, even if it's not related to your area."* While most of our sources had regularly made use of these resources, others reported that *"most of the training I get is directly from the folks I'm working with. It's easy to find people to bounce ideas off and ask questions."*

"You can attend any subject you like."

Most of our interviewees had an older associate mentor, and in addition *"part of the CareeRS program is that everyone has a partner mentor who you talk to about your career goals."* After this, associates are *"free to adapt to any other informal mentors."* While the majority found their associate mentor very useful – *"I speak with her daily"* – some felt that the partner mentor was less so: *"He just seems so busy that I don't want to bother him!"*

Offices

Reed Smith's base in Pittsburgh is home to nearly 300 attorneys, making it the largest in the USA. New York comes in second, with around 170 lawyers, while Philadelphia and Chicago each has around 150. The firm's other US offices, from largest to smallest, are in San Francisco, LA, Washington, DC, Houston, Princeton, Northern Virginia, Century City, Richmond, Silicon Valley and Wilmington.

"I think our office is the most incredible building in this town!"

"I think our office is the most incredible building in this town!" This excitable Pittsburgher added: *"It's gorgeous and brand new. The first couple of floors of the building*

See firm profile on p.688

are a hotel, so essentially our firm lobby is a hotel lobby." Associates have access to the hotel's spa and gym, as well as an in-house cafeteria or *"lions' den"* which is *"really convenient in the winter."* Interviewees also spoke fondly of the hotel's dog who greets them as they enter the building. *"She's so friendly and loves people – it's really welcoming!"* Visit our Twitter page to see photos of gorgeous Edie the boxer/labrador cross. Philly associates equally loved their naturally-lit, brand new office building, complete with *"fully ergonomic work spaces: all the offices have standing desks and chairs."*

Culture

Pittsburgh newbies described a supportive environment, in which people *"look out for others – they want me to be promoted and do well."* Socializing outside of work isn't a priority, however, and *"it's very much finish work and go home."* The sheer size of the firm means that juniors tend to be friendly within their group, but beyond this *"people generally keep to themselves."* One associate joked, *"I could wear the same outfit every day and nobody outside my group would notice!"*

Over in Chicago, one associate rhapsodized: *"You know how you hear of firms that are work hard, play hard? Well, we're work hard, play nice! I work with the most brilliant people who are so down-to-earth. It's still a very professional atmosphere, but these are people that I would happily have a drink with after work."* Junior New Yorkers were less gushing about their colleagues: *"It's not like we're all hugging all the time. You are encouraged to really take ownership of your time"* so, understandably, *"I work more with the people I like and less with those I don't."*

"We're work hard, play nice!"

Associate-partner relationships vary. New Yorkers reported having *"minimal interaction with partners, and when I do it's very professional and deferential."* One complex litigator noted being at *"the beck and call"* of certain partners: *"In BigLaw you're going to get difficult partners who don't necessarily keep the work/life balance of associates in mind."* Those in the corporate group meanwhile felt more encouraged to *"reach out to partners if you have any kind of questions in terms of career development or goals."* One corporate newbie added that *"partners are willing to take their time to work directly with you, to sit down and go over things."*

Hours & Compensation

As of September 2015, Reed Smith increased starting salaries, based on market adjustments, to $145,000 in Philadelphia, Wilmington and Princeton, and $140,000 in Pittsburgh. The billing target is 1,900 hours, although to be eligible for the profit-sharing bonus, associates need to bill 1,950. Corporate interviewees had no trouble meeting this number – *"I reached it a while back,"* one gladly reported, another cheerily noting *"the work finds me!"* Litigators, meanwhile, were less assured, as *"it's really difficult to have a consistent flow of work. If you have two slow months in a row, there's no way to make up that 100-hour deficit."*

"They care more about the quality of the product rather than simply hitting your hours."

If you don't manage to hit your hours, however, you won't be penalized: *"I think they care more about the quality of the product rather than simply hitting your hours. They look at the performance of the whole group, not just one person and why they had a bad week or month."* As far as vacation goes, the firm is *"extremely accommodating – they will go out of their way to not interfere with your holiday."* Official vacation policy for juniors at Reed Smith is three weeks, although one source confided, *"I ended up probably taking a lot more than I should! But you work hard here so you deserve a holiday."*

"It's not like we're all hugging all the time."

Pro Bono

"Pittsburgh is huge with respect to pro bono matters," one associate enthused. Juniors there spoke of adoption cases, legal name changes for transgender individuals and helping *"low income business owners to establish their business."* A generous 120 hours of pro bono count towards billables at Reed Smith, and a junior in Philadelphia remarked that *"you get a different colored ribbon on your door depending on how many pro bono hours you've done, so there's definitely an incentive there."*

"You get a different colored ribbon on your door depending on how many pro bono hours you've done."

The firm's ongoing commitment to pro bono through long-term projects was also repeatedly highlighted. New Yorkers, for instance, described Reed Smith's legal clinic: *"Once a month I go with a couple of other attorneys to senior centers to provide legal assistance and advice."* Over in Chicago, meanwhile, one junior had been working on a matter with the National Immigrant Justice Center: *"It's a case that our firm has been working on for the last 11 years or so."*

See firm profile on p.688

Pro bono hours
- For all attorneys across all US offices: 55,516
- Average per US attorney: 55

Diversity

The general feeling was that *"there's a great ratio of women to men,"* among the firm's associates, although *"you can see the drop-off when it comes to female partners."* The Women's Initiative Network of Reed Smith (WINRS) is very active, and every office has a liaison and a committee chair. *"Typically there are a couple of in-house networking events that we host, where we'll get together for cocktails with certain clients' women's initiatives. Sometimes we'll have a speaker come and discuss career strategy."*

"Cocktails with certain clients' women's initiatives."

As far as ethnic minorities and LGBT diversity goes, associates agreed that improvements could be made, although *"diversity has always been a key element for Reed Smith."* There is a diversity committee, *"an Asian affinity group, a black affinity group, and a couple of others,"* including LGBT and disability groups.

Get Hired

Generally, *"the more outgoing you are, and the more you're able to talk to people, the better you can direct yourself."* One source reiterated this point: *"People that do well here are self-starters. You need to be an entrepreneur in order to build your business both internally – in terms of your reputation and skill level within the firm – and externally, when you're a partner building your own book of clients."* More tangibly, *"when they recruit they look for strong writers, people who are on a law review and did well in legal writing class."* Go online for advice from Casey Ryan, Reed Smith's global head of legal personnel.

"The more you're able to talk to people, the better you can direct yourself."

Strategy & Future

"Reed Smith's strategy is to be the leading firm in five global industries: life sciences and health, energy and natural resources, financial services, shipping, and media and entertainment," global managing partner Sandy Thomas informs us. *"Our growth, be that adding lawyer talent or new geographies, is oriented around that strategy."*

Any specific locations that the firm is hoping to expand to? *"We have a number of regions where we are either not physically present, or we are, but are looking to expand. In Asia in particular, we have a very solid business that we think we can grow. We are also looking at central and Latin America."*

The Inside View

"People that do well here are self-starters. You need to be an entrepreneur in order to build your business."

See firm profile on p.688

Ropes & Gray LLP

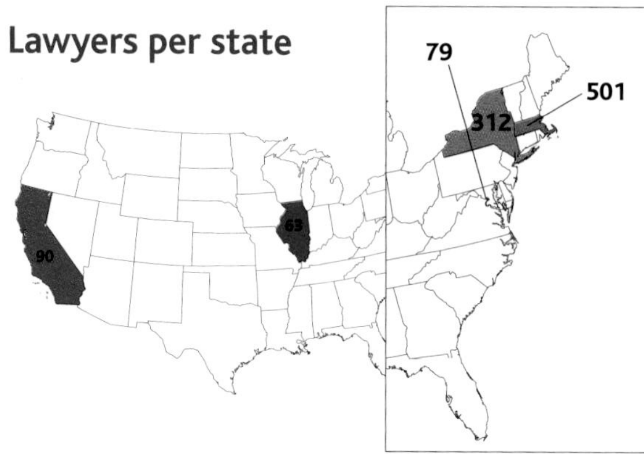

Largest US office: Boston
US offices: 6
International offices: 5
First-year salary: $160,000
Billable hours: 1,900 target
Summers 2016: 144 (all 2Ls)
Revenue 2015: $1.39 billion (+8.8%)
Partners made in 2015: 17 globally (13 in US)
Famous for: its Boston roots; second-to-none training

Boston-based Ropes & Gray prides itself on offering BigLaw work without the BigLaw burnout.

"THE last year has been very successful for Ropes & Gray, following a strong 2014," managing partner David Chapin tells us. However, Chapin is not focused on short term success but on the firm's long-term goals for 2020. *"Whether it's in five, ten or 20 years, there will be a number of firms – most think no more than 30 to 50 – that will be truly global and considered elite. Our goal is to be one of those firms."* Chapin continues: *"In 2015, for the first time in a while we did not open a new office. It is not that we have taken that option off the table, it is just that we are focused on building our current platform."* The firm's US offices are in Boston, Chicago, San Francisco, Silicon Valley, DC, and New York. Overseas branches are in Hong Kong, Shanghai, Seoul, Tokyo and London.

The firm's strong reputation in the USA – especially in Boston – merits *Chambers USA* rankings in areas including corporate/M&A, private equity, tax, litigation, banking & finance, and IP. Along with the high profile work, associates also spoke highly of Ropes & Gray's *"family-oriented"* culture and humane working hours: *"Everyone talks about the great work/life balance."* For our full interview with David Chapin, visit our website.

On chambers-associate.com...

- More on the tax practice
- Interviews with managing partner David Chapin and hiring partner Richard Batchelder

ASSOCIATES SAY...

The Work

For junior associates, work assignment is well regulated: *"There is an associate development manager (ADM) and they are intended to be the clearing house for work when you're a junior,"* one explained. *"A lot of your early work comes through them."* The ADM system was popular: *"One of the best things about the ADM is being able to tell them you've got too much on your plate. Declining work isn't a big deal and nobody will think any less of you."* Nevertheless, *"if you want to introduce yourself to a partner and express an interest in a field or topic, it's definitely encouraged."* Most junior associates are in the litigation, tax & benefits, and corporate groups. Corporate has subgroups including IP transactions, investment management, and private equity, and people tend to specialize in one by their third year. A handful of new associates join the labor & employment or restructuring practices.

"Right now I'm carving up a merger agreement."

In corporate, associates often work with private equity firms. *"I mostly do private equity transactions and lots of leveraged buyouts, but also drafting for M&A work,"* said one. Junior work involves a *"fair amount of diligence reporting and organization of consent documents."* Luckily, responsibility comes quickly in the department: *"After a year and a half you're treated like a mid-level*

See firm profile on p.689

The Inside View

Rankings in *Chambers USA*

Antitrust	Intellectual Property
Banking & Finance	Investment Funds
Bankruptcy/Restructuring	Labor & Employment
Capital Markets	Life Sciences
Corporate Crime & Investigations	Litigation
Corporate/M&A	Privacy & Data Security
Employee Benefits & Executive Compensation	Private Equity
FCPA	Real Estate
Healthcare	Securities
	Tax
	Wealth Management

For detail on ranking tiers and ranking locations, visit www.chambersandpartners.com

Recent work highlights

- Successfully represented Sony after 31 million Playstation and Qriocity users had their accounts hacked. The cases were dismissed due to lack of detail regarding the data breach
- Represented ex-BP employee Kurt Mix after he was accused of deleting texts regarding the company's 2010 oil spill
- Assisted the Adidas Group with the $280 million sale of its Rockport Shoe Business
- Provides ongoing advice to Goldman Sachs Asset Management regarding private equity funds and venture funds

associate," another explained. *"I mean this in the sense that you're working on a lot of agreements – I've worked on ancillary documents, LLC agreements and main purchase orders. Right now I'm carving up a merger agreement."*

Corporate associates in Silicon Valley often work with IP matters as *"it's the nature of the work out here."* Junior day-to-day work might involve commercial agreements, due diligence, purchase agreements, IP licensing agreements, M&A and risk analysis. Sources here also reported pleasing levels of responsibility early on: *"I've always found the amount of substantive work phenomenal and at times slightly unbelievable,"* one associate enthused.

Associates in litigation told us *"you're a free agent for the first couple of years. You work in general litigation, which is work in business and securities, and government enforcement."* These two practices make up the largest chunk of the litigation department, but associates tell us *"there's also the opportunity to work in labor & employment and antitrust"* in the third year. *"You get a good experience of the basics in your first year. That's great because work like that helps you keep your hours balanced."*

Day-to-day nitty gritty includes *"drafting responses, researching contractual issues and preparing interviews for witnesses in governmental investigations."* A New Yorker recalled working in *"FCPA* [Foreign Corrupt Practices Act] *investigations, international investigations and traditional business disputes like class actions."* Most litigators agreed that *"there is definitely the opportunity to do as much as you're willing to do. It's a steep learning curve, but the amount of support you get is great."* Happily, if things go belly up, *"there's not the idea that 'it's all on me' if stuff goes wrong. People always pitch in."* Read our expanded web feature on Ropes for feedback on the tax department.

Offices

"All our staffing and hiring is based around our one-firm philosophy," explains hiring partner Richard Batchelder. *"We do encourage mobility for associates by offering the flexibility to get to know our offices."* Associates agreed with this, with one Bostonian telling us: *"If you're at Ropes, you're going to end up working with everyone."* West Coast associates felt equally close to the other offices. *"The best thing about our offices is the effort Ropes puts into pairing you up with other offices. I've worked in the San Francisco office and try to work there a couple of times a year,"* said a Silicon Valley associate.

"If you've got binoculars you can probably watch the game!"

The firm's HQ takes up nearly 20 floors of the *"coolest building in Boston,"* the Prudential Tower. *"The office is gorgeous and it's comfortable to work in."* Glass walls offer unique views of Boston, from the *"sailboats on the Charles River"* to the bright lights of Fenway Park in the evening. *"If you've got binoculars you can probably watch the game!"* Associates in Boston share an office with a fellow junior before being promoted to their own office in their second year.

"I think most firms in New York look pretty similar," divulged one associate. *"You've got a few nice offices (like ours) and then a big group at the bottom of the pile with really terrible offices – so we're pretty lucky! We're in the Rockefeller complex which is great and very convenient. The firm could have moved to a cheaper space but they value this location."* Some associates found they were still sharing an office after their first year. *"You're supposed to get a new office in the second year. That's not happened for me yet but I can hear banging everyday – I'm hoping this means progress for the new office."* In summer 2015, Ropes announced plans to take over the entire 34th floor too.

See firm profile on p.689

The Culture & Get Hired

When we quizzed associates about Ropes' culture, buzzwords like *"supportive," "friendly"* and *"professional"* repeatedly cropped up. At each office, we got the impression that associates were comfortable with their colleagues, partners included: *"I feel comfortable talking to partners about totally random stuff like Broadway plays!"* Show tunes aside, associates found partners to be *"very open and helpful. They want to know all the associates and they make a point to treat first-years like people rather than somebody who just does doc reviews and research."* Broadly speaking, *"you're expected to run with tasks without having to have your hand held."*

"There isn't any room for intense law school types."

So who doesn't fit in here? *"People who are extremely intense aren't the kind of people who will wind up at Ropes,"* one associate mused. Nor rude people: *"There isn't any room for intense law school types – don't get me wrong, people here are hard-workers but there is nobody with super-intensity that leads to a competitive environment."*

Ropes makes *"an effort to provide opportunities for the those people who want the work social experience."* For example, the Boston tax department puts on *"regular cocktail hours."* However, events are few and far between as *"people here work late and they want to go home see their family."* That is not to say the firm never puts on events: *"We had our 150th anniversary so we had a big family picnic celebration in Central Park and each regional office did its own event."* Each office puts on its own holiday party, with one New Yorker remembering Christmas *"with a ton of booze and dancing – all that jazz!"*

"All our staffing and hiring is based around our one-firm philosophy."

Hours & Compensation

Boston associates believed that the 1,900 billable hours target was *"very achievable,"* while associates in the Big Apple believed it to be *"on the low end of targets for New York firms."* A corporate associate told us: *"It's like any corporate department in that there are peaks and valleys. If you're in the middle of a deal that's close to the end you're working 14 maybe 15 hours a day. On the flipside, when something closes it can be hard to make your average hours."* If work is on the slow side and associates are *"25 or 50 hours off target, it's not a big deal."* However, *"there's the possibility that you'll have your bonus reduced."* Average office hours were around 8.30am to 7pm but *"associates with kids are encouraged to go home at night and spend time with their family. That's really important to me."* One associate reflected: *"BigLaw can destroy your social life! At Ropes as long as you're getting your work done, nobody cares where you're getting it done."*

Diversity and Pro Bono

With 11 African American students, 13 openly gay students and a class where 56% are female, the 2016 summer program is one of Rope's most diverse yet. *"Don't regard diversity as something you can have happen by just putting a program in place. You have to live it everyday,"* explains managing partner David Chapin. *"Ropes has long been recognized as a place that's a tolerant and embracing work environment for those of different backgrounds. Honestly, I don't take too much comfort from this as the industry record is so poor. The fact that we're slightly more successful than other firms is a little comforting, but the entire industry could be doing better."* Associates agreed with their boss: *"There is still some way to go in terms of recruiting and retaining minorities,"* one admitted.

"Slightly more successful than other firms."

Several associates we spoke to were either members of the Women's Forum or involved in external bodies like the Asian American Bar. The firm has also made strides to improve diversity in its recruitment process and recently introduced the Trimmier Scholarship. The fellowship (named after Roscoe Trimmier, the firm's first African American partner), awards $25,000 to five diverse second-year law students. Recipients are also awarded a paid summer position with the firm after their second year.

Pro bono hours

- For all attorneys across the US offices: 98,174
- Average per US attorney: 96

Training & Development

Ropes offers standard orientation programs for first-years, and throughout the year juniors are encouraged to attend *"training events that are focused on improving your writing and research skills."* As one junior said: *"There are always great programs put on by the partners and senior associates about specific areas and cases. You get CLE credit for attending them, so it's all super convenient."*

The Inside View

See firm profile on p.689

A program unique to Ropes is its Go Program which hiring partner Richard Batchelder tells us *"stands for 'global opportunity."* He outlines the program *as "a few different components, from secondments at clients, to fellowships where each year we select a few associates to work in an office of their choice for 18 months."* One component is the Go First program which is *"geared for new associates who may want to start in one our offices with the idea that after a few years they would be able to transfer to another office permanently. So that's one of the ways we populate our offices in Asia for example – with home grown US transfers who express an interest in a move before they start."*

Strategy & Future

Ropes holds annual state of the firm meetings to keep its associates in the loop. *"Every year they talk about growth in each office,"* said one informed litigator. *"It's clear providing a full range of services to clients is important – that's the firm's long-term goal."* However, *"there isn't one magic formula,"* according to MP David Chapin. *"We need partners to be constantly thinking about ways that we can better connect our offices and clients. We need people to be thinking of Ropes & Gray as a global enterprise. We're looking to attract the clients that all large firms want."*

"I'm not giving our offers to those who have the best past, I'm giving out offers to those with the brightest future."
Richard Batchelder, hiring partner

See firm profile on p.689

Schulte Roth & Zabel LLP

Lawyers per state

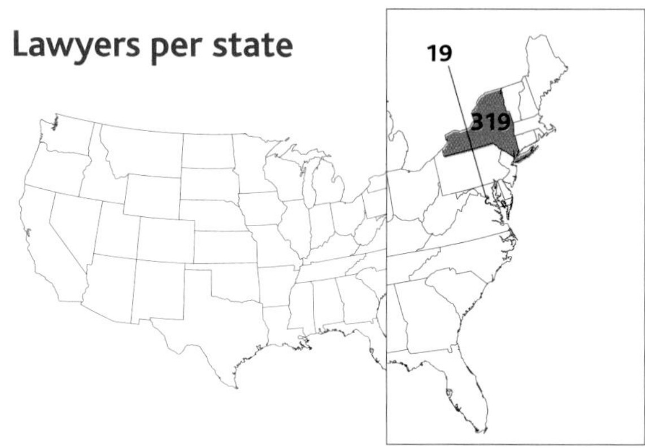

Largest US office: New York
US offices: 2
International offices: 1
First-year salary: $160,000
Billable hours: 2,000 target
Summers 2016: 37 (all 2Ls)
Revenue 2015: $405.5 million (+1.2%)
Partners made in 2016: 1 (in US)
Famous for: investment management work, including hedge funds

No need to hedge your bets if you're drawn to Wall Street: this midsizer outranks most in the district of greenbacks and gold.

IM is big at Schulte (pronounced *shuultee*). We're not talking about instant messaging. We're talking about investment management... that heady world of hedge funds and private equity in which Schulte Roth & Zabel excels. Within Wall Street's financial forest, Schulte is a relatively young buck, having been formed back in 1969 by an enterprising group of seven lawyers (all aged under 35) who broke away from Cleary, Fried Frank and Kaye Scholer to set up their own firm. Since then, Schulte has expanded its headcount to around 375 lawyers and earned itself a stellar reputation for hedge fund work, evidenced by a top *Chambers USA* ranking at national level, where it's also ranked for capital markets prowess. It also earns recognition in its hometown for tax, bankruptcy, corporate and real estate expertise.

"I knew that Schulte was best for investment management work," said one junior of why they came here. *"I knew what industry I wanted to work in, and got a good feel about the people I met with. People who work here are collegial and positive, and I enjoy the work culture."*

"I knew that Schulte was best for investment management work."

On chambers-associate.com...

- Interviews with hiring partner Bill Gussman

ASSOCIATES SAY...

The Work

Most juniors join the Big Apple base, although at the time of our calls there was a sprinkling of associates in the DC branch. The latter comprises around 20 attorneys in total, most of whom are litigators working on either securities matters or white-collar defense, we heard. Juniors in this line of work told us they'd *"written outlines of cross-examinations for witnesses, arranged for subpoenas to be served and driven round with investigators talking to potential witnesses,"* as well as handling research, doc review and drafting motions.

"We launched a fund with over 100 investors and I was in touch with them all."

However, it's the firm's premier rep in the hedge funds space that many sources cited as a major draw. Within the investment management group, *"a big chunk of the work is launching new funds, but then we also do a lot of work for existing funds as well."* One proud rookie declared that *"this year we launched a fund with over 100 investors and I was in touch with them all leading up to that, keeping them informed about documents and the timing of the launch."* Other common tasks for new recruits include *"reviewing and drafting documents like operating agreements for entities, subscription agreements, partnership agreements and side letters."* Client contact is also on the menu. *"Within a month of being*

See firm profile on p.690

Rankings in *Chambers USA*

Bankruptcy/Restructuring	Investment Funds
Capital Markets	Real Estate
Corporate/M&A	Tax

For detail on ranking tiers and ranking locations, visit www.chambersandpartners.com

Recent work highlights

- Advised global communications equipment company Aeroflex on a $1.46 billion merger with British aerospace manufacturer Cobham
- Represented hedge fund JANA Partners in its sale of a minority interest to New York-based private equity business Dyal Capital
- Succesfully secured a Chapter 11 reorganization plan for Quigley Company, a subsidiary of pharma giant Pfizer

here I was calling and emailing clients! It's nerve-racking but good that partners trust you. If you do good work, you get more work."

In terms of work assignment in the group, there's *"an assigning partner when you first start out."* Interviewees appreciated that *"you're staffed on matters to begin with so you don't have to try and awkwardly walk into people's offices."* However, *"once you have work you begin to gravitate naturally toward certain partners and request more work from them."*

Associates in the M&A group also make use of a formal assignment system. *"We have a weekly status report and we rate how busy we are. If you're slow you can reach out and say you've got availability. Early on that's important, but after you've worked with a number of people a lot of it comes organically."* Day-to-day life in this team also revolves around *"sophisticated money clients."* An eager interviewee explained that *"we work for a lot of hedge funds and private equity funds. A lot of the general transactions are the acquisition and divestment of portfolio companies."* A junior's duties include *"managing the checklist, making sure everything gets done, drafting the resolutions and the less complicated ancillary documents. Now I work on purchase agreements. I don't hold the pen on it but I do a lot of it!"*

"Partners always make time for questions."

Another area to get to grips with is shareholder activist work which *"involves certain funds holding interest in public companies and not liking how that company is performing, so they might nominate a specific person for the board of directors."* These matters require *"going through a whole process with different questionnaires and agreements. I get to do the initial run of drafting on the notice that's sent to the company and file it at the SEC."* We also spoke to associates in smaller groups like bankruptcy and IP, both of which support the larger practices and have a hedge fund-only clientele.

Training & Development

Incoming juniors gather in New York for a week of initial training that covers *"basic things like the compensation systems, firm structure and policies."* After that, first-years have regular practice-specific trainings. *"There are a bunch of lunchtime seminars on things like diligence, different types of deal structures, how to compile checklists... They're very helpful and thorough."* Informal training is also plentiful. *"There's lots of mentoring within my practice. Sources noted that they can "ask a ton of questions in the middle of real assignments"* and that *"partners always make time for questions, there's a real push on knowledge sharing. If you're working with someone they'll give you advice on how to draft something or how to negotiate a particular point if you're trying to get a provision into an agreement."*

Offices & Culture

The New York base has been undergoing a *"massive renovation"* since early 2016. Associates reckoned that the overhaul will introduce *"glass walls and a lot more natural light"* to the working environment, along with *"spaces for people to congregate and discuss things, or hang out."* Over in DC, we heard that there's plenty of space and *"we just had our office redone"* (although *"the only problem is that we're next to the Washington Post building which is currently being demolished – and the noise is ear-splitting!"*). The DC office *"has a very welcoming atmosphere – it's so small that everybody knows everybody and we do social activities regularly. They're not necessarily big things – like last Friday a partner invited us for drinks in his office because he has a nice whiskey collection."* There are also *"a decent number of more formal events where we have drinks and dinner somewhere."*

"The firm takes pride in people getting along."

Across both offices, many associates praised the firm's dress-down policy (*"It's awesome – I'm wearing sneakers right now!"* crowed one particularly casual associate), emphasizing that *"there's a lot of collegiality among juniors. We all get along and it's not a competitive atmosphere: nobody's boasting about how much they're billing."* According to one New Yorker, *"it's definitely not a stuffy place. It's hard for me to say it's relaxed – we're still a bunch of lawyers after all! Everyone here is really*

See firm profile on p.690

smart but you don't get the kind of 4.0 GPA psychopaths who are looking to bill 3,000 hours!" Another suggested that *"there's a really good culture that's driven by the fact that two of the named partners are still here, and the firm takes pride in people getting along. Partners have their doors open and that promotes a better atmosphere. There are very rarely frictions between people, and nobody is screaming or yelling!"*

Lots of interviewees pointed out that associates socialize together outside of the office (*"I've met a lot of friends at the firm – we have lunch and I see them on weekends"*). In addition, *"Schulte is renowned for its wonderful summer program. Everyone loves it, not just the summers, because they invite associates and partners to the events. I've been to Yankees games and a Beyoncé concert."* Also on the social calendar are holiday parties, speaker events (complete with *"light snacks and beverages"*) and *"preview movie nights."*

"One week I can bill over 60 hours and then 30 another week."

Although they had many positive things to say about the culture, most interviewees concurred that the possibility of staying on and making partner is rather remote. *"It's notoriously hard here. Almost every partner comes in from somewhere else. For associates it seems like you do your time here and then move on to greener pastures, which is kinda sad. We've lost a lot of good senior associates who would've made great partners."* The reasons for this? *"It's a smaller firm so they're hesitant to make any partners at all. Then there's an expectation gap in terms of timing. Here you need to stick around for 13 or 14 years if you really want an outside shot at making partner."*

Hours & Compensation

In order to be eligible for a bonus, associates need to hit 2,000 hours. Up to 200 hours of pro bono, marketing or recruiting work can count toward the billing target. The bonus increases by $10,000 increments for those who clock up 2,300 and 2,500 hours. Overall, sources thought that *"work is plentiful"* and *"the target is absolutely manageable."* However, some highlighted that *"the work fluctuates a lot. One week I can bill over 60 hours and then 30 another week. That makes it a little stressful. As a junior you can't really control the deal flow."* As one put it, *"we're always gonna be paranoid about making hours."* One interviewee admitted that *"there was a time when I got too much on my plate and couldn't get the documents to people fast enough. I went to the assigning partner and I felt they actually cared. They listen to associates who feel they're drowning."*

Typically, juniors tend to put in a solid ten hours a day at the office. Some felt that *"in the context of BigLaw, the work/life balance has been a lot better than expected. Of course, the bummer of BigLaw is that when you're not at work you're worried something might come up, checking your emails on a Saturday afternoon in case someone says you need to do something."* Another admitted: *"Explaining that to non-lawyers is difficult. It's not so much the hours, which can be crazy, but the lack of control over your own life and plans."* Associates appreciated that *"the firm is flexible about people working from home if necessary. It's really about getting your work done, rather than being glued to your desk."*

Diversity

Schulte *"definitely tries very hard"* when it comes to diversity. However, as with the majority of BigLaw firms, *"the partners are mostly white males"* (90% of partners are white and 13% are females). There are affinity groups for LGBT, African American, Asian American and Hispanic lawyers that *"try to plan a few events a year."* The women's initiative organizes occasional get-togethers like champagne tasting and a clothes drive for underprivileged women in business.

"We are comfortable in our own skin, with being a midsized, New York-centric, financial services-centric law firm."

Alan Waldenberg, executive committee chair

Pro Bono

The firm *"really values pro bono,"* associates testified, noting that Danny Greenberg, who spent nearly a decade as president and attorney-in-chief of the Legal Aid Society in New York, was recently hired by Schulte to act as special counsel overseeing the firm's pro bono program. Although some juniors informed us that *"I haven't done any pro bono because it's too hard to have outside commitments in this practice,"* several had taken on *"a ton"* of pro bono (200 hours of which can be counted toward the billing target). Some had helped nonprofits to achieve tax-exempt (category 501c3) status, while others had contributed to a suit against the UN relating to the spread of disease.

Pro bono hours

- For all attorneys across all US offices: 10,457
- Average per US attorney: 33

See firm profile on p.690

Get Hired

Hiring partner Bill Gussman informs us that Schulte looks for *"bright law students who are good communicators. We want the complete package, so we're not hyper-focused on a particular GPA cut-off. We ask ourselves, 'is this a person who's bright and who we can see ourselves working with'?"* He continues: *"There's a real human element about our approach. We are very collegial, we work well together and we're less formal than a lot of other firms – we're younger and more entrepreneurial. So that means we want somebody who tends to keep the door open, has a sense of humor, and is very bright – that's the standard we look for in a candidate. Of course, they need to have done very well but what makes them stand out is personality-driven."*

Strategy & Future

When it comes to strategy, executive committee chair Alan Waldenberg tells us: *"Frankly, we are comfortable in our own skin, with being a midsized, New York-centric, financial services-centric law firm. We've been very successful staying within those parameters and we've been able to grow by expanding within that box. We feel no need to go outside our box. The London office is closely related to practice in New York – we're very comfortable effectively being a one-office law firm."*

"I knew what industry I wanted to work in, and got a good feel about the people I met with."

See firm profile on p.690

Sedgwick LLP

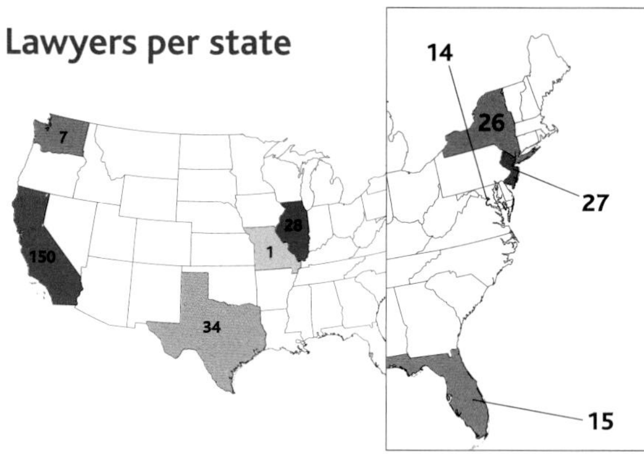

Largest US office: San Francisco

US offices: 14

International offices: 2 (including an affiliated office)

First-year salary: varies (case-by-case)

Billable hours: 1,950 required (2,000 to be bonus-eligible)

Summers 2016: no official summer program, but summer associates hired as needed

Revenue 2015: $183 million (-3.7%)

Partners made in 2016: 6 globally (5 in US)

Famous for: its complex litigation and insurance work

Sedgwick's prowess as a trial and litigation firm has been firmly bolstered since it opened its golden gate to a range of other practices.

FOUNDED in 1933, Sedgwick has grown considerably from its humble two-attorney beginnings in San Francisco. Nowadays laying claim to 14 offices across the USA and a further two abroad in London and Bermuda (an affiliated office), the firm most recently opened an office in Kansas City in 2014 to house its staff. And with growth has come variety: although it began life as a litigation firm, Sedgwick has since diversified to include areas such as business law, IP and real estate. In particular, this San Franciscan has an impressive insurance practice, ranking highly in *Chambers USA* within California for this area. It also ranks highly statewide for its construction work.

That said, Sedgwick's practice of origin still seemed to be the main draw for the associates we spoke to: *"I was very interested in litigation coming out of law school, and Sedgwick is one of the premier trial firms in San Francisco."* And the work itself wasn't the only pull, as another explained: *"It sounds like such a cliché, but I didn't want to end up being another cog in a machine. I was very excited to be at a place where if I proved myself early, I would get more substantive work early, and that has really panned out for me."* As well as California (San Fran, LA, Orange County), attorneys are to be found in Chicago, Dallas, Austin, Houston, Newark, New York, DC, Miami, Fort Lauderdale, and Seattle.

On chambers-associate.com...

- Chair Michael Healy talks strategy and recruitment

ASSOCIATES SAY...

Get Hired & Strategy

We asked juniors what sort of person the firm looks to hire, and most agreed that social skills were a must. *"I found out that in my first interview,"* one newbie told us. *"They were pre-screening me to see if I would be cool enough to take for drinks with the client!"* Another noted that *"Sedgwick doesn't necessarily look for the applicants from the best schools with the highest grades. Obviously grades are important, but it's more important to make sure the person will fit into our culture."* And be certain that the firm fits your interests; firm chair Michael Healy says that he looks for *"those that are interested in, and committed to, the type of practice we have."*

"We're comfortable with our geographical footprint."

In 2015, Sedgwick changed its formal summer program. Certain offices now take summer associates on a case-by-case basis – so candidates now have to apply directly to Sedgwick rather than through OCIs. This seems to be part of a broader strategy to focus on existing areas rather than expansion, as Michael Healy explains: *"Sedgwick*

See firm profile on p.691

Rankings in *Chambers USA*

Construction	Insurance

For detail on ranking tiers and ranking locations, visit www.chambersandpartners.com

is different than some of our peers in that we're committed to growing and bolstering our traditional areas of strength in our traditional cities." He adds: *"We're comfortable with our geographical footprint. We'd like to strengthen and broaden our expertise in the current offices."*

Recent work highlights

- Successfully defended Travelers Insurance against a coverage-related lawsuit brought by Travelers' client Raelco
- Currently defending Howmedica in a mass action litigation in connection with a toxic spinal implant
- Secured governmental approvals for state-of-the-art elevator systems in many California construction projects, including Levis Stadium and Santa Clara Gateway, coming to a total value of over $10 million

And the removal of the summer program isn't the only change at Sedgwick. Michael Healy was appointed firm chair in 2015, and in addition, *"there is a new insurance division chair, a new commercial division chair, and a new at-large member"* on the five-person executive committee. While hefty expansion isn't on the cards currently, Healy tells us that the firm has been bringing laterals into the cybersecurity & privacy group, an area which *"continues to grow in the US and in Europe,"* as well as *"five maritime partners to our San Francisco office earlier this year."* Read more about strategy and recruitment in Healy's online interview.

The Work

The three main pillars of work are complex litigation, commercial, and insurance, and newbies join one of these three groups. Despite this, the work is not strictly segregated according to practice area: *"The divisional differences don't actually affect my day-to-day, it's just the way they lump us into groups for organizational purposes."* As such, overlap between groups is fairly commonplace; we heard of newcomers in insurance, for instance, who had handled contract disputes and commercial litigation matters. Work allocation is an informal process, meaning *"you've got to get out there. Thankfully I've never been in need of work here, and now there's a few partners I work for on a regular basis."*

"The firm encourages you to go out and build a book of business."

In the insurance group, some had focused mainly on insurance coverage: *"When insurance claims come in, the insurer comes to us to give them an opinion as to whether or not the claim is covered by the policy."* Others, meanwhile, had done more on the litigation side – always on behalf of the insurer. Over in complex litigation, we heard of newbies who had worked on cases involving the school district, as well as *"a lot of landlord-tenant work and environmental toxic torts."* In the commercial group meanwhile, we spoke to juniors who had done work in construction, business litigation and retail. The latter usually involves defending retailers, with false advertising and deceptive pricing cases being cited as particularly common.

Our interviewees were generally very pleased with the level of responsibility they'd been offered. *"I'm going to court regularly, I'm taking depositions, and appearing in front of arbitration panels,"* one insurance junior told us. Another in the commercial group added that while some paper shuffling can be expected, *"they also encourage you to branch out – we're not just stuck doing doc review every day. I've been able to take and defend depositions, take hearings, argue motions, and I'm about to second chair a deposition."* Direct client contact is also fairly frequent; associates informed us that they are *"regularly on calls with clients,"* and one newbie appreciated that *"the firm encourages you to go out and build a book of business."*

Training & Development

Sedgwick organizes its training schedule through 'Sedgwick University', a program that offers classes and online resources on anything from *"how to manage complex litigation to the correct way to bill entries to clients."* The training sessions are officially split into seven schools: law, ethics, leadership, personal and professional development, finance, marketing and business development, and technology. Our interviewees also mentioned a weeklong 'Trial Academy' for midlevel associates. The course is conducted in Dallas *"with partners who act as judges, and you try two cases during the week. Everyone says it's one of the best experiences they've had at the firm."*

"Partners take time to go over things that I write."

Juniors *"have to attend a certain number of in-house training sessions to be in good standing,"* although many remarked that they had been given *"a ton"* of informal training and feedback too. One source noted that *"partners take time to go over things that I write and send them back to me, so I can see how to improve."* There is also a yearly formal review, at which point associates

See firm profile on p.691

"get a printout of feedback and constructive criticism, which is helpful."

Offices

The majority of newbies are herded into Sedgwick's San Francisco HQ, *"right in the heart of the financial district."* Associates loved their *"floor-to-ceiling windows,"* and the great views were a definite plus: *"I can see the bay and various iconic places in San Francisco like the Golden Gate Bridge."* Chicago juniors meanwhile enjoyed their *"very spacious"* offices and *"nice big windows."* The on-site gym and cafeteria were also appreciated – *"that's where I tend to eat breakfast and lunch."*

"It's really got that wow effect when you walk in."

Over in LA, the office is allegedly *"like a spa! We recently had the entire place remodeled from top to bottom,"* chirped an eager newcomer. *"Everything was repainted, there's a new kitchen, new fixtures, new lights – it's really got that wow effect when you walk in."* Another remarked that *"the main conference room has a view from Hollywood to Century City to Santa Monica, and on a clear day you can see the ocean – it's a pretty panoramic view."*

Culture

We've mentioned Sedgwick's cordiality in past editions of *Chambers Associate*, and we were told that little has changed on that front: *"For the most part, everyone here is very friendly and approachable. I'm not working with condescending or arrogant people."* One source highlighted that *"I never feel competitive with the other associates; there's no real cut-throat culture here."* They went on to add that although *"working at a firm of this nature is going to be stressful and intense, it's good to know that you don't have to look over your shoulder as you're facing the challenges!"* And this friendliness isn't limited to associates – partners too are *"very accessible, and they do a good job of communicating with younger associates. I go to informal lunches with partners, or into their offices to chat – I was just now talking to a partner about our weekends."*

"There's no real cut-throat culture here."

The phrase 'a good work/life balance' was frequently bandied about by the associates, but how does the firm promote this? *"I like the fact that it's very hands-off, and I very much make up my own hours,"* one source enthused. *"Most of my team have kids, so the firm is very diligent about keeping work off our plate for weekends as much as possible."* Others pointed out that socializing among colleagues helped support a more balanced lifestyle. *"We have a group that goes out regularly, and partners come along too,"* one junior told us, adding that *"there's a wine bar and cellar down the street and we go there all the time."* We heard that the firm itself is also good at arranging events: *"A couple of years ago Sedgwick instituted an associate retreat, which is in a different office each year,"* an interviewee informed us. The two-day event consists of a social gathering *"something like a baseball game,"* and *"an open forum to hear about what's going on at the firm and within your division, which is always interesting. It's a great way to meet other people across the firm."*

"We're committed to growing and bolstering our traditional areas of strength in our traditional cities."

Michael Healy, firm chair

Hours & Compensation

The 1,950 billable hours requirement at Sedgwick was generally considered *"very achievable."* While the firm expects associates to hit this number, one junior commented: *"I know some people have not hit their hours before, but it hasn't resulted in anything besides the firm helping them to get more work."* As far as base salary goes, *"we don't start at market, but it shows in the way we are afforded more flexibility with our hours, and I think it's a fair trade-off."* The firm tells us that salaries are *"extremely competitive"* given its size. Incoming associates' salaries vary on an individual basis depending on where they're based.

"We are afforded more flexibility with our hours."

Juniors need to bill 2,000 hours to get the first tier of bonus, which increases with every 50 additional hours above this. Once you hit 2,150, the increments increase to 75 hours. There were gripes about the salary in previous years – more specifically due to a lack of transparency. Unfortunately, *"that is a recurring issue. It's not 100% clear to me how they choose the raises or what to pay you,"* one newbie grumbled. Another added: *"Basically you show up for your end-of-year review and they tell you what your salary is for next year – there's no negotiation."*

This somewhat undiplomatic approach was criticized in a separate instance: *"They've just announced that they aren't going to give us a fee-sharing bonus if you bring in a new client."* Despite the grouching, however, many were satisfied with the system. *"If I wanted to take it*

See firm profile on p.691

easy and only hit 1,950, I could," one conscientious junior informed us, *"and some people do that who are very content. I far exceeded that number this year, but I was also well rewarded for it – it's really what you make of it."*

"It's really what you make of it."

Pro Bono

Exactly half of our interviewees had been involved in pro bono. They reported working on matters including immigration, veterans' affairs and legal guardianship cases. One junior remarked: *"I had a friend who did a pet owner dispute!"* As for those who hadn't been involved, one reason cited was that pro bono only counts toward the bonus: associates have to hit their 1,950 billing target before they can bill a total of 25 pro bono hours. Others were discouraged by the fact that pro bono projects weren't always readily available to them: *"There's not really a folder of things we can do,"* one source pointed out. *"You have to decide what you want to do, then you go to the pro bono partner and open a matter."*

Pro bono hours

- For all attorneys across all US offices: undisclosed
- Average per US attorney: undisclosed

Diversity

Sedgwick's five affinity groups aren't for keeping up appearances, and the feeling across the board was that *"the firm does a very good job of promoting diversity."* The African American Lawyers Forum, Asian Pacific Islander Forum, Hispanic Lawyers Forum, LGBT Action Committee and Women's Forum regularly organize events and presentations within the firm, as well as careers fairs aimed specifically at minority students. *"We also have a law school program here that invites diverse students to come to the firm and see what it's like,"* added one San Franciscan.

Nonetheless, as one associate deliberated, *"there's always the opportunity to be more diverse, although that's not specific to Sedgwick."* Another added that the persistent problem of diversity further up the ranks still needs to be addressed, because while *"at the bottom it looks diverse, the higher you go, the more that thins out."*

"I was very excited to be at a place where if I proved myself early, I would get more substantive work early, and that has really panned out for me."

See firm profile on p.691

Seward & Kissel LLP

Lawyers per state

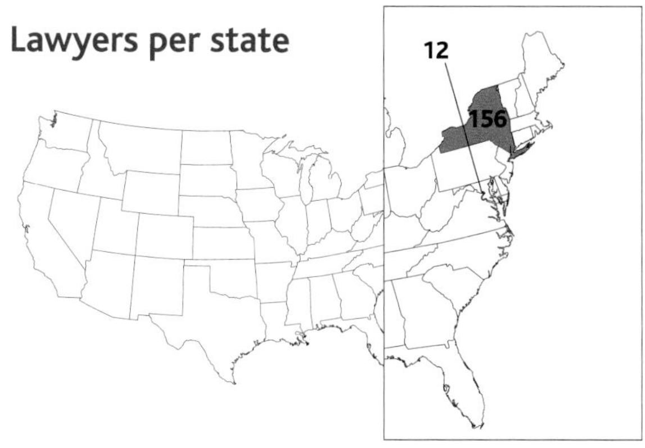

Largest US office: New York
US offices: 2
International offices: 0
First-year salary: $160,000
Billable hours: 2,000 target
Summers 2016: 18 (all 2Ls)
Revenue 2015: undisclosed
Partners made 2016: 3
Famous for: intellectual property, especially patents

If shipping and hedge funds float your boat, climb aboard this small but gold-laden galleon...

CELEBRATING over 125 years of successfully navigating the legal industry's sometimes stormy seas, Seward & Kissel (pronounced not 'sea-ward', alas, but 'soo-wood') employs around 155 lawyerly deck hands in New York and 12 in DC, making it one of the smaller ships in the BigLaw armada. But don't be fooled: when it comes to maritime finance and hedge funds, Seward can ignite some powerful broadside. Managing partner John Tavss tells us: *"The past year has brought a big uptick in transactional areas, so shipping finance has continued to prosper. Our investigations and enforcement litigation have also looked strong, so we've increased our hiring at both entry and lateral levels. Whereas the last few years we've taken on 15 or so new associates, we'll be bumping it up to 18 this year."*

Seward remains a sturdy hull when it comes career development, too. A smaller inflow of associates and leaner staffing models than bigger rivals mean *"lots of opportunities for one-on-one supervision with partners that are well respected in their fields."* Though *"dedicated to providing opportunities for career development,"* juniors here don't have to scrub decks into the early hours to prove their worth. Indeed, Seward provides a work/life balance that had interviewees shouting from the topmasts: *"I make the same money as associates at Skadden or Kirkland & Ellis, but the hours are far more favorable."* Another ahoyed: *"So many people at law school were desperate to be at a top 20 firm to satisfy their competitive streaks. I like to go home!"*

On chambers-associate.com...

- You're only 125 once! More information on S&K's big birthday bash

ASSOCIATES SAY...

Offices

Most new Seward & Kisselers head to the New York HQ, located in Battery Park Plaza. Not all are lucky enough to have their own office, but they liked the Lower Manhattan location for its waterfront calm: *"Far less stressful than being in the heart of Midtown and surrounded by skyscrapers,"* with *"jaw-dropping views onto the Hudson River and the Statue of Liberty."* Being *"just a short walk to Wall Street,"* it's no surprise that a large part of the office's work caters to the financial industry. However, practices such as litigation, real estate, bankruptcy, and trust & estates/tax/ERISA are also on offer.

"Jaw-dropping views onto the Hudson River and the Statue of Liberty."

In DC, a handful of junior associates supports the 12-strong team. Focusing predominantly on investment management, the cohort is *"less formally dressed than New York"* and *"still benefits from the support and resources you'd expect from a New York BigLaw firm."* The Capitol's office may be a minnow compared to New

See firm profile on p.692

Rankings in *Chambers USA*

Corporate/M&A
Investment Funds
Transportation

For detail on ranking tiers and ranking locations, visit www.chambersandpartners.com

York's, but for juniors *"work doesn't tend to overlap between the two offices, so most of the work you'll do is for partners and counsel based in DC."*

The Work

Upon receiving an offer of full-time employment, newbies state their practice area preferences. *"For the most part everyone's choices are honored,"* though it's worth pointing out that investment management and corporate finance take the lion's share, leaving a few to head to litigation, trusts & estates, real estate or bankruptcy. In 1949, S&K orchestrated the foundation of A.W. Jones & Co, the world's first hedge fund. Notching up high rankings in *Chambers USA*, the firm's investment management team continues to lead the field as far as hedge funds are concerned. Seward & Kissel's market share is second to none, servicing some 40% of the top 100 hedge funds based on assets under management. New starters are exposed to the full gamut of hedge funds work from day one, so expect to tackle *"anything from drafting the offering documents to establish a new fund, to helping some incredibly lucrative clients with SEC compliance concerns."*

"It's not just editing and proofreading for years on end!"

"Almost entirely driven out of New York," the litigation group is the beneficiary of a stack of clients from the funds practice. SEC civil investigations, contractual disputes and securities litigation are all common concerns, and interviewees were keen to point out that *"Seward has made a concerted effort to grow its white-collar crime offering in recent years."* Budding litigators start by completing research tasks, but are *"progressively entrusted with more responsibility."* A third-year revealed: *"I haven't completely escaped doc review, but have had the chance to lead interviews and draft findings into a final report. It's not just editing and proofreading for years on end!"*

Over in corporate finance, juniors are assigned to one of a number of subgroups, but *"you're free to approach partners from other teams if there's something you'd like to try."* M&A, capital markets and real estate are some of the options on offer, as is maritime finance. Awarded top marks in *Chambers USA*, the market-leading shipping team assists clients worldwide on matters such as loan agreements, ship purchases and joint ventures. *"It can be challenging to negotiate time differences,"* pointed out one source. *"A lot of shipowning companies are based in the Marshall Islands or the Bahamas. If a client based there wants to refinance their company to buy new ships then they'll commonly borrow from the US or the UK. The ships could be built in Korea, so you'll definitely work some late nights and early mornings when deals are winding up."* With so many jurisdictional particularities to keep up with, does it ever become too mind-boggling a process? *"The transactions are complex,"* answered one junior, *"but we receive lots of advice from foreign counsel, and partners make a point of sitting down and visualizing the transaction on a whiteboard so everyone can keep track on what's going on. It's challenging, but really interesting work."*

Recent work highlights

- Assisted Belgian crude oil shipping company Euronav in its $200 million IPO launch
- Helped global hedge fund management company Deimos secure private equity investment and subsequently acquire Guggenheim Global Trading
- Filing approximately 48 interpleader and ship arrest matters for ING Bank, in an attempt to win compensation from collapsed marine fuel company O.W. Bunker
- Represented Knightsbridge Shipping in its merger with Golden Ocean. With a combined fleet of 72 vessels, the combined Golden Ocean Group stands as one of the world's largest dry bulk shipping companies

Hours & Compensation

Though hours can at times be unpredictable, they're rarely taxing. *"Before I joined the firm, everyone I spoke to said that by New York BigLaw standards the hours are good,"* recalled one respondent. *"In my experience that's really been the strongest selling point. The pay is market, but we work fewer hours!"* There's no formal billing requirement, though associates do qualify for a bonus by hitting 2,000 hours. *"Bonuses are below market,"* though sources described this as *"a fair trade-off for a manageable working schedule."*

"It's not the kind of place where anyone burns out."

Most agreed that days in the office usually average out at around the ten-hour mark. However, interviewees felt that there's little pressure to stay in the evening if you're not busy. *"People here judge you on your work, so there's no need to run around like a headless chicken until midnight to prove your dedication!"*

See firm profile on p.692

When the vacation itch creeps in, juniors had *"no concerns about taking the full 20 days off. As long as you clear with colleagues to make sure someone can cover for you, and occasionally check your emails for anything urgent, you're good to go."* It's no surprise then that lawyers believed *"it's not the kind of place where anyone burns out."*

Pro Bono

"Pro bono opportunities tend to be more litigious than transactional," so many of our deal-doing sources hadn't taken on much. MP John Tavss was particularly keen to mention the firm's involvement with Her Justice, an organization that works in collaboration with New York law firms to provide legal services to indigent women. *"Her Justice – like many of the pro bono organizations that we work with – works with us on cases and provides a lot of mentoring for those who wish to get involved,"* he explains. *"It's been of huge interest to our summers and junior attorneys, as it gives them an opportunity to try out the sorts of work – areas such as divorce, immigration and custody law – that we don't otherwise specialize in."* All pro bono work can be counted toward associates' billable hours totals.

Pro bono hours

- For all attorneys across all US offices: 6,671
- Average per attorney: 31

Training & Development

To minimize any teething problems, juniors undergo a week of orientation training, covering all the basics such as how to bill, practice-specific seminars and a handful of CLEs. One third-year had observed *"an improvement in preliminary training since my year began. It seems now that there's a lot more in place to introduce starters to their practice areas. For us there was a lot of figuring it out as you go along, but first-years are now taught a universe of information to make sure they're up to scratch from the very start."*

> "You receive so much useful feedback throughout the year."

Rookies receive formal reviews at the end of each year, although the consensus view was that *"it'll rarely throw up any real surprises. You receive so much useful feedback throughout the year that you tend to know where you stand."* One corporate number-cruncher appreciated that *"when you're working on a new kind of deal there are so many different things that can leave you guessing. Thankfully, partners are of the opinion that the only bad question is the one you don't ask, and if you do a good job on something they'll tell you."* Litigators felt similarly encouraged, with one recalling an early success story: *"When I was in my first year, one of the reports I'd written led to a good result. The lit team holds lunches every other Thursday, and the leading partner gave me a shout-out for the work I did in front of the whole group. It was encouraging to know that if you do good work it will be recognized, even as a first-year."*

> "People are sociable in the office, but it's definitely a go home after work kind of place."

Culture

Such an approach paves the way for a culture that is *"very much team-oriented. Partners are really interested in associates' development, and associates are keen to help out, so it's really not the kind of workplace where people are out to ruin your day."* Though *"people are sociable in the office,"* Seward is *"definitely a go home after work kind of place."* Juniors tend to lead the line when it comes to socializing, but *"if someone closes a major deal or gets married then we'll celebrate it over a few glasses of wine."*

> ***"So many people at law school were desperate to be at a top 20 firm to satisfy their competitive streaks. I like to go home!"***

Naturally, the firm's 125th anniversary served as a perfect excuse to raise a few glasses. To find out more about S&K's big 125, head to our Bonus Features on chambers-associate.com.

Diversity

Interviewees judged the balance between male and female entry-level associates to be around 50:50, but *"aside from that there's definitely some work to be done when it comes to diversity."* They lamented that *"it's not an area that the firm seems to focus upon,"* citing a lack of affinity groups, pipeline programs or participation in any diversity recruiting events. *"I have no sense of whether or not we're making efforts,"* a junior admitted. *"I assume we are."* Consequently, some felt that *"considering we're based in New York, the firm could be doing a much better job to encourage people of ethnic minority backgrounds into the firm."* The figures match up too, with a whitewash of Caucasian attorneys making up 94% of partners and 86% of associates. S&K's recruiting partner Jack Rigney counters such criticisms by pointing out that *"though we do not have any formal programs in*

See firm profile on p.692

place, we are certainly aware that diversity in recruitment is important." One associated concurred: *"There has been an effort. It is clear that it's something that has been important."*

"Showing an invested interest in the types of work we do can really impress at interview."

Get Hired

"We're not a full-service firm, and our work is tailored to specific industry sectors," explained one junior, *"so showing an invested interest in the types of work we do can really impress at interview. Demonstrable prior exposure through internships or industry experience shows that you already have sought out relevant practical exposure, which you just wouldn't get at law school."* Jack Rigney elaborates further, stating that *"if you can quickly amass an intelligent understanding of the industry and its surrounding legal issues then you're off to a great start. Then it's a question of being confident when communicating with clients, and being productive and efficient while maintaining the integrity of your work. Throughout the application stage, applicants would do well to highlight examples of those kinds of qualities, because they are the sort of associates whom we expect to be very successful down the road."*

Strategy & Future

But regardless of rookies' aptitude and understanding, it's no secret that BigLaw in New York makes far fewer partners than it does associates. Jack Rigney believes that *"tenure and longevity here is better than most. Many of our summers have made partner, myself included. But the fact that our attorneys may be able to develop industry contacts, and act for many of these as a key contact point on matters, means that they become very attractive to the industry. We understand that a lot of our attorneys will be presented with fantastic offers over the course of their careers, and the only promise we make is that if they come here they will be well trained and welcomed in a friendly environment. Our goal is to develop lawyers to be well positioned to stay and become partner, as well as being marketable enough to go on to do great things elsewhere, should they want to."*

"Tenure and longevity here is better than most."

"I make the same money as associates at Skadden or Kirkland & Ellis, but the hours are far more favorable."

See firm profile on p.692

Shearman & Sterling LLP

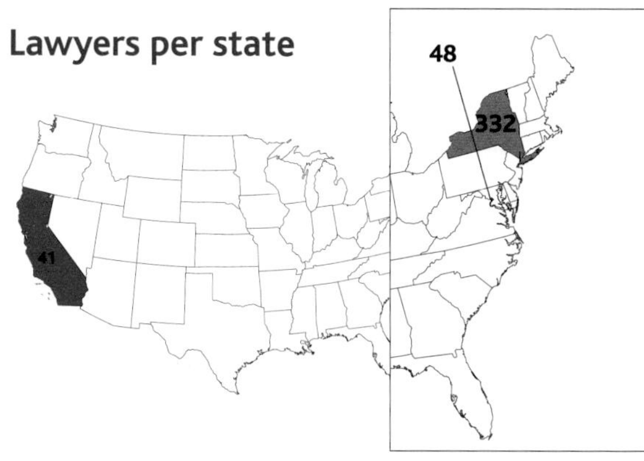

Largest US office: New York
US offices: 4
International offices: 16
First-year salary: $160,000
Billable hours: no requirement
Summers 2016: 78 (73 2Ls, 2 1Ls, 3 others)
Revenue 2015: $860.3 million (+1.8%)
Partners made 2016: 12 (4 US)
Famous for: international work, Wall Street roots, transactional heavyweight

From day one, Shearman offers sterling opportunities to grow and prosper as part of its burgeoning global network.

FOUNDED in 1873, Shearman & Sterling has built up a reputation for high-end matters that stretches far beyond its Wall Street beginnings. Corporate, projects and capital markets work draw the firm's biggest headlines, but Shearman is also recognized nationwide in *Chambers USA* for areas including banking & finance, securities litigation, international arbitration and tax. Shearman's New York HQ remains its largest US office, but presences in DC, Menlo Park and San Francisco complete the picture stateside.

Further afield, Shearman notches up over 30 additional rankings in *Chambers Global* for its work across 16 international offices. Showing no signs of slowing down, the firm opened a new Dubai office in September 2015. Is it difficult to keep so many irons in the fire? Not according to our associate sources, many of whom felt *"very lucky"* to have had the opportunity to travel to or work in foreign offices. *"Having a demonstrable interest in international work is essential,"* advised one. *"You'll routinely be working on globally-formed teams."*

The 'Chambers Global Top 30' places Shearman at number 16, based on law firms' worldwide practice strengths.

On chambers-associate.com...

- Interview with hiring partner Daniel Laguardia and director of legal recruiting Trisha Weiss

ASSOCIATES SAY...

The Work

The vast majority of new starters begin life in Shearman's NYC mothership, where most begin as generalists in either the corporate or litigation pools before specializing a few years in. The handful of associates that begin in the Bay Area and DC offices are channeled more toward particular practices. A sprinkling of New Yorkers also head to more focused groups such as IP transactional, financial restructuring & insolvency, and compensation, governance & ERISA.

Using rookies' weekly availability sheets, assigning coordinators dish out tasks as they see fit. *"The form does provide space to put forth any requests,"* one caller happily reassured. *"I had a colleague who was on a long M&A transaction, but it really wasn't her thing. She had a word and was subsequently transferred to another matter. You have to be honest, proactive and communicative to get what you want here."*

"You have to be honest, proactive and communicative to get what you want here."

Still, we did hear a few grumbles from litigators, who'd been routinely chugging through a glut of securities work. *"Everyone wants to work on white-collar government investigations,"* whined one, *"but there isn't really enough to go around."* Sources' levels of responsibility

The Inside View

See firm profile on p.693

Rankings in *Chambers USA*

Banking & Finance	International Arbitration
Bankruptcy/Restructuring	Investment Funds
Capital Markets	Latin American Investment
Corporate/M&A	Litigation
Employee Benefits & Executive Compensation	Projects
Environment	Real Estate
FCPA	Securities
Financial Services Regulation	Tax

For detail on ranking tiers and ranking locations, visit www.chambersandpartners.com

Recent work highlights

- Advised Bank of America, Merrill Lynch, Barclays, J.P. Morgan and Goldman Sachs as underwriters for $4 billion worth of Qualcomm's $10 billion bond offering
- Contesting gift tax deficiency rulings imposed by the IRS against media mogul Sumner Redstone. The alleged shortcoming stems from Redstone's purported gift of stock to his children in 1972
- Guided Nokia through the $3.1 billion sale of digital mapping business HERE, purchased by German car manufacturers Audi, BMW and Daimler
- Secured a complete vindication for former hedge fund manager Todd Newman, convicted of insider trading in 2012

varied wildly, so again *"you need to be vocal if you're not happy, or you could end up stuck on doc review and research tasks."* Smaller arbitrations were touted as a good way to notch up some experience: *"There's still some pulling of binders,"* but rookies were pleased to have helped draft witness statements and pieces of memorial.

Corporate juniors are most likely to eventually end up in M&A or capital markets, though finance, financial institutions advisory, financial restructuring, investment funds, project development and real estate all take new associates. Corporate clients fall in a number of different sectors, and *"it doesn't matter whether they're in the tech, aviation or financial spheres, the firm is just focused on its practice areas being the best they can."* Again, it's a case of 'ask and you shall receive,' as one financier pointed out. *"Initially I worked on a lot of deal management: reviewing offer certificates, collecting signature pages, drawing up schedules and identifying possible issues for midlevel associates. When I felt ready to take the next step, I asked to try drafting a credit agreement, and the partner I was working with supervised me throughout."*

"The prospect of spending half my summer program in a foreign office was never a concern."

Offices

Every year a few entry-level associates get the chance to work abroad permanently as US-track associates in one of Shearman's international offices. Even beforehand, freshmen can team up with their foreign counterparts by splitting their summer program between offices, which juniors felt *"really puts weight to Shearman's claim as a go-to for global experience."* Does spending five weeks abroad bear any consequences for that all-important exit offer? *"Not at all,"* shot down one globe-trotter. *"Over the past ten years Shearman has given out summer offers at a rate of 100%, so the prospect of spending half my summer program in a foreign office was never a concern."*

Training & Development

Reviews are held twice annually. The spring review compiles feedback from partners and seniors that the associate has worked with over the past year, and juniors found that *"people are as forthcoming with compliments as they are with suggestions for improvement."* A more informal fall review focuses on career development, posing questions such as *"'where do you want to be?'"* and *"'what resources can we give you to aid your development?'"* Sources felt *"well looked after"* and viewed the process as *"very associate-focused."*

"People are as forthcoming with compliments as they are with suggestions."

After an initial orientation week in their home offices, new starters flock to New York for a first-year conference. Later there's one for mid-level associates, and later still a conference for high-achieving sixth and seventh-years. At this stage, Shearman stages a three-day off-site program focusing on leadership skills and providing partnership pointers. Juniors viewed this ongoing investment as *"money well spent."* For hiring partner Daniel Laguardia, *"it's a great way for associates to build a network, and helps introduce them to different types of work from an early stage."*

Cross-office videocon training sessions keep rookies routinely updated with both their colleagues and any developments in their practice. Also favored was the role played by partners and seniors in fueling juniors' progress. *"They're highly adept at keeping you up to scratch with how you're getting on,"* raved one.

See firm profile on p.693

Culture

"We're the white shoe of white shoe firms," marveled one insider, *"and the experience and track record among our partners speaks for itself. But our ruthlessness in securing client results is juxtaposed by the very personal approach that people here take toward their colleagues. We're not a firm of screamers, which really surprised me when I summered."*

"We're not a firm of screamers."

In fact, New Yorkers found that *"Shearman puts a lot of emphasis on being part of the group, so it's important to show that you're involved and want to be part of the team."* Fortunately it's pretty easy to spark up a conversation, thanks in part to a 'library lounge' on the third floor. *"There are couches, TVs and even croissants provided,"* drooled one source. *"Management may regret the drop in productivity when March Madness kicks off!"*

"A little less formally dressed" than their Big Apple counterparts, DC's associates *"work on matters featured in the Wall Street Journal and New York Times"* but lap up *"the added benefit of not having to be in the big smoke."* A *"collapsed"* hierarchy means *"partners are very hands-on, and keen to get you involved with clients."* As for the Californian contingent, we heard that practice area teams from across the Menlo Park and San Francisco offices *"meet once a month over lunch or drinks,"* which *"helps us keep tabs on where we're all at."*

Diversity

"We're not all just square white guys," exclaimed one New Yorker. Propelled by a bustling network of snappy-titled affinity groups, Shearman *"strives to create a working environment in which lawyers from all walks of life can succeed."* WISER (The Women's Initiative for Success, Excellence and Retention), BLAQUE (Black Lawyers Aligned in the Quest for Excellence) and AVALANCHE (The Association of Various Asia-interested Lawyers Aligned for Non-discrimination, Community, Honor and Excellence...!) are just some of the groups on offer. One minority associate captured the vibe: *"My identity is never a concern, which frees up more time for me to focus on my work."*

"We're not all just square white guys."

Such provisions *"may have something to do with the firm's global footprint,"* associates speculated. *"Shearman values its diverse associate base, as having a range of skills to hand can be very useful."* A Big Apple source confirmed: *"A Hispanic colleague of mine has been drafted in on a number of matters with our Lat Am counterparts. Clients really appreciate being able to converse freely."*

Get Hired

"Our ruthlessness in securing client results is juxtaposed by the very personal approach that people here take toward their colleagues."

Shearman is *"looking to hire applicants who can demonstrate intellectual ability, collegiality and creativity, as well as an engagement and interest in the practice of law,"* says hiring partner Daniel Laguardia. *"Whether they've helped out at a legal clinic, written briefs, or helped government agencies on investigations, the most important thing is that students fully engage with what they are doing during their 1L summer. That will give them much more to talk about when it comes to interviews. We want to hear what they got out of it, what they learned from it, what was challenging and how they overcame those problems. It's all evidence that points toward a young professional who is trying hard to build a promising career, which is exactly what we're looking for."*

"The most important thing is that students fully engage with what they are doing during their 1L summer."

"It's also important to keep up to date with the business world," Laguardia adds. *"Read the business section in newspapers, and follow the top periodicals. Develop an understanding of the world in which we operate. Interviewees with a robust idea of how our firm fits into the global economic landscape are particularly impressive."* Read the full interview in our Bonus Features online.

Pro Bono

"One of the perks of being here is that pro bono work comes to you," explained an insider. *"It's not unheard of to get three or four emails in a day. There's a 25-hour minimum requirement, and pretty much everyone sails past that mark."*

"There's a 25-hour minimum requirement, and pretty much everyone sails past that mark."

See firm profile on p.693

With *"plenty of opportunities available"* for transactional associates, *"there's no need to slog away on litigious matters for the sake of doing your bit."* Deal-doers had helped local artists to get their businesses incorporated, launched social impact bonds to fund humanitarian work, and assisted charities in reforming their organizational documents. On the litigation front, *"everyone's done an asylum case or two,"* but juniors were most interested in Shearman's involvement with international criminal tribunals. *"We recently sent an attorney out to Rwanda to provide pro bono aid to the prosecutors at its international criminal tribunal,"* one rookie highlighted. *"We do a lot with the ICT in Cambodia too."*

Beyond its altruistic merit, pro bono work throws up some excellent fast-track development opportunities. *"You're the partner and have to take the reins, which is valuable,"* one respondent said. *"It's a good way to refine your skills."*

Pro bono hours

- For all attorneys across all US offices: 28,833
- Average per US attorney: 67

Hours & Compensation

Shearman doesn't enforce a particular billing target or requirement. However, some associates tipped us off about an unofficial target in their teams, with one stating: *"The goal is to try and break 2,050 hours."* With 11-hour days fairly standard, *"it isn't difficult to hit."* Bonuses are lockstep, and any variation is based on individual merit. *"Your general performance is a big consideration,"* said one insider.

"The goal is to try and break 2,050 hours."

Offices start clearing out by 7pm, and most Shearmanites will put in an extra hour or two from home later in the evening. *"We work a lot, but people are fine with that,"* one conceded. *"You wouldn't sign up to the army and then complain about going to war."* The flexibility to work remotely was appreciated: *"I thought face time would be a big thing and I wouldn't have much latitude for free time over evenings and weekends,"* recalled one junior. *"That hasn't been the case. Sure, it's important to get all of your work done, and some weeks will be far busier than others, but partners trust us to manage our own workload without needing to enforce clock-in times upon us. When you're off, you're off."*

Nevertheless, *"a late night at Shearman is a late night by anyone's standard."* Occasional all-nighters *"are a reality,"* but we were assured that *"you get to learn quite a bit during those busy times,"* and *"a strong sense of camaraderie makes it all a little more digestible."* In April 2016, the firm announced that associates and counsel in good standing can now work away from the office up to two days a month – a nice perk.

Strategy & Future

Shearman's 50-year Middle East presence received a shot in the arm in September 2015, following the opening of a Dubai office. *"We do a lot of work with the sovereign wealth funds in the Middle East and being in Dubai brings us closer to our clients,"* says global managing partner David Beveridge. *"We have no immediate plans for further expansion in the region,"* but when it comes to practices *"Shearman & Sterling is one of the world's best for litigation and arbitration work. In the past year our white collar, securities and securities defense groups have all performed particularly well. We've also added an IP litigation team and will continue to strengthen and grow as necessary. Our corporate practices also continue to deliver strong results, and we expect to expand those teams too, particularly in the US."*

"We're looking to hire applicants who can demonstrate intellectual ability, collegiality and creativity, as well as an engagement and interest in the practice of law."

Daniel Laguardia, hiring partner

See firm profile on p.693

Sheppard, Mullin, Richter & Hampton

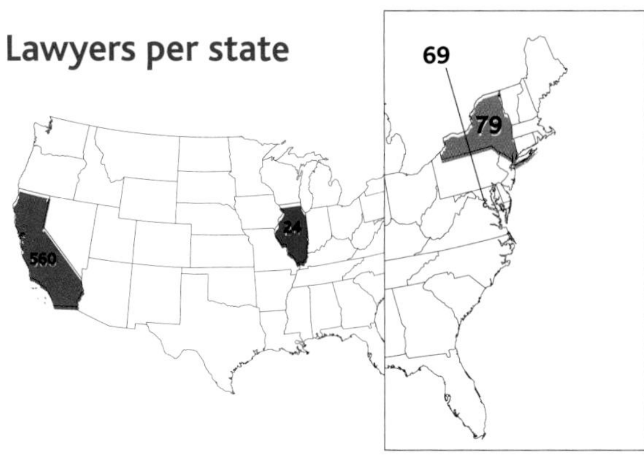

Largest US office: Los Angeles
US offices: 10
International offices: 5
First-year salary: $160,000
Billable hours: 1,950 required (including 50 creditable hours)
Summers 2016: 32 (31 2Ls, 1 1L)
Revenue 2015: $559.5 million (+9.6%)
Partners made in 2016: 11 globally (10 in US)
Famous for: California cool, consistent growth

Revitalized pro bono, restructured bonuses and revamped training... when Sheppard associates speak, management listens.

SHEP's rep for maintaining a laid-back California cool within the pressures of BigLaw attracts attorneys *"who value being congenial, social and having a life over sheer prestige,"* according to associates here. But Sheppard Mullin proves that being relatively mellow isn't a barrier to ambition. It's been expanding steadily for years and – with a string of already well-established California bases – the firm is currently concentrating on building up its offerings in Chicago, New York and Washington, DC. Across the Atlantic, the Brussels office is swelling as Sheppard recently added an EU competition and regulatory practice there.

Some BigLaw firms have expanded too quickly, crashed and burned, but Sheppard's growth has been considered and cautious. Chairman Guy Halgren explains: *"We've increased our revenue every year since 1992. We've never had a down year in 23 years, through thick and thin, throughout the financial meltdown, and we've done that without a merger or acquisition. We've recruited students out of law school and undertaken moderate lateral growth. That's our model for success and what we aim to do in the future."*

On chambers-associate.com...
- Interview with chairman Guy Halgren
- Interview with chief talent officer Bob Williams
- More on training and development

Well-regarded practices in *Chambers USA* encompass corporate, banking & finance, and litigation. More niche strengths include labor & employment, media & entertainment, government contracts (mainly out of DC), international trade, and Native American law.

ASSOCIATES SAY...

Strategy & Future
Chairman Guy Halgren tells us that enlarging the firm's industry expertise is its current focus. Healthcare and insurance have been in the frame for a couple of years but, Halgren notes, *"we've also added an emphasis on energy, games and social media, life sciences and hospitality."* Sheppard recently snapped up a three-partner IP team specializing in games and social media from Pillsbury.

"Grow into our skin."

"Our strategy remains to grow into our skin," Halgren continues. *"We like our footprint and we aim to do more for our clients in each of our existing locations."*

The Work
Business trial (general litigation) usually takes in the most newbies, closely followed by corporate and labor & employment. Some new attorneys also join government contracts, IP, finance & bankruptcy, and real estate.

See firm profile on p.694

Rankings in *Chambers USA*

Advertising	Healthcare
Antitrust	Insurance
Banking & Finance	Intellectual Property
Bankruptcy/Restructuring	International Trade
Construction	Labor & Employment
Corporate/M&A	Litigation
Environment	Media & Entertainment
Government	Native American Law

For detail on ranking tiers and ranking locations, visit www.chambersandpartners.com

Recent work highlights

- Represented California day spa Burke Williams against allegations of harassment and discrimination brought by an employee
- Assisted communications technology company Dialogic during an investigation by the SEC into the international operations of Dialogic's predecessor following allegations of fraud
- Advised French media company Banijay in its acquisition of a controlling interest in US television production company Stephen David Entertainment

The route to jumping on board with a practice area varies between offices. Some bases – NYC, DC and Orange County – follow Sheppard's tried and tested method: newbies are generally allocated to one of three preferences submitted after the summer program. Several smaller hubs, such as Century City and Del Mar, hire juniors into a specific group. Meanwhile LA and San Francisco are currently experimenting with a new approach: *"During your first four to six months as an associate you're in a general pool. Anyone can send you work until you decide which area you'd like to commit to."*

Business trial rookies tend to start out as generalists and can scoop up anything from construction, insurance or communications matters to white-collar crime, securities or privacy and data litigation. On smaller cases juniors do *"anything from discovery to drafting documents."* Larger matters tend to see them handling *"more research and drafting memos. You get a good experience in both situations. The bigger cases are intense while the smaller ones afford more responsibility from day one."*

"They put us out there early so we become comfortable."

Labor-oriented labor & employment associates *"assist labor negotiations and deal with arbitrations and unfair practices."* Those concentrating on the employment side tend to split their time between single-plaintiff harassment and discrimination claims, and class action suits on *"meal and rest cases or wage and hour violations."* Employment sources had gotten to work preparing depositions, drafting and responding to discovery requests and motions. One interviewee added: *"It's not unusual to appear in court at this stage in your career"* to argue motions for summary judgments and hearings. *"They put us out there early so we become comfortable."*

Sheppard's corporate attorneys encounter anything from venture financing and leveraged buyouts to M&A, IPOs and private equity matters. IP juniors can dabble in both patent litigation (patent infringement) and patent prosecution (applying for a patent). Anti-corruption, litigation, investigations and compliance matters are all up for grabs in government contracts.

Across practice areas, our sources didn't appear to have made much use of Sheppard's free market system to seek out work: *"I can't remember the last time I had to tell someone I was slow and needed more tasks,"* one inundated source reflected.

Hours & Compensation

Most of our interviewees had no trouble hitting the billable target of 1,950 hours although several acknowledged that discrepancies exist between practices: *"Some can be slow and others are so busy the 1,950 is a joke!"* Juniors tended to put in around ten or 11 hours a day at the office but were rarely disturbed once they'd left for home. *"They understand we have lives and there's no expectation we're constantly attached to our phones. Once I'd been in the bath and didn't see an email for a couple of hours. I apologized profusely but they understood I was out of office."* This midweek respect extends to weekends and time off: *"The last thing we want to do is disturb vacations as we know people need a break."*

"I apologized profusely but they understood I was out of the office."

In 2015, we heard some grumblings from associates that bonuses didn't match market rates. Soon afterwards, Sheppard restructured bonuses to bring them into line with the industry standard. Payouts now correlate to a tiered structure over and above the 1,950 hours. In 2015, the firm pushed back the annual bonus announcement to March (the billing cutoff takes place in September), which is really late. In 2016, it announced in January (the official line is that it announces bonuses during the first quarter). Although several juniors considered this late announcement a *"downside"* one suggested that *"maybe we did it to ourselves."* Sheppard floated the idea of shifting the billing year end from September to December to associates but, chairman Guy Halgren tells us, *"people*

See firm profile on p.694

did not want that pressure round the holidays so they overwhelmingly chose not to move it." Go online for more from Halgren on bonuses and other changes.

Training & Development

Associates are driving forward changes in the firm's training program after previous concerns over scant sessions. We heard chief talent officer Bob Williams has *"brought in a group of younger associates to brainstorm ways Sheppard could improve its formal education. The group's realizing it's not an easy thing to solve."*

"They've definitely made an effort to improve things."

The firm's not completely reliant on Bob Williams and co to come up with a final plan, though. The number of formal training sessions in each department have already been upped. *"They've definitely made an effort to improve things,"* one associate clarified. *"One of our practice area meetings was converted into a training session."* Go online to find out what other training Sheppard offers.

Culture

Alongside bringing associates on board to help improve training, the firm also runs an associates' council to raise any issues with management (it was this council that represented associates' views during bonus wrangling). Every few months the committee comes together to *"complain about everything,"* joked one source. *"There are no partners in there and a handful of associates are tasked with going to the firm's management and acting as the middle men"* to liaise over any concerns. *"Whether things actually change is a harder decision but we can voice our opinion,"* they reasoned. More informally, *"the partners don't dismiss us as juniors. Even in my first year they wanted to hear what I had to say on how things were handled."*

"Partners aren't stuffy and inaccessible."

New Yorkers in particular highlighted a *"strong sense of community. The partners aren't stuffy and inaccessible, and I've never once felt they consider me beneath them. We have a staff appreciation week, which speaks volumes. They want to make this a happy place."* This attitude appears to extend to the *"very jovial"* DC office: *"People have a good time here. Throughout the day we stop to have a chat or grab lunch together."* We even heard of juniors building extra time into their schedule to accommodate socializing.

Sheppard's known for its California cool attitude but West Coast juniors were keen to differentiate between offices. Del Mar *"is one of the most relaxed. We do a ton of work but there's not a lot of stress."* Vying for 'most laid-back office' is Century City – where *"partners take a vested interest in juniors"* – and Orange County, which *"is more easygoing than LA."* But even in the firm's Los Angeles HQ you'll find plenty of variation: *"Labor & employment has a ton of happy hours. There's so much socializing it's like a fraternity. In business trial the emphasis is more businesslike."*

Offices

The bulk of Sheppard's juniors are in the West Coast offices. LA takes on the most each year, with the rest spread around Century City, Del Mar and San Francisco. You'll also find a few others scattered between Orange County and Palo Alto. New York and DC each take a handful of first-years with one newbie occasionally popping up in Chicago.

"Everything but entertainment."

LA handles *"everything but entertainment"* while other offices have more specialized focuses. DC is, unsurprisingly, Sheppard's government contracts hub while half of Del Mar's attorneys work on IP. Century City is best known for hosting the firm's media & entertainment group.

"Our whole approach to interviewing is to hire people who will be long-term members."
Bob Williams, chief talent officer

Juniors reported a fair amount of inter-office collaboration on projects, particularly among offices in the Golden State. Annual practice area retreats bring everyone together for a weekend of sun on the California coast, although government contracts ignore this tradition and jet off for the bright lights of Vegas.

Pro Bono

As part of the firm's *"recommitment to doing as much pro bono as possible,"* Sheppard recently scrapped its hours cap. Unlimited pro bono now counts toward the billable target across the firm, bringing everyone on par with Sheppard's Big Apple base (limitless hours have been around for several years there). *"The firm has made an effort to underscore that all offices should be doing pro bono."*

See firm profile on p.694

And are they? One San Franciscan reckoned their office had recently seen *"a substantial increase in the amount of pro bono hours billed. We receive constant emails from our office's coordinators."* And Del Mar's pro bono committee *"tries to make lots of different types available"* to engage everyone. Immigration, asylum, housing rights, family law and adoption matters all frequently crop up firmwide.

Pro bono hours

- For all attorneys across all US offices: 26,632
- Average per US attorney: 36

Diversity

One interviewee surmised: *"I would say it feels diverse for BigLaw. Of course the numbers are what they are especially at the partnership level,"* where 91% are white and only 17.6% are female. Still, juniors noted that Sheppard *"is very transparent about the figures and they've definitely made diversity a priority."* When attorneys in the capital recently moved into new office space, for example, the women's group successfully lobbied for the addition of a 'wellness/nursing room', a multipurpose room for people who may not be feeling well and need to rest, as well as nursing mothers who may want to pump. Several sources also acknowledged *"the big push in recent years for the LGBT program."* Sheppard's 'Rock Your Interviews' events answer all the tricky questions diverse aspiring attorneys may have about law firm recruitment with the hopes of snapping up a few of them for the firm's summer program. The proof is in the pudding though and Sheppard's *"already seeing people who attended sessions come through OCIs."*

Get Hired

"Our whole approach to interviewing is to hire people who will succeed in our firm over the long term," partner and chief talent officer Bob Williams explains. *"Students can go through law school and not have much of an idea about what practice is like or the amount of work involved. Someone who understands this is less likely to leave the firm early."* Juniors with recruiting experience underscored the importance of *"asking thoughtful questions to demonstrate you've done your research."* So dig a little deeper than just the firm's homepage.

"Real responsibility and real management capability."

Prior work experience or a career can also be advantageous, Williams stresses, as candidates who demonstrate *"real responsibility and real management capability"* impress. Read more from Williams on our website.

"We like our footprint and we aim to do more for our clients in each of our existing locations."

See firm profile on p.694

Sidley Austin LLP

Lawyers per state

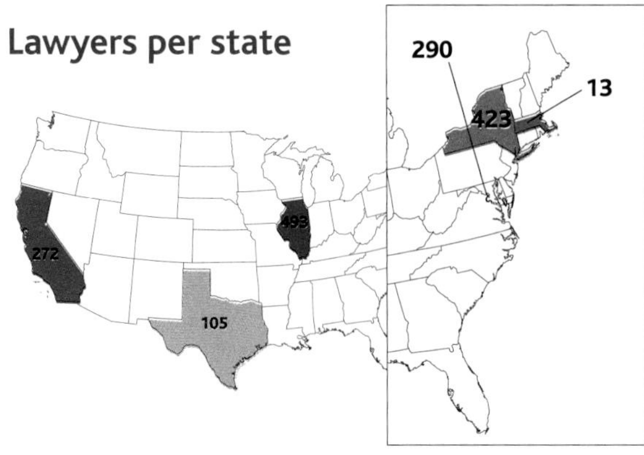

Largest US office: Chicago
US offices: 10
International offices: 9
First-year salary: $160,000
Billable hours: generally 2,000 target
Summers 2016: 188 (177 2Ls, 11 1Ls)
Revenue 2015: $1.867 billion (+6.7%)
Partners made in 2016: 24 (22 in US)
Famous for: appellate law and all things transactional; where the Obamas met

Associates at this supersized Chicagoan wrestle with appealing work and soak up the "*the Midwestern vibe.*"

SIDLEY Austin was founded by Norman Williams and John Leverett Thompson in Chicago in 1866 – long before the city's most famous export, the deep dish pizza, was invented. Today Sidley is known for many *Chambers USA*-ranked practices, one of the most eye-catching being its appellate group, which has seen the firm involved one way or another in around 40% of the cases the Supreme Court hears each term. These include landmark cases like *The United States v Lopez*, which ruled that Congress had exceeded its constitutional authority over the legality of guns in schools.

But appeals are far from the only topping on Sidley's deep dish legal pizza. Associates highlighted, for example, that *"for M&A and capital markets, Sidley is the clear choice."* Top-tier national rankings in *Chambers USA* include capital markets, climate change, product liability, and financial services regulation, as well as appellate law. Sidley's high marks are matched by its notable client roster, which in the early days included Abraham Lincoln's widow, Mary. Today's clientele includes Microsoft, PayPal and Bank of America, to name a few. Sidley's alumni are also worth mentioning. There's David Otunga, who joined after Harvard Law School before turning his hand (and limbs) to professional wrestling and the media. Then of course there are the Obamas (Michelle, then an associate, was mentor to a summer associate called Barack...).

On chambers-associate.com...

- Making A Murderer 2.0: The case of William Ziegler
- Interview with management and executive committee member Anne Rea
- Sidley on Media & Entertainment Law

ASSOCIATES SAY...

The Work

While litigators tend to start off as generalists, transactional rookies have more opportunities to specialize immediately, depending on the office they're in. Corporate in *"New York is officially split into M&A, capital markets and governance,"* and juniors here can pick one area sooner rather than later. In the Windy City, by contrast, corporate associates normally *"wait until their fourth year"* before specializing. Newbies had experienced *"an even mix of regulatory counseling and transactional work where banks call us and ask if their proposed strategy can be done. The twist is that Dodd-Frank threw a monkey wrench into things."* Those in the investment products & derivatives group quipped that *"we're one of those groups where people aren't sure what we do!"* They have three key groups – fund formation, trading documentation work and regulatory compliance – and junior tasks include *"drafting documents, client research and SEC filings, as doc review is only likely to be one ten-hour project."* Other transactional groups include: insurance & financial services; securities & derivatives

See firm profile on p.695

Rankings in *Chambers USA*

Antitrust
Appellate Law
Banking & Finance
Bankruptcy/Restructuring
Capital Markets
Climate Change
Communications
Corporate Crime & Investigations
Corporate/M&A
Employee Benefits & Executive Compensation
Energy & Natural Resources
Environment
ERISA Litigation
FCPA
Financial Services Regulation
Healthcare
Insurance
Intellectual Property
International Arbitration
International Trade
Investment Funds
Labor & Employment
Latin American Investment
Leisure & Hospitality
Life Sciences
Litigation
Media & Entertainment
Privacy & Data Security
Products Liability
Real Estate
REITs
Securities
Tax
Technology
Telecommunications
Transportation
Wealth Management

For detail on ranking tiers and ranking locations, visit www.chambersandpartners.com

enforcement & regulatory; global finance; pooled investment entities; and real estate.

General litigation *"is split into complex litigation, regulatory litigation, international arbitration and white-collar crime."* Other litigation subgroups include: IP; civil, criminal & constitutional; and regulatory & economic. On arrival, newbies get work from their assigned mentor to *"get their feet wet."* After this, assignment is a *"free market"* that grows via relationships. Once staffed, *"there's definitely some doc review but not as much as I thought."* Litigators had conducted legal research, drafted memos and prepped witnesses for interviews, among other things. Some sources had in addition *"been involved in pitching to clients, and now I get to draft the initial disclosures or summons,"* and others had *"been able to second-chair depositions."*

"Doc review is only likely to be one ten-hour project."

Practice group heads generally assign work to new associates, and work coordinators in most groups keep an eye on how busy people are. *"There's an overarching formal assignment system where we can see what work is on offer and can be used if we need it, but the majority of people get staffed through informal relationships. It's better this way."*

Recent work highlights

- Represented pharmacy benefit manager Catamaran in its $12.8 billion sale to UnitedHealth Group
- Represented Bank of America Merrill Lynch as financial adviser to Home Properties in its $7.6 billion sale to Lone Star Funds
- Represented Penguin Random House in the legal dispute surrounding the book *The Accidental Billionaires*, which was later adapted into the movie *The Social Network*

Training & Development

All are treated to a three-day firmwide general orientation in Chicago. Then it gets specific. Second-year transactional newbies are enrolled in *"Corporate College."* Sidley attorneys who are experts in the field give presentations in this three-day seminar. Litigators had roughly *"20 [mandatory] one-hour sessions on different topics."* However, the system is currently being *"revamped."* The old method featured sessions on cross-examination, direct examination, deposition training and closing arguments, concluding in a mock trial. The powers that be realized that this wasn't practical. *"It seems silly to go over closings, because first-years won't get anywhere near doing it in reality."* Now the program focuses on junior skills, including how to help partners prepare for depositions. *"In your fourth year you do a mock trial, as it's more career-appropriate."*

"20 [mandatory] one-hour sessions on different topics."

Reviews happen every six months. Like at most firms, associates ask partners who they have done substantive work with to review them. Reviews are then discussed in a meeting with the head of the practice group and a member of the appraisal committee. Reviewers rate associates *"on a scale of one to four"* on areas including *"substantive knowledge of the law, professional conduct, time management, writing and legal research."* However, Sidley stands out for its pre-review system, where associates meet prior to the formal review with a partner who isn't in their practice group. This is so that juniors can raise problems they may be facing with someone external.

Diversity

Associates thought that poor diversity *"is just a reality of the field of law, but Sidley really recognizes the need to work on this."* While some groups are *"still largely white and male,"* the most visible initiatives at Sidley are the programs targeted at women. Juniors detailed the firm's reduced hours policy, which allows parents to work on amended work schedules. *"One mother even made part-*

See firm profile on p.695

ner while on the program." Insiders were quick to reason that *"the firm is forward-thinking. People recognize that unless they make accommodations for women, they will lose valuable talent."*

"Sidley really recognizes the need to work on this."

The diversity committee and the committee on retention and promotion of women host *"a ton of events. We have different mentoring circles that deal with different things. For example, the mothers' mentoring circle has specific lunches and networking just for them."* Formal mentoring aside, associates felt that Sidley fosters an environment where *"there are some really awesome female seniors, who go out of their way to naturally mentor."* Other programs include *"regular webinars by the women's committee that help us with professional growth."*

Offices & Culture

With ten domestic offices (including the newly opened Century City base), Sidley's scope spans the States. However, *"the Midwestern vibe permeates all of them."* Juniors stressed that it's not *"cut-throat; we help each other and the partners work by your side."* While most juniors usually start out in their own office, New Yorkers found they generally share until their third year. DC has been undergoing renovations for the past year and now all associates have adjustable standing desks (which have been implemented throughout the majority of the other sites) and cupboards with dry-erase board doors. *"We're going for a futuristic, Silicon Valley-type feel."* HQ residents were happy with their office the way it is. Taking up 38 floors in the *"heart of downtown Chicago, it's the best location in the city. There is a gorgeous cafeteria and everything is themed in a mint green color."*

"Sidley's not a quirky firm, it's traditional but people know that."

Another theme that transcended location was the fact that *"everyone is nice; there's a no-jerk policy."* Another key feature is that *"it's a family-friendly firm."* Additionally, *"Sidley's not a quirky firm, it's traditional but people know that."* Different groups have different levels of commitment to social events. New York transactional newbies remembered that *"at the end of the summer we once hired a suite at the Yankee Stadium and watched the America v. Belgium World Cup game. We all had American beers and Belgian waffles."* However, Chicago litigators are the most adventurous, recently hosting an office mini-golf tournament where *"each group of people, whether it be juniors, midlevels, seniors, partners or secretaries, are in charge of making a different hole in the office and then we all play."*

Get Hired

Like most of BigLaw, *"there's more of an emphasis on top academics from top schools now."* But it still takes a lot to stand out from the crowd: *"The first thing that struck me on the other side of interviews was how important law review is. I've heard partners say, 'Yeah I like her, but she hasn't done law review.'"* Others suggested that hopefuls should demonstrate a specific interest in an area of law by at least being able to *"talk intelligently about what's going on in the sector."* Others recommended that students shouldn't *"fall into the trap of not promoting yourself. Bring the questions back to why you'd be a good candidate."*

"It's the best location in the city. There is a gorgeous cafeteria and everything is themed in a mint green color."

Hours & Compensation

There's some confusion about whether there's an official hours target. Some had *"never seen anything in writing,"* but most were certain that Sidley operates on the understanding that 2,000 hours is the minimum for bonus eligibility (of which 1,800 must be client chargeable). To achieve this, most attorneys work from around 9am until 7pm, as *"after 7pm it's not likely you'll see other people here."* But on the transactional side, horror stories featured public M&A workers *"getting in at 6am and leaving at 2am for a whole week."*

"Getting in at 6am and leaving at 2am for a whole week."

For bonuses themselves, *"my understanding is that if you reach the 2,000 hours, you should get the market bonus,"* associates believed. *"If you're above it, you can get above market rate."* Management and executive committee member Anne Rea clarifies that *"we also take into account the conditions in each local market."*

Pro Bono

"The firm is massively committed to pro bono," insiders claimed, even for transactional lawyers. The firm encourages it through regular email updates and the support of a full-time pro bono coordinator. Once attorneys reach the 1,800 hours target, 200 hours of pro bono work can count toward the 2,000 hours bonus threshold. Rookies described that *"the firm has a lot of strong partnerships with not-for-profit organizations."* Anne Rea reveals that *"this is done on an office by office basis. For example,*

See firm profile on p.695

our New York office has a longstanding partnership with Her Justice, an organization which helps victims of domestic violence." Rea also promotes the Public Interest Law Initiative (PILI) fellowship, *"where our incoming lawyers can start work at legal service agencies instead of starting at Sidley, and we pay their salary. "*

"I'm now working on an appellate brief. It's an incredible feeling."

Immigration is a key focus, and many associates have *"made visa applications based on domestic violence issues."* Others had drafted amicus briefs for the Supreme Court on death row cases. *"We have lots of death row cases in Alabama* [under the firmwide Capital Litigation Project, in conjunction with the Equal Justice Initiative in Alabama]. *I'm now working on an appellate brief. It's an incredible feeling."* Perhaps the most high-profile death row case recently was the William Ziegler appeal, who after being sentenced to death in 2001 was finally released from prison in 2015, after nearly ten years of work by Sidley attorneys. For more on the case, go online.

Pro bono hours

- For all attorneys across all US offices: 101,327
- Average per US attorney: 59

Strategy & Future

Sidley's future plans include becoming even more tech-savvy. With the new office in Century City and nine partners already calling it home, Anne Rea tells us that this has been to take *"advantage of key trends in the market such as representing private equity funds and media & entertainment companies."* She further reveals that *"our transactional practices have been incredibly busy. M&A, capital markets and other deal flow markets amounted to 40% of the firm's total firm work last year. "*

Sidley's growth has been planned with a *"longstanding no-debt policy."* Expansion occurs by apportioning existing revenue into new projects, to foster security and *"leave the firm bigger and stronger than when we joined. That is our legacy and our position for the future."* For more from Anne Rea, read our Bonus Features online.

"Leave the firm bigger and stronger than when we joined. That is our legacy and our position for the future."

Anne Rea, management and executive committee member

See firm profile on p.695

Simpson Thacher & Bartlett LLP

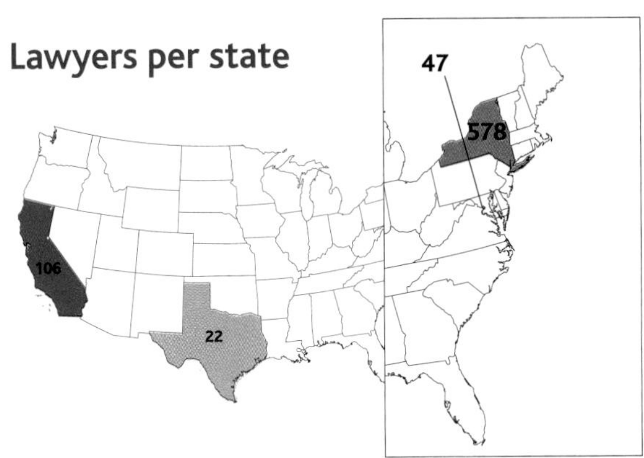

Largest US office: New York
US offices: 5
International offices: 6
First-year salary: $160,000
Billable hours: no requirement
Summers 2016: 140 (130 2Ls, 5 1Ls, 2 3Ls, 3 others)
Revenue 2015: $1.278 billion (+2.6%)
Partners made 2016: 9 globally (6 in US)
Famous for: its elite status and polite culture

Associates were adamant: "*You can't go wrong if you go to Simpson.*"

"WE'VE had a very good year, with solid activity in most areas of practice," chairman Bill Dougherty tells us. *"Relative to 2014 there was probably a little more variability; things slowed down and picked up in certain sectors during the course of the year."* The firm was founded in New York in 1884, and today its associates feel that *"there are few firms that offer strength in such a number of different areas."* A glance at *Chambers USA*'s rankings show there are no firms better than Simpson nationally for banking & finance, capital markets, M&A, private equity, insurance dispute resolution, and securities litigation work.

Despite this daunting reputation for excellence, associates we chatted to weren't intimidated. *"When I came to Simpson, everyone would chat with me casually, and say hello in the elevator,"* one junior reported. *"The people here are all very nice."* Bill Dougherty says this isn't accidental, that Simpson's culture is consciously created: *"We discourage competition among our associates. We want them to share their knowledge and experience with their colleagues, as we do at partner level."* He adds that *"we're really pleased with how our talent pool has developed since that's where we get the bulk of our partners from."* Read our full interview with Dougherty online.

On chambers-associate.com...

- White shoe: the term that law firms love to hate
- Interview with hiring partners Greg Grogan, Lori Lesser and Elizabeth Cooper
- Interview with chairman Bill Dougherty

ASSOCIATES SAY...

The Work

Corporate associates comprised 60% of our interviewee list, while just over a quarter were litigators. The remaining few were spread between real estate, tax, and ECEB (executive compensation and employee benefits). (One apiece worked in 'personal plan', serving individual and family clients, and 'exempt organizations', working with tax-exempt entities like charities.) Work assignment is a fairly formal process: across the board workflow is monitored through a centralized system. *"I do a weekly call with our staffing coordinator,"* one NYC corporate junior told us. *"We go through every single assignment that I'm on and discuss whether I have the capacity for something new. They're always really willing to talk through what you're doing – that's one of my favorite things about working here."*

"The rotation system obliges you to get that varied experience."

In litigation, *"all associates are generalists, so you're assigned to all different types of matters."* This includes providing analysis and advice on antitrust issues, a FCPA case on foreign bribery allegations, and *"we ran an internal investigation relating to an SEC subpoena over the misuse of corporate funds."* Interviewees reported getting *"managerial experience"* of the cases, as well as a fair amount of drafting for court documents. The clients are as diverse as the work: *"I've worked for a pharmaceutical company, done an internal investigation for a media corporation, and one client was a multinational*

See firm profile on p.696

Rankings in *Chambers USA*

Antitrust	International Arbitration
Banking & Finance	Investment Funds
Bankruptcy/Restructuring	Latin American Investment
Capital Markets	Litigation
Corporate/M&A	Private Equity
Employee Benefits & Executive Compensation	Projects
	Real Estate
Energy & Natural Resources	Securities
Environment	Tax
Financial Services Regulation	Technology
Insurance	

For detail on ranking tiers and ranking locations, visit www.chambersandpartners.com

Recent work highlights

- Representing Dell in its $67 billion acquisition of EMC
- Successfully defended HannStar Display, the world's largest LCD manufacturer, against $3.5 billion of price-fixing claims brought by Motorola
- Defending Alibaba in shareholder litigation and an SEC investigation arising from Alibaba's $25 billion IPO in 2014
- Represented Sterling Partners during its $925 million acquisition of eBay Enterprise
- Advising Office Depot in its proposed $6.3 billion sale to Staples

telecommunications company." When it comes to antitrust, *"most of our clients are private equity and other financial players."*

Corporate juniors begin their time at Simpson in a more structured way, rotating through three of the department's groups. Associates pick which groups they try (subject to availability), and after the third rotation they select which practice area they'd like to join full-time. *"The firm is pretty good about honoring the attorney's choice."* There are four main groups: *"People generally pick a combination of banking and credit, securities and capital markets, M&A, and fund formation – which involves working directly with the private equity group."* Other areas that associates can rotate through include real estate, public company advisory practice group, and ECEB. Associates loved this system. *"I now realize how valuable it is,"* one enthused, *"Simpson is strong in lots of areas, and the rotation system obliges you to get that varied experience."*

"I interfaced with clients very frequently and ran a closing by myself."

In the banking and credit group, interviewees described mostly private equity clients, as well as the odd public company. *"I've done work on the financing of leveraged buyouts, and a new practice is pursuing and creating credit facilities for existing funds."* This translates into a lot of drafting of ancillary documents, as well as *"helping with main documents on credit and merger agreements."* Those who had tried capital markets described being given *"the opportunity to do some more high-level work – I interfaced with clients very frequently and ran a closing by myself."*

Training & Development

Although there is continued training at all levels, *"it's more intensive during your first nine months or so. There's some kind of training once or twice a month"* at least. These sessions can be both substantive legal training or more generalized topics such as *"how to get assignments, how to be an effective attorney, and the best way to get feedback."* Litigators have deposition workshops, as well as training on topics like discovery and pleadings, while corporate newbies are introduced to various transactions.

"Everyone I've worked with is really interested in my learning."

Associates are assigned partner and associate mentors, although because *"people at Simpson are natural mentors,"* many juniors spoke of building their own mentor relationships more organically. *"There are a lot of educators here, and everyone I've worked with is really interested in my learning,"* one source commented. *"Even if it's not at that moment, the senior associate will explain to me what's going on and how it fits into the whole deal."*

Offices

The firm's New York headquarters unsurprisingly receives the vast majority of new associates, who described its location as *"very convenient; we're right across the street from Grand Central."* Juniors raved about the cafeteria: *"It's actually one of the biggest selling points of the firm!"* It sells a selection of hot and cold food, and the chefs *"can make you whatever you want."* Then there are the legendary Simpson cookies, made fresh every day, and apparently *"the best chocolate chip cookies in the whole of New York."* The office itself is currently being renovated: *"They've gone with a much more modern look, with glass doors and windows."* Although a few sources had reservations about a lack of privacy in the new glassy environment, *"it's not quite as exposing as I thought it would be – although it takes some getting used to."*

"They've gone with a much more modern look."

See firm profile on p.696

Over in Palo Alto – the second largest domestic office – the building is *"very open; there's a lot of light."* There is a cafe and an on-site gym, although *"most people use outside gyms, because this one is fairly small."* Much of the work in this office is (unsurprisingly given its location) technology-focused, while Asian clients and litigation are other particular focal points, *"especially for securities work."*

Culture

Most of our interviewees agreed that their initial impression of Simpson's amiable culture was a big draw, but did the reality match up? *"Yes, absolutely. Every single person I've worked with I'd like to work with again."* They felt Simpson's lack of billing target removed any potential competitiveness between associates. *"There's no feeling that if your group is slow, you need to panic because another group is super busy,"* one junior remarked, *"so it gets rid of those office rivalries."* Another added: *"Everyone understands that we're on the same side internally."*

"Sometimes I think people are too nice!"

We heard repeatedly that *"everyone is incredibly respectful – from junior associates to senior partners."* Many noted that the culture sweetens the pill of long working hours: *"I would get emails from the people I was working for, just saying 'Thank you. I know you were working late last night, but we really appreciate it.'"* Some found that this general politeness was at times a bit too polite. *"It's nice because you don't get people yelling or being rude, but I'm a very direct person, and sometimes I think people are too nice! They shy away from giving that constructive criticism."*

"This isn't really the place where everyone goes and grabs a drink on Friday after work," one junior told us. *"It's more 'finish work, go home.'"* That's not to say people are antisocial, though: *"It's not aggressively social in that there's a lot of pressure to go out, but there's always somebody to get a coffee or lunch with."* And many of our interviewees echoed the finding that *"I have met people here who I now count as real friends."*

Hours & Compensation

Sources assured us that *"on multiple occasions we've been told by partners that we really don't have to worry about how many hours we bill."* That said, as one junior highlighted, *"Simpson is not a charity, so it would be silly to say that no attention is paid to hours billed."* Another guessed: *"I would bet that 90% of the firm is between 1,800 and 2,200 hours for the year,"* and 2,000 hours is the usual ballpark figure for BigLaw firms. The centralized assignment system helps to keep associates busy, and also means that *"if the staffing partner asks why I'm slow, it's a very self-indicting thing to do, because it's his responsibility to get me staffed! It's therefore more a focus on 'are you busy, and will you be busy?' rather than 'give me a number.'"*

"It would be silly to say that no attention is paid to hours billed."

Associates generally work around ten hours a day, with weekend and late-night work during busy periods. Simpson has a lockstep system for salaries and bonuses, which our sources appreciated, as *"when you base bonuses on billable hours targets, you start to lose quality work over quantity."*

"We want individuals who are practical, who are commercial."
Greg Grogan, hiring partner

Pro Bono

"There are far more pro bono opportunities at Simpson than you can take advantage of!" corporate juniors in New York reported, after working on U visas for women who have been victims of domestic violence, and volunteering for The Door, an organization that provides a host of services to runaway LGBT youths. *"Simpson is partnered with them, so we go down once a week, three weeks every month."* The Big Apple office also has a legal clinic based in various Brooklyn high schools, which *"works with parents, largely on immigration issues."*

"People routinely go above 100 hours of pro bono."

Litigators meanwhile spoke of working with Public Counsel – the largest nonprofit law firm in the USA – as well as offering advice to veterans, and working on immigration and domestic violence cases. Pro bono hours are counted toward billables one-for-one, and there's no limit. Having no billing requirement also means associates felt a lot more comfortable doing a lot of pro bono: *"I'm not stressed that people will look at that number and question my billables."* As a result, *"people routinely go above 100 hours per year."*

Pro bono hours

- For all attorneys across all US offices: 44,773
- Average per US attorney: 60

The Inside View

See firm profile on p.696

Diversity

Overall, the consensus was that *"the firm does not feel incredibly diverse, but they are taking huge steps to try to change that."* There is a diversity committee for ethnic minorities and LGBT attorneys, as well as a women's initiative, which has *"lean-in meetings once a month. We also have more informal get-togethers like drinks or lunches."* As far as LGBT diversity goes, one second-year spoke positively: *"When I was a summer associate I knew a couple of LGBT people at the firm. Now I can easily think of three times as many LGBT attorneys."* This has made a huge difference, as now *"lots of people show up to events; you don't feel like you're one of very few people."*

"Lots of people show up to events."

Interviewees felt that racial diversity needed work, however. One junior pointed out the difficulties of this: *"It's often a chicken and an egg situation. If people don't see a lot of diversity, it's quite hard to convince them that we are diverse. I was more cynical before approaching from a recruiting perspective, and now I realize that it definitely is a priority."*

Get Hired

The academic requirements at Simpson are unsurprisingly *"stringent,"* although candidates need to demonstrate more than just academic intelligence. *"We want individuals who are practical, who are commercial,"* hiring partner Greg Grogan informs us, adding: *"We're business lawyers, and our clients want a heavy dose of common sense."* At interview, therefore, *"you should be able to hold a conversation with a stranger about topics that aren't on your resume."* Read more from hiring partners Greg Grogan, Lori Lesser and Elizabeth Cooper online.

"Our clients want a heavy dose of common sense."

Strategy & Future

"We've had great momentum now for the last three years or so," chairman Bill Dougherty tells us. Any big plans for 2016? *"There'll be points of emphasis. Notwithstanding low oil and gas prices, we're a big believer in our energy practice. We're seeing a lot of activity in healthcare. Technology has remained a critical area of focus throughout all of our offices, including those in Asia. Real estate is another group where we've seen tremendous activity."*

He also pointed out that *"2016 is an election year, and there tends to be a bit more caution in the deal environment as you get closer to the election, so we'll see how that plays out."* In addition, low oil prices mean that *"there will continue to be dislocation in the energy market, but that tends to generate different types of activity."* Go online to read our full interview with Dougherty.

"We're really pleased with how our talent pool has developed since that's where we get the bulk of our partners from."

Bill Dougherty, chairman

See firm profile on p.696

Skadden, Arps, Slate, Meagher & Flom LLP & Affiliates

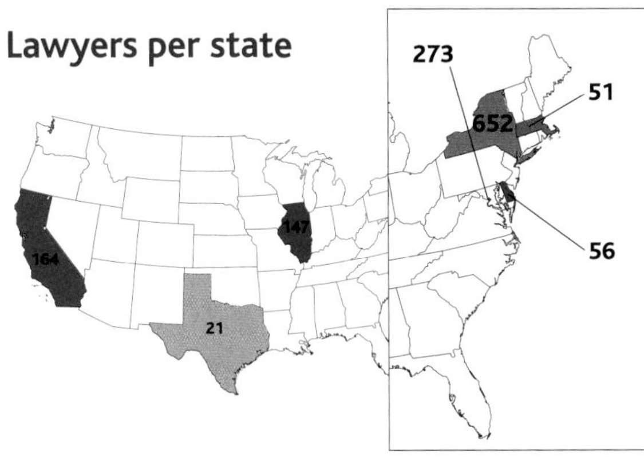

Largest US office: New York
US offices: 8
International offices: 15
First-year salary: $160,000
Billable hours: 1,800 target
Summers 2016: 212 (176 2Ls, 29 1Ls, 2 3Ls, 5 SEOs)
Revenue 2015: $2.41 billion (+4.1%)
Partners made 2016: 11 (9 in US)
Famous for: historically, muscling into deals white shoe firms wouldn't touch

Tough-as-nails Skadden provides the perfect setup for hard-working associates to blossom.

FOUNDED in 1948, Skadden spent the second half of the 20th century honing a shrewd commercial approach that set the precedent for BigLaw as we now know it. Capitalizing on the M&A boom of the freewheeling 1980s, the New York firm commanded high fees on corporate transactions by bringing Wall Street tactics into the boardroom, garnering a reputation for ruthless pragmatism and hard work that left clients counting their blessings, and Skadden counting the zeros.

Seen to be muddying the ever so white shoes of its market-leading competitors, the firm's modus operandi attracted some controversy, but was undeniably effective. Skadden now stands as one of the most revered and powerful brands on the legal circuit – a standing that was further bolstered in 2015 when it became the first ever firm to manage over $1 trillion worth of announced M&A deals in a calendar year. Its continued knack for success has seen it top *Chambers USA* for the number of first-class rankings it notches up, covering over 30 practice areas.

On chambers-associate.com...

- Bottom-dollar blues: Skadden's new productive hours target
- Skadden's offices

Perhaps mellowing in its golden years, associates at the firm assured us that *"the outdated assumption of Skadden as a big bad institution couldn't be further from the truth."* Admittedly, *"you're expected to go to great lengths to keep clients happy, so the hours can be challenging,"* but with that comes an acceptance that *"to keep standards high the working environment needs to be functional. Sniping at one another is not conducive to that, so we're not the sort to engage in office politics."*

"You'll get more of an education here than you ever got at law school."

The hours may be tough, but considering the profile of clients, complexity of deals and *"headline-grabbing cases"* passing through Skadden's doors, *"you'll get more of an education here than you ever got at law school."* Crucially, juniors felt that such an education set them up for an excellent career trajectory, wherever that may take them. The brand weight had associates *"batting off headhunters,"* but what really impressed was the fact that *"the firm is realistic about partnership opportunities. What you'll get here is the opportunity to work hard and make some excellent contacts, and when you decide that you'd like to make a career move the firm couldn't be more supportive."*

See firm profile on p.697

Rankings in *Chambers USA*

Antitrust	International Trade
Banking & Finance	Investment Funds
Bankruptcy/Restructuring	Latin American Investment
Capital Markets	Litigation
Chancery	Media & Entertainment
Corporate Crime & Investigations	Outsourcing
Corporate/M&A	Private Equity
Employee Benefits & Executive Compensation	Products Liability
Energy & Natural Resources	Projects
FCPA	Real Estate
Financial Services Regulation	REITs
Government	Securities
Insurance	Sports Law
Intellectual Property	Tax
International Arbitration	Technology
	Telecommunications

For detail on ranking tiers and ranking locations, visit www.chambersandpartners.com

Recent work highlights

- Represented EMC in its $67 billion acquisition by Dell – the biggest-ever technology deal
- Defending JPMorgan Chase against antitrust allegations relating to foreign exchange benchmark fixing
- Representing health giant Baxter International as selling shareholder in Baxalta's $32 billion combination with Shire
- Acted for Time Warner Cable in its $78.7 billion acquisition by Charter Communications

ASSOCIATES SAY...

The Work

Most newbies join Skadden's corporate & transactional group, where before deciding where to specialize those in New York have the opportunity pull two nine-month shifts in teams such as banking, corporate restructuring, finance, investment management, and M&A. Other offices offer more general corporate practices rather than a formal rotation. A handful of novices also slot into litigation & controversy or regulatory (which includes tax), though there's no rotation option in these groups.

"We learn by drinking from the fire hydrant!"

Wherever rookies end up they'll have access to a centralized work allocation system within their department, though it is worth pointing out that in smaller teams *"people are more likely to just knock on the door and see if you've got capacity."* That's not to say that the same doesn't happen in larger groups such as M&A, but according to one dealmaker *"most of our work comes through our group's assigning attorney. They'll meet up with you to see what you've got on and then spend ages making sure that workloads are balanced and cater to individual interests."*

"When it comes to the work itself, we learn by drinking from the fire hydrant," one interviewee joked. *"The hours are long and hard,"* but any pressure comes *"not from partners"* but *"from the cerebral challenge of the high-stakes work we take on."* Far from serving as small cogs in the corporate machine, sources felt *"encouraged to reach out for help,"* spurring a rate of development that *"would be much slower without the intensity we experience here."* Greater responsibility is usually afforded on more nominal tasks, with juniors hinting: *"It's inversely proportional to the size of the matter at hand."* That being said, *"you bite off as much as you can chew, as partners do monitor you to see what you're capable of and how quickly you can advance onto more complex tasks."*

Training & Development

To give them the confidence to go forth and prosper, Skadden's starters are immediately enrolled into the firm's four-week mini MBA program. It welcomes newcomers worldwide to New York for three days' briefing and a welcome dinner, all of which juniors found *"really useful going forward, as you gain contacts in different offices from the get-go."* Thereafter, they head back to their home offices for the remainder of the program, which covers issues such as *"financial modeling, marketing a business and reading financial statements."* Post-Fullbridge, associates are given a comprehensive heads-up on all things Skadden – practice areas, core values, expectations and resources – thanks to a two-week stint on the firm's Associates Comprehensive Education program.

"You gain contacts in different offices from the get-go."

Respondents found six weeks of initial training *"somewhat of an overload,"* but agreed that *"it demonstrates a commitment to our learning."* Further down the line, group-specific training sessions are staged, and rookies receive annual reviews (biannual in their first year). Interviewees did *"appreciate having the opportunity to formally address any issues,"* but added that *"partners here are extremely busy, so unless you're in a really small group you won't get a ton of informal feedback. It'd be nice to have more guidance on how our performance could affect our partnership prospects."*

The one thing that is for certain is that Skadden offers far fewer partnership promotions than associate hires. The firm's *"refreshingly honest approach"* toward this trend

See firm profile on p.697

means that *"there's no bullshit pretense that you'll make partner and live out the rest of your days here. Skadden's aim is to hire the best candidates to do great work before helping them jump onto the next opportunity."* Such support comes in the form of *"sit-down sessions to produce five-year career plans"* as well as *"regularly updated job opportunities and alumni contact information posted on the intranet."*

"More often than not you'll have something to do over the weekend."

Hours & Compensation

"When I speak to my friends from law school who are now practicing in other firms, I'm definitely leading the hours race," one source revealed. For those in the Empire State, that means that *"working until 10pm is pretty common,"* with a late night defined as *"anything after midnight."* Elsewhere one DC rookie moaned: *"More often than not you'll have something to do over the weekend,"* and interviewees in a number of different offices provided whispered accounts of *"sleep-under-your-desk nights."* Be that as it may, *"you'll never be asked to stay unnecessarily."* As one junior reasoned, *"I have friends elsewhere who've been asked to stay until two on the off-chance that they'll be needed. No one would dare pull that here."* All the same, *"the hours are undeniably long and doing them is different from reading about them. Bear that in mind!"*

Skadden's hours target was recently increased from 1,600 to 1,800. Find out more about this and Skadden's offices by heading to our website.

Culture

At Skadden, partners and senior associates hold *"high expectations when it comes to quality of work."* Granted, as a fresh face you're bound to have a few stumbles, but newer associates were confident that *"even if you were underperforming, I doubt people would be nasty or undermining. They'd probably just talk to you informally about the firm's expectations, and see if there was anything you wanted to discuss."* In fact, juniors in offices nationwide were keen to highlight a *"lack of shouting"* as one of the firm's true selling points. Of course, *"it can be tempting to panic when last-minute assignments fall on your desk,"* but *"the engrained reaction is for everyone to pull together to ensure that the client gets what they're looking for. They're relying on us to provide in the heat of the moment."*

"Even if you were underperforming, I doubt people would be nasty or undermining."

To avoid such panic, you're going to need a good planner and the wherewithal to keep it up to date: *"My colleagues here are some of the brightest people I've ever met,"* gushed one interviewee, *"but they're also some of the most organized."* A deal-doer added: *"On a lot of deals one of my tasks was to keep updated document checklists to keep tabs on what stage everything is at.*

"My colleagues here are some of the brightest people I've ever met, but they're also some of the most organized."

After a few months I found myself keeping similar checklists on other matters, even if I hadn't been asked to. It puts all of the work you're doing into context, maximizes your efficiency and helps to reduce your stress."

Pro Bono

"Skadden really takes pro bono seriously," trumpeted one junior. *"I was skeptical at my OCI because it's a claim that everyone tends to throw about, but there really are some good incentives to get involved here."* Pro bono counts hour-for-hour toward associates' hours target, and an award ceremony is thrown each year to recognize the firm's most prolific do-gooders. *"There have been points where billing work has been slow, so I've put in a ton of pro bono hours to compensate,"* recounted another source. *"We're expected to do that instead of waiting for work to fall on our desk."* Opportunities are both transactional and litigious, with sources having drafted organizational documents for NPEs (nonprofit entities), helped on guardian ad litem cases for children in custody disputes, and represented victims of human trafficking.

"There really are some good incentives to get involved here."

Pro bono hours

- For all attorneys across all US offices: 110,516
- Average per US attorney: 89.2

Diversity

Like many law firms, Skadden's upper echelons could be more diverse, but at junior and mid levels diversity efforts were unanimously praised. As one ethnically diverse associate put it, *"sometimes the challenges you face are overblown and sometimes they are very real. A lack of shared cultural references could in some circumstances hold you back, but Skadden acknowledges that and stages talks from high-standing partners with similar backgrounds. We'll discuss things like expectations of*

See firm profile on p.697

our parents versus your average American parents, and explore how that could affect your work. I really didn't expect Skadden to facilitate that dialogue."

"People here may be under stress, but their own identity is never the source."

The firm also hosts a wide range of affinity groups. Beyond representing women, ethnic minority groups and LGBT attorneys, there are also groups for veterans and parents. *"People here may be under stress, but their own identity is never the source."*

Get Hired

Skadden's strong diversity showing is boosted by a widely cast net during hiring. *"The firm was founded by a bunch of Jewish guys who couldn't get white shoe jobs back in the day,"* regaled one keen historian. *"There are a lot of concrete signifiers of that today. Skadden recruits well outside of the top 15 law schools, so as long as you're top of your class, you'll always be in with a shot."*

"Skadden recruits well outside of the top 15 law schools."

With spotless client service the name of the game, Skadden would-bes are advised to run all applications under the microscope before hitting the send button. *"If I see a typo on a resume it's a huge red flag,"* revealed one associate who'd helped with recruiting. *"It shows a lack of attention to detail, which is absolutely fundamental if you want to get anywhere at Skadden."* Equally important is the ability to impress clients, so *"if the conversation falls dead at interview or you're the type to eat marinara with your hands, you may want to look elsewhere."*

Strategy & Future

When strategy came into conversation, interviewees expressed frustration at Skadden's reticence to show its hand. *"We'd like there to be a little more transparency when it comes to big decisions,"* said several interviewees. *"When our hours targets were changed I ended up hearing about it via Google."*

"We'd like there to be a little more transparency when it comes to big decisions."

So what does executive partner Eric Friedman feel the future holds for Skadden? *"Our key focus has always been to secure great client outcomes,"* he says. *"The continued growth of our practice and geographic reach is what helps us deliver the best possible service, and we'll continue to take that approach in the years ahead."* Looking to delve a little deeper, we wondered if he had any key areas in mind. We didn't hear of any immediate plans, but were assured: *"We're continually looking to develop our resources and tap into new opportunities if they'll benefit our clients."*

"If the conversation falls dead at interview or you're the type to eat marinara with your hands, you may want to look elsewhere."

See firm profile on p.697

Snell & Wilmer LLP

Lawyers per state

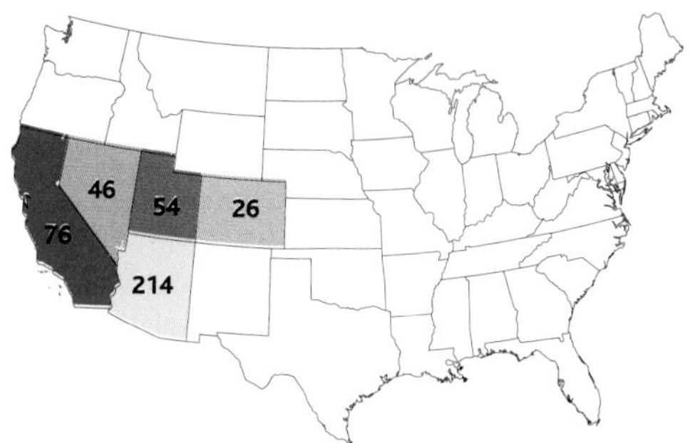

Largest US office: Phoenix
US offices: 8
International offices: 1
First-year salary: $115,000 - $160,000
Billable hours: 2,000 target
Summers 2016: 30 (28 2Ls, 2 1Ls)
Revenue 2015: undisclosed ($253 million in 2014)
Partners made in 2016: 6
Famous for: regional know-how

Participation in its local community lies at the heart of this mannerly Southwesterner, which operates a strict no jerk policy.

"WOULD you buy furniture from a store called Unpainted Huffhines?" scoffs Nathan Arizona in the Coen brothers' 1987 gem *Raising Arizona*. Well, maybe you would think twice about an Unpainted Huffhines dining suite. But would you buy legal services from Southwest stalwart Snell & Wilmer? If you happen to be a high-flying businessperson in Arizona then yes, you probably would. Among its practices are those linked to the local area, like water rights, mining, gaming and Native American affairs, but it's not just regional outfits that flock to this Phoenix-founded firm. High net worth individuals and multinational corporations like Wells Fargo and Starwood Hotels also grace the client roster. Since it was established in 1938, Snell has expanded beyond the Grand Canyon State into Nevada, California, Colorado and Utah, gathering up a troupe of around 400 lawyers. This spread of western territory is complemented by an international outpost in Los Cabos, Mexico.

Sources were *"drawn to the firm because of its reputation in the community"* and noted with approval that *"it's not a behemoth firm with thousands of attorneys, but it's big for Phoenix."* Look no further than *Chambers USA* for evidence of its prime place in this regional market – it earns a clutch of top-flight rankings in Arizona as well as recognition in other states. Indeed, interviewees outside the Arizonan capital described it as *"the best big firm that hires associates in Tucson"* and *"the best in Las Vegas as far as BigLaw goes: it has the sophisticated clients and all the resources I was hoping for."* Over in Salt Lake City, *"the quality of attorneys is second to none."*

On chambers-associate.com...

- An interview with the firm's new chairman Matt Feeney

ASSOCIATES SAY...

The Work

Around two-thirds of the class we interviewed from were beavering away in the firm's capacious litigation department. Incomers get a say in what group they join. *"Before you start they give you a form to fill out with your top three choices,"* a source explained. *"Some people might know from the beginning that they want to be in labor & employment and they'd go straight to that if the firm has a need for someone."* A hefty portion of associates take up a spot in the commercial litigation team, while another choice of destination is *"the litigation pool"* which *"enables new associates to get any work that's litigation-related, like product liability, healthcare or labor. That way you can get a feel for what interests you most, and slowly start to find your place."* On the transactional side of things, attorneys are sprinkled across corporate & securities, real estate, bankruptcy, IP, tax, natural resources and finance.

"They trust you and push you to step out of your comfort zone."

See firm profile on p.698

Rankings in *Chambers USA*

Corporate/M&A	Litigation
Environment	Real Estate
Labor & Employment	

For detail on ranking tiers and ranking locations, visit www.chambersandpartners.com

Work assignment is a fairly informal affair. *"It just kinda happens. If you don't have enough work you're encouraged to solicit it, but we get a lot of emails from partners asking for someone with capacity to join a project. Over time you build up a network and develop a steady flow of work."* Associates reckoned that this *"open market"* system doesn't require excessively sharp elbows. *"There's plenty of work to go around – it's not like there are attorneys all competing for assignments – so it works well."*

An interviewee who'd dived into the litigation pool had *"gotten my feet wet on a real variety of different-sized matters."* Areas sampled include employment, IP, product liability and attorney malpractice. *"On some cases it's just me and a partner, which allows me to take ownership, so I take the first draft of everything, do research projects and talk to the clients."* Commercial litigators weren't pigeonholed into a single field either. *"The clients range from individuals or startups, to financial institutions and pharma companies."* One piped up: *"In the beginning I focused on routine stuff like pleadings and discovery requests. Now I've just started my third year the majority of my time is spent researching and motion writing. At the moment I'm working on a complex motion for summary judgment in relation to a trade secret issue."* The responsibility levels shouldered by juniors are *"overwhelming at times and you question whether partners really know what they're doing by giving you certain things to do! But they trust you and push you to step out of your comfort zone, which is the best way to learn."* Inevitably, *"doc review comes with the territory of being a younger associate,"* but sources made it clear that *"it's a small portion of my practice."*

Meanwhile, transactional attorneys told us that *"the level of client contact is really great. You start off by emailing and making phone calls rather than going to in-person meetings, but now I have a ton of exposure to clients."* Again, variety is the name of the game: *"I'm rarely doing the same thing two days in a row."* For instance, the real estate team takes in work from *"land developers, builders, hospitality clients, multifamily developers, restaurants and sports teams"* and junior members handle *"a lot of drafting of leases and sale and purchase agreements along with property diligence and title and survey reviews."*

Recent work highlights

- Helped IceArizona, operator of NHL team the Arizona Coyotes, to win a temporary restraining order stopping the city of Glendale from terminating the lease for the Gila River Arena
- Acted for Wells Fargo on consumer litigation and class action matters in Arizona, Nevada, Colorado, Utah and New Mexico
- Represented Arizona State University Foundation in its \$35 million acquisition of a historic office building in Washington, DC

Training & Development

New recruits from across offices gather at the Phoenix HQ for a week of orientation that covers *"the ins and outs of billing and client etiquette"* followed by practice-specific training sessions. Throughout the year, there are further sessions *"covering different topics every couple of weeks or so – yesterday there was a mock motion to dismiss where the partners served as judges."* Although satisfied with the amount of training on offer, juniors repeated the familiar phrase that *"the best training comes from learning by doing."*

"Nobody's ever turned me away."

Associates agreed that support from more experienced colleagues isn't in short supply: *"Most partners and senior associates are cognizant of the need to give prompt feedback, so you can learn from your mistakes."* Juniors are assigned a formal mentor, but *"every day I go to different partners with questions because I know they have expertise in certain areas – nobody's ever turned me away."* Interviewees highlighted that 150 hours of training and shadowing can be counted toward the billable target.

Offices

Sources characterized the Phoenix office, located in the Arizona Center, as *"a bright, cheery kind of place"* and noted that the client meeting and waiting rooms have recently been spruced up. From the outside, *"it's very beautifully landscaped, surrounded by shops and restaurants – it looks very Southwestern."* All newcomers have an office to themselves, affording views of either Camelback Mountain or South Mountain.

"A bright cheery kind of place."

The Salt Lake City branch, home to around 50 attorneys, is located *"in the heart of downtown, with a beautiful mall just across the street and a Mormon temple on the corner."* Lawyers in Sin City work from *"very well*

See firm profile on p.698

cared-for offices with fantastic, panoramic views of Las Vegas. From one side of the building you can see the beautiful new High Roller Ferris wheel."

Culture

"One of the things that really sets us apart from other firms is the wonderful 'no jerk' policy. It runs from the top down and everybody buys into it," raved a source, whose declaration was backed up chairman Matt Feeney. *"We don't allow jerks around here,"* Feeney confirms. *"Good behavior is required!"* Associates happily informed us that they're *"also genuinely friends outside of work too."* In Phoenix, we heard that the culture *"tends to be pretty conservative"* particularly when it comes to sartorial matters. *"We're the only firm in town that still requires a shirt and tie every single day. It's a pretty formal place and very professional."* Other offices take a slightly more relaxed approach: *"In Las Vegas there's still a business formal dress code, but we can add a little more personal flair to it."*

"Everybody is rooting for you."

Being oppressed by a strict hierarchy doesn't seem to be part of the overall associate experience. *"When I'm talking to partners and feel nervous, that's a reflection of my own insecurity rather than anything they're doing: it's easy to go into their office and ask a question. It doesn't feel like anyone's trying to test you."* A newcomer appreciated that *"they don't put associates through a hazing process here. Everybody is here to help and rooting for you. I got an assignment the day before Thanksgiving but the partner said not to bother working on it until after the holiday. Nobody here is trying to break you or pull the rug out from underneath you."* One heartfelt associate emphasized that *"people really come and make Snell their home. Everyone gives you the tools to succeed. I'm in it for the long haul."*

Across offices, the social calendar features happy hours and networking events along with *"family activities, like a picnic at the zoo, ice skating, baseball games and a holiday party where someone dresses as Santa for the kids."* Winter festivities are also celebrated within departments, often with *"a trip to a fancy restaurant like a nice steakhouse in Scottsdale."* In addition to firm-organized fun, *"there are always informal happy hours. People will stop by your office and say 'hey we're meeting up to watch Monday night football – feel free to come along'."*

Hours & Compensation

Associates need to clock up 1,800 hours to be eligible for a bonus. There's also a 2,000-hour *"aspirational"* target. Of the former, interviewees reckoned: *"It's certainly manageable. It's a good amount of work but not so much that you'd never see the light of day."* Some of our sources also *"blew well past the 2,000-hour mark and still had time to see my spouse."* On average, juniors spend about ten hours in the office each day and appreciated that *"you're allowed the flexibility and autonomy to manage your schedule."*

"It's a good amount of work but not so much that you'd never see the light of day."

Snell uses a closed compensation system. While some thought this *"very fair,"* others felt that *"it only benefits a handful of people at the top."* According to Matt Feeney, *"when two people compare compensation, the only thing you can be sure of is that one person is not going to be happy. The closed system leads to a collegial working environment. I always say that the First Amendment doesn't stop at our doors and that associates are more than welcome to talk to each other about compensation, but we discourage it. Nothing good comes of it."*

"People really come and make Snell their home."

Pro Bono & Diversity

"There's no cap on the amount of pro bono hours you can work in a year," we heard. *"It's counted hour for hour toward your billable target as long as it's approved by the firm. They encourage us to get involved in lots of cases to get as much experience as we can."* All of our sources had been involved in pro bono, working variously on prisoners' rights cases, consumer disputes, guardianship matters and immigration issues.When it comes to diversity, interviewees recognized that *"there's a long way to go."* Many praised the women's initiative (*"they've been great as far as motherhood and maternity leave is concerned"*) but felt that *"there should be much broader racial diversity."*

"There's no cap on the amount of pro bono hours you can work."

Pro bono hours

- For all attorneys across all US offices: 15,315
- Average per US attorney: 36.6

Get Hired

"The firm looks for people with Midwestern values, people who are hard-working and respectful," agreed associates. *"Obviously they want bright people, but also some-*

The Inside View

See firm profile on p.698

one who's personable and involved in the community." Matt Feeney adds: "*We're a relationship-based firm: we focus very hard on relationships with our clients, with our colleagues – both lawyers and non-lawyers – and relationships with our communities. We take all three of these elements very seriously. Anyone thinking of becoming a lawyer at Snell needs to recognize that this is a service profession and to thrive here you need to be excellent at building relationships.*" Overall, "*we're looking for people who are excellent lawyers and good human beings.*"

"*Excellent lawyers and good human beings.*"

Strategy & Future

Matt Feeney took the reins as chairman in March 2015, following John Bouma's 30-year tenure at the top. Feeney's first year has seen Snell "*strengthen various practice groups and offices, especially our natural resources group, which is a fairly broad group that covers different disciplines, including environmental, water, oil & gas, and utilities. Our goal is to become one of preeminent natural resource firms in the West, and we're heading in that direction. We've also strengthened our IP practice on both the prosecution and litigation side.*"

"*Our goal is to become one of preeminent natural resource firms in the West.*"

Looking to the future, the firm remains opportunistic but cautious about expansion. "*We've been looking seriously at opportunities in Texas over the past three or four years, but so far nothing has presented itself that justifies us taking that step so we're approaching that market prudently. We're a debt-free firm so everything comes from cash flow.*"

"We're a relationship-based firm: we focus very hard on relationships with our clients, with our colleagues – both lawyers and non-lawyers – and relationships with our communities. We take all three of these elements very seriously."

See firm profile on p.698

Squire Patton Boggs

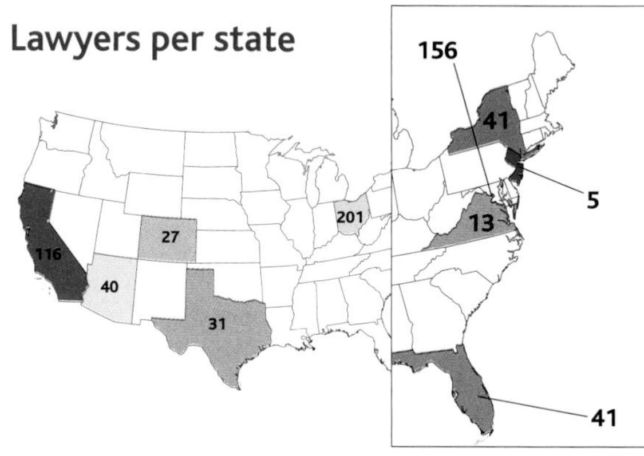

Largest US office: Washington, DC
US offices: 16
International offices: 29
First-year salary: $120,000 – $160,000
Billable hours: 1,950 required (1,900 for first-years)
Summers 2016: 28 (17 2Ls, 10 1Ls, 1 3L)
Revenue 2015: $929.1 million (+6.7%)
Partners made in 2016: 30 (16 in US)
Famous for: numerous mergers and appetite for international growth

Global expansion continues apace at this Midwest-founded go-getter.

ONLY a couple of years after the 2014 merger which created Squire Patton Boggs, this global firm announced a combination with Carroll, Burdick & McDonough. This California-based litigation and product risk management-focused firm may have only had 50 attorneys but its German regulatory practice proved a major attraction to SPB, and it brings additional offices in LA and Hong Kong.

This latest development is on a much smaller scale than the previous mega-union: Squire Patton Boggs emerged when Midwestern stalwarts Squire Sanders and public policy pros Patton Boggs interlocked in 2014. The merger gave the already established global network of Squire Sanders a boost to its Middle Eastern presence and, closer to home, considerably bolstered Squire's hold in Texas. Since this merger, the firm's been keen to strengthen and expand its international reach, so the addition of Carroll Burdick fits right in with this strategy. The firm has 28 overseas offices in total, spanning the UK, mainland Europe, Asia (including Australia) and the Middle East.

Squire Patton Boggs has 17 offices in the US. Most of the firm's attorneys are based in Washington, DC and Ohio (particularly the Cleveland office), but you'll also find lawyers in Arizona, California, Colorado, Florida, New Jersey, New York, Texas and Virginia.

On chambers-associate.com...

- We check in with global managing partner Steve Mahon
- A history of mergers, acquisitions and affiliations

ASSOCIATES SAY...

The Work

At the time of our calls, litigation had the greatest concentration of juniors with the rest spread across practices including corporate, public policy, IP, and environment. Litigators are encouraged to *"cast your net broadly"* and catch projects in areas such as fraud, class action disputes, breaches of contract and general commercial litigation. Corporate juniors are likewise invited to dabble; securities and public and private M&A were just some of the areas our sources had seen. Public policy juniors are attached to subgroups including: healthcare; financial services & tax; international; and transportation, infrastructure & local governments. In all these groups, associates can expect to spend plenty of time on Capitol Hill.

Whichever practice group they slot into, *"it doesn't feel very hierarchical,"* one typical source reckoned. *"Once you show the partners what you're capable of, you're given a lot more responsibility. No one has ever looked at me and said, 'You're a second-year, this is what they do.' If you're capable of handling it, they give you the task."*

"There is more synergy because of the combination."

See firm profile on p.699

Rankings in *Chambers USA*

Banking & Finance	Healthcare
Bankruptcy/Restructuring	Insurance
Corporate/M&A	Labor & Employment
Employee Benefits & Executive Compensation	Litigation
	Natural Resources
Environment	Telecommunications
Government	Transportation

For detail on ranking tiers and ranking locations, visit www.chambersandpartners.com

Recent work highlights

- Represented BP America in a class action suit concerning allegations that plaintiffs were injured by chemical emissions from a refinery flare
- Advised financial services company China Everbright on its $90 million acquisition of international automotive testing equipment manufacturer Burke E. Porter
- Filed a petition for Murray Energy to prohibit the Environmental Protection Agency from carrying out proposed regulations which restrict power plant carbon emissions

Work is allocated to juniors on an informal basis. *"I usually don't have to seek it out as we're busy enough that partners often give you a call to chat about new projects."* To find yourself on the deals which interest you most, one junior recommended *"indicating to a senior associate that you're keen to try out a matter they're working on and they may suggest you to a partner in future."* Some groups, such as corporate and private investment funds, require rookies to provide a weekly summary on their availability.

Now that a couple of years have passed since the merger which formed Squire Patton Boggs came about, we asked juniors if the union had influenced the kind of work they were seeing. *"One of the interesting things about the merger was that there wasn't a lot of overlap,"* one junior explained. *"We were very complementary in terms of strong groups and not a lot of merging took place within them. I've not had the chance to work outside of my legacy firm."* Others had seen an increase in opportunities; one junior attributed to the merger *"some very interesting matters I wouldn't have had access to without Patton Boggs"* coming on board. Others still reckoned *"there is more synergy because of the combination. I think it has gone really well; we can handle matters we wouldn't have been able to do before and we're able to better cross-sell on matters."*

Offices

Around a third of SPB's rookies were housed in Washington, DC. The rest were thinly strewn across Cincinnati, Cleveland, Columbus, Dallas, Denver, Miami, Northern Virginia, Phoenix and West Palm Beach. Juniors attached to practices with sizable teams in multiple offices, like corporate and litigation, often find themselves working with colleagues across the States, or beyond. *"I work with a ton of Squire lawyers across the globe,"* one litigator elaborated. *"If people need a US associate they reach out to a designated attorney who finds one of us to assist."*

"I work with a ton of Squire lawyers across the globe."

The firm's Washington, DC base is its largest in the US (Cleveland's not too far behind). DC is home to the firm's public policy and government relations group – it was this team's stellar reputation at Patton Boggs which caught the eye of Squire Sanders pre-merger, and the group is still pulling in top-tier *Chambers USA* rankings. DC's also one of the few offices to house both legacy Squire Sanders and Patton Boggs attorneys after Squire nudged its way into PB's offices in the Foggy Bottom district.

Culture

The DC office may have borne the brunt of upheaval surrounding the merger but now things have settled, the firm's focusing on encouraging integration between the two legacies. Although the two cultures were reportedly very similar, *"I think it has presented challenges,"* one legacy Patton Boggs source pondered. *"They're working to make it more cohesive between the two. I work with Squire's people in my team on projects and we're all in it together. Everyone gets along."* One way the firm's looking at *"blending the culture"* is by *"increasing its efforts on the social front"* with monthly happy hours leading the way.

"People have gotten really into it."

The cafeteria also sounds like it's, inadvertently, doing its bit to encourage increased cohesiveness. *"It's so cheesy but it runs a number of raffles,"* giving away things like pies in winter or gardening kits in spring. *"People have really gotten into it,"* we heard, with winners reportedly receiving *"loads of emails from the rest of us congratulating them on their pie; it's a megafirm but this office feels small. It's super-collaborative."*

Sources reckoned SPB's chain of Midwestern offices have given many of the firm's bases a *"very Midwestern feel. People are sincerely friendly and down to earth. It doesn't feel stuffy, competitive or cut-throat."* But bear in mind that this is a very global firm these days, with lawyers regularly working with colleagues in various of-

See firm profile on p.699

fices. High expectations on associates are tempered by colleagues who *"aren't stress-inducing."*

Training & Development

Sources informed us that most training at SPB tends to be *"on the job by learning as you go."* Transactional attorneys recalled *"webinars or seminars once in a while."* Litigators jetted off to Cleveland to take part in a deposition workshop hosted by the National Institute for Trial Advocacy (NITA). In 2015, the firm launched Squire Patton Boggs University (SPBU), building on a similar predecessor program. All new associates are flown to DC for a few days to attend *"a variety of workshops and sessions on things like how to work well within the firm and the kind of practices we have."*

"Up to you to seek out the level of training you want."

Most interviewees were fairly happy with the emphasis on hands-on training over structured sessions. *"It's really up to you to seek out the level of training you want,"* one litigator advised, though we did hear the public policy group is *"working to get training institutionalized again following the merger."* That said, the firm already offers standard BigLaw training opportunities through the Practising Law Institute (PLI), plus writing and public speaking coaching.

Pro Bono

Pro bono is another area where juniors are prompted to follow their own approach. Coordinators *"circulate set pieces or more institutional pro bono matters,"* but *"you're encouraged to seek out what you're interested in rather than just what the firm provides. It means pro bono is very individualized."* So juniors can handle *"anything so long as it goes through the formal conflict check; it could be a family law matter, wills and divorces or helping an individual with bankruptcy or foreclosure. The firm supports you on whatever you want to do."*

"Pro bono is very individualized."

Recently the firm filed a lawsuit against the St. Louis County police department on behalf of four journalists arrested while covering the Ferguson, Missouri protests. The suit was filed by Squire Patton Boggs' Public Service Initiative, which in February 2016 also helped secure the release of Louisiana prisoner Albert Fox, who spent 43 years in solitary confinement after being convicted of murdering a prison guard. Juniors can credit up to 100 hours of pro bono toward their billable target.

Pro bono hours

- For all attorneys across all US offices: 31,357
- Average per US attorney: 45

Hours & Compensation

Newbies are eased into the firm with a billing target of 1,900 hours, increasing to 1,950 from the second-year onward. *"The targets are achievable, there is no question about that,"* sources reckoned. Ten to 11 hour stints in the office plus a little extra billing from home after dinner seemed to be the norm among our sources. *"Face time is not important; if you do good work and you're responsible and responsive, everyone's happy."* Interviews reckoned the firm is *"pretty good at respecting vacations so long as you inform people in advance and plan around them. I can't think of anyone I know who's had to cancel one. That's a good sign!"* But don't count on being left entirely alone, as some sources had still taken the time to check and answer emails when on vacation.

"They're achievable, there is no question about that."

After the merger, Patton Boggs' lockstep bonus model was displaced by Squire Sanders' merit-based system, which takes into account billable hours, pro bono, firm citizenship and business development. *"That made me very happy; I work hard and I'm pleased with the compensation,"* one ex-Patton Boggs associate highlighted. *"One of the great things about this firm,"* another added, *"is that you reap what you sow."*

"We're gauging how we can leverage our platform to obtain more international work."

Diversity

"I think it's hard to tell where we fall with regards to diversity," one associate told us. Actually, with 22% female partners and 19% diverse associates, the firm's stats are fairly average for BigLaw. Another elaborated: *"It could be more diverse but I know they're trying to improve things."* Gender was the one area juniors felt was *"fairly diverse. There used to be a time when meetings were made up of all male partners and all female associates but now I'm working with a number of female partners."* The Women's Enterprise Group encompasses a number of committees, including those dedicated to business development, mentoring and a balanced hours policy.

See firm profile on p.699

The firm's commitment to LGBT associates also got a mention – *"they've made great efforts on that front"* – but we heard that *"ethnic diversity is lacking."* While sources knew various affinity and outreach groups exist – such as African-American/Black and Asian/Pacific Islanders groups – many were less sure of the initiatives or events they ran.

Get Hired

Aspiring SPB associates need to get those typing muscles flexing because *"there is a heavy focus on writing skills; the recruiting committee spends a lot of time of reviewing and reading samples,"* sources stressed. Juniors also felt the firm was keen to see a commitment to the local region they're applying to: *"We want to recruit people who will be here for the long haul and not those who are looking to try it out and then leave."*

"A heavy focus on writing skills."

Is there a typical attorney? *"I wouldn't say we necessarily look for people who are outgoing, but we like those who are sociable and personable."* But don't confuse that with being overly relaxed: *"People in the past have made the mistake of being too casual during interviews. Come in with professionalism."*

Strategy & Future

The impact from the Squire Sanders/Patton Boggs merger is still being felt, juniors reckoned: *"Even though it's two years on, we're still capitalizing on the synergies it has brought us."* This means *"becoming more global every day."* Interviews reckoned SPB's sights were set firmly on *"expanding its international reach. We're gauging how we can leverage our platform to obtain more international work."* Hence the merger with Carroll, Burdick & McDonough, which has a large presence in Germany and an office near Stuttgart, adding a third base to SPB's German network.

"We want to recruit people who will be here for the long haul and not those who are looking to try it out and then leave."

See firm profile on p.699

Sterne, Kessler, Goldstein & Fox P.L.L.C.

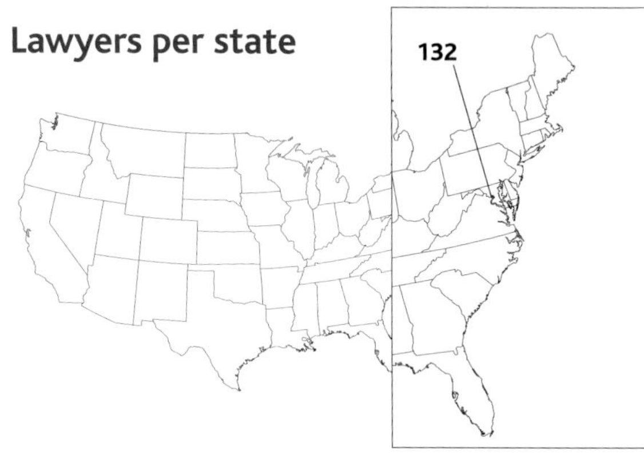

Largest US office: Washington, DC
US offices: 1
International offices: 0
First-year salary: $160,000
Billable hours: 1,900 or 2,000 target
Summers 2016: 5 (4 2Ls, 1 1L)
Revenue 2015: undisclosed
Partners made 2016: 4
Famous for: IP boutique with a strong emphasis on technical backgrounds

A renowned engineer once said: "*Science is about knowing, engineering is about doing.*" Sterne Kessler's associates know what they're doing.

"WE'RE dedicated to science and that's how we differentiate ourselves," one junior associate asserted when we asked which elements make up the compound that is IP boutique Sterne Kessler. *"We're working on legal matters very closely associated with engineering or science."* Launched in 1978 by name partner Robert Sterne, the firm set out to offer IP advice from attorneys steeped in technical knowledge: advanced degrees, PhDs and previous careers in labs or industry are a dime a dozen here.

The firm's so proud of its attorneys' technical heritage that lawyers' profiles on Sterne Kessler's website can be located by clicking on different 'elements' in the firm's own take on the periodic table. In fact the whole website put us in mind of a college textbook, complete with annotated cross-sectioned diagrams and terms like phylogeny, which had us whipping out the dictionary.

Patent prosecution may have been the firm's foundation stone when it was established almost 40 years ago but nowadays Sterne Kessler is propped up by *"the three pillars of patent prosecution, patent litigation and patent office matters."* The single-site Washington, DC firm earns top-tier *Chambers USA* rankings for patent prosecution work in the District of Columbia. And its formidable reputation means that despite only housing around 130 attorneys, it attracts megabrands like Google, adidas and multinational toy manufacturing company Hasbro.

On chambers-associate.com...

- Interview with managing director Mike Ray
- We chat with recruitment committee director and chair Don Featherstone
- More on Sterne Kessler's biotech, electrical and mechanical groups

ASSOCIATES SAY...

The Work

Sterne Kessler's emphasis on specialized know-how means that newbies are affiliated with a specific group from the beginning of the summer program. Litigation-designated associates solely handle contentious IP matters in a variety of areas, while those in the electrical, mechanical and biotech groups can experience both patent litigation and patent prosecution (applying for patent status). Both summer and junior associates undertake the bulk of their work from within their assigned team: *"A chemist isn't going to be working on something related to electrical engineering."* But rookies can reach out to other areas for tasks: *"If you're just researching, you don't have to be an expert in whatever the tech is used for."*

Biotech, electrical or mechanical newbies are allocated a point person who's *"intended to assign you tasks"* or *"connect you with people who can give you work."* Many of our sources had also sought out matters themselves.

See firm profile on p.700

Rankings in *Chambers USA*

Intellectual Property

For detail on ranking tiers and ranking locations, visit www.chambersandpartners.com

A single coordinator oversees all workflow in the litigation department but juniors are also free to reach out for assignments, provided they clear it with the coordinator first.

"I'm put in a position where I feel my opinion is relevant to what we're working on."

Litigators can work on patent infringement cases within a *"mish-mash"* of industries like pharmaceuticals, chemicals, energy, engineering, software and consumer products. *"If you express an interest in an area they'll try to give you work. Your skill set can be applied to litigation research so even if you don't have the technical know-how you can contribute to that team."* Juniors here primarily undertake *"first drafts of motions or pleadings, conduct discovery and document review, and respond to discovery requests. I'm pretty much taking the first crack at most things and have second-chaired depositions and oral arguments,"* one interviewee professed.

Although juniors in the biotech, electronic and mechanical groups predominantly handle assignments within their specialized field of expertise, tasks are similar across teams. Matters tend to fall into three categories: patent prosecution, opinion writing and patent litigation. Go online to read more about what each area involves. There's also a small *"but significant"* trademarks group. Sources in these groups were pleased with the responsibility afforded to them: *"I'm put in a position where I feel my opinion is relevant to what we're working on. I'm not just doing something for the sake of it."*

Get Hired

On the patent side, *"the majority of the attorneys here have science backgrounds, either in the lab or in industry."* Working for engineering or pharmaceutical companies and research institutions were just a few of the previous experiences we heard of. Certain practices require attorneys to hold specific degrees. "*We find that in chemistry and biotech, advanced degrees are mandatory. There are very few lawyers in that group that don't at least have a master's,"* recruitment committee chair Don Featherstone tells us. Check out our full interview with Featherstone online.

"Explain it like a scientist."

Recent work highlights

- Advised software company Veeam in litigation arising out of alleged false advertising published by competitors
- Represented fashion designer Tory Burch during an investigation launched by Converse into alleged trademark infringement
- Assisted prison communications provider Global Tel* Link to file ten inter partes review petitions against competitor Securus. The firm has also filed a number of patent applications for GTL

Sterne Kessler's *"picky attitude toward people with strong technical experience"* is reflected in interviews. One source recalled: *"I was asked a lot about my research and expected to explain it like a scientist, not like a layman."*

Culture

Juniors believed the abundance of similar backgrounds led to an identifiable type at the firm: "*I went through grad school in a lab and people there were laid back. When I went to law school I felt there was a difference between science and legal track students. At Sterne Kessler we have good blend of the easygoing science attitude, and the more serious legal attitude."* This results in *"a comfortable atmosphere. It's not that stressful here."* Others pointed out the environment isn't *"stuffy. The dress code is more on the casual side of business casual. If someone's in a suit you know they came from court."*

"It's geeky but I think it's nice."

Interviewees further felt there was a *"good camaraderie"* between attorneys. *"My point person is genuinely concerned about the career progression of the people he's helping."* But even senior lawyers who aren't designated to watch over juniors are cordial. *"No partner is unapproachable and no one is too important to talk to associates. I've not encountered many people with big egos who are difficult to deal with."* Or, another source added, *"gunners. Everyone is much more interested in working together."* Especially when they get to gossip: *"A lot of us really enjoy what we do. It's not uncommon to have conversations about the patents we're working on or the technology we've been seeing lately. It's geeky but I think it's nice."*

The firm's also keen to encourage employees to take their minds off work every once in a while. The winter retreat offers attorneys the chance to try anything from falconry to fishing, cooking classes to visiting a distillery, or bowling and paint-balling. *"It was a blast."* Back at the office associates can join Sterne Kessler's band, flag

See firm profile on p.700

football, softball or basketball teams. And they hold *"periodically random events like a ping pong tournament"* in the firm's games area.

Offices

All of Sterne Kessler's attorneys are located at the firm's New York Avenue base in downtown DC. The office itself is built within the shell of *"an old refurbished bus station,"* which still retains its art deco façade. *"It's pretty neat. I bring my friends by to look."*

"An old refurbished bus station."

Back in the 1990s comedy action flick *True Lies* was filmed in Sterne Kessler's filing department and kitchen. The firm even got a mention, although its name was changed to 'Sterne, Kessler, Goldstein and Kripnik'. Thanks to a recent office remodel you'd now be hard pressed to recognize the areas where Arnold Schwarzenegger interrogated Jamie Lee Curtis. A glass-partitioned interior has created more of a *"modern industrial"* vibe but a film poster in the caféteria reminds everyone of the firm's Hollywood moment. The café also has its own fully-staffed barista bar – complete with free coffee – and the games area which houses ping pong, table football and shuffleboard.

Training & Development

Upon arrival rookies are given an associate buddy. Buddies reside in the same practice group and are usually in the year above to *"answer all your stupid questions."* The firm's keen for associates to make the most of this relationship: *"They get annoyed if we don't use the lunch budget."* Sterne Kessler also launched in 2014 a career coach program to connect juniors with partners outside of their practice group. These external mentors *"can give us an objective take on any concerns."*

"An objective take on any concerns."

Newbies kick associate life off with two weeks of training on firm systems and the basics of patent prosecution and litigation. Thereafter, monthly practice group meetings outline strategy, case law and legal updates. Biotech associates also benefit from a weekly case law course taught by name partner and top life sciences patent litigator and prosecutor Jorge Goldstein. The firm's also *"very focused on writing training and hired a consultant writing specialist to come in."*

Hours & Compensation

Associates can choose their billable target to become bonus-eligible: 1,900 or 2,000 hours. As well as the hours component, a merit-based bonus comes into play for second-years and above. While most sources considered the targets reasonable, we heard of several who struggled to reach them. Although juniors admitted this was *"a source of concern, the firm's understanding. They tell you to write articles or undertake pro bono"* to bring hours up.

"There's no pressure to be here a certain number of hours."

Interviewees tended to put in around ten hours a day at the office. *"You don't expect to be working fewer hours than other professions but as law firms go I think it's fine."* Others pointed out: *"There's no pressure to be here a certain number of hours each day and be seen by everybody."* Once associates have left the office, evenings and weekends are *"normally unencumbered."*

"A lot of us really enjoy what we do. It's not uncommon to have conversations about the patents we're working on or the technology we've been seeing lately."

Vacations are also respected *"as long as you hit your hourly goal and don't take a break right in the middle of a big project you knew was coming."*

Pro Bono

Juniors believed they are allowed to count 50 pro bono hours toward the billable requirement. But we were hard pushed to find any interviewees who'd actually done any pro bono. *"It's available if you seek it out, but it's not brought up very often,"* one source acknowledged.

"Take advantage of our IP skills."

The firm does have an IP and human rights pro bono practice. The partner who founded it *"was thinking about how we could take advantage of our IP skills,"* one source explained. *"That can be limiting though as you're not going to have homeless people inventing things; it's typically corporations."* So the firm lends its hand to writing opinions for groups like Doctors Without Borders or advising *"Native American tribes who may need patent support."*

See firm profile on p.700

Pro bono hours

- For all attorneys: undisclosed
- Average per attorney: undisclosed

Diversity

"I would imagine that law, science and engineering are more male heavy than other professions," one interviewee thought. Does that mean Sterne Kessler finds it harder to hire diverse attorneys? *"I think based on the numbers we're doing okay,"* another junior mused. Although the gender divide among associates here is skewed heavily toward men, a quarter of the firm's partners are women (coming in above the BigLaw average of 17%). Interviewees commended *"several female partners who are working to drive additional diversity and provide more support to mothers and fathers."* We heard women partners also make themselves *"available to chat with female juniors and make an effort to get to know them."*

"Available to chat with female juniors."

In terms of race, *"there's not a large African American presence at the firm, although there are a few people of Asian descent."* The firm's diversity committee puts on several events to encourage attorneys to *"get to know one another. We held a session where we wrote down something others might not know about us and posted them in our common room."* Another event saw associates asking a panel of diverse attorneys and staff about their backgrounds.

Strategy & Future

"We're reasonably good at evolving with the legal landscape," one source considered. *"We started out as a patent prosecution firm. When patent litigation became profitable we launched our own group. Now patent office litigation is hot, we've become experts in that practice."*

"A big push to become involved in IPR work."

Patent office – or Patent Trial and Appeal Board (PTAB) litigation – has been on the up across the legal profession since 2012 saw the introduction of inter partes review (IPR) proceedings to challenge established patents. *"There's been a big push to become involved in IPR work,"* sources emphasized. *"Our PTAB offering has been really growing. We're gearing up to be at the forefront of this area."*

"We have over 60 PhDs among our staff; one of our distinguishing strengths is our technical firepower."

Mike Ray, managing director

See firm profile on p.700

Stroock & Stroock & Lavan LLP

Lawyers per state

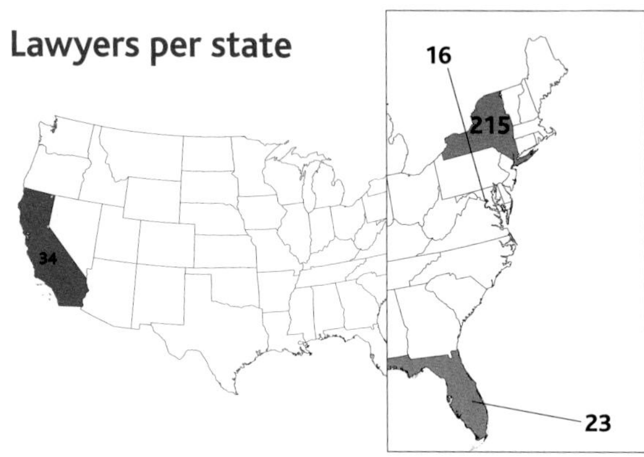

Largest US office: New York
US offices: 4
International offices: 0
First-year salary: $160,000
Billable hours: 2,000 target (incl. 200 non-billable)
Summers 2016: 14 (all 2Ls)
Revenue 2015: $265 million (+1.7%)
Partners made in 2016: 4
Famous for: being a BigLaw, midsized practice with big clients

BigLaw, big clients and the Big Apple... this compact New Yorker is bigger than it seems.

THE Wright brothers. The Cohen brothers. The Stroock brothers. All three pairs of siblings have shown that keeping it in the family is the winning formula. Sure, the Stroocks didn't invent air travel or *The Big Lebowski*, but their achievements are noteworthy, especially for the firm's modest proportions. *"Going after the biggest and the best,"* Stroock's clients include Goldman Sachs, American Express and Sophia Loren. *Chambers USA* scores Stroock highly in a raft of practice areas, particularly in real estate and media & entertainment (check out chambersandpartners.com for the full breakdown). *"We do sophisticated work for a prominent group of clients,"* co-managing partner Alan Klinger tells us. But the differentiating factor for juniors is: *"not being tremendously large, we can staff more leanly so our associates don't end up working as glorified paralegals. They are given a lot of responsibility very quickly."*

ASSOCIATES SAY...

The Work

Most newbies are split equally between corporate and litigation. The rest go into more niche areas including financial restructuring, IP and tax. Although *"real estate is Stroock's flagship practice,"* only 10% of new starters go there. Insiders believed that *"for the most part every office does litigation, real estate, general corporate and financial restructuring."* DC doesn't do litigation but *"has a lot of work in CFIUS* [Committee on Foreign Investment in the United States]. *LA and Miami have a big entertainment focus."* There's also the *"regular opportunity to cross-staff,"* according to a Big Appler. *"Miami and DC and LA – work goes back and forth between everyone."*

> *"It's a meritocracy."*

Typically, new associates start out as generalists in both litigation and corporate and *"as we progress we specialize. They're good at giving us work in our interest areas though."* Litigators are normally entrusted with *"either high-level administrative work or low-level legal work. You might be given a hundred pages of handwritten comments and told to type them up."* On the flipside, *"every litigation associate in the country will say that it's all doc review. But I've drafted briefs for various motions, memos for research assignments and I've also negotiated a settlement."* Insiders emphasized that this was the norm as *"it's a meritocracy. People don't have formal views on what juniors should be given, as opposed to a midlevel."*

Corporate fledglings described how they initially *"run managerial tasks like gathering documents."* Others elaborated they'd *"had to learn a topic in the morning and then present it in the afternoon to clients."* They

On chambers-associate.com...

- Interview with co-managing partner Alan Klinger
- Interview with hiring partner Claude Szyfer

See firm profile on p.701

Rankings in *Chambers USA*

Bankruptcy/Restructuring	Investment Funds
Capital Markets	Media & Entertainment
Insurance	Real Estate

For detail on ranking tiers and ranking locations, visit www.chambersandpartners.com

Recent work highlights

- Represented Goldman Sachs and Deutsche Bank, recovering $37 million of investment banking fees owed by CVR Energy
- Represented a branch of the Chinese government, China Film Group Corp., in investing in *Crouching Tiger, Hidden Dragon 2*
- Structured a complex, Section 892 compliant tax driven investment vehicle sponsored by J.P. Morgan Investment Management for properties valued at $2.5 billion
- Represented Bank of America in a $60 million loan to affiliates of L&L Holdings and Lubert Adler

generally relished the chance to *"do things out of my comfort zone, working closely with people who treat you simultaneously as a colleague and as a student."* Responsibility in real estate usually depends on the size of the deal. *"In very large deals, like portfolio lending, you do diligence work. You're likely to be in charge of the background agreements. Smaller deals are leanly staffed, so you can do the first draft of guarantees and loan agreements."*

Work in all groups is usually doled out by assigning partners who *"ask for availability emails detailing your commitments."* Most juniors liked that *"partners can approach you directly too."* Nonetheless, some warned that *"sometimes it can get out of hand. Once I was juggling six assignments, all urgent and time-consuming."*

Training & Development

Rookies are treated to a *"strongly structured first two weeks of basic training."* Associates then attend CLE courses that run once a week for the first six months. *"It's mandatory for first-years but optional for everyone else."* Other schemes specifically for litigators include *"a two-hour writing class led by the head litigator, which covers email, memo and brief writing."* Litigation, IP and financial restructuring collaborate for a mock trial. Summers play witnesses, *"non-legal staff are the jury and the managing attorney is the judge."*

> *"Most training is on the job, like a baptism of fire."*

Corporate interviewees get training on things like *"learning the shape of a transaction."* However, all associates found that *"most training is on the job, like a baptism of fire."* Some real estate associates lamented the fact that *"there used to be an attorney who would give us substantive training on purchase agreements, but it was scuttled as it wasn't billable."*

Reviews occur *"two times a year but there isn't a lot of feedback unless you seek it,"* some had discovered. However, those outside the NYC HQ painted a different picture: *"Whenever a deal closes they give you positive reinforcement. It's more formal in New York as you work with more people across the board, but here I get feedback directly."* In 2014, a benchmarking system was implemented for associates to measure their development against a baseline of experiences per class level, although recently some felt *"the focus on it has run out."* Others thought reviews *"entirely perfunctory! But it's hard to blame them as they are busy taking care of clients, which is how it should be."*

Offices & Culture

The New York office offers *"incomparable 360-degree views of Manhattan."* Insiders rhapsodized too about the refurbishment of the building's shared lobby, which is finally nearing completion following the damage wrought by Hurricane Sandy a few years ago: *"They are trying to give it a Google-esque feel!"* Meanwhile, LA associates feel like movie stars (or daytime TV fixtures, at the very least) whenever filming takes place outside their Century City base: *"Every other week there's a production crew outside. We'll often see our building in commercials."*

> *"There's no bandwidth for attacking each other."*

All juniors have their own offices except first-year New Yorkers, who initially *"share with second-years for six months. It makes you feel comfortable in the firm."* Stroock attempts to cultivate an environment where *"there's no bandwidth for attacking each other."* Does it succeed? "*People are playful.*"

Manhattan interviewees suggested that *"we could have more group drinks to build camaraderie."* Perhaps they could copy LA colleagues who praised their own *"habit of a happy hour which doesn't feel forced."* New Yorkers can, however, blow off steam in Stroock's *"softball team for both partners and support staff."* Cali associates similarly described *"our firmwide basketball league for all the different firms in LA. We play once a week."*

See firm profile on p.701

Pro Bono

The founding director of Stroock's Public Service Project, Kevin Curnin, coordinates pro bono work firmwide. Stroock has affiliations with many pro bono organizations including, LIFT (Legal Information for Families Today), Sanctuary for Families, and Her Justice. Sources praised the *"start-small, think-big clinic, which helps entrepreneurs without means get advice on their IP issues and what to do next."* Summers are also encouraged to get involved, with some running *"a debate camp for middle school low-income students."*

"It gives you more responsibility early on."

All interviewees recounted that it *"gives you more responsibility early on."* Some have already gone to court and *"argued motions to dismiss."* Others have argued *"habeas appeals to the second circuit."* One source stated: *"I get to do things I wouldn't normally do. For example, I've done work that we normally outsource. Now when I outsource work for billables, I understand behind the scenes and can be more specific in my requests."*

Pro bono hours

- For all attorneys across all offices: 15,646
- Average per US attorney: 57

Diversity

"The age of the old white man firm is gone," insisted one associate. However, like at other firms, diversity is much more prevalent in the junior classes than higher up. IP interviewees in particular stressed that *"this department is not diverse. There's one female partner and two female associates."* When asked if this was a product of the IP sector as a whole, a source replied: *"Last year I would have said that, but there were women this year who didn't get offers and I didn't know why."* Broadly speaking, fewer women do tech undergrad then law – and you need both to sit for the patent Bar.

"It's a working process over generations."

Nevertheless, Stroock acknowledges the problem and is attempting to fix it. Hiring partner Claude Szyfer divulges: *"Diversity and retention is a hard issue that all firms are dealing with at the moment. Over the past year, several of the lateral partners that we have brought on are women, which we know will help more junior associates in terms of mentoring etc."*

Firmwide events are hosted by a variety of affinity groups, including the Attorneys of Color, LGBT, Women's Affinity (SW) and Working Parents groups. Of specific note was the *"CLE put on by the partners to discuss the Supreme Court same-sex marriage case right before it came down."* However, most agreed that *"from the perspective of the world we live in as opposed to BigLaw, it's not particularly diverse. But it's a working process over generations."*

Hours & Compensation

The average Stroock associate works 12-hour days with a 2,000-hour yearly billable target. From this, *"200 hours can be non-billable legal work, which can include pro bono."* Juniors reasoned that *"for hours that aren't clearly pro bono you need to explain how this benefits the firm."* One newbie ventured that *"it's a black box what counts and what doesn't. I think it counts when you prepare CLE material or pitch to clients."*

"200 hours can be non-billable legal work, which can include pro bono."

Many mused that the target *"is achievable but depends on the cases you're assigned, which doesn't incentivize efficiency."* Bonuses, however, keep up morale, *"as generally associates don't stay late at night, but the pay is the same as those types of firms."* Juniors confirmed that *"it's pretty much lockstep with the industry. Last year's first-year bonus was $15,000"* ($3,750 prorated). Nevertheless, there is a *"merit component, so you can hit the target and not get a bonus if they feel that you were working sporadically slowly."*

"Our associates don't end up working as glorified paralegals."
Alan Klinger, co-managing partner

Get Hired

Stroock traditionally targets *"top-tier schools in the Northeast, as well as at regional law schools in New York and Los Angeles."* Hiring partner Claude Szyfer recommends that candidates should *"not just to be able to talk about their resume but talk about what drives them, which is a better barometer."* Insiders similarly advised that *"people at Stroock appreciate authenticity more than formality."* Further insight was given by New Yorkers, who stated: *"I would discourage anyone from saying 'I want to do litigation' if you're interviewing with litigation, as you can see right through that. No one after law school has any idea about anything!"* Instead, some suggested that *"you have to be dynamic and animated with a narrative that makes you memorable. Have an example for each answer from your life experiences."* For the full interview with Szyfer, go online.

See firm profile on p.701

"No one after law school has any idea about anything."

Strategy & Future

"In 2015, we've expanded our DC office by bringing in a real estate group from DLA Piper. Within a few years, I would be surprised if that office did not double in size," explains Alan Klinger (for the full interview, go online). However, juniors countered that *"there is a little bit of remnant stress from the layoffs a few years ago, but that is the nature of people, they are nervous. Now it's pretty much all hands on deck."*

Furthermore, sources hoped that in the future there would be more midlevel associates to act as intermediaries between partners. Some indicated that *"we've had smaller classes in the financial crisis so there aren't many people past fourth year. There aren't many people to look up to."* Nevertheless, interviewees agreed that *"Stroock has been smart in not overexpanding and managing growth."* HP Claude Szyfer agrees, stressing that *"we have never expanded recklessly in the past and so we haven't had to retrench like some other firms."*

"We have never expanded recklessly in the past and so we haven't had to retrench like some other firms."

See firm profile on p.701

Sullivan & Cromwell LLP

Lawyers per state

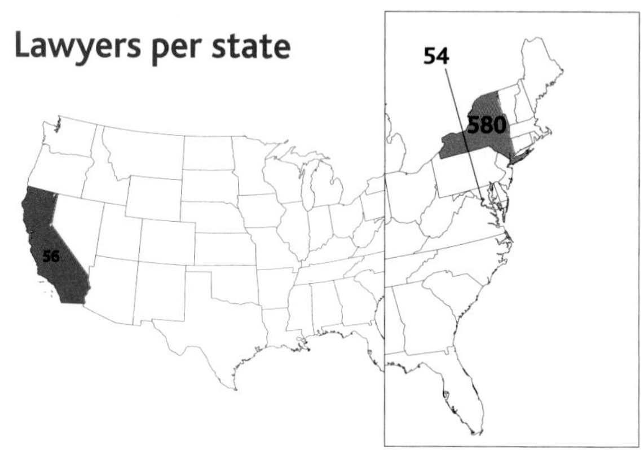

Largest US office: New York
US offices: 4
International offices: 8
First-year salary: $160,000
Billable hours: no requirement
Summers 2016: 144 (120 2Ls, 18 3Ls, 3 1Ls, 3 SEOs)
Revenue 2015: $1.314 billion (+2.98%)
Partners made in 2016: 6 (all US)
Famous for: perfectionism

If you like to put in 100% and have a "*fixation with getting things right*" then Sullivan & Cromwell may be a good match.

INDISPUTABLE prestige? Tick. 200-year history? Tick. A reputation for perfectionism, sky-high quality of work product, and rigorous client service? Tick, tick, tick. A plethora of *Chambers USA* rankings? Plethora of ticks. S&C unquestionably deserves top marks for the caliber of its national and international M&A, capital markets and corporate finance deals, and is also top of the class in securities and regulatory litigation, tax, real estate and energy work. Chairman Joe Shenker explains that while the effects of the 2008 financial crisis are still being felt, even now – and are thus still shaping some of the firm's practices – *"we also see significant 'strategic' M&A activity from clients that are expanding across national lines."*

Outsiders sometimes say Sullivan is synonymous with an old-fashioned, elitist Manhattan vibe. Our inside sources, however, told us this isn't true and that *"the culture isn't fratty or bro-ey."* But they did advise student applicants to understand the demands it places on its associates, particularly *"the firm's fixation with getting things right"* (see Culture below for more).

On chambers-associate.com...

- Interview with chairman Joe Shenker

ASSOCIATES SAY...

The Work

Associates were fairly evenly split between the general practice group (including corporate and other transactional practices) and litigation, with a couple in estate & personal, and tax. For members of the general practice cohort, *"the first 18 months are spent receiving work from multiple groups."* During this time *"assignments are run through a staffer, although on some occasions they can come from a partner."* There's also an associate development partner who oversees progress. Ideally, this is a time for newbies to explore their areas of interest before committing to one in particular. Insiders appreciated the system, had done *"most of what I felt I needed to know,"* and reckoned associates at other firms *"don't get to broaden their experience like we do."* At the end of the 18-month period, *"everyone gets to go where they want."*

> *"The responsibility is almost scary; you're definitely pushed out of your comfort zone."*

Sources in the corporate department admitted that they start with *"the basic first-year tasks like due diligence, checklists and document management,"* but soon enough found themselves *"doing tasks regarded as midlevel like drafting core transactional documents, having frequent interface with the clients, and direct contact with partners."* A second-year explained: *"I'm on a securitization deal and while I'm in charge of diligence I also draft*

See firm profile on p.702

Rankings in *Chambers USA*

Antitrust
Banking & Finance
Capital Markets
Corporate Crime & Investigations
Corporate/M&A
Employee Benefits & Executive Compensation
Energy & Natural Resources
Environment
FCPA
Financial Services Regulation
Insurance
International Arbitration
Investment Funds
Latin American Investment
Litigation
Projects
Real Estate
REITs
Securities
Tax
Wealth Management

For detail on ranking tiers and ranking locations, visit www.chambersandpartners.com

different registration documents, and on an M&A deal recently I wrote the first draft of the merger proxy statement." Another second-year commented that "*the responsibility is almost scary; you're definitely pushed out of your comfort zone.*" Litigators explained that there's an associate development partner here too, and a staffer to help with assignment, "*but you can also reach out to people. If there's an area you're keen on you put yourself out there. It's not rigid.*" One recalled: "*When I first arrived they gave me two folders and said here's who you need to call; I haven't gone back to the formal assignment since. S&C rewards initiative and lets you exercise as much autonomy as you want. Some people find that disconcerting.*" The work was "*a mixed bag, from doing prep work for depositions, to drafting parts of briefs, to a lot of legal research solving puzzles for the plaintiffs. There's certainly some doc review, but it's not all concentrated at the beginning; it can happen later on. The focus is on the specific work product that you're told needs achieving.*"

Pro Bono

More control over responsibility can be sought via pro bono. "*They aggressively encourage you to take it on, and it's a chance to get a lot of partner contact.*" The "*robust system*" is spearheaded by a specially appointed lawyer, but some juniors also found cases "*by talking to someone at a cocktail party and becoming interested in what they were doing.*" Work examples include "*a gay adoption case, immigration matters, transgender name changes, and Criminal Justice Act cases sometimes involving gun and drug charges.*" One had particularly enjoyed "*writing the first draft of an appellate brief with a senior associate, attending court hearings and preparing the attorney.*" Some corporate associates lamented that "*we don't have the added benefit of career enhancement like litigators do,*" but many were involved in pro bono nevertheless.

Recent work highlights

- Advised the world's biggest brewer, Belgian Anheuser-Busch InBev, on its acquisition of UK company SABMiller
- Represented the creditors' committee when Energy Future Holdings filed for bankruptcy
- Represented Cablevision in its acquisition by Altice for $17.7 billion
- Assisted Alcatel in its acquisition by Nokia for $16.6 billion
- Advised Israeli pharmaceutical company Teva in its $40.5 billion acquisition of generics business Allergan
- Successfully represented Argentinian Bank BCRA accused of being the government's 'alter ego' and covering $2.4 billion in defaulted Argentinian debt

"They aggressively encourage you to take it on."

Pro bono hours

- For all attorneys across US offices: 42,776
- Average per US attorney: 67

Hours & Compensation

While there's no specific pro bono requirement or official cap, and while there's no billable hours target either, it's understandable that industrious S&C associates think twice before seizing new work. Hours are pretty full on, with an average day starting at 9am and finishing between 8pm and 10pm. Whether these are all spent at the office or working remotely from home is "*up to us.*" Certain practice areas enable more predictable or slightly lighter schedules than others; one insider reckoned "*I'm here a lot less than M&A associates.*" Weekend work was not infrequent – "*you're expected to be on call*" – but again depended on practice areas.

"In California this schedule would be insane."

"*In California this schedule would be insane,*" one exclaimed with a tinge of pride, "*but in New York it's not atypical. The firm's official line will always be that they want people to take care of themselves, but no one will ever tell you you've been working too hard. It's up to you to make that time.*" Sources did observe that "*on a day-to-day basis people are understanding: you can't make plans five days a week, but everyone knows you need and want free time.*" Vacation days are "*valued. Usually no one bothers you.*"

Clearly racking up the hours isn't an issue at S&C, but associates were still grateful "*that there really isn't a number you have to aim for. I think I got to about 2,300, but there's really no emphasis on it.*"

See firm profile on p.702

Training & Development

Training on the other hand is emphasized. Several insiders agreed with one who enthused: *"Training is the best thing about the firm."* It starts in summer *"when you've got targeted training, but you're also invited to other programs across the firm. In the fall there's a big push to train junior associates, and it's not the same every year so you can return as a second-year and pick up new skills. Practice groups also meet once a month to share updates over lunch."*

Sources praised *"on the job"* support from team members, but observed that formal mentorship only really exists *"in theory."* Once associates are assigned to a practice group, they can express a preference as to who their formal mentor should be. Because many of our junior interviewees hadn't yet spent 18 months at the firm, most hadn't met their mentor or weren't sure how mentoring worked. Still, many noted that relationships formed naturally and that the *"associate experience committee"* was a good platform to voice concerns or seek support. The firm assures us that the associate development partners are charged with mentorship in the early days.

Feedback was similarly best consumed on the go: *"Generally if you ask for it on the job, you'll get it. The formal reviews happen once a year and comments mostly tend to be reassuring, but not specific."*

Culture

In previous years we picked up on S&C's pursuit of perfection as a driver of its culture. This theme came up again this year, with one venturing that *"the firm's fixation with getting things right reaches almost pathological levels."* While insiders did admit that *"there is a fear of being the weakest link and that can make anxiety run high,"* they conceded that *"all the mechanisms that are in place to help us achieve perfection, such as the word processing department dedicated to proof-reading overnight, do alleviate the stress."* Several reported not suffering anxiety at all.

"There is a fear of being the weakest link and that can make anxiety run high."

Most interviewees had enjoyed friendly and supportive relationships with peers, *"but your experience does depend on the partners you work with."* Episodes ranged from *"one partner I love working with because they're intimately involved with their matters and you never get the sense that they're too good to listen,"* to other anecdotes of impromptu weekend work and the occasional partner not being forthcoming with gratitude. Still, part of the focus on work *"might mean you don't go out for drinks with colleagues all the time, but on the flipside it takes the pressure off forced socializing."*

"The aftermath of the financial crisis has proven to us the virtue of our traditional focus on training our lawyers to be multidisciplinary."

Joe Shenker, chairman

Offices

Some socializing does occur though, of course, not least at *"4pm snack time."* Sources advised to get there quick *"because it can run out. But there's always the cafeteria, which is heavily subsidized and serves high-quality food for breakfast and lunch. There's been a push for healthy options and we're seeing it come to fruition."* Another notable perk of the Lower Manhattan digs was the *"new fitness center opened after Hurricane Sandy destroyed part of the office. It's useful to have showers at work."* The gym wasn't the only new addition, S&C also introduced *"associate lounges with TVs, computers which don't have website blocks so you can go on Facebook, foosball tables, soda machines and snacks."* In spite of these upgrades, the overall feel of the office was still described as *"quite old-fashioned, with carpet and mahogany in tan or muted colors. The views are great though and they're slowly refurbing the offices. Associates share for about a year and a half to two years, then get their own."*

"Foosball tables, soda machines and snacks."

Diversity

As with many big firms, insiders acknowledge both that *"they make a big effort,"* but that *"there's always room for improvement."* Sources in general practice got the impression that *"we have more women here than they do in litigation,"* and all agreed that *"at junior level the numbers are more encouraging than among partners."* One felt that *"while they're putting on events, and clearly trying to recruit and retain diverse candidates, I'm not sure it makes a difference: those who actually accept offers here tend to fit into the same category."* The diversity figures are in line with the NYC norm, and hiring partner Sergio Galvis adds: *"While much work remains to be done, US law schools have done a great job of attracting a more diverse pool of students in recent years and this has greatly benefited us."*

See firm profile on p.702

Get Hired

Sources suggested *"ignoring the firm's reputation as stuffy. Just come and meet the people and make up your own mind."* Some also warned against *"underestimating the job's demands on your personal life. You devote your life to your work and your social life just has to fit around that."* Sergio Galvis was also unequivocal that a candidate should be hungry for *"complex and challenging work,"* and that the associates should *"share a passion for excellence."* Concrete tips for getting your foot in the door included *"having really good grades, it's a reality of recruitment here. Also, make sure you express enthusiasm for what the firm does best in different areas of law. Don't come across as though you're just looking to cash a check for a few years."*

"You devote your life to your work and your social life just has to fit around that."

Strategy & Future

As in previous years, chairman Joe Shenker emphasizes the firm's steady growth in areas like energy, projects, restructuring, and IP. He also reiterates that Sullivan & Cromwell views itself as somewhere in between those firms that do *"everything for everyone"* and those that are totally niche. In further describing the intermediate space occupied by S&C he reveals that the firm's strategy going forward will be highly people-focused: *"The aftermath of the financial crisis has proven to us the virtue of our traditional focus on training our lawyers to be multidisciplinary practitioners who have a broad perspective and the ability to practice across geographies and specialties."*

"Make sure you express enthusiasm for what the firm does best in different areas of law. Don't come across as though you're just looking to cash a check for a few years."

See firm profile on p.702

Thompson & Knight LLP

Lawyers per state

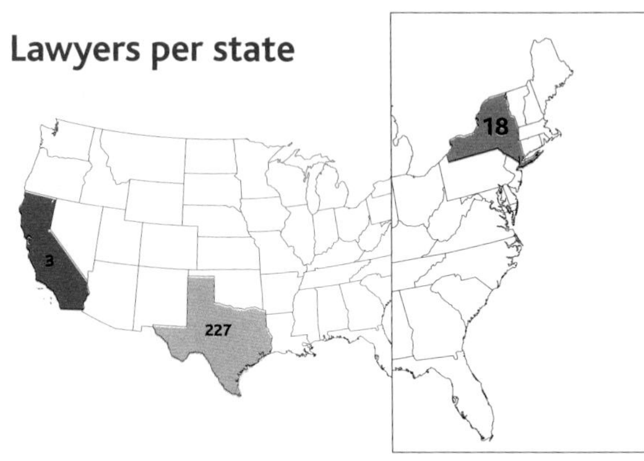

Largest US office: Dallas
US offices: 6
International offices: 5
First-year salary: $160,000
Billable hours: 1,900 required (2,000 after first year)
Summers 2016: 15 (10 2Ls, 5 1Ls)
Revenue 2015: $207.3 million (+2.8%)
Partners made in 2016: 8 (all US)
Famous for: its longstanding reputation in Texas; energy work

Knighted one of the best in Texas, this firm is *"such a great place to be mentored."*

WHEN Colonels Bill Thompson and Bob Knight joined forces in Dallas way back in 1887, they founded a firm which today boasts over 300 attorneys in 11 offices across five countries. Beginning life dealing with the basics of rural law, Thompson & Knight has grown up alongside Dallas: as the city grew into a bustling center for commerce, finance, technology, energy and technology, so too did T&K continue to expand and diversify its practices. While the firm's traditional expertise in the oil & gas industry gains it a high nationwide ranking in *Chambers USA*, the firm also ranks number one in Texas for its real estate work, and highly statewide in areas including corporate/M&A, healthcare, IP, and labor & employment.

Thompson's longstanding success in Texas and beyond was a key draw for the associates we spoke to: "*The firm has a reputation for having a lot of very fine lawyers. Pretty much anyone I spoke to who had dealt with Thompson was always positive about their experience,*" one junior revealed. Another added that "*the firm has been around for ages – it has a really successful track record.*" New managing partner Mark Sloan took over from Emily Parker in February 2016, and he informs us that 2015 has "*been very busy*" and "a very positive year for the firm financially."

ASSOCIATES SAY...

The Work

The corporate & securities practice generally takes the largest number of juniors, followed closely by the real estate & banking and trial groups. Bankruptcy & restructuring, employment & labor, finance, government & regulatory, IP, oil & gas, and tax have one or two newbies each. Newcomers split their summer between any two of these groups, and then indicate their preference at the end; interviewees assured us that it is *"very rare"* to not be offered your first choice.

In the corporate group, we were told that private equity is a very strong area for the firm, *"both on the fund formation side and the corporate company side."* M&A deals are also an important focus, *"anything from $100–500 million in size."* Unsurprisingly, this group reported a lot of work in the oil and gas industry, although there is also a separate oil & gas practice that focuses mainly on asset deals. Other corporate clients include those in the banking and finance, telecommunications, general retail, transportation and healthcare sectors.

"The firm encourages each associate to work with as many partners as possible."

On chambers-associate.com...
- Interview with new managing partner Mark Sloan
- Interview with hiring partner Jessica Hammons

See firm profile on p.703

The Inside View

Rankings in *Chambers USA*

Antitrust	Healthcare
Banking & Finance	Intellectual Property
Bankruptcy/Restructuring	Labor & Employment
Capital Markets	Litigation
Corporate/M&A	Real Estate
Energy & Natural Resources	Tax
Environment	

For detail on ranking tiers and ranking locations, visit www.chambersandpartners.com

Trial juniors reported *"a pretty broad exposure to a lot of different industries,"* including oil and gas, healthcare, general commercial, and antitrust and competition, *"representing parties in front of the DOJ and FTC as well as in private lawsuits."* One newbie added that *"the firm encourages each associate to work with as many partners as possible in order to find the best fit."* Over in real estate, we were informed that Thompson *"tends to be stronger on the lending side; we represent a lot of major lenders in real estate transactions."* At the same time, *"we have people who work a lot with developers who are constructing things like retail centers and office buildings."* Day to day, juniors reported being able to *"negotiate leases and purchase availment agreements, and I've had the chance to head up some smaller transactions."*

Each group has an administrator who *"reviews everyone's hours on a weekly basis in order to help distribute work fairly."* At the same time, *"there's definitely an organic element based on relationships that you build with partners."* Generally, sources appreciated this mixed system as a way to spread the work evenly between associates: *"It's a check and balance on the purely organic approach, so people don't get starved out."* As far as responsibility levels go, all of our interviewees seemed very happy with the level of tasks they were doing. One third-year told us: *"I'm transitioning into managing my own cases and delegating work to others. Partners will give you as much responsibility as you demonstrate you can handle."* Another real estate newbie added that *"I've done things that would usually be done by a fourth or fifth-year associate."*

Training

Associates are introduced to the firm with a program of weekly sessions for their first ten weeks, which cover *"day-to-day aspects like how to bill time and how to use the computers."* After this, there are regular sessions and CLEs on *"everything from IT trainings all the way to substantive legal trainings."* Sources also mentioned regular practice-wide meetings to discuss recent work matters and legal developments.

"We go through a full jury trial."

Recent work highlights

- Represented the Conflicts Committee of American Midstream Partners in its $162 million acquisition of a minority interest in Delta House from an affiliate of ArcLight Capital Partners
- Currently representing Southwest Airlines in a putative consumer class action relating to alleged breach of contract, unjust enrichment, and similar claims regarding the airline's frequent flyer program
- Acted for EnCap Investments in the formation of the $6.5 billion EnCap Energy Capital Fund X
- Advised Wells Fargo in connection with a $180 million loan to refinance Smith Haven Mall in New York

In the trial group, we heard about quarterly writing seminars and deposition trainings, as well as a Trial Academy *"that associates and summers do every summer. We go through a full jury trial and try a case before the senior partners."* Corporate juniors meanwhile described sessions on topics such as Section 16 of the Securities Exchange Act, *"and we had one big M&A training, with sessions every week for six months. They went over every part of the deal."* Dallas associates in particular pointed out that *"our office is very close to the local Bar Association where there are constantly lunches and seminars, and the firm encourages us to go to those as well."*

Culture & Development

Thompson's commitment to associate development was frequently highlighted: *"It's such a great place to be mentored,"* gushed one junior. *"I can go to the person I think is best equipped to answer my questions; no matter what it is they're always willing to talk to you."* This sentiment was undoubtedly encouraged by the fact that *"there isn't a huge distinction between partners and associates, so I feel comfortable going to partners with questions rather than asking associates first. Everyone is one cohesive team."* Others noted that the lean staffing of matters *"allows there to be a relationship with the partner – it's wonderful to see how an experienced attorney handles things. You're not just a faceless dump for work, you're encouraged to get as involved with the case as possible."* Newcomers are also formally assigned associate and partner mentors, and associates have yearly formal reviews and more relaxed midyear appraisals.

"You're not just a faceless dump for work."

Associates generally reported that the firm is sociable, *"but not overly so,"* as people mostly want to go home after office hours. That said, we did hear of fairly frequent happy hours – particularly to welcome new associates

See firm profile on p.703

– as well as *"various firm lunches where we can get together."* Others mentioned an intramural basketball team and a yearly firmwide retreat. It seemed that associates were more willing to interact with each other during the course of their working day: *"I've found that even the people I don't work with will reach out to me to go out for lunch; there's an emphasis on connection and developing relationships here."*

Offices

Two-thirds of the new associates on our list were in the Dallas HQ, while nearly a third went to Houston, and New York and Austin each had a lone junior. Thompson's other domestic offices are in Fort Worth and LA. Those in Dallas described *"a great building"* (One Arts Plaza) located *"on the edge of downtown."* The building has four on-site restaurants, and is *"a very short distance from uptown with a big selection of other restaurants,"* and the interior was described as *"very open, with huge windows in your office."*

"Very open, with huge windows in your office."

Over in Houston, we heard that the space is *"a little dated, but our lease is up next year so we might be moving."* While associates couldn't venture much further that this, we were informed that *"wherever we end up we'll do a full overhaul."* As it is, interviewees appreciated the on-site parking and convenient location on the edge of downtown, *"which is fantastic because I don't have to drive through the middle of it."*

Hours & Pro Bono

In order to be eligible for a discretionary bonus and advance to the next pay scale, first-years need to bill 1,900 hours (2,000 after the first year) including pro bono, and then rack up a further 200 hours of 'firm investment' time. This can include *"lunch trainings, writing articles, personal professional development such as keeping up with alumni, client development; a number of things that come with the job outside of working hours."* While juniors agreed that on paper this is a high requirement, the consensus was that *"people at other firms are doing that same amount but just not tracking them. I don't find it hard to meet the 200 hours at all in the course of my normal business, it's just a hassle to document it sometimes."* Another newbie pointed out that the investment hours *"are incredibly broad. I can even count having lunch with someone I went to law school with, or reading legal news."* The firm bumped up associates' base compensation to the New York scale in recent years, *"so our base scale increases in greater increments than it did before."*

"People at other firms are doing that same amount but just not tracking them."

Thompson awards up to 50 hours of pro bono toward the billable hours requirement, *"then there's a process for requesting more credit if your case runs longer."* One junior even reported: *"I heard of one associate who signed onto a pro bono case that was supposed to last ten hours, but went to, like, 500 hours – and he got credit for all of it."* We should add that 500 is unusually high. Examples of pro bono matters include asylum cases, pro bono divorces, and working for the Dallas Volunteer Assistance Program, which provides free legal help to low-income people in Dallas. Others mentioned helping out answering legal lines: *"That goes on once or twice a month; there's a set block of time and you man the phone lines while people call in with legal problems."* While there is a partner who coordinates pro bono in Dallas and Houston, one associate added that *"several partners and associates are involved in various pro bono activities around town, so there are always opportunities coming from those avenues as well."*

"We're looking to continue to grow our core practices and markets."

Mark Sloan, managing partner

Pro bono hours

- For all attorneys across all US offices: 4,805
- Average per US attorney: 35

Diversity

The general sentiment echoed by associates was that work needed to be done in this area: *"Truth be told I think that's an area of weakness for the firm; we could be more diverse."* Another junior added that *"we recently lost a number of our minority attorneys to other firms. We are focused on seeking out minority candidates, but it will take a while to rebuild our diversity figures."* Still others pointed out that while *"diversity is being made more of a priority, quite honestly I think at the moment there's clearly a generational divide."*

"Diversity is being made more of a priority."

Thompson has a diversity and inclusion committee as well as a women's initiative which does quarterly events. *"At Christmas we got together and stuffed stockings for a local charity, and we had a really fun cocktail-making*

The Inside View

See firm profile on p.703

event last fall that we invited all of our female clientele to. It's a mix of charity work and interacting with our female clients." The firm has a legal internship pipeline program, to encourage minority high school students in Dallas to pursue careers in the legal field, and also offers scholarships to diverse law students in Houston.

Get Hired

Our sources agreed that *"the firm hires all different sorts of people,"* so *"being a people person"* is important. Equally, *"a friendly person that doesn't take themselves too seriously"* does well at the firm, because as juniors reasonably pointed out, *"the more personable you are, the more people will want to work with you."*

According to TK's hiring partner, Jessica Hammons, at interview the firm is looking for *"polished, proactive candidates – those who come into the interview well prepared, and who have researched and know about the firm."* She continues that *"we also like to see students who have looked into the people who are interviewing them, so they can ask them specific questions."* Read her full interview online.

Strategy & Future

"We're anticipating a pretty busy year in 2016," MP Mark Sloan reports, *"so we're looking to continue to grow our core practices and markets."* He goes on to add that *"in particular the transactional area is busy, as well as the real estate, corporate and tax groups; those areas are really hitting capacity."* When we asked about the impact of recent low oil prices on practices, we were told that bankruptcy and restructuring has *"a lot going on,"* and *"we're seeing an increase in trial work."*

"We are concentrating on what we do best."

As far as geographical strategy goes, Sloan explains that *"we don't have offices randomly all over the place. The offices in Texas for instance fit in with our energy focus, while our New York office works well for our capital markets, real estate and trial groups. While we do have international posts, they are strategic, too."* Is any expansion potentially on the cards? *"We're really focused on what our markets are, and we're not interested in opening a far-flung office somewhere else; growth has to be strategic and we are concentrating on what we do best."*

"I'm transitioning into managing my own cases and delegating work to others. Partners will give you as much responsibility as you demonstrate you can handle."

See firm profile on p.703

Vedder Price

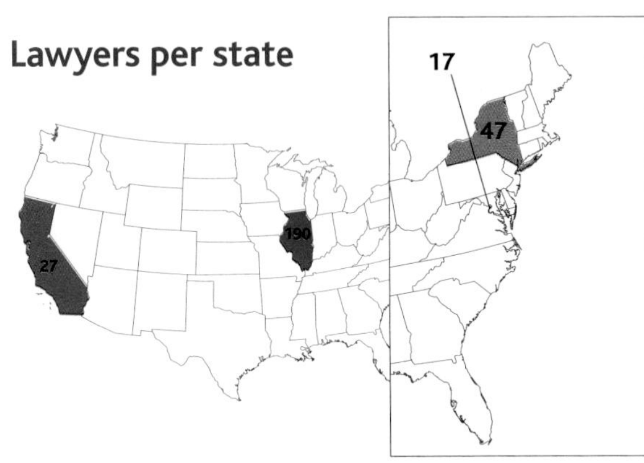

Largest US office: Chicago
US offices: 5
International offices: 1
First-year salary: $160,000
Billable hours: 1,850 target
Summers 2016: 14 (13 2Ls, 1 1L)
Revenue 2015: $238.3 million (+6.1%)
Partners made in 2016: 6
Famous for: transport finance; saving the *SS United States*

The price is right in many ways at Vedder, especially if asset finance floats your boat.

IN October 2015, when the historic luxury passenger ship the *SS United States* was due to be sold off for scrap, the nonprofit that owned the ship turned once again to Chicago's Vedder Price to help (lawyers here had helped the charity acquire the liner in 2011 and have provided pro bono legal support since then). True, with around 280 lawyers and five US offices, Vedder's a little smaller than many of the firms we profile in this guide, but its second-to-none knowledge of the transportation finance sector made it the ideal choice to help save this iconic flagship. *Chambers USA* awards Vedder the top ranking for its expertise in this area. It's not a boutique firm, however, and also gets the nod from *Chambers* for its banking & finance, bankruptcy, investment funds, employee benefits, labor & employment, corporate/M&A & private equity, and litigation: white-collar crime work.

The *SS United States* was huge: during the Cold War in the early 1950s it was secretly designed to be easily converted to carry 15,000 troops should war break out. Vedder isn't looking to become quite so big. As hiring partner Dana Armagno puts it, *"we're not trying to be a megafirm. We want to focus on what we do best, and be the best at it."* That said, steady expansion is very much on the cards. The firm opened its first West Coast office in San Francisco in 2013, and followed it up with an opening in Los Angeles in 2014. Back in 2011, Vedder made its first voyage overseas, launching in London.

On chambers-associate.com...

- Aviation finance law

ASSOCIATES SAY...

The Work

This isn't a place for people who don't know what area of law they want to practice. Summer associates spend all their time in one department, and that's the department they'll work in when they start full-time at the firm. The three groups on offer at Vedder are corporate, litigation, and labor & employment. *"While it might have been fun to get litigation experience,"* a transactional New Yorker told us, *"I knew I didn't want to build a career in it."* The corporate: global transportation finance (GTF) group and corporate: finance & transactions usually take the most new starters, followed by labor & employment. Litigation, corporate: tax, and corporate: investment services take one or two attorneys apiece.

> *"We staff our deals very leanly."*

Many firms talk about their 'high-flying' practice groups, but in Vedder's GTF team, this description is rather more literal. This is an asset-backed financing department where at least some of the assets can fly. The assets in question are, of course, planes, trains and ships. *"We're not a huge law firm, so we staff our deals very leanly."* Aviation finance isn't taught at most law schools, so newbies need to spend some time brushing up, but

See firm profile on p.704

Rankings in *Chambers USA*

Banking & Finance	Labor & Employment
Bankruptcy/Restructuring	Litigation
Corporate/M&A	Transportation
Investment Funds	

For detail on ranking tiers and ranking locations, visit www.chambersandpartners.com

Recent work highlights

- Represented Pizza Holdings in its purchase of the defunct Giordano's Pizza's assets from its bankruptcy trustee
- Represented the Import-Export Bank of the United States in connection with the issue of bonds for airlines in Brazil, Mexico, Ethiopia, Canada and the United States
- Helped Air Canada finance nine Boeing 747s

once that's done it's a short interchange from *"simple tasks like preparing checklists and reading conditions"* to *"doing the initial drafts of documents."*

Closely related to GTF is the finance & transactions corporate subgroup. This department does a lot of work in the private equity sector, representing either the funds themselves or the banks who lend to private equity houses. This gives the firm's budding lawyers a chance to do both corporate and financial tasks. Either way, there's a lot of responsibility. *"If it's a brand-new credit agreement the partner will do most of the drafting, but if it's an amendment, I'll do it myself,"* said one source of the finance work. Similarly, over on the M&A side, *"if it's a smaller deal I'll draft the asset agreement with the help of the partner."* Of course, responsibility varies according to deal size. But *"by the end of my first year I was running deals,"* recalled a source in Chicago.

"By the end of my first year I was running deals."

Offices

Vedder has two offices on each of the East and West Coasts, complementing its 190-lawyer Chicago HQ. This is by far the largest office and calls the Loop – Chicago's trendily named business district – home. It's certainly a handy location, although *"the general consensus is that the other offices are nicer."* This might not be the case for much longer, as a refurbishment is in the works. The DC office *"couldn't be more central,"* enthused a source here. It's situated on L Street, geographically and alphabetically next to the capital's famous K Street. It's the smallest of the East Coast offices, with a fluctuating population of lawyers that's *"never more than 20."* In the middle size-wise is New York with almost 50 lawyers in a Midtown high-rise.

Training & Development

"Vedder does a really nice job of training you," thought a source in transport finance. There's the traditional orientation period to help newbies get to grips with the firm's computer systems. This is followed by a range of practice area-specific lunchtime CLEs delivered by firm shareholders. *"You can only learn so much by listening to people,"* thought one insider. *"You need to get out there and get hands-on."* No lawyer, no matter how hands-on, is an island, and our sources thought very highly of the support they were given. *"I don't know if I lucked out, but my secretary's really helpful,"* admitted one associate. In addition, every new attorney gets a junior and senior mentor who they meet for lunch and a chat.

Associates are assessed twice a year in their first four years, and once a year after that. Every supervising attorney they've spent ten or more hours working with submits a detailed description of their work and rates the associate's performance according to various criteria, including work quality and contribution to the firm. Associates are then given a summary of each review. *"It seems like a pretty comprehensive process,"* sources who'd been reviewed thought. Interestingly, the process isn't anonymous: *"You're told straight up who said what."*

Hours & Compensation

Associates who bill 1,850 hours are eligible for a lockstep pay increase and a bonus. There's also a target of 2,000 hours, which qualifies associates for a higher bonus. *"You get a certain extra for every hour you've worked over 2,000,"* explained one junior. *"Hitting the hours isn't a problem,"* another told us confidently. *"There's plenty of work."*

"Hitting the hours isn't a problem."

Associates reckoned that Vedder Price is equally happy with them choosing to *"work 3,000 hours for the biggest bonus,"* as they are for associates to *"work a little less and not get a bonus at all."* An average workday begins between 8.30am and 9.30am, and finishes any time between 6pm and 9pm. All those we spoke to reported working remotely after getting home, and looming deadlines do signify late nights. *"The latest I've worked is 3am,"* a New Yorker told us, *"but a late night usually means midnight or 1am."*

Culture

"They try to cultivate an entrepreneurial spirit," one insider thought when asked about the firm's culture. By way of example, the source noted that *"if you bring in a*

See firm profile on p.704

new client, you'll get a cut of the fees." This is in contrast to other firms, which *"will just say 'thanks.'"* This isn't to say that money replaces manners – *"being from the Midwest, Vedder takes pride in being congenial,"* said an agent at Vedder in Chicago. *"I'm never nervous about approaching a shareholder,"* said another. *"There's no real hierarchy, and everyone's approachable."* We heard mixed reviews of the firm's social scene, with some attorneys telling us that *"all the associates try to do happy hour events,"* and others saying that *"this isn't the sort of place where your co-workers are supposed to be your best friends."* This isn't to say that lawyers are unfriendly, our source hastened to add, merely that Vedder is the kind of place where *"work isn't my life."*

"They try to cultivate an entrepreneurial spirit."

Diversity

"It's not extremely diverse," insiders admitted, *"but it seems like it's heading in that direction."* Diversity varies by office and practice group. The number of female attorneys is generally pretty good, with sources reporting either a 50/50 split, or slightly more women in recent incoming classes. As at other firms, diversity decreases as you go up the ranks of seniority; recent summer classes have been more diverse but *"when you look at the partners it becomes much less so."* Juniors were interested to see what happens at partnership level: *"There's a woman here who's up for partner,"* someone in Chicago highlighted, adding: *"She's on maternity leave, so how they handle that is of particular interest."*

"We'll always strive to do better."

As well as a hiring committee which is very diversity-focused, there's a specific diversity committee whose role is to develop programs to entice diverse candidates to the firm, and look at retention. Vedder regularly visits various minority careers fairs and takes one diversity 1L summer each year. *"We're proud of our successes,"* hiring chief Dana Armagno tells us, *"but we'll always strive to do better."*

Pro Bono

Pro bono is often more suited to litigation than transactional attorneys. Most Vedderites are transactional attorneys, so perhaps they could be forgiven for being a bit cautious when it comes to dipping their toes into the pro bono pond. That said, *"the firm is very open to transactional attorneys doing litigation bono work,"* and *"there are definitely corporate and IP opportunities."*

"Complete control."

The firm partners with organizations like the New York legal assistance group, the Chicago Bar Foundation's Adoption Assistance Program and the AIDS Legal Council of Chicago, and associates can treat up to 60 hours' worth of pro bono work as billable. Lawyers who had done pro bono raved about the experience, which offers *"complete control, a lot of drafting,"* and, for those doing litigation, *"the chance to go to court."*

Pro bono hours

- For all attorneys across all US offices: undisclosed
- Average per US attorney: undisclosed

"By the end of my first year I was running my own deals."

Get Hired

Vedder holds OCIs at a select number of schools near its offices in Chicago, New York and DC, although hiring partner Dana Armagno tells us that the firm is certainly open to write-ins from further afield. *"They often send an alumnus to conduct the interviews,"* recollected one source. At the callback stage, there are interviews with shareholders and associates, and a less formal lunch interview with two associates. Even the officially 'formal' interviews aren't too formal, we heard. *"There are no complicated interview questions,"* one associate reported. While the lunch interviews are supposed to be about *"seeing how a candidate handles themselves in a less formal situation,"* they also give applicants a chance to ask questions that they might not want to bother shareholders with, such as *"what's the work/life balance like?"* and *"what do you do all day?"*

"They always send an alumnus to conduct the interviews."

Because the firm hires summer associates straight into the departments they'll end up practicing in (corporate, litigation, or labor & employment), it wants candidates to demonstrate some experience in that area. *"This can be through having worked in a bank or in the aviation sector, having a business major at undergrad, or having taken the core business law modules at law school,"* says HP Dana Armagno. A demonstrated interest in the firm's practice areas is all well and good, but sources reassured us that it isn't necessary to be an aircraft geek or gearhead. *"I'm not even that into cars,"* someone in transport finance told us.

Strategy & Future

Quality over quantity appears to be Vedder's plan for the future. Take the firm's recent expansion to the West Coast.

See firm profile on p.704

Instead of growing *"haphazardly,"* sources there tell us the firm is *"looking to expand deliberately."* Whichever side of the country it's in, don't expect Vedder to deviate too wildly from its present course. *"We want to focus on becoming best in class in our core practice areas,"* reiterates hiring partner Dana Armagno.

"We're not trying to be a megafirm. We want to focus on what we do best, and be the best at it."
Dana Armagno, hiring partner

See firm profile on p.704

Venable LLP

Lawyers per state

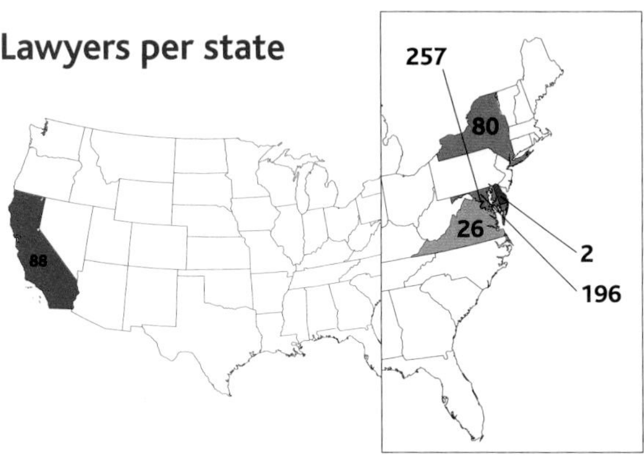

Largest US office: Washington, DC
US offices: 9
International offices: 0
First-year salary: $160,000
Billable hours: 1,900 required (1,800 for first-years)
Summers 2016: 34 (all 2Ls)
Revenue 2015: $477.2 million (+7.9%)
Partners made in 2016: 11
Famous for: summer bocce tournaments; all things government and regulatory

Venable in a nutshell? *"A strong regulatory practice, industry breadth, with a national presence,"* and a quirky culture that gives associates good vibes...

MOST associates told us they picked Venable for two main reasons: its *"great reputation"* in Baltimore and DC, and the *"down-to-earth vibe and people."* In fact, a couple contrasted their experiences of OCI and callbacks at Venable with the negative big New York firm stereotype. One had encountered at another firm in NYC *"a snooty woman dressed in way too much Prada,"* while the other chose Venable because they *"didn't want the snobbish, aristocratic type."* Here, by comparison, *"even from the first screening interview I had a good time, people had a sense of humor, and the callback was the same. I didn't feel anyone was hiding anything from me."*

While most lawyers – around three-quarters – are based in Maryland (where the firm was founded in 1900) and Washington, DC (the largest office), Venable has increased its national expansion in recent years. There are around 88 attorneys in California, 80 in New York, 26 in Virginia and a couple in Delaware. Practice area-wise, *Chambers USA* gives top and high marks for expertise including corporate/M&A, litigation, government, regulation, intellectual property, real estate, REITs, and employee benefits. Clients include Abercrombie & Fitch, BlackBerry and Sony Mobile. Associates relished *"the personal touch to things. We don't have an e-mail culture, partners just come and talk to you and people drop the pretense."* And we can't fail to mention Venable's rooftop bocce courts, where lawyers challenge each other to high-stakes games: the stuff of legend.

On chambers-associate.com...

- More on The Work
- All you need to know about bocce
- Interview with managing partner Lindsay Meyer
- Interview with Shannon Curry, legal recruiting manager and Kera Wise, senior director of attorney recruiting

ASSOCIATES SAY...

The Work

Associates praised Venable for its *"strong regulatory practice, industry breadth, with a national presence."* All interviewees worked in either government, litigation, business law or IP. Under that, there are specialist categories. For example, government associates can be part of groups that include regulatory, environmental or government contract work. DC insiders said that here *"most people go to regulation, several to commercial litigation, with at least a couple in IP. New York, LA and DC are hot spots for IP. But regulation is always the most popular in DC as there are loads of federal agencies here."*

> *"I've never had a doc review project; I'm afraid I don't know how to do it."*

The informal assignment system works on a relationship basis. *"As first-years, we have informal meetings*

See firm profile on p.705

Rankings in *Chambers USA*

Advertising	Labor & Employment
Bankruptcy/Restructuring	Leisure & Hospitality
Corporate/M&A	Litigation
Employee Benefits & Executive Compensation	Privacy & Data Security
	Products Liability
Energy & Natural Resources	Real Estate
Environment	REITs
Financial Services Regulation	Retail
Government	Tax
Healthcare	Technology
Intellectual Property	

For detail on ranking tiers and ranking locations, visit www.chambersandpartners.com

with practice group leaders and then fill out monthly project logs to see if we need to put the breaks on or get more work." Once staffed on matters, typical rookie tasks include *"a lot of research and drafting memos and emails to clients. I get to take the first stab at everything."* Sources in regulation indicated that *"I wouldn't say I was staffed to a case but more staffed to a client. I am the contact point for the client. I help negotiate contracts and sit in board meetings. The learning curve in regulation is steep. But you hit your stride in the first ten months and then you're expected to feel comfortable to not be as guided."* Juniors happily reported that *"I've never had a doc review project; I'm afraid I don't know how to do it! The most fulfilling work is when you help decide client strategy. Should we go to court or negotiate or find an innovative way to fix the problem? Then you research to back up your choice. I mostly spend my day researching and writing."* Transactional associates described how they were *"given more responsibility in smaller groups. I've been seconded to major clients' in-house legal teams. I've become the prime point of contact on deals and negotiated them."* For more on The Work, read our Bonus Features online.

Training & Development

"There is so much billable work it's more on-the-job training" than time-consuming formal sessions, explained one associate. Most liked this because *"diving in is much more valuable than watching a PowerPoint!"* Training is practice group-specific. For example, real estate newbies do things differently in the beginning with *"two to four hours of training every week where partners walk you through major topics. They make time for you."* Managing partner Lindsay Meyer explains that *"we've further enhanced the Venable Academy curriculum by introducing workshops on how to manage projects, communication, financial understanding and depositions in particular."*

Recent work highlights

- Acted as Maryland counsel to Blackstone Mortgage Trust on its acquisition of a $4.6 billion portfolio of commercial mortgage loans from GECC and its affiliates
- Serves as privacy counsel to the Association of Global Automakers (AGA). Members of the AGA include car makers like Aston Martin, Ferrari and Toyota, as well as suppliers including SiriusXM Radio and Bosch
- Assisted Coach, a New York design house of luxury accessories and lifestyle brands, in its securities compliance work

"Diving in is much more valuable than watching a PowerPoint!"

Juniors are treated to a yearly formal review which *"starts in September and a neutral third party comes around to discuss the evaluations from selected people you've worked with."* However, *"realistically you are evaluated on every assignment. It's about constantly developing and getting tricks that the partners wish they knew sooner in their own practices."* Others detailed the Preceptor Program for first-years which pairs new starters with an associate and partner mentor. Some felt that *"although there is a mentoring program, it very quickly drops out of people's minds."* However, respondents divulged that *"it's a resource on how to navigate the office and develop your career. All partners and seniors are willing to impart wisdom. There is a big focus on educating younger attorneys and giving them a platform for success. The firm has made an investment and wants to retain associates."*

Pro Bono

In 2015, Venable unveiled the Gerry Treanor Pro Bono Fellowship. Associates work for six months offering legal advice at either Bread for the City (a charity for vulnerable DC residents) or Maryland Legal Aid in Baltimore. Those who took part detailed how they were *"in court multiple times a week, meeting people for the first time and then going in front of a judge and arguing for them. It was a great experience."*

"You give quick and dirty advice."

For newbies who aren't attached to the project, there is a wealth of pro bono work on offer in-house. IP insiders disclosed that there is *"a wide variety of opportunities. I've advised clients who are extremely talented but lack the legal sophistication to deal with their patent being infringed."* Others detailed work on *"an asylum case, where I've helped draft and edit documents ready to file. I've coordinated expert reports and done general legal research. It's really good, you're only ever encouraged to*

See firm profile on p.705

get involved." Some have worked *"helping small charities become tax-exempt. You give quick and dirty advice. It's all been rewarding as you can really use this as a learning opportunity."*

All sources agreed that *"pro bono is a great way to ingratiate yourself in court and help people out. There's really no other way in the first four years that I would see inside a court, unless I was working for a small client."*

Pro bono hours

- For all attorneys across all offices: 28,869
- Average per US attorney: 36

Hours & Compensation

First-years have a reduced billable hour target of 1,800 hours per year, which then increases to 1,900 for second-years and above. To be bonus-eligible, juniors must reach 1,950 hours, of which 50 hours can be pro bono work. All associates concurred that *"people don't really shoot for bonuses: they aren't very much and it's not worth the time away from family."* Others added: *"They're a little lower than the industry and other firms of our size. The market rate is about $15,000, and we aren't close to that."*

> "Hours aren't something that keep people up at night."

Far from being disheartened, juniors praised the flexibility that this engendered. *"Hours aren't something that keep people up at night. In niche practice areas you can't predict when there will be a major case, so people don't get worried and there aren't repercussions."* While hours inevitably fluctuate between practice groups and depending on how busy people are, most felt that the *"hours are pretty reasonable and because we're not a face-time firm, there's a lot of freedom."*

Offices & Culture

Nine hubs span the States to make up the Venable network, with all associates starting out immediately in their own offices. The DC office takes pride of place as the largest of all outposts. However, the Baltimore founding office still has a hold over attorneys. *"DC has more people but Baltimore feels like the stronghold."* One Baltimore local joked that DC gives a frostier reception to new starters, whereas *"here it's more down to earth."* However, this was the extent of the rivalry between bases, as interviewees stressed that *"there's a strong interoffice synergy. For example, in litigation it's very common for the team to either go to DC or New York."*

> "There's a trophy and massive bragging rights."

Interviewees valued the time partners took to shoulder the bulk of the workload, instead of dumping it on associates. One even eulogized: *"Partners are very modest but brilliant and are real role models."* This camaraderie is enhanced by the balance between *"times to be serious and times to relax. Partners frequently invite associates to their homes for holiday or drinks parties."* Generally, *"they want you to bill but not burn out. For example, a partner told me that I wasn't taking enough time off."* But the standout event at Venable has to be the summer bocce tournament with its own purpose built roof-top court in DC and Baltimore. Things can get a little bit out of hand. Associates explained that *"there are three rounds and you play in teams of two. It's a big deal, there's a trophy and massive bragging rights. IP takes it way too seriously and we trash-talk."*

> **"I was worried about the hours being crazy, but we're not that type of firm and we have the best reputation."**

Diversity

"It's not very diverse," claimed one source. However, all interviewees extolled Venable *"for trying really hard."* They raised the fact that the firm is specifically trying promote female attorneys. The Women Attorneys at Venable group (WAVe), focuses on retention and promotion of women at the firm. They do this by, among other things, *"hosting lunch meetings and external speakers every month to focus on business development both internally and externally."*

> "Everyone is different and that's really valued."

Some juniors detailed that although there were more partners than female in their groups, at associate level it's a different story, with plenty of working mothers. Others said that *"for the most part it's a meritocracy. Everyone is different and that's really valued because we all give different perspectives to clients."*

However, although *"women at the firm are given a lot of opportunities, it comes down to individual choices. If you want to have kids they're very accommodating, but it comes to a point where you have to decide what comes first."* Still, the Diversity Committee oversees various initiatives. For example, Venable supports groups like the *"Asian American Bar Association. They pay the member-*

See firm profile on p.705

ship fees and sponsor dinner tables at different events. So they are working on it." There's also a 1L diversity program which takes scholars in the Baltimore and DC offices.

Get Hired

"Typically, you have to be top of your class, but we're definitely not restricted to the T14," explains legal recruiting manager, Shannon Curry and senior director of attorney recruiting, Kera Wise. Going further, juniors disclosed time-proven interview strategies. *"It's a cliché but it is true: the 'be yourself' tactic. You'll be working with these people a lot so you might as well get it all out there."* Others elaborated that *"we all go to interchangeably good law schools, get good grades. So they hire based on personality. In my interview I didn't talk about the law that much, but more about my own interests."*

"You should do your homework."

DC sources recommended that *"you should do your homework. Research the firm's practice areas because sometimes they're not always on the website. I tried to find alumni from law school who went to Venable, to learn more about the firm. When I interviewed, I could say, 'I spoke with X and this is interesting because Y.' It shows you are pursuing the firm. It's simple and doesn't take much time to set yourself apart from the pack."*

Strategy & Future

Explaining Venable's historic rearrangement from Baltimore to DC, associates said: *"We moved because the government and federal agencies are located in DC, so now we have a unique ability to access regulatory, policy and decision-making officials. We have had a recent push in state regulation practices. The intersection between business, politics and law happens in DC, so it was a good shift for the firm."* Insiders also revealed that *"we have a booming privacy group"* and budding litigators will be happy to hear that *"the two main litigation practices in IP and general commercial are also super-busy."* Others suggested that *"every department is always busy. To be any busier sounds terrifying."*

To furnish itself for the future, the DC HQ is *"moving to a new building, as upper management wants to equip all attorneys with the tools they need to thrive and succeed. They've spent a lot of time designing new work spaces to foster a collaborative environment. Don't worry, the bocce court is coming with us too! It's even written into the contract that we'll have another one."* Lindsay Meyer told us that *"our target is to move in by the first quarter of 2017. So we need to start spring cleaning."* For the full interview with Lindsay Meyer, go online.

"Even from the first screening interview I had a good time, people had a sense of humor, and the callback was the same. I didn't feel anyone was hiding anything from me."

See firm profile on p.705

Vinson & Elkins LLP

Lawyers per state

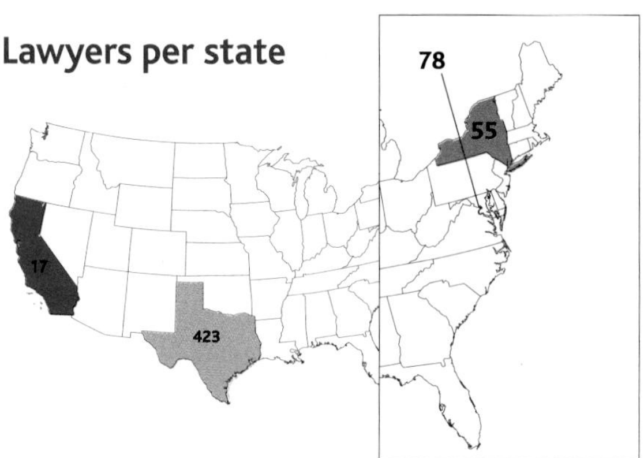

Largest US office: Houston
US offices: 7
International offices: 8
First-year salary: $160,000
Billable hours: 2,000 target
Summers 2016: 68 (45 2Ls, 20 1Ls, 1 3Ls, 2 others)
Revenue 2015: $627.7 million (-3.9%)
Partners made 2016: 10 (all US)
Famous for: leading the oil and gas scene

V&E has certainly got the power when it comes to the oil and gas industry, and associates were as much attracted to the firm's "*complex work*" as they were to its "*Texas can-do spirit.*"

AS one of the oldest and largest firms in Houston, it's hardly surprising that slick V&E has a well-oiled energy practice. The 99-year-old firm nabs a top spot nationwide in *Chambers USA* for its oil & gas litigation, regulatory and projects work. That said, energy is by no means the lone star practice area: it also comes top in Texas for an array of areas, including corporate/M&A, capital markets, bankruptcy & restructuring, real estate, tax, and general commercial litigation.

But the associates we spoke to were not only interested in V&E's *"great reputation."* As one gushed, *"I interviewed with a few firms, and V&E was the one place where people actually seemed relaxed, relatively happy, and actually interested in what I was doing."* Hiring partner Doug Bland emphasizes this point: *"People would describe V&E as a place where there is an open door at all levels. Our partners, associates and staff get along very well across the firm."* He adds that *"having interaction at all levels is an important attribute of the firm."* Revenue in 2015 was down 3.9% to $627.7 million, hardly surprising given the oil industry's current woes.

On chambers-associate.com...

- Vinson's vocations: more on the work
- Interview with hiring partner Doug Bland
- Interview with managing partner Mark Kelly

ASSOCIATES SAY...

The Work

The majority of the work is split into two broad departments: litigation & regulatory, and corporate. Under these umbrellas, associates are then separated into their practice groups. The corporate department accounted for around 60% of the junior associates on our interviewee list, and of these around half were in M&A & capital markets. The rest were divided between energy transactions & projects, finance, real estate and restructuring & reorganization. In litigation, two-thirds of juniors had joined CCL (complex commercial litigation), with the remainder dotted between energy regulation, general assignment litigation, environmental & natural resources, IP, and appellate. There is a third, much smaller department dedicated to tax-ECB [executive compensation and benefits]. Summer associates typically rotate through a number of these groups, which they then rank. The firm gets in touch just before graduation to see if any preferences have changed, before new first-years are assigned to a practice group.

"Loans anywhere between $200 million and $1.5 billion."

Those in M&A & capital markets described working on IPOs, private equity deals and *"a lot of SEC work. I've also been on public M&A."* When it comes to clients, our interviewees unsurprisingly mentioned a lot of energy

See firm profile on p.706

Rankings in *Chambers USA*

Antitrust	Intellectual Property
Appellate Law	International Trade
Banking & Finance	Labor & Employment
Bankruptcy/Restructuring	Latin American Investment
Capital Markets	Litigation
Climate Change	Projects
Corporate/M&A	Real Estate
Energy & Natural Resources	Tax
Environment	Technology
Government	

For detail on ranking tiers and ranking locations, visit www.chambersandpartners.com

Recent work highlights

- Advised Targa Resources Partners and Targa Resources Corp. in the $7.7 billion acquisition of Atlas Pipeline Partners and Atlas Energy
- Represented Pioneer Natural Resources Company in the sale of its Eagle Ford Shale Midstream business to Enterprise Products Partners for $2.15 billion
- Represented Related Fund Management in the formation of an approximately $1 billion fund, focused on real estate opportunities
- Served as issuer's counsel in Columbia Pipeline Partners' $1.2 billion initial public offering of common units

companies, plus private equity funds and public-private partnerships. Over in finance, one junior told us: *"I almost exclusively work on oil and gas-related matters, specifically syndicated finance. We represent both lenders and borrowers for loans anywhere between $200 million and $1.5 billion."* That said, there are *"various other industries"* that finance associates can get involved with, including real estate, insurance and commercial banks. How has the recent slump in oil prices impacted the day-to-day work? *"Over the past year, my time has been spent working with borrowers, trying to respond to this price environment that has implications for their loans,"* a third-year reported. *"I've also been advising lenders as to what would be a good way to tackle the situation with borrowers in the current price environment."*

Complex commercial litigation (CCL) associates described their practice area as *"pretty much the general litigation section of the firm; anyone who doesn't have a specific specialty will go there. We do False Claims Act work, white-collar, antitrust – basically anything that's not environmental, appellate, or energy litigation."* Responsibility levels within CCL varied. One interviewee remarked that they were *"better than expected. I've been able to file substantive motions in court, and I've got to draft small motions and revise some bigger pleadings."* Others, meanwhile, were less convinced: *"It's a lot of low-level doc review. They give you one assignment for a case, you do that and then you don't hear back from them."* Read more about some of the other practice areas online.

"Very productive."

Training & Development

Newbies spend an initial few days in Houston for *"team building and training for formal firm policies."* After this, interviewees noted the range of CLEs on offer. Corporate sources spoke of sessions on proxies, 10Ks and SEC filings, while litigators described training for brief-writing techniques, as well as classes *"explaining the different portions of the electrical grid and what our role is."* A DC litigator added: *"They've flown us twice to Houston for deposition, negotiation and legal writing trainings – those have been very productive."* V&E also recently piloted a writing improvement program.

New starters are assigned a partner mentor and an associate mentor. If they don't turn out great, don't panic, as six months later you get the option to switch mentors. In general, associates felt that they *"could go and ask anyone questions."* Further support comes in the form of a careers consultant who *"travels around to all the different offices – she's like a career coach! If you had a particular issue she can help you manage it."*

Offices

Around half of the juniors on our list were based in the Houston HQ, and gave the thumbs up to their exterior offices. *"We're pretty high up so it's cool seeing the storms come in."* For those with hunger pangs between meals, *"they've started a snack closet down in HR, which is full of healthy (and less healthy) snacks."* Juniors also appreciated the on-site Starbucks and a range of restaurants in the near vicinity.

"It's cool seeing the storms come in."

Over in Dallas, which takes around a fifth of new starters, the focus of the work is more diverse than the energy-centric Houston, and *"M&A and finance are two strong groups,"* as well as litigation. Dallas interviewees were excited by an upcoming move in 2018, as *"the office is a little bit outdated. It's the shape of an almost perfect square,"* which makes for *"a lot of empty space in the middle."* The new office will reputedly be *"a lot more glassy and more modern."* Washington associates meanwhile were chuffed with their *"beautiful"* office, which was built in 2011. *"There's a rooftop deck where we eat in the summer, which is really nice,"* and all associates have their own offices with *"floor to ceiling"* win-

See firm profile on p.706

dows looking out across Washington Circle. The energy regulatory, CCL and white-collar defense groups were picked out as being *"fairly well known here."*

Culture & Hours

The general consensus was that the firm's more family-oriented culture means there's not a huge emphasis on face time in the office. *"A lot of the associates have families, so the office really clears out between about 6.30 and 7pm. People still have work to do, but it's completely fine if you want to go home and work later on."* That's not to say that socializing never happens, however, and juniors mentioned frequent happy hours and lunches. They highlighted summer events in particular: we heard of a 'Top Chef' competition, and one associate excitedly recalled being taken to a Beyoncé concert. *"It was very unexpected and very fun!"* For those who are more into hitting balls than booty shaking, *"there's a very active baseball league in the Dallas office. It runs for 15 weeks and other firms in town participate."* The firmwide V&E prom in Houston, which takes place roughly every two years, is another high point. And in 2017, the firm will be pulling the party poppers and blowing up balloons as it celebrates its centenary...

"It's completely fine if you want to go home and work later on."

In past years, we've commented on V&E's relatively chilled-out *"Texan can-do spirit,"* and while most associates agreed with this, there were a few voices of dissent. *"I think it's actually the opposite, it's very stressful,"* one junior bluntly remarked. *"Certain partners are difficult to work with, and they set the culture that then trickles down to associates."* Mostly, though, opinions were far more positive: *"Everyone is very respectful; we have a truly open-door policy. I usually feel comfortable walking into a partner's office and asking questions on a type of matter that they've done."*

When it comes to compensation, first-years *"have a fixed low bonus regardless of hours,"* and after this bonuses are tiered at 2,000, 2,150 and 2,300 hours. We heard there was a fair amount of frustration regarding how bonuses had been calculated at V&E this year. *"In 2014, people who exceeded 2,300 hours and got positive reviews got up to 20% above Cravath,"* one junior explained. *"In 2015, with no warning, only fouth-years and up got 25% above. I billed far above 2,300 for no extra benefit."*

"The people here are extremely humane and polite."

Another frustration was that *"there's a lack of transparency, and it's inconsistent year on year. It would be more efficient to be open about the bonus system, because eventually we can piece it together anyway – it just takes longer and creates more angst this way!"* The firm replies that it had meetings with associates and explained how bonuses were calculated. A few sources felt the lower bonuses were a fair exchange for the work/life balance, however: *"I've been happy with my compensation. The people here are extremely humane and polite and my hours are very reasonable, so I think it's a fair trade-off."* The general consensus was that 2,000 hours is the *"unofficial official"* target.

"My gut feeling is that we will be opening some new offices, although we haven't announced anything yet, so stay tuned!"

Pro Bono

All of the associates we spoke to had participated in pro bono work, and many had done well over 100 hours in the past year, no doubt helped by the fact that there's no formal cap on the number of billable pro bono hours at the firm. (Although, as one associate pointed out, *"they probably won't like it if you meet your minimum hours through doing a lot of pro bono."*) Juniors felt that V&E truly respects this type of work. *"I've had timing conflicts where I've had pro bono meetings and client meetings at the same time, but because pro bono was scheduled before, that took priority."*

"Because pro bono was scheduled before, that took priority."

The firm has a dedicated pro bono counsel who regularly sends out emails with various opportunities available. Interviewees reported a large number of real estate-related matters, in the form of landlord-tenant cases, as well as helping nonprofit groups with the acquisition of land. Others mentioned participating in clinics and cases for veterans' affairs, and one Houstonite told us: *"We do a virtual clinic which people can participate in if they don't have time to take on an actual client."*

Pro bono hours

- For all attorneys across all US offices: 25,566
- Average per US attorney: 44

Diversity

Associates generally agreed that V&E is making progress in its male-female ratio. *"Among litigation associ-*

See firm profile on p.706

ates it's about 50:50 men to women, although at partner level it's far more male-heavy." The *"really strong"* women's initiative has been particularly active: *"We've done networking events with clients, speakers have come to talk, and we break out into smaller groups so you can speak to female partners about any concerns."* There is also *"a great new parent mentoring program: when you find out you or your partner are pregnant, you can be assigned to someone who has recently had a baby, to talk about your concerns regarding coming back to work."*

"Making positive steps."

While there is an active diversity committee that is *"making positive steps,"* several associates felt more could be done. *"I do think the firm is committed to diversity, but I think like most firms there may be a struggle in terms of how to manifest that commitment into concrete action. There is a diversity committee, a diversity scholarship, we organize events, we also have resources, not just financial but people who are available to us to discuss diverse matters. I think it's a good positive first step, but in terms of retention and promotion, for whatever reason our retention of diverse attorneys lags behind our retention of nondiverse attorneys."*

Get Hired

V&E's more informal work assignment system means *"the partnership rewards initiative in terms of getting the work you want. You can't just sit and wait for the work to come to you."* As such, *"you need to be a self-starter,"* not to mention *"outgoing and energetic,"* if you want to do well at this firm. And this forthcoming attitude needs to come across at interview, too: *"Grades get you the interview, but once there, you need to be able to have a back and forth – we don't want someone who's very stiff."* After all, *"if you can't talk to the interviewer then you're not going to be able to talk to the client!"* The firm's hiring partner Doug Bland expands on this: *"We like to hear candidates describe and explain what they do and what they think,"* he informs us. *"Through that we gain an understanding of how they organize and articulate their thoughts."* Read Bland's full interview online.

"You need to be able to have a back and forth."

Strategy & Future

Managing partner Mark Kelly reports a *"more challenging"* year in 2015, due to the slump in oil price. Nonetheless, he goes on to say that *"last year was our second strongest year as a firm,"* pointing to a boom in litigation, restructuring, finance and private equity, with a host of new laterals in those areas. *"While we may not be doing as many upstream IPOs, we're seeing a lot more financings, refinancings and restructurings,"* Kelly adds. When asked about any expansion plans on the horizon, we were told 2016 will likely see multiple offices open up shop: *"My gut feeling is that we will be opening some new offices, although we haven't announced anything yet, so stay tuned!"* Go online for Kelly's full interview.

"V&E was the one place where people actually seemed relaxed, relatively happy, and actually interested in what I was doing."

See firm profile on p.706

Waller

Lawyers per state

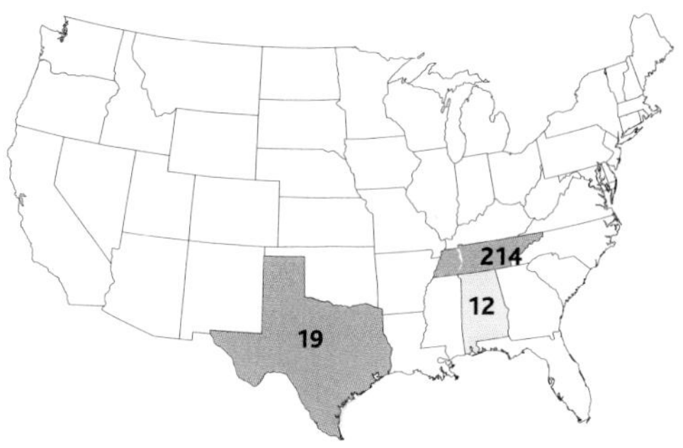

Largest US office: Nashville
US offices: 4
International offices: 0
First-year salary: $115,000
Billable hours: 1,800 target
Summers 2016: 9 (all 2Ls)
Revenue 2015: undisclosed
Partners made in 2016: 7
Famous for: healthcare work; being the top dogs in Tennessee

Nashville may have been the springboard for Taylor Swift's pop career, but Music City is also the setting for a love story between Waller and the healthcare industry...

THE appeal of Nashville spreads further than its renowned musical heritage. The city's robust economy, and its reputation as *"the healthcare capital of America,"* has seen several large firms move into the area in recent years for a slice of the action. And Waller, one of Nashville's largest and oldest firms, certainly stands up to the tough competition. For years it has upheld an excellent standing in the healthcare industry, having been consistently ranked by *Chambers USA* as the number one firm in Tennessee for this practice area. And Waller has more than just healthcare strings to its bow, also ranking top within the state for its corporate, environment, general commercial litigation, and real estate work. *"I think within the regional Southeast firms, Waller's among the most sophisticated transactional practices you'll find,"* one junior proudly told us.

The firm's chairman, Matt Burnstein, told us that the over the past year *"we've had substantial growth firm-wide,"* pointing in particular to the healthcare litigation and IP practices; the firm made an addition of seven patent lawyers in the first half of 2015. He was keen to emphasize, however, that *"we are a full-service firm with capabilities across pretty much every discipline."*

On chambers-associate.com...

- Waller's expert view on the Healthcare market
- Interview with Waller's chairman Matt Burnstein
- Interview with Waller's director of recruitment Bobby Weiss

ASSOCIATES SAY...

The Work

The majority of new associates at Waller are more or less evenly split between corporate, healthcare, or TAP (trial and appellate) work – the latter being the group that litigators join – and only one or two juniors go into IP, finance and restructuring, or labor and employment. In general, newbies agreed that there was not a formal system of work allocation, and that they had to be *"very proactive about going to partners and saying 'I want to work on this'."* In healthcare, corporate, and real estate, attorneys did however describe an *"availability system to track current workload,"* which associates fill out to indicate whether they need more work or are *"maxed-out."*

"You don't just sit and work as a cog in the machine."

Those in the specialized healthcare group described the work in general terms as *"primarily regulatory in nature with a real emphasis on assisting,"* which involves *"a lot of transactional work assisting any mergers or acquisitions with hospitals."* Although healthcare associates *"more or less take a back seat"* to the corporate lawyers

See firm profile on p.707

The Inside View

Rankings in *Chambers USA*

Banking & Finance	Labor & Employment
Corporate/M&A	Litigation
Environment	Media & Entertainment
Healthcare	Real Estate

For detail on ranking tiers and ranking locations, visit www.chambersandpartners.com

who drive the transactions, those dedicated to healthcare handle all the regulatory aspects, *"from deal structure to regulatory filing requirements."* Another junior added that working with other groups is the norm: *"We're brought in for finance and corporate deals, since we're specialized."* Day-to-day, this translates into *"everything from high level regulatory review to on-the-ground licensure aspects; making sure a client has all the licenses they need."* Over in the corporate group, the main body of work is divided into *"probably about 70% M&A and 30% securities work,"* with the M&A side usually having a *"healthcare spin given our client base of the big hospital management companies."* Associates reported *"a lot of drafting; everything from an asset purchase agreement to letters regarding consignment assents,"* as well as a fair amount of due diligence review.

Litigators described a lot of responsibility: *"You don't just sit and work as a cog in the machine,"* with tasks such as drafting motions to dismiss and summary judgments, and preparing witnesses for depositions. One second-year also described *"working on thinking of alternative dispute resolution measures to get a case with a construction group back at the mediation table,"* adding that, *"I'm doing major cases but in steps that I'm comfortable with."*

Training & Development

There is a three-day orientation for associates when they first join Waller, which covers aspects such as *"billing software, how to track hours, and information about HR."* After this, practice area-specific training depends on the group. Litigation attorneys have a more informal, learn-on-the-job approach, while corporate associates described a series of introductory 'lunch n' learns' involving *"presentations from partners in various practice groups, covering aspects which we might use in our work."* In the healthcare group, *"the practice leader has set up a monthly training session with a different partner over a different issue, rule or regulation."* This was well-received by healthcare associates, as *"our area is so specialized, and there's a lot of little rules; when you're presented with an issue sometimes you have to polish up on it."*

"If you're doing a good job it's more tacit approval and you'll get more work."

Recent work highlights

- Acted as special healthcare and real estate due diligence counsel in Ventas' $1.75 billion acquisition of Ardent Health Services
- Advised gaming machine provider Video Gaming Technologies, in connection with the $30 million sale of VGT to Aristocrat Leisure
- Represented Acadia in its $1.3 billion acquisition of CRC Health Group, a leading provider of treatment services
- Successfully defended Regions Bank against a lawsuit in excess of £12 million brought against the bank from Allstate Insurance

New starters are assigned a mentor or 'navigator' as Waller calls them, who were described as being *"very honest about breaking down firm politics; it's a very off-the-record, helpful relationship."* All associates have an annual and mid-year review, and while some felt that more frequent feedback would be useful, others told us that *"if you solicit feedback you're going to get it."* Another junior considered that *"if you're doing a good job it's more tacit approval and you'll get more work. Feedback tends to be for negative work, positive feedback comes at the review."*

Offices

Although 90% of the firm's attorneys are based Nashville, an associate in the Memphis office assured us, *"I don't feel cut off. There are times when as much as 80% of my work will be coming out of Nashville; they're always looking for help."* Another Nashville attorney noted, *"I'm working on transactions with lawyers in Memphis and Birmingham office, and on a regulatory issue with people in Austin."*

"All the partners and associates have floor-to-ceiling windows."

While some in Nashville felt that their building is *"a little 80s"* in style, litigators described their personal offices as *"awesome. All the partners and associates have floor-to-ceiling windows looking out over Nashville."* Over in Memphis, where *"the majority of us are corporate and securities attorneys,"* with a particular focus on the areas of life sciences, biotechnology, medical devices and emerging technologies, the brand new office was completed in 2014, and *"attorneys love it; people that visit from other offices seem pretty jealous!"*

Culture

Our interviewees didn't feel as though the firm's growth has had an impact on its culture – Waller is still *"chilled*

See firm profile on p.707

and down to earth." One junior added, *"there's not a feeling of competitiveness with associates in my group or other groups. I was in a partner's office the other day and another partner came in to brainstorm an issue, and suddenly there's four or five partners working together – it's very collaborative."* Approachable partners are part of this team-spirit: *"there's not a hard line in the sand that separates a partner from an associate,"* and although *"there are obviously some folks who are more senior who you show a certain amount of deference to, everyone else is pretty open and happy to talk to you."*

"There's not a hard line in the sand that separates a partner from an associate."

The firm organizes a lot of social events: there's a lunch with the chairman for new associates, and *"all new attorneys work together to plan the Christmas party, which is great because you get to know a bunch of people early on."* One litigator told us that *"tomorrow night we're going to a TAP dinner at one of our old partner's houses,"* and there is a yearly, firm wide retreat at a casino golf resort.

Nonetheless, the firm's reputation within the region means hard work is a given. *"Even though Waller is likely one of the better places to practice law in the Southeast in terms of culture and work-life balance, it's still the practice of law, so it does wear on you regardless."* And as one healthcare associate pointed out, *"I regularly work with big firms like Ropes & Grey and Kirkland & Ellis, and we're billing the same hours."*

Hours & Compensation

Associates are expected to bill 1,800 hours to be bonus eligible, and the amounts are discretionary (based on hours and other contributions). Associates generally felt that *"the bonus reflects all-round achievement, and billables are 98% of that."* Some of our sources mentioned that billing over this target may see a bonus increase, although *"there aren't set tiers – it depends on your group."* Most of our sources across practice areas felt that 1,800 was an achievable goal, and reported working around ten to 12 hours a day, as well as a few hours some weekends.

"Our board gave us a firm wide 5% bump in salary."

Generally interviewees were happy with their basic salary; one Memphis associate highlighted that *"compared to other Memphis firms that have a Nashville or regional presence it's among the highest."* In Nashville, compensation levels have been disrupted of late. We were told that Nashville-based Bass Berry & Sens recently raised their basic salary by around 10%. *"Our board responded to that very quickly, and gave us a firmwide 5% bump in salary,"* which came into place in January 2016. The starting salary is now $115,000, up from $110,000. There was certainly a sense from all of our interviewees that Waller is *"committed to giving the biggest bonus and having the highest-compensated associates"* in its markets.

Pro Bono

Juniors in Nashville receive emails every fortnight from the pro bono coordinator. The work itself includes some immigration cases and lease disputes, with one litigator mentioning *"a social security appeal for a client's son."* Another associate reported that *"we just set up an order for protection partnership with the Legal Aid Society. Any time a case comes up it's assigned to a different team and it rotates so you do about one a month."*

"It's considered in your evaluation as a good thing."

Those outside the Nashville office didn't feel as though they had *"had any opportunities presented,"* to do pro bono, while some in healthcare felt that the *"nature of our work is so different to the nature of pro bono cases."* The lack of enthusiasm we sensed could also be explained by the fact that pro bono hours don't count towards billables, although *"it's considered in your evaluation as a good thing."*

Pro bono hours

- For all attorneys: 2,835
- Average per attorney: 15

"Within the regional Southeast firms, Waller's among the most sophisticated transactional practices you'll find."

Diversity

While the majority of our associates did feel that there is *"room for improvement"* in the level of diversity at the firm, most agreed that *"it's something that we're working towards."* Waller has a diversity committee as well as a women's law council which is *"in the process identifying areas of growth and different ways to expand."* And as one second-year pointed out, *"even if your committee doesn't come up with anything groundbreaking, being involved and getting to know people is important."*

See firm profile on p.707

Get Hired

According to associates, a proactive attitude is important because *"There is more of a 'sink or swim' mentality here, and you're often expected to figure things out on your own."* Chairman Matt Burnstein reiterates this point, noting that *"a person is likely to thrive at Waller if he or she knows or can figure out what it takes to get a job done efficiently, in the absence of a set of definitive instructions."*

"You're often expected to figure things out on your own."

Others felt that the firm's commitment to its associates' career development means Waller is *"looking for longevity and ties to the community if possible, making sure we're not just a stopover to the next gig."* As Matt Burnstein adds, *"this environment of lifelong ties to the firm and good feelings toward us is a tremendous asset to developing young lawyers."*

Strategy & Future

Do associates see a future with the firm? Most were very positive on this front: *"It feels like once you've started here, you're here,"* no doubt helped by the fact that the firm is *"very transparent about making partner."* Waller's director of recruiting, Bobby Weiss, tells us that the firm makes a point of offering significant feedback and training programs, which help *"let associates know where they need to be,"* and *"ensure that the young attorneys will continue advancing at the pace they want and are expected to advance for partnership considerations."*

"Very transparent about making partner."

Others were less certain of a long-term career with the firm, however, particularly in the healthcare group, where *"a fair amount of people leave for other job opportunities, since healthcare work has a lot of mobility."* But you won't be discouraged from moving on if you so choose – in fact quite the opposite. Bobby Weiss describes Waller as having an *"open-door policy"* which *"allows people to go out and expand their skill set, then come back to the firm into leadership roles."* Many leavers go in-house, he says, and those who return come back with *"great institutional knowledge."*

"We are a full-service firm with capabilities across pretty much every discipline."

Matt Burnstein, chairman

See firm profile on p.707

Weil, Gotshal & Manges LLP

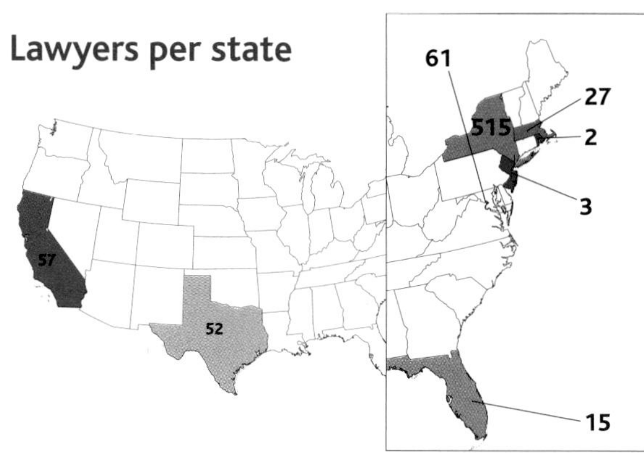

Largest US office: New York
US offices: 9
International offices: 11
First-year salary: $160,000
Billable hours: no target
Summers 2016: 97 (80 2Ls, 17 1Ls)
Revenue 2015: $1.164 billion (+1.1%)
Partners made in 2016: 9 globally (5 US)
Famous for: high-profile bankruptcy cases and a booming M&A practice

While Weil is best known for bankruptcy work, actually corporate and litigation have been the mainstays for quite a while...

LEHMAN Brothers. Enron. American Airlines. MF Global. General Motors. You guessed it, these are five of the biggest bankruptcies in history, and Weil Gotshal dealt with the fallout from each of these massive implosions. The countercyclical nature of bankruptcy/restructuring work reassured at least one associate that it *"gives us job security if the markets go bad."* Well up to a point, because most junior associates here are in the corporate and litigation practices, and bankruptcy only houses around 10% of Weil's lawyers.

"Fifteen years ago," executive partner Barry Wolf highlights, *"we set out to build a first-class private equity practice and then turn to M&A. We have built one of the top private equity practices and are now continuing to build out one of the top public M&A practices in the world."* Given today's healthier economy, *"the private equity practice will get stronger and M&A will continue to grow in terms of head count and revenue... In terms of our litigation practice... it speaks for itself and is top-flight."* Meanwhile, *"our restructuring practice might be slightly slower given the continuing strength of the US economy, but it is still extremely busy."* This 85-year-old New York stalwart achieves its highest (Band 1) *Chambers USA* rankings for bankruptcy, private equity, and litigation (specifically entertainment-related), and excellent ratings for other areas including general litigation, corporate/M&A, tax, intellectual property, and banking & finance.

On chambers-associate.com...

- Interview with executive partner Barry Wolf
- Interview with cochairs of the hiring committee Josh Amsel and Jackie Cohen

ASSOCIATES SAY...

The Work

First for some data. At the time of our calls, our interviewee pool of junior associates who joined Weil in 2013 and 2014 was distributed among the following practice groups (numbers in brackets): corporate (65); litigation (43); tax, benefits & executive compensation (9); and business finance & restructuring (7). Within litigation, the subgroups are complex commercial litigation (19), securities litigation (9), patent litigation (5), antitrust/competition (4), product liability/mass tort/environmental (2), employment litigation (2), and regulatory (2). In corporate, they are private equity/M&A (PEMA; 34), banking & finance (10), technology & IP transactions (7), capital markets (5), structured finance (4), private funds, (3) public company advisory group (1), and real estate (1).

Summer associates toward the end of their summer submit practice preferences. These are combined with partner assessments to determine where associates are assigned when they join as first-years. Specialist teams like patent litigation usually require prior expertise of some

See firm profile on p.708

Rankings in *Chambers USA*

Antitrust	IT & Outsourcing
Banking & Finance	Labor & Employment
Bankruptcy/Restructuring	Litigation
Capital Markets	Media & Entertainment
Corporate/M&A	Private Equity
Employee Benefits & Executive Compensation	Real Estate
	Securities
Intellectual Property	Sports Law
International Arbitration	Tax
Investment Funds	Technology

For detail on ranking tiers and ranking locations, visit www.chambersandpartners.com

Recent work highlights

- Advised DIRECTV in the tax aspects surrounding its $67.1 billion sale to AT&T
- Acted for real estate investment firm KTR Capital Partners in its $5.9 billion sale of a real estate assets operating platform to Prologis
- In one of the most talked-about restructuring deals of the year, advised supermarket giant A&P in the auction of 150 of its stores
- Major litigation wins for Weil clients CBS and P&G

sort, and *"someone's background plays into how work is assigned, with partners taking it into account to assign you work that you can do but that pushes you."* Generally, associates in larger groups indicate their availability for work in weekly reports, while those in smaller teams often work with one or two partners who dole out work. Many associates get work through a mix of the formal and informal methods. *"Partners are receptive to associates asking for work,"* sources told us. As a general rule, *"those who really care about the work and are hungry to ask for assignments lend themselves to better work."*

"Happy and surprised at the level of responsibility."

Associates in all groups can expect decent responsibility early on, *"depending on how much you are trusted and willing to take on."* A litigator, for example, relished lots of doc review and deposition prep because *"you have to be the owner of the facts,"* and was rewarded by being *"brought into depositions all across the country."* Another was *"very happy and surprised at the level of responsibility I've been given because in a lot of assignments I get the first crack at making a recommendation. If I don't think we can do it, people believe I did the necessary work and go with it."* That fact it's *"not given to five different associates for five different answers makes me give my best efforts."* Someone in the complex commercial litigation subgroup did lots of *"doc review, then I then got pretty involved and went to trial five or six times, and helped prep witnesses. Partners decide if they're comfortable giving you responsibility. It's needs-based but also depends if they like you and the interest you show."*

Corporate associates told us they're *"expected to do the heavy lifting like reviewing agreements for clients and summarizing key provisions."* In the big private equity subgroup, *"I am the point person for managing older portfolio companies, I'm staffed on private equity bids, draft memos, prepare for diligence calls. Leading them is more common for second-years but as a first-year I was able to do this. M&A is really case-specific. Clients are demanding so you need to interface with them, and juniors do get interesting work to do."* Deal sizes *"range from venture capital and middle market to billion dollar-plus. It depends on the fund cycle. This allows juniors to step up and take responsibility and work on things that end up in the newspaper."* In a smaller corporate team, work *"varies depending on the deal, but I'm normally drafting core documents, making closing checklists, talking with clients on the phone and via email."* Client contact is pretty good: *"I client-interfaced constantly in my first year,"* many revealed.

Training & Development

Associates explained that *"every two weeks there is a general firmwide training broadcast from office to office."* Other events are divided by practice groups and can count toward CLE requirements. Junior litigators are treated to evidence and deposition workshops in New York. Bostonian private equity newbies have *"concrete training such as reading contracts and then discussing what to do next with your group as a whole."* With two partners who are professors at NYU, it's no wonder that associates praise programs led by *"sharp and committed experts in their field who are always willing to teach."*

Initiatives such as *"Lunch and Learn,"* in which *"an associate and a partner prepare a topic to present to the group as a whole,"* are common in most offices. However, their frequency and subject areas differ. One associate hoped that there could be more balance between *"cutting-edge stuff"* necessary to keep ahead of the curve, and *"the basics."*

"Sharp and committed experts in their field."

In terms of appraisals, juniors undergo two yearly reviews. Some associates indicated that *"the reviews are pretty similar, so maybe they need to raise more improvement points which are glossed over now."* Nevertheless, associates choose their reviewers from a list of partners with whom they have worked. The feedback is then dis-

See firm profile on p.708

cussed in first an informal meeting. Two partners typically vocalize the *"collated feedback coupled with how you are doing in your class level."*

Offices & Culture

The New York HQ is in the *"iconic"* GM Building overlooking Central Park. First-year New Yorkers should expect to share with an office mate for at least three years. *"It's helpful in the beginning to ask questions and bounce around ideas with someone who can't get mad at you!"* Those in Boston have an annual *"moving day,"* where they move from first-year, single-windowed offices, to second-year, double-windowed residences. It might not be the GM Building, but Boston associates were quick to retort that *"you come here for the community and not the architecture,"* and mentioned they enjoy an office popcorn machine.

"We have to staff from other offices."

Regardless of location, associates attested that *"it says something about our culture that people in general want to spend time with each other outside of the office."* One junior based outside Manhattan assured us that *"we generate more work than we can staff, so we have to staff from other offices, including New York. We are New York-centric in the sense that it's the mothership, but we aren't dependent on it."* Most associates interviewed agreed that Weil is a place where *"you are given the freedom to approach problems how you need to, and there's an expectation that you can manage it and produce top-level work."*

Location also plays a part in the type of work encountered. Boston has been *"constantly running bids"* this year in a thriving PEMA group, with Dallas in a similar position. Silicon Valley holds the fort in patent litigation simultaneously with DC, which also has expertise in antitrust. New York is a leader in all things bankruptcy/restructuring, with the M&A team shining particularly bright.

Hours & Compensation

Hours vary based on office location and practice group. Some PEMA associates in New York mentioned occasional 2am finishes. However, on the whole, juniors found themselves arriving for work around 9am and leaving ten or 12 hours later. In past years, associates have told us tales of napping under their desks, which some wear as a badge of honor: *"Once or twice when a deal is closing, I'm here all night and I would sleep at my desk or under it, but that's because it's an emergency."*

"It's times of stress where personal relationships matter."

A Bostonian mused that it's *"times of stress where personal relationships matter and it's here that you build loyalty and can truly test the working environment."* Comparing their situation to peers at other similar BigLaw firms, some juniors felt that 1,800 hours was about the right number to aim for, although *"no one cares; it creates unnecessary stress, especially in corporate where we don't have control over our hours as deals can fall apart in minutes."*

Pro Bono

Pro bono is *"heralded at the firm,"* reported one interviewee. Each associate is expected to devote 50 hours a year to pro bono cases. However, in reality many have *"already eclipsed that by three or four times."* Firmwide emails make the rounds daily, coupled with lunchtime discussions that give further opportunities to engage in casework. There certainly is variety, with associates being granted the chance to work beyond their own practice areas. One associate highlighted that *"it's a great leeway to engage in whatever area I want."*

"If you are not doing it, you're asked why!"

The stakes have never been higher, as offices are actively encouraged to battle it out for the Pro Bono Cup. The Cup honors the office with the most pro bono hours, *"divided by the number of attorneys in that office,"* and is presented at a ceremony which is beamed across all offices, *"even the international ones."* The common attitude is: *"If you are not doing it, you're asked why!"*

Pro bono hours

- For all attorneys across all US offices: 40,000+
- Average per US attorney: 60

Diversity

Associates praised the firm's *"very concerted effort to focus on diversity, but there is room for improvement."* Affinity groups such as 'Women@Weil' in particular have a visible global presence. One associate remarked that *"there are initiatives that attract women at law school to get involved with 'Women@Weil' – it acts as a feeder toward the summer associate program."* Weil also has *"a long-standing practice of awarding diversity scholarships,"* say hiring committee cochairs Josh Amsel and Jackie Cohen. *"It started in respect to 1Ls and now we also have extended it to 2Ls. We encourage diverse candidates to apply by writing a personal statement about*

See firm profile on p.708

diversity and why they are particularly deserving of this scholarship. "

"Awarding diversity scholarships."

One initiative is the provision of direct access to the management committee by means of a liaison person within each affinity group. Also, a global task force has also been implemented to discuss the retention of women at the firm. Executive partner Barry Wolf stresses: *"We are entrepreneurial and are willing to try new things and be ahead of the pack."*

Get Hired

When asked what makes a candidate successful, the broad response was that it boils down to who will *"fit in here."* Grades can only get you so far. One associate asserted that *"GPA gets you the interview, but in the interview, it's very focused on the personality fit criteria: someone who is team-building, has ambition and a curiosity to learn."* Another stressed: *"It's clear we are looking for bright go-getters, but also people who pass the 2am test. They are the people you want to be in the office with past 2am."*

"We do expect you to throw yourself in."

Hiring cochairs Josh Amsel and Jackie Cohen add that the most successful candidates show *"enthusiasm, intellectual curiosity, pragmatism and sound judgment. We are a firm built by dynamic lawyers who are not afraid to forge their own paths – and we hope to find young lawyers who will see the world differently and are excited to 'think outside the box.'"* For the full interview with Amsel and Cohen, go online. Barry Wolf advises that, intellect aside, *"we are looking for people who want to be awarded a lot of responsibility and who are willing to step out and thrive in our diverse culture. I chose this firm in 1983 as a summer associate, having interviewed in 1982. I picked Weil because it has an entrepreneurial spirit and truly cares about its people. Thirty-one years on, it has really lived up to that.* " For the complete interview with Barry Wolf, visit our website.

Strategy & Future

Moving from strength to strength, it has been a good year for Weil's M&A practice in particular, which at the time of writing had accrued nearly $500 billion worth of completed transactions. In light of this growth, the firm's HQ is undergoing a complete transformation. Over the next three years, Weil plans to *"floor by floor, make every square foot brand new."* The reason for this change, according to Barry Wolf, is to *"make the space more efficient and compatible with how we work today."* Wolf aims to *"continue to strengthen the cultural hallmarks that are central to who we are as a firm, including our entrepreneurial and pioneering spirit."*

"Our true focus is on strengthening what we already have and integrating all our offices on a global level to an even further extent."

Barry Wolf, executive partner

See firm profile on p.708

White & Case LLP

Lawyers per state

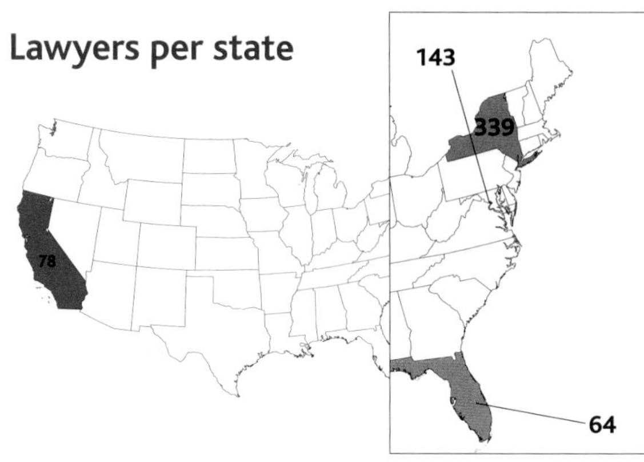

Largest US office: New York
US offices: 5
International offices: 34
First-year salary: $160,000
Billable hours: 2,000 target
Summers 2016: 102 (94 2Ls, 4 1Ls, 1 3L, 3 SEOs)
Revenue 2015: $1.523 billion (+1.5%)
Partners made 2016: 31 globally (8 in US)
Famous for: Big international network; travel opportunities

Grab your atlas, because megafirm White & Case is on the hunt for intrepid, worldly associates.

WITH almost 40 *"well-integrated"* offices worldwide, White & Case offers junior associates the opportunity to get involved in some seriously far-reaching matters. The firm's latest office addition (at the time of writing) is in Seoul, which opened in August 2015 to bolster its 20-year-old Korea practice.

Around two-thirds of White & Case's 2,000 lawyers are based outside of the firm's five US offices. Unsurprisingly, it tends to attract candidates whose appetite for the practice of law is matched only by their interest in market developments around the globe. No one typifies W&C lawyers' worldly wisdom better than chairman Hugh Verrier. Executive committee member David Koschik tells us: *"Hugh Verrier has worked for White & Case in three different continents, and it's a career path that many others have shared. There are a lot of opportunities to travel and work abroad for those who are interested."*

"Done a great job."

Stateside there's also plenty of encouraging news, as White & Case has spent the past year making efforts to improve the associate experience. *"There was sense that associates weren't as happy as they could have been, and mid-level retention wasn't looking so good,"* regaled one interviewee. *"The firm responded by establishing a 'great workplace taskforce', which, though it sounds corny, has done a great job."*

Powerful across the board, White & Case secures top rankings nationally in *Chambers USA* for corporate/M&A, international arbitration, and projects, but is also strong in areas such as banking, capital markets, litigation, antitrust, and energy. Search for White & Case on chambersandpartners.com and peruse the various global rankings directories (including *Chambers USA*) at your leisure.

ASSOCIATES SAY...

The Work

Upon arrival, newbies in New York, DC and LA choose whether they'd like to go into litigation or corporate. They then head to their respective assignment pools, which are headed by an administrator. It's their job to collect assignments from various subgroups, to ensure that starters get a good mix. Administrators were rated as *"really proactive, and keen to find out what you're interested in."* Crucially, *"saying 'thanks but no thanks' is much less intimidating when you can do it through your coordinator."*

Though a popular system, *"those who know where they want to practice will have to be patient. You are expected*

On chambers-associate.com...

- White & Case's soccer and volleyball galacticos

See firm profile on p.709

The Inside View

Rankings in *Chambers USA*

Antitrust	Latin American Investment
Banking & Finance	Litigation
Bankruptcy/Restructuring	Outsourcing
Capital Markets	Private Equity
Corporate/M&A	Projects
Energy & Natural Resources	Real Estate
Environment	Tax
Intellectual Property	Technology
International Arbitration	Transportation
International Trade	

For detail on ranking tiers and ranking locations, visit www.chambersandpartners.com

Recent work highlights

- Defended the LA Lakers in a claim alleging that its $3billion agreement with Time Warner Cable breached California's unfair competition law
- Providing regulatory advice to the lenders behind Liquefied Natural Gas's $3.5 billion Magnolia project. The project will establish a new liquefaction and export terminal in the Port of Lake Charles, Louisiana
- New York, Shanghai, Paris and eight other White & Case offices worked together to represent electric motor manufacturer Regal Beloit in its $1.44 billion purchase of Emerson Electric's Power Transmissions Solutions business
- Represented Barclays, Credit Suisse and several other major investment banks in connection with a $3.94 billion debt and equity financing for SS&C Technologies' acquisition of Advent Software

to try out at least one assignment with every subgroup before specializing." Generally speaking, after their first or second year in the corporate pool, associates in NY and LA join one of the corporate sections. Depending on the office, the sections include banking, capital markets, energy, infrastructure, project and asset finance (EIPAF), and M&A/corporate. Litigation pool members join either the competition (where IP, trade and antitrust reside) or disputes sections, eg commercial litigation, arbitration and white-collar, after one or two years depending on their home office. In DC, all new associates are placed in the litigation pool, but there is an option to join one of the corporate groups after their first year. In Miami, corporate associates are assigned to a practice group upon their arrival and litigators remain in the pool for one year. Palo Alto is a smaller setup, so juniors there are assigned to a practice group from the get-go.

"On many deals it's just you and a partner, so it's easy to ask questions."

To begin with, litigators *"stick to the simple stuff,"* occupying their time with a mix of memo writing, legal research, brief writing and *"some occasional doc review."* Once rookies have proven their worth, they're afforded *"a big jump in responsibility."* This not only results in advocacy opportunities – *"I argued two appeals in the state appellate court"* – but also paves the way for a step-up in managerial responsibility, *"supervising first-level reviewers, managing databases of people and working with the partner to handle production decisions."*

Corporate associates are exposed to clients from an early stage, which *"forces you to ensure you know the particularities of the deal inside out so that you can think on your feet, talk clients through your thought process and explain various aspects of the deal."* This may sound daunting, but insiders were *"impressed with the amount of strategic discussions we're privy to,"* as well as the fact that *"on many deals it's just you and a partner, so it's easy to ask questions."* Most deals have some international aspect to contend with, though the provenance can depend on which office you're in. As one Angeleno put it, *"In LA, our international scope is more Asia-facing, so we don't cover as many European deals as New York or DC."*

Training & Development

After office-specific IT training, newbies assemble in New York for an orientation week. *"It explained our business plan, the strengths of our individual offices and the resources that we have at our disposal, which really helped to reinforce exactly what we're about."* A big emphasis is placed on the firm's global credentials, so *"even the Mexico City starters come along."* Mixing with different offices so early on is *"undoubtedly beneficial, as we all work together regularly."*

"Even the Mexico City starters come along."

From then on, regular CLE sessions were popular amongst juniors, because as one New Yorker pointed out: *"They try to make sure they're applicable. It's more 'here's how to write a good brief,' as opposed to 'let's talk over a random esoteric point of law.'"* White & Case doesn't have a formal mentorship program, but *"if you seek out feedback, people definitely oblige."* In fact, *"this works well, as the training you receive is relevant to the work at hand."*

Offices & Culture

The firm's Big Apple HQ houses most new starters, followed by Washington, LA, Miami, and a smaller tech-focused outfit in Palo Alto. White & Case's offices are classed into three border-spanning designations: the Americas (which also ties in Mexico City and São Pau-

See firm profile on p.709

lo), Asia, and EMEA (Europe, the Middle East and Africa). Practice groups across the Americas offices regularly work hand in hand, though plenty of juniors had worked with European and Asian teams too.

The motive behind these groupings is simple: *"We're not just looking to operate in individual markets on a local basis,"* explains executive committee member David Koschik. *"Serving clients with multijurisdictional requirements is a big part of what we do, so we place a real premium on connecting and integrating our offices."* Sources corroborated this view, with one recounting: *"During interviews I spoke with juniors who had actually visited foreign offices. Having that wealth of opportunity really distinguishes us from other global firms."*

"We place a real premium on connecting and integrating our offices."

Interviewees were highly complementary of the so-called great workplace taskforce's recent improvements. *"They instantly brought in new coffee machines and better snacks,"* said a satisfied New Yorker. *"They're looking into revamping parental leave policies, and have also introduced upward feedback reviews. If particular partners aren't keeping up with their mentorship responsibilities then it'll be flagged, which is really encouraging."*

NYC callers also felt *"heavily involved in the design of our new office,"* set to open in the first quarter of 2017. *"They took surveys to see what interested us, and having seen the blueprints we're all very excited,"* one beamed. *"The gym will be on the 50th floor, looking out over the city skyline,"* and conveniently *"it'll only be five or six blocks from our current location."*

By and large, juniors found the firm *"a friendly place to be,"* where *"you can say what you feel without risk of judgment."* When it comes to social offerings, *"it's as busy as you want it to be. A lot of people are married or have families, but you can usually find someone to grab a beer with."* New lawyers are also encouraged to take part in firmwide networking events, with the annual White & Case World Cup particularly popular. Check our Bonus Feature online for more information.

Strategy & Future

2015 brought the closure of W&C's Munich office, inherited from a 2000 merger with Germany's Fedderson. According to David Koschik, *"we have offices in Berlin, Düsseldorf, Frankfurt and Hamburg which are well equipped to serve our Munich-based clients. We wanted to consolidate and strengthen our presence in those locations."*

"London and New York are crucial."

Last year we reported a New York and London-led push for transatlantic domination. Have other offices been left in the cold? *"Not at all,"* David Koschik replies. *"In fact, we've just recently opened offices in Seoul and Dubai. We're active in so many markets and long may that continue."* That said, *"London and New York are crucial, as so many of our clients in other target markets have dealings there. It makes sense to continue strengthening in those two hubs."*

How exactly does the firm aim to do this? *"Capital markets, disputes and M&A (including private equity) are the three practices we'd most like to push. We're strong in banking, international arbitration, project finance and many other practices too, but over the coming years we'll be putting the most effort into developing those three areas."*

"During interviews I spoke with juniors who had actually visited foreign offices. Having that wealth of opportunity really distinguishes us from other global firms."

Pro Bono

Of the 2,000 billable hours target, 200 can be earned doing pro bono work, as well as a mix of necessary non-billables such as recruiting, article writing and client development. *"Having that many hours to play with proves that for White & Case, pro bono isn't just lip service,"* one interviewee commended. *"It's difficult to do something meaningful in 20 to 30 hours."*

"For White & Case, pro bono isn't just lip service."

W&C is *"pretty open to associates' suggestions,"* though a NY-based pro bono coordinator is *"always shooting out emails"* for those left looking. Whether it's legal research for a same-sex marriage initiative, or arguing in court on criminal appeals, *"you can take on as much or as little as you want."* Thankfully there's *"always a partner or two on hand to guide you. I've worked on pro bono matters with partners, senior associates and counsel and we function as equals. Bouncing ideas off of one another so freely is a real confidence booster."*

Pro bono hours

- For all attorneys across all US offices: 59,753
- Average per US attorney: 86

See firm profile on p.709

"The last two summer classes have been increasingly balanced."

Diversity

How have associates rated the firm's efforts to promote diversity over the past 12 months? *"Recruitment is really trying,"* reflected one associate. *"We're an international firm that values languages, so obviously we already attract a mixed bunch, but the last two summer classes have been increasingly balanced."* However, when it comes to retaining diverse mid-levels *"there's still plenty to be done."* The upper echelons are *"predominately male,"* a trend that could be better countered through *"more concrete policies when it comes to flex time scheduling."* With any luck the establishment of the 'great workplace taskforce' will help to buck this trend. Encouragingly, in 2015 three female associates were among the eight promoted to partner in the USA. A recent improvement in affinity group activity bodes well, and associates were pleased to have noticed *"a lot more diversity events that include everyone, such as talks with high-standing female executives."*

Hours & Compensation

Associates hoped that the firm's morale-boosting turnaround would bring improvements to the vacation booking process. As with flex time, *"it'd be helpful to have a more formal set-up in place, as it all feels a little disorganized."* There are no limits to the amount of vacation people can take, which several felt *"can actually be limiting. I doubt many people take four weeks off each year."* Once vacation has been approved, *"people are respectful and try not to email you."*

"People usually cut you some slack if you've worked crazy hours."

If you don't hit your hours in your first year then *"as long as you haven't been hiding there's a good chance you'll make your bonus. Pro bono is a useful stopgap during quiet periods."* With such an international focus, hours vary wildly, so *"whereas some days you'll go home at 3pm, some days you don't go home at all."* Fortunately, *"the firm is reasonably understanding about working from home,"* and *"people usually cut you some slack if you've worked crazy hours. I've been allowed a few early finishes to compensate."*

Get Hired

In keeping with White & Case's global outlook, *"previous experience in multinational organizations is looked upon favorably, as is fluency in a foreign language,"* advises hiring partner Heather McDevitt. In fact, in the firm's 2016 recruitment season, 43% of all US summers spoke at least one foreign language. Clearly practices such as real estate are inherently more domestically focused, so *"we would never turn away candidates because they couldn't speak a second language."* However, *"if you're looking to go into international arbitration, for example, the ability to speak French or Spanish is more of an imperative."* Mandarin, Russian, Arabic and Portuguese were also flagged as particularly useful, but *"we operate globally so any language skills are a bonus."*

"Speaking a foreign language can lead you to new work."

Associates affirmed the importance of language skills, stating *"it's definitely something that they ask at interview."* Further down the line *"speaking a foreign language can lead you to new work, as partners regularly send e-mails searching for an associate who can speak Spanish or Hebrew or Russian, etc."*

"Previous experience in multinational organizations is looked upon favorably, as is linguistic fluency in a foreign language."

See firm profile on p.709

Wiley Rein LLP

Lawyers per state

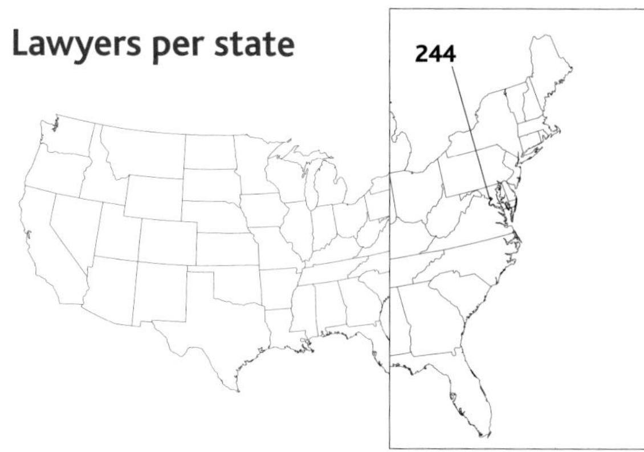

Largest US office: Washington, DC
US offices: 1
International offices: 0
First-year salary: $160,000
Billable hours: 1,950 target
Summers 2016: 11 (10 2Ls, 1 1L)
Revenue 2015: undisclosed
Partners made in 2016: 2
Famous for: telecoms expertise and government contracts work

Associates take the reins and steer their own career at this renowned DC thoroughbred.

AMONG the handful of firms who could claim to be king of K Street, Wiley Rein is a strong contender for the crown. Founder partner Dick Wiley is a communications industry heavyweight with a stint as chairman of the FCC under his belt and an Emmy to his name, awarded for his role in helping to create HDTV. In the past few years, cofounder Bert Rein has appeared in two much talked-about Supreme Court cases: he's helped Shelby County, Alabama, to challenge the 1965 Voting Rights Act and has been representing a white student who claimed that the University of Texas at Austin used affirmative action admission policies to discriminate against her.

"Easier for associates to have a voice."

Associates were delighted that *"the name partners are still active and practicing. I see them on a regular basis in the elevator and halls. The fact that this is our only office means that big decisions are made by people down the corridor, rather than an anonymous management committee that's spread across the globe. The structure of the firm makes it feel like a comfortable place rather than a faceless corporation. I don't want to say it's like a family because that sounds cheesy! But it is tight-knit."* The single-office setup also *"makes it easier for associates to have a voice. Everyone knows somebody on the associates' committee."*

On chambers-associate.com...

- We speak to the managing partner, chief talent officer, and chief marketing officer

Naturally, juniors were also drawn to the firm's *"expertise and strong practices"* – evidence of which is apparent in the firm's top-tier *Chambers USA* rankings for government contracts, insurance and telecoms work. The latter department has stacks of well-known clients, including AT&T, Verizon and Samsung, while the insurance group works for industry big-hitters like Chubb and XL Catlin.

ASSOCIATES SAY...

The Work

With around 250 attorneys in total operating under one roof, Wiley Rein's annual intake of new talent is pretty petite. At the time of our calls, there were four to five juniors in the insurance, government contracts and telecoms, media & technology (TMT) groups, with the odd attorney cropping up in the international trade, IP, election law, litigation and environmental departments.

In the communications and government contracts groups, there's a free-market system for getting work (*"it's up to you to fill your docket"*) although rest assured that *"when you first start they have a few assignments for you."* Overall, *"you get into the swing of things after a few months. Partners call you up and give you assignments and you end up working with some more than*

See firm profile on p.710

Rankings in *Chambers USA*

Franchising	International Trade
Government	Media & Entertainment
Insurance	Privacy & Data Security
Intellectual Property	Telecommunications

For detail on ranking tiers and ranking locations, visit www.chambersandpartners.com

others." The insurance group, meanwhile, is *"unique"* in having an assigning partner who *"helps you to navigate the free-market system. If you think you're getting slow and need more work, or if you're interested in a type of work you haven't been able to experience before, then he'll try to help you with that."*

"Partners call you up and give you assignments."

In government contracts, *"there are always bid protests floating around and appeals that go before the Armed Services Board or the Contract Board of Appeals. For my first six months I did a lot of research and writing for bid protests."* One source announced that *"I worked on a large internal investigation which was really fun. An employee had reported some mischarging on a government contract and I got to travel to interview all the people involved."* In addition, juniors might find themselves *"managing a massive document review and collection – it's been a little scary at times but it's given me a lot of responsibility. I'm on the front line answering calls, dealing with the discovery vendor and making decisions as to whether to elevate certain issues to partner level."* Daily life in the department also involves *"a lot of different variations of counseling and compliance work for clients who then two weeks later might find they have a protest to make."*

An insurance associate handily explained what the group does: *"It's nothing to do with car insurance or personal injury or health insurance. We counsel insurance companies that insure large companies. For instance, if Microsoft gets sued, which it does every day, it has insurance for that."* Typically, *"we do a lot of initial advising and counseling on whether claims that come in are covered under policies."* Juniors get stuck into *"coverage analysis, typically for professional liability insurance. I decide if there's coverage, what issues might come up, and then draft the analysis for partners to review."* When it comes to litigation, sources described *"writing briefs, filing motions and getting lots of client contact – the partners I work with really encourage me to get on calls and email clients directly."* Apparently, there isn't much doc review to get through, though one remarked brightly: *"I actually like doc review – it's kinda mindless!"*

"It's been a little scary at times."

Recent work highlights

- Acted for software company Citrix Systems in a bid protest before the Government Accountability Office, relating to software licenses and cloud computing for the US Department of Defense
- Successfully defended Boeing in a bid protest that challenged NASA's decision to award the aviation giant a $4.2 billion contract for ferrying crew to the International Space Station
- Advising on FCC satellite issues for AT&T following its $49 billion acquisition of DIRECTV Enterprises

TMT's capacious client list includes investment firms, technology companies, broadcasters, manufacturers and satellite companies. The associates we heard from had been dishing out regulatory compliance advice as well as taking a role in *"administrative law-focused litigation, involving federal regulatory agencies like the FCC."* A proud source declared that *"the partners handle the majority of communications, but I sometimes talk to the FCC directly, which is pretty great for my level. I also got the first pen on an appellate brief!"*

Training & Development

Sources seemed pleased with the support they'd received from partners. Outside of the annual formal evaluation, *"some partners get very enthusiastic about working with new attorneys and they'll sit down and go through what you did well and what you can improve on. It can be more difficult to get feedback from others. But you can learn what they like by looking at red lines on documents."* One suggested that *"senior associates are a little more cognizant that juniors really want feedback to know where they stand."* Juniors also get matched up with mentors who tend to be *"available to answer questions or proofread things to tell you if you're on the right path."*

"They get you up to speed."

In addition to standard orientation sessions (*"they get you up to speed on how to work in an office environment"*), new recruits have weekly practice-specific trainings. *"I probably had about 30 to 40 hours of training,"* recalled one approvingly.

Offices

In previous years we'd heard reports that the office was a bit behind the times in terms of décor. Apparently, *"there hasn't been a major renovation in a while,"* but sources did tell us that *"a bunch of conference rooms and kitchens have been upgraded and there are now marble tiles in the lobby."* One professed that *"it's not particularly*

See firm profile on p.710

lavish, but it gets the job done," while another pointed out that *"at a lot of other firms there's a trend for glass doors, which is awkward because everyone can see inside your office. It's nice that we have privacy here."*

"Not particularly lavish, but it gets the job done."

Hours & Compensation

Until recently there was a two-track system for billing targets – 1,800 hours and 1,950 – and a corresponding pay scale. When we interviewed associates, several grumbled that *"it created an unnecessary level of stress."* Although some thought that *"the 1,800 target relieved some pressure for first-years, especially when there's training that prevents you from billing hours,"* another declared that *"it created a false expectation that staying on the lower track won't impact your career in the long run."* Happily for associates, the firm has replaced this old dual system with a straightforward annual billable target of 1,950 hours. Bonuses are usually slightly below market.

"The 1,800 target relieved some pressure for first-years."

Most associates reported that they'll be toiling for an average of ten hours a day in the office, although obviously *"it ebbs and flows."* Sources were upbeat about the whole business of work/life balance. *"As lawyers we work a lot, but I do get to go out on weekends, I still have all my passions and hobbies and I hang out with my husband quite a bit."*

Culture

"I would say that the firm is kind of like a smart and dorky but lovable younger brother," chuckled an associate. *"We do really great work and there are a lot of brilliant people here from the best schools with the highest GPAs, but it's quite laid back, in that nobody makes you go out to bars for five hours after you've worked for 20 hours straight or anything like that. It's family-oriented, not a party firm."*

"Nobody makes you go out to bars for five hours after you've worked for 20 hours straight."

What about political affinities? Associates told us that election law groups can only work for one side and at Wiley it's Republican, so we were keen to find out if pro-conservatism permeates the entire firm. Associates thought not. *"We're not defined by the election law group, which is a practice where you have to pick a side and stick to it. In day-to-day life that doesn't come through very much. There are as many members of the Constitution Society here as there are members of the Federalist Society."* One source admitted that *"I struggled with coming here because of what I perceived as the firm's conservative stance in the election group. But it's not a problem at all, nobody tries to push that in your face and the firm is very supportive of diversity."*

Diversity & Pro Bono

"The firm works hard at increasing diversity," agreed sources. There are affinity groups, including a women's forum, and a pipeline scheme for diverse 1Ls. That said, associates weren't feeling complacent about the issue. *"The numbers are balancing out in terms of gender at associate level, but in terms of ethnic minority and LGBT lawyers there's a lot more to be done. And of course the partnership is still dominated by white males."*

When it comes to pro bono, associates can count 50 hours toward the billing target. All of our interviewees had taken on projects, including disability issues, child custody and human trafficking cases as well as with immigration and housing matters.

"Some partners get very enthusiastic about working with new attorneys."

Pro bono hours

- For all attorneys: 9,819
- Average per attorney: 37

Get Hired

Obnoxiousness is not an option, according to sources: *"I've never found a single associate here to be off-putting or arrogant. They want people who can work in a team, who aren't selfish and stuck-up."*

"Leaders in their law schools."

A genuine interest in Wiley's practices is obviously essential. Chief talent officer Kay Nash tell us that *"it's wonderful if someone has previous experience in the communications industry or government contracts, but it's not a mandatory requirement. We're looking for people who are talented, passionate and driven but also, more importantly, involved as leaders in their law schools. We want people who are connected with others in the community in addition to having the drive to succeed in private practice."*

See firm profile on p.710

Strategy & Future

Back in 2014, the firm initiated a 12-month review which saw it remove its bankruptcy practice and lose 48 lawyers and staff. Now, says managing partner Peter Shields, *"the first year of our strategic plan has gone successfully, and we're looking forward to continuing on this path. Our plan is focused on expanding our elite regulatory practices as well as our litigation capabilities, around the country and internationally – we want to solidify our relationships with other firms around the globe."*

"The first year of our strategic plan has gone successfully."

In the US, says Shields, *"we do not have plans to open other offices and are concentrated on growing our current platform – with both Wiley Rein and McBee Strategic in Washington, DC. However, we expect continued growth in enforcement areas including Federal Trade Commission matters, cybersecurity, and 'Internet of Things' innovations such as connected cars and health care technologies. As a DC-centric firm, we have prioritized developing our services to clients in need of policy and legal expertise in various areas of evolving government regulation. For example, we collaborate with industry thought leaders on commercial drone use."*

"Our plan is focused on expanding our elite regulatory practices as well as our litigation capabilities, around the country and internationally – we want to solidify our relationships with other firms around the globe."
Peter Shields, managing partner

See firm profile on p.710

Willkie Farr & Gallagher LLP

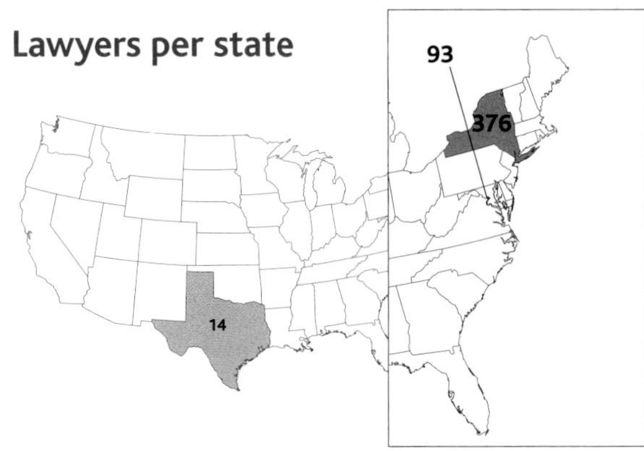

Largest US office: New York
US offices: 3
International offices: 6
First year salary: $160,000
Billable hours: no requirement
Summers 2016: 64 (62 2L, 2 1L)
Revenue 2015: $658 million (+2.8%)
Partners made in 2016: 5
Famous for: historic clients; insurance prowess

Unlike many firms, Willkie's usually busy in all economic weathers, evidenced by glowing financials year-in, year-out.

WILLKIE Farr & Gallagher was founded way back in 1888 as Hornblower & Byrne, with four lawyers in its single office. Multiple name changes later, Willkie has 650 lawyers in its nine offices around the world. Most are based in the US, New York in particular. The firm also has a good-sized Washington, DC office, and recently set up shop in Houston. Willkie has a long-running relationship with National League Baseball, and once counted Thomas Edison and a brokerage firm owned by Ulysses S. Grant as clients. Willkie continues to shine financially. The past several years have seen revenue rising steadily a few percent each year, and in 2014 it soared 14.5% to $640 million. It went up 2.8% in 2015.

Back in 2012, Willkie scooped up all 12 of Dewey & LeBoeuf's outgoing insurance partners, and its work in the insurance sector gets top marks from *Chambers USA*. Willkie's not a one-trick pony, however, and its private equity, corporate/M&A, investment funds, bankruptcy, tax, securities, litigation, and telecoms are among the other practices that pick up excellent rankings. *"We're busy in all business cycles,"* chair of the professional personnel committee Tom Henry tells us, *"whether that's a distressed market led by bankruptcy or a frothy one led by a traditional M&A offering."*

On chambers-associate.com...

- Interview with chair of the professional personnel committee Tom Henry

ASSOCIATES SAY...

Offices

"DC and New York operate to a large degree as one office," an associate in the capital told us. *"Generally DC associates are staffed on DC matters and vice versa,"* the informant continued, *"but you can be staffed on either Washington or New York matters depending on the firm's needs."* The ten-lawyer Houston office opened up in 2014 to serve Willkie's longstanding clients here, many of whom are in the energy sector. This Texas office sees a fair volume of referrals from NYC and DC.

> "You can be staffed on either Washington or New York matters."

"Post-renovation, it's going to be really nice," said an associate of the soon-to-be-done-up DC office, *"but right now it's a little dated."* No complaints about the location, though: *"We're on 19th and K Street, there are three major metro stations within a two-block radius, and it's a ten-minute walk to the White House."* New York also gets top marks for its location: *"We're located next to every subway, so that's really nice,"* said a Manhattanite of the firm's Midtown base.

DC has a *"smaller and more familiar"* atmosphere, according to our sources there, and new associates get their own offices on arrival. This is in contrast to New York where newbies share offices for their first year. *"It's a little irritating,"* admitted one, *"but you get your own of-*

See firm profile on p.711

Rankings in *Chambers USA*

Antitrust	Litigation
Bankruptcy/Restructuring	Private Equity
Corporate/M&A	Real Estate
FCPA	Securities
Insurance	Tax
Investment Funds	Telecommunications

For detail on ranking tiers and ranking locations, visit www.chambersandpartners.com

Recent work highlights

- Representing Cameron International in a dispute with its insurers arising out of the Deepwater Horizon oil spill
- Representing banker Anthony Allen in an upcoming trial alleging manipulation of the Libor rate
- Defending Barclays Bank against a New York suit claiming that it breached fiduciary duties by settling a previous dispute with the Saudi government
- Acted for the Hudson's Bay Company in its acquisition of GALERIA Holding, the owner of Germany's largest department store

fice quickly enough." Perhaps to make up for this, in New York 3.30pm every day is 'cookie time' in the office's attorney lounge. *"It's hard to resist their siren song!"* laughed an associate. The health-conscious among you may be interested to know that *"they're diversifying cookie time,"* with hummus and vegetables available on Tuesdays and crackers and cheese on Friday.

The Work

Litigation and corporate are the two biggest intake groups, followed by asset management, real estate, executive compensation & employee benefits, tax and IP. Departments operate a formal work assignment system. *"It's nice not to have a free-market system,"* one attorney ventured. *"If my hours are low I can just go to the assigning partner and say, 'Hey, I have 15 free hours.'"* Insiders also thought that the formality of the system helped prevent associates competing for work, as well as keeping them from getting swamped. *"If all the partners were emailing me directly, I imagine it would be hard to say no,"* opined a Washingtonian.

"We're not pigeonholed into a certain type of client."

"We're not pigeonholed into a certain type of client," said an associate in DC, and this generalist approach holds for New York too, in both litigation and corporate. Asset management is split into *"three big buckets:"* private equity; registered funds; and unregistered funds. Much of it is the same *"day-to-day work"* that any junior associate would do, including *"reviewing diligence documents to make sure the disclosures are current and proper,"* but there are also *"more substantive client-facing assignments"* on offer, including sitting in on client calls and *"direct interfacing."*

In addition to *"traditional commercial disputes,"* litigators can get involved in insurance bust-ups, FCPA investigations, securities disputes and antitrust work. Attorneys handling the old-fashioned commercial litigation cases will do traditional commercial litigation tasks such as *"research, drafting memos, doc review, discussing case strategy and drafting parts of motions."* On the more specialized areas, the work can get a bit wacky – for example attorneys doing FCPA work can find themselves helping to interview whistle-blowers or trawling through employee emails. The latter was described as *"fascinating"* by one associate, *"as you're reviewing emails that were sent years ago by people who had no idea that they could be checked."*

"It's not trite to say that there's a great camaraderie."

Culture

Contrary to what you might have thought, *"it's not trite to say that there's a great camaraderie,"* one of our sources enthused, at least not at Willkie. *"It didn't seem as cut-throat as some of the other places I interviewed at,"* said another. Insiders attributed this to the firm's billable hours requirement; more specifically its lack of one. *"We try to have each other's backs,"* one told us, *"but I can't help wondering, if we had an hours requirement would we be competing for work?"* This camaraderie is not just between members of the same class year; while there's *"an obvious hierarchy,"* relations with partners and senior associates are also top-notch. *"They try to help you become a better lawyer,"* said a DC-er of the firm's bigwigs.

"The partners are making diversity a priority at OCI level."

Diversity

Diversity at Willkie is *"a bit like at law school,"* we were told, in that *"incoming classes have been more diverse, but there's still a lot of work to be done."* Associates agreed that making the firm's partnership more representative was key to making the firm as a whole more diverse. *"A lot of diverse people are hesitant to come here because they're underrepresented at partnership level,"* speculated one. *"It's a cycle; if there aren't any female partners, women aren't going to want to stay long enough to make partner,"* added another. The powers

See firm profile on p.711

that be are aware of the situation, however, and juniors reckoned *"the partners are making diversity a priority at OCI level."* The firm has women's committees, and one initiative singled out for particular praise was an *"eye-opening"* implicit bias talk.

Hours & Compensation and Pro Bono

"It didn't even occur to me how big not having an hours target would be," admitted one lawyer, while another said: *"I have almost unilateral control over when I get in."* While no billing target means no internal rivalry, it doesn't mean no work. As one insider put it, *"no one is doing head checks at the start of the day, but getting out is harder."* A financier joked that in some of the busier departments attorneys *"sometimes almost wish there was a billing target."* Day-to-day hours were broadly similar to those worked at other firms. In the words of one attorney, *"I never leave before 6.30pm, but I rarely leave after 8.30pm."* Of course, deal deadlines and corporate timetables still apply, billable hours target or no, so some late nights are inevitable, and at least one attorney we spoke to had *"a couple of nights where I've slept at the office."* That said, with no targets to hit, *"there's less pressure to bill random hours."*

"My schedule has been so crazy."

Not only is there no billing target, but there's no cap on the number of pro bono hours associates can treat as billable. A frequent email is circulated letting people know what opportunities are in the pipeline. The firm regularly partners with the Lawyers' Committee in DC, and Her Justice in New York which works with domestic violence victims. Interested attorneys can complete a three or four-month externship here. Back at the office, pro bono work can range in size from *"small matters that juniors can handle with minimal supervision,"* to large partner-led cases, and includes asylum cases, LGBT rights work, helping incorporate nonprofit organizations and assisting the government in preventing the exploitation of recent immigrants. While there's *"a ridiculous number of pro bono opportunities if you have the time for them,"* not all the associates we spoke to had time. *"My schedule has been so crazy,"* lamented one. Similarly, some transactional attorneys worried that they lacked the skills to *"provide good pro bono advice."* These grumbles should become a thing of the past: 2015 saw pro bono hours billed at the firm jump by 50%.

Pro bono hours

- For all attorneys across all US offices: 30,458
- Average per US attorney: 62

Get Hired

"The OCI was more about my background," recollected one New Yorker, *"and about my knowledge of Willkie and what it does."* Instead of fishing for stock answers, the firm *"puts the ball in the person's court"* during interviews. *"They asked a lot of open questions and let me speak,"* recalled one former jobseeker. You'll need brains to work at Willkie – that's a given – but the firm also wants to make sure that new hires fit in with their colleagues. *"It's really important to Willkie that they find a good personality fit as well as an intellectual fit,"* explained another.

"Personality fit as well as an intellectual fit."

Teamwork is also high on the firm's agenda, according to professional personnel committee head Tom Henry. *"You'll be working with people in different departments, in different offices and with different strengths,"* he explains, *"so we want people who want to roll up their sleeves and be part of the team."* He also advises applicants to do their homework and find out more about the firm. Beyond this, though, there's no particular Willkie 'type': *"We attract a broad pool of people,"* he says, *"but the better informed an applicant is, the better they'll do."*

"We went into 2015 knowing we'd have big shoes to fill, and we exceeded our previous records."

Tom Henry, chair of the professional personnel committee

Training & Development

Newbies kick off their time at the firm with two weeks of orientation in New York, *"acclimating to the computer systems and learning how the support staff work,"* and completing a 'mini MBA.' This is then followed by department-specific bootcamps covering issues unique to individual practice groups. In addition, there are regular lunchtime CLEs. *"I think it would be helpful if it was all given again nine months later,"* thought one source, because *"you feel a little overwhelmed with information at the time."* The CLEs themselves cover everything from *"the mathematics of how to certify classes"* in antitrust litigation to *"a talk from an investment banker on how to read a balance sheet."*

See firm profile on p.711

Performance reviews take place annually, with a midyear review for first-years, although *"you only hear anything at the midyear point if there's something wrong."* Even at the annual review, associates told us, no news was good news. *"In practice, you go in and they're like, 'You're doing a good job, goodbye,'"* said one. When there is substantive feedback, it is often delivered *"using the sandwich method – they'll say, 'You did well on this, not so good on that, and well on this.'"* Feedback is sought on every matter that the reviewee spent 25 billable hours or more on over the previous year, and reviewers rate associates as meeting, exceeding or failing to meet expectations.

"A little overwhelmed with information."

Mentoring abounds, and begins during during the summer program, where each fledgling legal-eagle gets both a partner and an associate mentor. These are deliberately chosen from *"random"* departments, as *"summers don't know what group they want to be in."* Upon arrival full-time, each new associate gets a partner and associate mentor within their chosen group. *"The seniors I worked with were very willing to sit down and teach you things you didn't get formal training on,"* recollected one source.

Strategy & Future

"We went into 2015 knowing we'd have big shoes to fill, and we exceeded our previous records," says head of the professional personnel committee Tom Henry. He credits this to the firm's ability to do *"transformative, multijurisdictional deals,"* but also to the fact that Willkie *"does 'collegial' better than other firms."* A bold claim, given how often we hear that word, but Willkie deliberately scatters lawyers from different practice groups across the firm to foster idea-sharing.

As we mentioned at the start, Willkie is confident in its ability to operate in both calm and choppy economic waters. The firm's decision to open an office in energy hub Houston at a time of low oil prices is an example of this, according to Tom Henry. *"Energy work forms a growing part of our M&A and private equity practices,"* Henry explains, *"but because of the disruption of the energy markets, we can also bring our restructuring and bankruptcy expertise to bear."*

"If my hours are low I can just go to the assigning partner and say, 'Hey, I have 15 free hours'."

See firm profile on p.711

WilmerHale

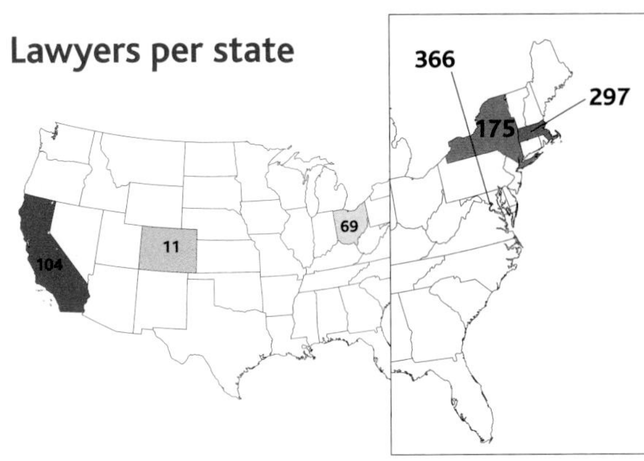

Largest US office: Washington, DC
US offices: 7 (including Dayton)
International offices: 5
First-year salary: $160,000
Billable hours: 2,000 target (though bonuses paid at 1,900 in 2015)
Summers 2016: 108 (104 2Ls, 4 others)
Revenue 2015: $1.14 billion (+6.4%)
Partners made 2016: 6 (all US)
Famous for: IP, litigation, antitrust, government work, transactional (especially in technology, life sciences and financial services sectors)

From DC to Boston to Palo Alto, there's plenty of high-level work available at this *"respectful, friendly and collaborative"* firm.

IT'S been a strong year for WilmerHale, whose 8.7% rise in partner profits accompanied a 6.4% total rise in revenue in 2015 to $1.14 billion. On a national level, the firm sweeps up a clutch of top-tier rankings in *Chambers USA* for areas such as appellate, antitrust & cartel, securities regulation, life sciences, and IP litigation. Favorable rankings also fall for Wilmer's international arbitration, FCPA [Foreign Corrupt Practices Act] investigations, and international trade practices, which are served by overseas offices in Beijing, Brussels, Frankfurt, Berlin and London.

The firm's securities litigation, bankruptcy/restructuring, and government relations groups also get recognition, the latter proving a big draw for some associate interviewees thanks to the career opportunities it presents for a future in public service. *"We have a strong record for sending people there – particularly as prosecutors in the US Attorney's office – and it's a path the firm really supports,"* enthused one insider. *"A stint in government provides knowledge and experience that can really benefit our clients, so even at interview we were told that there's always a revolving door between both entities."*

On chambers-associate.com...

- Sittin' pretty in Mile-High City: Wilmer's Denver office

But most attractive of all was the *"respectful, friendly and collaborative atmosphere"* at the firm. *"There's a real culture of support here that means we're encouraged to pursue our interests and never left to pick up the pieces,"* rookies agreed. *"Even when a crazy deal has gone awry, everyone is there in the trenches to ensure that no one is slogging away alone all night."*

ASSOCIATES SAY...

The Work

Around two-thirds of entry-level associates are split between the Boston and DC offices, with the rest spread around LA, New York and Palo Alto. Wilmer's litigation/controversy group snaps us the majority of new starters, though there's also space for fresh faces in the transactional, IP, regulatory & government affairs, and securities practice (which is divided into contentious and non-contentious work).

A centralized work allocation process not only *"helps you to find your feet,"* but remains at associates' disposal as they progress through the ranks. *"After a year or two you begin to develop workstreams with partners and senior attorneys,"* said one junior, *"so you won't always require the same degree of docket management as when you first started."* Still, *"it's an impeccable process. If you're running low you can just email your practice manager and they'll help you out, so you're never left on your own to solicit work."*

See firm profile on p.712

Rankings in *Chambers USA*

Antitrust	International Trade
Appellate Law	Life Sciences
Banking & Finance	Litigation
Bankruptcy/Restructuring	Media & Entertainment
Corporate Crime & Investigations	Native American Law
Corporate/M&A	Private Equity
Employee Benefits & Executive Compensation	Real Estate
FCPA	Securities
Financial Services Regulation	Startups & Emerging Companies
Government	Tax
Intellectual Property	Technology
International Arbitration	Telecommunications

For detail on ranking tiers and ranking locations, visit www.chambersandpartners.com

The litigation pool gives juniors the opportunity to try out a number of different practice groups, before specializing toward the end of their third year. *"The reality of working at such a government-focused outfit is that there's a lot of appellate work passing through the door,"* said a DC source, but others here and elsewhere had a more varied experience. As one New Yorker countered, *"there are plenty of opportunities to work on appellate cases, and I've helped out on a few of those cases with colleagues in DC. But no one in New York works exclusively on appellate. I've taken on plenty of general business litigation, IP lit, and some securities stuff too."* Associates' responsibilities *"ramp up quickly"* thanks to the fact that "*our teams really aren't that big. I routinely work directly with a partner, so there's no middle filter leaving you with all the doc review. From the start I was engaged in strategic planning, writing briefs and communicating with clients."*

> "There's no middle filter leaving you with all the doc review."

Wilmer's regulatory & government affairs group helps corporate clients – often from the aviation, defense, communications, financial services and pharmaceuticals sectors – to manage and litigate against government regulation. Rookies *"begin as the master of facts,"* so are *"responsible for keeping tabs on all the key documents, understanding the major issues for our client that arise out of the documents in the government's possession, and then forming theories on particular areas of focus."* Juniors that do a good job of keeping things running smoothly *"are recognized and rewarded with more managerial responsibilities."*

Recent work highlights

- Defending Intel in a second patent infringement lawsuit raised by AVM. The patent in question concerns the design of Intel's microprocessor products
- Investigating antitrust hurdles for Baker Hughes in preparation for the oilfield services company's upcoming $34.6 billion acquisition by Halliburton
- Keeping Google up to date regarding its public policy rights, and responsibilities as a search engine
- Orchestrated a $185 million IPO for gene therapy company Spark Therapeutics

Training & Development

"The firm takes our development very seriously," sources agreed. *"People are pretty open with their ambitions and partners try to help you if they can. If you're interested in going into government or in-house, then the online alumni database is a really useful resource."* The firm also assigns juniors a mentor who they meet with several times each year, and interviewees praised partners for the interest they take in associates' careers. *"One recently came up to me and said, 'I've been really thinking about your career, have you considered this?' It's great to feel that people are thinking about your development and how they can help you to advance."*

> "90% of the people I've worked with I've already met in person."

On a more formal basis, three days of orientation training are followed up by regular practice group sessions, featuring lectures, discussions and workshops. The training features useful pointers on areas ranging from legal writing to professional conduct and profile management. Then there are practice group retreats every year or so that bring lawyers together. *"Training and networking were the two main focuses,"* explained one insider. *"90% of the people I've worked with I've already met in person,"* said one IP whiz.

Offices

DC and Boston may be WilmerHale's biggest units, but there was no fear of smaller offices getting the satellite treatment. As one Californian said, *"we work regularly with other US offices: every day we're on the phone, e-mailing or teleconferencing one another, so there's really the feeling that we function as one network."* A large part of this cohesion is down to Wilmer's cross-office approach, which in the eyes of co-managing partner Bob Novick means "*we're really not organized by offices at all, but structured at a departmental level."* Administrative partners help to manage the running of individual offices, but *"if you're a litigator it doesn't matter which*

See firm profile on p.712

office you're in, you're managed as part of WilmerHale's litigation department," Novick continues. *"You're not in Boston, Frankfurt or Denver, you're in litigation. It's the same for all of our practices. Encouraging that degree of collaboration facilitates better training, better coverage of global issues, and easier and more efficient staffing."*

"We're really not organized by offices at all, but structured at a departmental level."

Wilmer's youngest US operation is in Denver. To find out more, head to the Bonus Features on our website.

Culture

The Boston office holds a happy hour every Friday affectionately known as CAMS [the Chowder and Marching Society]. When asked to elaborate about the name's origins, associates sighed: *"It's a longstanding firm tradition."* Still, *"it's a lovely way to end the week,"* and associates were impressed by the average turnout. *"There's free beer, wine and appetizers, and people will pop in, grab a snack and catch up. There's no pressure to attend, but people stop by for as long as they can."* Another Bostonian added: *"It's been a wonderful surprise to see that partners like getting involved. They're all such busy and impressive figures, but really make the time to help foster a friendly work environment."* In DC and New York, drinks in the office are a monthly occurrence, and those in the capital were keen on the themed spreads laid on. *"The theme often depends on which part of the year we're at. We don't all arrive in costumes, but the food and drinks usually have some unique additions. St. Patrick's Day, Hallowe'en and Thanksgiving are always good fun."*

"We all respect one another for our skills and intellect."

Such efforts help to create a working atmosphere devoid of any discernible hierarchical divisions. As one rookie in Palo Alto reported, *"it's normal to joke around with partners. We all respect one another for our skills and intellect, so there's no fear that you need to bootlick your superiors."*

Pro Bono

Pro bono work is headed up by a committee and an attorney in DC, who sends out larger cases across the firm's network of US offices. Juniors who wish to take on a case must first check in with their practice manager, to ensure they have sufficient space in the diary. *"Practice managers also keep us up to date with smaller local opportunities,"* added one insider. Sources had taken on *"a ton of pro bono work,"* thanks in part to the fact that there's no limit on the number of pro bono hours that can count toward the billable target. Consequently, many of our sources had been busy conducting interviews and writing briefs for a kaleidoscope of different cases. Excessive force claims against the police, cross-border child abduction cases and clemency petitions were some of the more interesting-sounding matters that hit our radar.

"I've done a ton of pro bono work."

Pro bono hours

- For all attorneys across all US offices: 99,822
- Average per US attorney: 97

"A stint in government provides knowledge and experience that can really benefit our clients, so even at interview we were told that there's always a revolving door between both entities."

Hours & Compensation

All of juniors' pro bono hours can count toward their 2,000 hour billable target. Ten-hour days seemed a reasonable daily stint across offices, and *"many leave at around 7pm to have dinner with their family before getting back online for a couple of hours at night."* Associates really appreciated such flexibility, and were keen to point out that it extends to maternity and paternity leave too: *"The firm's really supportive of that,"* they beamed. *"A lot of people who've recently had children come back on 80% while they're still figuring it all out."*

"A lot of people who've recently had children come back on 80% while they're still figuring it all out."

The bonus system had a bit of a shake-up recently, though *"the adjustments only affect those in their fourth year or above,"* according to chair of the DC office's hiring committee, Chris Davies. *"While our bonus program remains closely aligned with performance, we've chosen to shift a higher portion of total compensation back into base salaries for senior associates and counsel."*

Diversity

"Diversity is something we discuss regularly," revealed one associate. *"There are even diversity talks held which tie in with our legal training."* Wilmer's 'Diver-

See firm profile on p.712

sity Speaker Series' program stages networking events, which feature guest speakers from the government or particular industry sectors, who in recent events have covered matters as wide-ranging as diversity and inclusion in the financial services industry, to the firm's role in supporting South African lawyers in using the rule of law to combat apartheid. Lunchtime sessions staged by associates also *"cover developments in the US courts,"* we heard, *"things like the Supreme Court's handling of same-sex marriage. Covering both the legal and diversity-related points makes for some really interesting talking points."* With female lawyers making up 46% of associates, *"the ratio between male and female associates is pretty good,"* and there is a range of affinity groups help to represent female, ethnic minority and LGBT lawyers across the firm.

"Something we discuss regularly."

Get Hired

"There are three things we like to see in applicants," DC hiring chair Chris Davies explains. *"Initiative, imagination and articulation. Some of that is evident in an applicant's resume, and we're always interested to see which awards, life experiences and law school commitments they've listed. But that's your price of entry. During an interview, we really want to see aspiring lawyers who are passionate in describing what's listed on their resume. We want a sense of how deeply they were involved in certain groups or projects, because that can really hint at a young professional who is both fun to work with and dedicated to their work."*

Some big no-nos include apparent uninterest: *"If they show no passion or interest in their own work or the work of the firm then it's likely not a good fit, no matter how good their resume looks."* Arrogance won't get you far either: *"We really frown on that,"* Davies asserts. *"There's a fine line between self-possession and confidence, and coming across as self-important. Weeding out those that are too high in their own estimations is an important part of our hiring process. We spend a lot of time working with one another and want to work with people that we can enjoy being around."*

Strategy & Future

At the time of our research there were no big moves lined up for WilmerHale, but according to co-managing partner Bob Novick, *"we'll continue to build on our strengths and invest in all of our practices over the next couple of years."* Though *"there will still be growth on a lateral level,"* expect greater investment beyond Wilmer's *"geographically mature"* strongholds in Washington and Boston. *"The opportunity for growth is greater in New York,"* he adds. *"With some 200 lawyers it's already a good strong size, but the New York market is so busy that we'd be foolish not to focus a good deal of our resources there."*

"Wilmer has probably got the strongest IP litigation practice in the country," Novick claims, *"so we're definitely looking to take that strength and build out further. We offer IP litigation in our London office, and are looking at our prospects to grow that practice both in the UK and Germany."*

"The firm takes our development very seriously. People are pretty open with their ambitions and partners try to help you if they can."

See firm profile on p.712

Winston & Strawn LLP

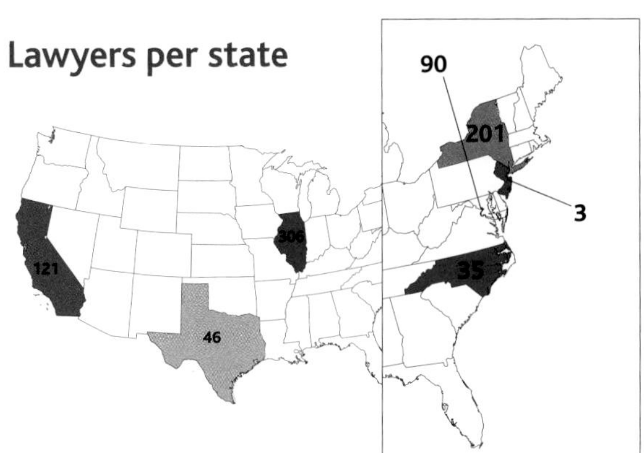

Largest US office: Chicago
US offices: 9
International offices: 10
First-year salary: $160,000
Billable hours: 2,000 required
Summers 2016: 67 (65 2Ls, 2 1Ls)
Revenue 2015: $818.3 million (+4.2%)
Partners made in 2016: 13
Famous for: being the oldest firm in Chicago; among the best in litigation with a burgeoning corporate group

One of Chicago's finest, this golden oldie is jazzing up its traditionally conservative image...

1853 was the year we could, for the first time, eat potato chips, protect our homes with a burglar alarm, enroll at the newly created University of Florida, and welcome the 14th President of the US, Franklin Pierce (usually ranked among the worst). That year long ago in the mists of time also saw the birth of Chicagoan stalwart Winston & Strawn. Despite the firm's impressive longevity, however, it isn't stuck in its ways. While Winston may once have had a reputation for being traditional, the associates we spoke had found this was changing: *"It's still conservative in some ways because it's a law firm, but even the most prominent partners are very nice and approachable,"* one junior told us. *"As a result, the rest of the culture is pretty open."*

And the culture isn't the only thing that's evolving; this conqueror of the courtroom continues to expand in litigation and other practices for which it's less well known. Winston's managing partner Tom Fitzgerald tells us that *"we're currently developing our corporate practice, with laterals this year from Pillsbury and McDermott, and we will continue to follow that strategy."* As well as general commercial litigation, top-ranked practices in *Chambers USA* include intellectual property, transactional media & entertainment, energy, and shipping regulation. Winston's corporate/M&A and private equity expertise in Illinois is also highly regarded.

On chambers-associate.com...

- Interview with managing partner Tom Fitzgerald
- Interview with Bill O'Neil, cochair of Winston's hiring committee

ASSOCIATES SAY...

The Work

Around 60% of new associates go into litigation, while corporate accounts for roughly a quarter of juniors. The rest go into smaller groups including energy, employee benefits, labor & employment, real estate, and tax. Work assignment for most is based on a free-market system, which associates appreciated: *"I was able to come in and align myself with partners who did the sort of work I wanted."* The system for New York newbies is more mixed: associates can talk to someone if they want more work or feel swamped, *"but it's not formalized – we're not obliged to get work through the assigning partner."*

"I was able to come in and align myself with partners who did the sort of work I wanted."

The litigation department offers associates a broad-ranging practice, which includes commercial disputes, patent litigation, white-collar crime, antitrust and bank fraud. *"I like the fact that for associates who don't want to specialize, you can diversify,"* one junior found. *"It's good to get experience in different areas – it can be monotonous otherwise."* For the younger associates, the

The Inside View

See firm profile on p.714

Rankings in *Chambers USA*

Advertising	Labor & Employment
Antitrust	Litigation
Banking & Finance	Media & Entertainment
Bankruptcy/Restructuring	Projects
Corporate/M&A	Sports Law
Energy & Natural Resources	Tax
Intellectual Property	Transportation
International Trade	

For detail on ranking tiers and ranking locations, visit www.chambersandpartners.com

Recent work highlights

- Currently representing Beef Products in a $1.2 billion defamation battle. The plaintiff is accusing ABC and journalist Diane Sawyer of defaming a beef trimmings maker by referring to its product as "pink slime," among other things
- Represented Invenergy in its sale to TerraForm of a 90.1% interest in a wind project portfolio for $2 billion
- Acted for TreeHouse Foods in the $2.7 billion acquisition of ConAgra Foods' private-label business
- Successfully defended Patriots quarterback Tom Brady in the 'Deflategate' scandal; the ruling saw his four-game suspension eliminated, though this saga rumbles on

day-to-day involves *"a fair amount of doc review and other tasks that are at the bottom of the totem pole,"* although more substantial duties include second-chairing a deposition and drafting initial motions. As you begin to climb the proverbial totem pole, responsibility levels increase. *"I've already taken depositions, argued motions in federal court, and had extensive briefing experience,"* one third-year told us proudly, adding that *"over the past eight months I've had more and more direct contact with the clients."* Among the clients that associates described were *Fortune* 100 companies, IP firms and technology companies.

When it comes to the fast-growing corporate group, we spoke to some newbies who had already begun to taper their practice. One junior explained the benefits of this: *"If you specialize earlier, you do the same types of tasks over again, and the partners start to trust you more. As a result I've been able to get more responsibility."* Others, meanwhile, were still in the more generalist stage. *"I've done some M&A, securities and lending – we have the ability to try everything until we decide what we like best."* We heard that private equity M&A was a particularly busy group, with deals ranging from *"north of $3 billion to as low as $1 million. I'd say Winston's sweet spot for private equity is generally below $500 million."* This translates into some fairly substantial tasks for the juniors: *"I've been able to take the first crack at drafting stock purchase or asset purchase agreements, and I've had some responsibility with negotiating ancillary issues."* One newbie added that *"I've also become the primary client contact on some deals."*

Pro Bono & Hours

For those who felt they hadn't yet had a chance to sink their teeth into meatier tasks, pro bono is a good way in. With four full-time pro bono attorneys, opportunities are abundant. On one domestic violence case, *"it's been great because the partner let the associates take the lead. The first depositions I took were for a pro bono case."* Another added: *"I've done two Seventh Circuit appeals, and I got to do all the briefing and the arguments myself."* Other examples we heard were immigration and adoption cases, and working on an assignment for the Hurricane Sandy Relief Fund. One source told us: *"I've done a few patent applications for small entities that normally wouldn't be able to afford our rates, such as those doing work in the Third World."*

"The first depositions I took were for a pro bono case."

Attorneys can count 100 pro bono hours toward their 2,000 hour billing target (increased from 50 a few years ago). Associates who hit this number receive the base bonus. After 2,200 they move to a higher tier bonus which increases in 100-hour increments, *"so I got rewarded for the extra work I did."* An added incentive to do more pro bono is that if associates hit their billables, they can count any extra pro bono hours towards a higher bonus. *"Once you hit 1,900 hours in regular billables, the firm will count however many pro bono hours on top of that,"* one newbie explained. *"I had a friend who billed 400 pro bono hours, but because he hit 1,900 hours he could count them all toward his bonus – it's nice padding."*

"I got rewarded for the extra work I did."

The sense was that associates are *"generally expected"* to reach the 2,000 hour mark, with most of our interviewees having no problem at all in reaching it. Those in corporate in particular cited a very busy year, and many had far exceeded the target. That said, there aren't huge repercussions for any who don't reach 2,000: *"I have friends that weren't able to hit it and they were fine – they just didn't get the bonus."* There's no formal vacation policy at Winston, which meant younger juniors sometimes felt uncomfortable taking time off: *"I didn't take vacation during my first year because I felt like it wasn't appropriate."* Generally, though, our interviewees reported taking around two weeks off.

Pro Bono Hours

- For all attorneys across all US offices: 50,767
- Average per US attorney: 64

See firm profile on p.714

Training & Development

First-years at Winston are introduced to the firm with a week of orientation in Chicago, followed by weekly, hour-long sessions on various topics. For litigators, topics include how to prepare for trial, steps for discovery, and how to perform doc review, and every two years newbies gather in the Chicago office for firmwide deposition training. For those in corporate, training is on *"anything from an overview of a private equity deal to secured lending and SEC filings."* Juniors in this department also spoke of doing sessions outside the firm: *"PLI* [Practising Law Institute] *has seminars throughout the year which we can go to for free. I recently did one on drafting M&A contracts."*

"You have to go and ask for feedback."

When it comes to feedback, the firm has a yearly evaluation which was described as *"very brief,"* and in the interim *"you have to go and ask for feedback."* Interviewees weren't bothered by this, however, particularly as *"everyone's willing to have that conversation with you."*

Culture & Offices

Some associates spoke of Winston's reputation for being fairly formal and conservative. Those in DC felt that *"it's definitely hierarchical. For instance, there's some extra capacity in the office, so technically everybody could have window offices, but in spite of this, first-years are required to have interior offices with no windows. Every year you move offices to a better view!"* Other DC juniors agreed, pointing to the smarter smart dress code, although *"there are people who also wear business casual, and our office has started doing jeans Fridays."*

"I've never once felt too timid to be able to ask questions."

Associates in the Chicago HQ reported a shift in the culture over the past few years. *"Previously, the firm had a reputation for being a bit formal, but I can tell you that in the past year alone it has changed dramatically,"* one newbie assured us. Another elaborated: *"I feel very comfortable with the people I work with. There's always an added layer of formality when you're working for a partner for the first time, but I've never once felt too timid to be able to ask questions."* And although many described Chicago as a family-friendly office, socializing isn't off the cards: *"We have happy hours every Friday, then within our group we do events every month, whether that's a training event or a completely informal cocktail hour at a bar or restaurant."* Interviewees also pointed out that the removal of 'Ms.', 'Mrs.' and 'Mr.' from office name plates, as well as the opening of a new café for all staff (and not just associates), had gone a fair way to expelling any formality that might have lingered. We're sure it also doesn't hurt that the office space itself is *"amazing,"* and associates all have their own exterior offices: *"Mine overlooks Lake Michigan, which is beautiful."*

"It's not stuffy at all!"

The Big Applers disagreed the most about Winston's traditional image. *"It's not stuffy at all!"* We were assured. *"It's a big firm so obviously we have all different kinds of people, but everyone hangs out and we have a lot of social events."* Another interviewee expanded: *"Every Friday we have a themed, officewide happy hour. We've had one for Mardi Gras and the Superbowl, and the firm puts on a food spread and an open bar. It's a nice time to relax and a great way to talk to partners and get new work."* The New York office, located in the MetLife Building above Grand Central, was praised for it's *"well-kept"* appearance, which is *"all marble and very polished."* Another source added: *"We're on the 42nd floor, so the views are pretty stunning."* Apparently, the cast and crew of *The Good Wife* even did some filming here. Juniors in New York share an office for their first two years.

Corporate has *"continued to be one of the fastest-growing parts of the firm."*

Diversity

"They're trying to make sure women are being promoted and that minorities are hired, but if you look at the makeup of the firm, right now it's not very diverse," one junior acknowledged. That said, the firm is *"definitely trying to fix that,"* in part through its very active women's initiative. *"We have a book club and dinners, and when new female partners were promoted they did a celebratory dinner and drinks for the female associates."* Someone else added: *"We did a wine and cheese pairing event for all the female attorneys in the Chicago office."* The firm also has a parental leave liaison, who *"helps to make it a more smooth transition"* for those leaving and returning from maternity or paternity leave.

Winston has a diversity committee and affinity groups for ethnic minorities and LGBT attorneys, and offers three scholarships to diverse summers every year, helping them pay for their third year of law school. While the firm is making efforts, *"it's still very Caucasian white male,"* particularly at partner level.

"It's not intelligence but attitude that differentiates a candidate."

See firm profile on p.714

Get Hired

Bill O'Neil, cochair of Winston's hiring committee, informs us that intellect, grit and interpersonal skills are the three key traits he looks for in a candidate. He continues that *"public sector experience is a plus. For example, an internship at the SEC or DOJ is attractive on a resume."* Read his full interview online. Associates echoed O'Neil's third point: that *"the firm wants someone who's personable,"* and this needs to shine through at interview. As one associate who had been involved in the recruiting process informed us, *"I assume most of the people we're speaking to are intelligent. We're not doing rocket science, we're doing legal paperwork, so to me it's not intelligence but attitude that differentiates a candidate."* After all, *"you don't want to be working on something until 2am with someone who is totally deadpan."* And an affable character is also useful because many at Winston *"have to be able to interact and respond to clients on a daily basis."*

Strategy & Future

We were told that in the past, associates felt that they weren't being kept in the loop at Winston, *"so now they're trying to get us more involved at different levels of the firm, and they're making the effort to tell us what's going on."* One newbie added that *"they had a meeting just over a year ago to explain some of the new policies related to pro bono, and about being more transparent with the path to partnership."* All attorneys now also receive a copy of the firm's finances. *"I think they've started to open up because of people telling them they're a bit closed."*

"They've started to open up."

The work has also seen a strategic shift in the past few years: *"Several years ago, Tom Fitzgerald made it a point to grow the corporate group, so by the time I came into the firm, it was already much larger than in the past, and it's continued to be one of the fastest-growing parts of the firm."* Go online to read what Fitzgerald has to say about strategy.

"You don't want to be working on something until 2am with someone who is totally deadpan."

The Inside View

See firm profile on p.714

Leading Law Firms

Akin Gump Strauss Hauer & Feld LLP

1333 New Hampshire Ave, NW, Washington, DC 20036
Tel: 202 887 4000 Fax: 202 887 4288
www.akingump.com

Main areas of work

Antitrust, communications and technology, cybersecurity, privacy and data protection, corporate, energy, entertainment and media, financial restructuring, global project finance, healthcare, intellectual property, international arbitration, international trade, investment funds, labor and employment, litigation, policy and regulation, Supreme Court and appellate and tax.

Firm profile

Akin Gump is a leading global law firm with more than 900 lawyers and advisors in the United States, Europe, Asia and the Middle East. Akin Gump is widely recognized for its strength in litigation and international arbitration, high stakes appellate work, financial restructuring, corporate transactions, investment funds, energy, global project finance and international trade and for its depth in regulatory and public policy, which allow the firm to provide a comprehensive suite of services for governments, companies and individuals worldwide. Collegiality, commitment, excellence, integrity and intensity form the bedrock of Akin Gump's core values. Akin Gump's dedication to the advancement of these values guides relationships within the firm and, most importantly, with its clients.

Recruitment details

- Number of 1st year associates: 42
- Number of 2nd year associates: 41
- Associate salaries: 1st year: $160,000
- 2nd Year: $170,000
- Clerking policy: Yes

Law Schools attending for OCIs in 2016:

American, Berkeley, Boston University, Cardozo, Catholic, Columbia, Cornell, Duke, Emory, Fordham, George Mason, George Washington, Georgetown, Harvard, Howard, UCLA, Houston, Michigan, New York University, Penn, USC, SMU, Stanford, Texas, Tulane, Vanderbilt, Virginia, William & Mary

Summer details

Summer associate profile:

Akin Gump seeks motivated candidates with outstanding academic credentials, overall achievement, leadership and interpersonal skills, and work experience. In addition, the firm looks for candidates who demonstrate the firm's core competencies: ownership, professional excellence, service and teamwork and client focus.

Summer program components:

Akin Gump summer associates work on real matters for real clients. Summer associates gain in-depth exposure to the firm's practice and hands-on experience with clients and work that interests them. With training, mentorship, teamwork and social activities, summer associates get a realistic and meaningful picture of firm life. Summer associates participate in pro bono projects through organisations with which Akin Gump has a pro bono partnership. These projects are geared to summer associates' interests and maximize front-line responsibility while ensuring appropriate supervision from experienced attorneys. Summer associates receive feedback on a project-by-project basis and at mid-summer and end of summer reviews.

Number of domestic offices: 12
Number of international offices: 9
Worldwide revenue: $930,000,000
Partners (US): 275
Associates (US): 364

Main Recruitment Contact: David H Botter, Firmwide Hiring Partner.
For a complete listing of our recruiting contacts go to www.akingump.com/en/careers/lawyers/recruiting-process/contact-us.html
Recruitment website: www.akingump.com/en/careers
Diversity officer: Karol Kepchar, Chair Firmwide Diversity Committee

Summer Salary 2016
1Ls: $3,077/week
2Ls: $3,077/week
1Ls hired? Select offices and through our Pro Bono Scholars Program
Split summers offered? Case by case
Can summers spend time in overseas office? No
Summers 2016: 54
Offers/Acceptances 2015:
43 offers, 34 acceptances

Firm Profiles

Akin Gump
STRAUSS HAUER & FELD LLP

Allen & Overy LLP

1221 Avenue of the Americas, New York, NY 10020
Tel: 212 610 6300 Fax: 212 610 6399
Email: legalcareers@allenovery.com
www.allenovery.com

Main areas of work

Banking, corporate, international capital markets, litigation, project finance, financial restructuring and insolvency, real estate and tax.

Firm profile

We are one of a group of truly international and integrated law firms with approximately 5,000 people working in 44 cities in 30 countries. This network has allowed us to become one of the largest and most connected law firms in our peer group with a global reach and local depth that is simply unrivalled. As more than 65% of our work involves more than two countries, our US practice—which operates principally from offices in Hong Kong, London, New York and Washington DC—is fully integrated with our offices in Europe, Asia, South America, Australia and Africa. We believe we have a special culture at Allen & Overy, which is founded on quality work, excellent working partnerships and collegiality.

Recruitment details

- Number of 1st year associates: 16 (NY/DC)
- Number of 2nd year associates: 11 (NY)
- Associate salaries: 1st year: $160,000 • 2nd year: $170,000
- Clerking policy: Yes

Law Schools attending for OCIs in 2016:

American, BC/BU, Brooklyn, Cardozo, Chicago, Columbia, Cornell, Duke, Emory, Fordham, Georgetown, George Washington, Harvard, Lavender Law, Michigan, NEBLSA, NLSC, Northwestern, NYU, University of Pennsylvania, Rutgers, Seton Hall, Stanford, St John's, Texas, UC Berkeley, UVA, Vanderbilt, Yale

Summer details

Summer associate profile:

At Allen & Overy, we operate in a dynamic, challenging environment which fosters creativity as well as professionalism. Our attorneys handle the most sophisticated and complex domestic and cross border transactions and cases for our clients. The ideal candidate should possess determination, vision, creativity, strength and breadth of character. He or she should be committed to working as part of an international team. One of the best features of the Allen & Overy team is the strength of the personal and professional relationships formed between colleagues. We maintain strong camaraderie around the world.

Summer program components:

We recruit on campus for all 5 summer programs (New York, London, Hong Kong, Singapore and Washington, DC). We typically host around 13-15 summer associates in New York, 3-4 in London, 2-3 in Hong Kong/Singapore, and 3-4 in Washington DC. Summer associates are treated as full-time associates and we make a point of offering considerable responsibility, working on top-quality transactions in various areas. We place great value on feedback and go to great lengths to match individual preferences with the work we assign. Summer associates can expect to receive ample partner attention and to gain invaluable experience. We take mentoring and development seriously and both are fundamental aspects of our program. We also expect our summer associates to have fun and plan social events to integrate them into our firm culture.

Head Office: New York, NY
Number of domestic offices: 2
Number of international offices: 42
Partners (US): 41
Senior Counsel (US): 9
Associates (US): 118

Main Recruitment Contact:
Erin Manna, Senior Coordinator, Lateral & Staff Recruitment
Hiring Partners: Charles Borden (DC), Erwin Dweck (NY), Laura Hall (NY)
Recruitment website: www.us.aograduate.com
Diversity officer: Elizabeth Leckie, Partner

Summer Salary 2016
1Ls: N/A
2Ls: $3,100/week
Post 3Ls: $3,100/week
1Ls hired? No
Split summers offered? Yes
Can summers spend time in overseas office? Yes, we run parallel summer associate programs in New York, London, Hong Kong, Singapore and Washington DC. Occasionally, summer associates have spent time in other international offices with US capabilities (such as Paris, Milan and Frankfurt)
Summers 2016: 24 (NY, LN, DC, HK)
Offers/acceptances 2015:
27 offers, 21 acceptances (NY, LN, DC, HK)

ALLEN & OVERY

Alston & Bird LLP

One Atlantic Center, 1201 West Peachtree Street, Atlanta, GA 30309-3424
Tel: 404 881 7000 Fax: 404 881 7777
Email: erin.springer@alston.com
www.alston.com

Main areas of work

Alston & Bird provides a full range of services to domestic and international clients. Our core practice areas are intellectual property, complex litigation, corporate and tax, with national industry focuses in healthcare, financial services and public policy.

Firm profile

Founded in 1893, Alston & Bird is a leading national AmLaw 50 firm. Counseling clients from what was initially a local context quickly expanded to regional, then national levels and now spans a global economic environment. Alston & Bird has overlaid its broad range of legal skills and business knowledge with a commitment to innovation and technology. Alston & Bird has been ranked on FORTUNE magazine's "100 Best Companies to Work For" list for 17 consecutive years, an unprecedented accomplishment among law firms in the United States. The recognition speaks to the culture of the firm and the environment in which we practice law and provide service to clients. Alston & Bird has been consistently recognized as a US law firm providing superior client service in the BTI Client Service A-Team. This recognition results from interviews with approximately 240 corporate counsel at Fortune 1000 companies.

Recruitment details

- Number of 1st year associates: 38
- Number of 2nd year associates: 51
- Associate salaries: 1st year: $135,000-$160,000 (based on location and patent bar membership)
- Clerking policy: Yes

Law Schools attending for OCIs in 2016:

American, Columbia, Cornell, Duke, Emory, Fordham, Georgetown, George Washington, Georgia, Georgia State, Harvard, Hofstra, Howard, Loyola, Mercer, Michigan, NYU, Northwestern, SMU, Stanford, Texas, UC Berkeley, UC Hastings, UC Irvine, UCLA, UNC, USC, Vanderbilt, Virginia, Wake Forest, Washington & Lee

Summer details

Summer associate profile:

Our lawyers have diverse backgrounds, varied social, cultural, civic, and educational interests and our summer associates are no exception. We value hard work, scholastic excellence and strong interpersonal skills.

Summer program components:

Our summer program provides students with substantive work for real clients, hands-on training opportunities, lawyer pairings to help foster relationships and a firm-wide retreat. Summer Associates work closely with their mentors to identify projects from our database that will allow for an authentic experience based on their legal interests. In addition to formal training programs, we offer out-of-office experiences to attend depositions, client meetings, hearings and other hands on learning experiences. Associate contacts ensure that summer associates have plenty of opportunities to interact with attorneys throughout the summer.

Head Office: Atlanta, GA
Number of domestic offices: 8
Number of international offices: 1
Worldwide revenue: $645,287,528
Partners (US): 340
Associates (US): 341

Main Recruitment Contact:
Erin L Springer
Hiring Partner: Elizabeth A Price
Recruitment website:
www.alston.com/alstoncareers
Diversity officers: Cari Dawson and John Latham

Summer Salary 2016
1Ls: $2,600/week (ATL, CLT, RTA) or $3,075/week (DFW, LAX, NYC, SVA, WDC)
2Ls: $2,600/week (ATL, CLT, RTA) or $3,075/week (DFW, LAX, NYC, SVA, WDC)
Post 3Ls: N/A
1Ls hired? Yes
Split summers offered? Yes, first half required
Can summers spend time in overseas office? No
Summers 2016: 46
Offers/acceptances 2015:
40 offers, 34 acceptances; several pending due to clerkships

ALSTON & BIRD LLP

Arnold & Porter LLP

601 Massachusetts Avenue, NW. Washington, DC 20001-3743
Tel: 202 942 5000 Fax: 202 942 5999
Email: recruitingdc@aporter.com
www.arnoldporter.com/en

Main areas of work

With Arnold & Porter LLP's more than 25 practice areas spanning a broad spectrum of legal practice, you can interact with experts across multiple fields and gain a wide range of hands-on experience. Our practices include appellate, antitrust, corporate, litigation, environmental, life sciences and healthcare regulatory, and intellectual property.

Firm profile

With nine offices in the US and Europe, Arnold & Porter is a preeminent international law firm with a longstanding tradition of complex and cutting-edge work at the intersection of law, public policy, and business. Highlights of our recent work include acting as primary environmental counsel for BP in the Deepwater Horizon oil spill case and historic settlement; in the past two years advising sovereign clients around the world on 27 sovereign deals with an aggregate value of more than $38 billion; and acting for the Republic of Colombia in its victory before the DC Federal Court of Appeals involving a $17 billion claim over rights to recover sunken treasure off the Colombian coast.

Our founders' spirit of service still shapes the Firm today, as demonstrated by our pro bono program and our attorneys' commitment to government service. The Firm and its lawyers have won dozens of pro bono awards in recent years, including the American Bar Association's prestigious "Pro Bono Publico" award. Many of the Firm's lawyers have held senior positions in the White House and in US government agencies.

Recruitment details

- Number of 1st year associates: 27
- Number of 2nd year associates: 27
- Associate salaries: 1st year: $160,000
- Clerking policy: yes

Law Schools attending for OCIs in 2016:

Brooklyn, Chicago, Colorado, Columbia, Denver, Duke, Fordham, George Mason, Georgetown, George Washington, Harvard, Howard, Loyola - Los Angeles, Michigan, NYU, Stanford, Texas, Tulane, UC Berkeley, UC Davis, UC Hastings, UCLA, UPenn, USC, UVA, Yale

Summer details

Summer associate profile:

Our Firm is a collection of independent, diverse personalities who share a common devotion to first-class legal work and client service. We seek candidates with outstanding academic and extracurricular achievements, as well as relevant work experience.

Summer program components:

Our summer associates experience first-hand the Firm's strong commitment to excellence, diversity, pro bono work, and professional development, working side-by-side with our attorneys on actual client matters. We seek to match assignments to the interests each summer associate has identified, including pro bono work. Our summer associates participate in the Firm's extensive training programs, including attending a retreat in the Washington, DC office. All summer associates have mentors and receive feedback on each assignment. Our summer program features a mix of events designed to appeal to a broad range of interests.

Head Office: Washington, DC
Number of domestic offices: 7
Number of international offices: 2
Worldwide revenue: $650,000,000
Partners (US): 224
Associates (US): 360 (includes 43 staff attorneys)

Main Recruitment Contact:
Jennifer Gewertz, Senior Manager of Attorney Recruitment
Hiring Partner: Ellen Fleishhacker and Darren Skinner
Recruitment website:
www.arnoldporter.com/en/careers

Summer Salary 2016
1Ls: N/A
2Ls: $3,080 per week
Post 3Ls: N/A
1Ls hired? No
Split summers offered? Yes
Can summers spend time in overseas office? No
Summers 2016: 38
Offers/acceptances 2015:
33 offers, 30 acceptances (2 pending)

ARNOLD & PORTER LLP

Axinn, Veltrop & Harkrider LLP

114 West 47th Street, New York, NY 10036
Tel: 212 728 2200 Fax: 212 728 2201
www.axinn.com

Main areas of work

Antitrust, intellectual property and complex litigation.

Firm profile

Axinn is a different kind of law firm. It combines the skills, experience and dedication of the world's largest firms with the focus, responsiveness, efficiency and attention to client needs of the best boutiques. Axinn was established in the late 1990s by lawyers from premier Wall Street firms with a common vision and has been joined by lawyers from the best firms and law schools who share that vision. Axinn is devoted to providing the highest conceivable quality of service in three practice areas: antitrust, intellectual property and high-stakes litigation. Axinn achieves that goal with world class skills and deep trial experience. Time and again, major companies have turned to Axinn for their biggest deals and cases, often on the eve of trial.

Recruitment details

- Number of 1st year associates: 3
- Number of 2nd year associates: 5
- Associate salaries: 1st year: $150,000 in CTO; $160,000 in NYO and DCO
- Clerking policy: Case by case

Law Schools attending for OCIs in 2016:

Berkeley, Chicago, Columbia, Connecticut, Duke, Fordham, George Washington, Georgetown, Harvard, Michigan, New York, Pennsylvania, Stanford, Virginia, Washington University in St Louis, Yale

Summer details

Summer associate profile:

Axinn is a top tier litigation boutique practicing in antitrust, IP and high-stakes corporate litigation. It seeks students who have achieved academic excellence and are entrepreneurial. Candidates must be among the top 25% of their law school class. Top 10% class ranking, law review and moot court experience is preferred. For the Antitrust Group, Axinn prefers that candidates have an economic or finance degree/ background. Science or engineering backgrounds are preferred for candidates who wish to work in IP. Patent bar admission is a plus for IP candidates.

Summer program components:

During their summer with Axinn, associates attend internal meetings and seminars to familiarize themselves with lawyers, clients and range of projects that comprise our practice. In addition, Axinn attorneys and outside professionals provide training in such topics as legal writing, litigation strategy and how to effectively utilize firm resources and support services. Each training experience emphasizes "learning by doing" and serves to enhance opportunities for summer associates to develop, exercise and build confidence in their skills. Each summer associate is assigned a partner and associate mentor, who are available to prioritize assignments and act as a sounding board. Axinn combines the prestige of a large firm with the collegiality of a boutique. Summer associates are invited to join events such as wine tastings, theater and museum outings and cooking classes.

Head Office: New York, NY
Number of domestic offices: 3
Number of international offices: 0
Partners (US): 24
Associates (US): 36

Main Recruitment Contact:
Rachel Rosado
Hiring Partners: Daniel Bitton, Gail Gottehrer and Jeremy Lowe
Recruitment website:
www.axinn.com/careers
Diversity officer: Jeremy Lowe

Summer Salary 2016
1Ls: N/A
2Ls: $2,884.61/week (CT)
$3,076.92/week (NY/DC)
Post 3Ls: N/A
1Ls hired? No
Split summers offered? Case by case
Can summers spend time in overseas office? N/A
Summers 2016: 4
Offers/acceptances 2015:
3 offers, 3 acceptances

Firm Profiles

Baker Botts LLP

One Shell Plaza, 910 Louisiana, Houston, Texas 77002-4995
Tel: 713 229 1234 Fax: 713 229 1522
Email: info@bakerbotts.com
www.bakerbotts.com

Main areas of work

Based on our broad experience and our in-depth knowledge of our clients' industries, we are recognized as a leading firm in energy and technology. Core practice areas include project development and finance; corporate transactions; complex business litigation; international arbitration; antitrust; intellectual property; environmental; compliance and enforcement; tax; employee benefits; and real estate.

Firm profile

Baker Botts is a globally respected law firm with offices around the world. Since 1840, we have provided the highest ethical and professional standards combined with our reach and depth of understanding of the law to help deliver better and more innovative solutions. We have advised on a broad range of issues, including many of the largest, most complex matters.

With a presence in the Americas, Europe, Asia and the Middle East, Baker Botts provides responsive services both domestically and internationally. This broad reach enables us to go wherever clients' industries go and respond to the challenges, minimize the risks and maximize the opportunities that are unique to their businesses and markets.

Recruitment details

- Number of 1st year associates: 64
- Number of 2nd year associates: N/A - advancement based on levels system
- Associate salaries: 1st year: $160,000 • 2nd year: $180,000
- Clerking policy: Yes

Law Schools attending for OCIs in 2016:

Baylor, Berkeley, Cardozo, Chicago, Columbia, Cornell, Duke, Fordham, Georgetown, George Washington, Harvard, Houston, Loyola Patent Program, LSU, Michigan, Northwestern, NYU, Pennsylvania, SMU, Stanford, Texas, Tulane, UC Hastings, UCLA, UC Davis, Santa Clara, USC, Vanderbilt, Virginia, Yale, Bay Area Diversity Career Fair, Boston College/ Boston University Job Fair, Harvard BLSA Job Fair, Lavender Law Job Fair, San Francisco IP Job Fair, Southeastern Minority Job Fair, Sunbelt Minority Job Fair, Texas in NY and DC Job Fairs.

Summer details

Summer associate profile:

Baker Botts lawyers are selected from the top graduates among the best law schools. We have formally established a set of core attributes we seek in candidates; some of which include leadership, collegiality, dedication, and commitment to excellence.

Summer program components:

Our philosophy is to allow summer associates to sample work in practice areas in which they are interested. Written and oral work evaluations are strongly encouraged and monitored. Each summer associate has both partner and associate advisors. All summer associates receive formal performance evaluations during the summer program. The firm sponsors numerous social activities, so that summer associates can meet our attorneys and learn about the offices and the local area.

Head Office: Houston, TX
Number of domestic offices: 7
Number of international offices: 7
Partners (US): 240
Associates (US): 329

Main Recruitment Contact: Elizabeth Krichmar, Director of Recruiting
Hiring Partner: Van Beckwith, Partner-in-Charge, Recruiting
Recruitment website: www.bakerbotts.com/lawstudents/
Diversity officer: Sylvia James, Diversity Counsel

Summer Salary 2016
1Ls: $3,077/week
2Ls: $3,077/week
Post 3Ls: $3,077/week
1Ls hired? Yes
Split summers offered? Yes
Can summers spend time in overseas office? No
Summers 2016: 112
Offers/acceptances 2015:
86 offers, 59 acceptances

Baker & McKenzie

300 East Randolph Street, Chicago, IL 60601
Tel: 312 861 8000 Fax: 312 861 8823
www.bakermckenzie.com

Main areas of work

Antitrust and competition, banking and finance, dispute resolution, employment, environment and climate change, intellectual property, IT/communications, energy, mining and infrastructure, mergers and acquisitions, pharmaceuticals and healthcare, private equity, real estate, securities, tax, trade and commerce.

Firm profile

For more than 60 years, Baker & McKenzie has provided sophisticated advice and legal services to many of the world's most dynamic and successful organizations. Baker & McKenzie serves more than half of the world's largest public companies as well as a broad spectrum of regional and local organizations. With more than 4,400 locally qualified, internationally experienced lawyers in 47 countries, the firm has the fluency to deliver a broad scope of quality legal services — consistently, with confidence and sensitivity for cultural, social and legal practice differences. Baker & McKenzie professionals share common values of integrity, personal responsibility and tenacity in an enthusiastic client-service culture. The firm is still guided by the entrepreneurial spirit and demanding standards of its founders and works to forge close personal relationships among its professionals in order to foster the responsiveness and accountability clients rightfully expect. The firm has a diverse and welcoming culture. Its lawyers and other professionals are citizens of more than 60 countries and are admitted to practice in nearly 250 jurisdictions. They have offices in 77 locations worldwide, including in 26 of the world's 30 largest economies. Baker & McKenzie also invests in communities where its people live and work and is a pioneer in teaming with its clients on corporate social responsibility efforts worldwide.

Recruitment details

- Number of 1st year associates: 32
- Associate salaries: 1st year: $160,000 in Dallas, Chicago, Houston, New York, Washington, DC, San Francisco/Palo Alto. $130,000 in Miami.
- Clerking policy: Case by case

Law Schools attending for OCIs in 2016:

Baker & McKenzie is committed to recruiting the highest caliber of talent for their Summer Associate Program. Particularly, they take great strides in recruiting at more than 30 distinctive law schools.

Summer details

Summer program components:

The Summer Associate Program is designed to introduce law students to the practice of law at Baker & McKenzie. Every effort is made to expose summer associates to all aspects of the firm's practice by receiving substantive legal work, professional training and networking opportunities. In addition, international clerkship opportunities are available for summer associates to gain meaningful work experience, aligned with their practice focus and intercultural experience, through a secondment in another office outside of North America.

Head Office: N/A
Number of domestic offices: 7
Number of international offices: 70
Worldwide revenue: $2.43 billion
Partners (US): 321
Associates (US): 318

Main Recruitment Contact:
Kristina Gajewicz, North America Recruiting Director
Hiring Partner: Scott Brandman, North America Hiring Partner
Recruitment website:
www.careers.bakermckenzie.com
Diversity officer: Floyd Mills, North America Director of Diversity

Summer Salary 2016
1Ls: $3,076/week for all US offices, except $2,500/week in Miami
2Ls: $3,076/week for all US offices, except $2,500/week in Miami
1Ls hired? Case by case
Split summers offered? Case by case
Can summers spend time in overseas office? Yes, through our International Clerkship Program
Summers 2016: 42 (includes Toronto office)
Offers/acceptances 2015:
37 offers, 33 acceptances (includes Toronto office)

BAKER & McKENZIE

Bracewell LLP

711 Louisiana St., Suite 2300, Houston, TX 77002
Tel: 713 223 2300 Fax: 713 221 1212
Email: client.services@bracewelllaw.com
www.bracewelllaw.com

Main areas of work

Bracewell's main areas of concentration are business and regulatory, technology, litigation and government. These areas breakdown into a number of core practices, including banks and financial institutions; energy; environmental strategies; financial restructuring; private investment funds; white-collar defense, internal investigations and regulatory enforcement; broker-dealer and market regulation; corporate and securities; finance; intellectual property; labor and employment; real estate and projects; strategic communications; tax; climate change; and public law.

Firm profile

Bracewell LLP is a global law firm with offices in Texas, New York, Washington, DC, Connecticut, Seattle, Dubai, and London. The firm serves Fortune 500 companies, major financial institutions, leading private investment funds, governmental entities and individuals concentrated in the energy, technology and financial services sectors worldwide.

Recruitment details

- Number of 1st year associates: 26
- Number of 2nd year associates: 20
- Associate Salaries: 1st Year: $160,000
- 2nd Year: $170,000
- Clerking policy: We encourage associates to pursue judicial clerkships if they are interested

Law Schools attending for OCIs in 2016:

Eighteen

Summer details

Summer associate profile:

Bracewell takes into account a number of factors when making its selection for summer associates. These include but are not limited to such academic-related areas as class rank, grade-point average and journal membership. In addition, the firm bases offers in part on the extracurricular endeavors of potential summer associates, such as professional/legal association involvement, internships and/or clerkships and law school fraternity memberships.

Summer program components:

The firm offers summer associate programs in all US offices, though demand in each office is determined from year to year. These programs vary by location, but range in length from 6-9 weeks. During this time, summer associates work in various practice areas – dictated by office locale – and attend hearings, depositions, trials, negotiations and client meetings. When not working at the firm, summer associates are encouraged to explore the city in which they live and are also invited to attorney dinners, all-clerk lunches and a summer associate retreat.

Head Office: Houston, TX
Number of domestic offices: 8
Number of international offices: 2
Worldwide revenue: $296,000,000
Partners (US): 201
Associates (US): 241

Main Recruitment Contact:
Jean Lenzner, Director Attorney Employment
Hiring Partners: Bryan Dumesnil and Ryan Holcomb
Recruitment website:
www.bracewelllaw.com/careers
Diversity officer: Marredia Rogers

Summer Salary 2016
1Ls: $3,077/week
2Ls: $3,077/week
Post 3Ls: N/A
1Ls hired? Yes
Split summers offered? Yes
Can summers spend time in overseas office? No
Summers 2016: 37 (27 2Ls, 10 1Ls)

BRACEWELL

Firm Profiles

Brown Rudnick LLP

One Financial Center, Boston, MA 02111
Tel: 617 856 8200 Fax: 617 856 8201
www.brownrudnick.com

Main areas of work

Antitrust; bankruptcy and corporate restructuring; complex litigation and arbitration; corporate, securities and M&A; distressed debt and claims trading; emerging companies; energy, utilities and environmental; finance; funds; government contracts; government law and strategies; healthcare; intellectual property; intellectual property litigation; international dispute resolution; life sciences; real estate; tax; white collar defense and government investigations.

Firm profile

Brown Rudnick, an international law firm with offices in the United States and Europe, represents clients from around the world in high stakes litigation, international arbitration and complex business transactions. Clients include public and private corporations, multinational Fortune 100 businesses and start-up enterprises. The firm also represents investors, as well as official and ad hoc creditors' committees in today's largest corporate restructurings, both domestically and abroad. Founded more than 60 years ago, Brown Rudnick has over 230 lawyers providing advice and services across key areas of the law. Beyond the United States, the firm regularly serves clients in Europe, the Middle East, North Africa, the Caribbean and Latin America. With its Brown Rudnick Center for the Public Interest, the firm has created an innovative model combining its pro bono, charitable giving and community volunteer efforts.

Recruitment details

- Number of 1st year associates: 13
- Number of 2nd year associates: 12
- Associate salaries: 1st year: $160,000
- 2nd year: $170,000 in Boston, NY, DC, and Orange County. $165,000 in Hartford and Providence
- Clerking policy: Yes

Law Schools attending for OCIs in 2016:

Boston College, Boston University, Columbia University, Harvard University, Georgetown University, New York University, University of California – Irvine, University of California – Los Angeles, University of Connecticut, University of Pennsylvania, University of Southern California, University of Texas, University of Virginia

Summer details

Summer associate profile:

Brown Rudnick recruits summer associates who are highly intelligent and creative and also possess those personal qualities that define our firm: hard driving but value oriented and pragmatic, entrepreneurial, always honest and ethical and highly collaborative.

Summer program components:

Brown Rudnick allocates significant energy and resources to provide each summer associate with a first hand experience of life as a lawyer at our firm. We offer a wide range of assignments, provide a robust training curriculum, including core legal and writing skills, business development and networking skills, as well as a fun social calendar.

Head Office: Boston, MA
Number of domestic offices: 6
Number of international offices: 3
Worldwide revenue: $192,400,000
Partners (US): 86
Associates (US): 70

Main Recruitment Contacts:
Lindsey M Baumgardner
Hiring Partner: Jeffrey L Jonas
Recruitment website:
www.brownrudnick/careers
Diversity officers: Sunni Beville, Franca L DeRosa

Summer Salary 2016
1Ls: $3,077/week
2Ls: $3,077/week
Post 3Ls: $3,077/week
1Ls hired? Case by case
Split summers offered? Case by case
Can summers spend time in overseas office? Case by case
Summers 2016: 9
Offers/acceptances 2015:
13 offers, 12 acceptances (100% offers made)

Cadwalader, Wickersham & Taft LLP

One World Financial Center, New York, NY 10281
Tel: 212 504 6000 Fax: 212 504 6666
www.cadwalader.com

Main areas of work

The firm offers legal representation in antitrust, banking, business fraud, capital markets, corporate finance, corporate governance, energy, executive compensation, financial restructuring, healthcare, intellectual property, litigation, mergers and acquisitions, private equity, private wealth, real estate, regulation, securitisation, structured finance and tax.

Firm profile

Cadwalader, Wickersham & Taft LLP, established in 1792, is a leading legal advisor to many of the world's top financial institutions and corporations, with offices in New York, London, Charlotte, Washington, Houston, Beijing, Hong Kong and Brussels. Our lawyers provide counsel on sophisticated and complex transactional, litigation, and regulatory matters to help our clients break new ground, achieve their business goals, and overcome challenges.

Recruitment details

- Number of 1st year associates: 36
- Number of 2nd year associates: 39
- Associate salaries: 1st year: $160,000
- 2nd year: $170,000
- Clerking policy: Case by case

Law Schools attending for OCIs in 2016:

Alabama, American, Berkeley, Boston College, Boston University, Brooklyn, Cardozo, University of Chicago, Columbia, Cornell NYC Job Fair, Duke, Emory NYC Job Fair, Fordham, George Washington, Georgetown, Harvard, University of Houston, University of Michigan, Minnesota, Northwestern, NYU, Penn, Stanford, University of Texas, Vanderbilt, University of Virginia, Wash U and Yale

Summer details

Summer associate profile:

Cadwalader is a community of talented and driven individuals committed to innovation and premier client service. We seek candidates with a record of academic and personal achievement, who exhibit excellent communication skills and professionalism and who are analytical and creative thinkers.

Summer program components:

Under the supervision of experienced attorneys, summer associates have an opportunity to make meaningful contributions to ongoing projects. You will work on diverse and challenging assignments in several of our areas, depending on your interests, participate in substantive and skills building sessions and take on pro bono work. Our goal is to expose you to the various aspects of the practice of law: meeting with clients; participating in strategy and negotiation sessions; conducting research; drafting memos, documents and pleadings; and attending closings, depositions and court appearances. Associate and partner mentors will work closely with you throughout the summer. In addition to getting feedback on individual projects by supervising lawyers, you will also participate in mid-summer and end-of-summer formal evaluations.

Head Office: New York, NY
Number of domestic offices: 4
Number of international offices: 4
Worldwide revenue: $463,500,000
Partners (US): 83
Associates (US): 195
Other attorneys: 96

Main Recruitment Contact:
Susan Harlow, Director of Legal Recruitment & Professional Development
Hiring Partner: Paul Mourning
Recruitment website:
www.cadwalader.com/makehistory
Diversity officer: Linda Wayner, Director of Diversity

Summer Salary 2016
1Ls: $3,075/week
2Ls: $3,075/week
Post 3Ls: $3,075/week
1Ls hired? Yes
Split summers offered? Case by case
Can summers spend time in overseas office? Case by case
Summers 2016: 47 (44 2Ls, 3 1Ls)
Offers/acceptances 2015:
36 offers, 30 acceptances

CADWALADER

Cahill Gordon & Reindel LLP

80 Pine Street, New York NY 10005
www.cahill.com/careers

Main areas of work

Antitrust, bankruptcy and restructuring, communications, corporate, corporate finance, corporate governance and investigations, crisis advisory, executive compensation and employee benefits, environmental, insurance, intellectual property, litigation, media, pro bono, real estate, tax and trust and estates.

Firm profile

Cahill has thrived for nearly a century by focusing on the most significant opportunities and the biggest legal challenges facing the top banking firms and global companies. Cahill is a firm where you can shape your own legal career. We believe that lawyers who practice in diverse areas are happier and more productive. We do not require immediate specialization and do not have formal departments or rotation policies. While among the most profitable New York-based law firms, our size is conducive to regular interaction between partners and associates. Opportunities abound for interesting work and unparalleled on-the-job training.

Recruitment details

- Number of 1st year associates: 34
- Number of 2nd year associates: 49
- Associate salaries: 1st year: $160,000
- 2nd year: $170,000
- Clerking policy: Yes

Law Schools attending for OCIs in 2016:

Albany, Boston College, Boston University, Brooklyn, Columbia, Cornell University, Duke University, Fordham University, Georgetown University, George Washington University, Harvard, Howard, New York University, Northwestern University, University of Michigan, University of Pennsylvania and University of Virginia (with job fairs and write-ins from a dozen more).

Summer details

Summer associate profile:

The firm seeks academically strong candidates who display good judgment, self-confidence and enthusiasm for the practice of law.

Summer program components:

Summer associates at Cahill gain first-hand experience of what it would be like to be an associate at Cahill. With substantive assignments and opportunities to gain valuable public interest work experience, attend client meetings, negotiations, court appearances and networking events, Cahill's summer associates develop a true understanding of the firm's practice. Formal and informal training, personal mentoring and comprehensive evaluations are components of the firm's summer program.

Head Office: New York, NY
Number of domestic offices: 2
Number of international offices: 1
Worldwide revenue: $364,500,000
Partners (US): 72
Associates (US): 209

Main Recruitment Contact:
Donna Manion
Hiring Partner: Brian Markley
Recruitment website:
www.cahill.com/careers
Diversity officers: Susanna Suh and Luis Penalver

Summer Salary 2016
1Ls: N/A
2Ls: $3,077/week
Post 3Ls: N/A
1Ls hired? Case by case
Split summers offered? Yes, with government or public agencies
Can summers spend time in overseas office? No
Summers 2016: 38
Offers/acceptances 2015:
35 offers, 34 acceptances

Chadbourne & Parke LLP

1301 Avenue of the Americas, New York, NY 10019-6022
Tel: 212 408 5100 Fax: 212 541 5369
www.chadbourne.com

Main areas of work

Bankruptcy, capital markets, corporate, intellectual property, international dispute resolution, Latin America, litigation, project finance, renewable energy, tax.

Firm profile

Chadbourne & Parke LLP is an international law firm with approximately 450 attorneys in 10 offices around the world. Headquartered in New York, Chadbourne takes great pride in its approach to the sharing of resources and the ability of all offices to work together seamlessly on cross-border matters. The Chadbourne culture is informal, friendly and entrepreneurial – qualities we have worked to maintain even as we have grown substantially in recent years. The people who work at Chadbourne – lawyers and staff alike – are our greatest assets, making our workplace vibrant, inviting and comfortable. We are seeking law students who will make a good long term fit at Chadbourne and its distinctive workplace. We want you to succeed here. Associates have substantial contact with both partners and clients and benefit from the collegial personality of Chadbourne. In addition, the firm's strong commitment to a diverse workplace creates an environment of respect and inclusion.

Recruitment details

- Number of 1st year associates: 13
- Number of 2nd year associates: 8
- Associate salaries: 1st year: $160,000
- 2nd year: $170,000
- Clerking policy: Yes

Law Schools attending for OCIs in 2016:

American, Brooklyn, Chicago, Columbia, Cornell, Emory, Fordham, Georgetown, George Washington, Harvard, Hofstra, Michigan, NEBLSA, Notre Dame, NYU, Penn, St John's, UVA

Summer details

Summer associate profile:

Chadbourne seeks candidates with top academic credentials, who possess excellent writing, analytical, communication and interpersonal skills. The firm values candidates who demonstrate drive, leadership and entrepreneurialism and uphold our core values of professional excellence, respect and inclusion.

Summer program components:

The goal of the summer program is to immerse students in the Chadbourne culture and give them a realistic sense of what life is like as an associate. The assignment structure enables summer associates to work on matters across all practice areas and to be trained through hands-on work and "shadowing" opportunities. Chadbourne strives to give the incoming associates solid skills in negotiating, drafting, researching, performing legal analysis, strategizing and developing business. At Chadbourne, professional development begins during your summer experience and the program is designed to give you solid tools to start your legal career. The summer program also has a vibrant social aspect, providing good food, good fun and, most important, opportunities for summer associates and attorneys to get to know one another.

Head Office: New York, NY
Number of domestic offices: 3
Number of international offices: 7
Partners (US): 74
Associates (US): 135

Main Recruitment Contact:
Lisa Featherson, Director of Legal Personnel & Associate Recruiting
Diversity officer: Lisa Featherson

Summer Salary 2016
1Ls: $3,077/week
2Ls: $3,077/week
Post 3Ls: N/A
1Ls hired? Yes
Split summers offered? Case by case
Can summers spend time in overseas office? Case by case
Summers 2016: 16
Offers/acceptances 2015:
17 offers, 14 acceptances

Choate Hall & Stewart LLP

Two International Place, Boston, MA 02110
Tel: 617 248 5000
Email: legalrecruiting@choate.com
www.choate.com

Main areas of work

Private equity and M&A, life sciences and technology companies, intellectual property and related litigation, finance and restructuring, government enforcement and financial litigation, insurance and reinsurance, complex trial and appellate, and wealth management.

Firm profile

Choate is one of the nation's premier law firms. Choate conducts its national and international practice through a single office model, with all lawyers under one roof in Boston. The firm's associate-to-partner ratio is low, affording junior lawyers opportunities to play important roles on matters and facilitating rapid career development. Lawyers know each other well and work together in dedicated client teams. That familiarity, proximity and continuity allows them to share knowledge easily and respond to clients' needs efficiently, seamlessly and immediately.

Recruitment details

- Number of 1st year associates: 12
- Number of 2nd year associates: 9
- Associate salaries: 1st year: $160,000
- 2nd year: $170,000
- Clerking policy: Choate offers compensation and progression credit, as well as a one-time clerkship bonus, to candidates who join the firm immediately following the completion of a federal district or circuit court clerkship or a federal or state supreme court clerkship

Law Schools attending for OCIs in 2016:

Boston College, Boston University, Columbia, Cornell, Georgetown, Harvard, New York University, Northeastern, Suffolk, University of Virginia, Yale and UConn

Summer details

Summer associate profile:

Choate seeks candidates who have a record of academic excellence and professional achievement. In addition to academic success, we seek candidates who are committed and who offer perspectives and talents shaped by a broad range of socioeconomic, racial, ethnic and personal backgrounds. We value proven leadership, dedication to team success, a strong work ethic and the ability to approach challenges thoughtfully and creatively.

Summer program components:

Choate's summer associates are involved in real work with real clients from day one. In recent years, summers have performed legal and factual research, drafted memos and briefs, helped prepare transactional documents, conducted diligence and managed deal closings, assisted in fact gathering, drafted estate planning documents, observed depositions and trials and worked on pro bono matters. Each summer associate is matched with a junior associate, mid-level associate and partner mentor, who provide guidance and feedback. The summer training program provides the opportunity to develop professional skills, learn about working at the firm and work with writing and communications coaches.

Head Office: Boston, MA
Number of domestic offices: 1
Number of international offices: 0
Worldwide revenue: $202,666,179
Partners: 64
Associates: 88
Other Attorneys: 15

Main Recruitment Contact:
Elaine Cohen Bortman, Chief of Legal Recruiting & Talent Development
Hiring Partners: Diana Lloyd and John Nadas
Recruitment website:
www.choate.com/careers

Summer Salary 2016
1Ls: $3,075/week
2Ls: $3,075/week
Post 3Ls: $3,075/week
1Ls hired? Yes, through the firm's 1L Diversity Fellowship program, through which Fellows receive a position in Choate's summer program and are eligible for a stipend of up to $10,000
Split summers offered? No
Can summers spend time in overseas office? N/A
Summers 2016: 17
Offers/acceptances 2015:
12 2L offers, 11 acceptances

Cleary Gottlieb Steen & Hamilton LLP

One Liberty Plaza, New York, NY 10006
Tel: 212 225 2000 Fax: 212 225 3999
www.clearygottlieb.com

Main areas of work

Antitrust and competition, banking and financial institutions, bankruptcy and restructuring, capital markets, corporate governance, derivatives, energy, environmental law, executive compensation and ERISA, intellectual property, international trade and investment, leveraged and acquisition finance, litigation and arbitration, mergers, acquisitions and joint ventures, private clients and charitable organizations, private equity, privatizations, pro bono, project finance and infrastructure, public international law, real estate, sovereign governments and international institutions, structured finance, tax, white-collar defense, securities enforcement and internal investigations.

Firm profile

Cleary Gottlieb embodies the principles of collegiality, collaboration, individuality and legal excellence while cultivating the finest legal talent in the world. Operating as a single, integrated worldwide firm with 16 offices in 12 different countries, Cleary Gottlieb has helped shape the globalization of the legal profession for more than 70 years.

Recruitment details

- Number of 1st year associates: 85
- Number of 2nd year associates: 89
- Associate salaries: 1st year: $160,000
- 2nd year: $170,000
- Clerking policy: Yes

Law Schools attending for OCIs in 2016:

Boston College, Boston University, Brooklyn, Cardozo, Chicago, Columbia, Cornell, Duke, Emory, Fordham, George Washington, Georgetown, Harvard, Howard, Lavender Law Career Fair, Michigan, Midwest California Interview Program, National Law School Consortium, NEBLSA Job Fair, New York Law, NYU, Northwestern, Ohio State, University of Pennsylvania, Stanford, Texas, Tulane, Washington University, Washington and Lee, William and Mary, UC Berkeley, UCLA, USC Gould, Vanderbilt, Virginia, Yale

Summer details

Summer associate profile:

We seek candidates who are confident in their abilities and creative in their thinking. We look for academically strong men and women of all races and nationalities who are enthusiastic about practicing law. We place a premium on openness, diversity, individuality and collegiality and look for candidates who do so as well.

Summer program components:

Cleary offers summer associates the flexibility to enjoy assignments in many practice areas or to focus on a particular discipline. The summer program consists of formal and informal training, partner and associate mentoring, optional overseas office rotations, pro bono work, comprehensive evaluations and social/networking events.

Head Offices: New York, NY and Washington, DC
Number of domestic offices: 2
Number of international offices: 14
Partners (US): 106
Associates (US): 442

Main Recruitment Contacts: Donna Harris (NY) and Georgia Emery Gray (DC)
Hiring Partners: Lisa Schweitzer (NY) and Michael A Mazzuchi (DC)
Recruitment website: www.clearygottlieb.com
Diversity officers: Sean O'Neal and Caroline Hayday

Summer Salary 2016
1Ls: N/A
2Ls: $3,077/week
Post 3Ls: N/A
1Ls hired? Yes - Washington Diversity Summer Associate Program
Split summers offered? Yes
Can summers spend time in overseas office? Yes
Summers 2016: 123
Offers/acceptances 2015: 120 offers

CLEARY GOTTLIEB

Clifford Chance US LLP

31 West 52nd Street, New York, NY 10019-6131
Tel: 212 878 8000 Fax: 212 878 8375
www.cliffordchance.com

Main areas of work

Banking and finance, capital markets, corporate/M&A, litigation and dispute resolution, real estate and tax, pensions and employment.

Firm profile

Clifford Chance offers the opportunity to join a major US practice and the world's leading international law firm. We are the first fully-integrated worldwide firm to provide coordinated legal advice to the world's leading financial institutions, corporations and governments. The combination of a large US presence with unparalleled resources in Europe, Asia Pacific, Latin America, Africa and the Middle East makes us uniquely qualified to handle complex cross-border and domestic transactions, disputes and investigations.

Recruitment details

- Number of 1st year associates: 27
- Number of 2nd year associates: 27
- Associate salaries: 1st year: $160,000
- 2nd year: $170,000
- Clerking policy: Yes

Law Schools attending for OCIs in 2016:

American, Boston College, Boston University, Brooklyn, Columbia, Cornell, Duke, Fordham, Georgetown, George Washington, Harvard, Howard, Michigan, Northwestern, NYU, Penn, St. John's, Virginia

Summer details

Summer associate profile:

Our summer program introduces students to our firm and our clients. All of our summer law clerks have the opportunity to spend two weeks working in one of our foreign offices.

Summer program components:

Each summer law clerk shares an office with a junior associate and is also assigned an associate mentor. Our training includes weekly seminars, practice group meetings and in-house and external training sessions. Feedback is given formally at a midsummer and final review meeting. Summer assignments are available from all of our practice areas and are coordinated by two assigning associates.

Head Office: London
Number of domestic offices: 2
Number of international offices: 33
Worldwide revenue: $2,139,000,000
Partners (US): 69
Associates (US): 195

Main Recruitment Contact:
Sarah Posner
Hiring Partner: Nicholas R Williams
Recruitment website:
www.cliffordchance.com/usrecruiting
Diversity officer: Zarrar Sehgal

Summer Salary 2016
1Ls: $3,077/week
2Ls: $3,077/week
Post 3Ls: $3,077/week
1Ls hired? No
Split summers offered? Case by case
Can summers spend time in overseas office? Yes
Summers 2016: 26
Offers/acceptances 2015:
26 offers, 25 acceptances

C L I F F O R D
C H A N C E

Cooley LLP

3175 Hanover Street, Palo Alto, CA 94304-1130
Tel: 650 843 5000 Fax: 650 849 7400
www.cooley.com

Main areas of work

Advertising, antitrust and competition, capital markets, class actions, commercial litigation, communications, copyright, corporate, corporate restructuring and bankruptcy, emerging companies, employment and labor, estate planning, financial services, government contracts, healthcare, education, IP litigation, insurance/reinsurance, investment funds, life sciences, M&A, patent prosecution and counseling, privacy and data protection, public companies, regulatory, real estate, retail, securities, tax, technology transactions, trademark, venture capital, white collar.

Firm profile

Cooley's lawyers solve legal issues for entrepreneurs, investors, financial institutions and established companies with a significant emphasis on technology, life sciences and other high growth industries. Clients partner with Cooley on transformative deals, complex IP and regulatory matters and bet-the-company litigation, often where innovation meets the law. Cooley goes to great lengths to maintain the culture of teamwork, collaboration, respect and excellence upon which it was established in 1920. Cooley strives to maintain an environment of inclusion and to create opportunities for professional growth and is proud to be one of Fortune's "100 Best Companies to Work For."

Cooley considers its commitment to the communities in which it resides to be one of its highest priorities and performs thousands of hours of pro bono legal services and other forms of community service annually.

Recruitment details

- Number of 1st year associates: 44
- Number of 2nd year associates: 55
- Associate salaries: 1st year: $160,000
- 2nd year: $170,000
- Clerking policy: Yes

Law Schools attending for OCIs in 2016:

Please refer to the Careers portion of our website for a list of the job fairs and campuses we will visit during the 2016 OCI season.

Summer details

Summer associate profile:

Successful summer associates are highly motivated, independent thinkers, with a collaborative spirit and an entrepreneurial mindset. They have excelled both in and beyond the classroom. They recognize that the greatest successes are those achieved by a team. They take ownership, inspire confidence and are motivated by a shared sense of purpose.

Summer program components:

Cooley's summer program is designed to give participants an unfiltered introduction to life and practice at the firm. It enables them to experience Cooley's commitment to providing extraordinary legal services in a professional and collaborative environment. Comprehensive training opportunities are provided through "Cooley College". Constructive feedback is provided at the conclusion of each assignment and in formal mid- and end of summer feedback sessions. Assigned mentors ensure that each summer associate is integrated into the firm over the course of the program.

Head Office: Palo Alto, CA
Number of domestic offices: 10
Number of international offices: 2
Worldwide revenue: $912,000,000
Partners (US): 300
Associates (US): 600

Main Recruitment Contact:
Carrie Wagner, Director of Legal Talent
Hiring Partner: Ryan Naftulin
Recruitment website:
www.cooley.com/careers
Diversity officers: DeAnna Allen, Partner and Amie Santos, Diversity & Inclusion Manager

Summer Salary 2016
1Ls: $3,077/week
2Ls: $3,077/week
1Ls hired? Yes, through Diversity Fellowship
Split summers offered? Yes
Can summers spend time in overseas office? No
Summers 2016: 64
Offers/acceptances 2015:
41 offers, 36 acceptances

Cozen O'Connor

One Liberty, 1650 Market Street, Philadelphia, Suite 2800 PA 19103
Tel: 215 665 2000 Fax: 215 665 2013
www.cozen.com

Main areas of work

Business/corporate, commercial litigation, government and regulatory, insurance coverage, intellectual property, labor and employment, real estate, private client services, subrogation and recovery.

Firm profile

Established in 1970, Cozen O'Connor delivers legal services on an integrated and global basis. As a first-generation law firm, we have not forgotten our entrepreneurial roots and continue to provide top-notch client service at unparalleled value as we have grown to one of the top law firms in the country. Our Business and Litigation Practice serves clients in the most effective and efficient manner, with professionals across disciplines working collaboratively to resolve any matter.

Recruitment details

- Number of 1st year associates: 14
- Number of 2nd year associates: 13
- Associate salaries: 1st year: $125,000-$155,000 (varies by office)
- 2nd year: Non lock step, merit-based compensation
- Clerking policy: Yes

Law Schools attending for OCIs in 2016:

Georgetown, Harvard, NYU, Penn, Penn State, Seattle University, Temple, UVA, University of Washington, Villanova, GW, Northwestern

Summer details

Summer associate profile:

Cozen O'Connor seeks summer associates who embody the best characteristics of our attorneys. We strive to find candidates who have distinguished themselves from their peers in academics, legal writing ability and oral advocacy skills. Our summer associates have diverse backgrounds including, but not limited to, prior work experience, military service and a demonstrated commitment to serving their communities through volunteerism.

Summer program components:

At Cozen O'Connor, we pride ourselves in providing our summer associates with a realistic experience of the responsibilities and high level of performance expected of the firm's associates. They take part in an extensive firm orientation and weekly training programs, such as a trial skills workshop where they have the opportunity to prepare and present a mock opening statement and take a mock deposition. Our writing mentors work closely with the summer associates to strengthen their legal writing skills and our associate mentors provide them with advice and guidance. Summer associates work on active cases and are relied upon to produce excellent work product. They are invited to practice group meetings and to attend hearings, depositions, or client meetings with their supervising attorneys. Summer associates receive assignments that allow them to become intimately familiar with the firm's various practice groups and their cases and clients and are encouraged to participate in pro bono matters.

Head Office: Philadelphia, PA
Number of domestic offices: 22
Number of international offices: 2
Worldwide revenue: $341,500,000
Partners (US): 402
Associates (US): 128

Main Recruitment Contacts:
Mindy J Herczfeld, Director of Legal Talent and Jill M Caughie, Associate Director of Legal Recruiting
Hiring Partner: Matthew J Siegel
Recruitment website:
www.cozen.com/careers
Diversity officer: Kimya S P Johnson

Summer Salary 2016
1Ls: $2,200-$2800/week, varies by office
2Ls: $2,400-$3000/week, varies by office
1Ls hired? Yes
Split summers offered? Case by case
Can summers spend time in overseas office? No
Summers 2016: 14 (2Ls)
Offers/acceptances 2015:
11 offers, 10 acceptances

Cravath, Swaine & Moore LLP

825 Eighth Avenue, New York, NY 10019
Tel: 212 474 1000 Fax: 212 474 3700
www.cravath.com

Main areas of work

Corporate, litigation, tax, executive compensation and benefits, trusts and estates.

Firm profile

Cravath is known as one of the preeminent law firms in the country. Each of our practice areas is highly regarded and our lawyers are widely recognized for their commitment to the representation of our clients' interests. We believe the development of our lawyers is our most important long term objective. Our partners come almost exclusively from the ranks of our own associates. We recruit the most talented law students and have our partners directly train the next generation of associates. Through our rotation system – a system in which corporate associates "rotate" from one practice group to another and litigation associates "rotate" from one partner to another – associates work directly with a small team of partners and associates. We have found that this system enables even our most recently hired associates to work directly with our clients and quickly to assume substantial responsibility for important matters, while at the same time preventing undue specialization.

Recruitment details

- Number of 1st year associates: 79
- Number of 2nd year associates: 74
- Associate salaries: 1st year: $160,000
- 2nd year: $170,000
- Clerking policy: Yes

Law Schools attending for OCIs in 2016:

Berkeley, Boston College/Boston University Job Fair, Brigham Young University New York Interview Program, Cardozo, Chicago, Columbia, Cornell Job Fair, Duke, Emory Job Fair, Fordham, George Washington New York Job Fair, Georgetown, Harvard, Harvard BLSA Job Fair, Howard, Lavender Law Career Fair, LeGaL LGBT Career Fair, McGill, Michigan, Midwestern/California New York Job Fair, Midwest-California-Georgia Consortium, Northeast BLSA Job Fair, New York University, Northwestern, Notre Dame New York Job Fair, Osgoode Hall, Stanford, Texas, Texas New York Job Fair, Toronto, Tulane/Washington University/Vanderbilt Job Fair, University of North Carolina, University of Pennsylvania, Virginia, William & Mary/ Washington & Lee Job Fair, Yale

Summer details

Summer associate profile:

Our summer program is designed to provide law students with an experience that mirrors the life of a first year associate. Summer associates experience the day-to-day working life of a Cravath lawyer and gain valuable hands-on experience working directly for, and with, our clients.

Summer program components:

Prior to the summer, we collect department and assignment preferences (type of matter or practice area, specific teams or partners). Upon arrival, summer associates are assigned to a partner from their selected department, along with an associate mentor. This partner is responsible for assigning work and providing feedback.

Head Office: New York, NY
Number of domestic offices: 1
Number of international offices: 1
Partners (US): 83
Associates (US): 373

Main Recruitment Contact: Lisa A Kalen
Hiring Partners: Karin A DeMasi and Eric L Schiele
Recruitment Website: www.cravath.com
Diversity officer: Kiisha J B Morrow

Summer Salary 2016
1Ls: $3,077/week
2Ls: $3,077/week
Post 3Ls: $3,077/week
1Ls hired: Yes
Split summers offered: Yes
Can summers spend time in overseas office: Yes
Summers 2016: 114

CRAVATH, SWAINE & MOORE LLP

Crowell & Moring LLP

1001 Pennsylvania Avenue, N.W. Washington DC, 20004-2595
Tel: 202 624 2500 Fax: 202 628 5116
www.crowell.com

Firm profile

Crowell & Moring LLP is an international law firm with more than 500 lawyers representing clients in litigation and arbitration, regulatory, and transactional matters. The firm is internationally recognized for its representation of Fortune 500 companies in high-stakes litigation, as well as its ongoing commitment to pro bono service and diversity. The firm has offices in Washington, DC, New York, Los Angeles, San Francisco, Orange County, Anchorage, Cheyenne, London, and Brussels.

Recruitment details

- Number of 1st year associates: 15
- Number of 2nd year associates: 22
- Associate salaries: 1st year: $160,000
- 2nd year: $170,000
- Clerking policy: No

Law Schools attending for OCIs in 2016:

We interview at the majority of the top 20 law schools and numerous diversity related and IP specific job fairs throughout the country.

Summer details

Summer associate profile:

The firm looks for highly qualified, entrepreneurial candidates with diverse backgrounds. We prefer candidate with law review, journal or moot court experience and/ or strong relevant legal employment experience, including judicial clerkships; as well as demonstrated leadership capabilities.

Summer program components:

The diversity in our summer program reflects the diversity of our firm at large. We want summer associates who take the practice of law and client service more seriously than they take themselves, who will contribute to the life of the firm, and who share our sense of responsibility to the community.

Most of our junior associates come from our Summer Associate Program. We want you to go back to law school knowing who we are, what we do, and how we do it. Work for summer associates includes mostly short-term projects that will allow you to experience as many practice areas and as many lawyers as possible.

Summer associates have the opportunity to participate in workshops and seminars on such topics as The Law Firm as a Business and Negotiations Training. In addition, the firm offers summer associates the opportunities to participate in our Public Interest Fellowship program and sign up for Live Events which are real-world activities like court hearings, client meetings, depositions, presentations and negotiations that summer associates may attend in order to observe Crowell & Moring attorneys in action.

Head Office: Washington, DC
Number of domestic offices: 7
Number of international offices: 2
Worldwide revenue: $363,039,506
Partners (US): 177
Counsel/Sr Counsel (US): 116
Associates (US): 148

Main Recruitment Contact:
Torey Phillips, Director of Attorney Recruiting and Development
Hiring Partner: Ryan Tisch
Recruitment website:
www.crowell.com/Careers/Lawyers
Diversity officer: Monica Parham

Summer Salary 2016
1Ls: $3,077/week
2Ls: $3,077/week
Post 3Ls: $3,077/week
1Ls hired? Yes
Split summers offered? Case by case
Can summers spend time in overseas office? No
Summers 2016: 17 firmwide
Offers/acceptances 2015:
15 offers, 14 acceptances

Firm Profiles

Curtis, Mallet-Prevost, Colt & Mosle LLP

101 Park Avenue, New York, NY 10178-0061
Tel: 212 696 6000 Fax: 212 697 1559
www.curtis.com

Main areas of work

Curtis represents clients across industry sectors, including multinational corporations and financial institutions, governments and state-owned companies, money managers, sovereign wealth funds, family-owned businesses, individuals and entrepreneurs. Curtis' attorneys provide legal services in international arbitration, energy, renewable energy and climate change, project finance and infrastructure development, international tax, mergers and acquisitions, private equity, restructuring and insolvency, litigation, banking and finance, capital markets, investment management, international investment, corporate law and real estate.

Firm profile

Curtis, Mallet-Prevost, Colt & Mosle LLP is a leading international law firm that provides a broad range of legal services to clients around the world. The firm operates worldwide throughout its offices in Europe, the United States, Latin America, the Middle East and Central Asia. Curtis' international orientation has been a hallmark of its practice for nearly two centuries. Curtis attorneys are trained as internationalists with a deep understanding of the cultural as well as business sensitivities associated with conducting business across borders.

Recruitment details

- Number of 1st year associates: 8
- Number of 2nd year associates: 9
- Associate salaries: 1st year: $160,000
- 2nd year: $170,000
- Clerking policy: Yes

Law Schools attending for OCIs in 2016:

Boston College, Boalt, Cornell, Columbia, Duke, Fordham, Georgetown, Harvard, New York University, St. John's, Stanford, University of Chicago, University of Pennsylvania, University of Virginia, Yale

Summer details

Summer associate profile:

The Curtis Summer Program is small and highly selective. Curtis chooses approximately 10 to 15 second-year law students to participate in our program. The summer program, which lasts 10 weeks, starts in late May and ends in early August. Grades and scores are not the only criteria for selection. Curtis looks for students who are confident, independent thinkers.

Summer program components:

The summer program is designed to give students a realistic view of the practice of law while at the same time teaching them real-world lawyering skills in a hands-on environment. Our summer associates quickly become assimilated as each summer associate is matched to a partner mentor and an associate advisor.

Summer associates receive assignments which are carefully selected to correspond with their interests and goals. Throughout the summer, summer associates join lawyers in meetings, closings, depositions and court proceedings. Formal training includes lectures, workshops, panel discussions and lunchtime programs on relevant topics.

Head Office: New York, NY
Number of domestic offices: 3
Number of international offices: 14
Worldwide revenue: $151,500,000
Partners (US): 52
Associates (US): 60

Main Recruitment Contact:
Raquel Lorenzo
Hiring Partner: Carl Ruggiero
Recruitment website:
www.curtis.com

Summer Salary 2016
1Ls: $3,077/week
2Ls: $3,077/week
Post 3Ls: N/A
1Ls hired? Yes
Split summers offered? Case by case
Can summers spend time in overseas office? Case by case
Summers 2016: 10
Offers/acceptances 2015:
8 offers for 2Ls, 8 acceptances

Davis Polk & Wardwell LLP

450 Lexington Avenue, New York, NY 10017
Tel: 212 450 4000 Fax: 212 701 5800
www.davispolk.com

Main areas of work

Capital markets, mergers and acquisitions, credit, litigation (including antitrust, bankruptcy, general commercial, IP, securities litigation and enforcement and white collar and government investigations), tax, private equity, investment management, insolvency and restructuring, corporate governance, intellectual property, financial institutions, global technology, environmental, executive compensation, real estate and trusts and estates.

Firm profile

Davis Polk & Wardwell LLP is a global law firm. For more than 160 years, its lawyers have advised industry-leading companies and major financial institutions on their most challenging legal and business matters. Davis Polk ranks among the world's preeminent law firms across the entire range of its practice. With approximately 900 lawyers in New York, Menlo Park, CA, Washington DC, London, Paris, Madrid, Hong Kong, Beijing, Tokyo and São Paulo, the firm operates from key business centers around the world to provide clients with seamlessly integrated legal services of the highest caliber.

Recruitment details

- Associate salaries: 1st year: $160,000 • 2nd year: $170,000
- Clerking policy: Yes

Summer details

Summer associate profile:

We seek to hire applicants from a variety of backgrounds with outstanding academic and non-academic achievements, leadership skills and creativity and with a demonstrated willingness to take initiative. We strive to find exceptional lawyers who share our commitment to excellence.

Summer program components:

Our summer program is designed to allow students the opportunity to experience work as a junior associate. Summer associates are encouraged to work on matters in any practice area of interest. There are no required rotations. Work assignments are made through two associates who take leave from their regular practices to assist each summer associate in shaping their summer work experience. In addition to working with our attorneys on the firm's current billable and pro bono matters, summer associates have the opportunity to attend practice area overviews and participate in multi-day interactive training sessions and workshops. The program also includes a wide range of cultural, social and mentoring activities to assist summer associates in getting to know their peers and our attorneys.

Head Office: New York, NY
Number of domestic offices: 3
Number of international offices: 7
Lawyers (US): 755

Main Recruitment Contact:
Cristobal V Modesto
Hiring Partner: Warren Motley &
Maurice Blanco
Recruitment website:
http://careers.davispolk.com

Summer Salary 2016
1Ls: $3,077/week
2Ls: $3,077/ week
Split summers offered? Yes
Can summers spend time in overseas office? Yes
Summers 2016: 145

Davis Polk

Debevoise & Plimpton LLP

919 Third Avenue, New York, NY 10022
Tel: 212 909 6000
www.debevoise.com

Main areas of work

Debevoise & Plimpton LLP has three main areas of practice: corporate (including mergers and acquisitions, private equity, investment funds, insurance, banking, leveraged finance, business restructuring and workouts, asset management, capital markets, corporate governance, structured and project finance, aviation finance, healthcare and life sciences, intellectual property, media and telecommunications, real estate, energy and environmental law), litigation (including white collar/regulatory, international dispute resolution, intellectual property, general commercial litigation, cybersecurity and data privacy, insurance, securities, antitrust, employment, bankruptcy and products liability) and tax and employee benefits.

Firm profile

Debevoise & Plimpton LLP is a premier law firm with market-leading practices, a global perspective and strong New York roots. Deep partner commitment, industry expertise and a strategic approach enable the firm to bring clear commercial judgment to every matter. The firm draws on the strength of its culture and structure to deliver the best of the firm to every client through true collaboration.

Recruitment details

- Number of 1st year associates: 77
- Number of 2nd year associates: 80
- Associate salaries: 1st year: $160,000
- 2nd year: $170,000
- Clerking policy: Yes

Law Schools attending for OCIs in 2016:

Benjamin N Cardozo, Brooklyn, Columbia University, Cornell University, Duke University, Fordham University, Georgetown University, Harvard, Howard University, New York Law School, New York University School of Law, Northwestern, Rutgers University, St. John's University, Stanford, Tulane University, University of Chicago, University of Michigan, University of Pennsylvania, University of Texas Law School, University of Virginia, Vanderbilt University, Washington University, Yale

Summer details

Summer associate profile:

Debevoise searches for dynamic, analytically strong and professionally curious individuals with an interest in and enthusiasm for the challenging deals and matters on which the firm works. In addition, the firm is interested in individuals from an array of different backgrounds as it prefers that its lawyer population is as diverse as its clients.

Summer program components:

Debevoise's summer program is structured to provide participants with the flexibility to explore as many practice areas as they wish. In order to accommodate the individual's evolving interests, the firm has chosen not to impose an assignment system that "rotates" participants through different areas of the firm. There are opportunities throughout the summer for formal evaluations, while informal feedback is given on a continuous basis. Social events are held for summer associates, which provide them with the chance to connect with other lawyers, of all levels, at the firm.

Head Office: New York, NY
Number of domestic offices: 2
Number of international offices: 6
Worldwide revenue: $756.9 million
Partners (US): 106
Associates (US): 327

Main Recruitment Contact: Sandra Herbst
Hiring Partner: Nicole Mesard
Recruitment website: www.debevoise.com
Diversity officers: Ezra Borut, Jonathan F Lewis (Diversity Committee Co-Chairs) and Rachel Simmonds-Watson (Diversity Manager)

Summer Salary 2016
1Ls: N/A
2Ls: $3,077/week
Post 3Ls: N/A
1Ls hired? No
Split summers offered? Yes
Can summers spend time in overseas office? Yes
Summers 2016: 70 (excluding SEOs and returnees; 68 in NY, 2 in DC)
Offers/acceptances 2015:
78 offers, 63 acceptances (NY and DC), some offers remain open.

Dechert LLP

Cira Centre, 2929 Arch Street, Philadelphia, PA 19104-2808
Tel: 215 994 4000 Fax: 215 994 2222

1095 Avenue of the Americas, New York, NY 10036-6797
Tel: 212 698 3500 Fax: 212 698 3599
www.dechert.com

Main areas of work

Dechert delivers legal expertise and commercial insight in our core practices: antitrust; banking and financial institutions; bankruptcy, business restructuring and reorganization; corporate; employee benefits and executive compensation; energy and natural resources; finance and real estate; financial services and investment management; intellectual property; international arbitration; international tax and private client services; international trade and government regulation; life sciences; litigation; and pro bono.

Firm profile

Dechert is a global specialist law firm focused on sectors with the greatest complexities, legal intricacies and highest regulatory demands. With 27 offices in the United States, Europe, Asia and the Middle East, the firm offers attractive locations in which to live and work. Dechert is a leading global law firm for pro bono services. *The American Lawyer* consistently ranks us in the top 10 law firm pro bono programs.

Recruitment details

- Number of 1st year associates: 64
- Number of 2nd year associates: 62
- Associate salaries: $160,000
- 2nd year: $170,000
- Clerking policy: Yes

Law Schools attending for OCIs in 2016:

Boston College; Boston University; Catholic University; Columbia; Cornell; Duke; Fordham; George Washington University; Georgetown; Harvard; Hofstra University; Howard; New York University; Northwestern; Stanford; Temple; UCLA; UC Berkeley; UC Hastings; Chicago; Connecticut; Michigan; North Carolina; University of Pennsylvania; Pittsburgh; USC; Texas; Virginia; Vanderbilt; Villanova; Yale

Summer details

Summer associate profile:

Strong academic background and communication, leadership, management and client relations skills indicating a high likelihood of success as a lawyer at the firm.

Summer program components:

Summer associates will discover firsthand what it's like to work at one of the world's most respected and dynamic global law firms. Our summer associates do not formally rotate through practice groups or departments; rather, they work across all the practice groups. A variety of work assignments allows summer associates to gain a broad perspective and get a close-up view of the practice of law. Beyond client-based assignments, we encourage summer associates to attend closings, depositions, hearings, oral arguments, trials, negotiations, and board meetings. Summer associates are assigned at least one associate mentor and one partner mentor and attend practice group meetings and training. We offer summer associate-specific training sessions throughout the program. Through our program, we provide summer associates with a realistic view of what it's like to practice law at Dechert.

Main Offices: Philadelphia / New York
Number of domestic offices: 13
Number of international offices: 14
Worldwide revenue: $890,232,713
Partners (US): 221
Associates (US): 387

Main Recruitment Contact:
Paul Giangola, Global Director, Legal Recruiting
Hiring Partner: James A Lebovitz, Firmwide Hiring Chair
Recruitment website:
www.dechert.com/careers
Diversity officer: Hector Gonzalez, Deputy Chair for Diversity and Chantel Moore, Global Director of Diversity

Summer Salary 2016
1Ls: $3,100/week
2Ls: $3,100/week
Post 3Ls: $3,100/week
1Ls hired? Yes
Split summers offered? Yes
Can summers spend time in overseas office? Yes, case by case
Summers 2016: 67 2Ls
Offers/acceptances 2015:
66 2L offers, 53 2L acceptances

Firm Profiles

DLA Piper LLP (US)

1251 Avenue of the Americas, 27th Floor, New York, NY 10020
Tel: 212 335 4500 Fax: 212 335 4501
www.dlapiper.com

Main areas of work

DLA Piper's core practices in the US are corporate, employment, finance, government affairs, intellectual property and technology, litigation, real estate, restructuring and tax.

Firm profile

DLA Piper is one of the largest business law firms in the world and serves its clients doing business around the world, with insight into both local and international considerations. We are one of the world's largest and most prominent legal service providers, located in more than 30 countries throughout the Americas, Asia Pacific, Europe and the Middle East, representing clients in a broad range of geographies and practice disciplines.

Recruitment details

- Number of 1st year associates: 37
- Number of 2nd year associates: Not lock step
- Associate salaries: 1st year: $160,000 in most markets
- 2nd year: Varies by market
- Clerking policy: Yes; Article III Federal and Appellate clerkship bonus (market based)

Law Schools attending for OCIs in 2016:

TBD

Summer details

Summer associate profile:

We promote a culture that is inclusive of all, where everyone has the opportunity to grow their career and where pathways to success are transparent. We look for well-rounded, energetic and entrepreneurial people. In general we recruit from the top 1/4 to the top 1/3 of law school classes.

Summer program components:

During the summer, with guidance from lawyers in the roles of mentors, we provide summer associates with a stimulating, realistic and exciting taste of legal life. Summer associates experience challenging days filled with client work, relationship-building opportunities and lively activities. All second-year summer associates attend a retreat hosted by one of our offices. During this three-day gathering, summer associates get to know one another and hear from firm leaders about the vision and values of the firm. Other topics include professional development, firm history, and pro bono. Our goal is for summer associates to experience what it is like to be on the DLA Piper team and, through the summer experience, envision their future as a knowledgeable, highly skilled, well-rounded DLA Piper lawyer.

Number of domestic offices: 29
Number of international offices: 63
Worldwide revenue: $2,543,152,599
Partners (US): 616
Associates (US): 515

Main Recruitment Contact: Diane Ross, Senior Director of Legal Recruiting
Hiring Partner: Ben Boyd, National Hiring Partner
Recruitment website: www.dlapiperlegalcareers.us
Diversity officer: Genhi Bailey

Summer Salary 2016
1Ls: $1,000/week
2Ls: $3,076/week in most markets
Post 3Ls: N/A
1Ls hired? Yes
Split summers offered? No
Can summers spend time in overseas office? No
Summers 2016: 33-35 2Ls,1Ls TBD
Offers/acceptances 2015:
32 offers and 30 acceptances

Duane Morris LLP

30 S. 17th Street, United Plaza, Philadelphia, PA 19103
Tel: 215 979 111 Fax: 215 979 1020

Main areas of work

Business reorganization and financial restructuring; corporate; employment, labor, benefits and immigration; energy, environment and resources; wealth planning, health law, intellectual property, litigation and real estate

Firm profile

Duane Morris LLP, a global law firm with more than 700 attorneys in offices across the United States and around the world, is asked by a broad array of clients to provide innovative solutions to today's legal and business challenges.

Recruitment details

- Number of 1st year associates: 11
- Number of 2nd year associates: 12
- Associate salaries: 1st year: $125,000-$150,000
- 2nd year: Non lock step compensation structure in place
- Clerking policy: Yes

Law Schools attending for OCIs in 2016:

University of Baltimore, Boston College, Boston University, Georgetown, Harvard, Howard, University of Maryland, Michigan, NYU, Penn, Temple, Villanova, among others.

Summer details

Summer associate profile:

Duane Morris strives to attract the best law students and to offer the ideal environment for lawyers at the beginning of their professional lives. We endeavor to improve our Summer Associates Program each year to make Duane Morris a meaningful and valuable destination for summer associates. The firm's summer associates rated the firm's program #12 nationally in The American Lawyer's 2015 Summer Associates Survey and a #1 ranking in the Philadelphia City ranking for 2015.

Duane Morris offers interesting challenges to law students who participate in our summer program. We believe the program offers a realistic picture of our practice to aspiring attorneys who have an interest in sharing our goals and serving our clients. Our program balances challenging work assignments with constructive feedback, work-related activities outside the office and enjoyable social events.

Summer program components:

The growth and development of each Duane Morris attorney furthers the central goals of the firm to provide the best legal services possible, to develop and build client relationships, and to ensure the stature and reputation of the firm with its clients. Duane Morris's Attorney Professional Development Program provides its summer associates and associates with comprehensive training and mentoring to support development of individual knowledge, skills and abilities in three broad categories: legal skills and substantive law, best business practices for the firm and practice development. Aside from these specific responsibilities, the mentors help introduce the summer associates to other lawyers in the firm and provide general guidance on any matter, whether or not related to particular work assignments.

Head Office: Philadelphia, PA
Number of domestic offices: 21
Number of international offices: 8
Partners (US): 362
Associates (US): 286

Main Recruitment Contact:
Peggy Simoncini Pasquay, Manager Attorney Recruitment & Relations
Hiring Partner: Kelly D Eckel, Esquire
Recruitment website:
www.duanemorris.com/site/careers.html
Diversity officer: Joseph K West, Esquire

Summer Salary 2016
1Ls: $2,692/week (Phila/Baltimore/NY)
2Ls: $2,884/week (Phila/Baltimore/NY)
1Ls hired? Yes, 1
Split summers offered? Case by case
Can summers spend time in overseas office? Case by case
Summers 2016: 22 (18 2Ls, 4 1Ls)
Offers/acceptances 2015:
17 offers (100%), 17 acceptances

Dykema Gossett PLLC

400 Renaissance Center, Detroit, MI 48243
Tel: 313 568 6800 Fax: 855 255 4354
www.dykema.com

Main areas of work

Dykema provides legal counsel to clients ranging from Fortune 500 corporations and middle-market businesses, to financial institutions, governmental entities and non-profits. Our practices include antitrust; appellate; automotive; banking; bankruptcy; class action; lending; litigation; construction; corporate; e-discovery; education; employee benefits and executive compensation; energy; environmental; estates and trusts; gaming; government policy; government investigations and compliance; healthcare; immigration; intellectual property and IP litigation; infrastructure; insurance; privacy, data security and e-commerce; private equity, venture capital and mezzanine finance; labor and employment; life sciences; mergers and acquisitions; product liability; public finance; real estate; securities and taxation.

Firm profile

With more than a century of experience and nearly 500 attorneys and other professionals, Dykema is one of the top law firms for business in the United States. Serving clients from our 15 offices in California, Illinois, Michigan, Minnesota, Texas and Washington, DC, we help clients address their most complex and sophisticated issues. We provide the highest quality legal counsel and exceptional client service from a work environment that thrives on cooperation, diversity and inclusion. Many of our attorneys and staff have made Dykema their home since the start of their careers. We consider this to be the highest compliment and one of the reasons for our ongoing success.

Recruitment details

- Number of 1st year associates: 20
- Number of 2nd year associates: 12
- Associate salaries: 1st year: $115,000-$145,000 (depending on office)
- 2nd year: Not lock step
- Clerking policy: Yes

Law Schools attending for OCIs in 2016:

Baylor, Detroit-Mercy, Howard, Illinois, Michigan, MSU, Northwestern, Notre Dame, OSU, St.Mary's, Texas Tech, U of T - Austin, UCLA, USC, Wayne State

Summer details

Summer associate profile:

A successful summer associate candidate will show initiative, excellent analytical skills and strong writing ability. We look for associates who are willing to work hard, have demonstrated leadership potential and enjoy working in a team environment.

Summer program components:

Dykema's summer associate program offers challenging assignments and a real life law practice experience with opportunities to participate in client, court and other formal settings. We integrate our summer associates into the firm via practice area and professional development activities, including a writing workshop with a professional writing instructor. We host social activities for summer associates to become better acquainted with us and our culture. We also provide summer associates with a senior and junior advisor. These advisors, together with our training, social activities and the substantive practice experience, have greatly contributed to the success of Dykema's summer program.

Head Office: Detroit, MI
Number of domestic offices: 15
Number of international offices: 0
Partners (US): 276
Associates (US): 141

Main Recruitment Contact: Sarah K Staup
Hiring Partner: Lisa A Brown
Recruitment website: www.dykema.com
Diversity officer: Sherrie L Farrell

Summer Salary 2016
2Ls: $1,900-$2,700/week
1Ls hired? Occasionally
Split summers offered? In Texas
Summers 2016: 31
Offers/acceptances 2015
15 offers, 10 acceptances

Epstein Becker & Green, PC

1227 25th Street, NW, Suite 700, Washington, DC 20037-1156
Tel: 202 861 0900 Fax: 202 296 2882

250 Park Avenue, New York, New York 10177-1211
Tel: 212 351 4500 Fax: 212 878 8600
www.ebglaw.com

Main areas of work

Healthcare and life sciences; employment, labor and workforce management; and litigation and business disputes.

Firm profile

Epstein Becker & Green, PC, is a national law firm with a primary focus on healthcare and life sciences; employment, labor and workforce management; and litigation and business disputes. Founded in 1973 as an industry-focused firm, Epstein Becker Green has decades of experience serving clients in healthcare, financial services, retail, hospitality and technology, among other industries, representing entities from startups to Fortune 100 companies. Operating in offices throughout the US and supporting clients in the US and abroad, the firm's attorneys are committed to uncompromising client service and legal excellence.

Recruitment details

- Number of 1st year associates: 9
- Number of 2nd year associates: 9
- Associate salaries: 1st year: Varies by practice and location
- 2nd year: Not lock step
- Clerking policy: Yes

Law Schools attending for OCIs in 2016:

American University, Boston University, Columbia, Cornell Law School, Fordham, George Washington University, Harvard Law School, Loyola University – Chicago, New York University, Seton Hall University, St Louis University, University of Houston, University of Maryland, University of Virginia

Summer details

Summer associate profile:

We look for law students who have a demonstrated interest in health law or labor and employment law through education and/or experience. EBG's summer associate positions are practice specific. Summer associate positions are either in the Healthcare and Life Sciences practice or in the Employment, Labor and Workforce Management practice. We prefer top one-third, law journal experience and strong writing skills.

Summer program components:

Training and development is an important goal of the summer program. Each summer associate is assigned an associate and a partner mentor to help guide them through the summer program experience. Summer associates are provided feedback throughout the summer – formally and informally. They have a midsummer review and an end-of-summer review. In addition, there is a series of educational sessions offered throughout the summer – typically two per week. Summer associates are given real assignments to work on so they have the opportunity to understand what it would be like to be a junior associate at EBG.

Head office: N/A
Number of domestic offices: 12
Number of partners (US): 121
Number of associates (US): 95

Main Recruiting Contact:
Amy Simmons
Hiring Partner: William Milani
Recruitment Website:
www.ebglaw.com
Diversity officer: Carrie Valiant

Summer Salary for 2016
1Ls: Varies by practice and location
2Ls: Varies by practice and location
Post 3Ls: N/A
1Ls hired? Yes, 2
Split summers offered? Case by case
Summers 2016: 9
Offers/acceptances 2015:
9 offers, 9 acceptances

Fenwick & West LLP

Silicon Valley Center, 801 California Street, Mountain View, CA 94041
Tel: 650 988 8500
www.fenwick.com

Main areas of work

Corporate, intellectual property, litigation and tax.

Firm profile

Fenwick & West provides comprehensive legal services to ground-breaking technology and life sciences companies – at every stage of their lifecycle – and the investors that partner with them. We craft innovative, cost-effective and practical solutions on issues ranging from venture capital, public offerings, joint ventures, M&A and strategic relationships, to intellectual property, litigation and dispute resolution, taxation, antitrust, executive compensation and employment law. For more than four decades, Fenwick has helped some of the world's most recognized companies become and remain market leaders.

Recruitment details

- Number of 1st year associates: 18
- Number of 2nd year associates: 22
- Associate salaries: 1st year: $160,000
- Clerking policy: Yes

Law Schools attending for OCIs in 2016:

Stanford; UC Berkeley; UC Hastings; UCLA; Santa Clara; UC Davis; Harvard; NYU; Columbia; University of Washington; Seattle University; Northwestern University; University of Chicago

Summer details

Summer associate profile:

At Fenwick, we both respect the individual and value collaboration. We seek out individuals with diverse backgrounds and personal experiences because we believe that the ability to bring diverse perspectives to serve our clients makes us highly-creative problem solvers and a stronger team. We look for passionate people with an entrepreneurial spirit, a self-starter mentality and intellectual curiosity. Ideal candidates will exercise and continue to develop good judgment, and take deep interest in their work and their clients. While for some practice areas, a higher degree in an area such as electrical engineering or a hard science is important, we seek individuals with a variety of backgrounds.

Summer program components:

Fenwick's ten-week summer associate program provides substantive, real-world legal work assignments. Summer associates will be able to take on a wide range of projects across our corporate, intellectual property and litigation groups, allowing for a personalized summer experience. We treat our summer associates like first-year associates, challenging them with interesting and varied work assignments. We pair each participant with a mentor and provide training and development programs throughout the summer that help students develop as an attorney. To enhance relationship building, the firm plans team building activities and social events throughout the summer. Fenwick also offers a split summer opportunity for 2L students where fellows spend the first seven weeks of the summer working as a Fenwick summer associate and the following three weeks at a Bay Area public interest organization.

Head Office: Mountain View, CA
Number of domestic offices: 3
Number of international offices: 1
Worldwide revenue: $363,590,000
Partners (US): 114
Associates (US): 226

Main Recruitment Contact: Julieta Stubrin
Hiring Partner: Bill Hughes and Carolyn Chang
Recruitment website: https://www.fenwick.com/pages/Careers-Law-Students.aspx
Diversity Officer: Gerald Audant and Felix Lee

Summer Salary 2016
1Ls: $3,076.92/week
2Ls: $3,076.92/week
Post 3Ls: An entry-level associate salary is $3,076.92/week and $160,000/year
1Ls hired? Yes
Split summers offered? Yes, on a case by case basis
Can summers spend time in overseas office? No
Summers 2016: 34
Offers/acceptances 2015:
20 offers, 18 acceptances

Firm Profiles

Finnegan, Henderson, Farabow, Garrett & Dunner LLP

901 New York Avenue, NW, Washington, DC 20001
Tel: 202 408 4000 Fax: 202 408 4400
www.finnegan.com

Main areas of work

Practice includes all aspects of patent, trademark, copyright, and trade secret law, including counseling, prosecution, licensing, patent office trials and litigation. Also, represent clients on IP issues related to international trade, portfolio management, the Internet, e-commerce, government contracts, antitrust and unfair competition.

Firm profile

Finnegan is a full-service intellectual property law firm, with a diverse blend of legal talent and cutting-edge scientific experience. Finnegan represents clients in a variety of industries including: alternative energy, biotechnology, pharmaceuticals, chemicals, consumer products, industrial manufacturing, medical devices, electronics and computers. Finnegan is positioned at the forefront of evolving intellectual property law issues and is a proven leader in the field.

Recruitment details

- Number of 1st year associates: 19
- Number of 2nd year associates: 24
- Associate salaries: 1st year: $160,000
- 2nd year: $170,000
- Clerking policy: Yes

Law Schools attending for OCIs in 2016:

Alabama; American; Arizona State; Berkeley; Boston College; Boston University; Duke; Emory; Florida; George Mason; George Washington; Georgetown; Georgia; Georgia State; Harvard; Hastings; Howard; Maryland; New Hampshire; UNC at Chapel Hill; Pennsylvania; Santa Clara; Stanford; University of Texas, Austin; Vanderbilt; Virginia; Washington

Summer details

Summer associate profile:

Summer associates at Finnegan are committed to excelling in intellectual property law. They are expected to demonstrate the ability to analyze complex legal issues, write clearly and persuasively, show initiative and manage time effectively. Above all, they are expected to be team players who work and interact well with others.

Summer program components:

Finnegan's summer associates have an opportunity to work on a broad range of matters in all of our practice areas. They complete substantive work related to their interests, receive extensive training and often have the chance to observe oral argument at the CAFC, participate in client meetings and attend depositions. Finnegan's summer program aims to acclimate students to firm culture and to prepare them for life as an associate. All summer associates are assigned both a partner and an associate mentor. Feedback is given formally at midsummer and final reviews.

Head Office: Washington, DC
Number of domestic offices: 5
Number of international offices: 5
Worldwide revenue: $308,099,651
Partners (US): 120
Associates (US): 141

Main Recruitment Contact:
Laurie Taylor
Hiring Partner: Scott Burwell
Recruitment website:
www.finnegan.com
Diversity officer: Sanya Sukduang

Summer Salary 2016
1Ls: $3,100/week
2Ls: $3,100/week
Post 3Ls: N/A
1Ls hired? Yes
Split summers offered? No
Can summers spend time in overseas office? No
Summers 2016: 28
Offers/acceptances 2015:
17 offers, 17 acceptances

FINNEGAN

Fish & Richardson PC

One Marina Park Drive, Boston, MA 02210
Tel: 617 542 5070 Fax: 617 542 8906
www.fr.com

Main areas of work

Fish & Richardson offers top-rated litigation, patent, regulatory, trademark, and copyright services to help clients maximize the value of their intellectual property.

Firm profile

Fish & Richardson is a global patent, intellectual property (IP) litigation, and commercial litigation law firm with more than 400 attorneys and technology specialists across the US and in Europe. Named number one for patent litigation in the US for 12 consecutive years, Fish maintains its elite position by consistently winning the most important, technically sophisticated, bet-the-company patent cases for clients such as Microsoft, 3M, Bose, Samsung, LG, Allergan, Bank of America, and Smith & Nephew. Since 1878, Fish has won cases worth billions in controversy—often by making new law—for the most innovative clients and influential industry leaders.

Recruitment details

- Number of 1st year associates: 25
- Number of 2nd year associates: 20 (US); 22 including Munich
- Associate salaries: 1st year: $160,000 • Clerking policy: Yes

Law Schools attending for OCIs in 2016:

Baylor Law School, Boston College, Boston University, Columbia, Emory, Fordham, Georgetown, George Washington, Harvard, NYU, Santa Clara University, SMU, Stanford, Temple, UC Berkeley, UC Davis, UC Hastings, University of Houston Law Center, UCLA, University of Michigan, University of Minnesota, University of Pennsylvania, University of San Diego, USC, University of Texas, University of Virginia, Vanderbilt Law School, Boston Lawyers Group Job Fair, Delaware Minority Job Fair, Patent Law Interview Program (Chicago), Southeastern IP Job Fair

Summer details

Summer associate profile:

Fish seeks students with excellent academic credentials and superior writing ability. For many positions, a scientific or technical background is preferred (required for patent prosecution candidates). Summer associates at Fish are given meaningful work assignments and plenty of opportunities to interact with the attorneys. They may prepare patent and trademark applications; conduct research for litigation cases; and attend client meetings, depositions, and even trials. They also receive one-on-one training from attorneys and participate in the firm's nationwide video conferences. In addition to informal feedback from attorneys throughout the summer, summer associates are given feedback on their work during midsummer and end-of-summer reviews. To help integrate summer associates into the firm and the city in which the office is located, Fish plans social events and assigns a mentor to each summer associate based on common interests, educational background, and other criteria.

Head Office: Boston, MA
Number of domestic offices: 11
Number of international offices: 1
Worldwide revenue: $394,959,808
Partners (US): 174
Associates (US): 142

Main Recruitment Contact:
Kelly Mixon Morgan, National Director of Attorney Hiring
Hiring Principal:
Betty Chen
Recruitment website:
www.fr.com/careers/
Diversity officer: Ahmed Davis, National Diversity Chair

Summer Salary 2016
1Ls: $3,100/week
2Ls: $3,100/week
Post 3Ls: N/A
1Ls hired? Yes
Split summers offered? Yes, with minimum week requirement
Can summers spend time in overseas office? No
Summers 2016: 42 (32 2Ls, 10 1Ls)
Offers/acceptances 2015:
37 offers, 26 acceptances (including 1 post-clerkship), 2 pending

FISH.
FISH & RICHARDSON

Firm Profiles

Fitzpatrick, Cella, Harper & Scinto

1290 Avenue of the Americas, New York, NY 10104
Tel: 212 218 2100 Fax: 212 218 2200
www.fitzpatrickcella.com

Main areas of work

All areas of intellectual property law, including patents, trademarks, copyrights, unfair competition and trade secrets.

Firm profile

Fitzpatrick, Cella, Harper & Scinto has grown to approximately 175 attorneys in New York, Washington, DC and Orange County, California. We have one of the premier patent litigation practices in the nation and also prosecute more than twice as many patents as any other New York-based firm. The quality and experience of our attorneys is second to none. In addition to superior legal qualifications, the overwhelming majority of our attorneys hold scientific or engineering degrees and many also have substantial industry experience. Our attorneys also have a long history of pro bono work, as well as active involvement in bar associations and community organizations.

Recruitment details

- Number of 1st year associates: 9
- Number of 2nd year associates: 9
- Associate salaries: 1st year: $160,000
- Clerking policy: Yes

Law Schools attending for OCIs in 2016:

American, Boston College, Boston University, Brooklyn, Cardozo, Columbia, Fordham, George Washington, Georgetown, Harvard, New York Law School, New York University, Notre Dame, Pace, Rutgers, Seton Hall, St John's, University of Houston, University of Michigan, University of New Hampshire and the University of Pennsylvania

Job Fairs/Consortia attending in 2016: Cornell Job Fair, Emory in New York, New York Interview Program, University of Connecticut NY Job Fair, and the Loyola Patent Interview Program

Summer details

Summer associate profile:

Fitzpatrick is looking for a diverse group of summer associates with science or engineering degrees. Our summer associates are team-oriented, motivated and have excelled academically. We like to see candidates that are enthusiastic about IP.

Summer program components:

Summer associates will have significant involvement in intellectual property matters, including playing substantive roles in litigation teams. Each summer associate has a partner and associate mentor to provide counsel and advice with assignments. Fitzpatrick will also provide formal training through seminars, a legal writing course, a fact investigation course and deposition workshop.

Head Office: New York, NY
Number of domestic offices: 3
Worldwide revenue: N/A
Partners (US): 54
Of Counsel: 7
Counsel: 3
Associates (US): 82

Main Recruitment Contact:
Nicole Cohen
Hiring Partner: Ha Kung Wong
Recruitment website:
www.fitzpatrickcella.com
Diversity officer: Tara Byrne

Summer Salary 2016
1Ls: $3,076/week
2Ls: $3,076/week
Post 3Ls: N/A
1Ls hired? Yes
Split summers offered? Only in exceptional circumstances
Summers 2016: 9
Offers/acceptances 2015:
7 offers, 7 acceptances

Foley Hoag LLP

155 Seaport Boulevard, Boston, MA 02210
Tel: 617 832 1000 Fax: 617 832 7000
www.foleyhoag.com

Main areas of work

Business crimes and government investigations; corporate finance and securities; corporate social responsibility; energy, technology and renewables; environmental litigation; government strategies; insurance recovery; international litigation and arbitration; investment management; labor and employment; licensing and strategic alliances; life sciences and health care; mergers and acquisitions; patent litigation; patent prosecution; professional liability litigation; tax; trademark, copyright and unfair competition.

Firm profile

For nearly seven decades, Foley Hoag has represented public and private clients in a wide range of disputes and transactions around the world. We have established a lengthy record of success in industries such as life sciences, health care, technology, energy/renewables, investment management, and professional services. We deeply understand our clients' businesses, priorities, strategies and industries. We are connected to the entrepreneurial community and detect emerging trends that will affect clients down the road. We have a reputation for an intellectual approach to case analysis and efficiently developing creative, compelling legal strategies. Foley Hoag lawyers are innovative, energetic and entrepreneurial, and we seek new lawyers who possess these same traits.

Recruitment details

- Number of 1st year associates: 14
- Number of 2nd year associates: 12
- Associate salaries: 1st year: $160,000
- 2nd year: $165,000
- Clerking policy: Foley Hoag provides salary and tenure credit, as well as a judicial clerkship bonus, to associates who join the firm upon completion of a federal district or circuit court clerkship or a state supreme court clerkship

Law Schools attending for OCIs in 2016:

Boston College, Boston University, Columbia, Cornell, Georgetown, Harvard, New York University, Northeastern, University of Pennsylvania, University of Virginia, and Yale.

Summer details

Summer associate profile:

We hire lawyers who have excelled academically, who are intellectually curious, and whose intelligence, character and creativity will inspire the confidence of clients and colleagues. We seek lawyers who take initiative, who strive for and achieve excellence, and who are motivated by a desire to make a difference - not only in their profession, but in their community as well.

Summer program components:

We work hard to build a summer associate program that provides a realistic look at life at Foley Hoag. Summer associates have the opportunity to choose their own assignments, experiencing as many or as few practice areas as they'd like. They work on real matters for real clients. They participate in team strategy meetings, go to court, attend negotiations, and assist in contract drafting. They receive on-the-job training, advice and feedback from seasoned partners and associates, and take part in seminars aimed at transforming their law school knowledge into real world skills.

Head Office: Boston
Number of domestic offices: 3
Number of international offices: 1
Worldwide revenue: $173,700,000
Partners (US): 112
Associates (US): 127

Main Recruitment Contact:
Dina M Wreede, Director of Legal Recruiting
Hiring Partner: Paul G Sweeney
Recruitment website: http://recruiting.foleyhoag.com/
Diversity Officer: Adam P Kahn, Co-Managing Partner

Summer Salary 2016
1Ls: $3,077 per week
2Ls: $3,077 per week
Post 3Ls: $3,077 per week
1Ls hired? Yes
Split summers offered? No
Can summers spend time in overseas office? No
Summers 2016: 15
Offers/acceptances 2015:
10 offers, 10 acceptances

Firm Profiles

Foley & Lardner LLP

777 E. Wisconsin Avenue, Milwaukee, WI 53202-5306
Tel: 414 271 2400 Fax: 414 297 4900
Email: rbradley@foley.com
www.foley.com

Main areas of work

With more than 850 attorneys spread across 17 domestic offices and 3 foreign offices, Foley's market-leading platform includes business law, government and public policy, international, intellectual property and litigation. Adding depth to our bench strength, we address and anticipate client needs across more than 60 core practice areas and 12 cross-disciplinary industry teams.

Firm profile

Foley provides award-winning business and legal insight to clients across the country and around the world. Creating legal strategies that help meet our clients' needs today – and anticipate their challenges tomorrow – Foley is continually recognized by our clients and the legal industry for our exceptional client service, thought-leadership, value, and innovative technology.

Recruitment details

- Number of 1st year associates: 34
- Number of 2nd year associates: 51
- Associate salaries: 1st year: $120,000-$160,000 (varies by geographic market)
- 2nd year: $130,000-$175,000 (varies by geographic market)
- Clerking policy: Yes

Law Schools attending for OCIs in 2016:

Boston College, Boston University, Columbia, Cornell, Duke, Florida State University, Fordham, George Washington, Georgetown, Harvard, Howard, Marquette University, New York University, Northwestern, Notre Dame, Stanford, UC-Berkeley, UC-Davis, UCLA, University of Chicago, University of Florida, University of Illinois, University of Iowa, University of Michigan, University of Minnesota, University of Pennsylvania, University of Southern California, University of Virginia, University of Wisconsin, Vanderbilt, Yale

Summer details

Summer associate profile:

Foley is looking for summer associates with an entrepreneurial spirit who bring diverse life and work experiences. Key attributes also include intellect, academic achievement, judgment and leadership abilities and excellent communication and interpersonal skills.

Summer program components:

We aim to introduce our summer associates to life as a Foley associate. Making significant contributions from day one, our summer associates are immersed in real world, practical experiences. Work is assigned on a project basis, which allows summer associates to experience a variety of practice areas and choose projects that match their interests. Summer associates receive a dedicated mentor and our training programs highlight Foley's culture, practice areas and strategic goals while developing and strengthening professional skills. To round out the experience, our summer associates participate in entertaining social events, including a firmwide retreat, where summer associates hear directly from firm leadership, participate in interactive workshops and training programs and build and strengthen relationships with our attorneys and other members of their class.

Head Office: Milwaukee, WI
Number of domestic offices: 17
Number of international offices: 3
Worldwide revenue: $682,000,000
Partners (US): 411
Associates (US): 457

Main Recruitment Contact:
Rebecca S Bradley
Hiring Partner: Robert A Scher
Recruitment website:
www.foleyrecruiting.com
Diversity officer: Eileen R Ridley

Summer Salary 2016
1Ls: $2,300-$3,100/week
2Ls: $2,300-$3,100/week
Post 3Ls: $2,300-$3,100/week
1Ls hired? Yes
Split summers offered? Case by case
Can summers spend time in overseas office? No
Summers 2016: 64
Offers/acceptances 2015:
54 offers, 46 acceptances

Firm Profiles

Fox Rothschild LLP

2000 Market Street, Philadelphia, PA 19103
Tel: 215 299 2000 Fax: 215 299 2150
www.foxrothschild.com

Main areas of work

Corporate; entertainment; financial restructuring and bankruptcy; intellectual property; labor and employment; litigation; real estate; taxation and wealth planning.

Firm profile

Fox Rothschild LLP is a national law firm with nearly 750 lawyers practicing in 22 offices coast to coast. Our lawyers provide a full range of legal services to public and private companies – from family-run businesses to multinational corporations. We also represent charitable, medical and educational institutions both in the United States and in more than 50 countries worldwide.

Recruitment details

- Number of 1st year associates: 14
- Number of 2nd year associates: 19
- Associate salaries: 1st year: $110,000-$145,000 depending on geographic location
- 2nd year: Non lock step compensation
- Clerking policy: Yes

Law Schools attending for OCIs in 2016:

Berkeley; Cardozo: Chicago; Chicago-Kent; Colorado; Columbia; Cornell; Delaware; Denver; Duquesne; Fordham; GWU; Georgetown; Loyola (Chicago); Loyola (Los Angeles); Minnesota; Mitchell Hamline; Nevada; Northwestern; Penn State; Penn; Pittsburgh; Rutgers; Seton Hall; SMU; St. Thomas; Temple; Texas; UCLA; UC Hastings; USC; Villanova

Job Fairs/Consortia attending in 2016: BC/BU NY Recruitment Program; Delaware Minority Job Fair; NJ Law Firm Group Minority Job Fair; Philadelphia Area Minority Job Fair

Summer details

Summer associate profile:

Our summer program is the foundation of our recruiting efforts. Each summer we invite a diverse group of bright, highly motivated law students to experience the practice of law at Fox Rothschild. Since the majority of our new lawyers come from the pool of second year summer associates who complete our program, we consider the summer program the most important component of the recruiting process.

Summer program components:

Our summer program is designed to expose summer associates to a realistic view of what it is like to practice law at Fox Rothschild. The program provides ongoing interaction with the attorneys on substantive assignments and during varied social events. Summer associates receive work assignments from all departments. We strive to ensure that the assignments given to summer associates are interesting and meaningful, with the results of that work used by our attorneys. Feedback is provided on an assignment-by-assignment basis, as well as through more formal mid-and end-of-summer evaluations. In addition, we encourage all summer associates to provide us with a detailed critique of all aspects of the summer program.

Head Office: Philadelphia, PA
Number of domestic offices: 22
Number of international offices: 0
Partners (US): 450
Associates (US): 227

Main Recruitment Contact:
Natalie Quinn, Associate Recruitment Manager
Recruitment website:
www.foxrothschild.com/careers
Diversity officers: Yesenia Gallegos and Prince Thomas, Diversity Committee Co-Chairs

Summer Salary 2016
1Ls: $1,900/week
2Ls: $2,211-$2,788/week
Post 3Ls: N/A
1Ls hired? Yes
Split summers offered? No
Summers 2016: 28
Offers/acceptances 2015:
16 offers, 16 acceptances

Freshfields Bruckhaus Deringer US LLP

601 Lexington Avenue, 31st Floor, New York, NY 10022
Tel: 212 277 4000 Fax: 212 277 4001
www.freshfields.com

Main areas of work

Freshfields' US offices concentrate on corporate and finance transactions, antitrust, tax, litigation and international arbitration, while the firm's US attorneys based in Europe and Asia focus on corporate and securities transactions.

Firm profile

With over 2,500 lawyers in 26 key business centers around the world, Freshfields combines an unrivalled breadth of expertise across practice areas and borders with tremendous growth opportunities within the US practices. This unique balance defines the firm's work style and culture. On one side, there's the friendliness, personal attention and lack of hierarchy one finds in a small firm; on the other, the comprehensive network, breadth of work and resources of an international organization. Freshfields prides itself on being a collegial firm, working and learning together in a cutting edge, global environment.

Recruitment details

- Number of 1st year associates: 16
- Number of 2nd year associates: 16
- Associate salaries: 1st year: $160,000
- 2nd year: $170,000
- Clerking policy: Yes

Law Schools attending for OCIs in 2016:

University of Chicago Law School, Columbia University Law School, Cornell Law School, Duke Law School, Emory University School of Law, Fordham University School of Law, George Washington University Law School, Georgetown University Law Center, Harvard Law School, University of Michigan Law School, New York University School of Law, Northwestern University School of Law, University of Pennsylvania Law School, Stanford Law School, Tulane/Vanderbilt/Washington University Job Fair, UC Berkeley School of Law, University of Virginia, Yale Law School

Summer details

Summer associate profile:

Freshfields recruits lawyers with many different talents and values individuality. The firm's ability to offer diverse skills locally and across international borders ensures clients have the very best advice possible. Freshfields operates a summer program for US law students in its New York, Washington, DC, Hong Kong, and London offices.

Summer program components:

Freshfields' 11 week summer program provides summer associates with exposure to several practice areas. Summer associates get substantive work supported by both formal and informal mentors. Most summer associates spend part of their summer in other Freshfields overseas offices such as London or Hong Kong.

Head Office: New York, NY
Number of domestic offices: 2
Number of international offices: 24
Worldwide revenue: $1.91 billion
Partners (US): 36
Counsel (US): 11
Associates (US): 128

Main Recruitment Contact:
Lesley Slater Stumphauzer
212 230 4674
Hiring Partner: Jerome Ranawake
Recruitment website:
http://www.freshfields.com/en/united_states/careers/

Summer Salary 2016
1Ls: $3,077/week
2Ls: $3,077/week
1Ls hired? Yes
Split summers offered? No
Can summers spend time in overseas office? Yes
Summers 2016: 25
Offers/acceptances 2015:
22 offers, 18 acceptances

Freshfields Bruckhaus Deringer US LLP

Fried, Frank, Harris, Shriver & Jacobson LLP

One New York Plaza, New York, NY 10004
Tel: 212 859 8000 Fax: 212 859 4000
www.friedfrank.com

Main areas of work

Antitrust and competition; bankruptcy and restructuring; corporate (asset management, capital markets, corporate governance, derivatives, environmental, finance, mergers and acquisitions, private acquisitions and private equity); energy and energy enforcement; executive compensation and employee benefits; financial services; intellectual property and technology; international arbitration; international trade and investment; litigation (antitrust litigation, commercial litigation, government contracts, healthcare fraud and compliance, securities and shareholder litigation, securities enforcement and regulation, white collar criminal defense and securities enforcement); pro bono; real estate (corporate; acquisitions, dispositions and related financings; restructuring and financing; leasing; land use, construction and development); tax; trusts and estates; white collar criminal defense.

Firm profile

Fried, Frank, Harris, Shriver & Jacobson LLP is a leading international law firm with offices in New York; Washington, DC; London; Paris; Frankfurt; Hong Kong; and Shanghai. Our lawyers regularly advise the world's leading corporations and financial institutions on their most critical legal needs and business opportunities.

Recruitment details

- Number of 1st year associates: 43
- Number of 2nd year associates: 30
- Associate salaries: 1st year: $160,000
- 2nd year: $170,000
- Clerking policy: Yes

Law Schools attending for OCIs in 2016:

Boston College, Boston University, Brooklyn, SUNY Buffalo, Cardozo, University of Chicago, Columbia, Cornell, Duke University, Fordham, Georgetown University, George Washington University, Harvard, Hofstra University, Howard University, University of Michigan, Northwestern University, New York Law, New York University, University of Pennsylvania, Rutgers – Newark, St John's University, University of Virginia, Yale

Summer details

Summer associate profile:

In hiring summer and full time associates, we look for energetic, motivated candidates who demonstrate a high level of intellectual ability and creativity, as well as a strong interest in working in a collegial setting.

Summer program components:

During the program, summer associates receive meaningful work assignments in a variety of practice areas, as well as attend court, client meetings, drafting and negotiation sessions and closings. They are also given significant opportunities to work on a range of pro bono matters. Each summer associate is matched with one partner mentor and two associate mentors, who review and provide feedback on assignments and guide them through the program. Working closely and socializing with partners, counsel and associates, our summer associates leave the program with a clear understanding of what Fried Frank can offer them as a place to begin their legal careers.

Head Office: New York, NY
Number of domestic offices: 2
Number of international offices: 5

Main Recruitment Contact:
Robert Edwards
Hiring Partners: Steven Steinman, Lisa Bebchick, and Michelle Gold (DC)
Recruitment website:
www.friedfrank.com/careers
Diversity officer: Don Smith

Summer Salary 2016
1Ls: $3,100/week
2Ls: $3,100/week
Post 3Ls: $3,100/week
1Ls hired? No
Split summers offered? Case by case
Can summers spend time in overseas office? No
Summers 2016: 72
Offers/acceptances 2015:
47 offers, 44 acceptances

Gibbons PC

One Gateway Center, Newark, New Jersey 07102
Tel: 973 596 4500 Fax: 973 596 0545
Email: firm@gibbonslaw.com
www.gibbonslaw.com

Main areas of work

The firm's main areas of practice include business and commercial litigation, corporate, criminal defense, employment and labor law, financial restructuring and creditors' rights, government affairs, intellectual property, products liability and real property and environmental.

Firm profile

With more than 200 attorneys, Gibbons is a leading law firm in New Jersey, New York, Pennsylvania and Delaware, ranked among the nation's top 200 firms by American Lawyer. Gibbons is one of only 20 law firms nationwide to be named to the National Law Journal's inaugural "Midsize Hot List", which recognized firms with fewer than 300 lawyers that have found innovative ways to position themselves and demonstrated creativity and success in recruiting and retaining top talent, developing practice areas, managing operations and generally navigating the economic downturn more effectively than did many larger firms. A 2009 winner of the prestigious Catalyst Award for its innovative Women's Initiative, Gibbons is ranked one of the top 50 firms nationwide for working women by Working Mother magazine. The firm has also been recognized among the Best Places to Work in America by the Society for Human Resource Management and Great Place to Work Institute, as well as in New Jersey, New York and Pennsylvania by NJBIZ, Crain's New York Business, Philadelphia Business Journal, and Central Penn Business Journal. Gibbons maintains offices in Newark, New Jersey; New York, New York; Trenton, New Jersey; Philadelphia, Pennsylvania; and Wilmington, Delaware.

Head Office: Newark, NJ
Number of domestic offices: 5
Number of international offices: 0
Partners (US): 135
Associates (US): 70

Main Recruitment Contact:
Peter J Torcicollo
Hiring Partner: Peter J Torcicollo
Recruitment website:
www.gibbonslaw.com
Diversity officer: Luis J Diaz

Recruitment details

- Number of 1st year associates: 0
- Number of 2nd year associates: 6
- Associate salaries: 1st year: N/A
- 2nd year: $135,000 + clerkship bonus
- Clerking policy: Yes

Summer details

Summer associate profile:

Since eliminating the firm's Summer Associate Program in 2003, Gibbons has focused on hiring new associates who have completed a judicial clerkship. Fully 70 percent of the attorneys in the Business and Commercial Litigation Department served for federal or state judges. These attorneys provide first-hand insight into the preferences and practices of federal and state judges, in addition to a well-developed knowledge of the inner workings of the courts, adding value for the firm's clients.

Gibson, Dunn & Crutcher LLP

333 South Grand Avenue, Los Angeles, CA 90071
Tel: 213 229 7000 Fax: 213 229 7520
Email: lripley@gibsondunn.com
www.gibsondunn.com

Main areas of work

Gibson, Dunn & Crutcher is renowned for both its litigation and transactional work. Major practice groups include antitrust, capital markets, class actions, environmental, electronic discovery, information technology, intellectual property, media and entertainment, mergers and acquisitions, securities, transnational litigation and white-collar defense. The firm is especially known for its appellate work, particularly in the US Supreme Court.

Firm profile

Gibson, Dunn & Crutcher is a full-service global law firm, with over 1,300 lawyers in 18 offices worldwide, including nine offices in major cities throughout the United States and over 170 lawyers in their London, Paris, Munich, Beijing, Brussels, Dubai, Hong Kong, Singapore and São Paulo offices. The firm is recognized for excellent legal service and its lawyers routinely represent clients in some of the most high-profile litigations and complex transactions in the world.

Recruitment details

- Number of 1st year associates: 87
- Number of 2nd year associates: 121
- Associate salaries: 1st year: $160,000
- 2nd year: $170,000
- Clerking policy: Yes

Law Schools attending for OCIs in 2016:

Berkeley, Chicago, Colorado, Columbia, Cornell, Duke, Fordham, George Washington, Georgetown, Harvard, Irvine, Loyola, Michigan, NYU, Northwestern, Pennsylvania, Pepperdine, San Diego, SMU, Stanford, Texas, UCLA, USC, Virginia, Yale

Summer details

Summer associate profile:

Gibson Dunn's summer program is the single largest means through which new lawyers become a part of our firm. Each summer, Gibson Dunn brings together approximately 125 of the most accomplished and ambitious students from the top law schools across the nation, providing them with real involvement in the high quality legal work that our firm does every day. Our summer associates are involved directly in the firm's representation of its clients, maximizing their exposure to the practical aspects of lawyering. In addition to interesting client work, the summer program includes many great social activities giving summer associates the chance to get to know each other and the lawyers of the firm.

Summer program components:

The firm provides significant and substantive training to our select group of summer associates. Each summer associate receives detailed feedback on the projects that they perform plus numerous formal training programs.

Head Office: Los Angeles, CA
Number of domestic offices: 9
Number of international offices: 9
Worldwide revenue: $1,535,271,000
Partners (US): 314
Associates (US): 768

Main Recruitment Contact:
Leslie Ripley, Chief Recruiting Officer
Hiring Partner: Steven E Sletten
Recruitment website:
www.gibsondunn.com
Diversity officer: Zakiyyah Salim-Williams

1Ls hired? Yes
Split summers offered? Yes
Can summers spend time in overseas office? No
Summers 2016: 125
Offers/acceptances 2015:
115 offers, 94 acceptances as of 1/22/16

GIBSON DUNN

Goodwin Procter LLP

www.goodwinlaw.com

Main areas of work

Corporate-based practices: financial institutions, intellectual property transactions and strategies, private equity, REITs and real estate capital markets, tax and technology and life sciences.

Litigation-based practices: business litigation, consumer financial services, intellectual property, products liability and mass torts, securities litigation and white-collar defense.

Firm profile

Goodwin is one of the nation's leading law firms, with offices in Boston, Hong Kong, Frankfurt, Los Angeles, London, New York, Paris, San Francisco, Silicon Valley and Washington, DC. Excelling at complex and sophisticated transactional work and precedent-setting, bet-the company litigation, the firm combines in-depth legal knowledge with practical business experience to help clients maximize opportunities, manage risk and move their business forward. The firm hires talented, motivated people committed to excellence, innovation, collaboration and client service and believes that every attorney and staff member deserves a supportive, meritocratic environment in which people of all backgrounds are given the opportunity to excel and thrive. Through an extensive and longstanding pro bono program, legal staff are encouraged to assist those unable to afford legal representation.

Recruitment details

- Number of 1st year associates: 59
- Number of 2nd year associates: 80
- Associate Salaries: 1st Year: $160,000
- 2nd Year: $170,000
- Clerking policy: Yes

Law Schools attending for OCIs in 2016:

Berkeley, Boston College, Boston University, Brooklyn, Catholic University of America, Columbia, Cornell, Duke, Emory, Fordham, George Washington, Georgetown, Harvard, Howard, Loyola Law School (Los Angeles), Northeastern, Northwestern, NYU, Santa Clara, Stanford, Suffolk, UC Davis, UC Hastings, UCLA, UNC, University of Chicago, University of Connecticut, University of Michigan, University of Pennsylvania, University of Texas, USC, UVA, William & Mary, Yale

Summer details

Summer associate profile:

Goodwin hires summer associates with exceptional academic records, demonstrated leadership abilities and excellent written, verbal and interpersonal skills.

Summer program components:

Goodwin's summer program provides summer associates with a realistic work experience mirroring that of a junior associate. We work closely with summer associates to understand their interests and provide opportunities to work on a broad range of assignments. Summer associates are encouraged to observe client meetings, court hearings, depositions, negotiations and attend practice area meetings. We provide leading litigation and business law training programs throughout the summer. Through our advisor program, each summer associate is paired with partners and associates to help integrate them into the firm.

Largest Office: Boston, MA
Number of domestic offices: 6
Number of international offices: 4
Worldwide revenue: $865,500,000
Partners (US): 318
Counsel (US): 84
Associates (US): 441

Main Recruitment Contact:
Ashley Nelson, Director of Legal Recruitment, Associate & Professional Track Hiring, or see the list of office-based recruiting contacts on our website
Hiring Partner: Kenneth J Gordon, National Hiring Partner
Recruitment website: www.goodwinlaw.com/law-students
Diversity officer: Laura Acosta, Senior Manager of Diversity & Professional Development

Summer Salary 2016
1Ls: $3,077/week
2Ls: $3,077/week
Post 3Ls: N/A
1Ls hired? Yes
Split summers offered? No
Can summers spend time in overseas office? Case by case
Summers 2016: 57
Offers/acceptances 2015:
65 offers, 60 acceptances

Goulston & Storrs

400 Atlantic Avenue, Boston, MA 02110
Tel: 617 482 1776 Fax: 617 574 4112
Email: jsmith@goulstonstorrs.com
www.goulstonstorrs.com

Main areas of work

Real estate, litigation, tax, private clients and trusts, capital markets, bankruptcy, corporate, employment, banking and finance, environmental, intellectual property.

Firm profile

Goulston & Storrs is an Am Law 200 law firm, with offices in Boston, New York, Washington, DC and Beijing. With nearly 200 lawyers across multiple disciplines, Goulston & Storrs is nationally recognized for its real estate practice, leading-edge corporate, capital markets and finance, litigation, and private client and trust practices. Our lawyers employ a proven team approach that values client outcomes over individual recognition. The firm's dedication to providing prompt, practical legal advice, cost-efficiently and tailored to our clients' business needs, has resulted in Goulston & Storrs being acknowledged for excellence by Chambers USA, BTI's A-Team for Client Service, Best Lawyers in America and other leading industry rankings.

Recruitment details

- Number of 1st year associates: 4
- Number of 2nd year associates: 5
- Associate salaries: 1st year: $160,000

Law Schools attending for OCIs in 2016:

Harvard, Georgetown University, Columbia University, Northeastern University, New York University, Boston College, Boston University, Suffolk University

Summer details

Summer associate profile:

We attract and hire people who: seek a sophisticated and challenging legal practice; are concerned about team success; are willing to work hard.

Summer program components:

As a summer associate, you have a unique opportunity to learn about the legal profession and the Boston area. Expect to live the law firm experience with direct partner and client exposure. Work assignments are substantive and include research and writing assignments, client meetings, conference calls, depositions and attending hearings. Your summer with Goulston & Storrs offers amazing work opportunities throughout several practice areas, assisting the firm's attorneys.

Head Office: Boston, MA
Number of domestic offices: 3
Number of international offices: 1
Worldwide revenue: $157,000,000
Partners (US): 113
Associates (US): 65

Main Recruitment Contacts:
Nancy Needle and Jen Smith
Hiring Partner: Bill Seuch
Recruitment website:
www.goulstonstorrs.com
Diversity Officers: Kevin O'Flaherty and Matt Epstein

Summer Salary 2016
1Ls: $3,100 per week
2Ls: $3,100 per week
1Ls hired? Yes
Split summers offered? Case by case basis
Can summers spend time in overseas office? No
Summers 2016: 7
Offers/acceptances 2015:
6 offers, 6 acceptances

Greenberg Traurig, LLP

Tel: 212 801 9200 Fax: 212 801 6400
Email: gtrecruiting@gtlaw.com
www.gtlaw.com

Main areas of work

Corporate and securities; litigation; real estate; health and FDA business; intellectual property and technology; global trade and investment; cybersecurity, privacy and crisis management; energy and natural resources; business reorganization and financial restructuring; tax, trusts and estates; government law and policy; public finance; entertainment and media; labor and employment; environmental; global practice group; and business immigration and compliance.

Firm profile

Greenberg Traurig, LLP is an international, multi-practice law firm with approximately 1950 attorneys serving clients from 38 offices in the United States, Latin America, Europe, the Middle East, and Asia. The firm works with clients to address their multi-disciplinary and cross-border needs. Providing associates with the type of client management and business development training previously offered only to partners are key elements to our associate programs.

Recruitment details

- Number of 1st year associates: 44
- Number of 2nd year associates: 69
- Associate salaries: 1st year: N/A
- 2nd year: N/A

Law Schools attending for OCIs in 2016:

Berkeley; Brooklyn; Chicago-Kent; Columbia; Cornell; Duke; FIU; Fordham; Georgetown; George Washington; Harvard; Loyola; NYU; Northwestern; Notre Dame; Santa Clara; SMU Dedman; Stanford; UC Hastings; UC Irvine; UCLA; Univ of Chicago; Univ of Florida; Univ of Illinois; Univ of Las Vegas; Univ of Miami; Univ of Michigan; Univ of Pennsylvania; Univ of Southern California; Univ of Texas; Univ of Virginia; Vanderbilt

Summer details

Summer associate profile:

We recruit students who excel in multiple areas, possessing what we call "3-D" skills (legal, business and leadership), as these are predictors for success in the Greenberg Traurig community.

Summer program components:

We provide summer associates varied professional opportunities to learn about our clients, our attorneys, our staff, our firm and our culture including:

- Day-to-day assignments, with direct shareholder contact
- Dedicated firmwide training and orientation
- Two mentors, one associate and one shareholder
- Mid-summer and end-of-summer review meetings with Summer Program leaders
- A variety of networking events and community outreach programs

An important objective of the program is for summer associates to transition from student to legal practitioner. Our attorneys and attorney recruitment staff help clarify and direct summer associates' decision-making about the start of their legal careers. The Summer Associate Highway blog provides an inside glimpse at Greenberg Traurig's summer associate program.

Head Office: Global
Number of domestic offices: 29
Number of international offices: 9
Worldwide revenue: $1,320,000,000
Partners (US): 968
Associates (US): 1017

Main Recruitment Contact:
Janet McKeegan
Hiring Partner: Bradford D Kaufman
Recruitment website:
www.gtlaw.com/Careers/Associates
Diversity Officer: Nikki Lewis Simon

Summer Salary 2016
1Ls: N/A
2Ls: N/A
Post 3Ls: N/A
1Ls hired? Yes
Split summers offered? CBC
Can summers spend time in overseas office? CBC
Summers 2016: 46
Offers/acceptances 2015:
37 offers, 37 acceptances

Hangley Aronchick Segal Pudlin & Schiller

One Logan Square, 27th Floor, Philadelphia, PA 19103
Tel: 215 568 6200 Fax: 215 568 0300
Email: marketingdept@hangley.com
www.hangley.com

Main areas of work

Hangley Aronchick Segal Pudlin & Schiller is a multi-faceted law firm that offers specialized legal solutions to a broad range of local, regional, and national clients. The firm is highly regarded nationally for its quality work, innovative strategies, and excellent results. With offices in Philadelphia, Harrisburg, and Norristown, Pennsylvania, and Cherry Hill, New Jersey, Hangley Aronchick offers a suite of diverse legal services, including litigation, business and corporate, insurance coverage, real estate, bankruptcy, education, environmental, family law, and tax and estate planning services.

Head Office: Philadelphia, PA
Number of domestic offices: 4
Number of international offices: 0

Hiring Partner: Daniel Segal, Chair of Hiring Committee
Recruitment website: www.hangley.com/careers/

Firm profile

Hangley Aronchick Segal Pudlin & Schiller is consistently recognized for excellence in legal practice, as well as for its ability to recruit talented attorneys. Founded in 1994, the firm is known for the sophistication of its matters, the roster of its clients and the quality of its work. In the Delaware Valley, the firm is unparalleled in its ability to attract the most highly qualified attorneys, both at the entry level and laterally. The firm includes former Philadelphia City Solicitors; Fellows of the American College of Trial Lawyers, the American College of Bankruptcy, and the American College of Real Estate Lawyers; members of judicial advisory committees; members of the American Law Institute; and adjunct faculty members at area law schools. For further information on the firm's practice areas and outstanding lawyers, readers are invited to visit the firm's website www.hangley.com

Recruitment details

- Number of 1st year associates: 1
- Number of 2nd year associates: 1
- Associate Salaries: 1st Year: $135,000
- Clerking policy: Yes

Summer details

Summer program components:

Hangley Aronchick Segal Pudlin & Schiller does not have a formal summer associate program, though the firm will consider extraordinary candidates for summer employment on occasion.

Harris, Wiltshire & Grannis LLP

1919 M Street NW, Eighth Floor, Washington, DC 20036
Tel: 202 730 1300 Fax: 202 730 1301
Email: attorneyrecruiting@hwglaw.com
www.hwglaw.com

Main areas of work

Harris, Wiltshire & Grannis is a boutique law firm, meaning we focus on solving fairly specialized legal problems extremely well. We have excellent trial litigators who handle government investigations and criminal defense matters as well as complex civil litigation. We also have an exceptional Supreme Court and appellate litigation group as well as one of the leading legal and government ethics practices. However, the firm started out as a telecom and technology firm and that is still our primary area of practice. We handle just about any kind of matter before the FCC, representing companies both large and small that are involved in all kinds of different technologies, from satellites to wireless phones to undersea cables to the Internet.

Firm profile

Work is an integral component of our lives; we gain personal and professional satisfaction from high quality legal advocacy, writing and critical thinking. We enjoy practicing together, working hard and giving our clients the absolute best representation. At the same time, we love our families and our friends and take pleasure in any number of avocations. Harris, Wiltshire & Grannis is a place where smart, dedicated attorneys do work of the highest quality and still live a normal life. Because this is central to the culture of the firm, we have no set billable hours requirement and no aspect of associate compensation is tied to the number of hours billed.

Recruitment details

- Number of 1st year associates: 2
- Number of 2nd year associates: 2
- Associate salaries: 1st year: $168,000
- 2nd year: $175,000
- Clerking policy: Yes

Law Schools attending for OCIs in 2016:

Chicago, Duke, Georgetown, Harvard, Michigan, Penn, Stanford, Vanderbilt, Virginia, Yale

Summer details

Summer associate profile:

We seek associates with superlative writing ability and a record of the very highest academic achievement. We will only hire a summer associate that we fully expect to become a superb lawyer and a trusted colleague.

Summer program components:

We treat summer associates like brand new associates. This means that, although summer associates necessarily require a different level of training and supervision, they will be doing the same work associates do, with the same people and under the same conditions. Harris, Wiltshire & Grannis associates are expected to perform as lawyers, not assistant lawyers and we want our summer associates to aim for the same high level of creativity, initiative and skill. Summer associates can expect to work in our telecommunications and technology, criminal defense and litigation, and appellate practices.

Head Office: Washington, DC
Number of domestic offices: 2
Number of international offices: 0
Partners (US): 26
Of Counsel (US): 3
Associates (US): 15

Main Recruitment Contact:
Jonathan Mirsky
Hiring Partner: Jonathan Mirsky
Recruitment website:
www.hwglaw.com/recruiting
Diversity officer: Brita Strandberg

Summer Salary 2016
1Ls: N/A
2Ls: $3,000/week
Post 3Ls: N/A
1Ls hired? No
Split summers offered? Yes
Can summers spend time in overseas office? N/A
Summers 2016: 3
Offers/acceptances 2015:
3 offers, 1 acceptance (2 other summers clerking after graduation)

Firm Profiles

Haynes and Boone, LLP

2323 Victory Avenue Suite 700, Dallas, TX 75219
Tel: 214 651 5000
Email: amanda.kelly@haynesboone.com
www.haynesboone.com

Main areas of work

Corporate/securities/M&A, private equity, hedge funds, business litigation (including IP, insurance coverage, environmental, energy, real estate, securities, healthcare and appellate), bankruptcy and restructuring, energy, banking and finance, franchises, intellectual property/technology, labor and employment and real estate.

Firm profile

Haynes and Boone, LLP is an international corporate law firm with offices in Texas, New York, California, Colorado, Washington, DC, Shanghai and Mexico City, providing a full spectrum of legal services.

Recruitment details

- Number of 1st year associates: 26
- Number of 2nd year associates: 34
- Associate salaries: 1st year: $160,000 (all offices)
- Clerking policy: Yes

Law Schools attending for OCIs in 2016:

Baylor, UC Berkeley, Columbia, Duke, Fordham, Georgetown, Harvard, Santa Clara, Southern Methodist University, Stanford, UC Davis, UC Irvine, UCLA, University of Houston, University of Pennsylvania, USC, University of Texas, University of Virginia, Vanderbilt, Cornell

Summer details

Summer associate profile:

To sustain what we feel is a blend of culture and sophistication of practice that is unmatched in the market, Haynes and Boone is looking for internally driven law students with a personality that would augment our firm's commitment to teamwork and a long-term approach to the practice of law.

Summer program components:

Our summer associates spend 8-10 weeks (depending on office) with us working in one or two of our practice areas. Each summer associate is given a supervisor who assigns them work and they are able to attend client meetings, negotiations, hearings, etc. Feedback is provided throughout the summer as well as through the mid-clerkship review. Our summer associates also enjoy several social events designed to get to know our attorneys.

Head Office: Dallas, TX
Number of domestic offices: 12
Number of international offices: 2
Worldwide revenue: $362,000,000
Partners (US): 230
Associates (US): 357 (including other attorneys)

Main Recruitment Contact: Amanda Kelly, Manager of Entry-Level Recruiting
Hiring Partner: Eric Williams
Recruitment website: www.haynesboone.com
Diversity officers: Kenya Woodruff, Partner of the Attorney Diversity and Inclusion Committee

Summer Salary 2016
1Ls: $3,077/week
2Ls: $3,077/week
Post 3Ls: $3,077/week
1Ls hired? Yes, in specific offices
Split summers offered? cbc
Can summers spend time in overseas office? No
Summers 2016: 2Ls: 39
Offers/acceptances 2015:
40 offers, 30 acceptances,
3 outstanding offers

Hogan Lovells US LLP

555 13th Street, NW, Washington, DC 20004
Tel: 202 637 5600 Fax: 202 637 5910
Email: irena.mcgrath@hoganlovells.com
www.hoganlovells.com

Main areas of work

Working at the intersection of law, business and government, across a wide range of industries, Hogan Lovells US LLP's global practices include corporate; finance; government regulatory; intellectual property, media and technology; litigation, arbitration and employment; and pro bono.

Firm profile

By joining Hogan Lovells, you will become part of a legal practice with a long tradition of excellence. Working as an integrated team, our lawyers provide sophisticated services on a broad spectrum of cutting-edge legal issues. Our unique global platform, collaborative culture and commitment to your professional development, provide an exceptional foundation on which to build a legal career – now and into the future. Hogan Lovells' pioneering US Pro Bono practice began more than 40 years ago when we were the first law firm to establish a separate practice devoted exclusively to providing pro bono legal services. Our culture of inclusion, which respects and values the diversity of all of our people, enhances the quality of Hogan Lovells' workplace and our ability to provide excellent legal services for clients. We prize our friendly, team-oriented environment, which encourages professional development, good associate-partner relations and early client contact.

Recruitment details

- Number of 1st year associates: 44
- Number of 2nd year associates: 75
- Associate salaries: 1st year: Varies by market - in most US offices $160,000
- 2nd year: Varies by market – in most US offices $170,000
- Clerking policy: Yes

Law Schools attending for OCIs in 2016:

American University, Baltimore, Boston College, Boston University, Brooklyn, Cardozo, Catholic University, Columbia, Colorado, Cornell, Denver, Duke, Florida, Florida International, Florida State, Fordham, George Mason, George Washington, Georgetown, Harvard, Howard, Maryland, Miami, Michigan, Minnesota, NYU, Pennsylvania, Stanford, Texas, UC Berkeley, UCLA, USC, UVA, Vanderbilt, Washington & Lee, William & Mary, Yale

Summer details

Summer associate profile:

With guidance from lawyer assignment coordinators/mentors, students do meaningful client work, and participate in training programs designed to develop and enhance legal skills. Summer Associates have opportunities to attend closings, depositions, and legislative and administrative hearings and meet with alumni and clients serving in prominent roles in government and business. In 2016, five US Summer Associates with strong interest in our transnational practices participated in a two-week program in the London office. All US Summer Associates attend a retreat in Washington where firm leaders share insights about Hogan Lovells' pre-eminent practices and strategic plans for the future, our vision and values, and commitment to diversity. Through group dinners and team building exercises, US Summer Associates get to know their colleagues from other offices and make life long connections.

Head Office (US): Washington, DC
Number of domestic offices: 13
Number of international offices: 36
Worldwide revenue: $1.82 billion
Partners (US): 397
Associates (US): 489

Main Recruitment Contact: Irena McGrath, Chief Associate Recruitment Officer
Hiring Partner: Timothy A Lloyd, Esq.
Recruitment website: http://careers-us.hoganlovells.com/
Diversity officer: Phyllis V Wan

Summer Salary 2016
1Ls: $3,080/week (in most offices)
2Ls: $3,080/week (in most offices)
Post 3Ls: $3,080/week (in most offices)
1Ls hired? Yes (in some offices)
Split summers offered? Case by case
Can summers spend time in overseas office? Case by case
Summers 2016: 83 (69 2Ls, 14 1Ls)
Offers/acceptances 2015:
67 offers, 52 acceptances (to date)

Holland & Knight LLP

701 Brickell Avenue, Suite 3300, Miami, FL 33131
Tel: 305 374 8500 Fax: 305 789 7799
www.hklaw.com

Main areas of work

Holland & Knight advises clients in a broad range of practice areas, including complex commercial litigation, corporate law, intellectual property, private wealth services, mergers and acquisitions, real estate and zoning law, and public policy and regulatory matters. Attorneys work collaboratively across practice groups and teams, drawing upon their depth and breadth of legal experience and industry knowledge to serve clients in the US and abroad.

Firm profile

Holland & Knight is a global firm with more than 1,100 lawyers and other professionals in 23 US offices, as well as Bogotá and Mexico City. Recent expansion has helped the firm penetrate new markets and attract sophisticated clients in the US and abroad. With a growing focus on Latin America, the firm leverages more than 30 years of experience in the region to advance client interests, from establishing a business in an emerging economy to expanding an international presence.

Recruitment details

- Number of 1st year associates: 27
- Number of 2nd year associates: 33
- Associate salaries: 1st year: $160,000
- 2nd year: $170,000
- Clerking policy: No

Law Schools attending for OCIs in 2016:

Boston College, Boston University, University of California, Berkeley – Boalt Hall, University of California - Los Angeles, University of Chicago, Columbia, Duke, University of Florida, Florida State University, Fordham University, George Washington, Georgetown, Harvard, New York University, Northwestern, University of Pennsylvania, University of Southern California, Stanford, University of Virginia, Yale and others.

Summer details

Summer associate profile:

Holland & Knight seeks candidates with superior academic credentials and diverse backgrounds who aspire to become leaders in the legal profession and their communities.

Summer program components

Holland & Knight's Summer Associate Program is structured to provide exposure to many diverse practice areas. Summer associates work on substantive matters and observe conferences, negotiations, oral arguments, closings, depositions, hearings and trials. These experiences provide a broad foundation to assist them in identifying the areas of practice on which they would like to focus as they begin their legal careers.

Head Office: No main office; Managing Partner resident in the Miami office
Number of domestic offices: 23
Number of international offices: 2
Worldwide revenue: $743,800,000
Partners (US): 604
Associates (US): 323

Main Recruitment Contact: Carrie Weintraub, Chief Professional Development & Human Resources Officer, carrie.weintraub@hklaw.com
Hiring Partner: Deborah E Barnard
Recruitment website: www.hklaw.com
Diversity officer: Tiffani G Lee

Summer Salary 2016
1Ls hired? Case by case
Split summers offered? Case by case
Can summers spend time in overseas office? No
Summers 2016: 42
Offers/acceptances 2015:
37 offers, 35 acceptances

Holland & Knight

Hughes Hubbard & Reed LLP

One Battery Park Plaza
Tel: 212 837 6000 Fax: 212 299 6131
www.hugheshubbard.com

Main areas of work

With offices in New York, Washington, DC, Los Angeles, Miami, Jersey City, Kansas City, Tokyo and Paris, Hughes Hubbard offers expertise in a wide-range of practice areas. Our team of more than 350 experienced practitioners works in over 30 specialized practices, from mergers and acquisitions, public offerings, corporate reorganization, real estate and cross-border transactions to general commercial litigation, securities litigation, international trade, anti-corruption and internal investigations, international arbitration and dispute resolution, product liability, antitrust, intellectual property, labor, employee benefits and tax, as well as niche practices such as art law and a credit card practice.

Firm profile

The firm has outstanding diversity scores and consistently receives high marks for its pro bono activities. The American Lawyer has consistently recognized Hughes Hubbard on its A-List of the nation's most elite law firms.

Recruitment details

- Number of 1st year associates: 30
- Number of 2nd year associates: 26
- Associate salaries: 1st year: $160,000
- 2nd year: $170,000
- Clerking policy: yes

Law Schools attending for OCIs in 2016:

Brooklyn Law School, Columbia University Law School, Cornell Law School, Duke University School of Law, Fordham University School of Law, George Washington University Law School, Georgetown University Law Center, Harvard Law School, New York University School of Law, Stanford Law School, University of Chicago Law School, University of Michigan Law School, University of Pennsylvania Law School, University of Virginia School of Law, Yale Law School

Summer details

Summer associate profile:

Hughes Hubbard recognizes that a successful recruiting effort is essential to the long-term success of the firm. We are committed to rendering services of the highest professional quality and, to that end, seek lawyers of exceptional ability, integrity and industry. We actively recruit candidates whose academic performance, energy, personality and character suggest that they possess the ability and desire to meet the challenges presented by a demanding practice and are prepared to develop rapidly and assume responsibility early.

Summer program components:

Summer associates work on real problems, not "make-work," and those problems often involve far more than library research. In recent years, for example, summer associates have assisted at depositions, court proceedings and closings. Summer associates participate in a wide variety of client meetings, witness interviews, negotiation sessions and fact-gathering projects and, on some occasions, they have traveled to other offices.

Head Office: New York, NY
Number of domestic offices: 6
Number of international offices: 2
Worldwide revenue: $394,000,000
Partners (US): $2,145,000
Per Lawyer (US): $1,185,000

Main Recruitment Contact: Mr Adrian B Cockerill
Hiring Partner: Mr George A Tsougarakis
Recruitment website: www.hugheshubbard.com/careers

Summer Salary 2016
1Ls: $3,100
2Ls: $3,100
Post 3Ls: $3,100
1Ls hired? Yes
Split summers offered? No
Can summers spend time in overseas office? Yes
Summers 2016: 22
Offers/acceptances 2015: 21 offers, 21 acceptances

Firm Profiles

Hughes
Hubbard
&Reed

Hunton & Williams LLP

2200 Pennsylvania Avenue, NW, Washington, DC 20037
Tel: 202 955 1500 Fax: 202 778 2201
www.hunton.com

Firm profile

Hunton & Williams is the legal advisor of choice for industry leaders on six continents. With more than 800 attorneys practicing from 19 offices across the United States, Europe and Asia, the firm helps clients realize new opportunities and solve complex problems with confidence. Founded in 1901, Hunton & Williams blends more than a century of experience in virtually every key legal discipline with a broad view of current business realities and a forward-looking perspective on emerging issues to provide legal and regulatory advice that will carry its clients well into the 21st century. The firm is regularly named by legal and business publications as among the top law firms for client service and as a place to work.

Recruitment details

- Number of 1st year associates: 28
- Number of 2nd year associates: 34
- Associate salaries: 1st year: $145,000-$160,000 (depending on location)
- Clerking policy: Yes

Law Schools attending for OCIs in 2016:

Columbia University; Cornell University; Duke University; Emory University; Fordham University; Georgetown University; George Washington University; Harvard University; Howard University; New York University; Southern Methodist University; University of California, Los Angeles; University of Michigan; University of Pennsylvania; University of Richmond; University of Southern California; University of Texas; University of Virginia; Vanderbilt University; Washington and Lee University; Washington University in St Louis; College of William and Mary

Summer details

Summer associate profile:

When recruiting summer associates, Hunton & Williams seeks high performing, team oriented and problem-solving law students. In addition to strong academic credentials and excellent written and verbal communication skills, applicants should have a solid record of success and leadership. Prior work experience, professional experience or advanced degrees also are valued.

Summer program components:

Hunton & Williams Summer Program is a focused, ten-week immersion in the real-world practice of law. Rather than simply shadowing experienced associates and partners, participants are actively engaged in practical work and training activities that support the goals of the firm and its clients while fostering professional development. While the program is customized, based on the career goals and interests of each summer associate, it generally includes leadership skills training, career mentoring, business development and client service training, practical experience, client interaction, pro bono opportunities, writing coaching, judicial clerkship counseling, and work projects and experience in the practice areas of interest.

Head Office: Washington, DC
Number of domestic offices: 14
Number of international offices: 5
Partners (US): 299
Counsel (US): 81
Associates (US): 312

Main Recruitment Contact:
See list of office-based recruiters located on www.huntoncareers.com
Hiring Partners: Kimberly C MacLeod and Thomas Y Hiner; Judith H Itkin, Partner in Charge of Lawyer Recruiting and Development
Recruitment website:
www.huntoncareers.com
Diversity Committee Co-Heads:
A Todd Brown, J Michael Martinez de Andino and Amy McDaniel Williams

Summer Salary 2016
2Ls: $2,800-$3,080/week
1Ls hired? No (Some offices may participate in a 1L diversity program.)
Split summers offered? No
Can summers spend time in overseas office? No
Summers 2016: 29
Offers/acceptances 2015:
33 offers, 32 acceptances

Irell & Manella LLP

1800 Avenue of the Stars, Suite 900, Los Angeles, CA 90067
Tel: 310 277 1010 Fax: 310 203 7199
www.irell.com

Main areas of work

Antitrust, appellate, art, bankruptcy reorganization and creditors' rights, class action defense, cyber liability and privacy, debt finance, entertainment litigation, insurance, IP litigation, IP transactions, litigation, media and entertainment transactions, mergers and acquisitions, patent, copyright and trademark, private equity and venture capital, professional liability defense, public offerings and private placements, real estate, securities law and corporate governance, securities litigation, tax and white collar defense.

Firm profile

Irell & Manella is a full service law firm with offices in Los Angeles and Newport Beach, California. Our unique practice and culture offers opportunities for talented law graduates to excel early in their careers. The quality of our work and the flexibility of our organization attract associates with the highest qualifications.

Irell's preeminent reputation brings clients to us from around the country and abroad and allows us to concentrate our physical presence in a single metropolitan area ensuring firm cohesion and a minimum of bureaucracy.

Recruitment details

- Number of 1st year associates: 6
- 1st year associate salary: $160,000
- Clerking policy: Yes
- Number of 2nd year associates: 17
- 2nd year associate salary: $170,000

Law Schools attending for OCIs in 2016:

Law Schools: Berkeley, University of Chicago, Columbia, Harvard, Michigan, Northwestern, NYU, Stanford, UCLA, UC Irvine, USC, Yale

Job Fairs & Interview Programs: Duke Regional Interview Program, Lavender Law, Loyola University Chicago Patent Law Interview Program, Los Angeles On Tour Interview Program (OTIP), Penn Regional Interview Program

Summer details

Summer associate profile:

We recruit the top candidates from the top schools. Consideration is given to participation in law school activities, undergraduate record, previous work experience, references and other factors. We look for individuals who are motivated, creative, show leadership, have a strong work ethic and are serious about being a lawyer.

Summer program components:

Our summer program is designed to allow summer associates to explore the various areas of our practice. Summer associates have the opportunity to participate in a mock wrongful death trial that is tried to a jury and presided over by a judge. Each summer associate is assigned a mentor and a work coordinator. Feedback is provided on each project by the assigning attorney and each summer associate has a mid-summer review to deliver additional feedback about his or her progress.

Head Office: Los Angeles, CA
Number of domestic offices: 2
Number of international offices: 0
Worldwide revenue: $199,850,000
Partners (US): 44
Associates (US): 64

Main Recruitment Contact:
Edith Gondwe
Hiring Partner: Ellisen Turner
Recruitment website: www.irell.com
Diversity officer: Kyle Kawakami

Summer Salary 2016
1Ls: $3,080/week
2Ls: $3,080/week
Post 3Ls: $3,080/week
1Ls hired? Yes
Split summers offered? Yes – first half of the summer only with a six week minimum
Summers 2016: 20
Offers/acceptances 2015:
20 offers, 15 acceptances. Some offers are outstanding to students who have accepted judicial clerkships.

Firm Profiles

Jackson Walker LLP

2323 Ross Avenue, Ste.600, Dallas, TX 75201
Tel: 214 953 6000 Fax: 214 953 5822
www.jw.com

Main areas of work

Bankruptcy; corporate and securities; energy; ERISA; environmental and legislative; finance; healthcare; intellectual property; labor and employment; litigation; land use; real estate; tax; wealth planning.

Firm profile

Jackson Walker is a Texas-based law firm with a national presence and global reach. With more than 350 attorneys, we're one of the largest firms in the state and we provide comprehensive services in a broad range of practice areas. Our practice now spans the globe and our corporate clients include some of the biggest names in business. We represent approximately 237 of the Fortune 500 companies and 69 of the Fortune 100. But we're also a good fit for smaller companies and our clients include family-owned businesses, local and regional government agencies, individuals and nonprofit groups.

Recruitment details

- Number of 1st year associates: 12
- Number of 2nd year associates: 19
- Associate salaries: 1st year: $160,000
- Clerking policy: Yes

Law Schools attending for OCIs in 2016:

Baylor, Chicago, University of Houston, Notre Dame, St Mary's, Southern Methodist University, South Texas, Texas Southern, University of Texas, University of Virginia, Texas on Tour Interview Program (Duke, Georgetown and Northwestern Universities), SUNBELT Minority Job Fair, Vanderbilt Job Fair

Summer details

Summer associate profile:

Candidates with leadership capabilities, academic excellence, strong interpersonal skills, community involvement and dedicated to practicing over the long term.

Summer program components:

We have a first half of summer program. Summers typically rotate through two practice areas and work on two or three projects at a time. Feedback is provided from the assigning attorney on each project and each summer has both a partner and associate mentor. Summers have the opportunity to attend client meetings, closings, negotiations, depositions, trials and courtroom hearings.

Head Office: Dallas, TX
Number of domestic offices: 7
Worldwide revenue: $221,500,000
Partners (US): 243
Associates (US): 99

Main Recruitment Contact:
Soraya Walden
Hiring Partner: Jim Ryan
Recruitment website:
www.jw.com/careers
Diversity officer: Bruce Ruzinsky

Summer Salary 2016
2Ls: $3,077/week
Post 3Ls: $3,077/week
1Ls hired? Case by case
Split summers offered? Yes
Can summers spend time in overseas office? N/A
Summers 2016: 25
Offers/acceptances 2015:
16 offers, 12 acceptances (2Ls only)

Jenner & Block LLP

353 North Clark Street, Chicago, IL 60654
Tel: 312 222 9350 Fax: 312 527 0484
www.jenner.com

Main areas of work

Appellate and US Supreme Court; communications; complex commercial litigation; content, media and entertainment; copyright; corporate; election law and redistricting; employee benefits and executive compensation; environmental and workplace health and safety law; government contracts; government controversies and public policy litigation; insurance recovery and counseling; international arbitration; media and First Amendment; mergers and acquisitions; patent litigation and counseling; privacy and information governance; private equity, investment funds and SBIC formation; professional responsibility; real estate; restructuring and bankruptcy; securities litigation and enforcement; tax; trademark, advertising, and unfair competition; white collar defense and investigations

Firm profile

Jenner & Block is a firm with global reach, comprised of more than 500 lawyers and offices in Chicago, London, Los Angeles, New York and Washington, DC. Our lawyers are widely recognized for securing significant litigation victories from the trial level through the US Supreme Court as well as producing results in sophisticated and high-profile corporate transactions. We are a firm with a conscience, committed to pro bono and public service, and to creating an unrivaled environment for superior talent. In 2015, *The American Lawyer* named us the number one Pro Bono firm for the sixth time in eight years.

Recruitment details

- Number of 1st year associates: 25
- Number of 2nd year associates: 30
- Associate salaries: 1st year: $160,000
- 2nd year: $170,000
- Clerking policy: Yes

Law Schools attending for OCIs in 2016:

Columbia University, Harvard University, Howard University, New York University, Northwestern University, Stanford University, University of California-Berkeley, University of California-Los Angeles, University of Chicago, University of Illinois, University of Michigan, University of Notre Dame, University of Pennsylvania, University of Southern California, Yale University

Summer details

Summer associate profile:

We seek summer associates who have excelled in law school, and have exceptional oral and written presentation skills, leadership experience, and strong interpersonal skills.

Summer program components:

Summer associates work with our lawyers and firm clients on a wide variety of complex cases and transactions. Among other things, our summer associates attend court hearings and closings, observe depositions and participate in strategy sessions with firm lawyers and clients. We also offer extensive training programs on a wide range of subjects. Summer associates are encouraged to attend department meetings, firmwide monthly associate lunches and weekly lunch-and-learn sessions. All summer associates have mentors and receive feedback from lawyers with whom they have worked.

Head Office: Chicago
Number of domestic offices: 4
Number of international offices: 1
Worldwide revenue: $464,891,012
Partners (US): 213
Associates (US): 221

Main Recruitment Contact: Alexis M Reed, Director of Lateral Partner Recruiting
Hiring Partner: Charlotte L Wager, Chief Talent Officer and Co-Chair of the Hiring Executive Committee
Recruitment website: www.jenner.com/joinus
Diversity officer: Jami de Lou, Associate Director of Talent Development, Diversity & Inclusion; Courtney Dredden, Diversity and Inclusion Manager

Summer Salary 2016
1Ls: N/A
2Ls: $3,077/week
Post 3Ls: $3,077/week
1Ls hired? No
Split summers offered? Yes
Summers 2016: 37 2Ls, 2 Pre-Clerks
Offers/acceptances 2015:
27 offers, 25 acceptances; 8 former summer associates will be judicial clerks

JENNER&BLOCK

Jones Day

51 Louisiana Avenue, NW, Washington, DC 20001
Tel: 202 879 3939 Fax: 202 629 1700
Email: recruiting@jonesday.com
www.jonesdaycareers.com

Main areas of work

Jones Day's practices cover the spectrum of transactional, litigation, regulatory and tax matters. Core practice areas: corporate/M&A, litigation/trial practice, government regulation, real estate, energy, healthcare, banking/finance, bankruptcy/restructuring, labor and employment, securities litigation, financial institutions, litigation/regulation, antitrust, tax and intellectual property.

Firm profile

The firm is a global legal institution based on a set of core principles and values – the most critical of which are integrity, dedication to the profession and a unity of purpose of and relentless focus on client service that transcends individual interests. Each lawyer is committed to the firm's foundation principles and values, which have a social purpose and permanence and ensure the distinctive quality and value of the legal services they provide their clients. This is one important aspect of what makes Jones Day the client service organization that it is. They function seamlessly across the globe and are truly One Firm Worldwide.

Recruitment details

- Number of 1st year associates: 119
- Number of 2nd year associates: 134
- Associate salaries: 1st year: $135,000-160,000 ($160,000 in Boston, Chicago, Dallas, Houston, Irvine, Los Angeles, New York, San Diego, San Francisco, Silicon Valley, Washington; $150,000 in Atlanta; $145,000 in Cleveland, Columbus, Detroit, Miami, Pittsburgh)
- 2nd year: Increase is merit based, not lock step
- Clerking policy: Yes

Law Schools attending for OCIs in 2016:

American, Benjamin N. Cardozo, Boston College, Boston University, Case Western, Chicago, Cleveland - Marshall, Columbia, Cornell, Dickinson, Duke, Emory, Fordham, George Washington, Georgetown, Georgia, Georgia State, Harvard, Houston, Howard, Illinois, Michigan, New York University, Northwestern, Notre Dame, Ohio State, Pennsylvania, Pittsburgh, San Diego, SMU, Stanford, Texas, UC Berkeley, UC Hastings, UC Irvine, UCLA, U Miami, USC, Vanderbilt, Virginia, Wisconsin, Yale

Summer details

Summer associate profile:

Jones Day lawyers share certain fundamental principles: exemplary integrity, a selfless dedication to the firm and its clients and a sense of responsibility and initiative that leads one to take ownership of assignments and to complete them at the highest level of quality legal service. Summer associates candidates are evaluated on their fit with this culture.

Summer program components:

Summer associates do real client work in their choice of practice areas. Mentors are assigned to provide one-on-one guidance. Each summer associate will have a formal, mid-summer review. Jones Day's dynamic culture and its global, multidisciplinary practice areas, provide the perfect training ground for summer associates and new lawyers.

Number of domestic offices: 17
Number of international offices: 26
Partners (US): 655
Associates (US): 875

Main Recruitment Contact:
Jolie A Blanchard, 202 879 3788
Hiring Partner:
Sharyl A Reisman, 212 326 3405
Recruitment website:
www.jonesdaycareers.com
Diversity coordinator: Jennifer Shumaker, 202 879 5430

Summer Salary 2016
1Ls / 2Ls / Post 3Ls: Cleveland, Columbus, Detroit, Miami, Pittsburgh: $12,083/month; Atlanta: $12,500/month; Boston, Chicago, Dallas, Houston, Irvine, Los Angeles, New York, San Diego, San Francisco, Silicon Valley, Washington: $13,333/month
1Ls hired? Varies by office
Split summers offered? Varies by office
Can summers spend time in overseas office? Case by case
Summers 2016: 136
Offers/acceptances 2015:
127 offers, 110 acceptances

K&L Gates LLP

K&L Gates Center, 210 Sixth Avenue, Pittsburgh, PA 15222-2613
Tel: 412 355 6500 Fax: 412 355 6501
www.klgates.com

Firm profile

K&L Gates is a fully integrated global law firm with approximately 2,000 lawyers across five continents. We have experienced dramatic growth in the past decade and now rank among the largest US-based law firms in the world. In 2016, for the second year in a row, we were recognized as being one of the 10 strongest US law firm brands by legal market research company Acritas. Our commitment to client service and dedication to delivering value to clients has resulted in four consecutive years on BTI's Client Service 30, placing in the top 10 the last two years. We were one of just two firms to have earned 45 national first-tier rankings—the highest number of national first-tier rankings among more than 12,700 firms—in the 2016 US News-Best Lawyers "Best Law Firms" survey. In 2015, The Financial Times ranked us as a Highly Commended firm in the Compliance & Technology category of its Innovative Lawyers - North America report in recognition of the ground-breaking digital content platform K&L Gates HUB, in addition to giving the firm a Commended ranking for our Cyber Civil Rights Legal Project.

The industry recognition K&L Gates has garnered over the past five years emanates from the foundation of a global community aligned on behalf of our clients. The people at K&L Gates are committed to working together to create a legacy for each other, the firm, our clients, and the communities we serve. We thrive in an inclusive and socially conscious environment that embraces diversity and takes a holistic approach to the career evolution of all our professionals.

We take pride in constantly striving for innovation, imagination, and an entrepreneurial spirit. We come up with big ideas and then roll up our sleeves to get the job done, guiding our clients through their most complex issues in a variety of industry sectors and across multiple regions of the world.

Recruitment details

- Number of 1st year associates: 77
- Number of 2nd year associates: 74
- Associate salaries: 1st year: varies by market
- 2nd Year: varies by market
- Clerking policy: Yes

Summer details

Summer program components:

As a summer associate, you will learn about our clients, our practices, our lawyers, and our culture. You'll sample projects from different practice areas, working as part of a team and participating in pro bono work that enriches the communities we serve. Through on-the-job experience and a formal training curriculum that includes an intensive writing workshop and practice-specific programs, our summer associates begin to develop the professional skills and competencies that will serve them well throughout their careers.

We pair our summer associates with mentors consisting of one partner and at least one associate, who provide guidance on seeking out and completing substantive work assignments, balancing workload demands, dealing with competing projects, integration into the firm's culture, and setting and achieving career goals. You will receive regular formal and informal feedback on your ongoing performance and developmental progress.

Number of domestic offices: 24
Number of international offices: 21
Worldwide revenue: $1,064,953,000
Partners (US): 631
Of Counsel (US): 89
Associates (US): 550

Main Recruitment Contact: Roslyn Pitts, Firmwide Director of Talent
Recruitment website: www.klgates.com/careers
Diversity officer: Valerie Jackson, Senior Advisor to the Management Committee and Firmwide Director of Diversity & Inclusion

Summer Salary 2016
1Ls: Varies by market
2Ls: Varies by market
Post 3Ls: Varies by market
1Ls hired? Yes
Split summers offered? Case by case
Can summers spend time in overseas office? No
Summers 2016: 81
Offers/acceptances 2015: 78 offers, 60 acceptances (2Ls only)

K&L GATES

Kasowitz, Benson, Torres & Friedman LLP

1633 Broadway, New York, New York 10019
Tel: 212 506 1700 Fax: 212 506 1800
www.Kasowitz.com

Main areas of work

Kasowitz, Benson, Torres & Friedman LLP, one of the largest litigation firms in the country, represents clients in high-stakes lawsuits involving antitrust, commercial banking, complex financial products, creditors' rights and bankruptcy, employment practices, entertainment, environmental, matrimonial, insurance recovery, intellectual property, international arbitration, mass tort and product liability, real estate, securities and white collar criminal defense litigation. The firm employs a decidedly aggressive approach to litigation and strives to achieve the most favorable results for its clients by focusing from the beginning of each case on preparation for trial. While litigation remains our core focus, the firm also represents clients in real estate transactions and corporate and government affairs matters.

Firm profile

Our success in implementing uniquely creative and successful legal strategies across practice areas has brought us clients with exceptionally interesting and challenging work. Such clients include leading companies in the high-tech, manufacturing, chemical, computer, energy, entertainment, consumer products, pharmaceutical and telecommunications industries, as well as major hedge funds, private equity firms, commercial banks, real estate developers and investors, regulated utilities and individuals.

Recruitment details

- Number of 1st year associates: 15
- Number of 2nd year associates: 16
- Clerking Policy: Yes
- Associate Salaries 1st year: $160,000
- Associate Salaries: 2nd year: $170,000

Law Schools attending for OCIs in 2016:

Columbia, Cornell, Fordham, Georgetown, NYU, NEBLSA Job Fair and Penn

Summer details

Summer associate profile:

Strong academic achievement, outstanding judgment, character and personal skills. Commitment to the practice of law and potential for growth.

Summer program components:

The primary objective of our summer program is to provide quality work assignments and professional experiences reflective of the depth and complexity of our practice. Summer associates learn about trying cases and drafting legal documents, motions and agreements and are exposed to courtroom appearances, depositions and client meetings. Our program provides an experience as close as possible to that of a first-year associate, as well as the opportunity to gain insight into the work and culture of the firm.

Summer associates participate in formal training programs, a partner lunch series and an associate mentor program, all of which assist with acclimation to the firm. Summer associates receive ongoing feedback from the attorneys with whom they work and are provided with formal mid and exit reviews.

The firm coordinates various charitable events during Give Back week. Kasowitz also hosts social events providing summer associates and our attorneys the opportunity to get to know one another in an informal environment.

Head Office: New York, NY
Number of domestic offices: 9
Number of international offices: N/A
Partners: 96
Associates: 134

Main Recruitment contact: Mindy J. Lindenman
Hiring Partner: Aaron H Marks
Recruitment Website: www.kasowitz.com
Diversity Officer: Jennifer Mercado

Summer Salary 2016
2Ls: $3,077/week
Post 3Ls: $3,077/week
1Ls hired? Case-by-case
Split summers offered? Case-by-case
Can summers spend time in overseas office? N/A
Summers 2016: 9
Offers/acceptances 2015: 6 offers/6 acceptances

Firm Profiles

Katten Muchin Rosenman LLP

525 West Monroe Street, Chicago, IL 60661-3693
Tel: 312 902 5200 Fax: 312 902 1061
www.kattenlaw.com

Main areas of work

Corporate, financial services, litigation, real estate, environmental, commercial finance, intellectual property and trusts and estates.

Firm profile

Katten is a full-service law firm with approximately 650 attorneys in locations across the United States and in London and Shanghai. Clients seeking sophisticated, high-value legal services turn to us for counsel locally, nationally and internationally.

Recruitment details

- Number of 1st year associates: 24
- Number of 2nd year associates: 31
- Associate salaries: 1st year: $160,000 (Charlotte: $140,000)
- 2nd Year: $170,000 (Charlotte: $145,000)
- Clerking policy: Yes

Law Schools attending for OCIs in 2016:

Chicago-Kent College of Law, Columbia, Fordham University, Harvard, Howard University, Loyola Law School Los Angeles, Loyola University Chicago School of Law, New York University, Northwestern University, University of California, Los Angeles, University of California at Berkeley, Boalt Hall, The University of Chicago, University of Illinois, University of Michigan, University of North Carolina, University of Pennsylvania, University of Southern California Gould, University of Virginia, Wake Forest University

Summer details

Summer associate profile:

Our Summer Associate Program is our most important recruiting activity. The program offers participants a realistic idea of what life is like for a first year associate. With our diverse client base, summer associates have the opportunity to work in each of our practice areas on a broad spectrum of assignments.

Summer program components:

We provide programs designed specifically for summer associates, including legal writing, negotiation, drafting and trial skills workshops, in addition to presentations introducing the firm's different areas of practice. Summer associates have the opportunity to directly observe lawyers and interact with clients as part of their training experience. We also encourage—and expect—our summer associates to participate in all of the attorney training and development programs presented by the firm and our various departments.

Head Office: Chicago, IL
Number of domestic offices: 11
Number of international offices: 2
Partners (US): 309
Associates (US): 256

Recruitment website:
For recruitment information and contacts, please visit:
www.kattenlaw.com/careers

Summer Salary 2016
Chicago/ Los Angeles/ New York/ Washington, DC:
1Ls/2Ls: $3,077
Post 3Ls: N/A
Charlotte:
1Ls/2Ls: $2,692
Post 3Ls: N/A
1Ls hired? Yes
Split summers offered: Case by case
Can summers spend time in overseas office? No
Summers 2016: 40 (32 2Ls, 8 1Ls)
Offers/acceptances 2015:
34 offers, 26 acceptances

Kaye Scholer LLP

250 W 55th Street, New York, NY 10019-9710
Tel: 212 836 8000 Fax: 212 836 8689
www.kayescholer.com

Main areas of work

Antitrust; bankruptcy and restructuring; corporate; crisis management; finance; government affairs; intellectual property, including global cybersecurity and privacy; litigation; national security, government contracts and regulatory compliance; private clients; real estate; and tax.

Firm profile

Founded in New York in 1917, Kaye Scholer combines the continuity and business acumen of a century-old law firm with a forward looking, results driven approach focused around lasting client relationships. With strengths in five core legal areas—corporate, finance, intellectual property, litigation and real estate—and focusing on two key sectors—life sciences and financial industries—we offer strategic guidance and legal services to public and private entities facing litigation, transactional or governance challenges. Our lawyers regularly advise on matters across multiple legal jurisdictions, including in the US, Canada, UK, EU and China.

Recruitment details

- Number of 1st year associates: 22
- Number of 2nd year associates: 24
- Associate salaries: 1st year: $160,000
- 2nd year: $170,000
- Clerking policy: Yes

Law Schools attending for OCIs in 2016:

BC/BU Job Fair, Columbia, Cornell, DuPont Minority Job Fair, Fordham, George Washington University, Georgetown University, Harvard, Howard University, Lavender Law Career Fair, Loyola Patent Law Interview Program, Midwest/California Interview Consortium, Northeast Black Law Students Association Job Fair, Northwestern University, New York University, St John's, University of Michigan, University of Pennsylvania, UVA, On Tour, Berkeley, Stanford

Summer details

Summer associate profile:

At Kaye Scholer, our summer associates receive work assignments that are equal in responsibility to the work assigned to first and second year associates. We look for summer associates with a "can do" attitude, who are professional, responsive, and have a genuine interest in our work.

Summer program components:

Kaye Scholer encourages summer associates to work on projects from all of our diverse practice groups to best help them achieve their individual goals. Summer associates participate in training sessions and are given front-line responsibilities on a variety of projects including legal research, drafting, negotiations, closings, client conferences and court proceedings. Summer associates are encouraged to work on pro bono cases across a wide range of areas. In addition, we offer a mentor program, informal feedback, and formal feedback including a midsummer review and an end of summer debriefing.

Head Office: New York City, NY
Number of domestic offices: 6
Number of international offices: 3
Worldwide revenue: $360,000,000
Partners (US): 113
Associates (US): 153
Counsel (US): 90

Main Recruitment Contact: Kiley Bostick
Hiring Partners: Salvatore Mastrosimone and Catherine Schumacher
Recruitment website: www.kayescholer.com/careers
Diversity officer: Satra Sampson-Arokium, Director of Diversity & Inclusion

Summer Salary 2016
1Ls: $3,100/week
2Ls: $3,100/week
Post 3Ls: N/A
1Ls hired? Yes
Split summers offered? No
Can summers spend time in overseas office? No
Summers 2016: 25 (21 2Ls, 4 1Ls)
Offers/acceptances 2015:
15 offers, 15 acceptances

Kilpatrick Townsend & Stockton LLP

1100 Peachtree St. NE, Suite 2800, Atlanta, GA 30309
Tel: 404 815 6500 Fax: 404 815 6555
www.ktrecruits.com

Main areas of work

Mergers and acquisitions, securities, domestic and international tax, employee benefits, financial institutions, global sourcing and technology, government relations, real estate finance and capital markets, real estate investment and development, chemistry and life sciences, patent litigation, trademark and copyright, electronics and software, medical and mechanical devices, bankruptcy and financial restructuring, complex commercial litigation, construction and infrastructure projects, environmental and sustainable development, government enforcement and investigations, insurance recovery, labor and employment, native american affairs.

Firm profile

Kilpatrick Townsend's attorneys fuel progress for innovative businesses of all sizes, types and markets. With more than 650 attorneys and professionals in 18 offices, we work together to make businesses better, smarter, more protected, and more successful. Kilpatrick Townsend ranked 73rd in the American Lawyer's 2015 AmLaw 100 Survey and had a record-breaking 126 attorneys honored by their peers in The Best Lawyers in America® 2016. In addition, the firm had over 75 tier 1 practice rankings, consisting of 16 national tier 1 rankings and 63 metropolitan tier 1 rankings in US News – Best Lawyers® 2016 "Best Law Firms."

Recruitment details

- Number of 1st year associates: 9 • Number of 2nd year associates: 14
- Associate salaries: 1st year: $135,000-160,000 • 2nd year: $140,000-195,000
- Clerking policy: yes

Law Schools attending for OCIs in 2016:

Emory University, Santa Clara University, University of North Carolina at Chapel Hill, University of Georgia, Wake Forest University, University of Virginia, George Washington University, Howard University, Duke University

Summer details

Summer associate profile:

We seek students who have demonstrated academic excellence (top 20%) and possess strong analytical and interpersonal skills. Participation and leadership in extra-curricular activities preferred. Technical backgrounds in engineering and science (eg, Electrical Engineering, Physics, Computer Engineering, Inorganic and Organic Chemistry) are required for patent practices.

Summer program components:

Our Summer Associate Program provides students with the opportunity to do substantive work in a variety of practice areas. Summer Associates can rotate among practice teams with a hiring need for which they have the required technical skills. Summer Associates also participate in three progress evaluations to review attorney feedback on all work product. The Summer Committee members in each office serve as mentors for the course of the program, providing guidance for evaluations, assigning work, and coaching associates as they rotate teams and ensuring a positive work/life balance.

Head Office: Atlanta, GA
Number of domestic offices: 15
Number of international offices: 3
Worldwide revenue: $411,328,000
Partners (US): 251
Associates (US): 233

Main Recruitment Contact: Lori Cates
Hiring Partner: Charlie Henn
Recruitment website:
www.ktrecruits.com
Diversity Officer: Lynda Murray-Blair

Summer Salary 2016
1Ls: $2600-3077/week
2Ls: $2600-3077/week
Post 3Ls: $2600-3077/week
1Ls hired? Yes
Split summers offered? Yes
Can summers spend time in overseas office? No
Summers 2016: 32
Offers/acceptances 2015:
14 offers, 13 acceptances

King & Spalding LLP

1180 Peachtree Street, NE, Atlanta, GA 30309-3521
Tel: 404 572 4600 Fax: 404 572 5100
www.kslaw.com

Main areas of work

Antitrust, appellate, banking and finance, corporate, energy, financial restructuring, government investigations, healthcare, intellectual property, international arbitration, international trade, litigation, pharma/biotech/medical device, real estate, tort and environmental and tax/ERISA.

Firm profile

King & Spalding has over 900 lawyers in 18 offices across the US, Europe, the Middle East and Asia. King & Spalding combines sophisticated legal practice with a commitment to excellence, collegial culture, investment in lawyer development, and dedication to community service.

Recruitment details

- Number of 1st year associates: 27
- Number of 2nd year associates: 41
- Associate salaries: 1st year: $160,000 (Austin, Houston, New York, San Francisco, Silicon Valley, Washington, DC); $135,000 (Atlanta, Charlotte)
- 2nd year: $170,000 (Austin, Houston, New York, Washington, DC); $165,000 to $170,000 (San Francisco, Silicon Valley); $140,000 to $170,000 (Charlotte); $140,000 (Atlanta)
- Clerking policy: Yes

Law Schools attending for OCIs in 2016:

Columbia, Duke, Emory, Fordham, Georgetown, Georgia State, Harvard, Howard, Mercer, NYU, St Louis, Stanford, University of Alabama, University of California – Berkeley, University of California – Hastings, University of Chicago, University of Florida, University of Georgia, University of Houston, University of Maryland, University of North Carolina, University of Pennsylvania, University of Texas, University of Virginia, Vanderbilt, Yale

Summer details

Summer associate profile:

King & Spalding offers an opportunity to work as part of a team on sophisticated legal matters for top clients in a collegial environment. We seek candidates who are well-rounded and intellectually curious with a demonstrated record of achievement and who also have diverse life and work experiences and outstanding interpersonal skills. Our summer associates experience what it is like to be a lawyer at King & Spalding and work on challenging matters for real clients. Our summer associates also get to know our lawyers in both professional and social settings.

Summer program components:

Summer associates work on matters in the practice group or groups in which they are interested. Assignment processes vary by office. Some offices have a formal rotation program while in other offices, our summer associates are assigned projects primarily in one practice group in which they are interested. Each summer associate is assigned at least one summer advisor who acts as a mentor.

Training: weekly luncheon seminars, attendance at practice group meetings, and in-house and external training sessions. Summer associates receive a formal mid-summer and end of summer evaluation, as well as ongoing project feedback.

Head Office: Atlanta, GA
Number of domestic offices: 8
Number of international offices: 10
Worldwide revenue: $1,018,000,000
Partners (US): 324
Associates (US): 318

Main Recruitment Contact:
Kate Ferguson
Hiring Partners: Bobby K Woo, Jr (Atlanta); Mike Stenglein (Austin); Mark V Thigpen (Charlotte); Penn C Huston (Houston); Andrew C Hruska (New York); Donald F Zimmer, Jr (San Francisco); Timothy T Scott (Silicon Valley); Robert K Hur (Washington, DC)
Recruitment website:
www.kslaw.com/careers
Diversity officer: Samuel M Matchett, Partner

Summer Salary 2016
1Ls: $3,100/week (Austin, Houston, New York, San Francisco, Silicon Valley, Washington, DC); $2,600/week (Atlanta, Charlotte)
2Ls: Same as 1Ls
Post 3Ls: Same as 1Ls
1Ls hired? Yes
Split summers offered? Yes
Can summer spend time in an overseas office? Generally, no
Summers 2016: 51
Offers/acceptances 2015:
45 offers, 37 acceptances

KING & SPALDING

Kirkland & Ellis LLP

300 North LaSalle, Chicago, IL 60654
Tel: 312 862 2000 Fax: 312 862 2200
Email: info@kirkland.com
www.kirkland.com

Main areas of work

Kirkland's main practice areas are corporate, intellectual property, litigation and restructuring.

Firm profile

Kirkland & Ellis LLP is a 1,600-attorney law firm representing global clients in complex corporate, dispute resolution and arbitration, intellectual property, litigation, restructuring, tax and technology matters. The firm has offices in Beijing, Chicago, Hong Kong, Houston, London, Los Angeles, Munich, New York, Palo Alto, San Francisco, Shanghai and Washington, DC. The firm's principal goals are to provide the highest-quality legal services available anywhere; to be an instrumental part of each client's success; and to recruit, retain and advance the brightest legal talent.

Recruitment details

- Number of 1st year associates: 140
- Number of 2nd year associates: 180
- Associate salaries: 1st year: $160,000
- Clerking policy: Yes

Law Schools attending for OCIs in 2016:

UC Berkeley; UC Hastings; UCLA; Cardozo; University of Chicago; Chicago – Kent; Columbia; Duke; Fordham; George Washington; Georgetown; Harvard; University of Houston; Howard University; University of Illinois; University of Michigan; New York University; Northwestern University; University of Notre Dame; University of Pennsylvania; USC; Stanford; University of Texas; Tulane; Vanderbilt University; University of Virginia; Washington University; Yale

Summer details

Summer associate profile:

Kirkland looks for candidates who show a record of outstanding academic achievement, evidence of initiative and a desire to assume early responsibility. Kirkland values individuals from diverse social, economic, cultural and personal backgrounds. The firm looks favorably upon law review, moot court and other indicators of intellectual curiosity and drive.

Summer program components:

Kirkland offers summer associates a realistic view of their future as lawyers at the firm. From day one, summer associates are allowed to choose challenging assignments that are of interest to them through Kirkland's open assignment system, including pro bono matters. Each office offers summer associates substantive, practice-specific training, writing workshops and numerous seminars on a variety of topics. Kirkland also hosts ample social events for summer associates. By the time they leave the firm, summer associates have a feel for Kirkland people, practice areas and culture and have a foundation on which to choose Kirkland to begin their careers.

Head Office: N/A
Number of domestic offices: 7
Number of international offices: 5
Partners (US): 700
Associates (US): 740

Hiring Partners: Elizabeth Deeley, Jason Kanner
Recruiting website: www.kirkland.com/careers
Diversity officer: Rina Alvarez

Summer Salary 2016
1Ls hired? Some offices
Split summers offered? No
Can summers spend time in overseas office? Yes, the London office has a summer program.
Summers 2016: 146
Offers/acceptances 2015:
133 offers, 112 acceptances

KIRKLAND & ELLIS

Kramer Levin Naftalis & Frankel LLP

1177 Avenue of the Americas, New York, NY 10036
Tel: 212 715 9100 Fax: 212 715 8000
Email: legalrecruiting@kramerlevin.com
www.kramerlevin.com

Main areas of work

Bankruptcy and restructuring; capital markets and M&A; commercial and white collar litigation; employment litigation; finance and banking; immigration; intellectual property; investment funds; real estate; land use and environmental; securitization; tax, employee benefits and individual clients.

Firm profile

Kramer Levin Naftalis & Frankel LLP is a premier, full-service law firm with offices in New York, Silicon Valley and Paris. Firm lawyers are leading practitioners in their respective fields. The firm represents public and private companies - ranging from Global 1000 to middle-market and emerging growth companies - across a broad range of industries, as well as funds, institutions and individuals.

Recruitment details

- Number of 1st year associates: 13
- Number of 2nd year associates: 18
- Associate salaries: 1st year: $160,000
- 2nd year: $170,000
- Clerking policy: Yes

Law Schools attending for OCIs in 2016:

Benjamin N Cardozo, Brooklyn, Columbia University, Fordham University, Georgetown University, Harvard, Hofstra University, New York University School of Law, St John's University, University of California at Berkeley, Boalt Hall School of Law, University of Michigan, University of Pennsylvania, Yale

Summer details

Summer associate profile:

We seek lawyers whose academic achievements, journal writing, and prior work experience demonstrate exceptional ability, motivation and potential for leadership.

Summer program components:

Our summer program offers a realistic experience. We fully involve summer associates in day to day practice and assign work comparable to that given to junior associates. Summer associates participate in our departmental meetings, firmwide events and training programs and are given opportunities to attend court hearings, discovery proceedings, negotiating sessions, closings, pro bono matters and client meetings.

Head Office: New York, NY
Number of domestic offices: 2
Number of international offices: 1
Worldwide revenue: $332,000,000
Partners (US): 95
Associates (US): 215

Main Recruitment Contact: Renée C Vanna, Director of Legal Recruiting
Hiring Partner: Kerri Ann Law
Recruitment website: www.kramerlevin.com/careers/
Diversity officer: Lauren Tapper, Director of Diversity

Summer Salary 2016
1Ls: $3,077/week
2Ls: $3,077/week
Post 3Ls: N/A
1Ls hired? Yes
Split summers offered? Case by case
Can summers spend time in overseas office? No
Summers 2016: 15
Offers/acceptances 2015:
12 offers, 11 acceptances

KRAMER LEVIN
NAFTALIS & FRANKEL LLP

Latham & Watkins LLP

885 Third Avenue, New York, NY 10022-4834
Tel: 212 906 1200 Fax: 212 751 4864
www.lw.com

Main areas of work

Corporate; environment, land and resources; finance; litigation; tax.

Firm profile

Latham & Watkins is a fully integrated, global law firm that takes pride in its culture of teamwork, diversity and inclusion, collegiality and a strong commitment to quality and professionalism that have helped the firm succeed for more than 75 years. Because we do not operate regions or offices as separate profit centers, and no single office serves as a headquarters for the firm, firm leadership is spread across the globe and the firm maintains a team-oriented focus. Clients rely on Latham's vast team of approximately 2,200 lawyers, located in the world's major business and financial centers, for their wide range of experience across practices, industries and global regions. Latham has received praise for its innovative approach to law firm management, which is grounded in the firm's devotion to the collaborative process and reaches across the firm's global platform. As a signatory to the Law Firm Pro Bono Challenge, Latham has a longstanding commitment to providing pro bono legal services and uncapped billable hour credit is given to pro bono work.

Recruitment details

- Number of 1st year associates: 150
- Number of 2nd year associates: 147
- Associate salaries: 1st year: $160,000
- Clerking policy: Yes

Law Schools attending for OCIs in 2016:

Berkeley, Boston College, Boston University, Chicago, Columbia, Cornell, Duke, Emory, Fordham, George Mason, George Washington, Georgetown, Harvard, UC Hastings, Houston, Howard, Illinois, UC Irvine, Loyola (LA), Michigan, Northwestern, Notre Dame, NYU, Ohio State, Pennsylvania, Stanford, Texas, Tulane, UCLA, USC, USD, Vanderbilt, Virginia, Wash U. (St. Louis), Yale and others.

Summer details

Summer associate profile:

We consider a number of factors in evaluating our applications for summer associate positions including academic and leadership achievements, a commitment to diversity and inclusion, initiative and willingness to assume early responsibility, maturity, judgment, non-academic experience, and extra-curricular activities.

Summer program components:

Latham's summer program is designed to give you a sense of life at the firm as a junior associate. As a summer associate, you will receive work assignments through the unassigned program, allowing you to explore our 50+ practice groups. Summer associates are also invited to participate in any training and CLE courses that are offered to our associates. Like a newly hired associate, you will be assigned a firm mentor who will help guide you through your summer. The summer associate review process is similar to the associate review process. Work reviews are read to you verbatim and a clear message regarding progress and standing is given. Summer associates also have the opportunity to participate in Summer Academy, a three-day professional development program.

Number of domestic offices: 10
Number of international offices: 21
Worldwide revenue: $2.650 billion
Partners (US): 456
Associates (US): 1014

Main Recruitment Contact: Debra Clarkson, Director of Global Recruiting
Hiring Partner: Manu Gayatrinath, Global Recruiting Committee Chair
Recruitment website: www.lw.com/careers
Diversity officer: Nadia Sager, Diversity Leadership Committee Chair

Summer Salary 2016
1Ls: $3,080/week
2Ls: $3,080/week
Post 3Ls: $3,080/week
1Ls hired? 1L Fellowship Program; others case by case
Split summers offered? Case by case
Can summers spend time in overseas office? Case by case
Summers 2016: 203
Offers/acceptances 2015:
176 offers, 166 acceptances, 7 pending

LATHAM & WATKINS LLP

Linklaters

1345 Avenue of the Americas, New York, NY 10105
Tel: 212 903 9000 Fax: 212 903 9100
www.linklaters.com

Main areas of work

Antitrust/competition, banking, bankruptcy, restructuring and insolvency, capital markets, corporate/M&A, energy and infrastructure/project finance, executive compensation and benefits, financial regulation, international governance and development, investment management, Latin American finance, litigation and arbitration, structured finance and derivatives, tax.

Firm profile

Linklaters LLP is a leading global law firm that has been advising the world's premier companies, financial institutions and governments on their most important and challenging assignments for over 175 years. With more than 2,600 attorneys based in 29 offices in 20 countries, we deliver an outstanding service to our clients anywhere in the world. We boast a strong US practice in New York and Washington, DC, that is reinforced by a global network of US lawyers extending across the world's major business and financial centers, including: Frankfurt, Hong Kong, London, Madrid, Milan, Moscow, Paris, São Paulo, Seoul and Singapore. Our team of US-qualified lawyers delivers integrated advice across multiple legal regimes and market practices, covering transactional, regulatory, disclosure, compliance, litigation and liability management issues globally.

Recruitment details

- Associate salaries: 1st year: $160,000 • 2nd year: $170,000
- Clerking policy: Yes

Law Schools attending for OCIs in 2016:

Brooklyn, Columbia, Cornell, Duke, Fordham, George Washington, Georgetown, Harvard, Michigan, NYU, Penn, UVA

Summer details

Summer associate profile:

We look for people who can make the most of everything Linklaters has to offer: those who will work hard, learn quickly and take responsibility early. You will need analytical intelligence, a high level of attention to detail, creativity, and the people skills required to work well with both colleagues and clients. It is also important to have a genuine interest in business and the financial world, a high level of commercial awareness, and the desire to be part of a global network.

Summer program components:

Linklaters' summer associates typically rotate through two practice divisions and may have the opportunity to spend time in more than one office. Summers are given real responsibility and are expected to participate in pro bono work in addition to working on billable matters.

Along with our dedicated summer associate training program, we encourage our summers to attend training sessions offered to our associates. Each summer associate is assigned a partner and associate mentor and receives two formal appraisals, one at the midpoint and one at the conclusion of the summer.

Number of domestic offices: 2
Number of international offices: 27
Partners (US): 43
Associates (US): 152

Main Recruitment Contact: Jennifer Katz-Hickman
Hiring Partners: Justin Storms and Paul Hessler
Recruitment website: www.linklatersuscareers.com
Diversity Partner: Peter Cohen-Millstein

Summer Salary 2016
1Ls: $3,077/week
2Ls: $3,077/week
Post 3Ls: $3,077/week
1Ls hired? Yes
Split summers offered? No
Can summers spend time in overseas office? Yes
Summers 2016: 18
Offers/acceptances 2015:
19 offers, 17 acceptances (2Ls only)

Linklaters

Lowenstein Sandler

1251 Avenue of the Americas
New York, New York 10020
Tel: 212 262 6700 Fax: 212 262 7402
www.lowenstein.com

Main areas of work

Corporate, venture capital, technology, intellectual property, investment management, fund formations, capital markets and securities, mergers and acquisitions, litigation, complex commercial litigation, white collar criminal defense, employment, insurance, pro bono, bankruptcy, real estate, tax.

Firm profile

Lowenstein Sandler is a leading national law firm intensely devoted to our client's success and deeply committed to our core values. We have built a reputation for pursuing every matter with creativity and passion. Our industry knowledge, entrepreneurial drive and proven commitment to our communities deliver a different and better law firm experience to our clients. We focus on building long-standing relationships and anticipating our clients' needs, rather than responding to them. Working side-by-side with our clients, we approach each case and each other with integrity and respect. And, our award winning pro-bono work enables us to connect individuals and communities with unimaginable success.

We pride ourselves on being a different kind of law firm – one deeply rooted in the interest of our clients, our communities and our colleagues.

Recruitment details

- Number of 1st year associates: 18
- Number of 2nd year associates: 17
- Associate salaries: 1st year: $160,000
- 2nd year: $170,000
- Clerking policy: Yes

Law Schools attending for OCIs in 2016:

Columbia, NYU, Harvard, Duke, UPenn, Yale, Notre Dame, Emory, Vanderbilt, Rutgers, Seton Hall, Santa Clara, Stanford, UC Berkeley, UC Hastings

Summer details

Summer program components:

Our summer program includes eleven weeks of real-world experience, working directly with lawyers in a variety of practice areas. The summer program offers educational seminars, mentoring, social events and, most significantly, participation in complex matters in the legal areas in which students have expressed interest, including pro bono work in the Lowenstein Center for Public Interest. Our summer program is the perfect balance between structure and flexibility, in-depth legal work and good fun.

Summer associate profile:

At Lowenstein Sandler we believe that what makes you different makes you successful. We are passionate about the things that make our firm unique and are committed to developing the next generation of attorneys with the same creative, entrepreneurial spirit. Enthusiasm, passion and commitment are core qualities of our ideal candidate. We seek individuals who possess genuine leadership qualities with a strong work ethic. We are a firm that thinks outside the box, so if you find yourself daring to be different, you owe it to yourself to have a look at Lowenstein Sandler.

Number of domestic offices: 6
Partners (US): 114
Associates (US): 187

Main Recruitment Contact:
Mona Patel, Manager of Entry Level Recruiting
Hiring Partner: Raymond Thek
Recruitment website:
www.lowensteincareers.com

Summer Salary 2016
1Ls: N/A in NY; $2,700/week in NJ
2Ls: $2,900/week in NY; $2,700/week in NJ
1Ls hired? Yes (NJ/CA only)
Split summers offered? No
Summers 2016: 25
Offers/acceptances 2015: 20 offers, 17 acceptances

Lowenstein Sandler LLP

Marshall, Gerstein & Borun LLP

233 S. Wacker Drive, 6300 Willis Tower, Chicago, IL 60606
Tel: 312 474 6300 Fax: 312 474 0448
Email: mgudaitis@marshallip.com
www.marshallip.com

Main areas of work

Marshall, Gerstein & Borun LLP is a Chicago-based intellectual property law firm having over 90 attorneys, highly qualified patent agents, and technical specialists, all dedicated to providing superior intellectual property counseling. We specialize in prosecution and litigation in all areas of intellectual property law. We litigate nationwide, primarily within the federal court system, and obtain patents and trademark registrations for our clients in the United States and foreign patent and trademark offices.

Firm profile

Marshall, Gerstein & Borun is at the forefront of intellectual property law. The Firm's professionals understand the hard science behind clients' innovations and how to devise, evaluate and execute intellectual property strategies. Fortune 500 corporations, small to mid-sized companies, non-profits and start-ups turn to Marshall Gerstein for comprehensive intellectual property solutions tailored to their needs. With almost 80 attorneys supported by a full team of patent agents, technical specialists and paralegals, the Firm assists clients with protection, enforcement and transfer of IP rights throughout the world.

- Nearly 90% of the Firm's attorneys and patent agents are admitted to practice before the US Patent and Trademark Office
- Nearly 90% of the Firm's attorneys have science or engineering degrees
- Nearly 50% of the Firm's patent agents and technical specialists have a PhD or other advanced technical degree

Recruitment details

- Number of 1st year associates: 1
- Number of 2nd year associates: 1
- Associate salaries: 1st year: $160,000
- 2nd year:
- Clerking policy: yes

Law Schools attending for OCIs in 2016:

Northwestern University, Notre Dame, University of Illinois, University of Michigan, University of Minnesota

Summer details

Summer associate profile:

We look for candidates with bright legal minds and demonstrated technical ability. The ideal candidate enjoys a thirst for learning, a dedicated work ethic, and an ability to work effectively in teams. Each candidate should have at least one technical/science degree, with an advanced degree preferred. Technical/science degrees are not requires for non-patent positions. We also appreciate the value diversity builds in our practice of law and look for candidates from diverse backgrounds that can bring a breadth of experience to our team.

Summer program components:

During the summer, we expose our summer associates to realistic, substantive legal assignments tackling issues across intellectual property disciplines, including litigation, prosecution, and transactional. Our summer associates will have one partner mentor and one associate mentor to work with throughout the summer. We also have many social events throughout the summer that take advantage of the culture and richness of Chicago.

Head Office: Chicago, IL
Number of domestic offices: 1
Number of international offices: 0
Partners (US): 43
Associates (US): 26

Main Recruitment Contact: Michele J Gudaitis
Hiring Partner: Julianne M Hartzell
Recruitment website: www.marshallip.com
Diversity Officers: Sharon M Sintich, Shelley C Danek

Summer Salary 2016
1Ls: $3,000
2Ls: $3,000
Post 3Ls: $3,000
1Ls hired? Yes
Split summers offered? Yes
Can summers spend time in overseas office? N/A
Summers 2016: 2
Offers/acceptances 2015: 5 offers, 4 acceptance

Mayer Brown LLP

www.mayerbrown.com

Firm profile

Mayer Brown is a leading global law firm with offices in 20 cities across the Americas, Asia and Europe. The firm's presence in the world's key business and legal centers enables it to offer clients access to local market knowledge and depth combined with a global reach. The firm's practice areas include: banking and finance; corporate and securities; litigation and dispute resolution; antitrust and competition; US Supreme Court and appellate matters; employment and benefits; environmental; financial services regulatory and enforcement; government and global trade; intellectual property; real estate; tax; restructuring, bankruptcy and insolvency; and wealth management.

Recruitment details

- Number of 1st year associates: 68
- Number of 2nd year associates: 52
- Associate salaries: 1st year: $160,000 plus significant market bonus opportunities
- 2nd year: $170,000 plus significant market bonus opportunities
- Clerking policy: Yes, the firm encourages clerkships, has pre-clerkship summer associate opportunities and pays clerkship bonuses.

Law Schools attending for OCIs in 2016:

Berkeley, Chicago, Columbia, Fordham, Georgetown, Harvard, Houston, Howard, Illinois, Loyola, Michigan, North Carolina, NYU, Northwestern, Penn, Stanford, Texas, Virginia, Wake Forest, Washington & Lee, Yale

Summer details

Summer associate profile:

Mayer Brown seeks to hire associates of exceptional promise from a variety of backgrounds. Because Mayer Brown seeks to hire associates with the potential to become partners at the firm, its hiring standards are rigorous. Above all, Mayer Brown is interested in candidates who share the firm's dedication to providing high-quality legal services and who have demonstrated superior academic ability and personal achievement.

Summer program components:

Summer Associates at Mayer Brown are not assigned to practice areas and there is no formal rotation between groups. The firm's goal is to expose summer associates to as many practices areas and attorneys as possible during the program. Each summer associate is assigned at least two attorney mentors and receives written reviews on every assignment. Each summer associate will attend development meetings with partners at mid-summer and at the end of summer.

Head Office: N/A
Number of domestic offices: 7
Number of international offices: 13
Worldwide revenue: $1.223 billion
Partners (US): 381
Counsel (US): 94
Associates (US): 402

Main Recruitment Contacts:
See www.mayerbrown.com/careers for office specific contacts
Hiring Partner: J Bradley (Brad) Keck
Recruitment website:
www.mayerbrown.com/careers
Diversity officer: Jeremiah DeBerry, Director of Diversity & Inclusion

Summer Salary 2016
1Ls: $3,077/week
2Ls: $3,077/week
Post 3Ls: $3,077/week
1Ls hired? Varies by office
Split summers offered? Case by case, office by office basis
Can summers spend time in overseas office? Atypical
Summers 2016: 67
Offers/acceptances 2015:
220 offers, 63 acceptances

MAYER•BROWN

McGuireWoods LLP

800 E. Canal Street, Richmond, VA 23219
Tel: 804 775 1000
www.mcguirewoods.com

Main areas of work

Antitrust and trade regulation, appeals and issues, banking and finance, class action, commercial litigation, corporate, data privacy and security, employee benefits, energy, environmental, financial services litigation, government/regulatory and criminal investigations, healthcare, insurance recovery, intellectual property, labor and employment, private wealth services, product liability and mass torts, real estate and land use, restructuring and insolvency, tax, technology and outsourcing, and trials.

Firm profile

McGuireWoods is a global law firm with approximately 1,000 lawyers and 21 strategically located offices worldwide. As a McGuireWoods lawyer, you'll reap the benefits of a resource-rich firm, but in the close knit, supportive environment you'd expect from a small firm. McGuireWoods is a distinguished, yet familiar place to work and grow. The backbone of our firm consists of six core values that guide everything we do – a commitment to excellence, client service, integrity, collegiality, community and diversity and inclusion.

Recruitment details

- Number of 1st year associates: 19
- Number of 2nd year associates: 23
- Associate salaries: 1st year: $115,000-$155,000 (depending on office)
- 2nd year: Varies – not lock step
- Clerking policy: Yes

Law Schools attending for OCIs in 2016:

University of Chicago, Duke University, Georgetown University, University of Illinois, University of North Carolina, Northwestern University, University of Notre Dame, University of Richmond, Vanderbilt University, University of Virginia, Wake Forest University, Washington and Lee University, William and Mary School of Law; Southeastern Minority Job Fair, Lavender Job Fair; CCBA Minority Job Fair

Summer details

Summer associate profile:

The selection process is highly competitive. Excellent academics, as well as superior writing and interpersonal skills are required. McGuireWoods is looking for highly qualified candidates with demonstrated leadership potential and a commitment to their law school communities. The firm values both legal and non-legal work experience in candidates.

Summer program components:

We have a 10 week summer program. Each summer associate is matched up with one or two associates and a partner mentor for the summer. The best kind of training comes from working alongside experienced lawyers on cases and transactions. Our summer program is designed to give our summer associates this kind of experience. Along with the on-the-job training, summer associates have numerous opportunities to attend department and industry team meetings to gain perspective of the work the firm handles. The firm also plans an annual three day summer associate retreat. The three days are filled with information and training sessions designed specifically for them. Topics include: legal writing, ethics and confidentiality, law firm economics, just to name a few.

Head Office: Richmond, VA
Number of domestic offices: 19
Number of international offices: 2
Partners US: 398
Associates US: 311

Main Recruitment Contact: Ann McGhee
Hiring Partners: John Adams and Naho Kobayashi
Recruiting website: www.mcguirewoods.com/careers
Diversity officer: Stacy Reyan

Summer Salary 2016
1Ls: $2,600–$2,900/week
2Ls: $2,600–$2,900/week
1Ls hired: Yes
Split summer offered: No
Can summers spend time in overseas offices: No
Summers 2016: 17
Offers/acceptances 2015:
16 offers, 14 acceptances

Milbank, Tweed, Hadley & McCloy LLP

28 Liberty Street, New York, NY 10005
Tel: 212 530 5000 Fax: 212 530 5219
www.milbank.com

Main areas of work

Milbank's practice areas include alternative investments, corporate, financial restructuring, leveraged finance, litigation (complex commercial, white collar and regulatory, securities and IP), pro bono, project finance, securities, structured finance, tax, transportation and space finance and trusts and estates.

Firm profile

Milbank is a premier international law firm handling high-profile cases and complex business transactions. We are a leader in corporate/finance work, including banking, capital markets, project and transportation finance and M&A. Our Litigation Group handles complex and high profile civil actions, SEC enforcements and white collar criminal matters. Our financial restructuring attorneys have been involved in every recent major reorganization in the US.

Recruitment details

- Number of 1st year associates: 51 (US), 68 (worldwide)
- Number of 2nd year associates: 74 (US), 85 (worldwide)
- Associate salaries: 1st year: $160,000 • 2nd year: $170,000
- Clerking policy: Yes

Law Schools attending for OCIs in 2016:

Albany, Berkeley, Boston University, Brooklyn, Cardozo, Chicago, Columbia, Cornell Job Fair, Duke, Emory Job Fair, Fordham, Georgetown, George Washington, Harvard, Howard, Lavender Law Job Fair, Loyola Los Angeles (LA), Michigan, New York University, New York Law School, Northwestern, University of Pennsylvania, St John's, Stanford, Texas Job Fair, Tulane/Washington University Job Fair, UCI (LA), UCLA (LA), USC (LA), Vanderbilt, Virginia, Yale

Summer details

Summer associate profile:

We are looking for summer associates with diverse backgrounds who demonstrate a high level of intelligence, creativity, leadership, determination and enthusiasm.

Summer program components:

Our program includes a rotation system enabling summers to rotate through several groups. Our comprehensive nine-session training program follows a company's lifecycle from inception to restructuring and includes in-session activities and post-class assignments. Summers are given mentors and receive formal reviews.

Head Office: New York, NY
Number of domestic offices: 3
Number of international offices: 9
Worldwide revenue: $771,000,000
Partners (US): 107
Counsel (US): 28
Associates (US): 345

Main Recruitment Contact: Amy Stisser
Hiring Partner: Rod Miller
Recruitment website: www.milbank.com/careers
Diversity officer: Salila Yohn

Summer Salary 2016
1Ls: $3,077/week
2Ls: $3,077/week
1Ls hired? No
Split summers offered? No
Can summers spend time in overseas office? Yes
Summers 2016: 65 (53 NY, 8 LA, 3 DC)
Offers/acceptances 2015:
55 offers, 54 acceptances (1 clerk deferred)

Mintz Levin

Head Office Address: One Financial Center, Boston, MA 02127
Tel: 617 542 6000 Fax: 617 542 2241
Email: jcarrion@mintz.com
www.mintz.com

Head Office: Boston
Number of domestic offices: 7
Number of international offices: 2
Worldwide revenue: $434.3m
Partners (US): 255
Associates (US): 190

Main Recruitment Contact: Jennifer Carrion
Hiring Partner: Adrienne Walker
Recruitment website: www.mintz.com
Diversity Officer: Tyrone Thomas

Summer Salary 2016
1Ls: $3,077
2Ls: $3,077
1Ls hired? Yes
Split summers offered? No
Can summers spend time in overseas office? No
Summers 2016: 18
Offers/acceptances 2015: 9 Offers Extended/8 Offers Accepted

Main areas of work

Antitrust; bankruptcy, restructuring and commercial law; communications; consumer product safety, corporate and securities; corporate compliance and investigations; crisis response, risk management and executive protection; employment, labor and benefits; environmental law; government law and contracts; health law; immigration; intellectual property; international; litigation; privacy and security; private client; private equity; product risk management and response; project development and finance; public finance; real estate; start-ups; tax; venture capital and emerging companies; white collar defense; government investigations and enforcement.

Firm profile

Mintz Levin is a multidisciplinary firm, characterized by innovation and an entrepreneurial drive that attracts interesting clients, from startups to large public companies, universities, non-profits and family-run businesses. Mintz Levin is dedicated to the continued professional growth of its attorneys at all levels. Incoming associates benefit from a formal orientation program that acclimates them to the Firm. New associates participate in an intensive three-day "base camp" to learn the substantive law of the area of practice in which they will be concentrating. This is followed by a curriculum designed to meet the professional development needs of each attorney at every step of his/her career.

Mintz Levin is proud of its formal mentoring programs that complement the collegiality of our Firm. The Firm has an extensive associate mentoring program run by a Firm-wide mentoring coordinator and on-site mentoring coordinators in each office.

Recruitment details

- Number of 1st year associates: 16
- Number of 2nd year associates: 13
- Associate salaries: 1st year: $160,000
- 2nd year: $170,000
- Clerking policy: Yes (but it depends on the situation)

Law Schools attending for OCIs in 2016:

Boston College Law School, Boston University School of Law, Columbia Law School, Fordham School of Law, Georgetown Law School, Harvard Law School, New York University, Northeastern University School of Law, University of California Los Angeles School of Law, niversity of San Diego School of Law, University of California Berkeley School of Law, University of Southern California Gould School of Law, University of Pennsylvania Law School

Summer details

Summer associate profile:

Summer associates are encouraged to work on assignments from a variety of practice areas. They attend trials, depositions and negotiations. They participate in legal writing workshops, a transactional case study, and a mock trial. Each summer associate is assigned an associate mentor, a member mentor and a writing mentor. Mentors are available for questions, and they facilitate informal feedback on work projects. Through work assignments and social events, our attorneys strive to provide each summer associate with an opportunity to get to know what a career at Mintz has to offer.

Morgan, Lewis & Bockius LLP

1701 Market Street, Philadelphia, PA 19103-2921
Tel: 215 963 5000 Fax: 215 963 5001
www.morganlewis.com

Main areas of work

At Morgan Lewis, we work around the world and around the clock to respond to the needs of our clients. We provide comprehensive corporate, transactional, litigation and regulatory services that address and anticipate challenges across rapidly changing landscapes. Our international team of lawyers and other specialists support clients across a wide range of industries, including financial services, energy and environmental, healthcare and life sciences, retail and technology.

Firm profile

From our 28 offices in the United States, Europe, Asia and the Middle East, we work across all major industries with clients that range from established, global Fortune 100 companies to enterprising startups. Our team comprises more than 2,000 legal professionals including lawyers, patent agents, employee benefits advisors, regulatory scientists and other specialists. We focus on immediate concerns and long-term goals, harnessing our resources from strategic hubs of commerce, law and government around the world. Founded in 1873, we stand on the shoulders of more than 140 years of excellence.

Recruitment details

- Number of 1st year associates: 74
- Number of 2nd year associates: 92
- Associate salaries: 1st year: $145,000-$160,000
- 2nd year: $150,000-$170,000
- Clerking policy: Yes

Law Schools attending for OCIs in 2016:

BC, Berkeley, BU, Chicago, Columbia, Cornell, Davis, Duke, Florida, Fordham, GW, Georgetown, Harvard, Hastings, Houston, Howard, Illinois, Miami, Michigan, NYU, Northwestern, Pennsylvania, Pittsburgh, Rutgers, Santa Clara, Stanford, Southern Methodist, Temple, Texas, UC Irvine, UCLA, USC, USF, UVA, Villanova

Summer details

Summer associate profile:

Highly motivated individuals from diverse backgrounds who have a record of outstanding academic achievement, as well as superior writing and analytical skills, a commitment to client service, initiative and an ability to succeed in a challenging, collaborative workplace.

Summer program components:

Our program provides insight into Morgan Lewis, its practices and culture through professional and social experiences. The summer program launches with a multi-day kickoff that brings summer associates from all offices together with firm leaders, other partners and associates. Summer associates have the unique opportunity to tailor their "ML Summer Experience" with the option of either spending the entire summer at the firm or spending a portion of the summer working on-site with a firm client or with a public interest organization. The client experience facilitates professional development by providing a deeper understanding of the operations and issues handled by in-house legal departments. While at the firm, summer associates work on matters typically assigned to first-year associates and participate in a generous mix of training opportunities to hone skills such as legal writing and presentation style.

Head Office: Philadelphia, PA
Number of domestic offices: 17
Number of international offices: 11
Partners (US): 649
Associates (US): 729

Main Recruitment Contact: Lindsay Callantine
Hiring Partners: Christina Edling Melendi
Recruitment website: www.morganlewis.com
Diversity officer: Kenneth Imo

Summer Salary 2016
1Ls: $3,080/week
2Ls: $3,080/week
1Ls hired? Case by case
Split summers offered? Case by case
Can summers spend time in overseas office? No
Summers 2016: 57
Offers/acceptances 2015:
56 offers, 50 acceptances

Morgan Lewis

Morrison & Foerster

425 Market Street, San Francisco, CA 94105
Tel: 415 268 7000 Fax: 415 268 7522
Email: fwattorneyrecruiting@mofo.com
www.mofo.com

Main areas of work

Appellate; business restructuring and insolvency; capital markets; clean technology and alternative energy; commercial litigation; emerging companies and venture capital; energy; financial transactions; intellectual property; life sciences; mergers and acquisitions; privacy and data security; real estate; securities litigation, enforcement and white-collar criminal defense; tax; and technology transactions.

Firm profile

Morrison & Foerster is a global firm of exceptional credentials. With 950 lawyers in 17 offices in key technology and financial centers in the United States, Europe and Asia, the firm advises the world's leading financial institutions, investment banks and technology, telecommunications, life sciences and Fortune 100 companies.

Recruitment details

- Number of 1st year associates: 46
- Number of 2nd year associates: 69
- Associate salaries: 1st year: $160,000
- 2nd year: $170,000
- Clerking policy: Yes

Law Schools attending for OCIs in 2016:

Berkeley Law, Cardozo, University of Chicago, Columbia, Cornell, UC Davis, Duke, Fordham, George Washington, Georgetown, Harvard, Howard, McGill, University of Michigan, Northwestern, NYU, UPenn, University of San Diego, Santa Clara, Stanford, University of Texas, UCLA, USC, UVA, Yale

Summer details

Summer associate profile:

Morrison & Foerster looks for individuals of exceptional intelligence whose academic and other achievements evidence their talent, motivation, energy and creativity.

Summer program components:

The summer program is intended to give summer associates a real sense of what it means to practice at MoFo.

Work is distributed using a central assignment system, taking into account your areas of interest. Typical assignments include writing briefs, motions, contracts and client memoranda, assisting in drafting and negotiation sessions, assisting in depositions and witness preparation and performing due diligence in corporate transactions, as well as pro bono assignments.

A variety of training programs are designed specifically for summer associates, including practice area presentations.

Each summer associate is assigned one or more mentors to help acclimate him or her to the firm. Mentors take their summer associates out to lunch, introduce their summer associates to the lawyers and staff in their practice group and office and act as a sounding board for any questions or concerns summer associates may have throughout the summer.

Head Office: San Francisco, CA
Number of domestic offices: 9
Number of international offices: 8
Worldwide revenue: $979,300,000
Partners (US): 247
Associates (US): 360

Main Recruitment Contact: Lesley Ficarri
Hiring Partner: Craig Martin
Recruitment website: http://careers.mofo.com
Diversity officer: Natalie Kernisant

Summer Salary 2016
1Ls: $3,080/week
2Ls: $3,080/week
Post 3Ls: $3,080/week
1Ls hired? Yes
Split summers offered? Yes, case by case
Can summers spend time in overseas office? Yes, case by case
Summers 2016: 83 (2Ls) +28 (1Ls)
Offers/acceptances 2015:
81 offers, 65 acceptances and 1 Open

MORRISON
FOERSTER

Munger, Tolles & Olson LLP

355 South Grand Avenue, 35th Floor, Los Angeles, CA 90071
Tel: 213 683 9100 Fax: 213 687 3702
www.mto.com

Main areas of work

For over a half century, attorneys from Munger, Tolles & Olson have been partnering with clients on their most important and complex cases and business deals. We maintain a national and international practice. Our principal areas of practice include bet-the-company litigation, and trials, class actions, white collar defense and investigations, corporate, labor and employment, environmental, real estate, financial restructuring and tax.

Firm profile

Munger Tolles has for decades intentionally maintained low-leverage. We believe our roughly one-to-one partner-to-associate ratio empowers all of our 200 lawyers to make an impact in the work we do for our clients. We are involved in some of the highest profile cases in the country and count among our clients Bank of America, Wells Fargo, LinkedIn, Facebook, Transocean, Edison International, Verizon, KB Home, LG Display, Yucaipa and Berkshire Hathaway.

Recruitment details

- Number of 1st year associates: 5
- Number of 2nd year associates: 14
- Associate salaries: 1st year: $160,000
- 2nd year: $170,000
- Clerking policy: Yes

Law Schools attending for OCIs in 2016:

Berkeley, Chicago, Columbia, Harvard, Howard, Michigan, NYU, Stanford, UCLA, USC, Yale

Summer details

Summer associate profile:

Our firm serves as a platform for individuals who want to actively solve their client's problems. We look for law students who have demonstrated excellence and leadership in their prior pursuits and who bring both intellectual curiosity and a sense of individuality to an already extremely talented and diverse group of lawyers. Unlike other law firms, where it has become common to expect that young lawyers will stay only a short time before moving on to other endeavors, we only hire lawyers we believe have the potential to ultimately join our (one-tier) partnership.

Summer program components:

Our summer program will provide you a realistic idea of what it is like to practice law at our firm. You will work closely with attorneys in various practice areas, doing meaningful assignments. Each summer associate is assigned a work coordinator and social advisor. Your work coordinator will find assignments that are of interest to you and provide guidance and feedback during the summer. Your summer will include invitations to attend our weekly lunches, training programs, social events and practice group meetings.

Head Office: Los Angeles, CA
Number of domestic offices: 2
Number of international offices: 0
Partners (US): 90
Associates (US): 116

Main Recruitment Contact: Kevinn Villard, 213 683 9242
Hiring Partners: Bethany Kristovich, Carolyn Luedtke, Gregory Weingart
Recruitment website: www.mto.com/careers

Summer Salary 2016
1Ls: $3,080/week
2Ls: $3,080/week
Post 3Ls: $3,080/week
1Ls hired? Yes
Split summers offered? Yes
Summers 2016: 20 2Ls, 3 1Ls
(1Ls are not eligible for offers)
Offers 2015: 28 offers

Nixon Peabody LLP

100 Summer Street, Boston, Massachusetts
Tel: 617 345 1000 Fax: 617 345 1300
Email: cfontane@nixonpeabody.com
www.nixonpeabody.com

Main areas of work

Business and finance; litigation and dispute resolution; real estate; intellectual property; private equity and investment funds; M&A; securities, public finance; tax; labor and employment; tax credit finance and syndication; affordable housing; government investigations and white collar defense; estate, trust and financial planning; health services; life sciences; energy; food and beverages; gaming and government relations.

Firm profile

We see the law as a tool to help shape our clients' futures. Our focus is on knowing what is important to our clients now and next so we can foresee obstacles and opportunities in their space and smooth their way. We ensure they are equipped with winning legal strategies as they navigate the exciting and challenging times we live in. The qualities that drive Nixon Peabody are extreme understanding of our clients and their industries, a future-leaning orientation, and a culture that taps collective intelligence to create value for clients. We provide counsel on the full range of corporate transactions, disputes and regulatory challenges.

Recruitment details

- Number of 1st year associates: 24
- Number of 2nd year associates: 21
- Associate salaries: 1st year: $160,000 in metro market offices
- 2nd year: $165,000
- Clerking policy: Yes

Law Schools attending for OCIs in 2016:

Nixon Peabody recruits from top tier law schools throughout the US including UC Berkeley, Cornell, Harvard, University of Michigan, Northwestern, NYU, UCLA and USC. In 2016, we expect to conduct interviews at various leading national and regional law schools.

Summer details

Summer associate profile:

We seek candidates with excellent academic credentials, solid research and writing skills, demonstrated leadership ability and sound judgment. We value innovation and collaborative work styles. Prior work experience and diversified outside activities are a plus.

Summer program components:

Our summer program lays the foundation for your career at Nixon Peabody. The program is intended to introduce you to as many opportunities as possible. We believe the more you learn over the summer, the better career choices you will make. You will be exposed to a range of practice areas and take part in billable client work and pro bono projects. In addition to exploring the practice of law, we also encourage our summer associates to get to know the Nixon Peabody attorneys in the cities in which we work. We provide formal and informal mentorship, various group training sessions and substantive feedback through our evaluation process.

Head Office: Boston, MA
Number of domestic offices: 13
Number of international offices: 3
Partners (US): 333
Associates (US): 229

Main Recruitment Contacts: Julie Zammuto and Cristina Fontane
Hiring Partner: John Snellings
Recruitment website: www.nixonpeabody.com/careers
Diversity officers: Jenny Kuenster

Summer Salary 2016
1Ls: $3,080/week
2Ls: $3,080/week
Post 3Ls: N/A
1Ls hired? Yes
Split summers offered? No
Can summers spend time in overseas office? No
Summers 2016: 22
Offers/acceptances 2015:
24 offers, 22 acceptances

Norton Rose Fulbright

1301 McKinney, Suite 5100 Houston, TX 77010
Tel: 713 651 5151 Fax: 713 651 5246
www.nortonrosefulbright.com/US/

Main areas of work

Antitrust and competition; banking and finance; corporate, M&A and securities; dispute resolution and litigation; employment and labor; financial restructuring and insolvency; intellectual property; real estate; regulations and investigations; tax

Firm profile

Norton Rose Fulbright is a global law firm. We provide the world's pre-eminent corporations and financial institutions with a full business law service. We have more than 3800 lawyers and other legal staff based in more than 50 cities across Europe, the United States, Canada, Latin America, Asia, Australia, Africa, the Middle East and Central Asia.

Recognized for our industry focus, we are strong across all the key industry sectors: financial institutions; energy; infrastructure, mining and commodities; transport; technology and innovation; and life sciences and healthcare.

Recruitment details

- Number of 1st year associates: 51
- Number of 2nd year associates: 28
- Associate salaries: 1st year: varies by market-$160,000 (CA, DC, NY, TX offices)
- 2nd year: varies by market
- Clerking policy: Yes

Law Schools attending for OCIs in 2016:

Baylor, Chicago, Columbia, Duke, Fordham, George Washington, Georgetown, Harvard, Houston, Howard, Loyola (CA), NYU, Penn, South Texas, Southern Methodist, St. Mary's, Texas, Texas Southern, UC-Irvine, UCLA, USC, Virginia, Vanderbilt, Washington University. Job fairs include Lavender Law, Southeastern Minority Job Fair, and Sunbelt Minority Recruitment Program

Summer details

Summer associate profile:

We recruit motivated, energetic and personable individuals with whom we will enjoy practicing law. We hire with a long-term view. Candidates should have excellent academic qualifications and demonstrate initiative.

Summer program components:

Essential to the long-term success of Norton Rose Fulbright, our summer associate program is the primary source of new legal talent. Our summer associates develop their skills by applying their education to active practice. From proofreading and drafting documents to carrying out legal research and attending meetings, our summer associates work on projects that sharpen their key legal skills. Summer associates participate in significant legal activities, such as client meetings, board meetings, depositions and court appearances. Summer associates also have the opportunity to participate in a variety of legal and business skills workshops and presentations. We offer team building and social activities that are unique to each of the cities in which we work and live. Our lawyers work hard, but they also enjoy spending time with one another and having fun. Summer associates and their families will find a wide selection of sports, cultural, artistic and other activities designed to appeal to a variety of interests.

Head Office: N/A
Number of domestic offices: 11
Number of international offices: 41
Worldwide revenue: $1,813,920,831
Partners (US): 289
Associates (US): 304

Main Recruitment Contact: Jaimee Slovak
Hiring Partner: Andrew Price
Recruitment website: www.nortonrosefulbright.com
Diversity Officer: Lisa Genecov

Summer Salary 2016
1Ls: varies by market ($3077 in CA, DC, NY, TX offices)
2Ls: varies by market ($3077 in CA, DC, NY, TX offices)
Post 3Ls: varies by market ($3077 in CA, DC, NY, TX offices)
1Ls hired? Varies by market
Split summers offered? Varies by market
Can summers spend time in overseas office? No
Summers 2016: 52 2Ls; 1Ls TBD
Offers/acceptances 2015: 47/57 associate offers; 33/47 accepted; 4 pending judicial clerkships

NORTON ROSE FULBRIGHT

Nutter McClennen & Fish LLP

Seaport West, 155 Seaport Blvd, Boston, MA 02210
Tel: 617 439 2000 Fax: 617 310 9000
www.nutter.com

Main areas of work

Business, intellectual property, litigation, real estate and finance, tax and trusts and estates.

Firm profile

Nutter McClennen & Fish LLP has deep roots in Boston and a long-standing reputation for business savvy and pragmatism. Nutter advises clients across a wide range of industries, including life sciences, medical devices, pharmaceuticals, banking and financial services, real estate, energy, and technology. The firm regularly represents major US global corporations and financial institutions, research universities, high technology and emerging companies, investors, developers, foundations, and families that select Nutter for the quality of its lawyers and its depth as a multi-service firm. Nutter was co-founded by Louis D Brandeis, who later became a renowned justice of the US Supreme Court. The founding partners' rich legacy continues to inspire and set an example for the firm. Today Nutter upholds the same standard of focused dedication, innovation, and unwavering commitment to client service that they set over a century ago.

Recruitment details

- Number of 1st year associates: 7
- Number of 2nd year associates: 6
- Associate Salaries: 1st Year: $145,000
- 2nd Year: Not lock step, based on a core competency system
- Clerking policy: Case by case

Law Schools attending for OCIs in 2016:

Boston College, Boston University, Harvard, New England School of Law, Northeastern School of Law, and Suffolk University

Job Fairs: Boston Lawyers Group Job Fair (diversity fair) and Patent Law Interview Program

Summer details

Summer associate profile:

Strong academic record. Intelligent, enthusiastic, confident and results-oriented team players with demonstrated interpersonal and communication skills.

Summer program components:

Our approach to the summer experience at Nutter is to provide our summer associates with as complete and accurate a view of the firm and our practice as possible. Summer associates divide their ten weeks between two departments. For those who desire exposure to other areas, assignment coordinators endeavor to provide them with projects tailored to their individual interests. Each summer associate receives two formal reviews, one at midsummer and the other at the end of the program. These reviews are intended to provide the summer associate with guidance and are based upon written evaluations by supervising attorneys. We expect attorneys to provide individual, ongoing, informal feedback to summer associates and encourage summer associates to solicit feedback directly from attorneys. Each summer associate is assigned mentors, from each department to which he or she is assigned. By the end of the program, our goal is for summer associates to have a thorough understanding of our client-base and the work environment they will encounter as full-time associates.

Head Office: Boston, MA
Number of domestic offices: 2
Number of international offices: 0
Partners (US): 76
Counsel (US): 20
Associates (US): 49

Main Recruitment Contact: Katherine A Thatcher, Director of Legal Recruitment
Hiring Partner: Matthew J Bresette
Recruitment website: www.nutter.com/careers
Diversity officer: Stephen J Brake, Chair, Diversity and Inclusion Committee

Summer Salary 2016
1Ls: $1,500/week
2Ls: $2,788/week
Post 3 Ls: N/A
1Ls hired? Yes
Split summers offered? No
Can summers spend time in overseas office? No
Summers 2016: 7
Offers/acceptances 2015:
7 offers, 4 acceptances

O'Melveny & Myers LLP

Tel: 213 430 6000 Fax: 213 430 6407
Email: info@omm.com
www.omm.com

Main areas of work

O'Melveny advises industry-leading clients on a full range of cutting-edge litigation, transactional, and regulatory matters. For a complete listing of our client services, please visit www.omm.com.

Firm profile

O'Melveny's clients shape markets, set precedents, and break boundaries. And for more than a century, O'Melveny has been right beside them, helping our clients achieve their most important goals. Regularly recognized for excellence and innovation, we are also committed to cultivating a diverse and inclusive environment and to strengthening our communities through pro bono work, which we treat as equal to billable work. Our unique talent development program—which includes a career development advisor, in-person upward reviews that allow associates to provide feedback to partners on their supervisory skills and an award-winning flexibility program—enhances your professional experience.

Recruitment details

- Number of 1st year associates: 33
- Number of 2nd year associates: 67
- Associate salaries: 1st year: $160,000
- 2nd year: $170,000
- Clerking policy: Yes

Law Schools attending for OCIs in 2016:

Berkeley, Brooklyn, Chapman, Chicago, Columbia, UC Davis, Duke, Fordham, Georgetown, George Washington, Harvard, Hastings, Howard, Lavender Law, Loyola, Michigan, Northwestern, NYU, Penn, Rutgers, Santa Clara, Southwestern, Stanford, Texas, UCI, UCLA, University of Washington, USC, UVA, Yale

Summer details

Summer associate profile:

O'Melveny is looking for summer associates with outstanding academic and personal credentials from diverse backgrounds. We strive to find students with strong interpersonal skills and a desire to work in a collegial atmosphere that values teamwork. In addition to activities like journal work and moot court, we look for a keen interest in O'Melveny's practices, culture, and attorneys.

Summer program components:

Our summer program offers an inside look at what it is like to practice at O'Melveny. During our ten-week program, summer associates work on major cases and transactions, support ongoing pro bono matters, participate in targeted training and development programs, and join in social events to get to know our attorneys. Experiential training includes our Advocacy Institute, Mock Deal Program, and opportunities to accompany O'Melveny lawyers to deal closings, client meetings, depositions, and court appearances. Our work coordination system ensures our summers are exposed to a variety of practice areas, attorneys, and types of work. Mentors, ongoing feedback, and a midsummer review help our summer associates make the most of their experiences.

Head Office: N/A
Number of domestic offices: 7
Number of international offices: 8
Worldwide revenue: $689,252,000
Partners (US): 184
Associates (US): 419

Main Recruitment Contact: Tina Metis, Firmwide Director of Attorney Recruiting
Hiring Partner: Allen Burton, Firmwide Hiring Partner
Recruitment website: www.omm.com/careers
Diversity officers: Walter Dellinger, Diversity Partner; Mary Ellen Connerty, Director of Diversity and Inclusion

Summer Salary 2016
1Ls: $3,100/week
2Ls: $3,100/week
Post 3Ls: $3,100/week
1Ls hired? Case by case
Split summers offered? Case by case
Can summers spend time in overseas office? No
Summers 2016: 92
Offers/acceptances 2015:
63 offers, 47 acceptances; some offers outstanding due to judicial clerkships

Orrick, Herrington & Sutcliffe LLP

51 West 52nd Street, New York, NY 10019
The Orrick Building, 405 Howard Street, San Francisco, CA 94105-2669
Tel: 212 506 5000 (New York) Tel: 415 773 5700 (San Francisco)
Email: ktumas@orrick.com
www.orrick.com

Main areas of work

Tech, energy and infrastructure, finance, corporate, litigation, appellate and intellectual property.

Firm profile

At Orrick, we focus on advising the tech, energy and infrastructure and finance sectors globally. Our work is split fairly evenly between transaction and litigation advice for some of the world's leading companies – like Microsoft, DISH Network, Pinterest and Credit Suisse, as well as more than 1,500 emerging companies. We're inspired by opportunities to make an impact with our clients. We're also inspired by the causes of our pro bono clients – we have one of the most active pro bono programs of any firm. We offer unique opportunities to advance at your own pace and take advantage of a wide range of business and legal training programs and flexible career options. We look forward to talking with you about opportunities at Orrick and learning about what inspires you.

Recruitment details

- Number of 1st year associates: 33
- Number of 2nd year associates: 16
- Associate salaries: 1st year: $145,000-160,000
- 2nd year: $155,000-170,000
- Clerking policy: Yes

Law Schools attended for OCIs in 2016:

Columbia University, Duke University, Fordham University, Georgetown University, George Washington University, Harvard University, McGeorge University, New York University, Santa Clara University, Stanford University, University of California – Berkeley, University of California – Davis, University of California – Hastings, University of California – Los Angeles, University of Chicago, University of Michigan, University of North Carolina, University of Pennsylvania, University of Southern California, University of Texas, University of Virginia, Vanderbilt University

Summer details

Summer associate profile:

We seek out candidates who bring interesting and diverse life experiences and perspectives. Beyond good grades and book smarts, we value creativity, judgment, a collaborative style and an entrepreneurial spirit. We also look for a little grit and resilience. In short, we want to be inspired by you. We believe in having fun while working hard on projects that make a tangible impact on the world, locally and globally. If you thrive in a collegial atmosphere and appreciate leadership transparency, we just may be the firm for you. Gunners need not apply.

Summer program components:

Your first day as a summer associate is the beginning of your Orrick career. Our goal is to immerse you in the firm, introduce you to our clients, engage you in the issues on which we are working and create opportunities for you to start building relationships that we hope will last a lifetime. Our summer associates classes are small – which means focused, and personal attention, practical training, varied assignments spanning across different transactional and litigation practice areas, extensive feedback and hands-on experience with real client matters.

Head Office: New York / San Francisco
Number of domestic offices: 11
Number of international offices: 14
Worldwide revenue: $913,000,000
Partners (US): 244
Associates (US): 351

Main Recruitment Contact: Kit Tumas
Hiring Partner: Lisa Simpson
Recruitment website: www.orrick.com/careers
Diversity officer: Lorraine McGowen

Summer Salary 2016
1Ls: $3,077/week
2Ls: $3,077/week
Post 3Ls: N/A
1Ls hired? Yes
Split summers offered? Yes, case by case
Can summers spend time in overseas office? No
Summers 2016: 48
Offers/acceptances 2015: 32 offers, 27 acceptances

ORRICK

Patterson Belknap Webb & Tyler LLP

1133 Avenue of the Americas, New York, NY 10036
Tel: 212 336 2000 Fax: 212 336 2222
Email: rlklum@pbwt.com
www.pbwt.com

Main areas of work

Patterson Belknap's practice combines skill in both complex litigation and transactional matters, including corporate, real estate, media and entertainment, intellectual property, sports, art and museum law, employee benefits and tax practices. The firm is regularly recognized in industry publications as a leader in litigation areas including intellectual property and false advertising. In addition, the firm has the leading personal planning and tax-exempt organizations practices in New York City.

Firm profile

Patterson Belknap Webb & Tyler LLP, founded in 1919, is a law firm based in New York City with more than 200 lawyers committed to maintaining its independence, its diversity and its focus of providing superior legal advice and service to clients. The firm delivers a full range of services across more than 20 practice groups in both litigation and commercial law. The National Law Journal has included Patterson Belknap on a list of firms which it considers to have "the nimbleness and adaptability that come from lean operations and strong client ties." The firm highly values public service and has consistently ranked at or near the top of The American Lawyer's annual pro bono survey.

Recruitment details

- Number of 1st year associates: 6
- Number of 2nd year associates: 9
- Associate salaries: 1st year: $160,000
- 2nd year: $170,000
- Clerking policy: The firm values clerkship experience and actively recruits judicial law clerks.

Head Office: New York, NY
Number of domestic offices: 1
Number of international offices: 0
Worldwide revenue: $187,900
Partners (US): 50
Associates (US): 112

Main Recruitment Contact:
Robin L Klum
Hiring Partners: Robert W Lehrburger and Sarah Zgliniec
Recruitment website: www.pbwt.com
Diversity officers: Peter C Harvey, TJ Tu and Richard R Upton, Co Chairs, Diversity Committee

1Ls hired? No
Summers 2016: 0
Offers/acceptances 2015: N/A

Program details

Patterson Belknap hires associates directly from judicial clerkships. We may also recruit in August 2016 to hire a select group of 3L law students graduating at the end of the 2017 school year. We look forward to meeting with outstanding law students through both clerkship and 3L recruiting.

Associate profile:

Patterson Belknap looks for smart, collaborative, intellectually curious people who desire early responsibility and are highly motivated to solve complex legal problems.

Patterson Belknap Webb & Tyler LLP

Paul Hastings

515 S Flower Street, 25th Floor, Los Angeles, CA 90071
Email: attorneyrecruiting@paulhastings.com
www.paulhastings.com

Firm profile

At Paul Hastings, our purpose is clear - to help our clients and people navigate new paths to growth. With a strong presence throughout Asia, Europe, Latin America and the US, Paul Hastings is recognized as one of the world's most innovative global law firms. In 2015, the firm ranked first on The American Lawyer's A-List and Vault's #1 Place to Work.

Main areas of work

With offices across Asia, Europe and the US, we have the global reach and wide-ranging capabilities to provide personalized service wherever our clients' needs take us.

Our practice areas include: anticorruption and compliance, antitrust and competition, complex commercial litigation, employment, finance and restructuring, global banking and payment systems, intellectual property, investment management, mergers and acquisitions, privacy and data security, private equity, real estate, securities and capital markets, securities litigation, tax, white collar defense and investigations.

Recruitment details

- Number of 1st year associates: 65
- Number of 2nd year associates: 55
- Associate salaries: 1st year: $160,000
- 2nd year: $170,000
- Clerking policy: Yes

Law Schools attending for OCIs in 2016:

Berkeley, University of Chicago, Columbia, Cornell, Duke, Emory, Fordham, Georgia, Georgetown, George Mason, GW, Harvard, Howard, Michigan, Northwestern, NYU, Penn, Stanford, UC Hastings, University of Houston, UC Irvine, UCLA, USC, University of San Diego, University of Texas, UVA, Vanderbilt, Yale

Summer details

Summer associate profile:

At Paul Hastings, it's smart business to build diverse teams rich in talent, experiences, and creativity. We seek students who exemplify the hallmarks of our successful associates: innovative, strong communication skills, achievement drive, interpersonal savvy, client service excellence and ability to be collaborative team members. Students should be committed to work for a dynamic and entrepreneurial law firm on complex legal matters across practices and offices to help our clients overcome challenges and move their business forward. Law students with outstanding academic credentials, superior writing skills, Law Review, Journal, or Moot Court membership are favorably considered.

Summer program components:

Our Summer Program serves as a cornerstone for the recruitment of outstanding associates and the future success of our firm. We are fully committed to the professional development and advancement of each summer associate. Summer associates are given substantive work with a variety of lawyers and a realistic view of practicing law at Paul Hastings. Our summer associates observe and, when possible, assist in trials, hearings, depositions and negotiations, and participate in client meetings and closings. Summer associates can also expect mentoring in a collaborative work environment.

Largest Office: New York, NY
Number of domestic offices: 10
Number of international offices: 10
Worldwide revenue: $1,056,500,000
Partners (US): 253
Associates (US): 438

Main Recruitment Contact: Cynthia Hasson, Director, Talent Acquisition
Hiring Partners: David Hernand, Teri O'Brien, Kristen Winckler
Recruitment website: www.paulhastings.com/careers/law-students
Diversity officer: Rhonda Mims, Managing Director, Corporate Social Responsibility

Summer Salary 2016
1Ls: $3,100
2Ls: $3,100
Post 3Ls: $3,100
1Ls hired? Yes
Split summers offered? Case by case
Can summers spend time in overseas office? In special cases, we may offer the opportunity to spend two weeks in one of our offices in Asia. The summer associate must have the appropriate language skills.
Summers 2016: 132
Offers 2015: 69

Paul, Weiss, Rifkind, Wharton & Garrison LLP

1285 Avenue of the Americas, New York, NY 10019
Tel: 212 373 3000 Fax: 212 757 3990
Email: lateralhiring@paulweiss.com, summerprogram@paulweiss.com
www.paulweiss.com

Main areas of work

Paul, Weiss is widely recognized as having leading litigation and corporate capabilities, and the firm has developed equally strong practices in the areas of bankruptcy and corporate reorganization, employee benefits and executive compensation, intellectual property, personal representation, real estate and tax law.

Firm profile

Paul, Weiss, Rifkind, Wharton & Garrison LLP is a firm of more than 900 lawyers, with diverse backgrounds, personalities, ideas and interests, who collaborate with clients to help them conquer their most critical legal challenges and business goals. Our long-standing clients include many of the largest publicly and privately held corporations and financial institutions in the United States and throughout the world. We have an unwavering dedication to representing those in need through our pro bono efforts, and have long been a leader in promoting diversity within our firm and the legal profession.

Recruitment details

- Number of 1st year associates: 120
- Number of 2nd year associates: 92
- Associate salaries: 1st year: $160,000
- 2nd year: $170,000
- Clerking policy: Yes

Law Schools attending for OCIs in 2016:

BC/BU NY Job Fair, Berkeley, Brooklyn, Cardozo, Chicago, Columbia, Cornell NYC Job Fair, Duke, Fordham, Georgetown, George Washington, Harvard, Howard, Lavender Law Career Fair, McGill, Michigan, Northwestern, NYU, Patent Job Fair at Loyola, Penn, Stanford, Texas Job Fair, Toronto, Virginia, Washington University, Yale

Summer details

Summer associate profile:

You should have a strong academic record and life experience and initiative and commitment to excellence in the practice of law.

Summer program components:

The summer associate program at Paul, Weiss is more than just legal training. It's your introduction to the rich variety and depth of life in one of New York's most unique law firms. You'll have the opportunity to shape your summer experience at Paul, Weiss. Choose one department to call your home, or select a variety of work from a number of different practice areas. You'll be matched with a team of lawyers including associates, counsel and partners. Your summer team will help you make connections with other lawyers at the firm and make informed decisions about the work you choose. In addition to your team, you'll be paired with a partner and an associate who will provide guidance and advice about your summer work. You'll receive training in both substantive areas of law and practical legal skills in a mix of highly interactive small group trainings, individual skills development workshops and more traditional classroom style presentations.

Head Office: New York, NY
Number of domestic offices: 3
Number of international offices: 5
Worldwide revenue: $1,109,547,000
Partners (US): 139
Associates (US): 560

Main Recruitment Contact:
Pamela N Davidson
Hiring Partners: Daniel J Toal and
T Robert Zochowski Jr
Recruitment website:
www.paulweiss.com/careers
Diversity officer: Danyale A Price

Summer Salary 2016
1Ls: $3,100/week
2Ls: $3,100/week
Post 3Ls: $3,100/week
1Ls hired? Yes
Split summers offered? Yes
Can summers spend time in overseas office? Yes
Summers 2016: 140
Offers/acceptances 2015:
149 offers, 124 acceptances

Paul|Weiss

Pepper Hamilton LLP

3000 Two Logan Square, 18th & Arch Streets, Philadelphia, PA 19103-2799
Email: recruit@pepperlaw.com
www.pepperlaw.com

Main areas of work

Our practice areas encompass nearly all areas of law and span many key industry sectors. Our largest and best-known practices include: pharmaceutical and medical device litigation, commercial litigation, corporate and securities, white collar litigation and investigations, intellectual property, construction law, investment fund services, life sciences, financial services, healthcare services, labor and employment, tax, real estate, environmental and energy, privacy and data security, technology, international matters and more.

Firm profile

We provide corporate, litigation and regulatory legal services to leading businesses, governmental entities, nonprofit organizations and individuals throughout the nation and the world. Our firm has grown from a two-person law office formed in 1890 to a sophisticated, large law firm with a national and international practice. We retain traditional values: respect for the rule of law, pride in an excellent work product and commitment to the client's cause. Pepper Hamilton is a diverse firm of men and women from a broad spectrum of backgrounds, united in these values. We use the breadth of our practices and the depth of our experience to help clients solve problems and realize business goals.

Recruitment details

• Number of 1st year associates: 15 • Number of 2nd year associates: 28
• Associate salaries: 1st year: Varies by office. $150,000 in Philadelphia; $160,000 in Boston, California and New York
• 2nd year: Varies by office • Clerking policy: Yes

Law Schools attending for OCIs in 2016:

We recruit from top national and regional law schools, as well as at diversity job fairs. Recruiting focus is based on which offices plan to host summer programs each year. In 2015, we conducted on campus interviews at the following schools: Boston College, Boston University, Cornell University, Drexel University, Fordham University, Georgetown University, Harvard University, Howard University, The Pennsylvania State University, Rutgers University – Camden, Suffolk University, Temple University, University of California - Irvine, UCLA, University of Pennsylvania, Univeresity of Southern California, University of Virginia, Villanova University, and Washington & Lee University.

Summer details

Summer associate profile:

We recruit candidates with strong academic credentials; superior writing and analytical abilities; excellent interpersonal skills; and law review, journal and/or moot court experience.

Summer program components:

Summer associates learn all aspects of what makes Pepper Hamilton a special place to start their careers. They immediately become part of teams to help solve sophisticated problems for our clients. Each summer associate is assigned a partner and an associate mentor to ensure a successful summer experience. We provide regular training programs and specific feedback on each assignment to ensure summer associates leave the firm ready to be attorneys at Pepper Hamilton.

Head Office: Philadelphia, PA
Number of domestic offices: 13
Number of international offices: 0
Worldwide revenue: $389,000,000
Partners (US): 227
Associates (US): 260 (inc. Of Counsel)

Main Recruitment Contact:
Kathryn M Graham, Director of Professional Recruitment
Hiring Partner: Daniel Boland
Recruitment website:
www.pepperlaw.com/careers/

Summer Salary 2016
1Ls: $2,900/week
2Ls: $2,900-$3,100/week
1Ls hired? Yes
Split summers offered? No
Summers 2016: 23
Offers/acceptances 2015:
20 offers, 18 acceptances

Perkins Coie LLP

1201 3rd Avenue, Suite 4900, Seattle, WA 98101-3099
Tel: 206 359 8000 Fax: 206 359 9000
www.perkinscoie.com

Main areas of work

Perkins Coie's practice areas include business; environment, energy and resources; intellectual property; labor and employment; litigation; personal planning; political law; product liability; real estate.

Firm profile

With offices across the United States and in China, Perkins Coie provides a full array of corporate, commercial litigation and intellectual property legal services to clients that span the range of entities in the business world – from Fortune 100 corporations to small, independent start-ups, as well as public and not-for-profit organizations.

Recruitment details

- Number of 1st year associates: 29
- Number of 2nd year associates: 30
- Associate salaries: 1st year: Varies by office
- 2nd year: Varies by office
- Clerking policy: Yes

Law Schools attending for OCIs in 2016:

Arizona State University, Brigham Young University, Chicago, Columbia, Cornell, Duke, Fordham, George Washington, Georgetown, Harvard, Loyola (Chicago), Loyola (Los Angeles), Michigan, Northwestern, NYU, Penn, Santa Clara, Seattle University, Stanford, Texas, UC Berkeley, UC Davis, UC Hastings, UC Irvine, UCLA, University of Arizona, University of Illinois, University of Oregon, University of Utah, University of Washington, USC, Vanderbilt, Virginia, Yale

Summer details

Summer associate profile:

Hiring criteria include demonstrated academic excellence, creative problem solving, leadership in and service to the community and dedication to excellence in the legal profession.

Summer program components:

Perkins Coie's summer program provides wide-ranging work opportunities and social events designed to promote interaction among summer associates, attorneys and staff. Supervising attorneys provide informal feedback after each assignment and they submit written, formal evaluations to the office hiring committee. The formal evaluations become part of each summer associate's midsummer and final evaluations. Summer associates have the opportunity for both informal and formal training throughout the program.

Head Office: Seattle, WA
Number of domestic offices: 16
Number of international offices: 3
Worldwide revenue: $710,000,000
Partners (US): 493
Senior Counsel (US): 68
Other Attorneys: (US): 24
Associates (US): 407

Main Recruitment Contact: Michael Gotham, Director of Legal Recruiting and Retention
Recruitment website:
www.perkinscoie.com/careers
Diversity officer: Theresa Cropper

Summer Salary 2016
1Ls: $2,200-$3,077/week
2Ls: $2,200-$3,077/week
Post 3Ls: N/A
1Ls hired? Yes
Split summers offered? Case by case
Can summers spend time in overseas office? No
Summers 2016: 64
Offers/acceptances 2015:
51 offers, 47 acceptances

Pillsbury Winthrop Shaw Pittman LLP

1540 Broadway, New York, NY 10036
Tel: 212 858 1000 Fax: 212 858 1500
www.pillsburylaw.com

Main areas of work

Regulatory: Whether working with a startup, a company in growth mode or a market leader, Pillsbury's lawyers help companies limit risk, achieve compliance, defend against investigations, advocate for new laws and challenge restrictions.

Litigation: Pillsbury's litigators handle complex commercial cases, matters of public interest, intellectual property challenges, tax controversies, insurance policyholder disputes, environmental claims, securities class actions, construction disputes and a wide variety of other assignments.

Business: Pillsbury's business teams partner with clients to help find capital, organize new companies, secure patents, purchase real estate, negotiate contracts, challenge competitors, guide investments, protect data, limit liability, outsource support services, minimize taxes, establish policies and expand markets.

Firm profile

Pillsbury is a leading international law firm with a particular focus on the energy and natural resources, financial services, real estate and construction, and technology sectors. The 2016 *Best Lawyers/US News & World Report* survey recognized our lawyers with 90 Tier 1 rankings, and the firm was again named as one of the most innovative law firms by *Financial Times*. Our lawyers are highly regarded for their forward-thinking approach, enthusiasm for collaborating across disciplines and unsurpassed commercial awareness.

Recruitment details

- Number of 1st year associates: 26
- Number of 2nd year associates: 33
- Associate salaries: 1st year: $160,000
- 2nd year: $170,000
- Clerking policy: Yes

Law Schools attending for OCIs in 2016:

University of California, Berkeley; University of California, Davis; University of California, Hastings; University of California, Irvine; University of California, Los Angeles; University of Chicago; Columbia; Cornell; Fordham; George Washington; Georgetown; Harvard; Hofstra; University of Houston; Howard University; Loyola Law School; University of Michigan; Northwestern; New York University; University of Pennsylvania; Stanford; University of Southern California; University of Texas; University of Virginia

Summer details

Summer associate profile:

Pillsbury seeks energetic, high-performing students who possess sound judgment, determination, common sense, excellent interpersonal skills, the ability to inspire confidence and the drive to produce high quality work and achieve outstanding results.

Summer program components:

Pillsbury's summer associates experience the firm's collaborative style by working side-by-side with attorneys in a variety of practice areas, on industry and client teams and on issue-specific projects. Pillsbury University offers training on everything from legal writing to client service basics to effective networking. Formal reviews supplement the extemporaneous feedback provided to summer associates by our lawyers.

Head Office: New York, NY
Number of domestic offices: 13
Number of international offices: 5
Worldwide revenue: $557,000,000
Partners (US): 344
Associates (US): 199

Main Recruitment Contact: Charles Curtis, Firmwide Director of Attorney Recruiting
Hiring Partner: Mariah Brandt
Recruitment website: http://careers.pillsburylaw.com/
Diversity officer: Rosa Walker, Director of Diversity and Inclusion

Summer Salary 2016
1Ls: $3,077/week
2Ls: $3,077/week
Post 3Ls: $3,077/week
1Ls hired? No
Split summers offered? Yes, but not preferred
Can summers spend time in overseas office? Case by case
Summers 2016: 44
Offers/acceptances 2015:
34 offers, 34 acceptances

Proskauer

Eleven Times Square, New York, NY 10036-8299
Tel: 212 969 3000 Fax: 212 969 2900
www.proskauer.com

Main areas of work

Private equity; corporate finance and securities; mergers and acquisitions; capital markets; litigation and dispute resolution; corporate defense and investigations; intellectual property; healthcare; labor and employment; employee benefits and executive compensation; real estate; environmental law; technology; media and communications; privacy and data protection; bankruptcy and restructuring; insurance coverage and recovery; and personal planning. The firm also has significant industry-focused experience across many fields, including financial services, life sciences, sports, media and entertainment, lodging and gaming and technology.

Firm profile

Proskauer is a global firm with more than 700 lawyers who are players in the world's major business and financial hubs. The firm's lawyers provide a full range of corporate, litigation, labor and employment, intellectual property, healthcare, private client services, real estate and tax services to businesses, not-for-profit institutions and individuals.

Recruitment details

- Number of 1st year associates: 61
- Number of 2nd year associates: 46
- Associate salaries: 1st year: $160,000 (except Boca Raton, New Orleans and Newark)
- 2nd year: $170,000 (except Boca Raton, New Orleans and Newark)
- Clerking policy: Yes

Law Schools attending for OCIs in 2016:

Boston College, Boston University, Columbia, Cornell, Duke, Emory, Fordham, George Washington University, Georgetown, Harvard, Howard, Northwestern, New York University, Rutgers, Stanford, Suffolk, Tulane, University of California (Berkeley, Los Angeles), University of Chicago, University of Connecticut, University of Illinois, University of Michigan, University of Pennsylvania, University of Southern California, University of Texas, University of Virginia, Vanderbilt, Washington University in St Louis, Yale

Summer details

Summer associate profile:

We look for well-rounded students who have demonstrated academic excellence, leadership, community service, intellectual curiosity, maturity and strong motivation to succeed.

Summer program components:

Summer associates are assigned projects, receive guidance and are promptly evaluated with a focus on skill enhancement and exposure to sophisticated legal practice. They are exposed to different departments via substantive assignments and shadowing opportunities with senior lawyers. Our program features a systematic procedure for review and feedback on all assignments. We offer seminars and activities to develop practice skills, provide insights into substantive legal issues and the basics of various practice areas. Cultural, recreational and social events include the Tony Awards and the NBA Draft, highlighting the firm's unique clients.

Head Office: New York, NY
Number of domestic offices: 8
Number of international offices: 5
Worldwide revenue: $822,300,000
Partners (US): 219
Associates (US): 438

Main Recruitment Contact:
Caroline K Menes
Hiring Partner: Michael T Mervis
Recruitment website:
www.proskauer.com/careers
Diversity officer: Peter Wilson

Summer Salary 2016
1Ls: $3,077/week (except Boca Raton, New Orleans and Newark)
2Ls: $3,077/week (except Boca Raton, New Orleans and Newark)
Post 3Ls: $3,077/week
1Ls hired? Yes
Split summers offered? Case by case
Can summers spend time in overseas office? No
Summers 2016: 76
Offers/acceptances 2015:
70 offers, 63 acceptances

Reed Smith LLP

225 Fifth Avenue, Pittsburgh, PA 15222
Tel: 412 288 3131 Fax: 412 288 3063
www.reedsmith.com

Main areas of work

Reed Smith is a global relationship law firm with more than 1,800 lawyers in 26 offices throughout the United States, Europe, Asia and the Middle East. Its lawyers provide litigation and other dispute-resolution services in multi-jurisdictional and other high-stakes matters; deliver regulatory counsel; and execute the full range of strategic domestic and cross-border transactions. Reed Smith is a preeminent advisor to industries including financial services, life sciences, healthcare, advertising, technology and media, shipping, energy and natural resources, real estate, manufacturing and education.

Firm profile

Reed Smith has been ranked consistently among the top law firms for client service and has been identified as one of the few large firms with a strategic focus on client satisfaction. Reed Smith has grown in large part because of its commitment to delivering high-quality service and developing long-term client relationships. Reed Smith is united by a culture that is defined by core values of quality, integrity, teamwork and respect, performance and innovation and improvement. These are further demonstrated through a firmwide commitment to diversity, pro bono and community support activity and the professional development of the firm's lawyers.

Recruitment details

- Number of 1st year associates: 45
- Associate salaries: 1st year: $125,000-$160,000
- Clerking policy: Yes

Summer details

Summer associate profile:

Reed Smith is looking for summer associates who have a combination of top academics, practical experience and superior analytical and writing skills. The firm values people who are mature and engaging and who demonstrate leadership capabilities and community involvement.

Summer program components:

Reed Smith offers law students first-rate work in a challenging and busy atmosphere where their contributions count from day one. Summer associates will become immersed in law firm life by completing assignments relating to actual client situations. Each assignment presents a fresh opportunity for summer associates to hone their research, writing, judgment, communication and analytical skills.

CareeRS is Reed Smith's competency-based career development program with a focus on role-specific professional training and development, including mentoring, and more developmentally oriented assessments tailored to the needs of associates. The firm offers its summer associates numerous chances to participate in both formal and informal training programs, such as: managing partner's forum, mediation and mergers and acquisitions clinics, law firm economics, cross-cultural training and legal writing. Summer associates also have numerous opportunities to participate in pro bono and community service projects and become acquainted with our Women's Initiative Network and Diversity and Inclusion Committees. Please visit www.reedsmith.com for more information about each of these initiatives.

Head Office: N/A
Number of domestic offices: 14
Number of international offices: 12
Worldwide revenue: $1.123 billion
Partners (US): 514
Associates (US): 449

Main Recruitment Contact:
Kevan Skelton, Global Director of Legal Recruiting
Recruitment website:
www.reedsmith.com
Diversity officer: Deborah Broyles, Partner and Director of Global Diversity & Inclusion

Summer Salary 2016
1Ls: $5,208-$6,667 semi-monthly
2Ls: $5,208-$6,667 semi-monthly
1Ls hired? Case by case
Split summers offered? Case by case
Can summers spend time in overseas office? No
Summers 2016: 47 (43 2Ls, 4 1Ls)
Offers/acceptances 2015: 51 offers, 49 acceptances

Ropes & Gray LLP

Prudential Tower, 800 Boylston Street, Boston, MA 02119
Tel: 617 951 7000 Fax: 617 951 7050
Email: hiringprogram@ropesgray.com
www.ropesgray.com

Main areas of work

From the boardroom to the courtroom, Ropes & Gray represents the world's leading companies on their most critical matters. On corporate transactional issues, the firm has been recognized as having top-ranked practices in private equity, M&A, finance, investment management, bankruptcy, healthcare, life sciences and intellectual property, among others. The firm also has been cited for its litigation experience and successful track record, including antitrust, appellate, complex business litigation, securities litigation and regulation, government enforcement and white collar criminal defense, IP litigation and privacy and data security.

Firm profile

Ropes & Gray, an international law firm with more than 1,000 attorneys and professionals in 11 offices in the United States, Europe and Asia, provides comprehensive legal services to leading businesses and individuals around the world. Clients benefit from the firm's unwavering standards of integrity, service and responsiveness. The firm is ideally positioned to address its clients' most pressing legal and business issues. In 2015, 1,400 lawyers, paralegals and other Ropes & Gray professionals worldwide logged 114,000 hours toward assisting our pro bono clients. In the US alone, over 740 of our attorneys dedicated 20 or more hours to pro bono legal service.

Recruitment details

- Number of 1st year associates: 102
- Number of 2nd year associates: 107
- Associate salaries: 1st year: $160,000
- 2nd year: $170,000
- Clerking policy: Yes

Law Schools attending for OCIs in 2016:

American, Berkeley, Boston College, Boston University, Brooklyn, Chicago, Columbia, Cornell, Duke, Fordham, George Washington, Georgetown, Harvard, Howard, Illinois, Michigan, North Carolina, Northeastern, Northwestern, Notre Dame, NYU, Penn, Santa Clara, Stanford, Suffolk, Texas, UC Davis, UC Hastings, UCLA, USC, UVA, Washington University in St Louis, Yale

Summer details

Summer associate profile:

Ropes & Gray chooses summer associates based on academic performance, personal skills, motivation, work and leadership experience, practice area interests and the ability to work well in a highly collaborative environment.

Summer program components:

Our goal is to provide summer associates with a realistic sense of what it is like to work at the firm by having them work on actual client matters and by giving them opportunities to get to know our attorneys through a variety of social events, activities and lunches. Our attorneys provide meaningful and timely feedback on work assignments and offer additional perspective through an end-of-summer formal review. Summer associates also benefit from our highly regarded training program, which provides both practice-specific and general soft-skills training designed to support summer associates' professional growth and development.

Head Office: Boston, MA
Number of domestic offices: 6
Number of international offices: 5
Partners (US): 257
Associates (US): 728

Main Recruitment Contact: Helen Long
Hiring Partner: Richard Batchelder
Recruitment website: www.ropesgray.com
Diversity officer: Lindsay Kendrick

Summer Salary 2016
1Ls: N/A
2Ls: $3,100/week
Post 3Ls: N/A
1Ls hired? N/A
Split summers offered? Yes
Can summers spend time in overseas office? Yes
Summers 2016: 144
Offers/acceptances 2015:
140 offers, 128 acceptances

ROPES & GRAY

Schulte Roth & Zabel LLP

919 Third Avenue, New York, NY 10022
Tel: 212 756 2000
Email: recruiting.department@srz.com

Main areas of work

Our specialties include business reorganization; distressed investing; employment and employee benefits; environmental; finance; individual client services; intellectual property, sourcing and technology; investment management; litigation; M&A; real estate; regulatory and compliance; securities and capital markets; structured finance and derivatives; and tax.

Firm profile

Schulte Roth & Zabel is a premier law firm serving the financial services industry from strategically located offices in New York, Washington, DC and London. We take a multidisciplinary approach in our work with a large and impressive array of global and forward-thinking institutional, entrepreneurial and individual clients, from advising clients on investment management, corporate and transactional matters, to providing counsel on regulatory, compliance, enforcement and investigative issues.

Recruitment details

- Number of 1st year associates: 34
- Number of 2nd year associates: 29
- Associate salaries: 1st year: $160,000
- 2nd year: $170,000
- Clerking policy: yes

Law Schools attending for OCIs in 2016:

Cardozo, Columbia, Cornell, Duke, Emory, Fordham, George Washington, Georgetown, Harvard, Howard, Michigan, NYU, Northwestern, Penn, Tulane, Vanderbilt, Virginia, Wash U

Summer details

Summer associate profile:

SRZ hires attorneys who are bright, personable and enthusiastic about early substantive responsibility and client contact. We seek candidates with outstanding academic achievement; high motivation and strong interpersonal skills.

Summer program components:

Our summer associate program allows students to receive substantive assignments from practice groups of their choice during two assigning periods. Summer associates have interaction with our clients, attend meetings and depositions and work on complex projects. Training and feedback are emphasized through regular departmental training sessions, a writing seminar, a corporate negotiation workshop, a trial advocacy program, and a pro bono week. These experiences are all designed to allow students to explore various areas of interest, get immersed in the firm culture and gain first-hand knowledge of what they will see as a junior associate. In addition to our top-notch training programs and hands-on work experience, we offer fun and exciting social activities that allow summer associates to spend time with their associate and partner mentors, develop relationships with our attorneys and get to know everyone outside of the office.

Head Office: New York
Number of domestic offices: 2
Number of international offices: 1
Partners (US): 89
Other lawyers (US): 249

Main Recruitment Contact: Alissa K Golden
Hiring Partners: William H Gussman, Jr, Taleah E Jennings, Jason S Kaplan
Recruitment website: www.srz.com/careers
Diversity Officer: Taleah E Jennings

Summer Salary 2016
2Ls: $3,077 per week
1Ls hired? No
Split summers offered? No
Can summers spend time in overseas office? No
Summers 2016: 37
Offers/acceptances 2015: 35 offers, 33 acceptances

Schulte Roth&Zabel

Sedgwick LLP

333 Bush Street, San Francisco, CA 94104
Tel: 415 781 7900 Fax: 415 781 2635
www.sedgwicklaw.com

Main areas of work

Sedgwick attorneys have skillfully managed complex litigation spanning multiple jurisdictions, from local to international. The firm has been retained in mass tort, class action, multi-district and market share litigation to defend and manage matters as national or regional trial counsel. We have served as national, regional and lead liaison counsel for a broad range of domestic and international companies in industries that include insurance, financial services, retail, pharmaceutical, automotive, media, food and beverage, and medical device manufacturing. Practice areas include antitrust and unfair competition, product liability, directors and officers liability, Bermuda Form, business litigation, intellectual property, healthcare, life sciences, real estate, property and casualty coverage, reinsurance, employment, insurance policy drafting/advice, international arbitration, and maritime.

Firm profile

Sedgwick LLP is a resolution-oriented firm. Founded in 1933, Sedgwick has grown into a broad-based international firm of 300 attorneys with 16 offices in the US, London and Bermuda. We have earned a reputation as a top litigation and trial law firm by winning cases and providing clients with sophisticated strategies. A significant number of our attorneys possess successful first-chair jury trial and arbitration experience. Sedgwick attorneys take pride in our longstanding client relationships and in our well-earned reputation for effective and economical representation of some of the world's largest companies. Sedgwick works with clients to assess and manage risks, providing effective solutions through all aspects of government enforcement and compliance initiatives.

Sedgwick also has a strong commitment to inclusion and diversity in the profession based on our belief that attorneys from diverse backgrounds and experiences, working toward a common goal, offer the best opportunity to deliver the superior legal services that our clients expect. We are honored to have been recognized for these efforts, including being named '100 Best Law Firms for Female Attorneys' and '100 Best Law Firm for Minority Attorneys' by Law360 and achieving a perfect score on the 2016 Human Rights Campaign Corporate Equality Index.

Recruitment details

- Number of 1st year associates: 4 • Number of 2nd year associates: 7
- Clerking policy: No

Summer details

Summer program components:

Sedgwick LLP does not have a formal summer program at the moment; however, the firm considers extraordinary candidates on an individual basis for summer associate positions at several of our offices. Participants receive excellent mentoring and training designed to expose them to the key practice areas of the firm. They receive firsthand courtoom experience, challenging 'first year' assignments, continuous evaluation and feedback and the opportunity to get to know the firm's attorneys professionally and socially.

Largest Office: San Francisco, CA
Number of domestic offices: 14
Number of international offices: 2
Partners (US): 110
Associates (US): 158

Main Recruitment Contact: Michele Blay, Director of Attorney Recruiting
Hiring Partner: Steve Di Saia
Recruitment website: www.sedgwicklaw.com/careers/
Diversity officers: James J S Holmes, Catalina Sugayan

Summer Salary 2016
1Ls: N/A
2Ls: Varies per office
Post 3Ls: N/A
1Ls hired? No

Seward & Kissel LLP

One Battery Park Plaza, New York, NY 10004
Tel: 212 574 1200 Fax: 212 480 8421
www.sewkis.com

Main areas of work

Investment management, corporate finance, global bank and institutional finance, litigation, maritime and transportation finance, capital markets and securities, business transactions, bankruptcy and corporate reorganization, real estate, taxation, trusts and estates, employee benefits, aviation finance, employment law, government enforcement and internal investigations and executive compensation.

Firm profile

Seward & Kissel offers our New York associates the broad experience and training of a large practice in the context of a moderately sized firm. We offer our Washington, DC associates a focused experience concentrating on our Investment Management, Corporate Finance and Capital Markets practices in the context of a small office environment.

Our associates have the opportunity to work on a wide range of challenging and stimulating matters within the practice areas of our particular offices.

Recruitment details

- Number of 1st year associates: 17
- Number of 2nd year associates: 10
- Associate salaries: 1st year: $160,000
- 2nd year: $170,000
- Clerking policy: Case by case

Law Schools attending for OCIs in 2016:

Our New York office participates in the following OCI programs: Albany, American, Boston College, Boston University, Brooklyn, Cardozo, Columbia, Cornell, Duke, Fordham, Georgetown, George Washington, Harvard, Midwest California Consortium, New York University, Tulane/Washington University/Vanderbilt Job Fair, Michigan, University of North Carolina, University of Pennsylvania, University of Virginia, and Vanderbilt.

Our Washington, DC office participates in the following OCI programs: Boston College, Boston University, Georgetown, George Washington, University of Virginia, Washington & Lee.

Summer details

Summer associate profile:

We rely heavily on our summer program for our hiring needs. The primary goals of the program are to provide summer associates with a realistic, broad-based view of our practice and an opportunity to become acquainted with our attorneys through our informal mentoring program, training sessions and social events.

Summer program components:

Assignments are from our practice areas.

Training: weekly seminars, practice group meetings and in-house training sessions. Feedback is given formally at the middle and end of the summer program.

Head Office: New York, NY
Number of domestic offices: 2
Partners (US): 52
Counsel (US): 20
Associates (US): 90

Main Recruitment Contact:
Royce Wain Akiva
Hiring Partner: Jack Rigney
Recruitment Website:
www.sewkis.com

Summer Salary 2016
1Ls: N/A
2Ls: $3,067/week
Post 3Ls: N/A
1Ls hired? No
Can summers spend time in overseas offices? N/A
Summers 2016: 17 (15 in NY, 2 in DC)
Offers/acceptances 2015:
17 offers, 17 acceptances (15 in NY, 2 in DC)

SEWARD & KISSEL LLP

Shearman & Sterling LLP

599 Lexington Avenue, New York, NY 10022
Tel: 212 848 4000 Fax: 212 848 7179
www.shearman.com

Main areas of work

Anti-corruption and Foreign Corrupt Practices Act, antitrust, capital markets, corporate governance, derivatives and structured products, environmental, executive compensation and employee benefits, finance, financial institutions advisory and financial regulatory, financial restructuring and insolvency, intellectual property, international arbitration, international trade and government relations, investment funds, litigation, mergers and acquisitions, project development and finance, real estate, sports, tax.

Firm profile

Shearman & Sterling LLP is a leading global law firm with approximately 850 lawyers in 20 offices in 13 countries around the world. Founded in 1873, Shearman & Sterling distinguishes itself by the way in which it harnesses the intellectual strength and deep experience of its lawyers across its extensive global footprint. The firm represents many of the world's leading corporations, financial institutions, emerging growth companies, governments and state-owned enterprises.

Recruitment details

- Number of 1st year associates: 52
- Number of 2nd year associates: 47
- Associate salaries: 1st year: $160,000
- 2nd year: $170,000
- Clerking policy: Yes

Law Schools attending for OCIs in 2016:

Shearman & Sterling LLP will be recruiting at the following schools or regional job fairs: American, BC, BU, Cardozo, Chicago, Columbia, Cornell, Duke, Fordham, Georgetown, George Washington, Harvard, Howard, Michigan, NEBLSA job fair, Northwestern, NYU, Osgoode, Penn, Stanford, Texas, Toronto, Tulane, Washington University, Vanderbilt, UC- Berkeley, UC- Hastings, UCLA, USC, UVA, Yale. In addition, the firm has resume collections at a number of schools.

Summer details

Summer associate profile:

We seek candidates who are bright, confident and enthusiastic about the practice of law and bring with them life, work, and educational experiences that will be highly valued by clients and colleagues alike. We also remain strongly committed to diversity and inclusion and overall excellence in our hiring. Finally, we expect that our associates will view collegiality and teamwork as important personal and firm values.

Summer program components:

Summer associates are given the opportunity to rotate through two practice groups. Partner and associate advisors are assigned during each rotation and, depending on the group, summer associates may attend client meetings, court hearings, depositions, or business trips. The firm has a robust training program for summer associates and also hosts a variety of social events.

Head Office: New York, NY
Number of domestic offices: 4
Number of international offices: 16
Worldwide revenue: $860,300,000

Main Recruitment Contact:
Trisha Weiss (Director of Legal Recruiting)
Hiring Partner: Daniel Laguardia, Linda Rappaport
Recruitment website: www.shearman.com
Diversity officer: Anna Brown (Director of Global Diversity and Inclusion)

Summer Salary 2016
1Ls: $3,077/week
2Ls: $3,077/week
Post 3Ls: N/A
1Ls hired? TBD
Split summers offered? No
Can summers spend time in overseas office? Yes
Summers 2016: 75
Offers/acceptances 2015:
62 offers (100% of 2Ls), 60 acceptances

SHEARMAN & STERLING LLP

Sheppard Mullin Richter & Hampton LLP

333 South Hope Street, 43rd Floor, Los Angeles, CA 90071-1422
Tel: 213 620 1780
www.sheppardmullin.com

Main areas of work

Sheppard Mullin is a full service Global 100 firm. A broad range of practice areas, including counter-cyclical practices, has allowed the firm to succeed through up and down economic cycles. Primary areas include antitrust; business trial; corporate and securities; entertainment, technology and advertising; finance and bankruptcy; government contracts; intellectual property; labor and employment; real estate, land use/ natural resources and environment; tax, ERISA and trusts and estates and white collar criminal defense. Clients are in industries ranging from aerospace and banking to entertainment and e-commerce and from real estate and retail to high tech and high fashion.

Firm profile

Founded in Los Angeles in 1927, there are now about 750 attorneys practicing in 15 offices (7 in California, and Chicago, New York, Washington, DC, Shanghai, Beijing, Seoul, Brussels and London). The firm remains a true partnership which governs itself through an elected, representative democracy. Stability is enhanced by skillful administration, excellent cost control and no firm debt. Core values include transparency in financial operations and governance, civility in the daily conduct of its business, advancement and celebration of diversity and inclusiveness and a vigorous pro bono program.

Recruitment details

- Number of 1st year associates: 31
- Number of 2nd year associates: 36
- Associate salaries: 1st year: $160,000
- 2nd year: $170,000
- Clerking policy: Yes

Law Schools attending for OCIs in 2016:

Berkeley, Chicago, Columbia, Fordham, George Washington, Georgetown, Harvard, Hastings, Howard, Illinois, Loyola (Los Angeles), Michigan, NYU, Northwestern, Southwestern, Stanford, UC Davis, UC Irvine, UCLA, USC, USD, USF, Virginia. Plus 3-4 job fairs (regional and/or diversity).

Summer details

Summer associate profile:

High academic achievement is a precondition to employment. But the firm is interested in more than that: it seeks associates who will succeed over the long term. It looks for associates who have the personal traits needed to become outstanding practicing lawyers: self-awareness, drive to succeed, capacity for hard work and an ability to work well with other people.

Summer program components:

The Summer Program gives students a realistic view of the way the firm practices throughout the year. Assignments include meaningful work on behalf of clients with partners and associates in litigation and/or transactional practice groups. All offices conduct clinical training programs with both a transactional component and a litigation component. Pro bono projects are assigned to those who express an interest. Social events offer exposure to the geographic area of the particular office.

Head Office: Los Angeles, CA
Number of domestic offices: 10
Number of international offices: 5 (Shanghai, Beijing, Brussels, London & Seoul)
Worldwide revenue: $559,500,000
Partners (US): 294
Associates (US): 279

Main Recruitment Contact:
Sally Bucklin (Manager of Attorney Hiring)
Hiring Partner: Bob Williams (Chief Talent Officer)
Recruitment website:
www.sheppardmullin.com
Diversity officer: Carol Ross-Burnett

Summer Salary 2016
1Ls: N/A
2Ls: $3,080/week
1Ls hired? No
Split summers offered? No
Can summers spend time in overseas office? No
Summers 2016: 31
Offers/acceptances 2015:
32 offers, 30 acceptances

SheppardMullin

Sidley Austin LLP

One South Dearborn, Chicago, IL 60603
Tel: 312 853 7000 Fax: 312 853 7036

787 Seventh Avenue, New York, NY 10019
Tel: 212 839 5300 Fax: 212 839 5599

Main areas of work

Antitrust; bankruptcy and restructuring; capital markets; communications; complex commercial litigation; employment and benefits; energy; environment; ERISA; FDA; financial institutions regulatory; global finance; corporate governance; healthcare; insurance; international trade; investment funds; IP; life sciences; M&A and private equity; privacy and data security; products liability; real estate; securities and derivatives enforcement and regulatory; securities litigation; securitization, Supreme Court and appellate, technology; transportation; trusts and estates; venture capital; white collar.

Firm profile

Sidley provides a broad range of legal services to meet the needs of our diverse client base. The strategic establishment of our offices in the key corporate and financial centers of the world has enabled us to represent a broad range of clients that includes multinational and domestic corporations, banks, funds and financial institutions. With over 1,900 lawyers in 20 offices around the world, talent and teamwork are central to Sidley's successful results for clients in all types of legal matters, from complex transactions to 'bet the company' litigation to cutting-edge regulatory issues.

Recruitment details

- Number of 1st year associates: 132
- Number of 2nd year associates: 132
- Associate salaries: 1st year: $160,000
- 2nd year: $170,000
- Clerking policy: Yes

Law Schools attending for OCIs in 2016:

Berkeley, Chicago, Columbia, Cornell, DePaul, Duke, Fordham, Georgetown, George Washington, Harvard, Howard, Houston, Illinois, Iowa, Chicago – Kent, Loyola, Loyola – LA, Michigan, Minnesota, New York University, Northwestern, Notre Dame, Pennsylvania, Santa Clara, Southern Methodist, Stanford, Texas, Toronto, UCLA, UC – Hastings, USC, Virginia, Washington University, Wisconsin, Yale

Summer details

Summer associate profile:

Sidley seeks candidates who have demonstrated academic success and possess strong leadership and interpersonal qualities. The firm looks for a diverse group of individuals who are motivated by highly sophisticated legal work practiced in a collegial and supportive environment.

Summer program components:

Sidley's summer associate program is an invaluable window into its practice and firm culture. Participants select projects that interest them and perform legal work under lawyer supervision. An essential component of Sidley's summer program is the opportunity to learn and develop professional skills. Hands-on training includes detailed reviews of each summer associate's work product, as well as more formal training programs such as writing seminars, a mock trial and a mock negotiation exercise. Each summer associate is assigned senior associates and partners to provide guidance and each participant receives a formal review at the midpoint of the summer program.

Head Offices: Chicago, IL; New York, NY
Number of domestic offices: 10
Number of international offices: 10
Worldwide revenue: $1,867,000,000
Partners (US): 619
Other lawyers (US): 973 (includes counsel and associates)

Main Recruitment Contact:
Jennifer L Connelly
Hiring Partners: Anthony J Aiello (CH), Kelly L C Kriebs (LA), John J Kuster (NY) and Rebecca K Wood (DC)
Recruitment website:
www.sidley.com/careers
Diversity officer: Sally L Olson

Summer Salary 2016
1Ls: $3,100/week
2Ls: $3,100/week
Post 3Ls: $3,100/week
Split summers offered? Case by case
Can summers spend time in overseas office? No
Summers 2016: 187
Offers/acceptances 2015:
97 offers, 80 acceptances to date

Simpson Thacher & Bartlett LLP

425 Lexington Avenue, New York, NY
Tel: 212 465 2000 Fax: 212 465 2502
Email: attorneyrecruiting@stblaw.com
www.simpsonthacher.com

Main areas of work

Clients in a wide array of industries and in jurisdictions around the world turn to Simpson Thacher to help them address their evolving business challenges. The firm is consistently ranked as one of the world's leading advisors for mergers and acquisitions, capital markets and banking activity, as well as private equity fund formation and investment management. The firm's litigation practice encompasses every type of complex litigation and is recognized as one of the most comprehensive, trial-ready litigation practices in the country.

Simpson Thacher also has leading innovative practices in the areas of antitrust, IP, tax, bankruptcy, real estate, executive compensation and employee benefits, exempt organizations and personal planning. Further, pro bono work is critical to the firm's identity and its record in this area is unparalleled.

Firm profile

Simpson Thacher & Bartlett LLP is one of the world's leading international law firms. The firm was established in 1884 and has more than 900 lawyers globally. Headquartered in New York City, the firm has offices in Beijing, Hong Kong, Houston, London, Los Angeles, Palo Alto, São Paulo, Seoul, Tokyo and Washington, DC. The firm provides coordinated legal advice and transactional capability to clients around the globe. Our focus on client needs is the hallmark of our practice and we value excellence in client service in all respects.

Recruitment details

- Number of 1st year associates: 106
- Number of 2nd year associates: 86
- Associate salaries: 1st year: $160,000
- 2nd year: $170,000
- Clerking policy: Yes

Law Schools attending for OCIs in 2016:

Berkeley, Brooklyn, Cardozo, Chicago, Columbia, Cornell, Davis, Duke, Emory Fordham, George Washington, Georgetown, Harvard, Howard, Michigan, NYU, Northwestern, Notre Dame, Pennsylvania, Santa Clara, St John's, Seton Hall, Stanford, Texas, Tulane, UCLA, USC, Vanderbilt, Virginia, Washington University, Yale

Summer details

Summer associate profile:

The firm looks for candidates with distinguished records of achievement, demonstrated leadership potential, a commitment to excellence and the ability to work cooperatively with clients and colleagues.

Summer program components:

The Simpson Thacher Summer Program is both challenging and satisfying. Summer associates work on assignments from all practice areas side by side with partners and associates on client projects of substantial complexity. Summer associates participate in frequent formal training programs geared to their needs and are also invited to attend other firmwide training programs. Summer associates have partner and associate mentors and are given prompt and specific feedback. At the end of the summer program, summer associates will have a thorough understanding of the firm's work and culture.

Head Office: New York, NY
Number of domestic offices: 5
Number of international offices: 6
Worldwide revenue: tbd
Partners (US): 154
Associates (US): 599

Main Recruitment Contacts: Susan Osnato, Chief, Legal Recruiting & Professional Development; Amy Claydon, Legal Recruiting Director
Hiring Partners: Elizabeth Cooper, Greg Grogan and Lori Lesser
Recruitment website: www.simpsonthacher.com
Diversity officer: Natalia Martín, Director of Diversity

Summer Salary 2016
1Ls: $3,080/week
2Ls: $3,080/week
Post 3Ls: $3,080/week
1Ls hired? Yes
Split summers offered? Yes, case by case
Can summers spend time in overseas office? Yes, subject to need and relevant language skills
Summers 2016: 135
Offers/acceptances 2015: 122 offers, 102 acceptances; 11 open for 2015/2016

Firm Profiles

Skadden, Arps, Slate, Meagher & Flom LLP

4 Times Square, New York, NY 10036
Tel: 212 735 3000 Fax: 212 735 2000
www.skadden.com
Twitter: @skaddenrecruit

Main areas of work

Antitrust, banking, complex mass torts/insurance litigation, corporate finance, corporate restructuring, energy and infrastructure projects, executive compensation and benefits, financial institutions, intellectual property and technology, investment management, litigation (including international arbitration, patent litigation and white collar crime), mergers and acquisitions, real estate, regulatory, structured finance, tax, trusts and estates.

Firm profile

Skadden attorneys work on bet-the-company issues around the world for leading Fortune 500 corporations, financial institutions, governments and cultural, educational and charitable organizations. Communication and expertise across our offices enable us to provide unparalleled service to our clients. Our attorneys, spread among 23 interconnected offices around the world, are engaged in more than 60 practice areas, many of which are specialized. We also encourage pro bono work, providing chargeable time credit. With fostering professional growth as a primary goal, our attorney development partners and Training Committee ensure that associates receive appropriate training and mentoring from the start of their careers. Our Diversity Committee promotes cross-cultural appreciation and competency through diversity and inclusion seminars, lunches, and our Facets diversity publication and lecture series. Our widely regarded summer associate program is designed to provide substantive practical skills training, exposure to various practices, as well as a sense of what it is like to be an attorney at Skadden.

Recruitment details

- Number of 1st year associates: 185
- Number of 2nd year associates: 170
- Associate salaries: 1st year: $160,000
- 2nd year: $170,000
- Clerking policy: Yes

Law Schools attending for OCIs in 2016:

Berkeley, Chicago, Columbia, Cornell, Duke, Georgetown, Harvard, Michigan, NYU, Northwestern, Penn, Stanford, Texas, UCLA, USC, Vanderbilt, Virginia, Yale

Summer details

Summer associate profile:

The breadth of our practice and the success it has enjoyed is largely due to the capabilities of our attorneys. We look for candidates who combine intellectual ability with enthusiasm and creativity. Successful candidates display high academic achievement in their law school and undergraduate education. Law Journal and/or Moot Court participation are preferred.

Summer program components:

One of the most comprehensive programs of its kind, our Summer Associate Program (offered in our Boston, Chicago, Houston, Los Angeles, New York, Palo Alto, Washington, DC, Wilmington, London, Hong Kong, Toronto and Tokyo offices) drives our hiring efforts. Summer Associates are assigned to active deals and litigations, providing them with work experiences similar to those of full time associates. For more information visit: www.skadden.com/recruiting.

Head Office: New York, NY
Number of domestic offices: 8
Number of international offices: 15
Partners (US): 310
Counsel (US): 175
Associates (US): 852

Main Recruitment Contact: Carol Lee H Sprague
Hiring Partner: Howard L Ellin
Recruitment website: www.skadden.com/recruiting
Diversity officer: Melique Jones

Summer Salary 2016
1Ls: $3,100
2Ls: $3,100
1Ls hired? Yes – Skadden 1L Scholars Program
Split summers offered? Yes – splits must spend at least 8 weeks with Skadden for first half
Can summers spend time in overseas office? Case by case
Summers 2016: 190
Offers/acceptances 2015:
191 offers, 157 acceptances, 20 offers open for 2017 or later

Firm Profiles

Snell & Wilmer LLP

One Arizona Center, Phoenix, Arizona 85004
Tel: 602 382 6000 Fax: 602 382 6070
Email: Recruiting@swlaw.com
www.swlaw.com

Main areas of work

Appellate, banking, bankruptcy, business and finance, class action, commercial litigation, construction, emerging businesses, employee benefits and executive compensation, environmental and natural resources, estate planning and taxation, financial services and securities, franchise, government investigations/criminal defense, healthcare, intellectual property, international, labor, mergers and acquisitions, municipal finance, professional liability, product liability, professional liability and tort liability, public utilities, legislation and real estate/land use.

Firm profile

Founded in 1938, Snell & Wilmer is a full service business law firm with more than 400 lawyers practicing in nine locations throughout the western United States and in Mexico, including Phoenix and Tucson, Arizona; Los Angeles and Orange County, California; Denver, Colorado; Las Vegas and Reno, Nevada; Salt Lake City, Utah; and Los Cabos, Mexico. The firm represents clients ranging from large, publicly traded corporations to small businesses, individuals and entrepreneurs. Snell & Wilmer and its lawyers have been recognized by clients and peers for exceptional legal skills and ethical business practices with various distinguished awards.

Recruitment details

- Number of 1st year associates: 15
- Number of 2nd year associates: 13
- Associate salaries: 1st year: $115,000 - $160,000
- Clerking policy: Yes

Law Schools attending for OCIs in 2016:

Arizona State University; Brigham Young University; Notre Dame; University of Arizona; University of California; Irvine; UCLA; University of Colorado; University of Denver; University of Iowa; University of Kansas; University of San Diego; University of Nevada; Las Vegas; University of Southern California; University of Utah; Vanderbilt; Virginia; Pepperdine; Loyola Los Angeles; Washington University in St Louis

Summer details

Summer associate profile:

Snell & Wilmer seeks to hire diverse individuals with the long-term potential to become partners at the firm. We are interested in candidates who have demonstrated high academic achievement, initiative and involvement in non-academic experiences or extra-curricular activities and possess strong interpersonal and communication skills.

Summer program components:

The firm appoints several senior associates to coordinate the program and assign summer associate projects. In addition, each summer associate is assigned a mentor, a partner reader and a reality partner. Summer associate mentors are responsible for making the summer a positive experience for each summer associate. Partner readers provide invaluable feedback on two written assignments a summer associate completes. The "Reality Snell & Wilmer" program matches summer associates with a partner who brings them into other cases and transactions, as needed, to simulate the day-to-day reality of working as an attorney.

Head Office: Phoenix, AZ
Number of domestic offices: 8
Number of international offices: 1
Partners (US): 212
Associates (US): 158

Main Recruitment Contact:
Abigail Raddatz, Director of Attorney Recruiting and Diversity
Hiring Partner: Adam E Lang, Anne M Meyer
Recruitment website: www.swlaw.com/careers
Diversity officer: Manuel H Cairo

Summer Salary 2016
1Ls: $2,211-$3,077/week
2Ls: $2,211-$3,077/week
Post 3Ls: $2,211-$3,077/week
1Ls hired? Case-by-case
Split summers offered? Case-by-case
Can summers spend time in overseas office? No
Summers 2016: 30
Offers/acceptances 2015:
15 offers, 14 acceptances

Squire Patton Boggs

4900 Key Tower, 127 Public Square, Cleveland, Ohio 44114
Tel: 216 479 8500 Fax: 216 479 8780
www.squirepattonboggs.com

Main areas of work

Aerospace, defense and government services; aviation; brands and consumer products; business immigration; chemicals; communications; competition – antitrust; construction and engineering; corporate; data privacy and cybersecurity; energy and natural resources; environmental, safety and health; financial services; government investigations and white collar; healthcare; hospitality and leisure; industrial products; infrastructure; intellectual property and technology; international dispute resolution; international trade; labor and employment; Latin America; life sciences; litigation; media and advertising; pensions; private investment funds; public and infrastructure finance; public policy; real estate; restructuring and insolvency; retail; sovereign and institutional investors; sports and entertainment; tax credit finance and community development; tax strategy and benefits; transportation, shipping and logistics.

Firm profile

Squire Patton Boggs offers the opportunity to join one of the strongest, most geographically diverse law firms in the world. With 45 offices in 21 countries, our global legal practice is in the markets where our clients do business. We have a team of more than 1,500 lawyers. Our client base spans every type of business, both private and public. We advise a diverse mix of clients, from Fortune 100 and FTSE 100 corporations to emerging companies and from individuals to local and national governments.

Recruitment details

- Number of 1st year associates: 11
- Number of 2nd year associates: 21
- Clerking policy: Yes

Law Schools attending for OCIs in 2016:

American, Case, Cleveland – Marshall, CUA, George Mason, Georgetown, GW Law, Harvard, Howard, Maryland, Michigan, Ohio State, UNC, UVA

Summer details

Summer associate profile:

Squire Patton Boggs is looking for summer associates with outstanding academic credentials, excellent communication skills, common sense, creativity, a strong work ethic and an ability to cultivate long term relationships with our clients and colleagues.

Summer program components:

A range of valuable experiences is structured around our three global messages:

Commercial: You will be given the opportunity to work side by side with our partners, attending depositions, hearings, deal negotiations and trials. In addition, you will cover legal writing and research, public speaking, negotiation and advocacy techniques.

Connected: You will be encouraged to attend practice group meetings and associate training programs to build your network of contacts within the business.

Committed: To get real value out of your program you will enjoy a collegial atmosphere with the support of a mentor for the duration of your summer with us.

Founding Office: Cleveland, OH
Number of domestic offices: 16
Number of international offices: 29
Worldwide revenue: $929,100,000
Partners (US): 272
Associates (US): 232
Other Attorneys (US): 167

Main Recruitment Contact:
Crystal L Arnold
Hiring Partner: Aneca E Lasley
Recruitment website:
www.squirepattonboggs.com/careers
Diversity Co-Chairs: Frederick R Nance, Alethia N Nancoo and Traci H Rollins

Summer Salary 2016
1Ls hired? Yes
Split summers offered? Case by case
Can summers spend time in overseas office? Yes
Summers 2016: 30
Offers/acceptances 2015:
1Ls 4 offers, 3 acceptances
2Ls 14 offers, 9 acceptances, 1 judicial clerkship

Sterne, Kessler, Goldstein & Fox P.L.L.C.

1100 New York Avenue NW, Suite 600, Washington, D.C. 20005
Tel: 202 772 8960 Fax: 202 371 2540
Email: ebusse@skgf.com
www.skgf.com

Main areas of work

Intellectual property.

Firm profile

Sterne, Kessler, Goldstein & Fox is dedicated to the protection, transfer, and enforcement of intellectual property rights. The firm's lawyers have the interdisciplinary background needed to develop, protect, and enforce valuable property rights for its clients. Most of Sterne Kessler's legal professionals hold an advanced level degree, including approximately 55 with a master's degree and over 55 with a doctorate in science or engineering. The firm's team of attorneys, registered patent agents, students, and technical specialists include some of the country's most respected practitioners of intellectual property law. The firm was founded in 1978, is based in Washington, D.C., and has grown to be one of the largest and highly regarded IP specialty firms in the United States and abroad.

Recruitment details

- Number of 1st year associates: 10
- Number of 2nd year associates: 8
- Associate salaries: 1st year: $160,000
- 2nd year: $170,000
- Clerking policy: Yes

Law Schools attending for OCIs in 2016:

American University College of Law, George Mason University Law School, George Washington University Law School, Loyola University Chicago School of Law (Patent Law Interview "PLI" Program)

Summer details

Summer associate profile:

Sterne Kessler seeks students with bachelor's degrees in science and/or engineering. All applicants must have at least a 3.0 cumulative GPA in undergraduate, graduate, and law school studies. United States Patent and Trademark Office and/or other industry work experience is a plus. Teamwork, motivation, collaboration, work ethic, and universal respect are core values of the firm.

Summer program components:

Each summer associate is assigned a senior-level and junior associate to help acclimate them to the firm and to answer any questions he/she may have during his/her tenure. Summer associates receive a full week of training in IP prosecution and litigation by experienced practitioners before ever taking an assignment. While hiring decisions lay at the practice group level, summer associates often have the opportunity to work on assignments from attorneys in other practice groups. Summer associates attend weekly practice group lunches where substantive topics are discussed and they participate in other professional development and technical training. Over the past several years, the firm has been consistently rated as a "best place to work" based on attorney and staff surveys conducted by The Washington Post and the Washington Business Journal.

Head Office: Washington, D.C.
Number of domestic offices: 1
Number of international offices: 0
Worldwide revenue: WND
Partners (US): 48
Associates (US): 87

Main Recruitment Contact: Emily Busse
Hiring Partner: Donald Featherstone
Recruitment website: www.skgf.com/careers and visit the firm's page on LinkedIn
Diversity Officer: Gaby Longsworth, Chair, Diversity Committee

Summer Salary 2016
1Ls: $2,900
2Ls: $3,100
Post 3Ls: N/A
1Ls hired? Yes
Split summers offered? CBC
Can summers spend time in overseas office? N/A
Summers 2016: 8
Offers/acceptances 2015: 6 offers, 5 acceptances

Firm Profiles

Stroock & Stroock & Lavan LLP

180 Maiden Lane, New York, NY 10038
Tel: 212 806 5400 Fax: 212 806 6006
Email: legalrecruiting@stroock.com
www.stroock.com

Main areas of work

Primary practice areas include capital markets/securities, commercial finance, commodities and derivatives, employee benefits and executive compensation, employment, energy and project finance, entertainment, environmental, financial restructuring, financial services/class action, government relations, insurance and reinsurance, intellectual property, investment management, litigation, mergers, acquisitions and joint ventures, national security/CFIUS/compliance, personal client services, private equity/venture capital, private funds, real estate and tax.

Firm profile

Stroock & Stroock & Lavan LLP provides transactional, regulatory and litigation guidance to leading financial institutions, multinational corporations, investment funds and entrepreneurs in the US and abroad. Our emphasis on excellence and innovation has enabled us to maintain long-term relationships with our clients and made us one of the nation's leading law firms for almost 140 years.

Recruitment details

- Number of 1st year associates: 14
- Number of 2nd year associates: 24
- Associate salaries: 1st year: $160,000
- 2nd year: $170,000
- Clerking policy: A $50,000 clerkship bonus is provided upon completion of a judicial clerkship with a federal court or state judge in the highest court of that jurisdiction.

Law Schools attending for OCIs in 2016:

New York Office: Boston C, Boston U, Cardozo, Columbia, Cornell, Duke, Fordham, Georgetown, Harvard, NEBLSA, NY Law School, NYU, Penn

Los Angeles Office: Loyola, UCLA, University of Chicago, USC

Summer details

Summer associate profile:

Successful summer associates are self-starters, quickly take ownership of their matters and are able to function at a high level early in their careers. While not a prerequisite, those with prior work experience and those who have held leadership positions typically do well at Stroock.

Summer program components:

The firm's program includes a flexible work assignment system, billable work across different practice areas, extensive training programs, pro bono opportunities, access to Diversity/Affinity Groups' activities and social events. In addition, each summer associate has a partner and an associate mentor, as well as a first-year office mate, which allows summer associates to quickly build relationships with and work alongside Stroock attorneys. Summer associates receive formal feedback at the mid-point and at the end of the summer, as well as when they complete assignments.

Head Office: New York, NY
Number of domestic offices: 4
Number of international offices: 0
Worldwide revenue: $265,000,000
Partners (US): 95
Associates (US): 192

Main Recruitment Contacts:
Halle Schargel and Yakiry Malena
Hiring Partner: Claude Szyfer
Recruitment website:
www.stroock.com
Diversity officer: Anita Rosenbloom

Summer Salary 2016
1Ls: $3,077/week
2Ls: $3,077/week
Post 3Ls: $3,077/week
1Ls hired? Case by case
Split summers offered? No
Can summers spend time in overseas office? No
Summers 2016: 14
Offers/acceptances 2015:
14 offers, 13 acceptances

STROOCK

Firm Profiles

Sullivan & Cromwell LLP

125 Broad Street, New York, NY 10004
Tel: 212 558 4000 Fax: 212 558 3588
www.sullcrom.com

Main areas of work

Sullivan & Cromwell brings a multidisciplinary approach to providing the fullest and most comprehensive legal advice to our clients. Our global practice includes four main groups: General Practice (corporate), Litigation, Tax and Estates and Personal.

Our lawyers are trained to be generalists through broad exposure to a wide range of challenging legal matters, many of which have a significant cross-border component. A substantial number of S&C's clients are non-US commercial enterprises and government entities and many of our US clients retain us for international matters. Our lawyers serve our clients through a network of 12 offices in New York, Washington, DC, Los Angeles, Palo Alto, London, Paris, Frankfurt, Tokyo, Hong Kong, Beijing, Melbourne and Sydney.

Firm profile

S&C has the most broadly and deeply trained collection of lawyers in the world. They thrive in our working environment, which is characterized by commitment to clients, leadership, professional development, broad experience, teamwork and commitment to community. Associates at S&C typically acquire leadership skills as lawyers more quickly than they would at other law firms, as they are given early responsibility for managing transactions, counseling clients and representing their interests in dealings with other parties. To supplement this on-the-job experience, we provide comprehensive training programs for associates as well as formal mentoring programs.

Recruitment details

- Number of 1st year associates: 92
- Number of 2nd year associates: 84
- Associate salaries: 1st year: $160,000
- 2nd year: $170,000
- Clerking policy: Yes

Law Schools attending for OCIs in 2016:

S&C interviews at top law schools around the country. Our lawyers are alumni of more than 135 law schools.

Summer details

Summer associate profile:

We are actively seeking people whose intellect, character, motivation and other attributes promise to make them outstanding lawyers.

Summer program components:

Training/Orientation: All summer associates participate in a formal orientation program, as well as a wide variety of training programs and skills workshops.

Advising/Assigning/Evaluations: Summer associates are assigned a partner advisor and an associate advisor, from whom they receive assignments. They are also matched with a junior associate, who is there to help with day-to-day matters at the firm. In addition, each summer associate is assigned to an Associate Development Partner, who oversees the distribution of summer associate assignments.

Events: Every summer, S&C organizes a variety of events, including professional opportunities, social events and charitable events.

Head Office: New York, NY
Number of domestic offices: 4
Number of international offices: 8
Partners (US): 139
Associates (US): 459

Main Recruitment Contact: Milana L Hogan, Chief Legal Recruiting & Professional Development Officer
Hiring Partner: Sergio J Galvis
Recruitment website: https://careers.sullcrom.com
Diversity officers: David Braff and Tracy Richelle High, Partners, Co-Chairs of the Diversity Committee

Summer Salary 2016
1Ls: $3,076/week
2Ls: $3,076/week
Post 3Ls: $3,076/week
1Ls hired? Yes
Split summers offered? Yes
Can summers spend time in overseas office? Yes
Summers 2016: 144 (120 2Ls, 3 1Ls, 18 3L pre-clerks, 3 SEOs)

SULLIVAN & CROMWELL LLP

Thompson & Knight LLP

1722 Routh Street Dallas, TX 75201
Tel: 214 969 1700
Fax: 214 969 1751
Email: lauren.mccann@tklaw.com
www.tklaw.com

Main areas of work

Bankruptcy and restructuring; corporate and securities; employment and labor; environmental; finance; government and regulatory; healthcare; intellectual property; oil, gas, and energy; real estate and real estate finance; tax; trial.

Firm profile

Established in 1887, Thompson & Knight is a full-service law firm with more than 300 attorneys that provides legal solutions to clients and communities around the world. The Firm has strong Texas roots, client-focused capabilities on the East and West Coasts, and strategic locations internationally in the Americas, North Africa, and Europe.

Our dedication to clients defines us well. According to Chambers USA 2015, Thompson & Knight has "an enviable client base," which includes the four largest US airlines, the two largest medical device companies in the world, seven of the top 10 US oil and gas exploration and production companies, and the largest real estate investment trust in the world, among others.

Our culture – the key reason for our success – emphasizes teamwork and an unparalleled commitment to excellence. Through our collective knowledge, our relationships, our high ethics, our team approach, and our dedication to the community, we make a positive impact on the people we serve. For more information on the Firm, please visit our website at www.tklaw.com.

Recruitment details

- Number of 1st year associates: 12
- Associate salaries: 1st year: $160,000
- Clerking policy: yes
- Number of 2nd year associates: 14
- 2nd year: $170,000

Law Schools attending for OCIs in 2016:

Law Schools: Baylor University; Duke University; LSU; South Texas College of Law; Southern Methodist University; Texas Tech University; University of Houston; Harvard University; University of Texas; Tulane University

Job Fairs: Lavender Law Career Fair; Southeastern Minority Job Fair; Sunbelt Minority Recruitment Program; Texas Interview Program; On Tour Job Fair; University of Oklahoma

Summer details

Summer associate profile:

Thompson & Knight's Summer Associate program is our principal source of hiring new Associates. Thompson & Knight has a collegial, team-oriented, and supportive culture. We offer challenging and fulfilling work in an atmosphere of mutual respect and appreciation. Our program provides an unparalleled educational experience and creates lasting relationships between our attorneys and Summer Associates, the future of our Firm.

Summer program components:

Summer Associates are assigned two practice areas to clerk in during their 6-8 week clerkship. They are also assigned a Partner and Associate advisor in each section during their time here. The Summer Associates receive a wide range of work and training opportunities

Head Office: Dallas, TX
Number of domestic offices: 6
Number of international offices: 5
Worldwide revenue: $207.5 million
Partners (US): 147
Associates (US): 79

Main Recruitment Contact:
Lauren McCann
Hiring Partner: Jessica Hammons
Recruitment website:
www.tklaw.com
Diversity Officer: Nichole Olajuwon

Summer Salary 2016
1Ls: $3,060/week
2Ls: $3,060/week
Post 3Ls: N/A
1Ls hired? Yes
Split summers offered? No, 1st half only
Can summers spend time in overseas office? No
Summers 2016: 15
Offers/acceptances 2015: 8

Firm Profiles

703

Vedder Price

222 North LaSalle Street, Chicago, IL 60601
Tel: 312 609 7500 Fax: 312 609 5005
Email: info@vedderprice.com
www.vedderprice.com

Main areas of work

Corporate, labor and employment, litigation.

Firm profile

Vedder Price is a thriving general-practice law firm with a proud tradition of maintaining long-standing relationships with its clients, many of whom have been with the firm since its founding in 1952. With approximately 300 attorneys and growing, Vedder Price serves clients of all sizes and in virtually all industries from offices in Chicago, New York, Washington, DC, London, San Francisco and Los Angeles.

Recruitment details

- Number of 1st year associates: 8
- Number of 2nd year associates: 10
- Associate salaries: 1st year: $160,000
- 2nd year: $165,000 – $170,000
- Clerking policy: No

Law Schools attending for OCIs in 2016:

Brooklyn, Chicago-Kent, Cornell, Fordham, George Washington, Georgetown, Loyola, Northwestern, Notre Dame, University of Chicago, University of Illinois, University of Michigan

Summer details

Summer associate profile:

Vedder Price recruits candidates with strong academics, excellent verbal and written communication skills, initiative and enthusiasm. Ideal candidates have a demonstrated interest in the practice area they are applying for, as evidenced by relevant course work and/or prior work experience. As Summer Associates will interact immediately with senior shareholders and clients, executive presence and maturity are valued.

Summer program components:

Summer Associates are integrated quickly into the practice area they are joining, through substantive work assignments, observation opportunities and training sessions. Summer Associates will work with an assigned associate advisor to receive practical advice and guidance. A firm-wide summer program orientation is hosted in Chicago during the first week of the program for the summer class to meet each other and engage with Firm Management. There are two formal review sessions, one at mid-summer and the other at the completion of the program, incorporating written attorney feedback regarding each completed project. Social events are frequent, both office-wide and in small groups, to ensure Summer Associates enjoy the collegiality of the Firm.

Head Office: Chicago, IL
Number of domestic offices: 5
Number of international offices: 1
Worldwide revenue: $238.3 million
Shareholders (US): 160
Associates (US): 113

Main Recruitment Contacts: Amanda Brummel and Elise Rippe, Managers of Legal Recruiting
Hiring Shareholder: Dana Armagno
Recruitment website: www.vedderprice.com/careers
Diversity Officer: Margo O'Donnell, Shareholder

Summer Salary 2016
1Ls: $3,077
2Ls: $3,077
Post 3Ls: N/A
1Ls hired? Yes (Diversity Scholar in the Chicago Office)
Split summers offered? No
Can summers spend time in overseas office? No
Summers 2016: 14
Offers/acceptances 2015: 11 offers, 10 acceptances

Venable LLP

575 7th Street, NW, Washington, DC 20004
Tel: 202 344 4000 Fax: 202 344 8300
www.venable.com

Main areas of work

Government and regulatory affairs, corporate law and business transactions, complex litigation, technology and intellectual property.

Firm profile

Venable is an American Lawyer 100 law firm. With approximately 650 attorneys in nine offices across the country, we are strategically positioned to advance our clients' business objectives in the US and abroad. Our clients rely on Venable's proven capabilities in all areas of corporate and business law, complex litigation, intellectual property, and regulatory and government affairs. Venable attorneys, many of whom have served in senior corporate, regulatory, prosecutorial, legislative and executive branch positions, understand the needs of their clients.

Recruitment details

- Number of 1st year associates: 31
- Number of 2nd year associates: 25
- Associate salaries: 1st year: $160,000
- Clerking policy: Yes

Law Schools attending for OCIs in 2016:

American University, Benjamin N. Cardozo School of Law, Berkley Law, Brooklyn Law School, Univ. of Baltimore, Catholic University, Cornell, UC Davis, Duke, Fordham, George Mason, Georgetown, George Washington, Harvard, UC Hastings, Howard, UCI Law, Loyola Law School (LA), UCLA, Univ. of Maryland, Univ. of Michigan, New York Law School, NYU, Univ. of Pennsylvania, Univ. of Richmond, Univ. of San Francisco, USC, Stanford, Vanderbilt, UVA, and William & Mary. We will also attend the Southeastern Minority Job Fair, Mid-Atlantic BLSA Job Fair, Western Region BLSA Job Fair, Northeast Region BLSA Job Fair, and Lavender Law Job Fair

Summer details

Summer associate profile:

We consider candidates whose personal and academic achievements demonstrate a commitment to excellence, who act with integrity, and who want to help clients solve problems in a large law firm environment.

Summer program components:

In 2015, Venable's summer associate program was ranked #4 Best Overall Summer Associate Program and #1 Best Prepares for Practice by Vault. Our summer associate program is designed to give our summer associates a realistic depiction of everyday life as a junior associate. Each summer associate is assigned a partner mentor and an associate mentor. Summer associates receive real work assignments on behalf of real clients – the same types of assignments our junior associates receive throughout the year. Assignments come from a mix of practice areas, and are supplemented with "take-alongs". Each assignment is reviewed after it is completed and each summer associate receives a formal midsummer and end of summer review by a member of the Hiring Committee. In addition to fun, local events, there are informal dinners, happy hours, and "take a partner to lunch" opportunities to get to know our attorneys. Venable also provides professional development workshops, such as legal writing, communication and time management, to the summer associates during the course of the program.

Head Office: Washington, DC
Number of domestic offices: 9
Worldwide revenue: $477,200,000
Partners (US): 287
Associates (US): 241

Main Recruitment Contact: Ms Kera M Wise, Senior Director of Attorney Recruiting
Hiring Partner: Mr Robert J Bolger, Jr
Recruitment website: www.venable.com/careers/
Diversity officers: Nora E Garrote, Kathleen S Hardway

Summer Salary 2016
1Ls: N/A
2Ls: $3076/week
Post 3Ls: N/A
1Ls hired? No
Split summers offered? No
Can summers spend time in overseas office? N/A
Summers 2016: 34
Offers/acceptances 2015: 37 offers, 37 acceptances

Vinson & Elkins LLP

1001 Fannin Street, Suite 2500, Houston, TX 77002-6760
Tel: 713 758 2222 Fax: 713 758 2346
www.velaw.com

Main areas of work

Antitrust; appellate; complex commercial litigation; condemnation; construction; employment, labor and OSHA; energy litigation; energy regulatory; energy transactions / projects; environmental and natural resources; finance; government contracts; government investigations and white collar; intellectual property; international dispute resolution; M&A/capital markets; media and entertainment; private equity; professional liability; real estate; restructuring and reorganization; securities litigation; tax – executive compensation and benefits.

Firm profile

Collaborating seamlessly across 15 offices worldwide, Vinson & Elkins LLP provides outstanding client service. Our lawyers are committed to excellence, offering clients experience in handling their transactions, investments, projects and disputes across the globe. Established in Houston in 1917, the firm's time-tested role as trusted advisor has made V&E a go-to law firm for many of the world's leading businesses, especially in the energy and finance industries. We bring competitive strength, insight and know-how to guide our clients through their most complex transactions and litigation.

Recruitment details

- Number of 1st year associates: 36
- Number of 2nd year associates: 48
- Associate salaries: 1st year: $160,000
- 2nd year: $170,000
- Clerking policy: Yes

Law Schools attending for OCIs in 2016:

Cardozo, Columbia, Duke, Fordham, George Washington, Georgetown, Harvard, Howard, LSU, Loyola University, Cornell Patent Law Program, NYU, Northwestern, South Texas, SMU, Stanford, The University of Texas, Tulane, UC Berkeley, University of Chicago, University of Houston, University of Maryland, University of Michigan, University of Pennsylvania, University of Richmond, UVA, Vanderbilt, Washington University, Washington & Lee, William & Mary, Yale

Summer details

Summer associate profile:

Vinson & Elkins hires talented and highly motivated individuals who desire a sophisticated legal practice.

We look for candidates who take initiative, offer diverse perspectives, are innovative and will enjoy working alongside top lawyers in a friendly and collegial environment.

Summer program components:

V&E's "one firm" mentality offers summer associates the opportunity to work on cross-office projects from a variety of practice areas of interest. As a summer associate, you'll experience hands-on legal training, develop mentoring relationships and get an understanding of what it is like to practice law at Vinson & Elkins.

Head Office: Houston, TX
Number of domestic offices: 8
Number of international offices: 8
Worldwide revenue: $627,700,000
Partners (US): 211
Associates (US): 304

Main Recruitment Contact: Gretchen Rollins, Director of Entry-Level Hiring
Hiring Partner: Doug Bland
Recruitment website: www.velaw.com/careers
Diversity officer: Renate Wagner, Director of Attorney Communications & Initiatives

Summer Salary 2016
1Ls: $3,077/week
2Ls: $3,077/week
Post 3Ls: $3,077/week
1Ls hired? Yes
Split summers offered? 10 week program, varies by office
Can summers spend time in overseas office? Case by case
Summers 2016: 66
Offers/acceptances 2015: 69 offers, 55 acceptances

Vinson&Elkins LLP

Waller

511 Union Street, Suite 2700, Nashville, TN 37219
Tel: 615 244 6380 Fax: 615 244 6804
www.wallerlaw.com

Main areas of work

Waller is a full-service general practice firm that advises clients across a spectrum of industries including healthcare, financial services, retail, hospitality, automotive, manufacturing, technology, media and entertainment, real estate, telecommunications and utilities. The firm prides itself on providing creative, cost-effective legal services and solutions to our clients, and providing advice and counsel in core legal areas such as corporate, M&A, litigation and dispute resolution, commercial finance, securities, bankruptcy and restructuring, environmental, intellectual property, real estate, tax, regulatory compliance, government investigations and government relations.

Recruitment details

- Number of 1st year associates: 7
- Number of 2nd year associates: 9
- Associate salaries: 1st year: $115,000
- Clerking policy: Yes

Summer details

Summer associate profile:

Waller recruits students who are diverse in thought, background and education, especially those with strong ties to the four Southeastern cities in which we are located. Individuals who have a track record of academic excellence and are motivated to learn and be integrated in a collegial environment will excel at Waller.

Summer program components:

Waller has continued to build on the successes of its groundbreaking Schola2Juris fall apprenticeship by transitioning the program to a summer associate experience. The firm's summer program still maintains the mentoring and teaching aspects of the fall apprenticeship in which students worked on hypothetical projects developed from actual transactions or matters that the firm has recently handled. With summer associates now in-house for the six-week program, students are afforded the opportunity to work on two different matters in distinct practice groups over the course of the internship. Waller attorneys guide the students through the hypothetical projects with the oversight of three mentors: a junior associate, mid- or senior-level associate and a partner. The hypothetical projects comprise for approximately half of program's workload, and students also have the opportunity to engage in live, time-sensitive matters in the remaining six practice groups not covered by their hypothetical projects. While working to create a more "practice ready" first-year attorney, Waller's summer program provides every student more ample working experience to determine which practice group would provide the best fit after graduation.

Head Office: Nashville, TN
Number of domestic offices: 4
Number of international offices: 0
Partners (US): 116
Associates (US): 107

Main Recruitment Contact: Bobby Weiss
Hiring Partner: Andy Norwood
Recruitment website: www.wallerlaw.com/join-us

Summer Salary 2016
2Ls: $1,800/week
1Ls hired? Yes
Split summers offered? Yes
Can summers spend time in overseas office? N/A
Summers 2016: 9
Offers/acceptances 2015: 7 offers, 5 acceptances

Weil, Gotshal & Manges LLP

767 Fifth Avenue, New York, NY 10153
Tel: 212 310 8000 Fax: 212 310 8007
www.weil.com

Main areas of work

The firm offers legal counsel in more than two dozen practices areas categorized by the following groups: business finance and restructuring, corporate, litigation and tax.

Firm profile

Founded in 1931, Weil, Gotshal & Manges LLP has been a preeminent provider of legal services for more than 80 years. With approximately 1,100 lawyers in offices on three continents, Weil has been a pioneer in establishing a geographic footprint that has allowed the Firm to partner with clients wherever they do business. The Firm's four departments, Corporate, Litigation, Business Finance & Restructuring, and Tax, Executive Compensation & Benefits, and more than two dozen practice groups are consistently recognized as leaders in their respective fields. Talented attorneys who want to tackle complex, challenging matters on behalf of world-class companies will find ample opportunities to shine in our uniquely entrepreneurial culture. Please see www.weil.com for more information, including awards and rankings.

Recruitment details

- Number of 1st year associates: 83
- Number of 2nd year associates: 79
- Associate salaries: 1st year: $160,000
- 2nd year: $170,000
- Clerking policy: Yes

Law Schools attending for OCIs in 2016:

Weil has a diversified approach to its recruiting process. Firm-wide, Weil interviews at over 45 law schools and job fairs and participates in resume collection programs at over 10 other law schools. For a complete list, please visit www.weil.com/careers.

Summer details

Summer associate profile:

Weil's summer associate program provides an exceptional opportunity for outstanding law students from across the nation to explore a career in the practice of law. Weil seeks candidates with exceptional credentials, both in terms of qualifications and character.

Summer program components:

Summer associates may work in a total of one to three departments of their choice. They are assigned to active transactional and litigation matters and attend client meetings, negotiations, depositions and court hearings. This enables them to gain a much clearer idea of their choice of future practice area and obtain a realistic view of what it is like to practice law at the firm. Weil organizes special seminars during the summer to discuss particular fields of specialization and topics of interest to law students and to provide training in such areas as negotiation, litigation and writing skills. The firm assigns both associate and partner mentors whose role is to guide the summer associate throughout his or her summer experience, both personally and professionally. Feedback is a critical element of the summer experience. Assigning attorneys regularly evaluate the summer associate's performance and written product, in much the same way that a senior attorney reviews a junior attorney's work. The summer associate's performance is formally evaluated twice during the summer.

Head Office: New York, NY
Number of domestic offices: 9
Number of international offices: 11
Worldwide revenue: $1.164 billion
Partners (US): 294
Associates (US): 745

Main Recruitment Contact:
Wesley Powell
Hiring Partners: Joshua Amsel and Jackie Cohen
Recruitment Website:
www.weil.com/careers
Diversity officer: Meredith Moore

Summer Salary 2016
1Ls: $3,077/week
2Ls: $3,077/week
Post 3Ls: $3,077/week
1Ls hired? Case by case
Split summers offered? Case by case
Can summers spend time in overseas office? Case by case
Summers 2016: 97 (including 1Ls)
Offers/acceptances 2015:
78 offers, 67 acceptances (excluding 1LS)

White & Case LLP

1155 Avenue of the Americas, New York, NY 10036
Tel: 212 819 8200 Fax: 212 354 8113
www.whitecase.com

Main areas of work

Antitrust, asset finance, banking, capital markets, commercial litigation, financial restructuring and insolvency, intellectual property, international arbitration, mergers and acquisitions, private equity, pro bono, project finance, tax, trade and white collar.

Firm profile

White & Case is a global law firm with longstanding offices in the markets that matter today. Our on-the-ground experience, our cross-border integration and our depth of local, US and English-qualified lawyers help our clients work with confidence in any one market or across many. We guide our clients through difficult issues, bringing our insight and judgment to each situation. Our innovative approaches create original solutions to our clients' most complex domestic and multijurisdictional deals and disputes. By thinking on behalf of our clients every day, we anticipate what they want, provide what they need and build lasting relationships. We do what it takes to help our clients achieve their ambitions.

Recruitment details

- Associate salaries: 1st year: $160k/$155k ($160k in LA, NY, SV, DC; $155k in MI)
- 2nd year: $170k/$160k ($170k in LA, NY, SV, DC and $160k in MI)
- Clerking policy: Yes

Law Schools attending for OCIs in 2016:

American, Bay Area Diversity, Berkeley, Boston College, Boston University, Chicago, Columbia, Cornell, Duke, Emory, Florida, Fordham, George Washington, Georgetown, Harvard, Howard, Irvine, Loyola, Loyola Patent Fair, McGill, Miami, Michigan, Mid-Atlantic BLSA, Northeast BLSA, Northwestern, Notre Dame, NYU, Penn, Pepperdine, San Francisco IP Job Fair, Stanford, Toronto, Tulane, UCLA, USC, Vanderbilt, Virginia, Washington University, Yale

Summer details

Summer associate profile:

We look for highly motivated individuals with excellent academic credentials, significant personal achievements and a strong commitment to the practice of law in a global and diverse law firm. Fluency in any second language is a plus.

Summer program components:

We pride ourselves on giving summer associates real work for real clients with real deadlines. You will have a full curriculum of training programs in addition to getting hands-on experience working side by side with our lawyers. Our assignment coordinators ensure that you receive exposure to a variety of work that is of interest to you, including pro bono matters. In addition to informal discussions, two formal reviews provide timely and meaningful feedback. Mentors are available to you throughout the summer. One of the highlights is the Summer Associate Conference that takes place in the NY office and provides an opportunity for our US summers to meet each other and learn more about the Firm, our people and our culture.

Head office: New York, NY
Number of domestic offices: 5
Number of international offices: 34
Worldwide revenue: $1,523,300,000
Partners (US): 179
Associates (US): 387

Main Recruitment Contact:
Jane P Stein
Hiring Partners: Matthew J Kautz and Owen C Pell
Recruitment website:
http://uslawcareers.whitecase.com
Diversity officer: Maja Hazell

Summer Salary 2016
1Ls: $3,077/week in LA, NY, SV, DC, $2,981/week in MI
2Ls: $2,981-$3,077/week
Post 3Ls: $2,981-$3,077/week
1Ls hired? Yes
Split summers offered? Yes
Can summers spend time in overseas office? Yes
Summers 2016: 100 (including 1Ls)
Offers/acceptances 2015:
65 offers, 63 acceptances

WHITE & CASE

Wiley Rein LLP

1776 K Street NW, Washington, DC 20006
Tel: 202 719 7000 Fax: 202 719 7049
www.wileyrein.com

Main areas of work

Communications, government contracts, insurance, international trade, intellectual property, regulatory, litigation.

Firm profile

In 1983, Wiley Rein LLP opened its doors with 39 attorneys and a mission to establish a distinctly Washington, DC firm providing exceptional, effective legal services. Now home to more than 250 attorneys practicing in almost two dozen areas of law, the firm has become an institution in the nation's capital. Offering our clients a unique integration of legal, regulatory and public policy expertise with an in-depth understanding of the business and technical underpinnings of the industries we serve, Wiley Rein employs an interdisciplinary approach that leverages the full breadth of our talent and knowledge and provides counsel derived from aggressive advocacy and extensive subject matter knowledge.

Recruitment details

- Number of 1st year associates: 11
- Number of 2nd year associates: 14
- Associate salaries: 1st year: $160,000
- 2nd year: $170,000
- Clerking policy: Yes

Law Schools attending for OCIs in 2016:

George Mason University School of Law, The George Washington University Law School, Georgetown University Law Center, Harvard Law School, Howard University School of Law, University of Virginia School of Law, Vanderbilt Law School, Washington and Lee University School of Law

Summer details

Summer associate profile:

Wiley Rein's summer associate program is the foundation of our recruiting efforts. We ensure that summer associates experience the excellence and diversity of our firm and we provide opportunities for each student to handle responsibilities typically assumed by first year associates.

Summer program components:

The defining feature of our program is the flexibility of work assignments. We assist students in tailoring their assignments so that they gain significant exposure to a wide variety of practice areas through our interactive database of assignments. In addition, summer associates receive an associate mentor to help integrate them into the firm and our practice. We host an extensive litigation skills training program in addition to other professional development and social events throughout the summer.

Head Office: Washington, DC
Number of domestic offices: 1
Partners (US): 118
Associates (US): 67

Main Recruitment Contact:
Kathy Schmidt, Senior Manager of Attorney Recruiting & Professional Development
Hiring Partner: Rachel A Alexander
Recruitment website:
www.wileyrein.com/careers.cfm
Diversity officer: Anna Gomez

Summer Salary 2016
1Ls: $3080/week
2Ls: $3080/week
Post 3Ls: N/A
1Ls hired? CBC
Split summers offered? No
Summers 2016: 10
Offers/acceptances 2015: 10 offers, 8 acceptances (1 received judicial clerkship)

Willkie Farr & Gallagher LLP

787 Seventh Avenue, New York, NY 10019
Tel: 212 728 8000 Fax: 212 728 8111
www.willkie.com

Main areas of work

Antitrust and competition, asset management, business reorganization and restructuring, communications, media and privacy, corporate and financial services, environmental, health and safety, executive compensation and employee benefits, government relations, insurance, intellectual property, litigation, private clients, real estate and tax.

Firm profile

Willkie Farr & Gallagher LLP was founded more than 125 years ago upon principles that still characterize our practice today. Our founders and memorable colleagues, like Wendell Willkie and Felix Frankfurter, established a strong foundation of integrity, innovation, pragmatism, flexibility and intellectual agility designed to continually meet the ever changing business needs of our clients. We continue our tradition of excellence by keeping nimble, working collaboratively together, with respect and professionalism, and by integrating this philosophy into our client relationships. Our clients not only rely on us for our creativity, skill, leadership, decisiveness and high-quality work, but because they know we are solution-oriented and we get the job done effectively and efficiently.

Recruitment details

- Number of 1st year associates: 54
- Number of 2nd year associates: 49
- Associate salaries: 1st year: $160,000
- 2nd year: $170,000
- Clerking policy: Yes

Law Schools attending for OCIs in 2016:

Brooklyn, Columbia University, Cornell, Duke, Fordham University, GWU, Georgetown University, Harvard, Howard University, NYU, Northwestern University, St John's University, University of Michigan, University of Pennsylvania, University of Texas, UVA, Yale

Summer details

Summer associate profile:

Willkie seeks motivated individuals who have excelled academically. We are looking for candidates who possess ambition, maturity, strong communication skills and the ability to work collaboratively with others.

Summer program components:

Willkie's summer program is a terrific introduction to the firm. We offer summer associates the opportunity to work side by side with our attorneys in practice areas of their choice. We offer departmental rotations during the course of the summer. In addition, summer associates participate in a presentation skills workshop, mock arbitration and corporate negotiation training seminars. Summer associates are evaluated twice during the program: once at mid-summer and then at the end of the program. In addition to providing an introduction to life as an associate, we provide a wide array of social events with the goal of helping our summer associates to get to know one another, our lawyers and the city.

Head Office: New York
Number of domestic offices: 3
Number of international offices: 6
Partners (US): 136
Associates (US): 295

Main Recruitment Contacts:
Christie Bonasera, Associate Director of Legal Recruiting (NY), Gail McGinley, Associate Director of Legal Personnel & Recruiting, (DC)
Hiring Partner: Elizabeth J Bower (DC); Sameer Advani, Joseph P Cunningham, David C Drewes, A Mark Getachew, Matthew J Guercio, Deirdre Norton Hykal, Danielle Scalzo; Angela Olivarez (TX)
Recruitment website:
www.willkie.com
Diversity officer: Kim A Walker, Director of Diversity & Inclusion

Summer Salary 2016
1Ls: N/A
2Ls: $3,077/week
Post 3Ls: N/A
1Ls hired? Case-by-case
Split summers offered? Yes, details by office
Can summers spend time in overseas office? Case-by-case
Summers 2016: 62
Offers/acceptances 2015:
74 offers, 67 acceptances

WILLKIE FARR & GALLAGHER LLP

WilmerHale

60 State Street, Boston, MA
350 S. Grand Avenue, Suite 2100, Los Angeles, CA
7 World Trade Center, 250 Greenwich Street, New York, NY
950 Page Mill Road, Palo Alto, CA
1875 Pennsylvania Ave, NW, Washington, DC

Main areas of work

Our global practice includes over 600 litigators with unmatched trial, appellate and Supreme Court experience; a preeminent securities law practice with over 130 lawyers; a regulatory practice that includes more than 110 lawyers who have held high-level government positions; an intellectual property practice enriched by the expertise of more than 170 attorneys and technology specialists who hold scientific or technical degrees; more than 200 seasoned corporate transactional lawyers and business counselors; and lawyers who focus on bankruptcy, environmental, labor and employment, private client, real estate and tax matters.

Firm profile

WilmerHale offers unparalleled legal representation across a comprehensive range of practice areas that are critical to the success of our clients. We practice at the very top of the legal profession and offer a cutting-edge blend of capabilities that enables us to handle deals and cases of any size and complexity. With a practice unsurpassed in depth and scope by any other major firm, we have the ability to anticipate obstacles, seize opportunities and get the case resolved or the deal done—and the experience and know-how to prevent it from being undone. Our heritage includes involvement in the foundation of legal aid work early in the 20th century, and today we consistently distinguish ourselves as leaders in pro bono representation. Many of our lawyers have played, and continue to play, prominent roles in public service activities of national and international importance—from counseling US presidents to opposing discrimination and defending human rights around the world. Most importantly, our firm stands for a steadfast commitment to quality and excellence in everything we do—a commitment reflected in the continued success of our clients across the globe and our dedication to the development of our attorneys.

Recruitment details

- Number of 1st year associates: 65
- Number of 2nd year associates: 51
- Associate salaries: 1st year: $160,000
- 2nd year: $170,000
- Clerking policy: Yes. The firm welcomes applications from judicial clerks. Approximately one-third of our recent incoming classes have come to the firm after serving one or more judicial clerkships. We value the experience of clerkships and give credit for clerkships for compensation and seniority purposes. We also pay a competitive bonus to incoming clerks.

Law Schools attending for OCIs in 2016:

University of California-Berkeley, Boston College, Boston University, University of Chicago, Columbia, Cornell, Duke, Fordham, George Washington, Georgetown, Harvard, Howard, Loyola Law School - LA, Michigan, Northwestern, Northeastern, NYU, University of Pennsylvania, Santa Clara, Stanford, Suffolk, University of California-LA (UCLA), University of California-Davis, University of Colorado-Boulder, University of Denver, University of Southern California (USC), University of Virginia, University of Washington, Yale.

Head Office: Boston, MA and Washington, DC
Number of domestic offices: 6
Number of international offices: 5
Worldwide revenue: $1.14 billion
Partners (US): 255
Associates (US): 568

Main Recruitment Contacts:
Beth Miller (firmwide)
Nancy Lam (Denver)
Terri Janezeck (Los Angeles)
Nancy Gray (New York)
Nancy Lam (Palo Alto)
Melissa Grossman (Washington, DC)
Hiring Partners:
Mark Fleming (Boston)
Randall Lee (Los Angeles)
Erin Sloane (New York)
Mark Flanagan (Palo Alto)
Chris Davies (Washington, DC)
Recruitment website:
www.wilmerhalecareers.com
Diversity officer: Nimesh Patel

WilmerHale
Continued

1225 17th Street #2600, Denver, CO
www.wilmerhale.com
www.wilmerhalecareers.com

Summer details

Summer associate profile:

We seek to hire an extraordinarily talented and diverse group of students whose academic and personal record of achievement demonstrates a commitment to excellence and who want to practice law at the highest and most demanding levels, while still enjoying lives enriched by public, professional and personal pursuits outside the firm. We have identified six competencies—commitment, confidence, oral communication, problem solving, teamwork and writing—that outline what constitutes outstanding performance at WilmerHale and are used to align our selection criteria and evaluations of candidates and summer associates with our expectations of attorneys. In addition, we seek individuals whose character, intelligence, judgment and training will inspire their colleagues and clients to have confidence in their advice and representation.

Summer program components:

By providing a realistic view of the firm through interesting work assignments, practical training and the opportunity to work and socialize with many of our lawyers, we give summer associates the insight needed to make an informed decision to join the firm after graduation or a clerkship. Summer associates do substantive client work and have the opportunity to try a broad range of practices or focus on a few, depending on their interests. Summer associates also have the opportunity to attend client meetings and trials whenever possible. Our mentors provide guidance and constructive feedback throughout the summer and make themselves available to their mentees as resources in the firm. We have developed training programs specifically for our summer associates designed to assist in their professional development by introducing the practical skills lawyers need and provide a sample of our training programs for our attorneys. Summer training topics include: research skills, leadership, negotiation skills, deposition skills, presentation skills/oral communication skills, legal writing, departmental panels and meetings, case studies and mock trials. In addition, summer associates receive a review of their work and are encouraged to provide feedback about their experience.

Summer Salary 2016
1Ls: $3,100/week
2Ls: $3,100/week
Post 3Ls: N/A
1Ls hired? Yes
Split summers offered? Yes
Can summers spend time in overseas office? Yes
Summers 2016: 104
Offers/acceptances 2015:
80 offers, 57 acceptances, 20 pending

Winston & Strawn LLP

35 West Wacker Drive, Chicago, IL 60601
Tel: 312 558 5600 Fax: 312 558 5700
www.winston.com

Main areas of work

Litigation, corporate and financial, intellectual property, labor and employment relations, tax, employee benefits and executive compensation, energy, environmental, government relations and regulatory affairs, healthcare, maritime, real estate, trusts and estates.

Firm profile

Throughout its more than 160 year history, Winston & Strawn LLP has handled many significant, high profile matters for its clients – from antitrust litigation to cross-border mergers, energy transactions to labor negotiations. The firm is a global law firm with more than 800 attorneys across the US, Europe and Asia. The firm's mission is to provide the highest quality legal services to meet the difficult legal challenges of the world's most important companies and organizations. Winston & Strawn is consistently honored by its clients for outstanding legal service.

Recruitment details

- Number of 1st year associates: 54
- Number of 2nd year associates: 52
- Associate salaries: 1st year: $160,000
- 2nd year: $170,000
- Clerking policy: Yes

Law Schools attending for OCIs in 2016:

Please visit the Careers section of winston.com for a list of OCI Schools.

Summer details

Summer associate profile:

Winston & Strawn prefers strong academic performance, participation in law review or other law school publications or competitive endeavors and a good balance of academic and interpersonal skills.

Summer program components:

Summer associates have the opportunity to learn about a wide range of Winston practice areas and the specialized skills each one demands. Individual department presentations allow summer associates to meet lawyers from specific practice groups who detail what they do in their daily practice. The Firm Highlights Lecture Series gives an inside look at some of the most publicized and interesting cases that the firm handled in the past year. In addition, the firm offers a practical training component that provides hands-on experience with activities such as drafting a legal research memorandum, negotiating a deal, drafting an IPO document, taking a deposition and trying a case in a mock trial. Summer associates learn from veteran Winston attorneys with years of experience and insight, who make the law come alive through examples, personal experience and anecdotes. In addition, summer associates have the opportunity to build relationships with attorneys through a variety of social activities throughout the summer.

Head Office: Chicago, IL
Number of domestic offices: 9
Number of international offices: 10
Worldwide revenue: $818,300,000
Partners (US): 359
Associates (US): 381

Main Recruitment Contact: Lisa A McLafferty, Director of Attorney Relations
Hiring Partner: Suzanne Jaffe Bloom, William C O'Neil, Co-Chairs, Hiring Committee
Recruitment website: www.winston.com
Diversity officer: Amanda Sommerfeld, Chair, Diversity Committee

Summer Salary 2016
1Ls: $3,077/week
2Ls: $3,077/week
Post 3Ls: N/A
1Ls hired? Yes
Split summers offered? No
Can summers spend time in overseas office? No
Summers 2016: 65
Offers/acceptances 2015:
54 offers, 48 acceptances

Regional Guide

Where to start your practice?
We assess the pros and cons of becoming an attorney in key legal markets across the US:

Alaska & Hawaii

The perks to lawyering in Hawaii are as clear as its sunny blue skies: a tropical climate, Hawaiian shirts in the office, and a laid back atmosphere where you don't have to practice the ancient art of Ho'oponopono (traditional dispute resolution and forgiveness) to feel goodwill toward your coworkers. A legal career in Alaska offers the advantages of mountain views, clear air and moose sauntering through your backyard.

Hawaii

HAWAII'S legal market is concentrated in downtown Honolulu, and the courts, government agencies and law firms there tend to be small in size. Local firms that offer summer programs include Carlsmith Ball, Goodsill Anderson Quinn & Stifel, Case Lombardi & Pettit, Starn O'Toole Marcus & Fisher, Damon Key Leong Kupchak Hastert, and the nattily named M4. Ties to the area, whether through family or education, are at a premium when it comes to getting recruited.

The University of Hawaii's prestigious Richardson School of Law is the surest way into a legal career in Honolulu. It offers state-specific courses in Native Hawaiian law, environmental law and Pacific-Asian studies. It only takes 85 students a year though, and its admission team tends to favor students who are already resident on the islands. Carving out a legal career in Hawaii isn't easy, and some aspiring lawyers hoping for a side of sun often turn to larger hubs like Miami or LA.

Hawaii is best known as a tourist hub, welcoming planeloads of lei-toting visitors all year round thanks to its tropical climate. Its development into a summer-sports paradise has posed some distinct legal challenges, many of which are related to Native Hawaiian rights. Native Hawaiians have protected access to fishing and hunting rights, as well as certain water sources and areas of land. But in a small and densely populated cluster of islands, these rights are increasingly challenged by businesses eager to expand their reach. The Native Hawaiian Legal Corporation provides legal assistance to communities and families whose lands and resources are under threat. Native Hawaiians are also battling for greater recognition by the federal government, or even independence. The state was an independent kingdom until the US illegally overthrew Queen Lili uokalani in 1893, and now Native Hawaiians comprise only 10% of the islands' populations. Senator Daniel Akaka tried to push through a bill for federal recognition of Native Hawaiians between 2000 and 2010, but efforts to establish nation-to-nation relations have floundered, in part due to Native Hawaiian frustration at the US government's failure to make reparations for its decades of colonialism.

Alaska

Chasing the Northern Lights isn't the only reason to head to America's chilliest state.

The bright lights of Anchorage, which houses 40% of Alaska's population and most of its businesses, shine on a small but lively legal market. The capital isn't the easiest place to live, thanks to inhospitable weather and seemingly endless winter nights, but for lawyers who can brave the freeze, there's the advantage of a close-knit community and more winter sports than you can shake a ski-pole at.

While other states wrestle with a dramatic oversupply of law graduates, Alaska has no such trouble. It's the only state without a law school. Seattle University's School of Law, which has long offered its students a summer program on Alaskan legal issues at its satellite campus in Anchorage, is on its way to remedying this: in 2014 it won ABA approval to allow students to spend not only their summers but their entire third year in Alaska.

Environment, natural resources and regulated industries are big practice areas in Alaska. It's no secret why: the state sits on vast oil reserves and is home to an impressive range of flora and fauna (black bears are often sighted within cities, and the Anchorage area in particular plays host to a lot of mountain goats and wolves). The interests of ecologists, native Alaskans, oil prospectors and the federal government are constantly rubbing up against each other, making for a lot of litigation work, often with a regulatory slant.

There are 13 *Chambers USA*-ranked law firms in Alaska. These include a handful of national names, like K&L Gates and Squire Patton Boggs, as well as Seattle or DC-based outfits that have spread their wings, among them Davis Wright Tremaine, Perkins Coie, Lane Powell, Dorsey & Whitney and Stoel Rives. The bulk of these firms have launched offices in Alaska to take advantage of all the oil and gas work, much of which involves exploration work or issues related to the Trans-Alaska Pipeline System. Big homegrown firms in Alaska include: Birch, Horton, Bittner & Cherot (which also has a Washington, DC office to serve the state of Alaska in government dealings); Durrell Law Group; Ashburn & Mason; Guess & Rudd; Atkinson, Conway & Gagnon; and Sedor, Wendlandt, Evans & Filippi.

The market might not be the most varied one out there, but if you're a fan of the climate there's a lot to be said for the lifestyle the region can offer. Just make sure you're not going to change your mind: flights to the lower 48 are lengthy and don't come cheap.

Law firms in Alaska:

Crowell & Moring

'As Washingtonian as House of Cards, and almost as much fun, Crowell & Moring offers the chance to do cutting edge work in a place that doesn't take itself too seriously.'

Holland & Knight

Founded in the lightning capital of the USA, Holland & Knight has sparky associates who appreciate the "good work/life balance."

K&L Gates

"We expanded very quickly so now we're looking to better establish ourselves."

Perkins Coie

'Rising in the West and settling in the East, this tech-savvy outfit has become a national star without losing its West Coast shine. Just don't call it a lifestyle firm...'

Boston & New England

In our associate happiness survey, young Bostonian lawyers were among the happiest and least stressed in the US. They think Boston law firms' reputation for stuffiness can get stuffed...

The Cradle students never want to leave

WITH a population of around 650,000 and tens of thousands more traveling in from the suburbs each day, Boston is New England's commercial center. To many in the region – whether from New Hampshire, Vermont, Rhode Island, Maine or Connecticut – the capital of Massachusetts is their city. There are over 100 colleges and universities in the Greater Boston area, and students here have access to *"some of the best and brightest professors and are able to study alongside other highly intelligent students,"* enthuses a source at Choate, Hall & Stewart.

The city's reputation for academic excellence means that it's crammed full of students for eight months of the year. In the summer, though, many head home for the holiday, *"and the dynamic totally changes,"* a junior associate at Nutter McClennen & Fish told us. *"The buses and trains suddenly become a lot quieter!"* Of course, *"with such a rich history and culture, the students are often replaced by tourists over the summer."*

All the associates we interviewed from Boston old-timer Choate had grown up and/or studied in New England. At Goodwin Procter, a source in the firm's Boston headquarters observed that *"they seem for each office to hire locally – there's an appreciation for Boston-area schools here."* According to our sources: *"Law students here are encouraged to build up a support network which often includes their peers, professors and members of the legal profession they come into contact with over the course of their studies."* This could go some way to explaining why so many graduates choose to stay in the area.

Boston is a top destination for building up a stonking resume thanks to the number of organizations offering externships and the breadth of pro bono opportunities available to aspiring lawyers. These can be vital in supplementing that all-important BigLaw application, with senior sources at Boston-based firms telling us they're on the lookout for students who've taken advantage of such opportunities. *"Don't be afraid to take on pro bono work during your summer program,"* advised one Beantowner. *"It's a great way to show you're interested in exploring Boston's legal scene."*

Your new social life

Colloquially known as The Hub, Boston has *"all the advantages of a much larger city,"* an associate at Nutter tells us. At the same time, *"it's not as overwhelming as some other cities. It's relatively easy to escape all the hustle and bustle."* Others went on to describe *"an impressive live music scene with plenty of smaller shows to complement the big headliners,"* and mentioned how seriously the city takes its sports teams. And for good reason too: the Bruins lifted the Stanley Cup in 2011 and the Red Sox won the World Series in 2013, so there's some serious sporting clout in this North-Eastern state. On the whole, interviewees felt Boston is *"more collegial than most cities. Whenever you go out you're likely to run into people you know, and any new restaurants or bars are discussed in the same circles."*

Boston is an undeniably expensive city, *"but you can still get good value for money,"* our sources insist, adding that *"one of the main advantages is its relative affordability compared to New York. Being able to afford a decent amount of space is a big plus. It's pricey, but living downtown is still doable."* Not that living a little further out is a problem: *"Boston is a very walkable city. You can live a reasonable distance away and still be within a ten to 15-minute bus or subway journey."*

Another bonus? The compact geography of New England means *"it's easy to hop in the car and have an adventure on the weekend, whether it's hiking in New Hampshire, strolling down Rhode Island's beaches or apple-picking in Vermont."*

Regeneration

Boston has long been associated with 'white shoe' firms and their reputation as strait-laced and somewhat stuffy.

However, the startup boom has seen a steady stream of tech businesses crop up in the city in recent years, transforming Boston's legal scene into *"a highly creative business culture,"* we hear. In the past, such businesses opted for the lure of Silicon Valley's more established technology and media industry, but now that trendy names like TripAdvisor and ZipCar have set up shop in the city, others are following suit. In turn, Boston has attracted the attention of some of the largest national and international firms, including Skadden, Jones Day and DLA Piper.

The modern, youthful ethos of hi-tech industry has trickled into many firms in the area. A Boston-based Goodwin Procter associate said that *"while there definitely remain a lot of partners who wouldn't be caught dead in anything besides a suit, there are many others who wear jeans more often than not."* Associates at Cooley chimed in to tell us that their office *"definitely doesn't have this so-called 'Boston attitude.' People don't take themselves too seriously; it's pretty lighthearted."* That's not to say the quality of candidates these firms seek has dropped, though. *"They really are looking for high achievers."*

Associates in Boston told us that the structure of the city's legal market means there's room to cut your teeth on smallish local matters while also gaining exposure to commercial clients of a national and international scale. With a healthy smattering of Fortune 500 companies, among them Staples and defense giant Raytheon, there's all the usual corporate and commercial litigation work one might expect of a BigLaw firm. This is set to grow in the years ahead, as demonstrated through General Electric's recently-announced plans to relocate its corporate headquarters to Boston. The move *"illustrates the strength and vibrancy of the Greater Boston economy,"* says Choate's chairman John Nadas. *"GE is one of the largest companies in the world. After considering many, many attractive options, GE chose Boston on the announced basis that Boston has the most dynamic and creative ecosystem in the country."* Many firms in Boston also undertake *"a good deal of estate planning and trustee work, much like the smaller firms,"* revealed an associate at Nutter. *"I think it's good that firms have the capacity to address these smaller individual matters."* And then there's the work that arises out of Boston's booming education and healthcare industries.

All in all, interviewees went on to tell us that *"this is a great city for doing interesting work with a little of the pressure taken off you – there's less of a national or global spotlight than in some of the headquarter offices of larger firms in New York."* At the same time, they were keen to note that *"Boston is one of the largest and most competitive legal markets outside New York, but its smaller Bar means that there's a greater sense of community. It's much easier here for juniors to take on leadership roles and be responsible for their own work. From an associate's perspective, that's fantastic for career development."*

Spotlight on Hartford

Hartford, Connecticut isn't just home to one of the largest stone arch bridges in the world: branches of some pretty well-known law firms reside here too, including Axinn Veltrop & Harkrider, Bracewell, Brown Rudnick and Dechert. Many insurance companies have their headquarters in Hartford – the city's not nicknamed the 'Insurance Capital of the World' for nothing – and it's a ripe place for young lawyers looking to get into insurance law. Plenty of other practices flourish here too. Small in size but big in ambition, fast-growing Axinn is ranked by *Chambers USA* as a top practitioner of general commercial litigation, and its Hartford office hosts the bulk of the firm's IP practice too. At bigger players like Brown Rudnick, it's a more complex operation covering practices as diverse as environmental law, government law and real estate. Associates here frequently work with colleagues from several offices at a time. *"At some point during your first few years, they pay for you to fly to another office and get to know your colleagues there. And if you need to be in another office for whatever reason, you can just call ahead and there'll be a room ready."*

Black coat, white shoes, black hat, Cadillac...

"Boston is a white-washed city," said a Goodwin Procter associate. *"So to improve diversity firms here have to fight against those circumstances as well as the lack of inclusion that's been inherent in the practice of law for so long."* At Choate, 82% of associates and a staggering 96% of partners are white. Likewise, Ropes & Gray is your classic firm where *"most partners are white males."* At the time of our research in 2016, 91% of R&G partners and 77% of its associates were white. All hope's not lost however: both of these firms and many of their peers are active on the diversity front, partly spurred by the demand to more accurately reflect their diverse client base. Check out **The Inside View** on each for more diversity stats and details on what they're doing to address the issue.

Here to stay

One benefit of legal life in Boston and New England at large is that *"you can build a long-term career here. The typical view of law firm life in places like New York is that you get there and stick it out for as long as you're willing to put up with the lifestyle sacrifices, and then you leave. It's not like that in Boston. Firms aren't used as a stepping stone with a large number of people leaving after three, four or five years. In fact, at most firms throughout the region you'll see as many sixth, seventh, eighth-year associates as you do juniors. The firms try to grow and develop people."* As one Nutter associate told us: *"To me, that makes a lot more sense. I definitely feel that the firm is more invested in me and that I can forge my own career path. You don't feel lost in some big corporate machine here. In fact, we get a lot more attention and exposure to higher quality work than in the larger offices in New York."*

On chambers-associate.com...
Boston's legal history

California

'The Governator' Arnie Schwarzenegger's famous proclamation that "*California has the ideas of Athens and the power of Sparta*" might be a touch grandiose, but California still boasts the highest population and highest revenues of any state...

THE distinctive perks of California living are pretty well documented: blissful weather, surfing, a laid back attitude and relentless positivity. As the writer Don DeLillo sourly quipped: *"Californians invented the concept of lifestyle. This alone warrants their doom."* Since it birthed the hippie in the 1960s, the state has increasingly combined its trademark brand of Cali-cool with impressive corporate credentials. California's claim to being a modern-day ancient Greece largely rests on the shoulders of the technological philosophers of Silicon Valley and the bronzed gods of Hollywood. Thanks to these industries, the state's GDP now measures up to that of the world's richest countries: in 2014 it was the eighth highest in the world, with $2.312 trillion to its name, beating both Italy and Russia and rapidly approaching Brazil, whose GDP sits at $2.346 trillion.

California cool

Although working in BigLaw is never a picnic, California law firms tend to offer a lighter, brighter lifestyle than their out-of-state counterparts. Our California junior associates tell us that *"instead of the older, stuffy dark-suit atmosphere in New York law firms that you see on TV shows, there's a lighter, brighter feeling here."* In a legacy of the hippies' famed contempt for the neck-tie, Cali-locals like Sheppard Mullin put the casual into dressing business casual – one associate there told us that *"I tend to hide behind my desk in my leggings a lot of the time, and a lot of partners wear jeans every day."* California litigation stalwarts Quinn Emanuel put them to shame in the dress-down stakes, though. Their co-founding partner Bill Urquhart is on record as saying that *"the only dress code we have is that you to have something between your feet and the carpet – and that's because our insurance company requires it!"* The firm's even issued QE-branded flip-flops to summer associates in the past.

Californians are linguistic pioneers, responsible for spreading the 'valley girl' and 'surfer dude' speech pattern stereotypes in the 1980s, and we can blame California for the infiltration of 'like' as a multipurpose conversational filler, as well as other gems like 'hella,' 'totally,' 'awesome,' 'dude,' and the underused 'gnarly.' We wouldn't recommend pulling out any of the above words in court, but words like *"relaxed"* frequently come up in our conversations with junior lawyers over the years, many of whom feel that *"people are more laid back here,"* wherever their firm is headquartered. This could be down to all that glorious vitamin D, part and parcel of a *"climate you can enjoy year-round."* Still, even at coastal offices, *"lawyers are really focused on living their professional lives; it's not like we're at the beach every weekend."*

Indeed, don't get carried away with visions of short working days and long evenings spent lazing on the sand. Perhaps this corporate associate in Gibson Dunn's LA office sums up the Cali approach to lawyering best: *"I leave the office around 7pm and work from home all the time. Most of the people I work with are good at not creating extra stress. They're flexible; they're not going to sweat someone's decision to work from home. You're given a lot of freedom when it comes to how and where you get your work done."* Note that the approach itself may be relaxed and flexible, but lawyers are still working those notorious BigLaw hours all the same. Turns out local lawyers save that sand-between-your-toes feeling for events like Sheppard Mullin's business trial retreat to Surf & Sand Resort on Laguna Beach.

A Tale of Two Cities

California was late to develop compared to other states, which makes sense considering part of its distinctive mythos is that people came there not out of necessity, but for the purposes of self-fulfillment and to put dreams into action. It's been shaped by two successive waves of self-starting, entrepreneurial energy, each of which has its own thriving hub. The first was the flood of movie-makers to Hollywood in the early 20th century. Initially they came to avoid paying Thomas Edison's fees (he had a patent on the movie-making process), as well as for the reliable sunshine and mild climate. As the studios grew through the 1920s and 1930s, writers, directors and technicians flooded in from around the world – with high numbers of displaced Jewish immigrants among their number – to create the world's first and most prolific movie industry.

Today, glamorous Hollywood clients flock to national firms' branches in Century City, the site of a former backlot for 20th Century Fox, for industry-specific services in areas like finance, employment and IP. One associate found the culture in Century City *"more trendy than in our other offices, because when your clients are cool production companies and you've got models and actors coming in, you have a different sort of attitude and interests. It's a very casual, low-key atmosphere."* If it's entertainment-related work that appeals most, check out *Chambers USA*'s top-ranked firms in the area, which include Akin Gump, Loeb & Loeb, Sheppard Mullin, Munger, Gibson Dunn and Davis Wright Tremaine.

Do robots dream of electric sheep?

The second wave of entrepreneurship shaping California's economy started in the 1940s and 50s, when the then dean of Stanford University encouraged graduates and academics to stay in the area to found businesses (this is how Hewlett-Packard got its start). A growing amount of hi-tech entrepreneurs powered by dreams of stardom on a rather smaller kind of screen stuck around, and the area became known as Silicon Valley. According to one anonymous Cali wit, the recipe for Silicon Valley was *"take one great research university, add venture capital, and shake vigorously."* Hollywood's supremacy is increasingly on the wane, but Silicon Valley goes from strength to strength. The speculation-driven industry is prone to booms and busts, but for now it seems to have seen off both the 2000–01 threat of the dot-com bubble burst and the more recent recession.

Stanford still feeds plenty of its hi-tech expertise into Silicon Valley: its graduates are responsible for eBay, Netflix, LinkedIn and Instagram, each of which got its start with dizzying sums of venture capital investment. The Valley has a reputation for throwing billions around in relaxed style, with megabuck deals sealed on a handshake. Law firms targeting the silicon dollar tend to set up outlets in Palo Alto. The area has a distinctive atmosphere: one White & Case junior based there told us that *"we adopt a Silicon Valley mentality, so we work hard and play hard too. People from our New York office make fun of us and say we shouldn't be dressed in business casual, but if you meet a client in suit and tie here they'll laugh you out the room!"*

"People from our New York office make fun of us and say we shouldn't be dressed in business casual."

Quinn Emanuel's Bill Urquhart reports that there has been *"a literal explosion of new tech companies in various hotspots across the country. For example, there is an area called Silicon Beach in LA which has attracted startups like Snapchat, as well as more established hi-tech companies like Google and big internet game companies like Electronic Arts."* The city's location and Hispanic cultural heritage mean that work often has a Latin American slant. Urquhart also tells us that *"our Los Angeles office provides lawyers the rare opportunity to do exciting work in Southern California where people go to relax, head for the beach and lay under palm trees."* As another BigLaw source based in Los Angeles raved, *"within two hours you can go to the desert, the beach or snow-skiing in the mountains."* This might be true on weekends, but as the US's second largest city, Los Angeles inevitably has a frenetic feel. One source felt that *"the best thing about working here is the diversity and richness of the city's culture, and the worst thing hands down is the traffic."*

Over in San Francisco, California's alternative heritage lives on in the form of health foods, organic farming and various eco movements. The state's environmental policies and targets are the strictest in the US – the city bans all its retailers from handing out plastic bags – and it has been named the greenest city in the US and Canada. In a less concrete (and potentially spurious) legacy, one survey found that 63% of Californians actually have hugged a tree. In any case, the area is a center for environmental law and green businesses like solar energy generation. Like LA, San Francisco is home to growing numbers of hi-tech businesses, including internet oversharers' favorites Instagram, Pinterest and Twitter. There's also plenty of corporate and finance work courtesy of the Financial District, home to the headquarters of national players like Wells Fargo, Gap and Levi Strauss.

San Fran has plenty of work for aspiring lawyers, but a move there comes with a mighty price tag. In its recently published National Rent Report, real-estate rental website Zumper found that of the one million active, one-bedroom listings it had analyzed, six of the 20 most expensive US cities for renters were in California. San Francisco and its surrounding areas were deemed the most expensive place to set up camp in the entire country, a position that has pushed up prices south of the Golden Gate City to promote the San Jose and Oakland metros to fourth and sixth place respectively. So while those starting salaries at BigLaw firms appear to be very generous, it's worth bearing in mind those dollars won't stretch as far as they could elsewhere, especially when it comes to housing. And if you're looking to buy? Well, San Francisco is one place where that'll be quite the challenge. The city's real estate market has reached dizzying heights, with the average homeowner's annual income standing at a nationwide high of $147,996. To put this into perspective, the salary required to buy a home in St. Louis, Missouri is $34,778.

Getting schooled

Of California's law school options, Stanford is arguably the most prestigious – it tends to come in the top three in various US law school rankings – and University of California Berkeley is not too far behind. Other respectable showings include UCLA, the University of Southern California (Gould), Loyola and Southwestern. Successful Cali-grads have a host of well-established local law firms to choose from: Orrick, Herrington & Sutcliffe, founded and headquartered in San Francisco, is one of the state's largest and oldest firms, while other prestigious California outfits include Morrison & Foerster (MoFo), litigation giant Quinn Emanuel, Gibson Dunn, and Sheppard Mullin.

There are also a host of boutiques catering to California's key industries, such as top-flight IP boutique Finnegan and property specialists Allen Matkins. And many BigLaw firms from across the US have Cali outposts, often in Silicon Valley or nearby San Francisco to profit from the area's surging tech industry. Los Angeles is also a desirable location thanks to its strong links with the Latin America market, while some large firms like Simpson Thacher use a Palo Alto base to extend their business further west. At this ST office one associate told us: *"We're very much Asia-facing on both the litigation and transactional side. We work on a lot of price-fixing issues with Asian companies."* Elsewhere, Orange County increasingly entices firms with its booming property market.

One for the money

California's government has one of the highest debt burdens in the US – partly a function of the state's 'bad debt' fueled housing crisis. The state's individual income tax system is broken down into ten brackets, and the top rate, at 13.3%, is the highest in the entire country. Economic challenges in recent years have included deep cuts at state government level, a surging birth rate that outstripped job levels, continued stagnant demand for housing in parts of SoCal, and a stronger dollar hurting California's tech exports. Still, sectors of California's economy are booming, and the state continues to lure in big businesses. As Bill Urquhart tells us, *"Northern California wasn't hurt by the recession as much as Southern California because of the strength of the tech industry. Construction is a big part of the Southern California economy. That segment of the economy really suffered. That industry has rebounded. Thankfully, I think the recession for the most part appears to be behind us in both Northern and Southern California."* All the signs point to a positive future for the Golden State. Of all US states, California leads the pack when it comes to revenue growth in the agriculture, manufacturing and technology industries. Workers' pockets have been a big beneficiary of this growth: in 2015 Californians' personal income increased by 6.3%, which was faster than any other US state.

Chicago & The Midwest

The Midwest has a knack for birthing top law firms: five of AmLaw's top ten are locals (DLA Piper, Baker & McKenzie, Jones Day, Sidley Austin, and Kirkland & Ellis), and the region is also the base for other serious national and international players.

MOST of these firms have sprung up in the fertile city ground of Chicago, but Columbus, Cleveland, Cincinnati, Minneapolis and Detroit are also significant legal centers in the Midwest. The region has a lot to offer junior associates, but don't think you can just waltz in unannounced; our BigLaw sources suggested applicants *"have a good explanation for being in the area. Just about everyone here has some kind of familial tie to the state. Firms want you to stay, and if you don't have a clear reason they'll be wondering how long it'll be before you leave for New York or Houston or wherever. That's a generality for Midwest firms. There are out-of-towners, but there's always a link."*

A local link should also set you in good stead in terms of your appreciation of 'Midwestern values,' often a big deal to firms based here – think humility, honesty, unpretentiousness, a hard-working attitude and wholesome Uncle Buck-style family loyalty (minus the urge to imprison miscreant teen boyfriends in the trunk). Lois Casaleggi, senior director of the University of Chicago Law School career services, explains: *"I think the culture inside law firms would be a little different compared to, say, New York. Midwesterners are generally a little more down to earth, friendly and polite. It's just a different vibe. However, the environment is also really hard-working – you're not going to be kicking your feet up."*

Our sources at Midwest firms concurred. Squire Sanders juniors told us that *"our firm's Midwestern in its attitude, meaning that it's much more laid back and low key. That doesn't mean we're not sophisticated or aggressive when we need to be, or capable of pulling off complex deals, but we're also very good-natured and easy to deal with, with no big egos."* An associate at Schiff Hardin felt similarly: *"We value our Midwestern culture, which means we value modesty and humility. We're not looking for showboats – we want people who are motivated to do an excellent job, but who aren't necessarily driven by competition."* Rookie associates felt that the region is a good place to raise children, thanks to relatively low property prices and *"family-oriented"* values that allow for a better work/life balance than in New York.

All things 'go

Home to the world's first skyscraper, a steel-framed high-rise built in 1885, Chicago is an urban jungle to rival any in the world. As America's third-largest city (behind New York and LA), Chicago has a predictably expansive legal market, with a surprisingly big emphasis on tech work. *"When people think about tech, they usually think Silicon Valley, but Chicago has a vibrant tech market that is not always as well known, with companies like Motorola and Groupon, to name just two,"* Casaleggi notes. *"There are a lot of media companies here, old and new. Part of the appeal is that it does a lot of things well. Locally the business community is so diverse and strong, and that feeds into the legal market."* It's a growing industry: in fall 2015 the Quarterly Census of Employment revealed that Chicago's largest county Cook County had notched up a 3.6% rise in employment in professional & technical services. Scientific research & development services grew by 21.1% in the same period, and an additional 6.2% also flocked to the city's computer systems design services sector. The city is also home to big media companies like regional television studios, radio corporations, and major newspaper publishers like Tribune and the now-depleted Sun-Times Media, which once housed Conrad Black's vast international media empire and still owns dozens of local newspapers.

Chicago started out as a blue-collar town, shaped by migrants from all over Southern, Eastern and Western Europe. These roots are evident in its most famous culinary inventions: artery-clogging deep dish pizza and the Chicago hot dog, dressed with mustard, onion and celery salt (add ketchup at your peril). The city's high murder rate – 269 were reported in 2015, up 12.5% on 2014 – topped the charts for US cities in 2015, though there have been strong police attempts to discourage gang violence recently. There's also lots of state money going into beautification projects. Casaleggi tells us that *"being on the lake is such a huge advantage – the water gives the city a different feel and opens up a lot of activities. There are bike paths, running paths, beaches, and you can rent boats. It's a city that is very abundant in green spaces, and there are parks everywhere."* As well as being famously windy, Chicago is also rather chilly, so in winter pedestrians make for the pedways – five miles of underground and overhead walkways that connect the city's downtown.

Charlotte Wager, chief talent officer at Chicago-headquartered firm Jenner & Block, tells us: *"I was struck by Chicago being a modern, metropolitan and sophisticated city with theater, opera, beautiful architecture, museums, parks and the magnificent lakefront, but without some of the stresses that come with living on either coast."* She reports that *"the Chicago legal community is small and close-knit – not necessarily in numbers but in the way it operates – which makes practicing law here all the more enjoyable. It's very supportive."* The Chicago Bar Association is a popular center for lawyerly life in the city, with its wood-burning fireplace, popular lunchroom and full program of social events, including the annual musical comedy revue. The show's been running for more than 90 years, and pun-tastic show titles like 'A Christmas Quarrel,' 'Pay Miserables' and 'The Merry Old Land of Lawz' suggest its wit is evergreen.

Put Your Hands Up 4 Detroit

Defeated by a population decline of more than 60% since its 1950s heyday, Detroit filed the largest-ever municipal bankruptcy case in 2013. But in the past few years the acres of boarded-up and crumbling houses and public buildings have attracted swaths of young professionals and empty-nesters to the city. Value for money and opportunity for investment has proven an attractive lure, and since 2008 the sale of luxury homes has risen by 107%. Detroit now offers a legal scene that stretches beyond foreclosures and bankruptcies, with real estate and emerging company work growing fast. Sarah Staup, director of professional personnel at Detroit-founded Dykema Gossett, tells us: *"We are seeing more and more younger associates living in Detroit. This past recruitment season we had a couple of people who wanted to be here. We wanted to put them in our suburban office* [in Bloomfield Hills] *due to their practice, but they wanted to be down here. Detroit has challenges, but it has growing sectors that are attracting young professionals and art groups."* Part of this is because *"the cost of living is really manageable. If you aspire to own a home, you are able to do that here."* Duane Morris, Foley & Lardner and Pepper Hamilton also have offices in Detroit; elsewhere in Michigan, there's Schiff Hardin and Dykema in Ann Arbor.

Staup goes on to tell us about *"up north, where there's so much natural beauty and all sorts of recreational opportunities. This state is an absolute find for anyone who's into the outdoors. And if you are into sports at all, it's a mecca."* Indeed, in addition to major league teams of the 'big four' variety (baseball, basketball, hockey and football), there's the lake and Michigan's Upper Peninsula, which offer every water-based diversion imaginable. There's also the country's only feather bowling alley in Detroit's Cadieux Cafe. We hear the quirky sport is a niche interest even in its homeland of Belgium.

A sailor went to CCC

The three Cs for a successful legal career in Ohio are Columbus, Cleveland and Cincinnati. Although they don't always boast the same big names as Chicago, each has a bustling legal market. Cleveland, birthplace of Jones Day and Squire Patton Boggs, has suffered from a bad rep in the past. Efforts to renovate the area and bring about an urban renaissance have been ongoing since the 80s, and in spite of ups and downs there are concrete results to suggest that the haters might just be out of touch with the real Cleveland. As one proud associate there said, *"at law school they told us we're one of the biggest legal markets between Chicago and New York."*

The medical center Cleveland Clinic has been ranked as one of the top five hospitals in the US and is widely recognized as a big contributor to Ohio's thriving bioscience industry. The city isn't lagging behind culturally either: a $350 million architectural renovation of the Cleveland Museum of Art was initiated in 2002 with a view toward catering to citizens and tourists, and there's also the Rock n Roll Hall of Fame, designed by top dog of modern architecture I M Pei, on the lakefront, as well as the Playhouse Square, the second-largest performing arts center in the US (right behind the Lincoln Center).

Columbus is the capital of the Buckeye State, and its swing-state politics have attracted an *"unusual number of top political minds,"* says one Ohio State student. Culture is the order of the day in Columbus: the local cuisine is highly revered, and annual music and arts festival ComFest comes highly recommended. Speaking of cuisine, Cincinnati once adopted the moniker 'Porkopolis' for its thriving pork industry in the 19th century – apparently the excess of pork fat that came as a result provided Messrs Procter and Gamble with the means to build a thriving soap business. For the most part, the city's broken free of its porky past and is increasingly a retreat for hipsters setting up microbreweries. Another claim to fame is the Cincinnati Reds, America's first official baseball team.

Money talks

The Midwest has been called America's breadbasket, and indeed its rich soil makes it some of the most lucrative farmland in the world. As well as wheat for your daily loaf, there's soybeans, corn and cattle in abundance. Over the past few years, farmers have been struggling with drought conditions as well as unexpected torrential rain, both of which have prompted them to ramp up the pressure on the government to maintain crop insurance payments. So-called 'ag-gag' laws are another farming legal battleground: these essentially ban journalists and protesters from filming inside agricultural facilities or taking on jobs with the intention of reporting on their findings.

Industry is the other traditional cornerstone of the Midwestern economy, particularly in Michigan, where the economy is driven by the 'big three' automobile manufacturers that have dominated the home-grown scene for nearly a century: Chrysler, Ford and General Motors. Detroit's dramatic rise and decline has become a lesson in the unreliable fortunes of the American motor industry. When times are good, orders surge. When times are bad, potential customers are thin on the ground, and those that remain are more likely to be tempted by the growing variety of foreign imports.

Barack Obama opted to bail out the motor industry in 2009 by handing Chrysler and General Motors billion-dollar loans. Since then, the industry has made an impressive turnaround. Low replacement rates during the recession mean that the average American car is now a grand old age of 11.5 years, an all-time high. This is good news for manufacturers, because as the economy recovers and household wealth grows, the demand for new vehicles is surging. Sarah Staup feels that *"we have finally turned the corner, and there's a positive horizon ahead – we're used to getting tough economic news in Michigan, so we can recover pretty quickly."*

The Midwest as a whole continues to pull out of the recession, and former industrial centers are forging new identities as their inner city areas regenerate and redevelop. Still, there are plenty of long-term challenges to the region's economy. An aging population, combined with a historical resistance to immigration, means the workforce is shrinking, even as the demand for jobs picks up. Meanwhile, the strong dollar is a threat to Chicago's growing tech expertise, and long-term it's hard to be sure that the recovery of the automobile industry will stay on the road to success. For young lawyers, though, the region offers a wide array of international BigLaw options, combined with low house prices, the promise of a livable work/life balance, and a more low-key way of life.

New York & DC

The brightest young lawyers interested in corporate law, litigation or government work flock to New York and DC. Will you be drawn into the melting pot?

NEW YORK

Appetite for a Big Apple

EVERYONE wants to monkey around in the concrete jungle. *"It's got everything: the best food and the most diverse culture of any city. It's the best city in the world."* Those who crave a spot in the heart of the legal action in Manhattan, though, be warned: the location comes at a hefty premium. Even on a BigLaw starting salary of $160,000, rents are a stretch: *"$3,000 a month for a shoebox"* makes us question how Carrie could afford those Manolos.

For those willing to commute, New York's most populated borough, Brooklyn, is a popular place to look. However, with the average price of property now at $700,000, it's no longer the budget location it once was. *"Queens or New Jersey are now the most viable options,"* NYC associates tell us. Partners, with a vastly superior budget and often bigger families, *"tend to live on the Upper East or Upper West sides. There's more open space and the apartments are bigger."*

Gold digga?

In May 1792, 24 stockbrokers signed an agreement outside 68 Wall Street (called the Buttonwood Agreement, as the ink was put to paper under a buttonwood tree) that led to the founding of the New York Stock Exchange (NYSE), today the largest stock exchange in the world. Most, if not all, of the trillions of dollars' worth of financial transactions the exchange hosts are conducted electronically these days, in seconds; but beneath the streets in the vaults of the Federal Reserve Bank of New York, 50 feet below sea level, you'll find more gold bullion than in any other gold repository anywhere on the planet. There are around 530,000 gold bars with a combined weight of 6,700 tons, worth hundreds of thousands of dollars.

The financial services industry employs almost 450,000 people in NYC and accounts for roughly 35% of the city's income. The likes of Goldman Sachs, Morgan Stanley, JPMorgan Chase and Bank of America Merrill Lynch require legions of legal advisers, in pretty much every area of law you can think of, from employment to capital markets, white-collar defense to restructuring and tax. The vast amounts of work provided by banking giants remain a big draw for the largest US and international law firms in Manhattan today, as well as smaller niche players. However, as Bess Sully, director of talent development at New York-based Kaye Scholer, points out: *"Not all New York legal work is dictated by Wall Street. While every kind of finance work, from straightforward banking and finance to IPOs and LBOs, is available, other areas such as IP and environmental law are generating a lot of revenue."*

> ***"Not all New York legal work is dictated by Wall Street."***

Around 10% of the Fortune 500 is headquartered in the city (and more in New York state), including Pfizer, American Express and Time Warner. New York has the highest proportion of overseas employers of any US city: one in ten private sector jobs is with a foreign company based in the city. Foreign law firms, including the UK's magic circle firms (such as Linklaters, Clifford Chance, Freshfields and Allen & Overy) have offices in New York and DC to serve international clients conducting business in the region, as well as to compete in the US market themselves.

No city for old men (or Californians)

We asked junior associates if the New York City cliché of insanely long work hours is accurate. Mostly yes, they replied, but it's not just the city's lawyers who could do with some more downtime. *"To be honest, people in other industries have to work just as hard,"* one associate reflected. They were surely thinking of investment bankers – or perhaps over-worked bartenders – when they added: *"Being an attorney is probably less extreme than other professions."* Still, one admitted that *"working in this city can be a little crazy; being on call 24 hours a day can be a little wearing. We probably work harder than in other parts of the country."* Others agreed: *"In*

California this schedule would be insane. But the cut-throat image is overplayed."

Get on up, stay on the scene

While dreams of becoming a lawyer in New York were dashed for many graduates coming into the industry in the days after the recession, the situation seems to have picked up, with big firms like Cravath, White & Case, and Kaye Scholer all hiring more summers in 2016 than the previous year. That said: *"Junior associates are doing a different kind of work,"* says Bess Sully, director of talent development at Kaye Scholer, noting that at KS at least: *"They're no longer carrying out admin tasks. It's been more cost-effective to outsource those."* Luckily for young lawyers, there's a trend toward *"retaining people longer"* in order to make the most of their experience and expertise. As you'd expect, culture and entertainment-wise New York is *"awesome,"* associates confirmed. There's a seemingly infinite number of visitor attractions and things to do in your spare time; among our sources, the Museum of the City of New York came especially highly recommended, as did the NYC Transit Museum, a little off the beaten track in Brooklyn. Fitness freaks will be pleased to know New York *"is a really active city. It's easy to go running, cycling or just for a wander round Central Park with friends."* And if for some reason you tire of the metropolis, *"you can head out to the beach or mountains,"* both of which are accessible via car or New York's decent public transport infrastructure.

"New Yorkers rule the world."

The final word must go to the associate who described New York as *"overwhelmingly awesome. It sucks you in. It's hard to live here then go somewhere else. New Yorkers rule the world."*

WASHINGTON, DC

Under (a little less) pressure

While a career in Washington, DC carries similar (if not greater) prestige to New York, *"the culture is a little more laid back and less intense,"* according to junior associates based here. *"We are a bit more civilized,"* one junior joked, *"and have a better understanding of balance."* One DC-er noticed that their firm *"isn't buttoned up or formal, and it's a more collegial and family-friendly environment than my friends at New York firms experience."* Part of the reason for this could be the government setting, as one junior put it: *"In the government there is a tradition of valuing quality of life."* Compared to the perceived excesses of BigLaw in New York, *"here there's a happy medium. There isn't a need to sit in your office twiddling your thumbs if you are not doing work. The work ethic here is very, very strong, but it's a targeted effort."* Of course, *"there are still the normal pressures exerted by billing and client needs."*

"Within a matter of months I was on the Hill, advocating directly to congressional staff."

"Being close to the political and legal heart of the nation is an exciting prospect," juniors told us of DC's appeal for young lawyers. Government-related work can be a big part of DC associates' workload, depending on the firm: one associate told of *"representing local government and regional transport authorities on urban policy issues,"* while another told us that *"within a matter of months I was on the Hill, advocating directly to congressional staff and in meetings with members of Congress."* That said, there are certainly places where, as one source put it, *"we talk politics every now and then, but it doesn't overshadow the firm. If you're a corporate lawyer or a litigator here, you can have a completely independent practice."* Increasingly, DC associates have been reporting on *"working for a lot of small businesses and start-ups."*

'The City of Magnificent Intentions'

Charles Dickens coined this nickname for the then fledgling capital city of the United States in 1842 during his tour of the nation. It was only in the late 1860s, following the end of the Civil War, that DC really started to turn intentions into reality. The population grew, peaking at over 800,000 after World War Two thanks to a boom in the number of federal government employees. Today there are over 650,000 people living in DC, though the wider Washington metropolitan area has a population of almost six million. The federal government remains at the heart of the District, employing nearly 240,000 people, according to the Bureau of Labor Statistics. Service industries over the years have flocked to the city to assist those who work in government and, as in the case of many law firms, to help with the very workings of government.

The DC economy didn't suffer as much as other places during the recession, largely because of the steady flow of government-related work that needs to be done, recession or no recession. DC *"is a little insulated,"* NALP's executive director Jim Leipold confirms. *"There is so much regulatory and government work that it is less exposed to the ups and downs in the economy."*

Working for the man

What sort of government-related work do associates do? Here's a snapshot from interviewees at various DC firms:

- *"I did the gamut of healthcare public policy."*
- *"30% of what I do is representing foreign governments on the international law side of things."*
- *"I have been very active in the role of policy interpretation around the health reform bill."*
- *"I work a lot in government investigations, healthcare regulatory and compliance."*
- *"Our group does anything that would be considered FCC [Federal Communications Commission] work."*
- *"Our clients are mutual funds and hedge fund managers. We basically do filings they have to do. We also act as experts for the enforcement and litigation groups."*
- *"We had a lot of post-Fukushima energy regulation to worry about."*
- *"Our clients come from all over the world."*
- *"My work is very DC-based because so many government agencies are here."*
- *"After just a year I'm considered a privacy and data securities specialist, recently working on an FTC regulatory enforcement action."*

House of the rising sum

Washington used to be an attractive option for bright, ambitious lawyers who wanted top-notch work but were put off by New York's sky-high rents and apartment prices. However, DC is less and less cheap these days. *"Over the last ten years, everything has changed,"* one associate said bluntly. *"There's been a dramatic increase in house prices, and rents – high already – have only climbed higher."* Some hoped that *"with new buildings going up all the time, prices should stabilize soon."*

Many DC workers commute in from the surrounding suburbs or even further afield from areas like Maryland and Virginia. Once you're in town it's pretty easy to get around on foot. *"Walkability is brilliant,"* enthused one junior. Many lawyers in the District get around by walking or taking the metro as *"DC's roads have a tendency to be too busy at times,"* though we did hear from one who mainly biked. A King & Spalding source this year described their *"hilariously idyllic walk to work: I'm in the background of most of the tourist photos! We also have this crazy amazing rooftop where we watch fireworks on the fourth of July. The only downside is when you're trying to do a conference call and the White House motorcades go off."*

DC doesn't have the same constant buzz of New York, but there's plenty to keep you entertained if you know where to look. *"Venture away from the Mall and there are great restaurants and bars on the 14th Street corridor,"* one source hinted.

"The only downside is when you're trying to do a conference call and the White House motorcades go off."

The Pacific Northwest

The Pacific Northwest drips coolness: with its grunge heritage and a techy future ahead, is it patently the place to be for young lawyers?

Lately things, they don't seem the same

Seattle: nestled between the picturesque Puget Sound and Lake Washington, flanked by the Olympic and Cascade Mountains, loomed over by Mount Rainier; for many it's synonymous with its old Hendrix and Cobain days, for some it's still reminiscent of jazzy nights with Ray Charles and Quincy Jones. And while these musical legends left a rich legacy in this culturally complex city – as well as some of their old stuff (the Experience Music Project is worth a trip for Cobain's smashed guitars alone) – the city has now put down its broken guitar, emerged gracefully from the grunge period, and got itself on the straight and narrow. So much so that Starbucks is a staple, and even ooze chicness, provided you find the original branch down at Pike Place Market, where they've been spelling customers' names wrong since 1971.

Believe it: today Seattle is a hub for green industry, a model for sustainable development, one of the fastest-growing cities in the country and a major gateway for trade with Asia thanks to its port, the 8th largest in the US. It is home to massive businesses such as Amazon, Starbucks, Boeing, department store Nordstrom and freight forwarder Expeditors International. For obvious reasons, Microsoft is also based here. Time to put down your skinny mocha and do some serious work...

With the lights out, it's less dangerous

Portland – aka the City of Roses – is Oregon's commercial and cultural epicenter. This verdant haven is home to the country's largest wilderness park within city limits, covering a whopping 5,000 acres. It also plays host to the smallest (Mill Ends Park is no more than a two-foot diameter circle). Among Portland's many pull factors are rose gardens, abundant outdoor activities, liberal values, microbreweries and coffee enthusiasm. It has been named the 'Greenest City in America' by Popular Science in 2008, a title Grist surpassed by dubbing it the second greenest city in the world, after Reykjavik. If it's falafel off a cart you're after, Portland is where it's at: both US News & World Report and CNN have named it the best place in the world for street food.

But it's not all pretty flowers and culinary delights. Portland is known for attracting big businesses, most notably athletic and footwear manufacturers: adidas, Nike, Columbia Sportswear, Li Ning (China's largest footwear manufacturer), Hi-Tec Sports and Korkers all call Portland home. KinderCare, Laika, The Original Pancake House, The Spaghetti Factory and Leatherman also reside here.

"Will the last person leaving SEATTLE – turn out the lights."

On April 16, 1971, real estate agents Bob McDonald and Jim Youngren put these words on a billboard near SeaTac International Airport in protest of the phenomenon known locally as the 'Boeing Bust'. The Boeing company had previously established Seattle as a center for aircraft manufacturing, but following the oil crisis and a costly debacle over the Boeing 747, the company suffered and many were forced to leave the area in search of alternative work.

Thankfully the area recovered and underwent a technological revolution as a stream of new software, biotechnology and internet companies led to an economic revival. This began with Microsoft's 1979 move from Albuquerque to nearby Bellevue. Seattle then became home to a number of tech companies, including Amazon, Nintendo of America and T-Mobile USA.

Portland underwent a similar change in the 90s, welcoming computer components manufacturer Intel, which is now one of the area's largest employers. Today Greater Portland is home to more than 1,200 tech companies, which has led to the nickname 'Silicon Forest' in homage to the area's arboreal abundance. Nearby Boise, aka 'The City of Trees' in Idaho, has also seen a rise in technology investment and hi-tech industry in recent years; resident businesses include Hewlett-Packard and Microsoft.

Degrees of knowledge

The Pacific Northwest has a *"somewhat typical legal market in the sense that you'll find practice groups in all traditional legal sectors, including litigation, corporate, real estate and land use, taxation and IP,"* says Paul Danielson, recruiter for BCG Attorney Search. However, the area hasn't escaped the influence of its tech-focused residents. Danielson explains: *"While not on par with the Silicon Valley in terms of relative revenue and the sheer number of tech-based companies, the tech sector's significance to the overall Pacific Northwest economy is what has driven the demand for patent prosecution work historically. While the demand for patent litigation associates and partners has waned recently due to a rash of hiring in the Pacific Northwest which left firms fully staffed on that front, patent prosecution remains strong in these sectors."* With regards to hiring patent litigators though, watch this space, as he explains *"it goes in cycles."*

Danielson further updates us in 2016 confirming that over the past few years *"finance, lending, M&A and litigation have all increased in demand and are very strong at the moment. Litigation is a particularly active market in Seattle right now, so lateral litigation candidates looking to move to Seattle should jump on the opportunity. Taxation work has also ticked up, which is expected at this stage in the market cycle."* He explains this is due to a growth in wealth following the business boom, and then families and businesses responding with tax planning.

> ***"Nearly all openings call for a technical degree in computer science, electronic engineering or physics."***

There's an important caveat to consider for all IP-related opportunities in the region, Danielson warns, particularly at midsized and major firms: *"Nearly all openings call for a technical degree in computer science, electronic engineering or physics, as well as direct experience with things like software, programming, wireless communications and microchip technology."*

There are also plenty of other practice areas thriving in the region at the moment. Danielson notes: *"Portland and Seattle have both enjoyed significant and steady population growth due to the attractiveness of the region from a quality-of-life perspective, and this in turn has driven demand for legal services in real estate and land use, as well as litigation positions that emphasize experience with construction disputes, which we see on a relatively regular basis. There is also plenty of transactional work to be had, as many major brands, manufacturers and retailers are headquartered in the area and nearby."*

While most industry sectors in the Pacific Northwest were mangled by the recession, Danielson says that *"employment has generally come back online at a steady pace."* However, *"overall demand is still depressed compared to pre-crash levels. For instance, housing and real estate jobs have come back considerably relative to their recession lows, but if you zoom out a bit they are still slightly below pre-recession levels."*

Livin' La Vida Legal

We'll be blunt: it rains a lot in Seattle. One Perkins Coie associate called it *"the coolest city with the worst weather."* Despite this, Paul Danielson asserts that *"it is often not as bad as claimed, and many residents prefer it because it contributes to the lush and verdant nature of the local environment."* An associate at K&L Gates (Bill Gates' dad gave the firm its current name) agreed: *"If it didn't rain so much, it wouldn't look like this. When the clouds go away, it's beautiful."* Of course, what's *"not as bad as claimed"* for one person might be just plain awful for another. Danielson presents us with an example: *"During my first year of college in the greater Seattle area, there were over 100 days in a row where it rained at some point, often throughout the entire day. That will get to you after a while."*

> ***"You'd be looked at strangely if you wore a suit to work and weren't going to court."***

The region's renowned *"relaxed"* and *"quirky"* vibe lends itself an *"informal legal atmosphere,"* our sources agreed. A Perkins Coie associate said: *"When I interviewed in other cities, I got taken to the country club, but that just doesn't happen here. It's a very laid back legal environment. People aren't the mythical figures you see at the New York firms, and you'd be looked at strangely if you wore a suit to work and weren't going to court. There's more of an emphasis on a balanced lifestyle too. We have days when we work late, but it's not as regular as in the other legal markets that I've worked in. I like being able to have a life outside of work."*

While you could argue this comes at a price since, historically, salaries in the region have been on average between 20 and 30% lower than in the major legal markets, Danielson notes: *"We have been seeing a small but potentially significant shift in thinking among many firms towards raising their compensation packages, in part to be competitive for top candidates from other markets, but more likely because the economic and population boom in Portland and Seattle have led to a rapid rise in the cost-of-living, particularly housing."* If this happens, then billable hours or billable rates and bonuses will all have to increase. Another thing to consider is that the Pacific Northwest is now targeted by techies working in the Bay Area trying to avoid San Fran and Silicon Valley's super-high rents, which is in turn causing a rise in Portland house prices. This is unlikely to dip again.

Major law schools in Portland include Lewis & Clark, the University of Oregon and Willamette, while Seattle has the University of Washington, Seattle University and Gonzaga University. Cooley, Davis Wright Tremaine, DLA Piper, K&L Gates, Stoel Rives, Sedgwick and Perkins Coie all have a big stake in the region's commercial market, though legal work for local businesses and individuals is often performed by *"solid midsized regional firms or local firms"* because it's a smaller market. Getting hired here isn't a walk in the park, Danielson explains: *"Because the Portland and Seattle areas are so desirable in terms of the quality of life, and because the legal markets are smaller relative to major cities like New York, Chicago, Los Angeles and San Francisco, competition for law firm jobs is fierce. You also see a relatively low turnover at the associate and partner level, because people simply tend to stay put once they are established."*

"Aside from the generally positive credentials like a degree from a prestigious law school, top grades and clerkship experience, Pacific Northwest firms place a high degree of emphasis on having local ties and/or extensive familiarity with the region," he continues. *"A part of this is due to the weather – as lush and beautiful as the region is, a number of recruiting coordinators I have met with from Portland and Seattle firms have stories of lateral associates departing within a year or two after discovering the weather did not agree with them."* Our associate sources agreed, with one saying: *"I think employers look for good grades, but also some sort of connection geographically. Firms are looking for people who are going to stay; that's a big part of it."*

"You also see a relatively low turnover at the associate and partner level, because people simply tend to stay put once they are established."

The Southeast

A steadily recovering banking sector, a growing technology industry and relatively low living costs have seen major cities such as Miami, Atlanta and Charlotte become increasingly diverse and vibrant economic centers...

WITH the headquarters of some of the largest multinationals located in the South East, there is plenty of complex and high-value work on offer in the region. As such, there are plenty of opportunities available for a budding attorney to build an interesting and fulfilling career here, in a less costly environment than is available in New York or Washington up the coast.

Not-so-small-town America

The three major hubs for those looking to embark upon a legal career in the South East are Atlanta, Georgia; Charlotte, North Carolina; and Miami, Florida. Compared to New York, the go-to location for many ambitious young attorneys, these cities are positively deserted, all with populations well below one million. A lower population density has a lot of positives, though, not least the price of real estate and cost of living, both of which are significantly lower than in the great metropolises of Chicago or New York. As one Charlotte-based associate put it: *"Here in the South East you can have all the benefits of living in a big city but with that lovely small town feel to it."* Their smaller size has not stopped these three cities from attracting the attention of many national and multinational companies whose presence helps make local business communities cutting-edge places to work.

City Too Busy To Hate

Atlanta set down roots in 1837 at the intersection of two great railroads. After complete destruction during the Civil War, the city rose from the ashes and, capitalizing on its position as the primary transport hub for the South East, grew into a vibrant cultural and economic center. Excellent rail and highway links enable national businesses here to access markets across the country, while Hartsfield-Jackson Atlanta International airport (the busiest in the world by both passenger volume and aircraft traffic since 1998) opens up the rest of the globe. Atlanta's bustling business community that thrives today is a nod to the city's nickname, coined during the days of the civil rights movement: the City Too Busy To Hate.

Atlanta's transport links have helped its economy become both expansive and very diverse. The city's rail connection remains, as it houses the classification yards of both Norfolk Southern and CSX. Many major companies have their national or international headquarters within the city's metropolitan area, including UPS, Coca-Cola, Delta Air Lines and Home Depot.

Georgia contains the highest concentration of colleges and universities of any of the southern states, and 28% of African Americans in Atlanta hold a bachelors degree, second in the US only to DC at 32%. An abundance of bright young graduates has helped the city to build up thriving media and technology sectors. The city is a major television programming center and home to the headquarters of Cox Enterprises, which owns the nation's third largest cable television service and publishes over a dozen major daily and weekly local newspapers. Other notable television channels based here are Cartoon Network and several CNN subsidiaries.

Although Georgia and Atlanta in particular were badly hit by the financial crash and recession, there have been signs of a steady recovery over the past few years. Many of the jobs created recently have been in the highly paid finance and professional services sectors – areas where legal advice is often required, which is good news for lawyers in the area. Many national and international firms view Atlanta as an essential part of their network of domestic offices, with the likes of Jones Day, DLA Piper and Greenberg Traurig all maintaining offices in the city.

Many perceive southern firms to embody a certain gentility and, as a result, an old-fashioned approach to work. However, we've heard the opposite from associates in Atlanta. *"Our Atlanta office is much more relaxed than the others; it's casual, and you quickly get to know almost everyone in the office,"* said one junior. Compared to the Big Apple, Atlanta's smallish size and less intensive working culture are big selling points to many, but one trade-off is that nights out are not as regular. As a Finnegan associate explained: *"People tend to be a bit older, so they often have a spouse and kids they want to get home to after work. But on weekends we'll invite each other to our kids' birthdays, summer barbecues, that kind of thing."* On the plus side, the cost of living is lower in Atlanta than the likes of New York, and house prices even fell a couple of years ago, meaning that a BigLaw starting salary of $160,000 stretches even further.

The hornet's nest

Charlotte, North Carolina was first incorporated in 1768. Since then it's grown into a major financial market, second only to New York as a US banking center (in terms of the value of assets held). NCNB is still in residence, although it is now in the form of the national headquarters of Bank of America. Until 2008, homegrown banking giant Wachovia also operated out of Charlotte, but that year it was bought by Wells Fargo, and Wachovia's Charlotte office is now home to the East Coast operations of Wells Fargo. *"The presence of these huge national and international banks brings a sophistication to the legal work you don't get in many other regional locations,"* thought an associate at K&L Gates.

Charlotte also plays host to 13 Fortune 500 companies, including Duke Energy and Sonic Automotive. Other major businesses span a huge range of sectors, from television production (Time Warner Cable and Fox Sports 1) to food and drink (Compass Group USA and Coca-Cola Bottling Co. Consolidated). Charlotte is also home to over 240 companies tied to the energy sector, including Babcock & Wilcox, Siemens Energy and Toshiba, earning it the title 'The New Energy Capital'. *"As a city it's making great strides at bringing in new industries,"* said one associate. *"Lots of companies are relocating here, and the economy is really diversifying. I definitely get the impression it's on the up and up – they're building a new railyard and expanding the airport as well."* With that growth comes an increased need for legal services of many different kinds – good news for local lawyers.

This isn't all that commends a legal career in Charlotte, however; there's also the *"beautiful weather, great travel opportunities and great universities,"* a local source pointed out. The city has all the amenities one might expect: *"Plenty of shows, plays and art museums. And lots of upmarket stores like Armani and Chanel. The restaurants really are fantastic too."* The cost of living is low, with one associate enthusing: *"On a BigLaw starting salary you can live like a king in Charlotte! Join the best athletics club, eat out every night and even afford to drive around in a brand-new BMW!"* Another thought: *"If you work in a regional office here of a firm with a global presence, you get the best of both worlds. It's easy to maintain a work/life balance, and you get to draw upon resources from all across the world."* Our sources were all of the opinion that *"the city is definitely recovering from the hit the banking sector took in 2008. Right now, Charlotte is hiring!"*

Welcome to Miami

Miami was founded in 1896 and grew rapidly. The late 20th century, following the Cuban Revolution and upheaval across the Caribbean and Latin America, saw an influx of wealthy Cubans and others from the region. Today, Miami is a multicultural and colorful international, financial and cultural center whose growth has outpaced the national average in the past year. As a result, the city has continued to attract a wide range of businesses and corporations from around the world, and household names like American Airlines, Office Depot and Motorola all have their headquarters here. Miami is very closely intertwined with the Spanish-speaking nations of the Caribbean and Latin America, and it has a very large population of native Spanish speakers, second in size only to El Paso, Texas. Many multinationals have taken advantage of these language skills and ease of access and established their Latin American headquarters in the city, including Western Union, Microsoft and Canon.

As a result, Miami has developed a very diverse professional services industry – perfect for an aspiring attorney seeking a varied and challenging career. According to an associate at Holland & Knight, *"Miami is THE legal city in Florida. The reason is that it's culturally vibrant and very international – especially because of the Spanish-speaking influences."* The city is a thriving trade hub, with the Port of Miami and Miami International Airport some of the busiest ports of entry in the country. Tourism also sucks in money, and one in seven of the world's cruise passengers sets off from Miami.

Putting down roots

South Eastern natives could not speak more highly of the atmosphere and working culture common to firms and offices in the region. As one associate explained: *"We're expected to cope with complex matters and to produce great work, but there's more of a balance. No one's working an 80-hour week like some in New York. I think possibly it's something to do with that traditional Southern hospitality. It's really just an ability to relate to others and to understand where they're coming from."* Also, being based in a smaller urban community means that being an attorney still carries the kind of weight more common a century ago. *"As a lawyer you're a well-respected member of the community. This carries a certain level of prestige though also big expectations."*

This sense of community and pleasant atmosphere often makes it easier for associates to stay at a firm long-term.

Employers *"expect you to work hard and put the hours in, but they know family is important and respect that. They allow you to reach your own balance,"* said one associate, while another told us: *"I work with a lot of parents and, say, if their kid had a soccer game then, barring the imminent closing of a major deal, they can get there and log back in later when it suits them."* Our sources felt the emphasis is *"definitely on the long-term. They want you to stay and put down roots. The scales tip in favor of people staying put for the seven or eight years it might take to make partner, rather than heading up and out."*

So, you're set on a career in the South East. What next?

"You really need to be able to demonstrate a commitment not just to the law and the firm, but to the city you plan to be based in," thought our associate sources. *"Firms here want people to stay, not head off after a few years."* In order to demonstrate you're serious about a certain city, it *"would be best to attend law school in that state – unless, of course, you're at a top-tier firm elsewhere."* One associate urged applicants *"to summer down here at a law firm or intern in another local industry – either is very attractive to firms. Explore other options as well, such as clerking or pro bono work. It will really give you a chance to see what we're all about and why people love it here so much!"*

"Miami is THE legal city in Florida. The reason is that it's culturally vibrant and very international especially because of the Spanish-speaking influences."
– Holland & Knight associate

Texas

With its harsh criminal punishment and strident self defense laws, the South gets a lot of stick for its approach to law enforcement. Read on to discover why so many young lawyers look beyond the stereotypes and have 'gone to Texas' for an exciting and fulfilling legal career.

Everything is bigger in Texas...

...SO they say, and not just with regard to the intimidating food portions. Land in Texas and the South is cheaper than elsewhere, particularly in contrast to Chicago and New York, making the area popular with big families; playgrounds in Texas now bustle with an above-average number of kids. As Karen Sargent of the career services office at Southern Methodist University notes: *"Texas is a great place for young families. There are excellent school districts and lots of ways to get involved with the community. It's bringing people in from all over the world."* For a state that often receives bad press for its conservative values, you may be surprised to learn that San Antonio, Texas' second biggest city, boasts the largest community of gay parents in the US.

The state is welcoming to more than just those who want to settle down. *"Houston's a great place to live for young people,"* an associate at Baker Botts in Houston attested. *"You can live close to the office and enjoy a short commute and relatively low cost of living. Generally, younger folks might rent an apartment close in for a bit, then look for a house with a yard and a few bedrooms when they want to start a family."* Already the state's biggest city, Houston has been a popular destination for young attorneys in the past few years. As an associate at Bracewell stipulated: *"I think Houston has garnered a lot more national recognition as a good place to live with a good legal market, since we weathered the recession better than some cities. In the past it might have seemed weird for people to move to Texas if they didn't already have connections with the state, but now it's completely normal."*

An abundance of investment opportunities has bred pretty healthy legal markets. Dallas and Houston are two of the largest markets in the country, with the Dallas/Fort Worth area housing more than 10,000 corporate HQs, more than anywhere else in the States. As such, Texas firms have opened their doors to a flood of lateral hires over the past few years. One Haynes & Boone associate told us: *"There's been a lot of change in the Houston market over the last few years, with many national and international firms opening up here. We've seen people leaving the traditional Texan firms to go to them, so there's been more in the way of turnover than normal."* Since 2010, Latham & Watkins, Sidley Austin, Quinn Emanuel, Kirkland & Ellis, Arnold & Porter, K&L Gates, Reed Smith, and Katten Muchin have all launched Houston branches. Longstanding Texan firms are increasingly under pressure to up their game since young associates looking to start their careers now have a lot more choice of where to go.

Houston and Dallas rank among the highest-paying metropolitan areas in the country for lawyers, and most associates in Texas can expect to earn the same as their New York counterparts. Since the state doesn't collect individual income tax, however, the standard BigLaw salary goes a lot further here: according to a recent CNN survey, a salary of $160,000 in Dallas gets you the same buying power as someone raking in $374,772 in New York. Inevitably, the state's social services have suffered from these low tax rates, but for young lawyers they're highly alluring.

But it's not just lawyers that are falling for the Lone Star State. Despite the recent plummet in oil prices, Texas remains a popular destination for tradesmen, professionals, families... anybody in fact. In a recent survey by the US Census Bureau, the state housed eight of 2015's top 20 US counties when measured by population gain. According to the Texas A&M University Real Estate Center, swelling numbers have pushed Texas' median home price up by 37% in the past decade, topping out at $189,000 in January 2016. Still, living in Texas remains a steal compared to the likes of LA or New York.

Oh my gush!

A thick black soup rained down on Texas and the South in the early 20th century and continues to shape the economic landscape to this day. The oil discoveries of the so-called Gusher Age fueled a meteoric rise in the area's fortunes, and these days a number of high-profile petroleum companies are based in the state, among them ExxonMobil, ConocoPhillips, Valero, Halliburton and Marathon Oil. These Fortune 500s generate not only power but also a healthy check for lawyers, with energy work a huge component of many local firms' business.

The boom time may well be up in this respect, though. Due to an increasing global supply and falling demand, oil prices plummeted by nearly 66% in 2015, and the number of actively drilling rigs decreased by 75%. The state produces more than a third of the United States' total oil output, and such disparaging figures posed a huge blow to the sector, with employment dropping by 19.4% in 2015. Still, such fluctuations bode well for the state's legal workforce, prompting a rise in bankruptcy, restructuring and employment-related work. Amanda Kelly, manager of attorney recruitment at Haynes and Boone, remains optimistic: *"Despite the downturn in energy prices, the Texas economy is still robust. For law school students the array of jobs available here, coupled with the low cost of living, continues to make Texas very enticing."* Karen Sargent of SMU chimes in to note that *"a number of North-Eastern schools are now bringing their students down here to recruit."*

Whatever happens on that front, the energy sector isn't Texas' only pull-factor. As Kelly points out: *"Many people don't realize that Texas is second only to New York in the number of Fortune 1000 company headquarters. Our firm serves 20% of the Fortune 500 corporations in a wide variety of industries, including energy, technology, aviation, transportation and healthcare so we are diversified and staying busy. Right now, for example, real estate has ramped up nicely, and a good amount of our work is coming in from outside Texas, especially on the IP side."* Sargent adds: *"I'd say intellectual property law was originally the rocket docket in East Texas – we have a US patent and trademark office opening in Dallas now, and IP is a big focus of our law school. Obviously energy is big here, but that ebbs and flows with the economy. On the corporate side, we're a center for some of the largest corporations in the country, and that brings in a big deal of M&A work. Law firms are now moving into the Dallas area for IP and transactions, where they'd previously moved to Houston for energy."*

Gone to Texas

The Panic of 1819 saw the first wave of mass migration to Texas. Droves of Americans flocked to the state with crippling debts hard on their heels, leaving only the simple message 'Gone To Texas,' or 'GTT,' fixed to their doors. Today it's lawyers and other corporate workers who are relocating to the Lone Star State en masse: since the millennium, one million more people have moved to Texas from other states than have left, with many seeking out a cheaper way of life and a less regulated climate in which to do business.

As a result, Texas' traditionally resource-fueled economy has become increasingly tech-oriented as the likes of Dell and AT&T plant HQs in the state; many have opened operations in The Silicon Hills of Austin in particular, including Facebook, eBay, Google and Apple. To maintain its competitive edge in a time of fast-developing technology and fickle alliances, certain cities have resorted to facelifts. *"San Antonio, for example, is a very family-oriented city,"* a Jackson Walker associate told us, *"but there's a growing culture of nightlife benefiting from the growing number of tech firms bringing young professionals into the city."*

"Dallas is now drawing in young people who are attracted to the economy and are moving into all the new developments," Karen Sargent tells us. *"They're moving into areas that are becoming heavily populated with young people, and they're having a good time."* The city has been investing in its Arts District and green spaces in particular; Houston is likewise intent to create a greener, more attractive city, spending more than $6 billion on regeneration projects over the past 15 years. *"Houston has really been developing its downtown area,"* an associate at Baker Botts confirmed. *"Discovery Green park has blossomed into a popular spot, hosting events and music to draw people down at weekends. They've made an effort to make it a really nice place."* And then there's the capital: *"I think Austin is probably the best place to be living in Texas right now,"* said a Baker Botts associate based there. *"It really lives up to its slogan, 'Keep Austin Weird.' There's a great music scene and great food, and it's really lively. I think a lot of it has to do with the University of Texas being here, so it's more collegey."*

Ask a Texan about life in the South and they'll tell you it gets hotter than a honeymoon hotel. Starched collars are bound to wilt in the tropical warmth, but apparently Houston's got an innovative way to beat the summer heat: *"It's really brutal, but we've got an air-conditioned tunnel system downtown – all the offices are connected underground, with restaurants, dry cleaners and so on. It's like a ghost town above ground because you can go straight from your car to the office."*

Law and border

So the South has come a long way to cast off its image as resource-rich and intellect-sparse; it has also largely shifted the racial demographics which dominated up until the 1980s. While it's true that Southern cities were the domain of white men in the days of oil, the past three decades have seen the population become far more diverse.

Houston boasts the title of America's most ethnically diverse metropolitan region, pipping even New York to the post. Its proximity to the Mexican border has seen the Lone Star try to protect itself from Mexican immigration and influence, historically pushing for insularity in the face of progression, but like its world-famous TexMex fusion, the cultures have largely come to coexist. And with the immigration of Latinos, Asians and African-Americans over the past few decades, the state has become a melting pot of cultures from all corners of the globe. These changing demographics have led some to speculate whether Texas might eventually become a blue state politics-wise.

What can you expect of life as a lawyer in Texas and the South?

Our interviewees in Texas and the South have long been quick to sing the praises of southern culture, telling us a big part of that is respecting people's personal lives outside of work. *"We have a very family-friendly environment,"* an associate at Jackson Walker said. *"When we have social events we try to involve spouses whenever possible, and I feel like the firm respects my personal time. You're expected to work hard and provide excellent client service, but I definitely feel like the partners and other attorneys want me to enjoy my family time, to be a well-rounded person and get involved with community. The attitude here is that that's the right thing to do."*

According to an associate from Waller: *"In the South there's a greater attention to form and decorum. If you're a jackass around here, you ain't gonna last long."* It's fitting that 'Texas' originates from the word 'tejas', which means 'friends' in the Caddo language. But friendliness doesn't detract from the serious work Southern lawyers do. When we asked Karen Sargent, of SMU, if practicing law in the South was more laid back than in New York, she replied: *"It's more about civility. The attorneys here all know each other and their reputation is on the line at all times. They make sure to maintain civility in the legal profession."*

The emphasis on a life outside of work doesn't necessarily mean you'll have fewer billables in the South. The big local firms in Texas – Haynes and Boone, Baker Botts and Bracewell – all have 2,000 hour billing targets, the same target that DLA Piper in New York, Katten Muchin in Chicago, Irell & Manella in LA and Hunton & Williams in Richmond all set their associates. (In fact, you can find firms in those high-octane markets with even lower billing targets: Dechert and Epstein juniors, for example, are set 1,950 hours each.) Granted, working for Haynes and Boone or Baker Botts won't be the same as slugging it out at the traditional New York firms, many of which set no targets because it's assumed juniors will fly past them anyway, but it's worth noting that at firms like Haynes and Boone and Bracewell associates aren't compensated on the lockstep scale favored by NYC firms if they fall short of their targets. At Bracewell there's a reduced compensation track, and at Haynes juniors told us they were put on *"the old Texas compressed scale"* if they didn't rack up 2,000.

Index of leading employers by US state

Below is a listing of law firms by the US States where they are ranked in *Chambers USA*

Connecticut

Delaware

District of Columbia

Florida

Georgia

Idaho

Illinois

Louisiana

Maryland

Massachusetts

Michigan

Minnesota

Nevada

New Hampshire

New Jersey

New York

Utah

Virginia

Washington

Wisconsin

Diversity figures among the firms in *Chambers Associate*. Read the firm's Inside View for the full picture.

Firm	Women partners	Women associates	Ethnic minority partners	Ethnic minority associates	LGBT partners	LGBT associates
Akin Gump	19.0%	43.2%	12.4%	19.5%	2.1%	2.4%
Allen & Overy	20.0%	38.0%	10.0%	31.9%	12.5%	6.0%
Alston & Bird	22.8%	41.7%	7.8%	29.6%	2.9%	5.3%
Arnold & Porter	20.4%	50.5%	11.6%	24.1%	4.4%	7.0%
Axinn	12.5%	33.0%	0.0%	37.0%	4.8%	8.1%
Baker & McKenzie	28.0%	50.0%	10.0%	22.0%	0.9%	2.0%
Baker Botts	19.0%	40.1%	9.9%	23.1%	2.1%	2.7%
Bracewell	22.1%	46.4%	7.8%	18.5%	0.6%	1.9%
Brown Rudnick	15.0%	49.0%	Not given	Not given	Not given	Not given
Cadwalader	17.9%	39.3%	10.8%	30.6%	1.2%	3.6%
Cahill	20.0%	44.0%	7.0%	18.0%	6.0%	1.0%
Chadbourne	15.8%	38.5%	8.4%	20.5%	2.1%	1.0%
Choate	19.0%	44.0%	4.0%	18.0%	3.0%	6.0%
Cleary Gottlieb	19.0%	49.0%	12.0%	34.0%	5.0%	7.0%
Clifford Chance	10.0%	47.0%	19.0%	41.0%	1.0%	4.0%
Cooley	22.4%	52.9%	11.9%	24.0%	1.9%	2.0%
Cozen O'Connor	25.0%	52.0%	8.0%	21.0%	1.5%	4.0%
Cravath	18.0%	39.0%	7.0%	20.0%	4.0%	4.0%
Crowell	22.3%	58.4%	9.7%	31.2%	1.1%	3.2%
Curtis	10.7%	42.4%	19.7%	27.2%	5.4%	1.7%
Davis Polk	19.0%	42.0%	10.0%	32.0%	2.0%	7.0%
Debevoise	18.7%	50.0%	10.3%	32.9%	3.7%	5.0%
Dechert	14.5%	42.9%	6.8%	24.3%	3.0%	2.0%
DLA Piper	20.4%	43.1%	12.6%	26.8%	1.2%	1.6%
Duane Morris	23.6%	39.2%	9.0%	16.9%	1.2%	1.3%
Dykema	28.0%	60.0%	8.0%	25.0%	2.0%	1.0%
Epstein	27.0%	57.0%	14.0%	10.0%	Not given	Not given
Fenwick & West	20.4%	41.8%	16.8%	38.3%	1.8%	3.0%
Finnegan	24.0%	43.0%	13.0%	35.0%	2.0%	2.0%
Fish & Richardson	20.0%	29.0%	13.0%	35.0%	2.0%	1.0%
Fitzpatrick	16.0%	43.0%	7.0%	20.0%	1.0%	Not given
Foley & Lardner	19.0%	42.0%	8.0%	23.0%	1.0%	5.0%
Fox Rothschild	24.0%	45.0%	7.0%	19.0%	1.0%	2.0%
Freshfields	22.0%	50.0%	14.0%	23.0%	Not given	Not given
Fried Frank	15.0%	43.0%	40.0%	19.0%	1.0%	4.0%
Gibbons	20.0%	42.0%	6.0%	18.0%	2.0%	4.0%
Gibson Dunn	17.5%	44.3%	9.6%	24.8%	1.9%	5.7%

Firm	Women partners	Women associates	Ethnic minority partners	Ethnic minority associates	LGBT partners	LGBT associates
Goodwin Procter	24.0%	50.0%	7.0%	25.0%	2.0%	4.0%
Goulston & Storrs	19.0%	53.0%	2.0%	20.0%	3.0%	5.0%
Greenberg Traurig	22.0%	49.0%	12.0%	21.0%	Not given	Not given
Hangley	29.0%	41.0%	Not given	Not given	Not given	Not given
Harris, Wiltshire & Grannis	25.0%	60.0%	0.0%	0.0%	9.0%	13.0%
Haynes and Boone	20.0%	40.0%	11.0%	29.0%	2.0%	2.0%
Hogan Lovells	25.0%	50.0%	9.0%	26.0%	2.5%	3.0%
Holland & Knight	23.0%	48.0%	12.0%	20.0%	3.0%	1.0%
Hughes Hubbard	23.0%	48.0%	8.0%	30.0%	1.0%	4.0%
Hunton & Williams	17.4%	47.7%	9.4%	15.3%	0.7%	2.0%
Irell & Manella	9.0%	33.0%	16.0%	20.0%	2.0%	5.0%
Jackson Walker	22.0%	44.0%	13.0%	27.0%	1.0%	2.0%
Jenner & Block	26.8%	41.3%	7.2%	19.9%	4.7%	11.7%
Jones Day	23.4%	46.5%	9.7%	20.1%	Not given	Not given
K&L Gates	Not given	Not given	Not given	Not given	Not given	Not given
Kasowitz	23.0%	44.0%	11.0%	16.0%	1.0%	4.0%
Katten Muchin	23.8%	45.0%	7.1%	21.4%	1.1%	2.5%
Kaye Scholer	19.0%	50.0%	6.0%	22.0%	2.0%	2.0%
Kilpatrick Townsend	23.2%	39.8%	7.3%	29.0%	2.0%	2.2%
King & Spalding	22.7%	46.9%	9.0%	16.0%	Not given	Not given
Kirkland & Ellis	23.2%	39.8%	7.3%	29.0%	2.0%	2.2%
Kramer Levin	13.0%	46.0%	7.4%	14.0%	3.2%	4.1%
Latham & Watkins	21.0%	43.0%	8.0%	19.0%	2.0%	4.0%
Linklaters	16.7%	45.0%	11.9%	38.0%	4.8%	6.5%
Lowenstein	Not given	Not given	Not given	Not given	Not given	Not given
Marshall Gerstein	26.0%	38.0%	7.0%	12.0%	2.0%	0.0%
Mayer Brown	18.0%	39.2%	7.8%	21.6%	2.1%	2.2%
McGuireWoods	18.7%	43.5%	6.3%	17.9%	0.5%	0.6%
Milbank	13.6%	44.0%	12.8%	31.2%	1.8%	4.0%
Mintz Levin	22.3%	48.9%	14.8%	20.3%	Not given	Not given
Morgan Lewis	22.5%	52.3%	7.5%	24.5%	2.3%	3.5%
Morrison & Foerster	22.0%	46.0%	14.0%	32.0%	3.0%	5.0%
Munger Tolles	23.3%	39.8%	19.8%	22.7%	3.5%	6.3%
Nixon Peabody	21.1%	51.1%	8.1%	23.1%	3.3%	4.4%
Norton Rose Fulbright	22.0%	44.0%	8.0%	23.0%	Not given	Not given
Nutter	29.0%	33.0%	3.0%	10.0%	1.0%	2.0%
O'Melveny & Myers	17.4%	44.1%	9.2%	27.4%	3.3%	5.5%
Orrick	20.0%	47.0%	21.0%	37.0%	3.0%	5.0%
Patterson Belknapp	16.0%	49.5%	15.6%	15.6%	8.0%	6.3%
Paul Hastings	21.3%	45.0%	11.1%	31.7%	2.8%	1.4%
Paul, Weiss	23.0%	38.0%	11.0%	22.0%	5.0%	6.0%

Firm	Women partners	Women associates	Ethnic minority partners	Ethnic minority associates	LGBT partners	LGBT associates
Pepper Hamilton	21.0%	45.0%	8.0%	18.0%	2.0%	3.0%
Perkins Coie	23.1%	45.0%	11.2%	24.9%	2.8%	3.6%
Pillsbury	20.7%	43.1%	10.8%	29.6%	4.0%	5.1%
Proskauer	17.0%	45.0%	5.0%	21.0%	1.0%	3.0%
Reed Smith	22.0%	50.0%	10.0%	22.0%	Not given	Not given
Ropes & Gray	25.0%	45.0%	9.0%	23.0%	3.0%	6.0%
Schulte Roth	13.0%	43.0%	10.0%	28.0%	2.0%	2.0%
Sedgwick	30.0%	50.0%	13.0%	29.0%	2.0%	1.0%
Seward & Kissel	9.0%	46.0%	7.0%	15.0%	N/A	1.0%
Shearman & Sterling	18.0%	37.6%	9.1%	34.3%	1.8%	5.8%
Sheppard Mullin	17.6%	47.2%	8.9%	36.5%	5.3%	2.13%
Sidley Austin	23.3%	48.7%	9.9%	26.1%	2.4%	3.8%
Simpson Thacher	20.1%	41.7%	8.4%	27.4%	1.9%	3.9%
Skadden	20.0%	45.0%	9.0%	31.0%	1.0%	5.0%
Snell & Wilmer	16.0%	32.3%	9.9%	16.5%	1.4%	0.0%
Squire Patton Boggs	22.0%	37.0%	15.0%	19.0%	Not given	Not given
Sterne Kessler	27.0%	28.0%	26.0%	27.0%	2.0%	1.0%
Stroock	18.0%	39.0%	7.3%	21.0%	1.0%	2.7%
Sullivan & Cromwell	20.0%	38.0%	9.0%	24.0%	6.0%	5.0%
Thompson & Knight	26.5%	39.0%	5.4%	20.8%	Not given	Not given
Vedder Price	16.0%	41.0%	10.0%	23.0%	Not given	Not given
Venable	24.5%	51.1%	8.3%	19.8%	0.5%	2.2%
Vinson & Elkins	14.0%	38.0%	8.0%	21.0%	4.0%	2.0%
Waller	17.0%	36.0%	3.6%	13.2%	Not given	Not given
Weil	21.0%	51.0%	9.0%	27.0%	2.0%	3.0%
White & Case	17.0%	49.0%	21.0%	38.0%	1.0%	3.0%
Wiley Rein	25.0%	55.0%	11.0%	22.0%	2.0%	0.0%
Willkie Farr	14.5%	46.1%	8.7%	21.2%	4.3%	2.7%
WilmerHale	25.4%	46.0%	9.1%	21.8%	1.5%	3.5%
Winston & Strawn	22.0%	43.0%	8.0%	22.0%	1.0%	5.0%

The *Chambers USA* Awards for Excellence 2016

Award 1

Antitrust

Shortlist:

Dechert LLP
Hausfeld LLP
Latham & Watkins LLP
Simpson Thacher & Bartlett LLP
Skadden, Arps, Slate, Meagher & Flom LLP
Weil, Gotshal & Manges LLP
White & Case LLP

Winner: Simpson Thacher & Bartlett LLP

Award 2

Bankruptcy

Shortlist:

Brown Rudnick LLP
Jones Day
Kirkland & Ellis LLP
O'Melveny & Myers LLP
Pachulski Stang Ziehl & Jones LLP
Quinn Emanuel Urquhart & Sullivan, LLP

Winner: Jones Day

Award 3

Construction

Shortlist:

Farella Braun + Martel LLP
Jones Day
Kilpatrick Townsend & Stockton LLP
Peckar & Abramson, P.C.
Thompson Hine LLP
Varela, Lee, Metz & Guarino

Winner: Kilpatrick Townsend & Stockton LLP

Award 4

Corporate Crime & Gov't Investigations

Shortlist:

Covington & Burling LLP
Debevoise & Plimpton LLP
Gibson, Dunn & Crutcher LLP
Jones Day
Kirkland & Ellis LLP
Quinn Emanuel Urquhart & Sullivan, LLP
Ropes & Gray LLP

Winner: Gibson, Dunn & Crutcher LLP
Client Service: Ropes & Gray LLP

Award 5

Corporate/M&A

Shortlist:

Cravath, Swaine & Moore LLP
Davis Polk & Wardwell LLP
Latham & Watkins LLP
Skadden, Arps, Slate, Meagher & Flom LLP
White & Case LLP
Wilson Sonsini Goodrich & Rosati

Winner: Skadden, Arps, Slate, Meagher & Flom LLP

Award 6

Employee Benefits & Executive Compensation

Shortlist:

Cleary Gottlieb Steen & Hamilton LLP
Davis Polk & Wardwell LLP
Debevoise & Plimpton LLP
Groom Law Group
Latham & Watkins LLP

Winner: Latham & Watkins LLP

Award 7

Energy/Projects: Oil & Gas

Shortlist:

Baker Botts LLP
Caldwell Boudreaux Lefler
King & Spalding LLP
Latham & Watkins LLP
Steptoe & Johnson LLP
Vinson & Elkins LLP

Winner: Vinson & Elkins LLP

Award 8

Energy/Projects: Power (including Renewables)

Shortlist:

Chadbourne & Parke LLP
Latham & Watkins LLP
Milbank, Tweed, Hadley & McCloy LLP
Morgan, Lewis & Bockius LLP
Skadden, Arps, Slate, Meagher & Flom LLP
Steptoe & Johnson LLP

Winner: Chadbourne & Parke LLP

Award 9

Environment

Shortlist:

Arnold & Porter LLP
Beveridge & Diamond PC
Crowell & Moring LLP
Hunton & Williams LLP
Latham & Watkins LLP
Sidley Austin LLP

Winner: Beveridge & Diamond PC

Award 10

Finance

Shortlist:

Cahill Gordon & Reindel LLP
Cleary Gottlieb Steen & Hamilton LLP
Cravath, Swaine & Moore LLP
Davis Polk & Wardwell LLP
Kirkland & Ellis LLP
Latham & Watkins LLP
Simpson Thacher & Bartlett LLP
Weil, Gotshal & Manges LLP

Winner: Davis Polk & Wardwell LLP

Award 11

Financial Services & Securities Regulation

Arnold & Porter LLP
BuckleySandler LLP
Covington & Burling LLP
Davis Polk & Wardwell LLP
Morgan, Lewis & Bockius LLP
Sidley Austin LLP
Sullivan & Cromwell LLP
WilmerHale

Winner: Sidley Austin LLP

Award 12

Healthcare

Epstein Becker & Green PC
Hogan Lovells US LLP
Hooper Lundy & Bookman PC
Jones Day
McDermott Will & Emery LLP
Proskauer Rose LLP

Winner: Hogan Lovells US LLP

Award 13

Insurance

Shortlist:

Covington & Burling LLP
Debevoise & Plimpton LLP
Jones Day
Latham & Watkins LLP
Simpson Thacher & Bartlett LLP
Squire Patton Boggs
Sutherland Asbill & Brennan LLP

Winner, Insurer: Debevoise & Plimpton
Winner, Policy Holder: Latham & Watkins LLP

Award 14

Intellectual Property

Shortlist:

Fross Zelnick Lehrman & Zissu PC
Irell & Manella LLP
Kirkland & Ellis LLP
Morrison & Foerster LLP
Quinn Emanuel Urquhart & Sullivan, LLP
Sidley Austin LLP

Winner: Kirkland & Ellis LLP
Client Service: Sidley Austin LLP

Award 15

International Trade

Shortlist:

Arnold & Porter LLP
Cassidy Levy Kent LLP
Covington & Burling LLP
Hogan Lovells US LLP
King & Spalding LLP
Steptoe & Johnson LLP

Winner: Covington & Burling LLP

Award 16

Investment Funds

Shortlist:

Cleary Gottlieb Steen & Hamilton LLP
Fried, Frank, Harris, Shriver & Jacobson LLP
Kirkland & Ellis LLP
Paul, Weiss, Rifkind, Wharton & Garrison LLP
Proskauer Rose LLP
Willkie Farr & Gallagher LLP

Winner: Cleary Gottlieb Steen & Hamilton LLP
Client Service: Fried, Frank, Harris, Shriver & Jacobson LLP

Award 17

Labor & Employment

Shortlist:

Gibson, Dunn & Crutcher LLP
Jones Day
Morgan, Lewis & Bockius LLP
Ogletree, Deakins, Nash, Smoak & Stewart, PC
Proskauer Rose LLP
Seyfarth Shaw LLP

Winner: Morgan, Lewis & Bockius LLP

Award 18

Privacy & Data Security

Shortlist:

DLA Piper LLP (US)
Hogan Lovells US LLP
Morrison & Foerster LLP
Ropes & Gray LLP
Wiley Rein LLP
ZwillGen PLLC

Winner: Morrison & Foerster LLP

Award 19

Product Liability

Shortlist:

Bowman and Brooke LLP
Covington & Burling LLP
King & Spalding LLP
Quinn Emanuel Urquhart & Sullivan, LLP
Sidley Austin LLP
Venable LLP
Wheeler Trigg O'Donnell LLP
Williams & Connolly

Winner: Williams & Connolly
Client Service: Covington & Burling LLP

Award 20

Real Estate

Shortlist:

Dechert LLP
Gibson, Dunn & Crutcher LLP
Greenberg Traurig, LLP
Kirkland & Ellis LLP
Simpson Thacher & Bartlett LLP
Stroock & Stroock & Lavan LLP
Sullivan & Cromwell LLP

Winner: Sullivan & Cromwell LLP
Client Service: Simpson Thacher & Bartlett LLP

Award 21

Tax

Shortlist:

Caplin & Drysdale, Chartered
Latham & Watkins LLP
Miller & Chevalier Chartered
Morrison & Foerster LLP
Simpson Thacher & Bartlett LLP
Skadden, Arps, Slate, Meagher & Flom LLP

Winner: Miller & Chevalier Chartered

Award 22

Litigation: Business Trial Lawyers (individuals)

David M. Bernick - Paul, Weiss, Rifkind, Wharton & Garrison LLP
John C. Hueston - Hueston Hennigan LLP
William F. Lee – WilmerHale
Mike McKool - McKool Smith
Diane P. Sullivan - Weil, Gotshal & Manges LLP
Beth Wilkinson - Wilkinson Walsh + Eskovitz

Winner: David M. Bernick - Paul, Weiss, Rifkind, Wharton & Garrison LLP

Award 23

Litigation: White-Collar Crime (individuals)

Shortlist:

Susan E. Brune - Brune Law PC
Mark S. Cohen - Cohen & Gresser LLP
Gary Lincenberg - Bird, Marella, Boxer, Wolpert, Nessim, Drooks, Lincenberg & Rhow PC
Aaron R. Marcu - Freshfields Bruckhaus Deringer LLP
Matthew I. Menchel - Kobre & Kim
Paul Schectman – Zuckerman Spaeder LLP
David Schertler – Schertler & Onorato LLP
Debra Wong Yang - Gibson, Dunn & Crutcher LLP

Winner: Debra Wong Yang - Gibson, Dunn & Crutcher LLP

Award 24

Lifetime Achievement

Elkan Abramowitz
Morvillo Abramowitz Grand Iason & Anello P.C.

Award 25

Outstanding Contribution to the Legal Profession

Jonathan L. Mechanic
Fried, Frank, Harris, Shriver & Jacobson LLP

Useful Resources

General

American Bar Association (ABA)
Chicago HQ:
321 North Clark Street
Chicago, IL 60654
Phone: 312 988-5000
DC office:
1050 Connecticut Ave. NW
Suite 400
Washington, DC. 20036
Phone: 202 662-1000
www.americanbar.org

The National Association for Law Placement (NALP)
1220 19th Street NW
Suite 401
Washington, DC 20036-2405
Phone: 202 835-1001
www.nalp.org

National Institute for Trial Advocacy (NITA)
1685 38th Street, Suite 200
Boulder, CO 80301-2735
P: 1.800.225.6482

Diversity

Disability:
National Association of Law Students with Disabilities (NALSWD)
Contact: via website
www.nalswd.org

LGBT:
National LGBT Bar Association
1875 I Street NW, 11th Floor
Washington, DC 20006
Phone: 202 637-7661
E-mail: info@LGBTbar.org
www.lgbtbar.org

Minorities:
Asian American Legal Defense and Education Fund (AALDEF)
99 Hudson St, 12th Fl
New York, NY 10013
Phone: (212) 966-5932
E-mail: info@aaldef.org
www.aaldef.org

Hispanic National Bar Association (HNBA)
1020 19th Street NW, Suite 505
Washington, DC 20036
www.hnba.com

Lawyers' Committee for Civil Rights Under Law
1401 New York Avenue, NW,
Suite 400
Washington, DC 20005
Phone: (888) 299-5227
www.lawyerscommittee.org

Minority Corporate Counsel Association (MCCA)
1111 Pennsylvania Avenue, NW
Washington, DC 20004
Phone: (202) 739-5901
www.mcca.com

The NAACP Legal Defense & Educational Fund
40 Rector Street, 5th floor
New York, NY, 10006
(212) 965-2200
www.naacpldf.org

National Asian Pacific American Bar Association (NAPABA)
1612 K Street NW, Suite 1400
Washington, DC 20006
Phone: (202) 775-9555
www.napaba.org

The National Asian Pacific American Law Student Association (NAPALSA)
Contact: via website
www.napalsa.com

National Bar Association (NBA)
1225 11th Street, NW
Washington, DC 20001
Phone: (302) 842-3900
www.nationalbar.org

National Black Law Students Association (NBLSA)
1225 11th Street NW
Washington, DC 20001-4217
Phone: (202) 618-2572
E-Mail: info@nblsa.org www.nblsa.org

Practicing Attorneys for Law Students Program (PALS)
42 West 44th Street
New York, NY 10036
Phone: (212) 730-PALS
E-Mail: info@palsprogram.org
www.palsprogram.org

The National Latina/o Student Association (NLLSA)
E-Mail: info@nllsa.org
www.nllsa.org

South Asian Bar Association of North America
www.sabanorthamerica.com

Women

Ms.JD
Email: staff@ms-jd.org
http://ms-jd.org

National Women's Law Center
11 Dupont Circle, NW, #800
Washington, DC 20036
Phone: (202) 588-5180
E-Mail: info@nwlc.org www.nwlc.org

New York Women's Bar Association (NYWBA)
132 East 43rd Street, #716,
The Chrysler Building
New York, NY, 10017-4019
Phone: 212-490-8202
E-mail: info@nywba.org
www.nywba.org

Women's Bar Association of the District of Columbia & WBA Foundation
2020 Pennsylvania Avenue, NW
Suite 446
Washington, DC 20006
Phone: 202-639-8880
E-Mail: admin@wbadc.org www.wbadc.org

Pro Bono

American Civil Liberties Union (ACLU)
125 Broad Street, 18th Floor
New York NY 10004
Phone: 212-549-2500
www.aclu.org

Equal Justice Works
1730 M Street NW, Suite 1010
Washington, DC 20036-4511
Phone: (202) 466-3686
www.equaljusticeworks.org

Legal Aid Society
199 Water Street
New York, NY 10038
Phone: (212) 577-3300
www.legal-aid.org

New York Legal Assistance Group (NYLAG)
7 Hanover Square, 18th Floor
New York, NY 10004
Phone: (212) 613-5000
E-mail: volunteer@nylag.org

Pro Bono Institute
1025 Connecticut Avenue, NW
Suite 205
Washington, DC 20036
Phone: (202) 729-6699
www.probonoinst.org

Public Counsel Law Center
610 South Ardmore Avenue
Los Angeles, CA 90005
Phone: (213) 385-2977
www.publiccounsel.org

Notes